# HISTOLOGY

## ARTHUR W. HAM, M.B., F.R.S.C., D.Sc.

*Professor and Chairman, Department of Anatomy,
Faculty of Medicine, University of Toronto, and
Senior Research Associate, Division of Biological Research,
The Ontario Cancer Institute, Toronto, Canada*

D0002268

### FIFTH EDITION

666 Figures, Including 9 Plates in Color

J. B. LIPPINCOTT COMPANY    Philadelphia and Montreal

# Preface to the Fifth Edition

During the fifteen years that have elapsed since the first edition of this book was published the investigation of minute structure has deepened from the study of units that could be discerned with the light microscope to the study of the infinitely smaller units that became visible in the electron microscope and it has now deepened further into the general area of molecular biology which is concerned with the organization of molecules which possess biological functions. This recent and tremendous advance in knowledge has of course had a profound influence on the subject matter of histology and it has considerably influenced the writing of this edition in ways that will now be described briefly.

Much of the new knowledge has led to a much closer relation between histology and biochemistry, and this introduces a complication in an histology textbook because histology is studied somewhat in advance of biochemistry in the usual curriculum. Accordingly, if advantage is to be taken of correlating histology and biochemistry, at least some elementary biochemistry must be introduced in a histology textbook. To assist in this matter this edition, in Chapter 2, has a new section dealing with the chemical components of tissue and some explanation about what happens to these as a section is processed and how the chemical components that remain in the section react with stains. Then, in Chapter 4, fairly extensive accounts are given of the methods that are employed in modern histology and, since many of these are also employed in biochemical studies, an opportunity is provided for achieving further correlation between the two subjects. By this time enough groundwork has been laid to achieve still further correlation with biochemistry in the following chapters on cell structure and cell biology.

The new knowledge has required that the cell, in particular, be considered at much greater length than formerly; for example, in this edition there are three chapters on cell structure and cell biology instead of the one chapter in the previous edition. However, it is important to point out that instead of making the subject more difficult the new knowledge about cell structure and cell biology has made the study of the cell so much more intelligible that its study, if not easier, is much more satisfactory than it was before. The student now has the great advantage of being able to visualize a working model of a cell. He can visualize how certain unblocked segments of DNA molecules serve as patterns for the synthesis of molecules of messenger RNA which thereupon transmit the information inscribed on them to sites of protein synthesis. He can visualize how protein destined for secretion is formed by amino acids being linked together in proper sequences and how these are segregated in membranous vesicles and how the contents of these are delivered to the golgi apparatus where the product is further modified and then packaged in membranous bags and delivered through the secretory surface of the cell. He can understand how DNA duplicates itself to maintain genetic continuity in cells. These and many other relatively recent findings make it far easier to visualize cells as consisting of components which play particular and interrelated roles. In other words, the student now has the great advantage of studying a working model instead of trying to memorize the names and appearances of the parts of the unassembled jig-saw puzzle that so many of us had to learn when we studied cell structure years ago.

Another area of importance to histology and in which there have been many interesting advances is that of the cellular basis for immunologic reactions. This has been taken into account in this edition as follows: A beginning is made in Chapter 4 in the discussion given there about immunofluorescence technics. The story continues with the description and discussion of plasma and mast cells in the chapter on loose connective tissue, is developed still more in the chapter on leukocytes, particularly in the discussion on lymphocytes, and finally is considered in detail in the chapter on lymphatic tissue with regard to both lymph nodes and the thymus. Much of this discussion should be of interest to medical students and those interested in the immunological problems involved in the homotransplantation of tissues and organs.

It may be noticed that the order in this edition has been changed. This was done both to save space and to match more closely the order followed in the usual histology course. When this book was first written so little attention was being paid to intercellular substances that it was thought desirable to emphasize the nonliving components of the body by having a chapter about intercellular substance immediately follow the chapter on the cell. Now, however, intercellular substances have come into their own, so this undue emphasis is no longer required, and intercellular substances are considered in the chapters on connective tissue.

As a result of what has already been described and because of many other alterations in the chapters dealing with myeloid tissue, bone, and muscle, most of the first half of this edition represents new copy. The chapters in the second half of the book, which deal with the systems, have not been revised as extensively as those in the first half, partly because most of the new developments in knowledge lent themselves to being incorporated more readily in the first half of the book. Nevertheless, almost all of the later chapters have been revised and, in particular, much of the chapter on endocrine glands and almost all of the section dealing with the liver was rewritten.

It perhaps should be remarked that much or most of the new knowledge does not displace that which existed before. Most of what has been learned from light microscopy is just as important as ever. For example, learning about the fine structure of hepatocytes is not a substitute for learning about the structure of liver lobules at the level of light microscopy. The fact is that much more information must now be presented in a histology textbook than heretofore and it is therefore inevitable that a textbook on this subject must be longer instead of shorter if it is to present intelligibly minute structure and its significance at the various levels at which it now should be described.

Despite the extensive changes made in this edition, every effort has been made to preserve the character of the book established in previous editions. As was done in them, much care has been taken not to introduce words and concepts in early chapters without explaining them. So far as was possible, the book has been arranged so that each chapter represents a step which lifts the student to a position where he can easily take the next. It should be emphasized that this is a textbook; it is designed, not to be read in bits and pieces, but progressively from chapter to chapter. Furthermore, since there is no special course given to students to integrate the information they gain in studying different subjects into a usable body of knowledge much effort has gone into pointing out how histology integrates with other subjects. Finally, much effort has also gone into making the presentation as interesting as possible—or perhaps this should be said another way; that histology is a very interesting subject and much effort has gone into trying to prevent its presentation from becoming dull.

ARTHUR W. HAM

# Acknowledgements

The increasing use of the newer technics, described in Chapter 4, over the past 4 years has led to the subject matter of Histology not only expanding in content but also extending in depth, where it merges with much of modern cell biology. Consequently, there is now so much material that should be dealt with in a book on Histology that it has become almost impossible for any single individual to cover the broad and deep field without a great deal of help. I have been fortunate in that there have been many colleagues and friends to whom I could turn for advice about various matters dealt with in this edition. In every instance they have extended assistance with the greatest good will. In mentioning the names of some of those who have helped, I should like to make it clear that although they deserve great credit, I alone should be blamed if it should transpire over the next 4 years that any interpretations I have placed on the findings I was aware of when this was written were less conservative than they should have been.

Consistently, throughout the preparation of this edition, my good friend Dr. Charles Leblond, has taken time from his busy life to help me. On many occasions we have spent several days together, discussing the new developments in histology and what should be included in this textbook. Several times, following our discussions, Dr. Leblond has gone to the trouble of preparing tentative drafts of manuscript dealing with new material related to one of his many special interests, and this, of course, made my work much easier. Moreover, Dr. Leblond provided many illustrations for me from his laboratory; some of these were specially prepared for the specific purpose of serving as teaching, textbook illustrations. His influence extends to many more pages than those on which it is obvious, and I am deeply grateful to him for his stimulating help.

I have also received much assistance and encouragement from my immediate colleagues in the Division of Biological Research of The Ontario Cancer Institute. Dr. Louis Siminovitch, with his broad knowledge of the chemistry of heredity, was always ready to read manuscript critically and make pertinent suggestions for improvement when the part of Chapter 6 that deals with this matter was being written. Dr. Arthur Axelrad assisted me greatly in preparing the material on chromosomes and chromosome abnormalities and, in addition, we had many instructive conversations about the thymus and many other matters. Dr. Allan Howatson, as in past editions, was most helpful with regard to matters relating to electron microscopy and fine structure and provided me with many new illustrations, as did also Mrs. June Almeida. Drs. E. A. McCulloch and J. E. Till provided assistance and illustrations with regard to the material on the spleen-colony technic. Dr. D. F. Parsons was most informative about the newer work on mitochondria and provided illustrations. Dr. Bernhard Cinader was always willing to discuss immunology with me when I needed expert help, and I learned much from him.

My colleagues on the clinical side of The Ontario Cancer Institute also provided help. Dr. D. M. Whitelaw took a great interest in the presentation regarding lymphocytes and gave me much material assistance in this connection. Dr. R. Hasselback aided me greatly in revising the chapter on platelets and fibrin and read other chapters critically for me. Dr. J. W. Meakin assisted me in the revision of parts of the chapter on endocrine glands, much of which he read critically for me. Dr. M. G. Williams helped in revising the section on melanin pigment.

Much help was also received from colleagues in other Departments of the Faculty of Medicine, University of Toronto. Dr. H. Z. Movat of the Department of Pathology gave me access to findings not yet published and provided me with many electron micrographs of various cells of connective tissue and cells of lymphatic tissue under conditions of antigenic stimulation. Dr. J. W. Steiner of the same Department gave most generously of his time, and he and his staff provided me abundantly with electron micrographs illustrating the details of nuclear and nucleolar structures and also the fine structure of the liver. Dr. Steiner read, criticized and generally helped in preparing the manuscript relating to these two important sections. Dr. Calvin Ezrin of the same Department assisted with the preparation of the section dealing with the cells of the anterior lobe of the pituitary gland and supplied a color illustration. Dr. W. S. Hartroft kindly read and made helpful suggestions regarding the chapter on the kidney and gave me advice about bringing it up to date. Dr. W. R. Harris of the Department of Surgery provided information and illustrations regarding the blood supply of bone. I am grateful to Dr. John Barrie for reading the material dealing with the lung and making many useful suggestions regarding its revision. Dr. Don Thompson of the Department of Pathology gave me much help in making such revision as was made in Chapter 29.

Many individuals outside of my immediate environment also provided much assistance. Dr. George Palade who, beginning with the second edition of this book, published in 1953, provided me with beautiful electron micrographs and has done so for each subsequent edition, again supplied me with further ones for this edition and took time to answer by correspondence many questions I asked about matters to which they related. I continue to be especially grateful for his very generous and kind help. Dr. Samuel Dales also supplied me with electron micrographs and much helpful comment. Dr. Alex Novikoff read the manuscript dealing with cytoplasm and gave me helpful advice and illustrations of lysosomes. Dr. R. C. Buck of the Department of Microscopic Anatomy, University of Western Ontario, supplied me with several electron micrographs as well as giving me a good deal of assistance in connection with preparing the section dealing with mitosis. Dr. Murray Barr again gave me some help and much encouragement. Dr. Norman Nadler of McGill University provided very extensive and detailed assistance in bringing the section on the thyroid gland up to date and provided many new illustrations. Dr. Yves Clermont of the same University most kindly read the chapter which deals with the testis and provided new material, including illustrations. Dr. Jennifer Jowsey made many useful suggestions about improving the chapter on Bone and provided an illustration.

Assistance was received from others still farther away. Dr. Norman Hancox and Dr. B. Boothroyd of the University of Liverpool provided me with a selection of electron micrographs illustrating various cells of bone. I am most grateful to Dr. Charles Ford for promptly providing beautiful photomicrographs of human chromosomes for inclusion in this edition, together with some words of encouragement.

In addition to those already mentioned I am grateful to many others who kindly supplied illustrations for this edition, namely, Drs. K. Arakawa, C. G. Biava, R. I. Birks, Sam Clark, Jr., J. E. Dowling, B. Droz, N. V. P. Fernando, L. Herman, H. van Heyningen, J. H. Humphrey, S. Ishii, A. M. Jézéquel, J. G. Lafontaine, W. R. Lockwood, K. Miyai, J. D. McNabb, H. H. Mollenhauer, M. Nagai, T. Oosaki, M. Petersen, M. J. Phillips, K. R. Porter, A. Rich, R. M. Salter, G. Sainte-Marie, M. D. Schoenberg, R. and M. Silberberg, F. S. Sjöstrand, N. S. Taichman, B. F. Trump, J. J. Vazquez, J Weiner, J. C. Wyllie and D. Zucker-Franklin.

I remain grateful to all those who assisted in previous editions. In particular I wish to thank my former colleague and collaborator in the 4th edition, Dr. T. S. Leeson, for the assistance he provided in preparing that edition and to express regret that the new position he understandably accepted separated us by some 2,000 miles, which made it impracticable to attempt to work together closely as collaborators on this edition; therefore, I have had to prepare it without his assistance.

Once again, Miss Mary McConnell, while shouldering many other responsibilities, has prepared, to her high standards, all the copy for the publishers, a task which often encroached on her own time, and once again I am deeply grateful to her. I also thank Mr. R. Escoffery for preparing for me many special sections and photographs in connection with this edition. I wish also to thank my wife who, day after day, read proof for me and then helped to prepare the Index. My publishers also deserve my thanks; they have been as considerate and helpful as possible. It has been a pleasure to work once more with Mr. Stanley A. Gillet, who has again been in charge of editing the manuscript as it was received.

ARTHUR W. HAM

# Contents

## Part One

## What Histology Is and How It Is Studied

1. THE NATURE AND THE SCOPE OF HISTOLOGY; ITS INTEGRATION WITH OTHER BIOLOGIC SUBJECTS; THE ROUTE FOLLOWED IN ITS STUDY . . . . . . 3

2. HOW HISTOLOGY IS STUDIED . . . . . . 7
   The Paraffin Technic . . . . . . 7
   The Chemical Components of the Body and How They Are Affected by the Procedures Just Described . . . . . . 10
   The Staining of Sections . . . . . . 14
   Other Ways of Preparing Sections . . . . . . 15

3. THE STUDY AND THE INTERPRETATION OF SECTIONS . . . . . . 17
   Why 3-Dimensional Visualization Is Necessary in Histology . . . . . . 17
   How Reconstructions Are Made . . . . . . 17
   Some Aids To Making Mental Reconstructions . . . . . . 18
   How To Study a Section . . . . . . 19

4. SPECIAL METHODS USED FOR STUDYING HISTOLOGY AND CELL BIOLOGY . . . . . . 28
   Histochemistry—Some Examples of Representative Technics . . . . . . 29
   Radioautography . . . . . . 31
   Microincineration . . . . . . 35
   Immunofluorescence Technics . . . . . . 37
   The Electron Microscope . . . . . . 39
   The Use of the Interference and the Phase Microscopes for the Study of Living Unstained Tissue . . . . . . 48
   Ways in Which Living or Fresh Tissue Can Be Studied Outside the Body or in the Living Body . . . . . . 51

## Part Two

## Cell Structure and Cell Biology

5. GENERAL FEATURES OF CELLS . . . . . . 57
   Introduction . . . . . . 57
   The Physiologic Properties of Protoplasm . . . . . . 58
   Differentiation—The Process Whereby Cells Become Specialized . . . . . . 59
   Some Generalizations About the Consequences of Differentiation (Cell Specialization) . . . . . . 60

6. NUCLEI . . . . . . 64
   The Microscopic Study of Cells in Sections in the Laboratory . . . . . . 64
   How Nuclei Appear in Sections . . . . . . 65

x   Contents

6. NUCLEI—(*Continued*)

The Chromatin of the Interphase Nucleus . . . . . . . . . . 66
How the Body Cells of Females Can Be Distinguished From Those of Males
by Examining the Chromatin of Interphase Nuclei . . . . . . 68
Chromatin and Chromosomes; the Changes That Occur in Cell Division
(Mitosis) . . . . . . . . . . . . . . . . . . . 71
The Phases of Mitosis . . . . . . . . . . . . . . 74
Effects of Colchicine on Mitosis . . . . . . . . . . . 80
The Morphology of Metaphase Chromosomes and Their Classification . . 81
Polyploidy . . . . . . . . . . . . . . . . . . 85
Chemistry and Histochemistry of Chromatin and Chromosomes . . . 86
Introduction to Chemistry of Genetic Material; How Information Is Stored
in DNA . . . . . . . . . . . . . . . . . . . 88
The Chemical Basis of Genes . . . . . . . . . . . . 89
How DNA Molecules Are Duplicated . . . . . . . . . . 90
The Study of DNA Synthesis by the Use of a Radioactive Label and Radio-
autographs . . . . . . . . . . . . . . . . . . 91
Some Matters That Have Been Clarified by Labeling Nuclei with Radioactive
Thymidine . . . . . . . . . . . . . . . . . . 93
The Fine Structure of Chromosomes . . . . . . . . . . 97
Effect of Radiation on Chromosomes and Mitosis . . . . . . . 98
How Genetic Information in the Chromosomes Is Made Operative in the Cell . 99
Nucleoli . . . . . . . . . . . . . . . . . . . 102
The Nuclear Membrane (Also Termed the Nuclear Envelope) . . . . 107
Nuclear Sap . . . . . . . . . . . . . . . . . . 109
Nuclear Changes Indicative of Cell Death . . . . . . . . . 112

7. THE CYTOPLASM . . . . . . . . . . . . . . . . . 115

Organelles and Inclusions . . . . . . . . . . . . . 115
The Golgi Apparatus . . . . . . . . . . . . . . . 127
The Fine Structure of the Golgi Apparatus . . . . . . . . . 129
Lyosomes . . . . . . . . . . . . . . . . . . . 142
Cytoplasmic Inclusions . . . . . . . . . . . . . . 145
Significance of the Newer Knowledge About Cells to the Problem of Cell
Differentiation . . . . . . . . . . . . . . . . . 152

# Part Three

# The Four Primary Tissues and Their Subdivisions

8. THE FOUR PRIMARY TISSUES; EPITHELIAL TISSUE . . . . . . . . 165

Introduction . . . . . . . . . . . . . . . . . . 165
A Suggestion on How To Study the Tissues . . . . . . . . . 165
Epithelial Tissue . . . . . . . . . . . . . . . . . 165
Embryologic Origin of Epithelium . . . . . . . . . . . 167
Types of Epithelium Found on Wet Surfaces . . . . . . . . 170
The Internal Support in Epithelial Cells and How Epithelial Cells Are Held
Together in Membranes . . . . . . . . . . . . . . 174
Stratified Epithelial Membranes . . . . . . . . . . . . 184

9. EPITHELIAL TISSUE—(*Continued*) . . . . . . . . . . . . 188

Epithelial Glands . . . . . . . . . . . . . . . . 188

10. CONNECTIVE TISSUE . . . . . . . . . . . . . 200
    Introduction . . . . . . . . . . . . . . 200
    Loose Ordinary Connective Tissue . . . . . . . . . 200
    The Intercellular Substances of Loose Connective Tissue . . . . 203
    Collagenic Fibers . . . . . . . . . . . . . 203
    Elastic Fibers . . . . . . . . . . . . . . 208
    Reticular Fibers . . . . . . . . . . . . . . 208
    The Amorphous Intercellular Substance of Loose Connective Tissue . . . 209
    The Staining of the Ground Substance of Loose Connective Tissue (Hyaluronic
      Acid) . . . . . . . . . . . . . . . 210
    Tissue Fluid . . . . . . . . . . . . . . . 211
    Hydrostatic Pressure and the Formation of Tissue Fluid . . . . . 213
    Absorption of Tissue Fluid . . . . . . . . . . . 214
    Edema . . . . . . . . . . . . . . . . 216
    Some Causes of Edema . . . . . . . . . . . . 216
    Intercellular Substances and Aging . . . . . . . . . 221

11. THE CELLS OF LOOSE ORDINARY CONNECTIVE TISSUE . . . . 224
    The Development of Connective Tissue . . . . . . . . 224
    The Cells of Loose Ordinary Connective Tissue . . . . . . 226
    Features of Plasma Cells . . . . . . . . . . . 238
    Mast Cells, Histamine, Anaphylaxis and Allergy . . . . . . 246
    Dense Ordinary Connective Tissue . . . . . . . . . 251

12. THE CELLS OF BLOOD . . . . . . . . . . . . 257
    Leukocytes . . . . . . . . . . . . . . . 257
    The Basis for Classifying Leukocytes . . . . . . . . 259
    The Study of Leukocytes in a Stained Blood Film . . . . . 261
    Granular Leukocytes . . . . . . . . . . . . 262
    Nongranular Leukocytes . . . . . . . . . . . 270
    The Life Span and the Functions of Lymphocytes . . . . . 273
    The Functions of Lymphocytes . . . . . . . . . . 275
    Sensitivity of Lymphocytes to Radiation and Radiomimetic Drugs . . . 281
    Some Problems Associated With Identifying Certain Leukocytes Seen in a
      Blood Film . . . . . . . . . . . . . . 283

13. THE CELLS OF BLOOD—(Continued) . . . . . . . . . 287
    Red Blood Cells (Erythrocytes) . . . . . . . . . . 287

14. PLATELETS AND FIBRIN . . . . . . . . . . . . 298
    The Two Basic Hemostatic Mechanisms . . . . . . . . 298
    The Formation of Platelet Plugs That Seal Off Blood Vessels . . . 298
    Coagulation . . . . . . . . . . . . . . . 300
    Coagulation and Its Dependence on Extrinsic or Intrinsic Factors . . . 301
    The Study of Platelets in the Laboratory . . . . . . . 302
    How Platelets Are Counted . . . . . . . . . . . 304
    The Formation and Life-Span of Platelets . . . . . . . 304
    A Few Examples of Defects in Hemostatic Mechanisms . . . . 305

15. HEMOPOIETIC TISSUE . . . . . . . . . . . . 308
    Some General Considerations . . . . . . . . . . 308
    Lymphatic Tissue . . . . . . . . . . . . . 309
    Lymph Nodes . . . . . . . . . . . . . . 313
    The Spleen . . . . . . . . . . . . . . . 327
    The Thymus . . . . . . . . . . . . . . . 338

16.  HEMOPOIETIC TISSUE—(*Continued*) . . . . . . . . . . . 351
      Myeloid Tissue . . . . . . . . . . . . . . . 351
      The Development of Myeloid Tissue . . . . . . . . . 351
      The Cells That Form Along Line 1 . . . . . . . . . . 352
      The Appearance of Sinusoids in Sections . . . . . . . 353
      How the Production of Free Cells Is Maintained . . . . . 355
      Other Cells in Bone Marrow . . . . . . . . . . . 369
      The Study of Bone Marrow in Clinical Medicine . . . . . 370

17.  THE SUPPORTING CONNECTIVE TISSUES: CARTILAGE AND BONE . . 373
      Cartilage . . . . . . . . . . . . . . . . . 373
      The Development of Cartilage . . . . . . . . . . . 377
      The Growth of Cartilage . . . . . . . . . . . . 377
      Nutrition of Cartilage . . . . . . . . . . . . . 378
      General Considerations About the Transplantation of Cartilage . . . . 381

18.  BONE . . . . . . . . . . . . . . . . . . . 384
      The Differences Between Calcified Cartilage and Bone . . . . 384
      Special Types of Preparations Are Required for a Rounded-Out Study of Bone . 387
      The Development of Bone . . . . . . . . . . . . 388
      What Is Meant by the Terms Intramembranous, Endochondral and Heterotopic
        Ossification . . . . . . . . . . . . . . . 393
      Intramembranous Ossification . . . . . . . . . . . 394
      Bone Growth and Bone Resorption . . . . . . . . . . 398
      The Different Appearances Presented by Bone Surfaces on Which Bone
        Deposition of Bone Resorption Is Occurring . . . . . . 400
      Osteoclasts . . . . . . . . . . . . . . . . 402
      The Further Growth of the Skull . . . . . . . . . . 407
      Endochondral Ossification . . . . . . . . . . . . 408
      The Growth of a Long Bone as a Whole . . . . . . . . 420
      How Shafts of Bone Grow in Width . . . . . . . . . 424
      The Remodeling of Compact Bone That Occurs Throughout Life . . 428
      How Certain Nutritional and Metabolic Factors Can Affect Growing Bones
        and the Structure of Bones in the Adult . . . . . . . 431
      Periosteum and Endosteum . . . . . . . . . . . . 436
      Wolff's Law . . . . . . . . . . . . . . . . 436
      The Repair of Fractures . . . . . . . . . . . . . 436
      The Repair of a Simple Fracture . . . . . . . . . . 437
      The Transplantation of Bone . . . . . . . . . . . 444
      Transplants of Cancellous Bone . . . . . . . . . . 447
      The Blood Supply of a Long Bone and Its Various Parts . . . . 449
      The Blood Supply of the Metaphysis of a Growing Bone . . . . 450

19.  JOINTS . . . . . . . . . . . . . . . . . . 458
      Introduction . . . . . . . . . . . . . . . . 458
      Syndesmoses . . . . . . . . . . . . . . . . 459
      Synchondroses . . . . . . . . . . . . . . . 460
      Synostoses . . . . . . . . . . . . . . . . 460
      Synovial Joints . . . . . . . . . . . . . . . 462

20.  MUSCULAR TISSUE . . . . . . . . . . . . . . . 476
      Classification of Muscle . . . . . . . . . . . . . 477
      Smooth Muscle . . . . . . . . . . . . . . . 477
      Striated, Skeletal or Voluntary Muscle . . . . . . . . 482
      Development and Growth of Striated Muscle Fibers . . . . . 494

20.  MUSCULAR TISSUE—(*Continued*)
How Striated Muscles Are Harnessed . . . . . . . 496
Blood Vessels and Lymphatics . . . . . . . . 497
The Efferent Innervation of Striated Muscle . . . . . . 498
Cardiac Muscle . . . . . . . . . . . 501

21.  NERVOUS TISSUE AND THE NERVOUS SYSTEM . . . . . 507
Preliminary Considerations . . . . . . . . 507
An Account (In Which Important New Terms Are Introduced) of Some Steps
in the Evolution of Nervous Tissue . . . . . . . 508
The Development of the Central Nervous Tissue . . . . . 516
Morphogenesis of the Spinal Cord . . . . . . . 517
Morphogenesis of the Brain . . . . . . . . 518
Histogenesis of the Spinal Cord . . . . . . . . 520
Differentiation of the Inner Layer and the Formation of the Ependyma . . . 520
Differentiation in the Middle Layer and the Formation of Gray Matter . . . 522
Differentiation in the Outer Layer and the Formation of White Matter . . . 522
Histogenesis of Nervous Tissue of Brain . . . . . . 525
The Cells of the Nervous Tissue of the C.N.S. . . . . . . 526
Microscopic Structure of the Spinal Cord . . . . . . 538
Microscopic Structure of Some Parts of the Brain . . . . . 541
The Meninges . . . . . . . . . . . 546
Formation, Circulation and Absorption of Cerebrospinal Fluid . . . 549
The Peripheral Nervous System . . . . . . . . 551
The Development of the P.N.S. . . . . . . . . 553
Microscopic Structure of Spinal Ganglia . . . . . . 554
Microscopic Structure of Peripheral Nerves . . . . . . 555
Nerve Injuries and the Degeneration and the Regeneration of Peripheral Nerves 564
The Autonomic Nervous System . . . . . . . . 567

# Part Four

# The Histology of the Systems

22.  THE CIRCULATORY SYSTEM . . . . . . . . . 581
Some Mechanical Problems Inherent in a Circulatory System . . . 581
The Microscopic Structure of Arteries . . . . . . . 583
Nervous Control of Arteries and Arterial Pressure . . . . . 588
The Microscopic Structure of Capillaries . . . . . . 590
Control of the Capillary Circulation . . . . . . . 591
The Fine Structure of Capillaries and Venules . . . . . 594
Veins . . . . . . . . . . . . . 596
The Transplantation of Blood Vessels . . . . . . . 599
Arteriovenous Anastomoses . . . . . . . . 600
Heart . . . . . . . . . . . . . 600
Impulse-Conducting System of the Heart . . . . . . 604
The Lymphatic Division of the Circulatory System . . . . . 609

23.  THE INTEGUMENTARY SYSTEM (The Skin and Its Appendages) . . . 613
Introduction . . . . . . . . . . . 613
General Microscopic Structure . . . . . . . . 613
Microscopic Structure of the Thick Skin . . . . . . 615
Microscopic Structure of the Thin Skin . . . . . . 621

23.  THE INTEGUMENTARY SYSTEM (The Skin and Its Appendages)—(*Continued*)

Hair Follicles . . . . . . . . . . . . . . . . . . 623
Sebaceous Glands . . . . . . . . . . . . . . . . 630
Pigmentation of the Skin . . . . . . . . . . . . . 632
Blood Supply of the Skin . . . . . . . . . . . . . 635
Skin Grafting . . . . . . . . . . . . . . . . . 638
Nails . . . . . . . . . . . . . . . . . . . . 640

24.  THE DIGESTIVE SYSTEM . . . . . . . . . . . . . . 645
Introduction . . . . . . . . . . . . . . . . . . 645
The Lips . . . . . . . . . . . . . . . . . . . 647
The Cheeks . . . . . . . . . . . . . . . . . . 648
The Tongue . . . . . . . . . . . . . . . . . . 648
The Teeth . . . . . . . . . . . . . . . . . . . 652
The Salivary Glands . . . . . . . . . . . . . . . 669
The Hard Palate . . . . . . . . . . . . . . . . 671
The Soft Palate . . . . . . . . . . . . . . . . . 671
The Pharynx . . . . . . . . . . . . . . . . . . 672
The Palatine Tonsils . . . . . . . . . . . . . . . 673
General Plan of the Gastrointestinal Tract . . . . . . . 674
The Esophagus . . . . . . . . . . . . . . . . . 678
The Stomach . . . . . . . . . . . . . . . . . . 680
Fine Structure . . . . . . . . . . . . . . . . . 684
The Small Intestine . . . . . . . . . . . . . . . 688
The Large Intestine . . . . . . . . . . . . . . . 697

25.  PANCREAS, LIVER AND GALLBLADDER . . . . . . . . . 706
The Pancreas . . . . . . . . . . . . . . . . . . 706
The Liver . . . . . . . . . . . . . . . . . . . 711
Some Functions of the Liver Dependent on Its Structure and Position . 712
The Liver Acinus . . . . . . . . . . . . . . . . 721
The Cytology and Fine Structure of the Liver . . . . . . 726
The Cytoplasm of Hepatic Cells . . . . . . . . . . . 727
The Gallbladder . . . . . . . . . . . . . . . . . 737
A Note on Jaundice . . . . . . . . . . . . . . . 739

26.  THE RESPIRATORY SYSTEM . . . . . . . . . . . . . 744
Introduction . . . . . . . . . . . . . . . . . . 744
The Nasal Cavities . . . . . . . . . . . . . . . . 746
Paranasal Air Sinuses of the Nose . . . . . . . . . . 748
The Pharyngeal Tonsil . . . . . . . . . . . . . . 749
The Larynx . . . . . . . . . . . . . . . . . . 749
The Trachea . . . . . . . . . . . . . . . . . . 751
The Bronchial Tree . . . . . . . . . . . . . . . . 752
The Development of the Lungs . . . . . . . . . . . . 763
Innervation of the Smooth Muscles of the Bronchi and the Bronchioles . 768

27.  THE URINARY SYSTEM . . . . . . . . . . . . . . . 772
Some General Considerations . . . . . . . . . . . . 772
The Basic Mechanisms of Excretory Tubules . . . . . . . 772
The Nephrons of Higher Animals and How They Function . . . 773
The Unilobar (Unipyramidal) Kidney . . . . . . . . . . 775
Lobules and Medullary Rays . . . . . . . . . . . . . 778
The Multipyramidal or Multilobar Kidney of Man . . . . . 779
The Nephron of the Kidney of Man: Its Parts and Their Functions . . 781

27. THE URINARY SYSTEM—(*Continued*)
  The Proximal Tubule . . . . . . . . . . . . . 795
  Loops of Henle . . . . . . . . . . . . . . 799
  The Distal Convoluted Tubule . . . . . . . . . 800
  Other Features of the Kidney . . . . . . . . . 800
  The Circulation of Blood Through the Kidney . . . . 802
  Lymphatics of the Kidney . . . . . . . . . . 805
  Postnatal Growth of the Kidney . . . . . . . . 806
  The Ureter . . . . . . . . . . . . . . . 807
  The Urinary Bladder . . . . . . . . . . . . 808
  The Urethra . . . . . . . . . . . . . . . 808
  Innervation of the Urinary System . . . . . . . 809

28. THE ENDOCRINE SYSTEM . . . . . . . . . . . 814
  Introduction . . . . . . . . . . . . . . . 814
  The Pituitary Gland or Body (Hypophysis Cerebri) . . 815
  Other Parts of the Pituitary Gland . . . . . . . 828
  The Thyroid Gland . . . . . . . . . . . . . 831
  Does the Thyroid Gland Provide an Example of a Secluded Antigen . . . 844
  The Parathyroid Glands . . . . . . . . . . . 845
  The Adrenal (Suprarenal) Glands . . . . . . . . 852
  Islets of Langerhans . . . . . . . . . . . . 866
  The Pineal Body . . . . . . . . . . . . . . 875

29. THE FEMALE REPRODUCTIVE SYSTEM . . . . . . . 884
  Introductory Remarks About Sex . . . . . . . . 884
  The Parts of the Female Reproductive System . . . . 884
  The Ovary: Ovulation and Hormone Secretion . . . . 890
  The Oviducts . . . . . . . . . . . . . . . 909
  The Body and the Fundus of the Uterus . . . . . . 911
  The Placenta . . . . . . . . . . . . . . . 917
  The Cervix . . . . . . . . . . . . . . . . 927
  The Mammary Glands (Breasts or Mammae) . . . . 934

30. THE MALE REPRODUCTIVE SYSTEM . . . . . . . . 946
  The Parts of the System and Their Functions . . . . 946
  The Testes . . . . . . . . . . . . . . . . 949
  The Epididymis . . . . . . . . . . . . . . 964
  The Ductus Deferens . . . . . . . . . . . . 965
  The Seminal Vesicles . . . . . . . . . . . . 965
  The Prostate Gland . . . . . . . . . . . . . 966
  The Penis . . . . . . . . . . . . . . . . 969
  The Male Urethra . . . . . . . . . . . . . 971

31. THE SYSTEM OF SENSORY RECEPTORS . . . . . . . 975
  Introduction . . . . . . . . . . . . . . . 975
  Receptors Concerned in Cutaneous and Deep Sensibility . . 975
  The Olfactory Organ . . . . . . . . . . . . 978
  The Eye . . . . . . . . . . . . . . . . . 981
  Taste Buds . . . . . . . . . . . . . . . . 1006
  The Ear . . . . . . . . . . . . . . . . . 1007

INDEX . . . . . . . . . . . . . . . . . . . 1025

PART ONE

# What Histology Is and How It Is Studied

# 1  The Nature and the Scope of Histology; Its Integration With Other Biologic Subjects; the Route Followed in Its Study

Before journeying into new territory it is helpful to consult a map that gives information about the nature of the area that will be visited and the route that will be followed. It is equally helpful, before beginning the study of a new subject, to obtain some idea of its nature, its position in relation to certain other subjects, and the route that will be followed in a course of instruction in the new subject. Therefore, an attempt will be made here to present some information on these three matters.

It is appropriate to begin by giving a definition. The word histology is derived from the Greek *"histos"* and *"logos"* which mean "tissue" and "study or science of," respectively. However, although describing histology as "the study or the science of the tissues" provides an acceptable definition, it is not very informative because it does not explain the meaning of tissues and the particular sense in which this term is used with regard to animals.

The English word *tissue* was taken from the French *tissu* which means "weave" or "texture." Anything that is woven together can be called a tissue; indeed, a connected series of falsehoods, woven together to form a plausible story, can properly be referred to as a "tissue of lies."

**How Histology Evolved From Gross Anatomy.** The word *tissue* came into anatomic use chiefly because of the work and the writings of Bichat, a brilliant young French anatomist (1771-1802). As he dissected bodies he became impressed by the fact that the various layers and structures that he described or peeled apart were of different weaves and textures, and so he made a classification of these various components of the body on the basis of their different textures. This first classification of the tissues was made without the help of the microscope, for although microscopes were coming into general use at that time, Bichat refused to use one. Therefore, it is something of a paradox to think that the science of the tissues—*histology*—which is now studied exclusively with the microscope, began with an anatomist who refused to use this instrument.

Other anatomists did not entertain Bichat's doubts about the value of the microscope and began to explore the structure of the various parts of the body with it; as a result, the microscopic structures of various parts of the body that previously had been studied only with the naked eye and the magnifying glass were elucidated successively.

It might be thought that the new insight into body structure gained from the use of the microscope would detract from Bichat's concept of the body's being composed of different tissues. But instead, the use of the microscope showed much more clearly than could be determined from gross observations that the concept of the body's being built of certain tissues was indeed correct. Of course, the microscope led to a modification of Bichat's views, for it showed that instead of there being 20 or more different tissues as Bichat had described, there were only 4 basic tissues; but in justice to Bichat it should be said, as the student will learn, that each of these 4 basic tissues generally is divided into several subtypes.

The advent of the microscope therefore permitted the structure and the nature of the tissues to be gradually elucidated, and this, as well as raising the stature of histology as a scientific discipline, had the further effect of increasing the scope of histology because it showed that the microscopic anatomy of any part of the body was to be explained by the particular tissues that entered into its composition and the particular ways in which they were arranged and combined to make that part of the body a functional structure. As a result of the finding that all microscopic anatomy was to be explained by different arrangements of tissue, microscopic anatomy came to be considered, not as a separate discipline, but as an extension of histology. Therefore, histology is a subject that deals first with the nature and the microscopic structure of the tissues, and secondly with the ways in which these are employed and arranged to account for the different microscopic structures and organs of the body.

It is hoped that the foregoing will indicate that there are two main parts to a histology course. The first is the study of the basic building materials of the body—the 4 basic tissues and their various subtypes. The second is the way in which the building blocks are arranged to account for the particular microscopic structure possessed by different parts of the body. The two divisions of the subject are not at all sharp, but it is helpful for the student to realize that approximately the first half of this book deals primarily with the nature and the classification of tissues and the second half primarily with the ways in which these are arranged to account for the particular microscopic appearance (the microscopic anatomy) of different organs and other important structures of the body.

The advent and the use of the light microscope did something more; it eventually revealed clearly that there were both living and nonliving components entering into the composition of the body. The former consist of small units or *cells*, which are well-limited packages of living matter of a size of the order of 1/1,000th of an inch (0.02 mm.). The nonliving components, since they were distributed between cells, were termed *intercellular substances*, and sooner or later they were shown to exist in the form of fibers or jellies of different degrees of firmness. Since living cells are soft, it became obvious that it was the nonliving intercellular substance that gave form to the body; and indeed, that the *body could be viewed as an edifice of intercellular substances in which cells live as residents*.

**Integration of Histology With Physiology.** Moreover, the use of the microscope showed that there was a profound division and specialization of labor among the cells of the human body, and this permitted the study of function (physiology) to be brought down to the level of cells. Indeed, the cells of the body proved to be as different from one another as are the various people who make up a modern society. In the latter, one group of people is specialized to grow grain, another to make bread, another to make bricks, another to build houses, another to make clothing, and so on. And, just as specialized workers must exchange their various products and services with one another, the various specialized cell groups in the body must likewise exchange with one another. Exchange, of course, requires a transportation system, and in the body this is provided by the great blood vascular system. The general arrangement that the microscope disclosed in the body was that almost every cell lives close to a small tributary of the blood vascular system from which it takes what it needs and into which it delivers its specialized products which are needed by cells in other sites. Waste products also are emptied into the system, ear-marked for elimination from the body by special organs that perform this function. Of course, all this specialized activity and continuous exchange must be regulated properly lest surpluses pile up in one quarter and famines occur in others. Regulation, in turn, requires a communication system; this is provided primarily by the nervous system which sends its wirelike nerves to all groups of specialized cells. An additional communication system is employed for some cell groups; this involves the dispatch into the bloodstream of *chemical messengers* called *hormones*; these, on reaching their targets, arouse activity in special cell groups that are often far removed from where the message was dispatched.

**Integration of Histology With Pathology.** The development of knowledge about the body that was made possible by the microscope was, of course, of the greatest importance with regard to pathology—the study of disease. To give a few simple examples, it became possible to understand how death could occur when the cells of only one part of the body—on whose specialized activities the whole body depended —were seriously injured or destroyed. It became possible to understand that cells in some part of the body sometimes multiplied in an unrestrained way so as to invade other parts of the body and destroy these; this was the first time that the nature of the disease called *cancer* was clarified. It became clear that obstructions in the transportation system, such as blockages in the blood vessels caused by blood coagulation, could lead to the death of vital parts of the body and that the local destruction of nervous tissue could likewise interfere with the welfare and the operation of parts whose functions were dependent on the communication system. Many more examples could be given, but it should be said that one man stands out in the application of histology to the understanding of disease—the German pathologist Rudolf Virchow (1821-1902). It is perhaps of interest to note that the problems of an economic community, whether it be a community of cells or of people, in which there is a specialization of labor and a consequent dependence on the continuous production and exchange of goods and services between specialists, are so similar that biologists have some preparation to understand the economic problems of modern societies. Virchow became so interested that, in addition to making his great contribution to the understanding of disease, he became a political figure of considerable stature in Germany. Finally, to round off his career, he became a great anthropologist.

**The Developing Integration of Histology With Biochemistry.** The resolving power of the light microscope was great enough to reveal not only that cells in various parts of the body are structurally specialized to perform special functions but also indications of a specialization of structure for the performance of different functions within the cell itself. With the development, during the 1950's, of methods that permitted the great resolving power of the electron microscope to be brought to bear effectively on the study of biologic materials, it was established that there was indeed a profound degree of structural specialization within cells. This finding gave impetus to biochemists and histologists to attempt to determine the particular functions of these different structural components of cells. Advantage was taken of the fact that different cell components have different densities; this permitted their separation by differential centrifugation, and by the biochemical study of different fractions so obtained, much was learned about the particular biochemical functions of different cell components. The functions of different parts of the cell were also studied while in position within the cell by the technics of the rapidly developing science of histochemistry. As a result, the functions and the chemical interdependence of many individual structural components of cells have now been established, and a whole new world has been opened up for further exploration, a world that involves the relation between structure and function at, or close to, the molecular level; this area in general is termed molecular biology. Consequently, it has become impossible for the biochemist who discusses the chemistry of cells to refrain from describing intracellular structure. It has likewise made it impossible for the histologist or the cytologist to discuss intelligently the various structures within the cell without discussing their biochemical functions, and, at this level particularly, histology integrates closely with biochemistry.

The foregoing, it is hoped, will acquaint the student first with the nature and, secondly, with the scope, of histology. It is hoped that it will also indicate that *as knowledge deepens, the borders between different biologic disciplines become less distinct.* Indeed, at the level of the cell, the disciplines of histology, cytology, biochemistry, cell physiology and genetics become sufficiently interwoven to pose a problem as to how and where teaching in this area—which is generally referred to as *cell biology*—should be conducted. As matters stand, students will receive instruction in this area in several different courses, and in some instances in special courses. One very practical result of the breakdown of interdisciplinary borders at the level of the cell is that the student will find that what he now learns in one subject will help him to learn, and pass examinations in, other subjects.

**The Route Followed in a Course of Instruction in Histology.** We are now in a position to discuss briefly the route that will be followed in this book and probably also in the usual course of histology.

We have shown that in order to study the microscopic anatomy of the various organs and parts of the organ systems of the body, it is desirable to possess a thorough knowledge of the 4 basic tissues, because the organs are all built of tissues. Accordingly, as has already been described, our route passes through the tissues before proceeding to the microscopic structure of the organs and allied structures. Next, we have explained that there is much new knowledge about cells; and indeed, there are so many interesting things that should be learned about cells in general before it is practicable to begin learning about the various ways in which they are specialized to perform special functions in the different tissues, that before beginning the study of tissues we shall first study cell structure and cell biology in some detail. Therefore, our route will lead from cells to tissues and from tissues to the microscopic anatomy of organs. But, even before we begin the study of cells, we must describe the methods by which cells, tissues and organs are studied in histology, for these are the methods that the student will either use or at least understand if he is to learn from them. Accordingly, the route we shall follow will be (1) how histology is studied, (2) cell structure and cell biology, (3) the tissues of the body and (4) the microscopic anatomy of the parts of the organ systems.

# 2    How Histology Is Studied

We shall begin by describing the simplest and most common method used in the study of histology. However, before doing so we must mention that although there are 4 basic tissues, each with a name of its own, in describing *histologic methods* the word *tissue* is not qualified but used in a nonspecific way; that is, anything cut from the body is referred to simply as a piece of tissue.

**The Term "Section."** The student, in the histology laboratory, will mostly study, with his microscope, preparations termed *sections*. A section is a very thin slice of tissue, laid flat on a glass slide, stained and mounted in a medium of proper refractive index and covered with a very thin square piece of glass called a *coverslip*. It is usual for the student to be provided with, or have access to, a box of sections cut from all representative tissues and organs of the body.

The various ways by which sections can be prepared for general and special purposes constitutes much of the subject matter of *histologic technic*. Many books have been written about this subject; several are listed at the end of this chapter for any reader who wishes detailed information.

Although the usual student who takes a course in histology does not need an exhaustive knowledge of histologic technic, he should know enough about it to study various kinds of sections intelligently. Here, information will be given at that level. Most sections for student use are prepared by the *paraffin technic*.

### THE PARAFFIN TECHNIC

The several steps in the preparation of a section by this technic will now be described.

**1. Obtaining the Tissue.** Tissue for microscopic sections should be obtained as soon as possible after death or, if obtained at operation, as soon as possible after the tissue is removed so that the tissue can be *fixed* (next step to be described) immediately.

The small piece of tissue that is taken, which will subsequently be sliced into thin slices for sections, should be cut from the body with a minimum of handling, and using a very sharp knife. A dull knife or scissors squeezes tissue and distorts the arrangement of cells in the piece taken. Furthermore, the piece should be not a "chunk" of tissue but a slice thin enough so that the fixative that will be employed in the next step will penetrate it quickly and thoroughly.

**2. Fixation.** As soon as a person or an animal dies, his tissues begin to undergo progressive changes due to autolysis, that is to say, self-digestion or *postmortem (after death) degeneration*. The same changes begin in a piece of tissue that is removed from a living body at operation. These autolytic processes alter the appearance of the tissue, and, if they are allowed to proceed for any length of time, they render tissue unfit for study with the microscope. As will be learned, autolytic changes occur more quickly in some tissues than others, and the rate at which they occur is related to temperature; that is one reason for refrigerating bodies on which postmortem examinations are to be made.

Postmortem degeneration is prevented or arrested when tissue is placed in certain fluids called *fixatives*. The chief function of a fixative is to penetrate the tissue and "set" its components in a state that is as close as possible to their state in life. Fixatives also kill any bacteria that might be present which otherwise might grow in the dead tissue and alter its appearance still further. Another function of fixatives is that they harden tissue so that it can be sliced into thin sections more readily. In addition, some fixatives increase the affinity of certain components of tissue for dyes that are subsequently used in staining. Fixatives "set" and harden tissue chiefly by coagulating sols and, indeed, if no chemical fixatives are available, the sols of tissue, like those of the white of an egg, can be coagulated and hardened by heat.

Probably the commonest fixing solution

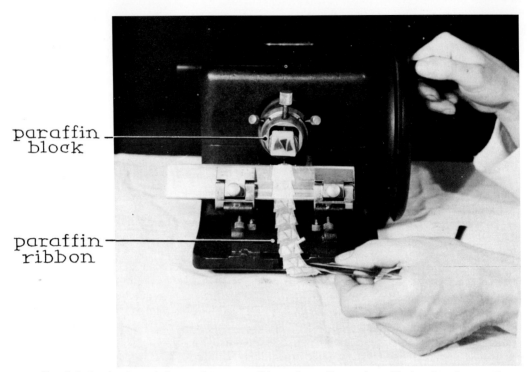

paraffin
block

paraffin
ribbon

FIG. 2-1. A microtome being used to cut a ribbon of paraffin sections. Notice that the paraffin block has 3 pieces of tissue embedded in it, and the outline of these may be seen in each of the sections whose edges are adhering to one another to form the ribbon.

used is a 4 per cent solution of formaldehyde. However, a great variety of other chemicals are used, among them mercury bichloride, potassium dichromate, acetic acid, picric acid, osmic acid and ethyl alcohol. Many of the better fixatives are mixtures. These are often named after the people who devised them— for example, Bouin's fluid. There is no perfect fixative, and the choice of one usually is determined by the particular tissue component that is to be studied and by the stain that is to be used.

3. **Dehydration.** Tissue contains much water. In making a paraffin section a piece of tissue must be thoroughly and completely infiltrated with paraffin wax. Paraffin, of course, is not soluble in water, and a piece of tissue with its normal water content could lie in melted paraffin wax for days without becoming infiltrated with wax. This difficulty is overcome by a 2-step procedure. First, the piece of tissue, fresh from the fixative, is placed successively in solutions of alcohol of increasing strength, ending with a couple of passages through absolute alcohol. As a result of this process all the water in the tissue is replaced by alcohol. This step is known as dehydration. Other dehydrating agents are also available (see modern books on histologic technic if information on this matter is required).

4. **Clearing.** At first thought, it might seem that this first step brought us no further along in our attempt to infiltrate a piece of tissue with paraffin wax because alcohol, like water, is not soluble in paraffin. But, happily, certain chemicals are soluble both in alcohol and in melted paraffin wax; these are often termed *clearing agents*. Xylol, toluol, chloroform, benzene and cedar oil are examples. So the piece of tissue is taken from the absolute alcohol and placed in a clearing agent, and, just as the alcohol replaced the water, the clearing agent replaces the alcohol in the tissue. (Clearing agents are so called because some of them tend to make tissue translucent.)

5. **Embedding.** The piece of tissue is now put into melted paraffin wax in an oven warm enough to keep the wax liquid. Following this, while still in the oven, the original wax is replaced by fresh wax at frequent intervals. By this time the wax has permeated the tissue and replaced all the clearing agents. This paraffin is allowed to harden in the form of a block that contains the piece of tissue. A paraffin "block" containing 3 separate little pieces of tissue and mounted on a microtome is illustrated in Figure 2-1.

Today, the various steps from fixation to infiltration by paraffin are often done automatically by tissue-processing machines.

6. **Sectioning.** The ease with which thin shavings can be cut from a candle suggests the reason for embedding tissues in paraffin. Tissue embedded in, and so impregnated with, paraffin may be sliced very thinly. For most kinds of microscopic work the slices must be extremely thin, usually between 3 and 10 *microns* (a micron is 1/1,000 mm.). To cut such thin slices necessitates special equipment, a slicing machine, sturdy yet capable of delicate movements, called a *microtome*, and an extremely sharp, heavy knife, a *microtome knife* (Fig. 2-1).

A microtome has an arrangement whereby a paraffin block can be firmly attached to it, and it operates so that when the crank is turned, the paraffin block is swept past the edge of the knife and then back again. Between each full stroke the paraffin block is moved a few microns nearer the knife edge. Hence, each sweep of the block past the knife results in a thin slice being cut from the face of the block. Each slice, after it is cut, tends to adhere to the knife edge until it is displaced by the next slice, and then it adheres to the free edge of the slice that displaces it. In this fashion a *paraffin ribbon*, consisting of individual slices adhering to one another, comes away from the machine (Fig. 2-1). Each slice, of course, passes through the tissue embedded in the block, hence each slice of paraffin contains a slice of tissue. On close inspection of Figure 2-1, the 3 pieces of tissue in each paraffin slice may be seen.

7. **Attaching Sections to Slides.** A ribbon of paraffin sections is gently laid down (lower right of Fig. 2-2), and the individual sections are carefully separated from one another by a

Fig. 2-2. A ribbon of paraffin sections from the microtome is shown at the lower right. The individual sections in such a ribbon are separated and floated on a little water on glass slides, and wrinkles in them are straightened on the warm plate as shown at left.

scalpel. One surface of a glass slide is now made a little sticky by rubbing it with a weak solution of egg albumen or some other adhesive medium. Then a little water is floated over the slide, and a single paraffin section is floated on the water. The slide is warmed very gently on a heated plate so as to straighten out any wrinkles that may have formed (Fig. 2-2), for they form easily; then the water is drained off, and the paraffin section adheres to the slide. To make sure that it adheres, the slide is dried in an incubator for a few hours.

8. **Preparation for Staining.** Since most dyes that are used to stain sections are in the form of aqueous solutions, the paraffin that still infiltrates the thin slice of tissue that is now mounted on a slide must be removed before staining can be accomplished. Accordingly, the slide to which the paraffin-infiltrated

thin slice of tissue adheres is dipped, first into clearing agent to dissolve out the paraffin, next into absolute alcohol to dissolve out the clearing agent, next into jars of successively weaker solutions of alcohol and then finally into a jar of water. If the slide were examined at this point with an ordinary light microscope it would reveal little detail that would lend itself to interpretation; it would be like examining an exposed but undeveloped photographic negative. Contrast between different components in the thin slice of tissue, so that they may be distinguished, is obtained by using suitable dyes to stain the section. Commonly, at least two dyes are employed, one after the other.

Before describing some of the dyes commonly used to stain histologic sections, and such information as exists about their actions, we must turn our attention to the other side of the coin; that is, what are the materials in a section of tissue with which dyes can react? Here, we must first describe briefly something of the chemistry of the components of living tissue and then consider what is left of these in a paraffin section whose preparation required exposing the original tissue and the thin slices cut from it to the many chemical procedures already described.

## THE CHEMICAL COMPONENTS OF THE BODY TISSUES AND HOW THEY ARE AFFECTED BY THE PROCEDURES JUST DESCRIBED

Approximately 65 to 70 per cent of the human body is water, 15 per cent protein, 10 to 15 per cent lipid (fats and fatlike substances), 5 per cent inorganic material and around 1 per cent carbohydrate. Body tissues contain also a small percentage of organic substances of low molecular weight that are difficult to classify except in a miscellaneous group. Each of these main types of substance will now be considered briefly, as will what happens to them in the various procedures involved in preparing a paraffin section to the point where it is ready for staining.

1. **Water.** The free water of tissue is all removed by the dehydrating agents that are used as a preliminary to embedding in paraffin.

2. **The Proteins.** Proteins are the most important component of living tissue; this was probably first recognized by the Dutch agricultural chemist, Gerard Johannes Mulder, who wrote in 1838 that without protein life would be impossible on our planet. He was the first to use the word protein in his writings, the word is derived from the Greek *pröteios* which means "of first rank."

There are thousands of different proteins in the body. Since the molecules of proteins are in general of great size, they are termed *macromolecules*. Protein macromolecules are made up of nitrogen, carbon, hydrogen, oxygen and usually some sulfur.

Since some body protein is continuously being broken down, new protein has to be synthesized just as continuously if the body is to remain healthy. Since nitrogenous waste products resulting from protein breakdown are continuously lost from the body, new nitrogen-containing building blocks for protein synthesis must be taken into the body if the body is to replace with new protein the old protein that is lost. The common source of nitrogen-containing building blocks for protein is protein in the diet; this is broken down by digestion in the intestine to building blocks, and these are absorbed into the body and used to make new protein. This is why an adequate source of dietary protein is essential for the maintenance of health. Through carelessness, ignorance or want, diets are often inadequate in this respect.

Gelatin is a familiar protein. Dissolved in warm water its molecules are dispersed and remain suspended in the water for which they have an affinity; the colloidal solution so formed is spoken of as a *hydrophilic* (water-loving) *sol*. Placed in the refrigerator, however, the sol sets into a *gel*. Proteins exist both as gels and sols in the living body. The proteins that are normally in the form of gels are found mostly in, and indeed they mostly constitute, the nonliving intercellular substances that give form to the body; therefore, these proteins can be termed *structural proteins*. Gelled proteins are relatively unaffected by most fixing solutions and the other reagents used in preparing a section, although some reagents can be used which make them swell. This is true of the protein from which commercial gelatin is prepared; that is, *collagen*, an important intercellular substance in the body. Other proteins, however, particularly many of those that are contained within and make up the greater parts of living cells, are normally present in a sol type of colloidal solution. Most of these protein molecules are enzymes. Since such molecules are normally suspended in an aqueous medium, they could be washed out of tissue, hence *an important function of a fixative is to precipitate these proteins* so that they stay more or less in place as a section is being prepared. Different fixatives do this by somewhat different means. Formaldehyde, for example, enters into combination with protein macromolecules, forming linkages with and between them. Certain other fixatives act either by abstracting the water from the hydrated macromolecules of sols or changing the electrolyte concentration to the point where the macromolecules of the sol are no longer maintained in colloidal solution, but precipitate from it.

Each of the thousands of different protein macromolecules of the body is assembled, more or less in a linear manner, from simpler molecules known as amino acids. As will be learned in the student's biochemistry course, there are only about 20 of these: glycine, alanine, valine, isoleucine, leucine, phenylalanine, tyrosine, cystine, cysteine, methionine, serine, thionine, aspartic acid, glutamic acid, lysine, arginine, histidine, proline, hydroxyproline and tryptophan. The fact that thousands of different protein macromolecules can be made from only 20 amino acids is to be explained as follows: (1) the total *number* of amino acid molecules in each type of protein macromolecule is different from that of every other type of protein macromolecule, and it is generally large, for many protein macromolecules consist of thousands of amino acid molecules; indeed, some protein macromolecules are large enough to be seen in the electron microscope; (2) the *relative percentages* of amino acids differ in different proteins, and, indeed, not all the amino acids are represented in some proteins; (3) the sequences in which the amino acids are arranged along protein macromolecules is different in different proteins; and (4) the over-all structure of protein macromolecules of different types differs to some extent, as will be described presently.

The amino acids all have in common an

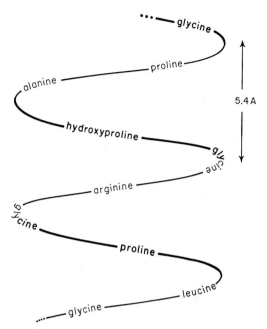

Fig. 2-3. Part of the helix of a collagen molecule. The front part of the coils is drawn as heavy lines; and the back part, as thin lines. The distance between 2 coils is 5.5 Å (0.00054 μ).

The amino acids glycine, proline and hydroxyproline are particularly abundant in collagen.

acidic carboxyl group and a basic amino or imino group. They differ from one another by their other groupings. When amino acids are assembled into protein macromolecules, the carboxyl group of one becomes linked with the amino group of the next one, whereas the other groupings on each amino acid, known as side chains, remain free. The linear assembly of amino acids builds up the chainlike protein macromolecule. The chain is often wound into the form of a regular helix, a small part of which is shown in Figure 2-3. There are also other arrangements, for example, the hormone insulin, which was the first protein macromolecule whose precise structure was elucidated, consists of two chains that are partly helicoidal and which are connected by two bridges built up by side chains and consisting of 2 sulphur atoms each. Side chains may be involved in many more than two bridges, and as a result, a main protein chain may become convoluted in a complex manner, as for instance in the protein ribonuclease.

The various amino acids from which protein macromolecules are assembled yield different kinds of side chains. The side chains of some amino acids contain groupings that ionize to form acids, while the side chains of other amino acids contain groupings that ionize as bases. Since protein macromolecules have both kinds of amino acids, proteins can act either as acids or bases depending on conditions, and so proteins are said to be *amphoteric* (*amphoteros* = both). But since different proteins vary in their respective contents of amino acids that ionize into acids and those that ionize into bases, different proteins, at the point of neutrality, are either predominantly acid or basic, and this is of importance, as we shall see later, with regard to their staining with acid and basic dyes.

Proteins may be conjugated with other substances such as phosphoric acid (phosphoproteins), sugars (glycoproteins) and nucleic acids (nucleoproteins). The last deserve special comment here.

NUCLEOPROTEINS AND NUCLEIC ACIDS. Unlike glycoproteins, nucleoproteins are readily split into their component proteins and nucleic acids. Thus in sections, the nucleic acids may be readily removed with specific enzymes, as will be described later, while the proteins are left in the section. The nucleic acids rank with proteins in biologic importance. Nucleic acids consist of linear arrangements of units termed nucleotides. Each nucleotide is composed of a pentose sugar, a phosphate group, and a base; the arrangement is illustrated here in Figure 2-4 and also in Figure 6-21 B, which is in Chapter 6, where nucleic acids will be discussed further.

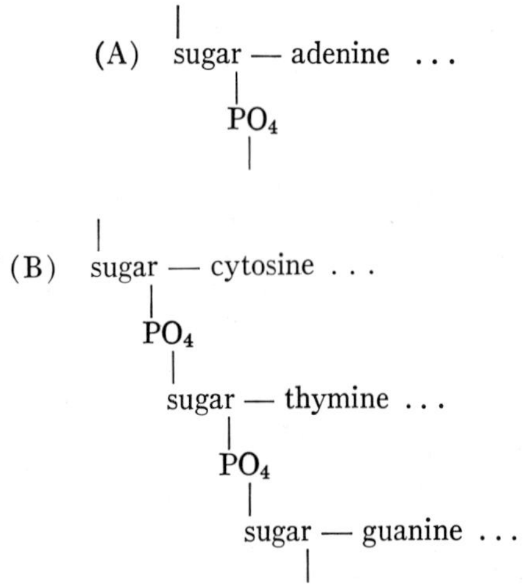

Nucleic acids are found in all living cells and only in living cells; they are not a component of intercellular substance. There are only two kinds of nucleic acid; the first is termed deoxyribonucleic acid (commonly abbreviated to DNA), and the other, ribonucleic acid (commonly abbreviated to RNA). These are both preserved in cells by the usual fixatives. Since the nucleic acids will be considered at some length in Chapter 6, they will not be described further here.

3. **Lipids.** Most of the fat in the body represents stored food and exists in the form of large droplets within special fat cells, as will be described later. In addition to this fat, however, fatty materials enter into the composition of many complex compounds in many different kinds of cells. Both the pure fat and the fat-containing compounds are dissolved away in preparing the usual paraffin section, because fats are extracted from tissue by alcohol and particularly by clearing agents. A very few compounds containing lipid materials may remain stainable, but for the most part the former presence of fat in tissue is indicated in the usual paraffin section only by the presence in the section of rounded empty spaces. However, if tissue is fixed in osmium tetroxide, the fat present is rendered sufficiently insoluble in alcohol and clearing agents to be demonstrable in paraffin sections, for the osmium combines with the fat to form an insoluble, blackish complex.

4. **Inorganic Materials and Other Substances of Low Molecular Weight.** It has been mentioned already that at least 65 per cent of the body is water. It should now be observed that numerous inorganic salts as well as organic substances of low molecular weight (acetate, certain hormones and vitamins, etc.) are dissolved in this water to different extents, depending on location. Furthermore, in certain tissues (bones, teeth and some cartilage), relatively insoluble salts, chiefly of calcium, are precipitated during life; hence deposits of mineral are normal constituents of these par-

$$
\begin{array}{l}
\qquad\qquad | \\
\text{(A)}\quad \text{sugar — adenine} \;\ldots \\
\qquad\qquad | \\
\qquad\qquad \text{PO}_4 \\
\qquad\qquad |
\end{array}
$$

$$
\begin{array}{l}
\qquad | \\
\text{(B)}\quad \text{sugar — cytosine} \;\ldots \\
\qquad | \\
\qquad \text{PO}_4 \\
\qquad | \\
\qquad\quad \text{sugar — thymine} \;\ldots \\
\qquad\qquad\quad | \\
\qquad\qquad\quad \text{PO}_4 \\
\qquad\qquad\quad | \\
\qquad\qquad\qquad \text{sugar — guanine} \;\ldots \\
\qquad\qquad\qquad\qquad |
\end{array}
$$

FIG. 2-4. (A) A nucleotide. (B) A chain of nucleotides in a nucleic acid.

ticular tissues. Moreover, certain minerals, for example iron and zinc, are concentrated to some extent in certain cells in the body.

The inorganic salts and substances of low molecular weight that are dissolved in water in the body are lost to varying extents when tissue is immersed in the usual aqueous fixatives. (If these substances are to be retained in the sections, the freeze-drying technic, to be described later, should be used.) With the routine paraffin method, salts and small molecules that are not lost in the fixative usually will be extracted during dehydration and clearing. However, the mineral deposits in teeth, bone and cartilage are so insoluble that they are not materially affected by aqueous fixing solutions unless the latter contain acid. In order to cut sections of these calcified tissues, measures usually are taken after fixation to dissolve the deposits by the use of *decalcifying solutions*; these contain acids or acid salts and act to convert relatively insoluble salts to soluble salts, which wash away. When tissues are decalcified they may be processed in the ordinary way, but when sections are cut, only the organic material which the mineral formerly impregnated is left to mark the location of the mineral in the living. (By special technics it is possible to cut sections of some calcified tissues without previously removing the mineral from them, but, as might be imagined, cutting stonelike materials with a knife is not easy.)

As already noted, certain body cells may contain concentrations of certain minerals under normal conditions and to a much greater extent in certain diseases. For example, there are diseases characterized by accumulations of iron and copper, respectively, in parts of the body. Any substantial aggregation of mineral is generally sufficiently insoluble to withstand ordinary processing and so can be demonstrated by special technics in paraffin sections.

5. **Carbohydrates** exist in body tissues both as simple sugars and as polymers. The simple sugars are organic substances of low molecular weight and are commonly dissolved away in preparing a paraffin section. The molecules of the polymers, like those of proteins, are usually of a large size and hence are also termed *macromolecules*. By taking proper precautions, carbohydrate macromolecules can, for the most part, be retained in tissue through the processing required in preparing a paraffin section. The carbohydrate macromolecules are of 3 types.

A. The simplest is animal starch—*glycogen*—and is found in many cells of the body. Glycogen is a polymer composed of many molecules of glucose attached to each other in straight or branching chains. It was formerly believed that glycogen was dissolved by aqueous fixatives from cells which had stored it, but it is now recognized that, whereas glycogen hydrolyzes quickly after death, and as a result becomes increasingly soluble, most of it will remain if the tissue is fixed immediately after death or removal from the body, even if aqueous fixatives are used.

B. A second type of carbohydrate polymer, which is found within many of the intercellular spaces of the body, is characterized by the presence of prominent acidic side chains and therefore is referred to as *acid mucopolysaccharide*. This type of polymer also contains mildly basic side chains, usually acetylated hexosamines. The acidic side chains may be either simple organic acid groups—COOH—or sulfuric acid groups. The type that contains the former is a jellylike material known as hyaluronic acid. The slippery fluid that fills joint cavities is a solution of hyaluronic acid. Hyaluronic acid is also distributed in many other intercellular substances where it permeates between other intercellular substances. The polymers that contain sulfuric acid groups may be in the form of either sols or gels; the most common are firm gels. An example of the latter is the chondroitin sulfuric acid of cartilage.

The acid mucopolysaccharides that have sulfuric acid groups are often referred to as sulfated mucopolysaccharides. The sulfated mucopolysaccharides are fixed readily in tissue by ordinary fixatives. The retention in a section of the more soluble hyaluronic acid, particularly in sites where it is not closely associated with other components of intercellular substance, may present some problems.

C. A third type of macromolecule in which carbohydrate is a component is composed of both protein and carbohydrate. Here the carbohydrate fraction is composed of simple sugars (glucose, galactose, fructose, etc.) attached together as well as to sialic acid. Substances of this type will be referred to as *glycoproteins*. The slippery mucus of saliva (a sol) is a glycoprotein. Mucus, as we shall see, is made in certain types of cells, and its fixation in them presents some problems. In general, fixatives that are acidic and contain some alcohol fix it in position most firmly.

Having now described what is left in a section that has been processed by the paraffin technic to the point where it is ready for staining, we shall next consider what happens in the staining procedure.

## THE STAINING OF SECTIONS

**Staining With Basic and Acid Stains.** It is common practice to stain sections with at least two stains, one after the other. Generally the first stain used is a basic stain and the second an acid stain. When the stained section is examined, it will be seen that the basic stain has colored certain tissue components and the acid stain has colored certain others. The tissue components that are colored by the basic stain are referred to as being *basophilic* and those colored by the acid stain as *acidophilic* which, of course, means that these tissue components respectively *love* basic stains and acid stains. The most commonly used (but not necessarily all) basic stains impart a blue-to-purple color to the tissue components with which they combine, and the most commonly used (but not necessarily all) acid stains impart a pink-to-red color to the tissue components with which they combine. This is true of the commonly used combination of hematoxylin and eosin; so, in a section stained with these two dyes, basophilic components of tissue are colored blue-to-purple with the basic dye, hematoxylin, while acidophilic components of tissue are colored pink-to-red with the acid dye, eosin.

The bulk of the material in a section that is thus colored is protein or conjugated protein. So, if we are to understand how basophilic and acidophilic substances differ, we must learn why, under normal conditions, some proteins stain with basic stains and some with acid stains. But we must first learn the difference between acid and basic stains.

In order to color anything, stains must dissociate in an aqueous solution into anions and cations. The ability of stains to impart color depends on their having a color-bearing

organic grouping in either the anions or the cations into which they dissociate. If the color-bearing grouping is in the cation, the stain is said to be a *basic stain*. If the color-bearing grouping is in the anion, the stain is said to be an *acid stain*.

Proteins that have predominantly acid groupings tend to stain well with basic stains because when these groupings dissociate, the anions of these acid groupings which were formerly bound to H ions become available to react with and become firmly bound to the color-bearing cations of the basic stain. On the other hand, the predominantly basic groupings of basic proteins dissociate into fixed cations and free OH ions, and the color-bearing anions of the acid stain can then combine firmly with the cations of the dissociated basic groupings.

**Staining With Hematoxylin and Eosin—an H and E Section.** It was pointed out above that histologic sections are commonly stained with two dyes. The first is hematoxylin, which colors basophilic material blue or purple. Hematoxylin does not act as a basic stain directly but indirectly because a substance called hematein—a basic stain—forms in hematoxylin solutions. The second dye is the acid stain *eosin*, which colors acidophilic material (sometimes called eosinophilic material) pink or red. Sections stained in this manner are often referred to as H and E sections.

Another term encountered in connection with staining is mordants; these are chemicals that are sometimes used to facilitate the uptake or the retention of some dyes. For example, one staining method known as iron hematoxylin depends on the sections being first treated with an iron salt (which in this case is a mordant) which combines with certain proteins only, and later the stain attaches itself to the bound iron, as was shown by Puchtler.

A few stains act merely by dissolving in some tissue component. The typical example is that of the Sudan dyes, which stain lipid by dissolving into structures rich in one or the other of the lipids.

Other staining methods are used to supplement what can be learned from H and E sections, and these will be described either in Chapter 4 or periodically throughout the text in relation to the structures they are specially used to elucidate.

**Mounting.** After the section is stained, it must be treated in some way to convert it into a permanent preparation, and this must be done with materials that have suitable optical properties.

The first step is to remove the water from the section by passing it through solutions of alcohol of increasing strengths. After absolute alcohol, the section is transferred to a solution of clearing agent. The slide is wiped dry except for the area containing the thin slice of tissue (which is now permeated with clearing agent). A drop of mounting medium (for example, Canada Balsam) is put on the section or on a coverslip, and the coverslip is dropped gently on the section so that the mounting medium covers and permeates the slice of tissue. Then, as the coverslip is pressed firmly onto the section, the mounting medium spreads out to form a thin film (which contains the slice of tissue) between the coverslip and the slide. The subsequent "setting" of the mounting medium firmly attaches the coverslip to the slide. Satisfactory mounting media must be capable of displacing the clearing agent in the slice of tissue and of "setting" into an inert solid possessing a proper refractive index.

## OTHER WAYS OF PREPARING SECTIONS

Three other methods are employed fairly extensively for special purposes.

**Paraffin Infiltration by the Freeze-Drying Method.** When it is desired to retain small molecules in sections, it is necessary to avoid preliminary treatment of tissues with fixatives, dehydrating solutions or clearing agents which would wash out these molecules. This is done by the freeze-drying method. In using this method, fresh tissue is frozen in liquid air, or in isopentane chilled in liquid nitrogen. Dehydration is accomplished by storing the frozen tissue in a chilled chamber which is kept exhausted of air and vapor by means of a vacuum pump (certain chemicals are used to help to remove the vapor). When all the water of the tissue has turned to vapor and has been removed, the temperature can be raised to that of melted paraffin, into which the tissue is placed (or it can be placed in paraffin oil at a lower temperature), where it becomes infiltrated with the melted wax (or the oil). It is

FIG. 2-5. A section being cut by the celloidin method.

recommended that this step also be carried out under a vacuum.

**The Frozen Section Technic.** In employing this method, a piece of tissue which is fresh or has been hardened in fixing fluid is placed on the stage of a microtome that has an outlet below the stage, through which carbon dioxide gas can be released to cool the stage sufficiently for the piece of tissue to become frozen. This makes the tissue firm enough to allow fairly thin slices to be cut from its surface by the microtome knife which, in this type of microtome, is arranged so that it sweeps over the surface of the frozen block of tissue horizontally. The slices are gathered from the knife with a brush and, after allowing them to become flattened out on water, they are gently placed on slides to which they adhere, and so can be stained.

Frozen sections are increasingly commonly cut in a cryostat, which is a piece of apparatus that permits the microtome knife as well as the block of tissue to be kept below freezing so that the whole operation of preparing the section is conducted at the same low temperature.

Certain of the solutions, particularly the clearing agents, through which the tissue is passed in preparing the paraffin section dissolve out the fat that the tissue contains. Frozen sections can be prepared without exposing the tissue to these fat solvents. Hence, frozen sections can be stained profitably with specific fat stains. Another advantage of frozen sections is that they can be prepared very quickly; that is why the pathologist uses this technic at the operating room for his "quick section" diagnosis. But, in general, frozen sections are thicker than paraffin sections and not as satisfactory for general work. However, when cut in a cryostat, they can be of good quality and eminently suitable for certain kinds of histochemical studies.

**The Celloidin Method.** Celloidin is a celluloidlike material in which tissue can be embedded after suitable preliminary treatment. The procedures employed require no heat; they are all carried out at room temperature; hence, celloidin embedding does not tend to cause as much shrinkage of tissue as do the steps employed in paraffin embedding. Furthermore, relatively large objects, such as teeth, can be sectioned to best advantage by the celloidin method because the celloidin holds all their different parts firmly in place. Possessing these advantages, celloidin sections obviously have great usefulness. But preparing these takes longer, and they are usually thicker than paraffin sections. They are cut on a heavy microtome which has a knife mounted so that its edge may be drawn across the face of the block at an angle (Fig. 2-5).

The preparation of ultrathin sections for study with the light microscope will be described in Chapter 4 in connection with electron microscopy.

## REFERENCES

### GENERAL REFERENCES ON HISTOLOGIC TECHNICS

Armed Forces Institute of Pathology: Manual of Histologic and Special Staining Technics, ed. 2, New York, McGraw-Hill-Blakiston, 1949.

Baker, J. R.: Principles of Biological Microtechnique, New York, Wiley, 1958.
————: Staining *in* Gray, Peter (ed.): The Encyclopedia of Biological Science, p. 969, New York, Reinhold, 1961.
Carleton, H. M.: Histological Technique, ed. 3 (Oxford Medical Publications), London, Oxford, 1957.
Clayden, E. C.: Practical Section Cutting and Staining, ed. 3, London, Churchill, 1955.
Conn, H. J.: Biological Stains, ed. 7, Baltimore, Williams & Wilkins, 1961.
Gomori, G.: Microscopic Histochemistry: Principles and Practice, Chicago, Univ. Chicago Press, 1952.
Gray, P.: Handbook of Basic Microtechnique, ed. 2, New York, McGraw-Hill-Blakiston, 1952.
————: The Microtomist's Formulary and Guide, New York, McGraw-Hill-Blakiston, 1954.
Gurr, E.: A Practical Manual of Medical and Biological Staining Techniques, London, Leonard Hill Ltd., 1953.
Krajian, A. A., and Gradwohl, R. B. H.: Histopathological Technic, ed. 2, St. Louis, Mosby, 1952.
McClung's Handbook of Microscopical Technique, ed. 3, New York, Hoeber, 1950.
McManus, J. F. A., and Moury, R. W.: Staining Methods: Histological and Histochemical, New York, Hoeber, 1960.
Romeis, B.: Mikroskopische Technik, München, Leibniz, 1948.
Simmons, J. S., and Gentzkow, C. J.: Medical and Public Health Laboratory Methods, ed. 6, Philadelphia, Lea & Febiger, 1955.

### SPECIAL REFERENCES ON THE FREEZE-DRY METHOD

Bell, L. G. E.: The application of freezing and drying techniques in cytology, Internat. Rev. Cytol. *1*:35, 1952.
Harris, R. J. C.: Biological Applications of Freezing and Drying, New York, Acad. Press, 1954.

### REFERENCES ON THE CHEMICAL COMPONENTS OF TISSUES

See textbooks of biochemistry and of histochemistry.

# 3    The Study and the
## Interpretation of Sections

## WHY 3-DIMENSIONAL VISUALIZATION IS NECESSARY IN HISTOLOGY

In the study of gross anatomy, the student may both see and make dissections. By this method he can find out where an artery or a nerve comes from and where it goes; he can lift up muscles and look underneath them and can inspect organs from many different aspects. Dissections, then, allow the various structures in the body to be studied in their 3 dimensions. However, there is another method of studying anatomy that is useful for supplementing the information gained from dissections: that of studying cross sections of the human body. Cross sections are essentially slices cut across a whole frozen body at different levels. Learning gross anatomy by studying cross sections alone would be difficult because the cut surface of a cross section, which is all that may be seen when it is examined, presents only 2 dimensions. Without other knowledge, one could not tell from a single cross section how far any organ, blood vessel or nerve seen in that particular cross section extended up or down the body, or whether it became larger or smaller above or below the section being studied. To tell this it would be necessary to examine consecutive cross sections, but it is easier to gain this knowledge from dissections, in which the structures of the body may be seen in 3 dimensions.

Since it is not practical to learn microscopic structure by making dissections that allow things to be seen in 3 dimensions under the microscope, most microscopic anatomy must be learned from the study of thin slices cut through the various tissues and organs of the body. This, then, presents much the same problem as would occur if the student were forced to learn gross anatomy from only the study of cross sections. Of course, in microscopic anatomy, longitudinal and oblique sections may be used as well as cross sections;

nevertheless, it is a great handicap to have to learn 3-dimensional structure from thin slices which, for all practical purposes, have no depth. For example, a single thin slice cut from an organ may give a false impression of its architecture. This can be illustrated easily by cutting slices through such a simple thing as a hard-boiled egg. As is shown in Figure 3-1, no single one of the 4 slices illustrated would give a person who never had seen an egg a correct idea of its structure. For this reason, in the study of an organ it is usual to use several sections, taken from different sites and in different planes. Even so, the structure of some organs is so complicated that it has been necessary to make what are called *reconstructions* in order to learn the details of their microscopic structure.

## HOW RECONSTRUCTIONS ARE MADE

To make a reconstruction, say, of a small but typical part of an organ, the whole part is embedded and cut into serial sections. Each section is mounted and numbered in the order in which it was cut. Then the first one cut is put into a microprojector, an instrument which projects a greatly enlarged image of a section on a screen. However, the screen is first covered with a thin, transparent material such as cellophane so that the image of the section thrown on the screen may be carefully traced out of the cellophane, both with regard to its outline and its important internal detail. Then the cellophane sheet is removed from the screen and placed on a wax plate, the thickness of which is decided by multiplying the thickness of the section by the number of diameters it was magnified on the screen. The drawing on the cellophane is retraced over the wax plate so as to make an impression on it. Next, the wax plate is cut with a knife or a fine saw so as to conform to the tracing in outline and also in all important detail in the interior of the section. The finished wax plate

17

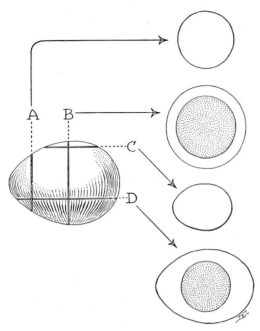

thus becomes a greatly enlarged replica of the tiny thin piece of tissue that was mounted on the slide (Fig. 3-2). The same procedure is employed for each successive serial section until finally a greatly enlarged replica of every section cut from the original part of the organ is obtained. The wax plates now are put together in the right order, and when this is accomplished, one has a huge replica of the whole part of the organ, one large enough to study with the naked eye. Cuts may be made into this in such a way that different segments can be removed at will, and this allows one to see and understand its various internal structural features.

## SOME AIDS TO MAKING MENTAL RECONSTRUCTIONS

Enough time is not available for the student to make any reconstructions himself—except mental ones—and these must be made almost every time that the microscope is used. When the student looks at any section, he always should try to visualize the series of sections that would lie above and below the one under view. This helps one to appreciate the structure of the organ in 3 dimensions, and this appreciation helps, in turn, to explain why certain things appear as they do in the single slice being studied.

The art of making mental reconstructions, of visualizing in 3 dimensions when only 2 are

FIG. 3-1. Diagram showing how sections cut through an object in different planes or at different levels may give different impressions about its structure. A hard-boiled egg is shown at the left side of this illustration. Notice how cross sections cut at A and B would be different from one another and in turn different from longitudinal sections cut at C and D.

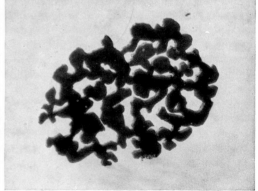

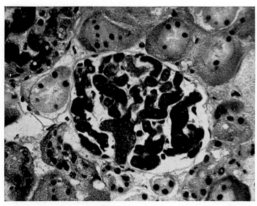

FIG. 3-2. (*Left*) A medium-power photomicrograph cut through the glomerulus of a kidney whose blood vessels were injected with a material that shows black in the photomicrograph. (*Right*) A photograph of a wax reconstruction of a similarly prepared glomerulus (but not the same one).

seen, may be learned by a difficult method or an easy one. The difficult way is to plunge immediately into the study of histologic sections; the easy way is to practice first on some common and familiar objects. Now it so happens that some common and familiar objects are very much like certain things in the body. For example, most organs of the body contain a complicated assortment of tubes, partitions and cords; and these extend throughout the substance of organs in every direction and may follow straight or curved paths. Some organs, indeed, consist of little more than these three things. The lung, for example, contains tubes that carry air and tubes that carry body fluids. It is riddled with partitions, and it contains some nerves that are in the form of cords. Therefore, sections cut through the lung will pass through tubes and partitions, and some of them through cords; and as all these run in many different directions, a section cuts them at many different angles. So if the student has a knowledge of how straight tubes, curved tubes, partitions and bundles of cords appear in slices cut through them at different angles (Figs. 3-3 to 3-6), he will be able not only to recognize these various structures for what they are when he sees them in a section, no matter at what angle they are cut, but also, by deducing the various planes in which they must have been disposed to present the particular appearance they present in the section, he will be able to build up a mental 3-dimensional reconstruction of the piece of organ or tissue from which the single slice under observation was cut.

Therefore, it is of the greatest importance, in learning to interpret sections, to become familiar with the appearances presented by slices cut through straight tubes, curved tubes, partitions and bundles of cords in different planes. Figures 3-3 to 3-6 are provided to assist in this matter. The student is advised to study them carefully, and then, as he proceeds to the study of histologic sections, to be prepared to refer back to these 4 figures frequently. Those students who are relatively deficient in their aptitude for visualizing 3 dimensions from seeing only 2 are advised to purchase some plasticine of different colors and construct models, and then to slice up the models with a knife so that they may have direct experience in associating the 2-dimen-

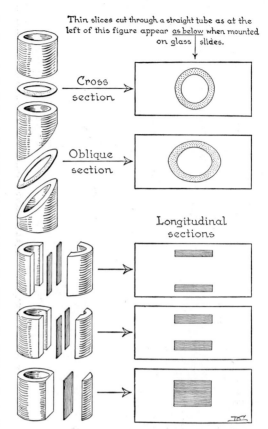

FIG. 3-3. Diagram showing how sections cut through straight tubes in different planes have different appearances when mounted on slides and viewed through the microscope. Notice that it is possible to cut a longitudinal section of a tube without having a lumen in the section.

sional appearances presented by cut surfaces with the 3-dimensional models from which the slices are cut.

## HOW TO STUDY A SECTION

### INSPECTION WITH THE NAKED EYE

The student, before examining a section with the microscope, should hold the section to the light and examine it with the naked eye. Some reasons for this are:

1. The *color* of the stained slice of tissue may give a clue about the particular tissue that has been sectioned. For example, lymphatic tissue (described later in this book) has a great affinity for hematoxylin; hence, blue patches seen with the naked eye suggest

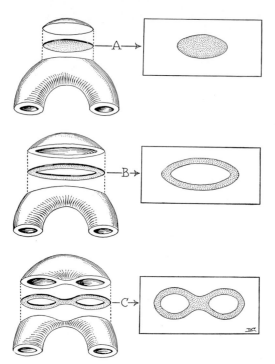

FIG. 3-4. Diagram showing the different appearances of sections cut through a curved tube at different levels.

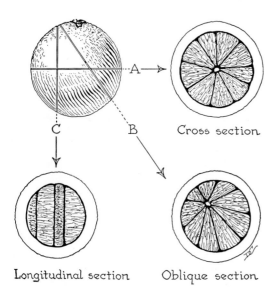

FIG. 3-5. Diagram showing the different appearances presented by sections cut in different planes through an object which contains partitions (an orange).

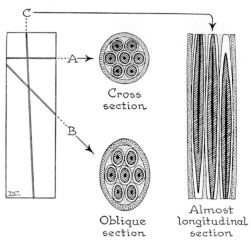

FIG. 3-6. Diagram showing how the appearance of sections cut through a cable containing many insulated wires differs according to the plane in which the section is cut.

its presence. Another example is provided by fat tissue, for, in paraffin sections, it absorbs almost no color; hence, irregular, seemingly empty spaces seen with the naked eye suggest the presence of fat.

2. The outer and, if present, the inner *profile* of the slice of tissue may give clues about the particular structure or organ that has been sectioned. For example, from an inspection by the naked eye, some sections appear as rings; this suggests that they are cross sections cut through tubular structures, and this narrows the number of possibilities that must be considered in their identification. Generally, it is easy to recognize sections of joints, the eye, the fingernails or the toenails, and so on, from their profiles. Furthermore, many blocks of tissue that are obtained for sectioning are cut from organs so that the capsule of the organ is left on one side of the block. The capsular surface is generally smooth, whereas the other surfaces that have been cut with a knife are generally ragged. This can be noted from an inspection by the naked eye, and this gives the orientation necessary to examine the section intelligently.

## INSPECTION WITH THE MICROSCOPE

In the following text, a description of some of the parts of the microscope will be more or less combined with an account of how the instrument should be used to study a section to best advantage.

**The Mirror and Illumination.** Many modern microscopes have built-in illumination; that is, the lamp is mounted within the base. If not, a separate lamp is used, but then a mirror is necessary to direct the beam of light toward the object. The mirror (Fig. 3-7) has two surfaces: one flat and the other concave. For low-magnification work the concave surface may be used instead of the condenser (to be described presently) to focus the beam of light on the object. However, for high-power work a condenser (Fig. 3-7) is essential. Under these circumstances, the built-in lamp or mirror directs the beam of light through the condenser, and for this purpose the plane surface of the mirror is used. For studying stained sections, artificial light should be passed through a *ground glass* and a *blue filter*, or, if a blue filter has a ground surface, it may be used alone.

**The Condenser.** The condenser (Fig. 3-7), as its name implies, converges the roughly parallel beam of light that comes from the mirror below so that a cone of light emerges from its upper surface (Fig. 3-7). This converging cone of light passes through the aperture of the stage of the microscope and is directed at the section that is mounted on the stage (Fig. 3-7).

In using the high-power and the oil-immersion objectives it is of great importance to adjust the condenser to obtain optimum illumination of the section. This may be done as follows. The condenser, which can be moved up and down by a rack-and-pinion movement (Fig. 3-7), is adjusted so that an image of the light source, or, if the lamp has a lens and an aperture, the aperture itself, is focused in the plane of the object. A slight adjustment of the mirror or the lamp aperture may be necessary to ensure that the field is illuminated completely and uniformly.

**If the Field Under View Cannot Be Illuminated Brightly by Moving the Condenser.** With student microscopes it is not unusual for the condenser to slip down the sleeve into which it is fitted (Fig. 3-7). Under these conditions good illumination cannot be obtained, because the condenser cannot be raised high enough. This state of affairs should always be suspected when illumination is poor. The sim-

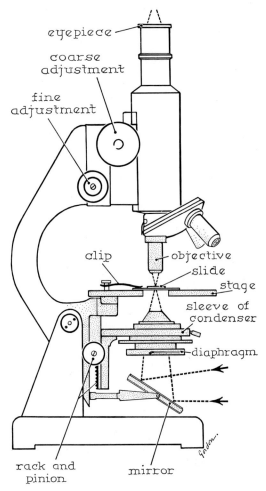

FIG. 3-7. Diagram of a microscope.

ple and obvious remedy is to push the condenser up its sleeve as far as it will go and then to tighten the little screw that fastens it in position.

An iris diaphragm, called the substage diaphragm, generally is built into the condenser just below the lenses. Its purpose is to provide a means for controlling the width of the beam of light entering the objective lens. Too wide a beam may cause glare, so the aperture should be reduced in size only to the point where glare is eliminated.

Further closure of the diaphragm, or lowering the condenser, sometimes is resorted to in order to improve contrast, but it should be realized that the increased contrast obtained in this way is gained at the expense of a loss in resolution. If lack of contrast is a problem, it is best to use a special type of microscope called a phase-contrast microscope which will be described in a later section.

**The Stage.** Today it is the fashion for students to buy microscopes with mechanical stages. To a right-handed person, the mechanical stage is controlled by the right hand, while the left hand manipulates the fine adjustment of the microscope. This is done first to keep the section in focus as the slide is moved about. If a mechanical stage is not available, a right-handed student should use only one clip to hold the slide in place, the clip that he would naturally put in position with his right hand. This clip should be pushed down firmly. With this arrangement, 2 fingers of one hand may be used to move the slide about, and the other hand may be used to manipulate the fine adjustment.

**The Objectives.** Student microscopes have 3 or better 4 objectives: (1) a very low-power objective that magnifies about 3 times and is used to scan the section; (2) a low-power objective that magnifies 10 times; (3) a high-power objective that magnifies 40 times; and (4) an oil-immersion objective that magnifies from 90 to 100 times.

The objectives are mounted on a revolving nosepiece; this has the form of a turntable and allows any objective to be swung into place below the microscope. The standard objectives supplied on new microscopes are commonly parfocal, which means that when the microscope is adjusted with any objective so that the image is in focus, the image will still be approximately in focus when any other objective is swung into place. However, if objectives that have been purchased independently are used, it cannot be expected that they will be parfocal; hence, each one that is used must be focused separately. In addition to the 3 standard objectives (10, 40 and 90 $\times$), it is desirable for the student microscope to have also a "scanning" objective which magnifies only 3 to 4 times. There should be accommodation for this objective also on the revolving turntable into which the other three objectives are screwed. Proper illumination of the relatively large area that can be seen with a scanning objective requires an additional lens that can be swung in place over the condenser and which should be swung *out* of place when any of the other 3 objectives are used.

**The Importance of Low-Power Objectives.** Beginners are too inclined to assume that the value of an objective varies directly with its ability to magnify. As a consequence, beginners tend to use the higher-power objectives too much and the low-power objectives too little. It is said that a famous pathologist, to combat this tendency, used to remove all the high-power objectives from the microscopes of those who came to study with him when they first arrived, and would release them only when the students had learned the enormous value of the low-power objectives.

The first rule in studying a section is to examine it with the naked eye. The second rule is to examine all of the section with the scanning objective and the low-power objective before using the higher powers. As the student gains experience, he will rely more and more on the thorough study of a section with the low-power objectives for identifying sections in ordinary laboratory work and at examinations.

**Use of the High-Power Objective.** In examining a section with the low-power objective a certain area may be seen which warrants a more detailed examination. Before switching to the high-power objective the section should be maneuvered under the low-power objective so that the area to be examined further is in the center of the field of vision. It should be realized that the high-power objective encompasses a much smaller field than the low-power objective; hence, if the area warranting further investigation is at one side of the low-power field it may be excluded from view when the high-power objective is used. So, areas to be examined with the high-power objective always should be centered first with the low-power objective. Likewise, areas to be examined with the oil-immersion objective should be centered first with the high-power objective.

**Use of the Oil-Immersion Objective.** The use of the oil-immersion objective is associated with a special difficulty: the objective must approach the coverslip of the section very closely. Hence, in bringing a section into focus with the oil-immersion objective there is a danger of making a direct contact between the coverslip of the slide and the objective, and this may cause injury to either or both. Probably the best way to bring the oil-immersion objective into focus safely is this: After centering the particular area to be examined with the high-power objective, raise the tube of the microscope with the coarse adjustment and switch on the oil-immersion objective. Place a drop of oil on the part of the slide that lies directly over the center of the condenser. Then lower the tube of the microscope, watching it from the side, until the objective is seen just entering the drop of oil. At this point the oil-immersion lens is still above the point at which the section would be in focus. So, one can now look through the microscope and lower the tube slowly with the fine adjustment until the field comes into focus. If it does not come into focus with a turn or two of the fine adjustment, it is best to stop and question whether or not something has gone wrong. Two possibilities should be considered: (1) there may be no stained part of the section under the oil-immersion objective, either because the slide was moved or because there is an open space of some sort in the section near its central part; or (2) the objective is *below* the level at which it is in focus. If color can be seen on looking down the microscope, the first possibility has become negated, and if the color has become better defined with focusing downward, the chances are that the objective is still above the point of focus and can be safely lowered somewhat farther. But, if there is reason to doubt, the tube should be raised, the oil wiped off the objective and the slide, the area centered with the high-power objective again and the rest of the procedure repeated. It is always best to proceed very cautiously until considerable experience has been gained.

**The Eyepiece.** The resolution of the microscope, that is, the ability to improve the detail of an object, is due only to the objective. The eyepiece (also called the ocular) enlarges the image produced by the objective but does not improve its quality.

Most microscopes are equipped with 2 or 3 eyepieces, which magnify 5, 8, 10, 12 or 15 times. For general use, the 8 $\times$ or 10 $\times$ eyepieces are recommended.

Very commonly eyepieces become dirty or misty. To know whether specks or hazy areas are due to dirt or smears on the eyepiece the student should rotate the eyepiece while look-

# Microscope Eyepiece Pointer

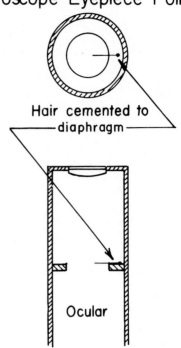

FIG. 3-8. If the top lens is unscrewed from the eyepiece, it will appear as in the upper picture, and a hair can be cemented to the diaphragm with a small drop of Canada balsam. The lower diagram shows the position of the hair in a longitudinal section of the eyepiece.

ing down the microscope. All spots and hazy areas that turn with the eyepiece are on the eyepiece. To clean them, a common procedure is to breathe on the lenses and then rub them with lens paper until they are clear and bright. However, loose specks generally remain after this procedure, and they must be blown off, not with the breath, but with a blast of air from a rubber syringe that is kept for this purpose. Any small syringe, such as an ear syringe, that can be purchased very cheaply from any medical supply house, serves this purpose well, and every student should have one.

Beginners should mount pointers in their eyepieces so that they can indicate to their teachers appearances that puzzle them. A pointer is mounted as follows: Remove the eyepiece from the microscope and unscrew and remove the top lens. Look down the eyepiece and see a circular shelf with a central aperture

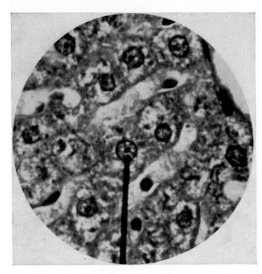

FIG. 3-9. This shows how a pointer in the eyepiece can be used to indicate a particular structure in the section under view. In this section of liver, the end of the pointer reaches and extends slightly over the edge of the nucleus of a liver cell. The nucleolus is seen just off the end of the pointer.

that is about halfway down the eyepiece tube (Fig. 3-8). Cut a little piece of straight hair just long enough for it to project from the side to the center of the tube. Place a tiny drop of Canada balsam or immersion oil on the shelf and then, with a pair of tweezers, lower the hair onto the shelf so that the part of the hair that rests on the shelf is in the drop of oil. Adjust the hair with the tweezers so that it lies flat on the shelf and so that its free end reaches just short of the center of the tube, as shown in Figure 3-8. Then the top lens is screwed back into place. Figure 3-9 shows how the pointer can be used to point to a particular structure in a section.

### Estimating Approximate Size With the Microscope

Only a small part of a section can be viewed at any one time with the microscope. The area of the section that can be seen at any one time is circular. The width of this circular area of the section varies with the magnification being employed; the greater the magnification the smaller the area of the section that can be seen. For example, with the low-power objective and the 10 × eyepiece, the diameter of the part of a section that can be viewed at any one time is around 1.5 mm. or 1,500 $\mu$ (a micron, indicated hereafter by the symbol $\mu$, is one 1/1,000th of a millimeter). However, with the oil-immersion objective and a 15 × eyepiece, the diameter of the area is about 0.1 mm. or 100 $\mu$. It is helpful to know the approximate diameters of the parts of sections that occupy the field under conditions of different combinations of objectives and eyepieces. If this is known, the size of objects seen in the field can be measured, but only *approximately*, by comparing them with the width of the field. For example, if the diameter of the area seen with an oil-immersion objective and a 15 × eyepiece is only about 100 $\mu$, objects one tenth as wide as the field are roughly 10 $\mu$ wide. For the convenience of the student, the following table gives in round numbers (for microscopes vary somewhat) the approximate widths of the areas of sections that can be seen under different magnifications.

For the electron microscope the unit of measurement commonly used is the *millimicron*, which is one 1/1,000th of a micron, or the Ångstrom unit, which is one tenth of a millimicron. The Greek letter $\mu$ is commonly used for micron, the symbol m$\mu$ for millimicron, and the symbol Å for Ångstrom unit.

### Photomicrography

The many students who are amateur photographers may wish to take photomicrographs. All that is needed is a good microscope and some inexpensive or even homemade equipment.

| Eyepiece | Objective | Magnification | Width of Circular Area of Section Seen |
|---|---|---|---|
| 5 × | Low-power 10 × | 50 | About 3 millimeters or 3,000 microns |
| 10 × | Low-power | 100 | About 1.5 millimeters or 1,500 microns |
| 10 × | High power 40 × | 400 | Nearly 0.4 millimeters or 400 microns |
| 10 × | Oil-immersion 90 × | 900 | About 0.15 millimeters or 150 microns |
| 15 × | Oil-immersion 90 × | 1,350 | Slightly less than 100 microns |

No other lenses besides those of the microscope are required. The camera need be no more than a light-proof box with a hole in one end and a slot for taking a film pack, a plate holder or a ground glass at the other. An old plate camera from which the lenses have been removed is better than a homemade box because the bellows allows the magnification to be varied.

In taking photomicrographs, the microscope is used as a projector. A strong light source should be used, and the light from it should be directed so that it strikes the substage condenser squarely. The end of the microscope tube containing the eyepiece is pushed through the hole at one end of the camera, and the ground glass is put in the other. Then a section can be put on the stage. When the microscope is focused, a sharp image of the part of the section under view appears on the ground glass. A picture may be taken by turning off the light, replacing the ground glass with film or a plate, and turning on the light for a period of time required. The expert will use a light meter to determine the time of exposure, but it can be determined easily by trial and error. Once the exposure time for low-power pictures has been learned, those for the higher powers can be calculated roughly by multiplying the low-power exposure time by the number of times the magnification is increased with the objective being used.

Histologic sections usually contain an assortment of blues and reds, and it is desirable to obtain contrast between these two colors in black-and-white prints. This entails the use of filters and films with suitable color sensitivity. Books on photomicrography should be consulted for detailed information about the various combinations of filters and films that can be employed. Generally, however, in photographing H and E sections, good results may be obtained if a green filter is used with film that is sensitive to all colors.

### ARTEFACTS

The first few minutes a student looks down a microscope at a stained section are not likely to be encouraging ones. A kaleidoscopic assortment of colors will meet his eye, and literally hundreds of different tissue ingredients will seem to be present. He can derive comfort from realizing that there are only 3 categories of materials in the human body: (1) cells, (2) intercellular substances and (3) fluids; hence, these 3 things are all that are contained in any perfect section of normal tissue. Furthermore, these 3 things have distinctly different appearances under the microscope. Hence, to make definite progress toward becoming a good practical histologist, one has to learn not hundreds of different appearances but only 3.

However, all sections are not perfect. Even the most careful preparation of a section alters the arrangement of the tissue elements to some extent, and errors in technic alter it considerably. Sections, then, may exhibit flaws, and these are called *artefacts* because they are artificial appearances caused by technical procedures.

Artefacts may confuse a student who is commencing to classify the things he sees into cells, intercellular substances and fluids. Therefore, it is best to have some idea of their appearance when first beginning the study of sections, so that an undue amount of time will not be wasted on them. The common artefacts and their causes will now be discussed.

The different chemicals with which tissue is treated in making a section may cause considerable *shrinkage* in its substance. This may result in portions of tissue which were adjacent in life being pulled away from one another, as has occurred at the sites indicated by arrows in Figure 3-10 A.

Sometimes the fixative is imperfectly removed from tissue, and crystals of it remain behind. The appearance these present is indicated by arrows in Figure 3-10 B. The appearance of any other foreign material added during the preparation of the section is somewhat similar, but it depends, of course, on the nature of the material.

Paraffin sections are so thin that it is not unusual for them to become somewhat wrinkled or folded as they are cut, and sometimes these little wrinkles or *folds* cannot be entirely smoothed out when the section is being mounted on a slide. These appear in a section as shown in Figure 3-10 C and D.

Microscopic nicks in the microtome knife cause a characteristic defect. As the knife sweeps across the paraffin block in a straight plane, any nick in it creates a defect in the section and appears as a straight line across it.

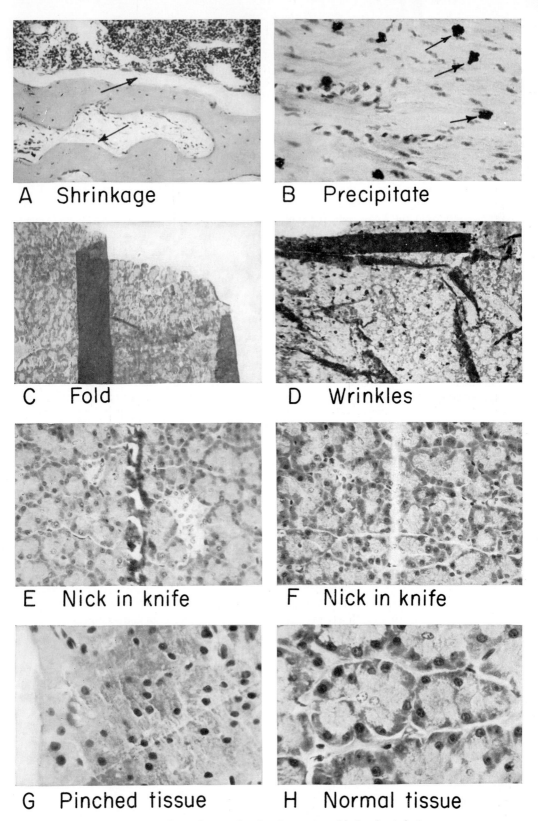

FIG. 3-10. Photomicrographs showing various kinds of artefacts.

Figure 3-10 E and F show 2 examples of defects caused in this way. The picture in E shows one caused by a large nick, and the one in F by a small nick. Any curious appearance in a section that is seen as a straight line that passes from one of its sides to the other is most likely to be an artefact of this type.

Another type of appearance that is often seen in sections which may lead to the incorrect surmise that the tissue under view has been the seat of pathologic change is the artefact produced by the rough handling of tissue as it is being cut from the animal body. Commonly, in obtaining tissue, forceps are used to hold a piece that is being cut away; sometimes the cutting is done with scissors (instead of a very sharp knife) and dull ones at that. The pinching caused by holding living tissue with forceps and cutting it with dull scissors profoundly affects the appearance it presents in stained sections. This appearance is illustrated in Figure 3-10 G. Figure 3-10 H shows how the tissue would have appeared had it not been mistreated. This type of artefact presents an appearance somewhat similar to that of tissue that has undergone postmortem degeneration, which is discussed in Chapter 6.

The fixation of cells that have a large content of carbohydrate polymers is associated with a special difficulty because the penetration of the fixative from one side into the substance of the cell may push the carbohydrate mass ahead of it. The place where this type of artefact is most obvious is the liver where the cells may contain large amounts of the carbohydrate polymer, glycogen. When sections of tissue cut from tissue in which this fixation artefact has occurred are stained, for example, by the PAS technic, which colors glycogen deeply, the magenta-colored glycogen, which appears black in a photomicrograph, is seen to be located in the halves of the cells that are most distant from the surface of the liver from which the fixative penetrated (Fig. 3-11). The surface of the liver,

Fig. 3-11. Photomicrograph of section of liver stained for glycogen by the PAS method. Glycogen appears dark. The fixative penetrated the tissue from the surface above. The glycogen in most cells has shifted ahead of the fixative, so that it is concentrated in the bottom part of each cell.

from which this fixative penetrated, is seen at the top of the illustration.

### REFERENCES

Since the material in this chapter is mostly advice which the author found was helpful to students who were beginning laboratory work, it is not the kind of subject matter about which references can be provided. However, any student who wishes to read further on the light microscope or photomicrography will find reference books on these subjects in his college or university library.

# 4 Special Methods Used for Studying Histology and Cell Biology

The first 3 chapters have been directed toward preparing the student for the laboratory study of sections made from various parts of the body. Such a study constitutes the backbone of the usual laboratory course in histology. However, there is much more to the subject than can be learned from studying ordinary stained sections. Much of the information inherent in modern histology has been obtained by the use of what we will here term *special methods*. Since the modern student must at least become familiar with much of the knowledge that has been gained by the use of special methods, he should know something of them. Their description constitutes the subject of this present chapter.

For a beginning it may help to classify special methods into three broad groups.

1. The first group generally utilizes sections and some form of light microscopy. The most important of these are:

A. **Histochemistry,** which in general entails using biochemical procedures to identify and sometimes quantitate certain chemical components of tissue in sections. Generally included under histochemistry are also (B) and (C).

B. **Radioautography.** This method entails making radioactive tracers available to cells of animals. Different tracers become incorporated into different specific chemical components of tissue. The sites where various tracers become incorporated can be determined by sectioning the cells or tissues and coating the sections with photographic emulsion as will be described shortly. This method provides information about what different tissue components are made from, where they are made, and what happens to them afterward.

C. **Fluorescence Microscopy.** This method takes advantage of the fact that a body will react to any foreign macromolecules by making specific protein macromolecules, called antibodies, which will specifically combine with the kind of foreign macromolecules which gained entrance to the body. Antibodies can be conjugated with dyes that fluoresce under ultraviolet light. If a section is flooded with fluorescent antibody that is specific for some particular type of foreign macromolecule, the fluorescent antibody will seek out and attach itself to macromolecules of this type, and so the distribution of these particular macromolecules in tissues can be determined by locating sites of fluorescence in sections illuminated by ultraviolet light.

2. **Electron Microscopy.** The size of the detail made visible by light microscopy is unalterably limited by the wavelength of light. The useful magnification attainable with the light microscope is only about 1,000 diameters, and it is only somewhat greater with a microscope using ultraviolet light. The development of the electron microscope, and of methods for preparing tissue for examining tissue preparations in it, has made it possible to obtain effective magnifications of up to 100,000 times or even more. It is not surprising that the developments in the field of electron microscopy have revolutionized the study of histology.

3. **Phase and Interference Microscopy of Fresh Tissues.** In the second chapter it was explained that the processing of a paraffin section leads to the loss of many substances from the tissue and also chemically alters many tissue components that remain. It is therefore desirable to study tissue under the microscope without any preliminary treatment, and if possible while the tissue is still alive. However, the study of fresh untreated tissue with the ordinary light microscope is difficult because there is little contrast between

different tissue components. The phase and the interference microscopes both permit contrast to be obtained in fresh tissue. These instruments, together with other means for manipulating fresh and living tissues, have permitted new knowledge to be gained about cells and tissues.

All these special methods, together with certain others, will now be described in turn and in more detail.

## HISTOCHEMISTRY—SOME EXAMPLES OF REPRESENTATIVE TECHNICS

As was described in Chapter 2, the tissues of the human body are variously composed of proteins (including nucleoproteins), lipids, carbohydrates, inorganic salts and miscellaneous substances. The branch of histology known as histochemistry is concerned with methods for demonstrating various types of substances in cells and intercellular material, as well as estimating the amounts present. A few examples of different types of histochemical reactions will be given here; others are described from time to time in later portions of this book in relation to the tissues or organs to which they particularly apply.

**Methods for Proteins.** Much of the substance in histologic sections is protein. Hence, technics devised for the histochemical detection of proteins stain nearly every part of every section. These technics make use of reagents capable of combining with the side chains of proteins and of imparting color to them. A well-known chemical test specific for phenolic side chains (contributed by the amino acid tyrosine) is the Millon reaction; this colors proteins present in sections yellow. The amount of yellow color present in any given site in a section may be measured in a microscope using monochromatic light and a sensitive photometer, and by this means the concentration of protein present can be calculated.

**Methods for Enzymes.** More interesting perhaps than general protein reactions, such as the one described above, are specific reactions which allow the identification of particular proteins, particularly *enzymes*. Reactions catalyzed by enzymes are of fundamental importance in the maintenance of life. Enzymes are all named by adding the suffix "ase" to

the name of the substance (the substrate) on which they act. Thus all enzymes that remove a phosphate group from an organic substance are known as *phosphatases*. If the substrate on which a phosphatase acts is, for example, a glycerophosphate, the phosphatase that removes its phosphate is known as *glycerophosphatase*.

Two main types of technics are used to locate phosphatases and many other enzymes in sections; these methods differ according to whether the substrate used is natural (or similar to natural substrates) or artificial.

The method of Gomori for demonstrating phosphatases is a "natural substrate" method. The tissue section is incubated with, for example, glycerophosphate. If phosphatase is present in the tissue in the section, it splits phosphate off from the glycerophosphate. A soluble calcium salt that is included in the incubation medium combines with the released phosphate to form a precipitate of calcium phosphate at the site where the enzyme was present. The precipitate is demonstrated by first treating the section with a solution of cobalt salts which results in cobalt replacing the calcium in the precipitate, and then treating it with ammonium sulfide which converts the precipitate to a readily visible black cobalt sulfide. The black sites in the section then indicate the places where the enzyme glycerophosphate was originally present in the tissue.

Similar principles may be used to detect a variety of enzymes. For example, to search for lipase, the substrate used is a water-soluble stearic ester (produced by the combination of a natural substance, stearic acid, with an ester of polymannitol, known as Tween 60, a commercial detergent). Lipase in the tissue releases free stearic acid from the substrate, and the stearic acid so released will combine *in situ* with a calcium salt that was included in the medium. The insoluble calcium salt so obtained is made clearly visible by treating it with lead salts which convert the precipitate to lead stearate, and this is then transformed by ammonium sulfide into black lead sulfide.

The "artificial substrate" methods utilize synthetic organic substrates. Perhaps the most widely used substrates of this kind are composed of beta naphthol combined with whatever grouping is under study (e.g., a beta naphthol-phosphate for detection of phosphatases, a beta naphthol-stearate for detection of lipase, etc.). When the tissue enzyme acts on such a substrate, beta naphthol is liberated. A diazonium salt included in the medium combines with the free beta naphthol to give a colored azo compound at the site of enzyme activity.

Methods for the detection of some *oxidizing enzymes* should also be mentioned. Peroxidases (which release oxygen from hydrogen peroxide) are detected by incubating tissue sections in a medium containing benzidine (which is colorless) and hydrogen peroxide. Sites of peroxidase activity then acquire the yellow-to-brown color of oxidized benzidines. Some *dehydrogenases* can be detected in tissue sections because they react with colorless tetrazolium derivatives and transform them into deeply stained formazans which crystallize at the sites of enzyme activity.

An ingenious method devised by Daoust for the detection of the enzyme RNAse, which has the ability to break down the nucleic acids of the RNA type, deserves mention. This method, inspired by the radioautographic technics, consists in coating fresh tissue sections (cut at low temperature in a cryostat) with a gelatin film that contains RNA. The section, thus sandwiched between the glass slide and the gelatin film, is allowed to stand long enough for the RNAse of the section to break down the RNA that is present in the film immediately above the sites of RNAse. Hence, when the film is stained with toluidine blue, which is an excellent stain for RNA, the film is stained except in sites where RNAse was present in the section, for at these latter sites the RNAse broke down the RNA in the film, and so none is left to be stained.

**Nucleic Acids.** The histochemistry of nucleic acids is considered in Chapter 6.

**Lipids.** Perhaps because of the difficulty of retaining lipids in sections, the histochemistry of lipids is somewhat crude. The simple technic of using colored dyes that are soluble in fat, such as Sudan III and Scarlet red, has been mentioned already. These dyes on dissolving into fatty structures impart an orange color to the sites of their adsorption. The British dye Sudan black B is said to be taken up preferentially in phospholipids and cholesterol and thus seems to emphasize structures rich in these substances. Osmium tetroxide

also seems to dissolve into fat droplets, and often to blacken them; however, it is not understood why some, and not other fatty materials, undergo blackening.

**Carbohydrates.** Several methods are used to detect carbohydrate-containing macromolecules. The periodic acid-Schiff technic for glycogen and glycoproteins, and the colloidal iron method and metachromatic staining for acid mucopolysaccharides deserve special mention.

1. *Glycogen.* The periodic acid-Schiff (commonly abbreviated to PA-Schiff or even PAS) technic is a two-step procedure based on the application to histology of two reactions well known to chemists. Periodic acid reacts with the 1, 2 glycol groups (-CHOH-CHOH-) which occur in each one of the glucose residues making up the glycogen chain. On treatment with periodic acid both members of each glycol group yield an aldehyde (-CHO), so that the polysaccharidic chain of glycogen becomes a polyaldehydic chain. The second step is to treat the sections with a well-known reagent for aldehydes; this is basic fuchsin bleached with sulfurous acid, usually known as the Schiff reagent. Aldehydes combine with the bleached dye to produce a *magenta* or *purple* colored complex (see Fig. 27-13), which is readily seen in the microscope. In the case of glycogen, a bright purple reaction product is seen. Accordingly, it is said that glycogen is a PAS-positive substance.

Glycogen is readily broken down by amylase, the enzyme present in saliva, and after treatment with this ezyme, it can be washed out of sections. Hence, when a PAS-positive substance is found in a cell, it is customary to incubate a section in purified amylase (or in saliva) to extract glycogen and stain again by the PAS method. Disappearance of the purple material proves that the material was glycogen.

2. *Glycoproteins.* Many structural proteins as well as secretory materials contain proteins conjugated with carbohydrates. These glycoproteins are composed of hexose units which have 1, 2 glycol or 1, 2-amino alcohol groups (-CHOH-CHNH$_2$-). The latter, like the former, can be oxidized to aldehydes with periodic acid. Subsequent treatment with the Schiff reagent gives a characteristic magenta color to glycoprotein sites. Glycoproteins,

however, are not dissolved by amylase treatment; thus sites where they are present in sections are termed amylase-resistant, PAS-positive sites. However, some caution must be used in interpreting the results. The time of action of periodic acid must be kept under 10 minutes; otherwise certain other substances that may be present (e.g., acid mucopolysaccharides) might become reactive. Even with a short exposure, weak reactions are produced by proteins, because of aldehyde being liberated from some amino acids situated at the end of protein chains.

3. *Acid Mucopolysaccharides.* The methods available for the detection of acid mucopolysaccharides are only moderately satisfactory. One method makes use of metachromatic staining and will be described in connection with intercellular substances in Chapter 10. The other, known as the colloidal iron technic, takes advantage of the fact that at pH 2.5 the acid groups of acid mucopolysaccharides bind colloidal iron, which may then be stained by one of the methods used for the detection of iron (to be described presently).

**Inorganic Salts.** One of the oldest methods in histochemistry is that devised by M. Perls in 1867 for the detection of iron ionized in the ferric form. To demonstrate iron in sections by Perls' method, tissue is fixed in a neutral solution such as neutral formalin, because any acid in the fixative dissolves ferric ions. When sections are exposed to a solution of ferrocyanide, sites of iron are revealed by the formation of blue ferricyanide—a reaction known as the Prussian blue test.

Iron salts, as well as calcium and other salts, may be detected in sections by the technic of microincineration; the latter technic is described later in this chapter.

## RADIOAUTOGRAPHY

### INTRODUCTION

It is of obvious importance to know what happens to various nutritive substances that are absorbed into the body from the lumen of the intestine. For many years the study of this matter was often difficult and necessarily somewhat indirect because there was no way by which given substances could be followed from the time they were absorbed until they were either broken down to provide energy or

incorporated into some body component. Furthermore, there was no way of telling whether or not the absorbed substance was incorporated into a body component that had a long existence, or only a short one (which would require that it be constantly replenished). It was likewise difficult to obtain any information on the lengths of time that certain body substances lasted, or whether they moved from one place to another. When it became possible to label nutritive and other substances with radioactive tracers, much precise information could be obtained on many of these matters because the particular molecules or substances that were labeled could be followed thereafter by their labels. One way that this is done, after a tracer is given, is by means of detecting and estimating the radioactivity in intact body parts or various fractions of tissues by means of Geiger counters. The technic used in the histology and histopathologic laboratory is even more direct and depends on locating radioactive substances in ordinary tissue sections, because sites of radioactivity in sections affect photographic emulsions placed directly above them (see Fig. 4-1). Briefly, radioautography is a technic which depends first on the fact that a label, which is a radioactive isotope of some element, can be incorporated into the chemical structure of substances that are used by the body and secondly on the fact that the substances so labeled behave just the same as unlabeled substances and become incorporated into macromolecules in the body for shorter or longer periods of time; while the labeled substances are present, these macromolecules can be located in tissue sections because their label emits radiation which will affect photographic emulsion placed over the section (Fig. 4-1).

### DEVELOPMENT OF THE METHOD

The possibility of locating radioactive substances in tissue sections by exposing the sections to photographic emulsions was first exploited systematically by Lacassagne and his group in 1925. They traced polonium, an emitter of alpha particles, after it was injected into rabbits, by pressing sections cut from the tissues of the rabbit, or in some instances the faces of the paraffin blocks from which the sections were cut, against photographic plates.

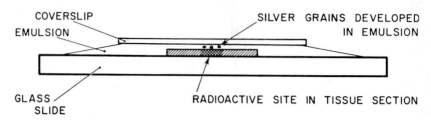

COVERSLIP                                  SILVER GRAINS DEVELOPED
EMULSION                                         IN EMULSION

GLASS                           RADIOACTIVE SITE IN TISSUE SECTION
SLIDE

FIG. 4-1. Diagram of a radioautograph prepared by the coating technic.

Then, after developing the plates and taking note of the sites where they had been affected, they examined under the microscope the sections that had been held against the plates, and were thus able to gain a rough idea of the sites in the sections which were emitting radiation. Although this work indicated the possibilities of radioautography, it did not permit radioactive sites in tissue to be localized with any precision. Much credit is due to C. P. Leblond and his associates for pioneering new developments in the technic which have led to its becoming an extremely useful and precise tool.

**Coated Radioautography.** To make radioautography more precise, it was necessary to devise some method for integrating section and emulsion into a single unit where they would be in intimate contact with one another. This was accomplished by the so-called *coating technic* devised by Belanger and Leblond in 1946. Their technic involved removing emulsion from Eastman Kodak medium lantern plates in the dark, melting it, and then spreading it directly onto sections which were mounted on slides. Further improvement arose from the introduction of the so-called nuclear emulsions, which contain a high concentration of very sensitive, uniformly sized silver bromide crystals. These nuclear emulsions are available in bulk and are readily melted for coating the sections (Kopriwa and Leblond, 1962). Their use has made it possible to localize radioactive sites in sections with great accuracy.

**The Preparation of a Coated Radioautograph.** Tissue from animals given a substance labeled with a radioactive isotope is fixed and sectioned. Indeed, the section may even be stained. (No substance capable of inhibiting the response of the emulsion, such as heavy metallic salts, should be present in the fixative or stain that is used.) The sections are

then taken to the dark room where they are coated with photographic emulsion and dried. The coated sections are left in a lightproof box for a suitable length of time, during which time each minute amount of isotope in the section of tissue acts as a point source of radiation and the rays it emits affects such emulsion that they reach by bringing about the ionization of silver atoms in each crystal of silver bromide that is hit. When the preparation is developed and fixed like an ordinary photographic negative, the crystals of silver bromide that have been hit appear as little dark dots which are commonly called *grains* (Fig. 4-1). The sites of grains in the emulsion indicate radioactivity in sites below the grains and indeed, as will be described presently, by using beta emitters with short tracks, very thin sections and thin layers of emulsion, the grains that are seen can be related to the particular cell or tissue component directly or almost directly under them.

**The Stripping Film Method.** This method, developed in 1947, employs a special kind of film which readily permits the emulsion to be stripped from its backing. This step is, of course, carried out in the darkroom, and the stripped emulsion is placed on the surface of water in a dish. A glass slide with a section mounted on it, but with no coverslip, is then slipped under the floating stripped emulsion and brought up under it so that the layer of emulsion rests flat on the section. Subsequent steps are much the same as in the previous technic. The stripping method has the advantage, for the inexperienced worker with a minimum of equipment, of giving some assurance that the emulsion is of fairly constant thickness, and this is important in quantitative work, which involves the counting of numbers of grains.

**Some Factors Concerned in Obtaining Precise Localization of Radioactive Emitters**

in Sections. A radioactive label in a tissue section serves as a point source of radiation, and so gives off rays in all directions. If the label used is a high energy emitter, such as $P^{32}$, an emitter of beta particles, that is electrons endowed with high energy, then, not only do the electrons emitted at right angle to the section affect the emulsion directly above the label, but the electrons it gave off at angles would also reach the emulsion, even though they had to travel longer distances to reach it. Hence they would affect emulsion for considerable distances to either side of the emitter, and, as a consequence, the site of the label could not be localized with precision. It is therefore desirable to use low-energy beta emitters, since they give off electrons with short tracks, which ideally are long enough to reach emulsion that is directly above the label and not long enough to reach the emulsion if they extend off at various angles from the point source. Accordingly, tritium is commonly used for radioautography because the electrons that it emits have a low *average* energy (5.7 KeV) which gives them a range in water of about 1 micron. It is therefore obvious that some of the emission from tritium in the deeper part of anything but a thin section would not reach the emulsion at all and hence that it is desirable to have the emulsion as close as possible to the tissue components in the section and that the sections used for detecting tritium be as thin as possible so that the short tracks of the emitted particles will extend through the section and reach the emulsion.

### DIFFERENT SUBSTANCES ARE LABELED WITH DIFFERENT LABELS FOR DIFFERENT PURPOSES

The nutritive substances absorbed from the intestine are small molecules, and many of these when they are taken into the body are assembled into macromolecules. The smaller molecules that are labeled are termed *precursors,* and when they are incorporated into larger molecules in the body, the substance into which they are incorporated and which they then label is referred to as a *product.* Generally a precursor can be given to an animal so that it remains available for about an hour; if the animal is then killed, such precursor as is still in tissue (since it is a small molecule) is washed out as the section is

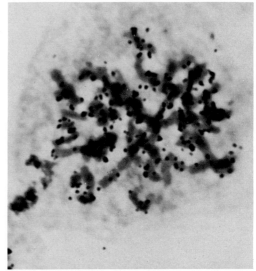

FIG. 4-2. Radioautograph of an air-dried preparation of an L cell from a culture that was given a 16-hour exposure to tritium-labeled thymidine. The labeled thymidine was taken up as the DNA was being duplicated, and enough time elapsed for the cell to enter mitosis; this cell was obtained when it was in the metaphase. The dark grains that are seen over the chromosomes are due to the short tracks of beta particles from the tritium causing ionization in the overlying photographic emulsion. (Stanners, C. P., and Till, J. E.: Biochim. et biophys. acta *37*:406)

processed. The product, however, into which labeled precursor has been incorporated, being a large molecule, is fixed in position by the use of a suitable fixative, and hence it is available for being detected *in situ* by radioautography.

Most of the kinds of macromolecules described in Chapter 2 under "The Chemical Components of Tissue" represent products that can be labeled by means of the administration of suitable labeled precursors under conditions when the macromolecules are being synthesized. To study the synthesis of many kinds of protein macromolecules it is customary to administer an amino acid, for example, leucine, which has been labeled with tritium. Because the protein collagen contains much glycine and proline, these amino acids labeled with tritium are especially good precursors to use for labeling collagen that is

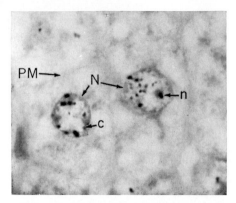

Fig. 4-3. Radioautograph showing newly
formed RNA in two liver cells. Each cell
shows a round nucleus. In one of the nuclei,
a nucleolus is visible; in both some grayish
material, chromatin, may be seen.

The cells came from an animal given an
injection of cytidine-H³ 20 minutes before
sacrifice. Since cytidine-H³ is a precursor
of nucleic acids, both RNA and DNA may
be labeled. Here the DNA was extracted
from the section by DNAse. The section
was then stained with H and E, coated with
photographic emulsion and exposed.

After development the above preparation
was obtained. Black silver grains indicative
of the presence of a radioactive product are
seen over the cell nucleus (mainly over
nucleolus and chromatin). It thus appears
that RNA is synthesized in these parts of
the nucleus. (Amano and Leblond: Exp.
Cell Res. *20:250*)

being synthesized. For labeling carbohydrate
macromolecules it is customary to use glucose
labeled with tritium. As will be described in
Chapter 6, thymidine, labeled with tritium, is
used to study the synthesis of deoxyribonucleic
acid (Fig. 4-2). The problem of studying the
synthesis of ribonucleic acid (RNA) is more
complicated because there is no specific precursor of RNA. However, its synthesis can be
studied by using either cytidine or uridine
labeled with tritium, provided that a further
step is taken. Both of these nucleosides serve
as precursors for both DNA and RNA, and so
both nucleic acids that are being synthesized
when either of these labeled precursors are
available are labeled. However, the RNA that
is synthesized when the labeled precursors are
available can be studied in radioautographs if
the section from which the radioautographs

are made are first treated with the enzyme
DNAse, for this enzyme removes DNA (labeled and otherwise) from the tissue and
leaves only the RNA to affect the emulsion
that is applied after the DNA has been removed. Figure 4-3 shows RNA located by
this technic.

The mineral deposits in cartilage and bone
can be labeled, as they are deposited, by radioactive isotopes of calcium or phosphorus.
Carbohydrate-containing organic intercellular
substances being synthesized in the body can
be labeled with radioactive glucose. Sulfated
mucopolysaccharides that form in the body
can be labeled as they form by giving animals
radioactive isotopes of sulfur. Hemoglobin
contains iron, so radioactive iron is much used
in the study of red blood cell formation and
destruction. Since the hormones of the thyroid
gland contain iodine as one of their chemical
components, radioactive iodine has been much
used in the study of the formation of hormones by this gland. Finally, since the half-
life of different radioisotopes varies, those
used must have a half-life long enough to
permit an experiment to be concluded. For example, $I^{131}$ has a half-life of only 8 days, and
therefore it can be used only for short-term
experiments. Tritium ($H^3$) has a half-life of
12 years, and $C^{14}$ a half-life of 5,600 years, so
both the latter can be used in long-term experiments.

### Determining the Site of Synthesis and the Migration of Products

If sections are taken very shortly after a
labeled precursor is given, radioautographs
prepared from the sections reveal the site of
synthesis of the product of which they are becoming a part. If sections are prepared from
animals treated similarly, but allowed to live
for progressively longer periods of time, the
movement of the product can be followed.
Some products stay where they were formed,
but others move. For example, as was shown
by Warshawsky *et al.* in Leblond's laboratory,
protein macromolecules destined for secretion
in certain gland cells are synthesized in the
basal parts of the cells. They then migrate to
another part of the cell where they are assembled into large granular bodies, and
finally they are discharged from the cell. The
time sequences for all these events, as well as

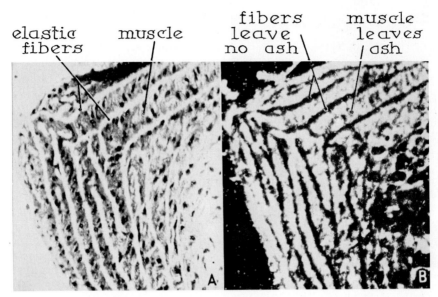

FIG. 4-4. (A) A medium-power photomicrograph of a section of the wall of a rat's aorta stained with H and E. (B) A photomicrograph of a similarly cut section which was incinerated. With darkfield illumination the ash shows up as white and an absence of ash shows up as black. (Ham, A.: Arch. Path. *14*:613)

migration pathways, can be established very accurately by the radioautographic method as is described in Chapter 8.

**Quantitative Radioautography.** As has been shown by Gross, Bogoroch, Nadler and Leblond, the number of grains that appear over a given site in an emulsion depends among other factors on the amount of radioactivity that is present in the section directly under the site where grains appear. Accordingly, if say, the synthesis of some protein is being studied by the use of a labeled amino acid, the rate at which the number of grains over the site of synthesis is found to increase in sections taken at successively longer periods of time after a labeled precursor is given an animal gives information about the rate of synthesis of that particular protein product. However, a protein formed in some site may either migrate or it may be metabolized and replaced *in situ* with freshly synthesized protein. If it migrates, its migration can be studied as described in the preceding paragraph (and in more detail in Chap. 7). If it is metabolized, the rate at which the number of grains over the site disappear in sections taken at successively later times when no further label is available to mark the protein that replaces it gives in-

formation about the rate of breakdown of the product. *Hence, the time taken for protein macromolecules of this kind to be replaced* (its turnover time) *can be calculated*. The same technic can be used for the study of the turnover time of other kinds of macromolecules. The assessment of such dynamic events in tissue sections by radioautography represents its major conquest.

## MICROINCINERATION

The minerals in different parts of tissue can be studied by the technic of microincineration. This was evolved by Policard and brought to a high state of development on this continent by Scott and in Great Britain by Horning. In the usual employment of this technic, paraffin sections of tissue fixed in a solution of alcohol and formalin are mounted on slides and placed in an electric furnace. The temperature of the furnace is raised slowly to a point where all the organic matter of the section is burned off and only the mineral skeleton of the tissue is left on the slide. This may be studied conveniently with darkfield illumination with which, for example, calcium appears white (Fig. 4-4).

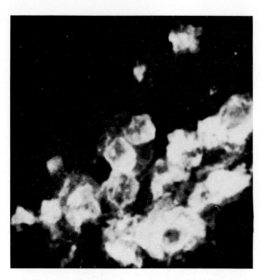

FIG. 4-5. High-power photomicrograph (taken with a darkfield condenser) of a section of a kidney of a hamster that was infected at birth with polyoma virus. The section was treated with antibody that was prepared by injecting polyoma virus into a rabbit. The antibody to polyoma virus was then conjugated with a fluorescent dye. Since the fluorescent antibody combines specifically with polyoma virus, the cells that contain virus fluoresce under ultraviolet light and appear white against a dark background of cells that do not contain virus and hence do not attach fluorescent dye.

## FLUORESCENCE MICROSCOPY

The human eye can detect light of only certain wavelengths. The wavelength of ultraviolet light or of x-rays is too short to register on the eye as light. However, there are certain unique substances that have the property of giving off visible light (light of a longer wavelength) when they are exposed to ultraviolet light or even to x-rays. Such substances are said to be fluorescent, and the fact that they give off visible light when exposed to ultraviolet light is taken advantage of in the technic known as *fluorescence microscopy*. Although this technic permits those naturally occurring fluorescent substances that are present in the body to be detected in histologic sections, a more important use of the technic hinges on the fact that there are certain fluorescent dyes which can be used *directly* to selectively combine with certain specific body

components so that these can be identified in sections because they fluoresce. What is more useful still is the technic termed *immunofluorescence* microscopy which will be described shortly.

**Equipment Required for Fluorescence Microscopy.** If suitable sections are prepared from tissue that contains either naturally occurring fluorescent substances, or substances that have been made fluorescent by experimental procedures that will be described presently, their sites in sections can be determined by examining the sections (with certain precautions) in a usual type of microscope equipped with an ultraviolet light source and a dark-field condenser. The microscope, unlike a true ultraviolet microscope, does not require special quartz or other types of objectives and eyepieces that transmit ultraviolet light, for the observer of fluorescence looks for visible light emitted from sites in the section, and, of course, visible light is transmitted by ordinary objectives and eyepieces. Nevertheless, if these sites in the section are to be made fluorescent, they must be illuminated from below by light of a shorter wavelength than that which they emit. Accordingly, the light source that is employed must be one that emits light in the ultraviolet range. Any light that it emits of wavelengths longer than those in the ultraviolet must be filtered out. The wavelengths in the ultraviolet spectrum that are used in fluorescence microscopy are generally long enough to pass through an ordinary condenser in appreciable amounts; hence, a condenser of the dark-field type generally is employed so that fluorescent sites can be seen easily against a dark background (Fig. 4-5). Since light of relatively long wavelengths in the ultraviolet spectrum is employed, some of it, after passing through the nonfluorescing parts of the section, may continue on through the objectives and the eyepieces. Accordingly, *to prevent injury to the eyes from this invisible light*, filters which exclude ultraviolet rays but permit the passage of light in the visible spectrum, must be inserted in the eyepiece for inspecting sections. A filter which excludes ultraviolet but permits the passage of visible light must also be used in the eyepiece for photographing sites of fluorescence in sections; otherwise, ultraviolet light passing through the nonfluorescing parts of the section may fog the photographic film.

**Naturally Occurring Fluorescent Substances.** There are several naturally occurring groups of fluorescent materials in the body; of these groups, one of the most interesting is the porphyrins. Free porphyrins may exist in normal tissue in minute concentrations. *Free porphyrins serve no known normal function,* but in certain disease states they accumulate in the skin and make it photosensitive. Porphyrins assume importance in normal biologic functions when they enter into combination with iron. The iron complex of protoporphyrin is called *heme,* and the latter is a constituent of hemoglobin and several important enzymes concerned in oxidations.

Some of the vitamins are fluorescent—vitamin A and vitamin $B_2$ (riboflavin).

**Direct Use of Fluorescent Dyes.** There are several dyes that fluoresce and can be used to stain ordinarily nonfluorescing cell and tissue components, so that these cell and tissue components can be demonstrated. For example, acridine orange combines with both the DNA and the RNA of the cell (described in Chap. 6). When cells stained with this fluorescent dye are examined, the DNA fluoresces with a green-to-yellow color, and the RNA with an orange-to-red color (Bertalanffy). Other fluorescent dyes used for certain purposes are thioflavine S, thioflavine T, rhodamine B and primulin.

## IMMUNOFLUORESCENCE TECHNICS

In order to describe these technics, we must comment briefly, and in as simple a fashion as possible, on a subject that will be dealt with in more detail in later parts of this book; namely, an important way in which the body reacts to disease agents or other foreign materials that gain entrance to it.

**The Terms Antigen and Antibody.** Although the body contains thousands of different kinds of macromolecules, it remembers them all, for it exhibits an amazing discriminatory ability to distinguish between its own macromolecules and those that are foreign. The body reacts against foreign macromolecules but not against its own. This is why we recover from, for example, infectious diseases caused by viruses. The protein macromolecules of viruses are different from those in

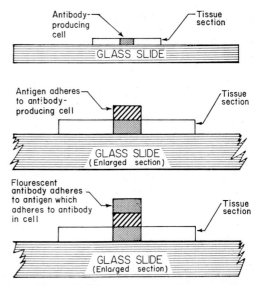

Fig. 4-6. Diagram representing steps in the sandwich technic. Sizes of objects illustrated are of course greatly out of proportion.

the body. Hence, when viruses gain entrance to the body their macromolecules are recognized as foreign, and machinery is set in motion to eliminate them. Macromolecules with a molecular weight of over 10,000 that are foreign to a given body are termed *antigens* (*anti* = against, *generare* = to produce) in relation to that individual body, because they induce reactions in that body that are directed against them. An important part of the reaction is the production of the body of substances that are termed *antibodies;* so-named because they specifically combine with, and lead to, the inactivation of the particular antigens that induce their production.

Figure 4-13 is an illustration that shows two kinds of virus particles which are morphologically similar, but one kind (V1) is slightly larger than the other (V2). The larger kind cause warts in man, and the smaller kind cause tumors in mice and hamsters. Antibody was made by injecting one kind into rabbits; then both kinds of virus particles were mixed with the antibody that was made in the rabbit. The antibody (Fig. 4-13, Anti) combined with, and only with, the type of particle that was the antigen that was injected into the rabbits. It has only recently been possible to demonstrate antibodies in the EM.

It is possible to label an antibody that has

been made in response to some particular antigen, and which is specific for that antigen, with a fluorescent dye. If a section which contains some of the same antigen that was injected into an animal to induce the formation of this particular antibody is flooded with the fluorescent antibody, the fluorescent antibody will stick to the antigen at sites where it is present. Antibody that has not adhered to antigen can then be washed from the section, and the section can be examined under the microscope with the equipment already described, where it will be found that sites where antibody has adhered to antigen in the section will fluoresce. By this means, sites of particular antigens can be located in sections. This is how the virus that was multiplying in certain cells in an animal were located in Figure 4-5.

### How the Cells That Make Antibodies Can Be Located by the Immuno-fluorescent Technic; the Sandwich Technic

For many years there was much uncertainty about the particular types of cells in the body that had the special task of producing antibodies. This will be discussed in later chapters; here, we shall consider only how immunofluorescence technics made this discovery possible.

If a particular antigen is injected into an animal every few days over a certain period of time, the animal produces increasing amounts of a specific antibody to the injected antigen. The antibody gains entrance to the blood, so, if blood is collected at a suitable time after the injections have ceased, it will contain a high titer of antibody to this antigen. Since the antibody is in one fraction of the serum (the globulin fraction), and since the fraction can be separated from the rest of the blood, the antibody can be obtained in a reasonably concentrated state. The antibody so obtained can be conjugated with a fluorescent dye so that it will fluoresce under ultraviolet light.

Next, to locate the particular cells in the animal that produced the antibody, the animal is killed and sections are prepared from pieces of tissue, taken from its various parts, and fixed in a special manner. In the beginning it was necessary to use frozen sections cut in a cryostat. Now the technic can be used on specially fixed material, embedded and cut in paraffin (see Sainte-Marie). Suitably processed sections which contain the antibody-forming cells (see Fig. 4-6) are flooded with the antigen that was used to induce the formation of antibody. Since antibody is still in the cells that were producing it in life, and since the antibody has an affinity for the specific antigen with which the sections are flooded, the antigen adheres to those cells that were engaged in making the antibody to this particular antigen (Fig. 4-6). The sections can then be washed, and the antigen that has not combined with antibody washes away. Next, the sections are flooded with some of the antibody that was conjugated with a fluorescent dye, and this, in turn, sticks to the antigen that has adhered to the cells that were producing antibody to this antigen (see bottom illustration, Fig. 4-6). Finally, the sections are examined in the fluorescence microscope, and the cells that have fluorescent antibody attached to them (these are the cells that originally made the antibody) can be identified (Fig. 15-7 *left, right*). This technic is generally referred to as the *sandwich technic* because it necessitates making a sandwich which has a layer of antigen between two layers of antibody.

### How the Technic Can Be Used To Locate Specific Types of Macromolecules in Tissue Sections

Let us suppose that some particular type of macromolecule can be extracted from some organ of the body but it is not known which particular cells of that organ make this substance. The particular cells that make these macromolecules can often be ascertained by the immunofluorescent technic, as will now be explained.

Macromolecules, which perform some special function in one species, while similar chemically to the macromolecules that perform the same function in another species, often differ from them because macromolecules that perform the same function in different species generally have slightly different arrangements of amino acids in their respective structures. Hence, if a pure substance made of macromolecules that are extracted from an organ of an animal of one species is injected into an animal of another species, it will, in due course, evoke the formation

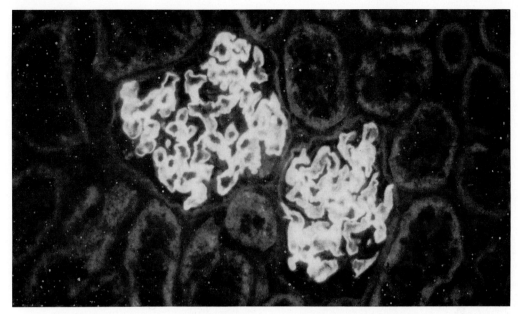

FIG. 4-7. This shows how the immunofluorescence technic is used to demarcate some tissue component with a fluorescent antibody. Here, the immunofluorescence technic demonstrates the same structures shown in the reconstruction of the capillaries of glomeruli of the kidney (Fig. 3-2). The student should compare that illustration with this one. The glomerular capillaries are demarcated here because the material of which they are composed was used in another animal as an antigen and the antibody made in the other animal to this antigen attached itself to the basement membranes of this present animal when it was injected into it. The attached antibody was then located in sections by the sandwich technic. (Hammer, Vazquez and Dixon: Lab. Invest. *12*:8)

of specific antibodies to it. If this antibody is then collected and labeled with a fluorescent dye, it can be used to flood sections cut from the organ of the animal of the first species; here it affixes itself to the macromolecules which constituted the antigen used to induce the formation of the antibody in the second species. Hence, when sections are examined under ultraviolet light, the tissue component to which fluorescent antibody adheres fluoresce and so can be identified as the tissue component that acted as the antigen. This, for example, is the way that proof was afforded that J-G cells in the kidney (to be described later) produce a substance called *renin*, that raises blood pressure.

The fact that a specific tissue component of one animal (for example, basement membranes of kidney glomeruli of a rat) can be antigenic in another species and that antibody made to this particular rat tissue by an animal of another species, in this case a rabbit, can be used to locate the specific tissue component of the first animal is beautifully illustrated in

Figure 4-7. The way this picture was obtained (courtesy of Jacinto J. Vazquez) and which involved making a different kind of a sandwich, is described in the caption.

By procedures similar to this, the sites of production or residence of many body substances can be located.

## THE ELECTRON MICROSCOPE

**History.** As Abbé showed in the latter part of the last century, the resolving power of the light microscope is irrevocably limited, not by the quality or the nature of lenses that it is within man's capacity to construct, but by the wavelength of light. With ordinary illumination, this means that no two objects separated by less than 0.2 microns can be resolved clearly as distinct entities by the light microscope. By taking advantage of the shorter wavelength of ultraviolet light, the resolving power can be approximately doubled, but this requires the use of quartz or some other kind of lenses that transmit ultraviolet light and a

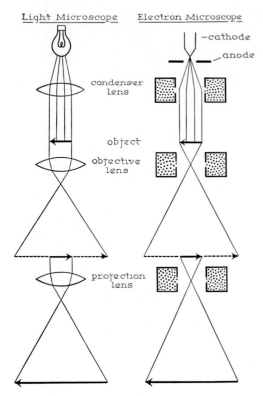

Light Microscope    Electron Microscope

−cathode
anode
condenser
lens
object
objective
lens
projection
lens

Fig. 4-8. Diagram showing optical paths in light and electron microscopes.

fluorescent screen for viewing objects. Ultraviolet microscopes would probably have been used more to gain this extra resolving power had it not been for the revolutionary development which followed the finding in the 1920's that suitably-shaped magnetic or electrostatic fields could be used as true lenses for an electron beam, and that the electrons could be accelerated to speeds at which their wavelength would be an almost negligible factor in resolving objects with them.

The first electron microscope was built by 1931 by Knoll and Ruska, and by 1933 they had constructed an instrument in Germany that had a resolving power greater than that obtainable with a light microscope. The first electron microscope built in North America was constructed in the Department of Physics at the University of Toronto by Prebus and Hillier who were working under the direction of Professor Eli Burton.

Commercial instruments of high quality became available many years before the electron microscope was shown to have general appli-

cation to the study of cytology, histology and histopathology. The chief problem was that of devising methods whereby tissue preparations of sufficient thinness could be obtained for use in the instrument. An early method was evolved by Porter by which cells were grown in tissue cultures so that their cytoplasm extended out from them in films that were thin enough to be penetrated by an electron beam. However, general application of electron microscopy to the study of histology came only after it became possible to cut sections of around a millionth of an inch in thickness.

**Terminology.** In order to save space it is desirable to use an abbreviation for the term *electron microscope*; otherwise these two words would have to be spelled out hundreds of times. One abbreviation that has been used often is E/M, another is EM; the latter will be used here.

The structure revealed by the EM over and above that which can be resolved with the light microscope is generally termed "fine structure." This term seems preferable to ultrastructure, which is sometimes used, because the latter term means *beyond* structure.

**Comparison of Optics of Light and Electron Microscopes.** In obtaining a magnified image with the light microscope, advantage is taken of the fact that rays of light bend as they pass from a medium of one refractive index into one of another. By using glass with curved surfaces (lenses), light from a small object can be bent so that it produces a large image (Fig. 4-8). In the EM, advantage is taken of the fact that the paths of electrons can be influenced similarly by magnetic fields. Accordingly, the lenses of the EM are magnetic fields, and the strength of these fields can be varied by the amount of current that is passed through the coils of wire (stippled in Fig. 4-8) which excite the fields.

In describing an EM it is convenient to compare its lens systems with those of the light microscope. The optics of both are shown in Figure 4-8, but in using this figure the student should keep in mind that the light microscope shown at the left is upside down.

In the ordinary microscope, light from a suitable source is focused with a condenser lens (Fig. 4-8). The condenser lens directs a strong beam of light through the aperture of

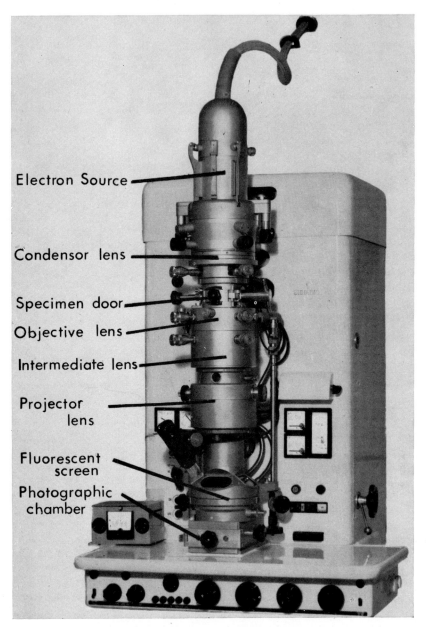

Electron Source

Condensor lens

Specimen door

Objective lens

Intermediate lens

Projector lens

Fluorescent screen

Photographic chamber

FIG. 4-9. A Siemens electron microscope.

the microscope stage and *through* the specimen, for example, a stained section that is on the stage (Fig. 4-8); the specimen is termed the *object* (Fig. 4-8). The light that passes through the specimen is focused by the objective lens (Fig. 4-8). The objective lens brings an *image* of the object into focus somewhere between the objective and the projection lenses. The projection lens, which is the one in the eyepiece of the ordinary microscope, can further magnify the image up to 10 or 15 times and can be used to bring the enlarged image into focus either on a screen or on a photographic plate placed at the site indicated by the bottom arrow (Fig. 4-8).

The optics of an EM are illustrated at the right of Figure 4-8. The whole instrument (Fig. 4-9) is, in essence, a demountable cathode-ray tube in which a vacuum must be maintained by continuous pumping. From the

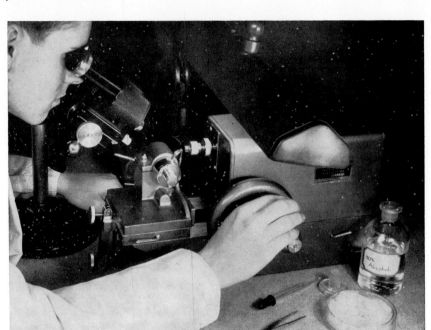

FIG. 4-10. Photograph of an "ultra" microtome in operation. This is of the type designed by Porter and Blum. Observe that the operator requires a binocular microscope to see the thin sections that are being cut by the instrument.

cathode, which is a V-shaped tungsten filament (Fig. 4-8, *top right*) that can be heated electrically, electrons are emitted and attracted toward the anode (by a potential difference of 50,000 to 100,000 volts). The anode has an aperture in it so that a diverging stream of electrons passes through it (Fig. 4-8, *right*). The diverging stream is focused by the condenser lens (a magnetic field) and directed at the object (Fig. 4-8, *right*), which, for our purposes, is generally an unbelievably thin slice of tissue prepared as will be described presently. As the electrons pass through the section, more are scattered out of the beam by some parts of the section than by others.

Those electrons that are scattered by the specimens are removed from the beam by the blocking action of a very fine aperture placed at some position in the objective lens. This aperture which is only about 30 microns in diameter plays an important part in obtaining contrast in the electron microscope and can be said to work by subtractive action. The remaining electrons (those not scattered, and hence not subtracted from the beam) are focused by the objective lens and an enlarged

image is obtained thereby (Fig. 4-8, *right*). This image is enlarged further first by a lens known as an intermediate lens and secondly by a projection lens; the latter projects the image onto the fluorescent screen (Fig. 4-9).

Like ultraviolet light and x-rays, electrons do not register as light in the eye. However, like ultraviolet light and x-rays, they make certain substances fluoresce, and they also affect photographic film. So, as with the ultraviolet microscope, a fluorescent screen must be used for focusing the image obtained with the EM, and then a photographic film or plate can be substituted for the screen and exposed. Those parts of the final image that correspond to parts of the section that scatter electrons strongly will be dark on the fluorescent screen, light in a photographic negative and dark on a print made from the negative. Conversely, those parts of the image of the section that correspond to parts of the section that do not scatter electrons strongly will be bright on the fluorescent screen, black on the photographic negative and light on a print made from the negative.

There is not much point in greatly enlarging an ordinary photomicrograph because the amount of detail in the photographic image is limited by the wavelength of light. However, there is every reason for making great enlargements of negatives exposed in the EM because these negatives contain a vast amount of detail that can be detected by the unaided eye only in greatly enlarged prints.

It is important for the student to realize that he can learn as much or more about the fine structure that is revealed by the EM by studying enlarged prints of negatives exposed in the EM than he can by using the instrument itself. This is in contrast with the light microscope, for with the latter instrument the student generally can learn more by studying sections than he can from photomicrographs.

## How Sections Are Prepared for Electron Microscopy

As has been noted already, a major obstacle to the use of the EM in histology in the early days was the seeming impossibility of ever being able to cut sufficiently thin sections. Electrons penetrate matter so poorly that they will not pass through even the thinnest sections used in light microscopy. For electron microscopy, sections must be less than 1/10 of a micron in thickness, preferably about 1/40 of a micron (almost exactly 1 millionth of an inch) for the best results. To achieve sections of this thinness many improvements over pre-existing methods had to be made. First, microtomes with special advance mechanisms capable of operating in the range required for electron microscopy, that is from 1/10 to 1/40 micron, had to be designed (Fig. 4-10). Furthermore, it was found to be important to avoid having the block pass back over the knife edge on the return stroke after the cutting stroke was completed. Accordingly, ultramicrotomes are usually designed so that the block takes a circuitous course and bypasses the cutting edge on the return stroke. Another improvement involved using the fractured edge of a piece of plate glass as a cutting knife for the new microtomes (Fig. 4-11). More recently, specially ground diamond knives have become available, and their use is increasing. The cutting edge of a diamond knife is no sharper than that of a glass knife but it is so very hard that it can be used for a much longer time than a glass knife.

Fig. 4-11. Close-up photograph of the block of tissue (seen at the apex of the pyramid) approaching the edge of the glass knife. Observe that there is a little reservoir on the upper surface of the knife; as the sections are cut they float onto the fluid in this reservoir.

Moreover, the hardness of a diamond knife makes it particularly useful for cutting sections of very hard tissues.

New and improved embedding media were also necessary before satisfactory thin sections could be secured. A plastic material, *n-butyl methacrylate*, proved to be very useful and, at first, was used almost universally. However, methacrylate has some disadvantages; the main one is that it shrinks during polymerization and so distorts the tissue embedded in it. Another is that the electron beam may sublime the methacrylate and, as a consequence, certain delicate structures that ordinarily are held in place by the embedding medium are permitted to shift position slightly when it is sublimed. In view of these disadvantages, attempts have been made to find better embedding media, and several have been found which do not cause as much distortion as methacrylate and do not sublime when bombarded by electrons. Among the newer embedding media are the epoxy resins, Epon and Araldite.

Since the EM resolves such minute detail, it is of the greatest importance that the tissue from which sections are cut be fixed as perfectly as possible. It was shown some time ago by Strangeways and Canti that of all fixatives osmium tetroxide ($OsO_4$) produces the least alteration in cells. These results were fully confirmed in early EM studies, and since then solutions of osmium tetroxide have been generally employed as the fixatives of choice. A considerable improvement was effected when Palade introduced buffered solutions of osmium tetroxide.

For many years the latter was the only fixative of much practical importance to electron microscopists. However, its use is associated with one serious disadvantage; that is, after its use, it is impossible to study the cytochemistry of the cell by means of enzyme digestion. Subsequently, it was found that potassium permanganate preserves fine structure in reasonable condition and also allows certain digestion procedures to be carried out. More recently still, it has been shown that a succession of two fixatives, first an aldehyde and then conventional osmium tetroxide, produces results that are comparable with the best osmic fixation. By using this combination, histochemical technics can be applied to the tissue between the two fixing procedures. The buffered aldehydes that give the best results are formalin, acrolein and, particularly, gluteraldehyde; these allow the retention of the cell's fine structure, yet still permit the use of many histochemical technics. It is fortunate then that after enzyme digestion the material can be post-fixed in osmium tetroxide, fine structure that had been preserved by the aldehyde now being endowed with the means for contrast in the EM, for osmium, which scatters electrons strongly, is normally taken up to different extents by different tissue components. Other salts of heavy metals act in a similar manner and are also sometimes used to increase contrast. Such solutions are referred to as "electron stains." One which has come into common use is *lead hydroxide;* some of the electron micrographs in this book were taken from sections stained in this way.

### SOME TECHNICAL POINTS RELATIVE TO CUTTING AND MOUNTING SECTIONS FOR ELECTRON MICROSCOPY

In order to achieve satisfactory fixation for EM studies, only very small blocks of tissue can be used; these are commonly about 1 cu. mm. in size. After the tissue is embedded, the block so obtained is trimmed further so that the slices cut from it are only about 1/4 mm. square. Since the slices cut from the block are only about 1 millionth of an inch in thickness, it is obvious that they would be almost invisible to the naked eye. Therefore, their manipulation must be carried on under a light microscope of the type commonly used for making delicate dissections (Fig. 4-10). Since the extremely thin sections are very fragile, they can be handled only by floating them, as they are cut, onto the surface of a liquid. A small cuplike reservoir containing a mixture of alcohol, or acetone, and water is attached to the back of the cutting edge of the knife for this purpose (Fig. 4-11). As the sections are cut they float on this mixture in the form of a ribbon. Relatively thick sections appear to be colored by reflected light, but sections sufficiently thin for study appear colorless or silvery. The problem of obtaining proper support for these very thin sections and yet permitting the passage of electrons through them is solved by mounting the sections on little copper grids, each of which is coated with a very thin supporting film of formvar (a plastic) or carbon. The copper grid supports the film, and the film supports the section. Electrons can pass through the holes in the grid, and penetrate through the supporting film and the parts of the section that overlie the holes in the grid.

Thin sections, so mounted, are placed on the specimen holder of the microscope and inserted into the instrument. A high vacuum must be produced in the instrument before the electron beam can be switched on and the specimen examined. Controls are provided for moving the specimen around, changing the magnification and the brightness of the image, and so on (Fig. 4-9). The magnification can be changed easily by turning a knob which controls the current passing through the intermediate or projector lens. Focusing of the image is accomplished not by moving the object up and down as in the light microscope but by altering very slightly the objective lens current. The focal length of the objective lens is altered thereby, and the image may be brought into sharp focus on the fluorescent screen. The focusing must be done very accurately, and as an aid to sharp focusing it is customary to observe the screen through a low-power binocular microscope. The photo-

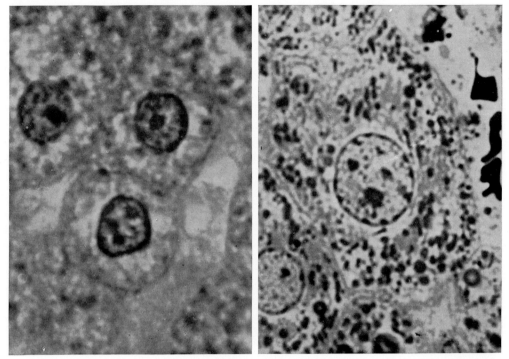

FIG. 4-12. Photomicrographs (× 2,500) showing the difference between the appearance of cells in sections prepared by the ordinary paraffin technic and by methods evolved for electron microscopy which permit much thinner sections to be obtained. The section of liver shown on the left was prepared by the paraffin technic from tissue fixed in Bouin's fluid. It was cut with a 4-$\mu$ setting on the microtome and stained with H and E. The section on the right was cut from material fixed in glutaraldehyde and post-fixed in osmium tetroxide. It was cut at 0.5 $\mu$ and stained with a buffered solution of toluidine blue. Much more detail can be seen in both nucleus and cytoplasm; in particular note how well the mitochondria in the cytoplasm are shown. Thin sections like this help to bridge the gap between low-power electron micrographs and ordinary sections prepared by the paraffin technic. (Preparations by R. Escoffery)

graphic plate lies immediately below the screen. To take a micrograph the screen is tilted out of the way, and the electron beam is allowed to hit the photographic emulsion for a few seconds. The exposed plate is developed and fixed in the usual way.

The depth of an ordinary paraffin section is much greater than the depth of focus obtainable with high-power objectives of the light microscope, so that in scanning a section completely with the light microscope it is necessary not only to traverse the whole area of the specimen but also to focus up and down. This is not so with the EM. Owing to the narrow aperture of the electron beam the depth of focus at the object is relatively great (approximately 1 micron), and this distance is much greater than the thickness of the sec-tions used (about 1/40th of a micron). Hence, objects at all depths in the section are in focus at one time, even structures that overlap.

**The Use of Ultrathin Sections for Light Microscopy.** The student who is familiar with appearances seen with light microscopy may find it difficult at first to interpret electron micrographs. From light to electron microscopy is not so much a step as it is a jump.

There are two important reasons for electron micrographs differing from ordinary photomicrographs: (1) their much greater magnification and (2) the better fixation and thinner sections employed for electron microscopy. In the usual electron micrograph everything appears anywhere from say 10 to 50 or more times as large as with the oil-immersion

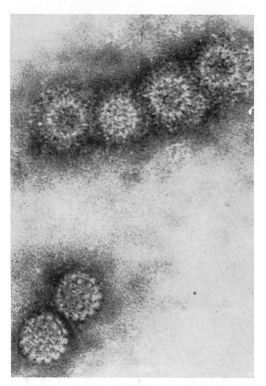

FIG. 4-13. Electron micrograph (× 300,-000) of 6 negatively stained virus particles. The upper 4 particles are polyoma virus, and the 2 lower particles are the virus of human warts. The two kinds of particles have a similar structure and appearance except that the particles of wart virus are slightly larger. Before being negatively stained this preparation was treated with antibody to polyoma virus which was made by injecting polyoma virus into rabbits. The polyoma antibody has combined with, and hence is attached only to, the 4 polyoma particles. The antibody can be seen as delicate short strands that more or less radiate out from the little knobs which stud the particles to which they are attached. (Almeida, J., Cinader, B., and Howatson, A.: J. Exp. Med. 118:327-340)

objective of the light microscope, and this, together with the fact that a wealth of detail may appear within objects that can barely be resolved with the light microscope, makes the transition from light to electron microscopy difficult. Examining very low-power electron micrographs before examining the more usual ones taken at great magnification may be helpful.

Another procedure that is helpful for bridging the gap between light and electron microscopy entails the light microscope study of sections prepared similarly to those prepared for electron microscopy but stained and mounted for light microscopy. Until recently this could not be done very effectively because fixation with osmium tetroxide and embedding in methacrylate interfered with ordinary staining procedures. Recently, however, the introduction of glutaraldehyde for fixation and the use of epoxy resins for embedding have made it possible to use many staining methods on very thin sections. Sections prepared by these methods, but for use with the light microscope instead of the EM, are usually cut at thicknesses between 0.5 and 1 micron, and this is most easily done with a diamond, instead of a glass, knife. Such sections can be stained with H and E and, even though they are thus colored, because of the way they are fixed and because they are so thin, they resemble what is seen with the electron microscope much more than do sections prepared by the paraffin technic (see Fig. 4-12).

**Negative Staining.** Only recently has this technic been used in electron microscopy. In the technics discussed previously, contrast in the EM is generally obtained because heavy metal atoms become attached to various tissue components, and hence some parts of the section become more electron dense, and hence darker on the fluorescent screen, than others. With negative staining, however, the particular object being examined, for example, virus particles (Figs. 4-13 and 4-14), or a small component of cells, is allowed to retain its own slight electron density and contrast between it and its environment is obtained by surrounding it with a substance of great electron density. As a result, the object appears light against a dark background, and so has a "negative" appearance. The electron-dense material most commonly employed for this procedure is a solution of phosphotungstic acid. Since the material to be examined must be surrounded on all sides by the contrast agent, which permeates into even the finest interstices presented by the surface of the object under examination, the technic cannot be applied to embedded tissue but only to structures that can be obtained in some sort of suspension. The surface detail that can be obtained by this method has had considerable

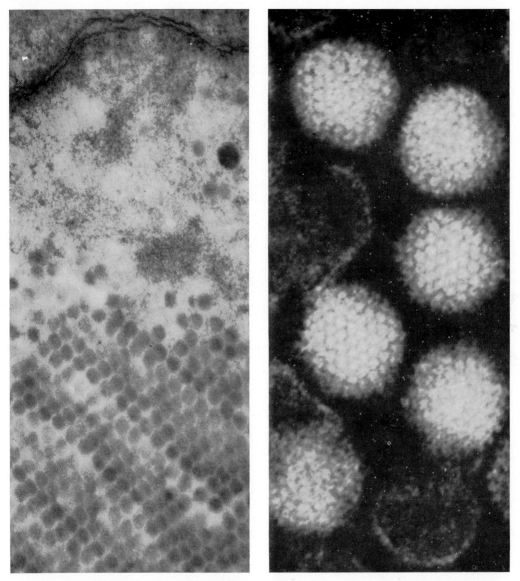

FIG. 4-14. (*Left*) Electron micrograph ($\times$ 70,000) of thin section of a cell infected with adenovirus which has multiplied in its nucleus. The adenovirus particles can be seen in the lower part of the illustration arranged in the nucleus in a crystallinelike array. (*Right*) Electron micrograph ($\times$ 500,000) of a negatively stained preparation of adenovirus particles. Note that the negative staining procedure reveals much more detail about their contours than can be seen in thin sections. The little projections of protein that stud the particles are termed capsomeres. (Preparation by June Almeida)

application in elucidating the fine structure of virus particles (Fig. 4-14) and certain structures within the cell (Fig. 7-21).

**Histochemical Technics and Radioautography With the Electron Microscope.** Many of the methods used to detect nucleic acids, carbohydrates and proteins—particularly enzymes, for instance phosphatase—are now being adapted to localization at the electron microscope level. Very precise localization has been obtained by several authors, particularly Barnett.

Radioautographs can be examined in the EM. Thin sections are coated with a thin layer of emulsion (with only one thickness of silver crystals). After exposure and develop-

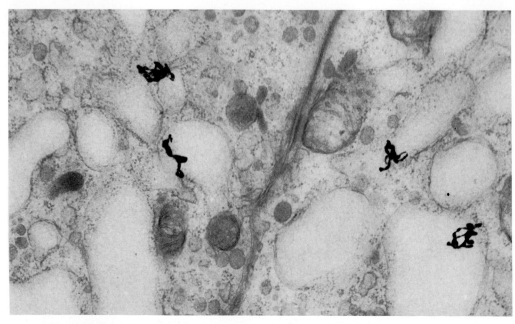

FIG. 4-15. EM radioautograph (× 280,000) showing newly formed protein in parts of 2 thyroid cells. The specimen was obtained from a rat given leucine-H³ 1 hour before its death. Since leucine-H³ is a precursor of protein, newly formed protein will be labeled. Here the filamentous black silver grains, 4 of which may be seen, straddle rough-surfaced vesicles of the endoplasmic reticulum, indicating the sites of their synthesis. (Preparation by B. A. Young)

ment, the silver grains appearing over the specimen may be examined in the electron microscope. However, the presence of gelatin over the section clouds the fields. By careful treatment of the sections with either acidic or basic solutions, it is possible to remove most of the gelatin without displacing the silver grains, and thus it is possible to see the fine structure of the tissue distinctly. The silver grains which appear as tiny but solid dots under the light microscope show under the EM as black filamentous structures (Fig. 4-15). It is therefore possible to inject a precursor and locate the sites of synthesis and migration of a product with the help of the electron microscope, and to achieve very precise localization.

## THE USE OF THE INTERFERENCE AND THE PHASE MICROSCOPES FOR THE STUDY OF LIVING UNSTAINED TISSUE

The study of living unstained cells is difficult with the ordinary light microscope because there is so little contrast between their different parts. Two developments, the *interference* and the *phase microscopes*, have made studies of living cells much easier and more profitable. The principles on which they operate will now be described briefly.

Light waves can differ from one another in their (1) amplitude, (2) wavelength and (3) phase, as will now be described.

1. The amplitude of a light wave is responsible for its intensity; the greater its amplitude, the greater its intensity. If light is passed through a neutral filter, its intensity is diminished (Fig. 4-16) because the filter diminishes the amplitude of the wave that passes through it (Fig. 4-16).

It might be thought that the various tissue components in an unstained section or in a living fresh preparation of tissue would each act like a neutral filter of a different degree of opacity and so reduce the amplitude of the waves that pass through them to different extents. Unfortunately, however, although most tissue components do indeed act like neutral filters, they all transmit about the same amount of light, and so, with the ordinary microscope, they all appear to be about the

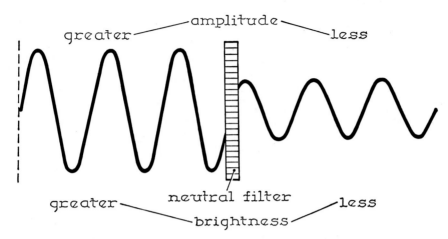

FIG. 4-16. Diagram showing how the amplitude of light waves is decreased by the waves passing through a neutral filter.

same degree of brightness. Hence, they cannot be distinguished readily from one another (Fig. 4-18, *left*). Accordingly, histologists were driven to the use of stained sections, which take advantage of the attribute of light waves next to be described.

2. The wavelength of light—the distance between two successive crests of waves—determines its color. The wavelength of red light is greater than that of green, and that of green is greater than that of blue. Filters that absorb light of different wavelengths can be constructed; for example, a green filter transmits only light that has the wavelength of green light; it absorbs red and blue light.

When sections are stained, say with H and E, the different tissue components in them take up one or the other of the two dyes to become colored blue and red to different extents. When such sections are examined with the microscope the various red-and-blue tissue components in them act as blue-and-red filters (of different degrees of color selectivity and opacity), and so each tissue component can be recognized because it transmits light of a different color and amplitude to the eye.

3. In the foregoing it has been shown that the various components in a preparation of *unstained* tissue do not change the amplitude of the light waves that pass through them to very different extents and do not absorb light waves of different wavelengths to different extents. Hence, on the grounds of amplitude and wavelength, light waves that pass through an unstained specimen cannot be readily dis-

tinguished from one another (Fig. 4-18, *left*). However, the different components in unstained tissue do alter the phase of light waves that pass through them to different extents. This fact is not easily taken advantage of, because phase differences as such are not discernible to the eye. If somehow phase differences could be converted into differences of amplitude different tissue components in unstained preparations could be made to appear of different degrees of brightness and so be distinguished easily from one another (Fig. 4-18, *center* and *right*). The phase and the interference microscopes are designed to accomplish this aim, as will now be described.

Anyone who has seen the waves on a lake sweeping around both sides of an anchored boat and then reuniting has seen an illustration of the principle that is employed. When the waves that come around one side of the boat join with those coming around the other side of the boat, one of two things may happen: the combining of the waves may result in the formation of waves that have either (1) a greater or (2) a smaller amplitude than the individual waves that join one another. To illustrate, in Part 1 of Figure 4-17, *left*, two waves, A and B, of the same amplitude and length are shown as being in phase with one another, that is, the peaks and the troughs of each are directly above one another. If two such waves are combined, as is shown in the lower left corner of this figure, the resulting wave has a greater amplitude than each of the original two. Even if the waves are slightly

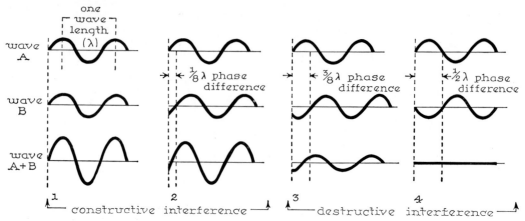

FIG. 4-17. Diagrams showing how light waves can interfere with one another to increase or decrease the amplitude of the resultant waves.

out of phase with one another, as is illustrated in Part 2 of Figure 4-17, the amplitude of the resulting wave is still greater than that of each of the waves that combined (but less than that of the wave that results from the combining of two similar waves that are perfectly in phase with one another). When waves interfere with one another to form waves of greater amplitude, the interference is said to be constructive. However, if waves of a given amplitude are considerably out of phase with one another, as is illustrated in Part 3 of Figure 4-17, their combining results in waves that are smaller than the original ones, and, indeed, if they are completely out of phase with one another, they can obliterate each other completely, as is shown in Part 4 of this illustration. It can be seen readily from Figure 4-17 that by variously combining light waves that are out of phase with one another it is possible to produce combined waves of greater or lesser amplitude and hence of greater or lesser brightness. This is the principle used in the phase and the interference microscopes to provide contrast between tissue components that are of approximately the same relative opacities. However, to do this, two sets of waves must be used.

Although two sets of waves are obtained and reunited in both the interference and the phase microscopes, the way in which this is accomplished differs. In both instances the two sets of waves must be derived from the same source; thus they are said to be *coherent*.

In the interference microscope, two sets of waves are obtained before light reaches the object; this is done by placing a beam-splitter in the condenser. The beam-splitter allows one beam to pass directly through it to the object; this is called the *object beam*. A second beam passes out from the beam-splitter parallel with, but a short distance off from, the object beam. This is called the *reference beam*, and it passes up, not through, the object but at one side of it, ideally through some clear area close to the cell or whatever object is being examined. On reaching the objective lens, the reference and the objective beams are recombined by another beam-splitter, used, as it were, in reverse.

So far we have discussed two beams. However, it should be understood that the object beam contains a multitude of light waves that pass through all the different parts of the object. For example, if a cell is being examined, some light waves would pass through some parts and others through other parts. These two parts of the cell would alter the phase of the waves that pass through them to a different extent. When the multitude of waves in the object beam are reunited with the corresponding multitude of waves in the reference beam, the light waves that passed through one part will interfere with the reference beam (the waves of which are all in the same phase) differently from the light waves that passed through the other part; hence, there will be differences in amplitude between the two resultant sets of waves. This will permit the two parts to be distinguished by their different degrees of brightness.

Since the phase of the light waves in the

reference beam is practically unaltered it provides a standard for measurement. By seeing how much interference is caused by waves that pass through different objects, it is possible to measure quantitatively the extent to which these objects alter the phase of the waves that pass through them. Hence, the interference microscope can be used as an interferometer to provide quantitative data.

In the phase microscope, two beams from the same light source are obtained in a different way from that employed in the interference microscope. No beam-splitters are used. Instead, an annular diaphragm is placed in the condenser so that all the light that strikes the object is in the form of a hollow cone. On striking the transparent object, light acts as it does when it strikes a diffraction grating, by giving rise to two types of waves. One type passes through the object in a straight line; these form the *undiffracted* waves. However, other waves are diffracted by the object, and their course is changed somewhat. These constitute the *diffracted* waves.

The different components in the object diffract to different extents the light waves that strike them. Consequently, the relative intensity (amplitude) of the diffracted and the undiffracted waves that arise as light strikes these components of the object varies. With some components the undiffracted light would be of much greater amplitude than the diffracted, but with others not so great. Of course, if the diffracted and the undiffracted waves from any given component in the object were combined, they would not necessarily differ greatly in amplitude from the combined waves from any other component. But advantage is taken of the fact that the relative amplitudes of the diffracted and the undiffracted beams from different components differ. This is done by inserting a phase retarder in the objective. Phase retarders, depending on the type used, act by retarding primarily either the diffracted or the undiffracted waves from the different components of the object. Different components of the object diffract light to different extents. Accordingly, the percentage of diffracted and undiffracted light that emerges from each component in the object is different. When a phrase retarder (that affects *either* the diffracted light *or* the undiffracted light) is inserted in the objective, it

will, depending on the kind used, retard the phase of *either* the diffracted or the undiffracted light from every component in the object equally. But, since the percentage of diffracted and undiffracted light from every component in the object is different, it is obvious that a recombination of the diffracted and the undiffracted light from each component in the object, after the phase of one or the other kind has been altered by the phase retarder, will result in different amounts of interference between the recombined waves from each component in the object, and this, of course, affects the amplitude of these waves, and this in turn results in different components of the object exhibiting contrast with one another in terms of brightness or darkness. The extent to which any component in the object diffracts light is, of course, dependent on the surrounding medium of that component of the object. Therefore, it is possible to alter the ability of any component of the object to diffract light by the use of different mounting media which have different refractive indices. Different components can be made lighter or darker than certain others by using phase retarders that act primarily on the diffracted or the undiffracted rays; hence, it is possible to have either "dark" or "bright" contrast objectives. Figure 4-18 shows how the same unstained cell, removed fresh from the inner lining of the cheek, appears when viewed with the ordinary light microscope (*left*), the phase microscope (*center*) and the interference microscope (*right*).

## WAYS IN WHICH LIVING OR FRESH TISSUE CAN BE STUDIED OUTSIDE THE BODY OR IN THE LIVING BODY

Tiny pieces of tissue removed from a living animal body can be mounted on slides in salt or other types of solution and examined with the microscope as they are or after being teased apart. For phase microscopy the preparations should be very thin. If the ordinary light microscope is used, the study may be facilitated by the use of *supravital stains* (for example, Janus Green B). Supravital stains depend for their staining qualities on cells' being alive. However, supravital stains are generally toxic, and although cells must be

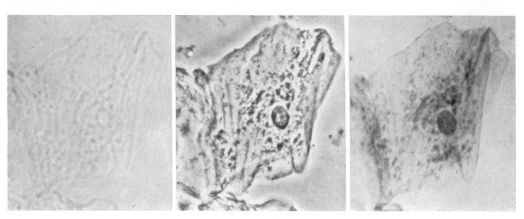

FIG. 4-18. Photomicrographs of the same unstained epithelial cell made with the ordinary light, phase and interference microscope respectively. The cell was obtained from the inside of the cheek. (Preparation by W. G. B. Casselman)

alive to be stained properly by them, they subsequently kill the cells that they stain.

It is possible to examine certain parts of an animal body under the microscope without separating the part from its blood supply. Perhaps the easiest tissue to examine in this way is the web of a frog's foot. This is sufficiently thin to allow light to pass through it. The mesentery of the frog can also be similarly studied while alive; it is pulled out through a small incision and spread over a slide on the stage of a microscope and covered to keep it from drying. Both these procedures nicely demonstrate the circulation of the blood.

**The Quartz-Rod Illuminator.** Knisely has studied less accessible organs and structures by utilizing an ingenious method for conducting light to them by means of rods of fused quartz. These convey light even around corners, because the refractive index of quartz is such that all light is reflected within the rod; hence, light can be delivered to deeply situated organs which otherwise would be almost impossible to illuminate sufficiently well for microscopic examination. By the use of the quartz-rod illuminator, Knisely has made very impressive contributions toward obtaining an understanding of how blood circulates through certain organs and toward what is known as the "sludging of blood." The method is also employed to great advantage in the transillumination of the eye; the technic here has been specially described by S. Bensley.

**Transparent Chambers.** Very clear observa-

tions can be made through certain types of glass windows (or windows made of other transparent materials) that can be inserted by surgical procedures into some parts of the body. Sandison devised this method in 1924; he cut holes in rabbits' ears and, using the borders of these as window frames, he sewed in double windows that fitted the window frames closely. The two panes were separated from each other slightly by transparent spacers, and the space between them was filled with a suitable salt solution. From the living "window frame" cells and blood vessels grew into the space between the two panes of the double window, and by placing the rabbit ear on the stage of a microscope, with the window directly under the objective, he was able to observe the growth and the movement of the living cells that grew in between the two panes of the window. This work was begun and carried out under the direction of E. R. Clark who, with E. L. Clark, later devised the further improvements and refinements of the method by which they were able to perform their many illuminating studies, particularly on the smaller blood vessels of the body.

**Micrurgy.** The dissections that can be performed on fresh living tissue under a microscope by means of instruments held with the hands are limited, because it is not possible to make freehand movements of the delicacy required. However, movements of the greatest delicacy can be made because of the development of what is known as micromanipulative technic (micrurgy, which means "small work"). Mechanical devices have been constructed which are affixed to a microscope and allow the turn of a screw or some other easily controlled movement to act through reduction gears or similarly functioning mechanisms so that gross movements of the hand cause movements of only the most minute latitude in the instruments under the microscope. The instruments which can be used are of different sorts, but all are minute. With the use of such equipment, fine dissections can be accomplished, injections can be introduced with great accuracy, and many other actions can be performed which otherwise would be impossible.

## REFERENCES

### HISTOCHEMISTRY

Glick, D.: Techniques of Histo- and Cytochemistry. A Manual of Morphological and Quantitative Micromethods for Inorganic, Organic and Enzyme Constituents in Biological Materials, New York, Interscience, 1949.

Graumann, W., and Neumann, K.: Handbuch der Histochimie, Gustav Fischer, Stuttgart, 1959-1965 (continuing series).

Lillie, R. D.: Histopathologic Technic and Practical Histochemistry, ed. 2, New York, McGraw-Hill, 1954.

Lison, L.: Histochimie et Cytochimie Animales: Principes et Méthodes, vols. 1 and 2, Paris, Gauthier-Villars, 1960.

Pearse, A. G. E.: Histochemistry, Theoretical and Applied, ed. 2, London, Churchill, 1960.

Wegmann, R. (ed.): Histochemistry and Cytochemistry, Proceedings of the First International Congress, Paris, 1960, New York, Pergamon Press, Macmillan, 1963.

### RADIOAUTOGRAPHY

Bélanger, L. F., and Leblond, C. P.: A method for locating radioactive elements in tissues by covering histological sections with a photographic emulsion, Endocrinology 39:8-13, 1946.

Caro, L. G., and van Tubergen, R. P.: High-resolution autoradiography. I. Methods, J. Cell Biol. 15:173, 1962.

Granboulan, Philippe, Granboulan, Nicole, and Bernhard, Wilhelm: Application de l'autoradiographie à la microscopie électronique, J. Microscopie 1(1):75, 1962.

Kopriwa, B. M., and Leblond, C. P.: Improvements in the coating technique of radioautography, J. Histochem. Cytochem. 10:269-284, 1962.

Lacassagne, A., Lattés, J., and Lavedan, J.: Etude expérimentale des effets biologiques du Polonium introduit dans l'organisme, J. Rad. Elect. 9:1-14, 1925.

Leblond, C. P.: Time dimension in histology, Am. J. Anat. 116:1-29, 1965.

Nadler, N. J.: Some theoretical aspects of radioautography, Canad. J. M. Sci. 29:182-194, 1951.

Nadler, N. J., Young, B. A., Leblond, C. P., and Mitmaker, B.: Elaboration of thyroglobulin in the thyroid follicle, Endocrinology 74:333-354, 1964.

Pelc, S. R.: The stripping-film technique of autoradiography, Int. J. Applied Rad. Isotopes 1: 172-177, 1956.

Warshawsky, H., Leblond, C. P., and Droz, B.: Synthesis and migration of proteins in the cells of the exocrine pancreas as revealed by specific activity determinations from radioautographs, J. Cell Biol. 16:1-23, 1963.

### MICROINCINERATION

Horning, E. S.: Micro-incineration and the inorganic constituents of cells in Bourne, Geoffrey (ed.): Cytology and Cell Physiology, Chap. 7, London, Oxford, 1951.

Policard, A.: Twenty years of microincineration; cytological results, J. Roy. Micro. Soc. 62:25, 1942.

### FLUORESCENCE MICROSCOPY

Cherry, W. B., Goldman, M., and Carski, T. R.: Fluorescent Antibody Technics in the Diagnosis of Communicable Diseases, U. S. Dept. of Health, Education and Welfare, Public Health Service Pub. No. 729, Washington, D. C., U. S. Gov't. Print. Off., 1960.

Coons, A. H.: Fluorescent antibody methods in Danielli, J. F. (ed.): General Cytochemical Methods, pp. 399-422, New York, Acad. Press, 1958.

Loofbourow, J. R.: Fluorescence: Methods in Glasser, O. (ed.): Medical Physics, vol. 1, pp. 446-451, Chicago, Year Book Pub., 1944.

Nairn, R. C. (ed.): Fluorescent Protein Tracing, ed. 2, Edinburgh, Livingstone, 1964.

Sainte-Marie, G.: A paraffin embedding technic for studies employing immunofluorescence, J. Histochem. Biochem. 10:250, 1962.

### ELECTRON MICROSCOPY

#### Historical

Burton, E. F., and Kohl, W. H.: The Electron Microscope, ed. 2, New York, Reinhold, 1946.

Freundlich, M. M.: Origin of the electron microscope, Science 142:185, 1963.

### *Technics for Electron Microscopy*

Kay, D. (ed.): Technics for Electron Microscopy, Springfield, Ill., Thomas, 1961.

Pease, D. C.: Histological Techniques for Electron Microscopy, New York, Acad. Press, 1960.

Wischnitzer, S.: Introduction to Electron Microscopy, New York, Pergamon, 1962.

### *Atlases and/or Books Dealing Primarily With the Fine Structure of Cells, Tissues and Organs*

Porter, K. R., and Bonneville, M. A.: An Introduction to the Fine Structure of Cells and Tissues, ed. 2, Philadelphia, Lea & Febiger, 1964.

Rhodin, J. A. G.: An Atlas of Ultrastructure, Philadelphia, Saunders, 1963. (NOTE: Rhodin's *Atlas* contains a most extensive bibliography relating to the fine structure of cells, tissues and organs.)

### PHASE AND INTERFERENCE MICROSCOPY

Barer, R.: Phase contrast microscopy, Research *8*:341, 1955.

Bennett, A. H., Jupnik, H., Osterberg, H., and Richards, O. W.: Phase Microscopy: Principles and Applications, New York, Wiley, 1951.

Zernike, F.: How I discovered phase contrast, Science *121*:345, 1955.

———: Phase contrast, a new method for the microscopic observation of transparent objects, Physica *9*:686, 1942.

### TRANSPARENT CHAMBERS AND OTHER TECHNICS FOR VIEWING LIVING CELLS IN VIVO

Algire, G. H., and Legallais, F. Y.: Recent developments in the transparent chamber technique as adapted to the mouse, J. Nat. Cancer Inst. *10*:225, 1949.

Bensley, S. H.: Microscopic studies of the living iris, Anat. Rec. *138*:39, 1960.

Bloch, E. H.: The bulbar conjunctiva of man as a site for the microscopic study of the circulation, Anat. Rec. *120*:349, 1954.

Clark, E. R.: The transparent chamber technique for the microscopic study of living blood vessels, Anat. Rec. *120*:241, 1954.

Forbes, H. S.: The fused quartz rod technique for transilluminating living internal organs *in situ* for microscopic study, Anat. Rec. *120*:265, 1954.

———: Study of blood vessels on cortex of living mammalian brain—description of technique, Anat. Rec. *120*:309, 1954.

Knisely, M. H.: An improved fused quartz living tissue illuminator, Anat. Rec. *71*:503, 1938.

———: A method of illuminating living structures for microscopic study, Anat. Rec. *64*:499, 1936.

Moore, R. L.: Adaptation of the transparent chamber technique to the ear of the dog, Anat. Rec. *64*:387, 1935-1936.

Sandison, J. C.: A new method for the microscopic study of living growing tissues by the introduction of a transparent chamber in the rabbit's ear, Anat. Rec. *28*:281, 1924.

———: The transparent chamber of the rabbit's ear, Am. J. Anat. *41*:447, 1928.

Zweifach, B. W.: Direct observation of the mesenteric circulation in experimental animals, Anat. Rec. *120*:277, 1954.

### SUPRAVITAL STAINING

Bensley, R. R.: Studies on the pancreas of the guinea pig, Am. J. Anat. *12*:297, 1911.

Cunningham, R. S., and Tompkins, E. H.: The supravital method of studying blood cells *in* Downey, H. (ed.): Handbook of Hematology, vol. 1, sec. IX, New York, Hoeber, 1938.

Hall, Byron E.: Evaluation of the supravital staining method *in* Downey, H. (ed.): Handbook of Hematology, vol. 1, sec. XI, New York, Hoeber, 1938.

### MICRURGY

Chambers, Robert: New apparatus and methods for the dissection and injection of living cells, J. Roy. Micro. Soc. *42*:373, 1922.

———: Recent developments of the micromanipulative technique and its application, J. Roy. Micro. Soc. *60*:113, 1940.

Reyniers, James A. (ed.): Micrurgical and Germ Free Technique, Springfield, Ill., Thomas, 1943.

———: Studies in micrurgical technique, V and VI, Anat. Rec. *56*:295, 307, 1933.

# PART TWO

# Cell Structure and Cell Biology

# 5    General Features of Cells

## INTRODUCTION

There has been an explosive development of knowledge about cell biology over the past decade. Contrary to what might be assumed, this has made both the learning and the teaching of histology easier than it was before. The reason for this seeming paradox is that much of the new knowledge relates to the elucidation of the functions and the interrelations of many components of cells that previously had to be remembered as individual and unrelated entities. It has now become possible to assemble, theoretically, the various parts and components of cells into a working model, the operation of which can, up to a point, be understood. When the student has some concept of how a cell works, the various interrelated parts of the model become meaningful to him and hence easily remembered.

In the next two chapters we shall take up the various parts of the cell, choosing an order that will fit, so far as possible, the study of cells in the laboratory. It is hoped that this order will also permit the parts of a working model of a cell to be assembled gradually and logically in the mind. But first there are some preliminary matters and some general features of cells and cell populations that must be described briefly and this is done in this chapter.

**Origin of Term.** The word *cell* (*cella* = a small room) was introduced into biology by Robert Hooke, an ingenious scientist of the 17th century. Hooke built a microscope and, on examining some thin slices of cork with it, found the cork to consist of tiny empty compartments separated from one another by thin walls which are now known to be composed of nonliving material. However, Hooke termed the compartments *cells*. It was found much later that the compartments of *living* plant tissue, in contrast to those of cork, were each filled with a little body of semifluid material, and so the term cell came to include the bodies that were in the compartments of plants as well as the compartments themselves. When animal tissues were studied under the microscope, it became obvious that they too were composed of tiny little bodies of material like those in the compartments of living plants. In animal tissues, however, only some of these little bodies were found to be enclosed in compartments of nonliving material; others were disposed in layers or groups without being separated from one another by compartment walls but only by their own delicate surrounding membranes. So, with regard to animal tissues, the word cell is no longer used for compartments made of nonliving materials but only for little bodies that are comparable to those that live in compartments in plants.

An organism composed of only a single cell, such as a bacterium or an amoeba, can manifest the properties of life and reproduce its own kind in a suitable nutritive medium. Many of the cells of man, planted in suitable media in glass containers, can live, and some at least, for a time, can reproduce their own kind in this environment. Cells are the smallest units of living matter that can be isolated and still independently carry on the processes of life.

**Protoplasm.** The material of which cells are composed is called *protoplasm* (*protos* = first, *plasma* = something formed or molded). The use of this word for the material that cells are made of is perhaps more understandable if it is explained that this word, which was coined by the distinguished investigator Purkinje in 1840, was first used with reference to the formative material of embryos, which material we now know is cellular.

Protoplasm is a general term for the complex material that cells are made of and which functions as living material. This material has been defined by Huxley as the physical basis of life. It is important to understand that life is not a static property of protoplasm but depends on, and arises out of, the continuous chemical activity that occurs in protoplasm.

The point should perhaps be made that protoplasm is not an inert medium in which the chemical processes of life proceed, because the protoplasm is itself involved in the chemical processes of life, and for this reason it is always changing.

**Metabolism.** The sum total of all the chemical reactions that proceed in a cell constitutes its *metabolism* (*metabote* = change). Some metabolic reactions are concerned with the breakdown of protoplasm; these are termed *catabolic* (*kata* = down, *ballein* = to throw). Others are concerned with the synthesis of protoplasm; these are termed *anabolic* (*anabole* = a rising up). Growth is dependent on anabolic reactions overshadowing catabolic reactions. Most of the chemical reactions involved in metabolism are catalyzed by enzymes. As was explained in Chapter 2, the most important components of protoplasm are proteins. Moreover, many of these are enzymes; indeed, a vast number of different enzymes is present in every cell. Each is extraordinarily specific and acts on its particular substrate by combining with it. The complex so formed becomes reactive so that the substrate of the enzymes enters into reactions which it would not otherwise have entered into under the physical conditions existing in the cell. Enzymes bring about reactions in cells that would require drastic procedures to effect in test tubes; for example, many of the reactions, catalyzed in cells by enzymes, could only be effected otherwise by the use of great heat and strong chemicals.

## THE PHYSIOLOGIC PROPERTIES OF PROTOPLASM

Speaking generally, the functions that any kind of cell can be observed to perform express one or more of what are termed the properties of protoplasm. There is a time-honored list of these that the student should learn well for the study of both histology and physiology. They are (1) irritability, (2) conductivity, (3) contractility, (4) absorption and assimilation, (5) excretion and secretion, (6) respiration and (7) growth and reproduction.

Before describing these briefly it should be pointed out that all these properties of protoplasm are demonstrable in an organism that consists of but a single cell, such as an amoeba. Since the protoplasm of an amoeba must be able to function in all seven ways if it is to live and propagate, it is like a jack-of-all-trades who, having to be able to do a lot of things, is unable to do any of them as well as a specialist. Basic to the understanding of the histology of a multicellular organism is the fact that the properties of protoplasm have been divided up to a considerable extent, with different properties being more or less delegated to different families of cells. This leads to there being different kinds of cells with different appearances in the body. Another point is that the development of a cell's ability to express certain properties well is often associated with corresponding inability to express certain others. Hence, the different kinds of cells in a multicellular organism are dependent on one another and, as we shall see, this creates many problems that are solved in various ways.

The basic properties of protoplasm will now be described briefly.

1. **Irritability** was defined a long time ago as the basic property of protoplasm that enables cells to respond in some way, for example, by contracting, when they are stimulated. Cells differ with regard to the extent to which they possess this property; this can be said another way, namely, that some cells are more *sensitive to stimulation* than others. The measure of irritability is in effect the measure of the sensitivity of cells to different magnitudes and different kinds of stimulation. Irritability can be highly specialized, for example, the photoreceptors of the eye are sensitive to light to which they respond by firing off nervous impulses.

2. **Conductivity** refers to the ability of protoplasm to conduct a wave of excitation from the point where the cell is stimulated to some distant part of the cell. That protoplasm has this property is easily demonstrated by the fact that responses can be observed to occur in a part of a cell other than that to which a stimulus is applied and even in other cells that are in contact with the one stimulated.

3. **Contractility** refers to the ability of the protoplasm of a cell to alter in such a way that the cell or a part of the cell becomes shortened in some direction.

4. **Absorption and Assimilation.** Absorption refers to the ability of cells to take up fluid and dissolved substances through their surfaces. Certain fluids, and substances dissolved in fluids, may be absorbed directly through the surface membranes of cells. A modification of the process is known as *pinocytosis* (*pinein* = to drink); this process involves fluid material being encapsulated by little vesicles that form from little infoldings of the cell membrane and then migrate into the substance of the cell. The taking up of particulate matter, another type of absorption, is described as *phagocytosis* (*phago* = I eat); this depends on particles at the surface of cells being enfolded by the cell membrane and then drawn into the substance of the cell.

**Assimilation** refers to the processes by which material taken into a cell is utilized (metabolized) in some way, for example, for the production of energy, the building up of protein or the storage of food.

5. **Excretion and Secretion.** Excretion refers to the ability of the protoplasm of cells to extrude waste products (excreta) from cell surfaces. If the product that is excreted is not a waste product of metabolism, but a useful substance, for example, a digestive juice or a hormone, the process is termed *secretion*.

6. **Respiration** refers to the process whereby food and oxygen, taken in by cells, interact in reactions catalyzed by enzymes to eventually form water and carbon dioxide. The process yields energy.

7. **Growth and Reproduction.** The use of the word growth in relation to any part of the body implies an enlargement of the part occasioned by an increase in the total amount of protoplasm or of intercellular substance of the part, or usually both. Enlargement caused by a part of the body becoming swollen with water is not growth. An increase in the amount of protoplasm in any part of the body can be achieved by the cells of the part becoming larger, and such an increase does occur in most cells during childhood. Far more significant is the increase in the amount of protoplasm achieved by cells keeping a more or less constant size but becoming more numerous, and this, of course, requires that some of them undergo division. Growth by means of cell multiplication instead of increase in cell size is desirable, for there is a limit to the

size that cells can attain and still function efficiently because they must absorb food and oxygen from their surfaces and deliver the waste products of metabolism through their surfaces. If a cell became so large that its central part were too far removed from a surface for diffusion mechanisms to operate effectively, it would suffer.

The term *reproduction* can be used with regard both to cells and to individuals. The reproduction of cells is accomplished by individual cells each dividing into two daughter cells. The reproduction of individuals is discussed in later chapters which deal with the reproductive systems of the body.

## DIFFERENTIATION—THE PROCESS WHEREBY CELLS BECOME SPECIALIZED

A single cell, the fertilized ovum, by continued cell division, gives rise to all the cells of a body. The fertilized ovum, and the first generations of cells that develop from it, show no particular specialization for the expression of any of the properties of protoplasm except growth and reproduction. But, as further generations of cells are formed, the cells of different parts of the enlarging mass of cells begin to become different from one another as they begin to become specialized to express certain of the properties of protoplasm. For example, certain cells evolve in which the properties of irritability and conductivity are highly developed; these become what are known as nerve cells. Other cells develop in which the basic property of contractility is so exploited that it becomes their dominant feature; these are known as muscle cells. Still other cells become highly specialized for absorption and still others for secretion.

The process by which the cells that develop from the fertilized ovum thus become different from one another is termed *differentiation*. Since a particular specialized function performed by a cell is dependent on that cell's possessing the physical equipment required for expressing that particular function, specialization for different kinds of function results in specialized cells having different physical equipment and hence different appearances. Because of this the histologist is able not only to tell different kinds of specialized cells apart from their over-all appearances, but also to correlate both the external appearance and the internal structure of cells with specific functions.

Possible mechanisms involved in cell differentiation will be considered at the end of Chapter 7.

The advantages gained because of cell specialization are obvious. Therefore, we shall next discuss some of the consequences of specialization, for these are not so obvious and are of concern to many important problems in histology and to the study of disease.

## SOME GENERALIZATIONS ABOUT THE CONSEQUENCES OF DIFFERENTIATION (CELL SPECIALIZATION)

**A Loss of Potentiality.** One generalization that can be made about the consequences of differentiation for specialized function is that differentiation entails a loss of *potentiality* on the part of the cell that differentiates. The word potentiality, used with regard to cells, refers to their capacity to form or become any of a great variety of different kinds of cells. Thus the fertilized ovum is said to be a *totipotent cell* because it can form any of the various kinds of specialized cells that exist in a body. However, the total potentiality of the ovum is retained only by the germ cells to which it gives rise and not by the body cells that develop from it. The development of a body is dependent on differentiation occurring in the body cells and, as a result of this differentiation, the body comes to be composed of different cell families. A consequence of this is that the members of each of these families lose their ability to form or become cells of other families; in other words, differentiation is generally associated with a restriction of the potentiality of the differentiating cells so that they become unable to become or form cells of any family type other than that of the family to which they belong.

**A Loss of Reproductive Capacity.** Just as differentiation involves a restriction of a cell's potentiality, it seems also to impair, sooner or later, a cell's capacity for reproducing itself. Species are perpetuated, not because the differentiated body cells of individuals of that

species live forever, but because the totipotent germ cells carried by individuals are perpetuated through countless generations of individuals of the species. Since only germ cells are perpetuated indefinitely, there is some reason to believe that such cell differentiation as occurs to form a body places restrictions on the reproductive capacities of the body cells. The restrictions on reproductive capacity that result from cells differentiating into body cells is apparent in some cells immediately after birth but, in other kinds of cells, it may not be apparent during the lifetime of the individual. However, there is some reason to believe that body cells could not continue to reproduce themselves forever even in the most favorable environment and hence that the restriction placed on the reproductive capacity of cells because of their becoming body cells is a factor which limits the life span of members of any species.

We shall now consider how 3 categories of cells in the body vary with regard to their reproductive capacities and whether any arrangements exist whereby the body is maintained even if some specialized cells cannot reproduce. Later we shall consider briefly the problem of whether or not any body cells could reproduce themselves indefinitely under appropriate conditions, and in connection with this we shall discuss briefly the disease called cancer.

**Category 1.** By the time of birth there are some cells in the body in which a highly differentiated state seems to have been attained at the expense of a complete loss of any future reproductive capacity. Moreover, there is no provision for the replacement of these specialized cells if they wear out or are destroyed. Nerve cells are the classic example of cells of this sort. We are all born with all the nerve cells that we will ever possess, and throughout our lives there is a continuous diminution of the number that we possess as they wear out or are destroyed.

**Category 2.** There are many kinds of cells in the body that become highly specialized to perform some special function and which either wear out or are lost from body surfaces, often at a rapid rate. However, whereas the differentiated cells of members of this second category of cells, like nerve cells, are unable to reproduce, there is, unlike the situation with nerve cells, provision for the replacement of specialized cells of this category. This is accomplished by means of there being associated with the highly differentiated cells, cells of the same family type which have not yet differentiated to the point where they have lost their ability to reproduce. In general, cells of the latter type are termed the *stem cells* or *germinative cells* of the family to which they belong, and they, by reproducing themselves, keep up a supply of cells of that particular family type so that some are always available to differentiate and take the place of those that are lost. This means that in many parts of the body there is a continuous, and often rapid, *turnover of the cell population;* the *cell population* thus exists in a *steady state* although its individual members change. Cell families of this second category have been much studied by Leblond and his group who have shown, for example, that the specialized cells that line the greater part of the intestinal tract have a life-span of only a few days, after which they are lost into the lumen of the gut. The old cells that are discarded are all replaced with fresh cells at the same rate as that at which old cells are lost. The cells that cover our bodies in the outer layer of the skin likewise have a limited life-span before they are shed. Our highly specialized red blood cells are incapable of reproduction and last only about 4 months, and so they must be continuously replaced. Even the tissue of our bones deteriorates and is here and there dissolved away and must be replaced throughout life. So, in many parts of our bodies, there is a continuous turnover of the cell population of the part, with the older and most highly differentiated cells, which cannot reproduce, being lost from a surface or disposed of in some other way, their places being taken by new cells that differentiate out from a pool of stem cells.

**Category 3.** There are still other kinds of cells in the body which appear to represent an exception to the rule that specialized function interferes with reproductive capacity, for there are many examples of highly differentiated cells which, under certain circumstances, can reproduce themselves. However, such highly specialized cells as retain reproductive capacity are generally not called upon to use

their reproductive capacity very often after the growth of the organ in which they live is completed. Cells of this category are found mostly in organs where the cells have a long life-span, and in which cell division seldom occurs after full growth has been attained. The cells of the liver are examples of this category. Under normal conditions, liver cells live for a long time, and hence cell division is seldom seen in a normal adult liver. However, if two thirds of the liver of an experimental animal is removed at operation, the cells of the remaining third undergo division and reproduce themselves so rapidly that the liver is restored to its former size in only a few days. The cells of other organs, for example, the cells that make the external secretion of the pancreas, and the cells of many glands that make hormones, are highly specialized and, under normal conditions, seldom reproduce themselves, for they live a long time but, under altered conditions, they can undergo division and so demonstrate that even though they are specialized, they have not lost the ability to reproduce themselves.

It is obvious from the description of the three general categories of cells given above that it is impossible to make a hard-and-fast generalization to the effect that a loss of reproductive capacity is always a consequence of cell specialization. Such a generalization would hold for cells in the first two categories but not for those in the third. However, what we have been considering is what can be studied in an individual over the normal life of that individual. It is another problem to consider whether or not body cells, in a suitable environment, could continue to reproduce themselves indefinitely, or whether, as a consequence of their being body cells, a limitation is placed on their reproductive capacity. One way this intriguing problem has been approached is by means of transplanting body cells into suitable nutritive solutions outside the body and attempting to determine whether in this environment the cells would continue to reproduce themselves indefinitely, as will now be described.

**Studies on the Reproductive Capacities of Cells in Cell Cultures.** That living cells could be transferred from the body to suitable solutions where their growth could be studied directly with the microscope was first demonstrated by Harrison many decades ago. By this method he was able to see nerve fibers growing from nerve cells. Subsequently it was shown that certain body cells would multiply in suitable media. The technic is termed the *in vitro* (*vitrum* = glass) method although, instead of glass receptacles, plastic ones are now commonly used to contain the nutritive media and cells. The methods and technics of tissue culture are described in books written about this subject; some are listed in the references.

Several decades ago there was general opinion to the effect that certain body cells of the stem cell type could, under suitable conditions in vitro, multiply indefinitely. This widespread opinion was due primarily to the experiments of the late Alexis Carrel who, with his colleagues, maintained by subculturing, a strain of chick-derived fibroblasts for over 20 years, when the experiment was terminated. Since 20 years was a much longer time than the chick from which the cells were obtained would have lived, and since the indications were that, had the experiment been continued, the cells would have continued to multiply as long as they were properly tended, the general conclusions from this work were that certain body cells could be immortal under the right conditions, and this concept of course inferred that aging was not caused by stem cells becoming unable to reproduce themselves.

More recently, however, the matter has been shown to be more complicated than was thought. It is true that since Carrel's time many lines of cells have been shown to lend themselves to continuous cultivation in cultures. But when these cells were studied by the newly developed methods for identifying their chromosomes (described in the next chapter) and which were not available in Carrel's time, it has become apparent that cells of the lines that proliferate indefinitely have undergone alterations in their chromosome content, and hence the cells of these lines that multiply indefinitely are not normal cells. Furthermore, the cells of most of the cell lines that can be cultivated indefinitely will, on being injected into hosts identical with those from which the cultivated cells were obtained, grow as malignant (cancer) cells and destroy their hosts.

**The Nature of Cancer.** In order to discuss this problem further, and for other important reasons, we must briefly describe cancer. The disease commonly called cancer seems superficially to be extremely simple. The common explanation is that some body cell, often of the stem cell type, undergoes a genetic change which is of such a nature that the genetically altered cell is much less susceptible than its neighbors to those factors which control cell populations in the body, and so it multiplies under conditions where the multiplication of normal cells would be restrained. The escape of such cells from growth-control mechanisms is associated more or less reciprocally with a loss of their ability to differentiate and hence to manifest specialized functional properties, and because of these properties cancer cells are commonly said to devote their energies to growth instead of function. Since the change that occurs in body cells, and which makes them into cancer cells, is in their genetic mechanism, cancer cells pass on their unsocial characteristics to all their progeny and, as a result, a cancer, once it is initiated, continues to grow, and unless it is removed or destroyed in its early stages, the multiplying cells of the cancer invade other tissues and organs and even become disseminated by the lymph and the bloodstream to other parts of the body where they set up new centers of growth, called secondary growths or metastases.

By losing their ability to differentiate, cancer cells in a sense achieve the requisites for body cell immortality. They, of course, are not able to demonstrate immortality in the body in which they develop, for if they are left to multiply in that body they will destroy it. But, if they are removed, and thereafter grown in vitro, some kinds at least can be propagated indefinitely. Furthermore, if the cells of a cancer that originate in an experimental animal are regularly transferred to other animals of the same strain, they will continue to propagate indefinitely, and indeed, on continued transplantation they often experience further mutations by which they become even more malignant than when they originated. Some cancers have been maintained in mice by this means for decades. Cancer cells therefore seem to be able to reproduce themselves indefinitely.

Studies in vitro therefore seem to suggest

that unless body stem cells undergo a malignant transformation, they cannot be propagated indefinitely. Therefore, the ability to respond to influences that bring about differentiation, that exists in normal stem cells, would stem to be associated with factors that limit their reproductive capacity.

**Animal Experiments on the Problem.** The problem of whether or not normal stem cells can proliferate indefinitely is a difficult one to study by means of transplantation experiments in inbred animals because transplanted cells are so similar to those of their identical host that they are difficult to follow. However, the problem has been investigated in an ingenious manner as follows.

A sufficiently large dose of whole-body radiation given to an animal is lethal because the chief effect of radiation is that it makes the stem cells of the host unable to divide. The stem cells are therefore unable to keep up the supply of differentiated cells that are needed for the maintenance of the body. The effect of lethal irradiation is exerted most prominently on the tissues in which there is a considerable turnover of the cell population, for example, on cells which give rise to the cells of the blood; hence a lack of blood cells is an important cause of death after extensive irradiation. However, an irradiated animal that would have died can be saved if it is suitably injected with cells from the blood-forming tissues of an identical and normal animal, for the stem cells in the transplanted blood-forming tissue multiply in their new hosts and, in due course, give rise to more mature cells which provide new red blood cells, granular leukocytes and platelets for the transfused animal.

However, it has been shown that if the cells of the blood-forming tissues that have repopulated the blood-forming tissue of an irradiated animal, from blood-forming stem cells that were transfused into it, are used in turn to transfuse another irradiated animal, and then the cells that repopulate the blood-forming tissue of this animal are used, in turn, to transfuse still another irradiated animal, and so on, the cells of the blood-forming tissue become decreasingly effective in regenerating further blood-forming tissues and eventually will not save the lives of irradiated animals that are transfused with them. So both these experiments in vitro and in vivo give some suggestion to the effect that body stem cells are unable to multiply indefinitely. Hence it may be that even *the capacity* to differentiate into any kind of a body cell is necessarily associated with some limitation on the reproductive capacity of that cell.

## REFERENCES

References for Chapter 5 are grouped with those for Chapters 6 and 7 and will be found at the end of Chapter 7.

# 6     Nuclei

## THE MICROSCOPIC STUDY OF CELLS IN SECTIONS IN THE LABORATORY

The members of some cell families, like the members of some families of people, live close together, while those of other cell families become distributed through many parts of the body. It is easier for the student to begin studying cells in sections of some part of the body where cells of the same family type, and which have the same appearance, live close together. Such an arrangement is to be found in the liver; hence we shall begin our study of the microscopic appearances of cells by describing the most common cells seen in a section of this organ. Even here, however, there are some cells of other family types; we shall consider these later.

**Some Suggestions for the Beginner.** The student at this time should not attempt to learn the microscopic structure of the liver; this is not described here but in a later chapter of this book. For the present, sections of the liver should be examined only to learn the appearances presented by cells in an H and E section of mammalian tissue.

Before examining a section of liver with the low-power objective, the beginner should recall that every cell has 2 main parts and that these stain differently. The more central part of each cell is occupied by a round or ovoid body that is basophilic and hence is colored blue-purple in an H and E section. This body is termed the nucleus (nut) of the cell (Fig. 6-1). The remainder of the cell, the part that surrounds the nucleus, is termed *cytoplasm* (labeled in Fig. 6-1), and this generally is colored pink in an H and E section.

Mammalian cells seen in sections do not commonly appear as they are depicted in a diagram made of a single cell; that is, as discrete rounded bodies. However, since the *nuclei* of cells *do* appear as discrete rounded bodies (as in Fig. 6-1), the beginner, who has a picture of a cell as a discrete rounded body in his mind, may easily mistake nuclei for whole cells. In the study of sections of mammalian tissue *most* cells do not appear either as discrete or as rounded bodies; indeed, as for example in sections of liver prepared by *ordinary* technics, the cell boundaries between adjacent cells may not be very distinct (Fig. 6-1, cell boundary not apparent here). Accordingly, the student must be on guard against making the commonest error made by beginners, that of thinking that nuclei are whole cells.

Even if the beginner keeps in mind that he must not mistake nuclei for whole cells, he may find it difficult to identify cells when he first examines a section, because he has no concept of how large cells are in relation to the size of the field he sees under the microscope. Hence, it may be helpful here to say that liver cells are about 20 microns in width, and that the field seen with the low-power objective and a 10 $\times$ eyepiece is around 1,500 microns wide. Hence, at this magnification it would take about 70 cells to extend from one side of the field to the other, and so at this magnification cells appear as very small objects (Fig. 6-2). To see detail in either nuclei or cytoplasm it is desirable to use greater magnifications. With the high-power objective it takes only about 20 cells to extend across the field, and with the oil-immersion objective it takes around 7 cells. If the oil-immersion objective is used in conjunction with a 15 $\times$ eyepiece it takes only 4 or 5 cells to extend across the field, as is shown in Figure 6-1. Since, at these higher magnifications, it takes relatively few cells to extend across the whole field, it becomes easy to identify them, and the higher magnifications, say oil-immersion with a 10 $\times$ eyepiece, should be used to study detail in them.

We are now prepared to begin the study of the two parts of the cell, the nucleus and the cytoplasm. This chapter will be devoted to nuclei.

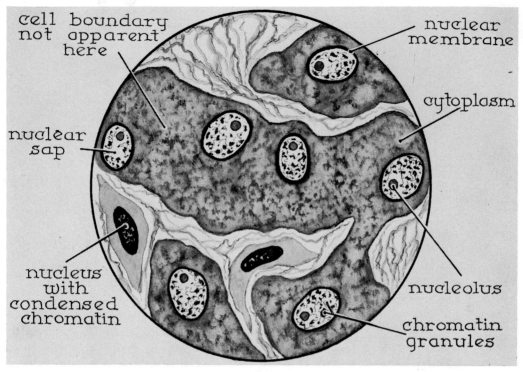

FIG. 6-1. Drawing of cords of liver cells from an H and E section as seen with the oil-immersion objective and a 15 × eyepiece. The circular area of the section that can be seen with this magnification is less than 100 $\mu$ wide, and it takes only about 4 large liver cells to bridge the area from side to side. Notice the open-face type of nuclei and the condensed chromatin type.

## HOW NUCLEI APPEAR IN SECTIONS

With the oil-immersion objective nuclei are seen as rounded-to-ovoid blue-purple bodies. In a section of liver, most of the nuclei that are seen are of what are termed the *open-face type* because some detail can be seen in their interiors (Fig. 6-1). Another type, less commonly seen, are the nuclei of cells of another cell family. These nuclei are smaller and almost evenly dark-staining and are described as "nuclei with condensed chromatin" (Fig. 6-1), for reasons to be described presently. Before describing the structure of open-face nuclei, we must explain what is meant by the term *interphase* nuclei.

**Interphase Nuclei.** The appearance of nuclei becomes greatly altered when a cell is in the process of dividing into 2 cells, and a few pages further on this matter will be considered in detail. But first we shall describe nuclei in cells that are not in the process of division; such nuclei commonly are termed *interphase nuclei* because they are the nuclei of cells that are *between* 2 successive phases of division. Almost all the nuclei in a section of normal liver are of the interphase type. Most show the following features:

### THE OPEN-FACE TYPE OF INTERPHASE NUCLEUS

1. With the light microscope each open-face nucleus is seen in an H and E section to be limited by a reasonably well-defined dark-blue staining membrane, the *nuclear membrane* (Fig. 6-1).

2. Within each nucleus there may be one or more rounded and generally blue-staining bodies; these are the largest and roundest of the bodies within the nucleus. This body, or these bodies, are termed the *nucleolus* (Fig. 35) or *nucleoli*.

3. Within each nucleus there are numerous particles of blue-staining material that are of irregular shapes and smaller than nucleoli. This material is referred to as *chromatin*

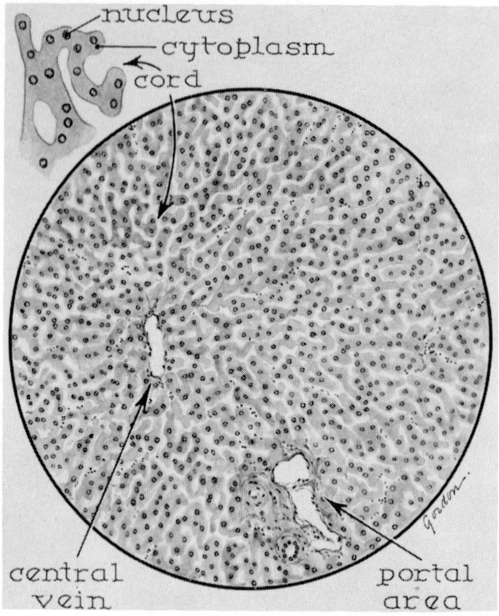

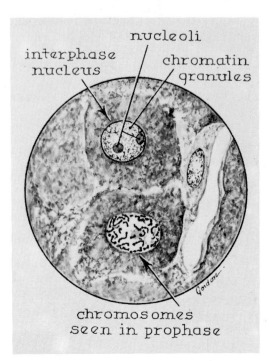

FIG. 6-2. Drawing of the field that is seen
with the microscope when an H and E section of a human liver is examined with the
low-power (10 ×) objective with a 10 ×
eyepiece. (*Upper, left*) A small area of the
field is reproduced at a somewhat greater
magnification so that liver cords, nuclei and
cytoplasm can be identified.

FIG. 6-3. An H and E section of regenerating rat liver under oil-immersion. The
upper cell contains an interphase open-face
nucleus. The nucleus of the lower cell has
entered the prophase of mitosis, and it contains rodlike chromosomes instead of chromatin granules.

(*chrome* = color) because it stains well. Individual particles of chromatin are sometimes
termed *chromatin granules* (Fig. 6-1).

4. The space in the nucleus not occupied
by chromatin and nucleoli is filled with a
semifluid material called *nuclear sap*. In
stained sections this material is represented
by very pale-staining or almost clear areas
(Fig. 6-1).

### THE CONDENSED CHROMATIN TYPE OF INTERPHASE NUCLEUS

As noted previously, some of the nuclei seen
in a section of liver are smaller, more solid
and darker than those of the open-face type;
these are termed nuclei with condensed
chromatin (Fig. 6-1). These are the nuclei of
a different family of cells from those that have
open-face nuclei. Such nuclei have the same
components as interphase nuclei of the open-
face type but less nuclear sap; hence the
other components of the nucleus are packed so
tightly together they cannot be individually
distinguished in ordinary sections.

Although it is convenient to describe nuclei

as being of the open-faced or condensed
chromatin type, there are, as might be expected, some nuclei in the cells of the body
that have appearances somewhere between the
two extremes. The reason we shall now concentrate on open-face nuclei is because these
are the only kind in which the various components of a nucleus can be seen clearly. Having
learned the components of open-faced nuclei,
the same components can then be visualized
as existing in nuclei whose components are
condensed to the point where they cannot be
seen as individual entities.

We shall now consider in some detail the 4
components of the nucleus that were previously listed. We shall take them up in the
following order (1) chromatin, (2) nucleoli,
(3) nuclear sap and (4) nuclear membrane.

### THE CHROMATIN OF THE INTERPHASE NUCLEUS

The chromatin in open-faced nuclei generally appears in sections in the form of parti-

cles. The chromatin particles of cells of different kinds differ; in some kinds of cells the particles are fine, lightly stained and distributed like dust throughout the nuclei, but in the nuclei of other cells the chromatin is characteristically coarsely clumped and heavily stained. The degree of clumping of chromatin and hence the depth to which particles stain depends on the method of fixation as well as on cell type and cell maturity. Whether the chromatin of nuclei is fine or coarse can be a helpful aid in determining cell types; for example, it helps the hematologist to identify certain kinds of cells that appear in blood in certain diseases of the blood-forming organs.

**What are Chromatin Particles?** The chromosomes of a cell are contained in its nucleus. The genes, which determine the heredity of the cell, are distributed along the chromosomes. The word chromosome was coined, not from any appearance seen in an interphase nucleus, but from appearances seen in cells that were in the process of division. As will be described in more detail later, when a cell passes from the interphase (the phase between divisions) into the prophase of cell division, the chromatin granules that characterize the interphase nucleus, and which are shown in the upper cell in Figure 6-3, are no longer seen; their place is taken by little deep blue-staining rodlike bodies called *chromosomes* which are illustrated in the lower nucleus in Figure 6-3, and which were given this name because they are deeply-colored bodies (*chroma* = color, *soma* = body).

For many years it was believed that after each division of a cell the chromosomes broke up into the chromatin granules that characterize the interphase nucleus. It was also believed that when an interphase cell again entered the process of cell division the chromatin granules were re-assembled into chromosomes. This hypothesis seemed increasingly unlikely as more and more was learned about genes and gene action, because the reassembly of innumerable bits of chromatin, that contained different genes, into chromosomes, would invite innumerable accidents, such as genes belonging to one chromosome being incorporated into another, and so on. But it was very difficult to show, or to under-

FIG. 6-4. A very high-power photomicrograph of a squash preparation of plant cells pretreated with sodium cyanide to cause the coils of the strands of the chromosomes to unravel; stained by means of the Feulgen reaction. (Dr. A. R. Gopal-Ayengar and Prof. Lesley Coleman, Department of Botany, University of Toronto)

stand how, chromosomes remained intact, each with its own complement of genes, through the interphase when nothing but a sprinkling of chromatin could be seen in nuclei in stained sections. The use of phase microscopy for studying fresh unstained preparations helped to solve this problem because, under these conditions, the chromosomes of some kinds of cells could be seen in the interphase to exist as long wavy and very delicate strands, much too delicate to be stained as distinct strands in a fixed tissue preparation. It was known by this time, moreover, that the chromosomes that could be stained when a cell was dividing were composed of strands wound into tight coils (see Fig. 6-4) and that this made them sufficiently dense to be visible in stained sections. It also was shown by phase microscopy that some portions of the generally extended chromosome strands that could be seen in interphase nuclei did not become uncoiled following cell division but instead remained tightly coiled throughout the interphase. Accordingly, whereas the coiled chromosomes of dividing cells become uncoiled over most of their lengths when division is over, there are some segments of them that do not, and it is now

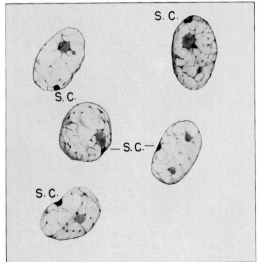 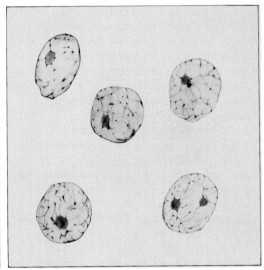

FIG. 6-5. (*Left*) Oil-immersion drawing of nuclei in the stratum spinosum of the epidermis of a female obtained by biopsy as they appear in a section stained with Harris's hematoxylin and eosin. The sex chromatin (s.c.) (now commonly called Barr bodies) lies against the inner surface of the nuclear membrane as it does in most tissues. (*Right*) A preparation in all respects similar except that the epidermis is from the skin of a male. There is no Barr body visible. (Preparations by Margaret A. Graham and Murray Barr)

generally believed that it is the sections of chromosomes that remain tightly coiled in interphase nuclei that constitute dense enough little aggregations of material to be visible after staining in interphase nuclei where they appear as if they were *granules* or *particles* of chromatin.

Since the uncoiled extended portions of interphase chromosomes are also composed of chromatin, but are not dense enough to constitute visible stainable objects, and since the tightly coiled sections of interphase chromosomes do constitute dense enough bodies to be visible when stained in sections, where they appear as chromatin granules, chromatin is classified into two types on the basis of density. Chromatin therefore is said to be heteropyknotic (*hetero* = one or the other of two; *pyknosis* = dense) which, of course, means that it may be of one of two densities. The dense kind (the coiled portion of chromosomes) is said to be *positively heteropyknotic* and the less dense kind (the extended portions of chromosomes) *negatively heteropyknotic*.

Another terminology with regard to chromatin evolved from genetic studies which showed that some portions of chromosomes

were genetically active while others seemed to be inert. The genetically active portions of chromosomes came to be termed *euchromatic*, the good kind (*eu* = good), and the genetically inert, *heterochromatic* (the other kind). Although there is perhaps no justification for a definite rule about the matter, there are so many instances in which the extended portions of interphase chromosomes are genetically active, and the coiled sections inactive, that the term heterochromatic is often used to refer to the coiled (positively heteropyknotic) sections of chromosomes, and these, of course, in interphase nuclei appear as particles of chromatin. With this in mind, we can now describe how it is possible to distinguish, in human tissue, the body cells of females from those of males by examining the chromatin of their interphase nuclei.

## HOW THE BODY CELLS OF FEMALES CAN BE DISTINGUISHED FROM THOSE OF MALES BY EXAMINING THE CHROMATIN OF INTERPHASE NUCLEI

For over 100 years countless microscopists

in many countries studied innumerable sections of human tissue without anyone ever noticing that the interphase nuclei of females were slightly, but definitely, different from those of males. The discovery that there was a sex difference in nuclei was not made until 1949, in which year Barr and Bertram noticed that there was a little stainable body of chromatin to be seen in the nerve cells of female cats that could not be seen in similar cells of male cats. Figure 21-17 illustrates the appearances they saw in female and male cat nerve cells. Barr and his colleagues quickly extended their study to other kinds of cells and to other species. The little body that they observed in female cat nerve cell nuclei was usually found apposed to the nucleolus (Fig. 21-17) and this led them at first to name it the nucleolar satellite. Curiously enough, the little body was not found in this position in other kinds of cells, but instead apposed to, and more or less flattened against, the inner surface of the nuclear membrane (Figs. 6-5 and 6-6). Accordingly, the term nucleolar satellite was dropped and the little body is now generally referred to as a Barr body.

**The Chromosomes of Cells of Males and Females.** The cells of the human body develop from a fertilized ovum that has 46 chromosomes, hence the body, or as they are commonly termed, _somatic_ (_soma_ = body) cells that develop from it each have 46 chromosomes. The chromosomes of the fertilized ovum are derived from germ cells, half from the unfertilized ovum, and half from the male germ cell that fertilizes the ovum. The chromosomes of a normal female germ cell are 23 in number. One of these is a sex chromosome; the other 22 are termed _autosomes_ (_auto_ = self). The sex chromosome of female germ cells is always of the X type. Male germ cells also each possess 22 autosomes and 1 sex chromosome; the sex chromosome may be either an X chromosome or a Y chromosome (the morphology of these will be described later). Maleness is dependent on the Y chromosome, so a female germ cell (which always has an X chromosome) that is fertilized by a male germ cell that carries an X chromosome will have an XX combination of sex chromosomes and so will become a female with each of its body cells afterward possessing 44 autosomes and 2 X chromosomes.

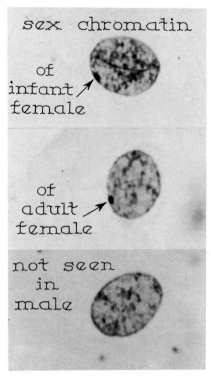

FIG. 6-6. Photomicrographs of epithelial cells from the oral mucosa stained with cresyl-echt violet (× 2,000). The upper two nuclei have Barr bodies which are indicated by arrows. (Moore, K. L., and Barr, M. L.: Lancet 269:57)

If the male germ cell that fertilized an ovum has a Y chromosome, the fertilized ovum will possess 44 autosomes and an XY combination of sex chromosomes and, because of its having a Y chromosome, it will develop into a male and all its body cells will possess 44 autosomes plus an X and a Y chromosome.

**What constitutes the little body of chromatin that can be seen against the nuclear membrane in the body cells of females but not in males?** Opinion has changed in the last few years about its constitution. At first it was thought that (1) since X chromosomes are larger than Y chromosomes, the total amount of chromatin in a pair of X chromosomes would be greater than the total amount of chromatin in an XY combination of sex chromosomes, and (2) the amount of chromatin in an XX combination would be sufficient to constitute a stainable body in an interphase nucleus while the total amount of chromatin in an XY combination of chromosomes would not be enough to constitute a stainable visible body in the interphase nuclei of cells of males. This first concept of the nature of a Barr body had to be modified because, as new methods evolved for studying and mapping the chromosomes of dividing body cells of man (methods which will be described a little later), and as patients with certain sex anomalies were studied by this latter means, it became apparent that the Barr body in the interphase nuclei of females was not to be explained by 2 X chromosomes together making a visible body; instead the appearance was caused by 1 X chromosome being coiled tightly along most or all of its length during the interphase. As a result of its tight coiling it would be a dense enough body when stained to constitute a visible (Barr) body.

If the appearance of a Barr body is due to only one X chromosome, it might be asked why Barr bodies are not seen in the nuclei of cells of males, for these of course have an X chromosome. The fact is that an X chromosome remains heterochromatic (positively heteropyknotic) during the interphase only if it has a companion X chromosome that is euchromatic. This is a fortunate arrangement, for if both X chromosomes in the cells of females were heterochromatic in the interphase, neither would be able to give off genetic information. It would seem that 1 genetically active X chromosome is all that is required to provide such genetic information as is required from X chromosomes in cells during the interphase. If there are 2 (or even more X chromosomes in body cells, as occurs in some anomalies), only one remains active; the others rest, as it were, in a heterochromatic state, and in that state they appear as Barr bodies. In the cells of males, which have only 1 X chromosome, there is of course a need for this X chromosome to be genetically active during the interphase if the cell is to have the benefits of the genetic information that it carries. This, of course, does not explain why the single X chromosome in the cells of males remains euchromatic in the interphase; it merely points out that it is important that a single X chromosome should remain euchromatic.

**How the Test Is Performed on Living Sub-**

jects. For the first few years after Barr's discovery, the test was commonly performed by excising a tiny piece of skin from a living subject (this is called taking a skin biopsy) and then cutting and staining sections of it (Fig. 6-5). More recently, Moore and Barr showed that the test can be performed by simply making a smear of the cells that readily come off the inside of the cheek when a metal spatula of the type commonly used for analytical weighing is drawn across it. The cells are smeared onto a glass slide that has been coated with a thin layer of egg albumin and are fixed by immersing the slide in 95 per cent ethyl alcohol. The slide is then passed through graded alcohols to distilled water and stained with cresyl violet (Fig. 6-6).

**Form and Disposition.** Barr bodies in the cells of females are seen to best advantage in open-face nuclei, particularly those that are relatively large and pale—the so-called vesicular (*vesicule* = a little bladder) type. A Barr body appears as a little dark mass, often planoconvex in form, that is pressed against the inner side of the nuclear membrane (Figs. 6-5 and 6-6). Generally, it has a diameter of about 1 micron so that it is clearly visible *if the plane of the section passes through it*. But it should not be expected that it will be seen in every open-face female nucleus that is examined, because the section may not cross the nucleus in the right plane. Even in smears, every female nucleus need not show sex chromatin, because it may be on the upper or the lower part of the flattened nucleus and not at its periphery where it shows up best.

The nuclei of male cells may demonstrate bits of chromatin close to the nuclear membrane, which sometimes might be interpreted as Barr bodies; the probable explanation for this is that some chromatin particles (not belonging to sex chromosomes) accidentally have been shifted to a position close to the nuclear membrane. Accordingly, since a Barr body cannot be seen in every female nucleus, and since chromatin masses approximating the appearance and the position of Barr bodies can sometimes be seen in male nuclei, the presence or absence of Barr bodies cannot be determined by a hasty examination of a section or a smear but only by examining, say, 100 consecutive nuclei and then calculating the percentage of cells in which this appearance was noted. In general, the appearance given by a Barr body is *very often* apparent in the nuclei of female cells (usually in over 90%), and a similar appearance is rarely seen in the nuclei of male cells (usually in less than 10%).

**Anomalies Involving the Sex Chromosomes.** There are occasional disorders of development due to the number of sex chromosomes in somatic cells being more or less than usual. In some of these conditions the test for Barr bodies may not indicate the true chromosomal sex of the affected individual. Two examples will be given.

There is a condition, termed *Klinefelter's syndrome*, in which the somatic cells of the affected individual each contain 2 X and 1 Y chromosomes. Such an individual, because his cells each possess a Y chromosome, is a chromosomal male. However, the fact that his cells each contain 2 X chromosomes results in one of the X chromosomes being heterochromatic, and hence his cells give a positive test for Barr bodies; thus, by this test, he would seem to be a female. Such individuals, although they have the general physical form and genitalia of a male, are infertile and appear less masculine than normal males in certain respects.

Another condition, which in its extreme form is termed *Turner's syndrome*, results from the somatic cells of an individual having in addition to their autosomes, only 1 sex chromosome, and this is the X type. Since such individuals have no Y chromosomes, they are chromosomal females, but, since they do not have 2 X chromosomes in their somatic cells, but only one, that chromosome remains euchromatic, and so their cells do *not* give a positive test for Barr bodies. Hence, by this test they might be falsely considered to be males. Individuals afflicted with this condition are female in form, short in stature, sexually immature and infertile. Furthermore, they may have congenital defects in organs not related to the reproductive system as, for example, the heart.

## CHROMATIN AND CHROMOSOMES; THE CHANGES THAT OCCUR IN CELL DIVISION (MITOSIS)

The process of cell division is called *mitosis*

(*mitos* = thread; *osis* = a condition) because in the condition of mitosis threadlike bodies are seen in the nucleus instead of chromatin granules (compare the two nuclei in Figure 6-3). Threadlike bodies are called *chromosomes* (*chroma* = color; *soma* = body), for they stain avidly with basic dyes.

A nucleus in the process of mitosis is commonly referred to by histologists and pathologists as a *mitotic figure*. It is very important for the student to be able to recognize mitotic figures in stained sections, so their appearances should be learned well.

**Where Mitotic Figures Are Normally Seen.** Mitotic figures are common in sections of the developing embryo and fetus because the growth of the body is dependent on cell division occurring in its various parts. Mitotic figures are also common in postnatal life in certain parts of the body for two reasons. First, the growth of the body in postnatal life is dependent on cell division in many of its parts, and hence sections of these will reveal numerous mitotic figures. Secondly, even in adult life, as has already been explained, there is a considerable turnover of the cell population in many parts of the body where functioning cells have only a short life span, and in these parts cell division must occur just as often as cell loss or death; hence under normal conditions, sections of these parts of the body exhibit many mitotic figures.

Finally, in many parts of the body where cell turnover is relatively rare, under normal conditions, the repair of an injury or the regeneration of lost tissue can lead to much cell division, and so, in regeneration and repair, mitotic figures become numerous even in many tissues in which they are ordinarily scarce. For example, although mitotic figures are seldom seen in the liver, material for the classroom study of mitotic figures in this organ can be obtained easily by operating on a rat and removing two thirds of its liver. When this is done the cells in the remaining third of the liver undergo mitosis at such a rapid rate that the cell complement of the liver is restored in a few days' time, so sections taken from regenerating rat liver reveal many mitotic figures.

**Recognition of Mitotic Figures in Sections.** The important point to realize in looking for mitotic figures in a section is that the appear-

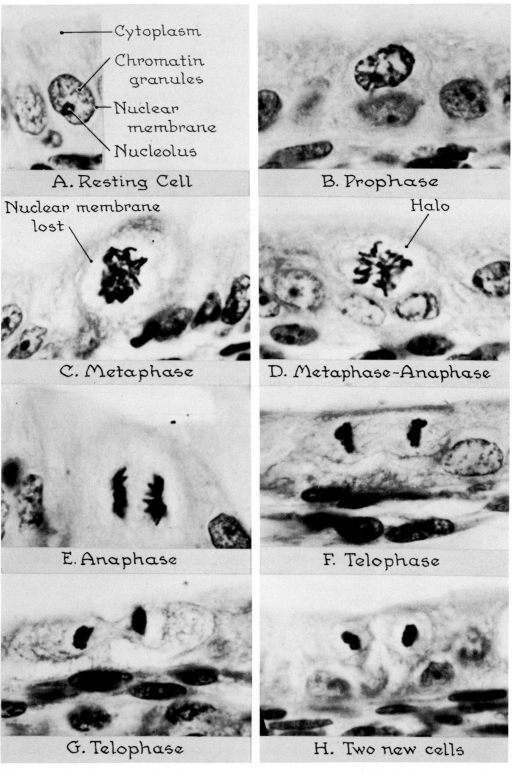

Cytoplasm

Chromatin granules

Nuclear membrane

Nucleolus

**A. Resting Cell**

**B. Prophase**

Nuclear membrane lost

Halo

**C. Metaphase**

**D. Metaphase-Anaphase**

**E. Anaphase**

**F. Telophase**

**G. Telophase**

**H. Two new cells**

FIG. 6-7. Oil-immersion photomicrographs taken from sections of the lining of the uterus of a rat that was injected 48 hours previously with a large dose of female sex hormone. The illustrations show the different stages of mitosis.

ances of nuclei that have become familiar from studying interphase nuclei completely change. First, as mitosis proceeds the nuclear membrane dissolves so that the *nucleus no longer appears as a sharply delineated round-to-ovoid body* (see A, B and C, Fig. 6-7). Second, the nucleolus melts away; (see A, B and C, Fig. 6-7); and third, instead of chromatin granules being seen in the site occupied by the former delineated nucleus, larger dark-staining little rods, the chromosomes (B, C and D, Fig. 6-7), are seen instead. The rodlike chromosomes are curved and bent more often than they are straight, and with good resolution, each can be seen to be more or less split longitudinally into two halves (Fig. 6-8). It has already been observed that in the interphase, chromosomes are long extended threads, being coiled tightly into helical coils only here and there along their course. In mitosis they become coiled along their whole lengths and so become much shorter and hence much denser bodies, dense enough to stain along almost their whole lengths.

The coiled nature of certain plant mitotic chromosomes can be demonstrated beautifully by treating them with reagents which cause a slight separation of the individual coils of the thread that is wound into a tight helix (Fig. 6-4). The enormously long threads that constitute chromosomes or chromatids in interphase nuclei must of course become coiled very extensively if they are to assume the appearances of relatively short rodlike structures during mitosis. The way in which they are coiled in different plants and animals has been much studied and in many instances appears to be very complex, involving coils of different orders. For a discussion of this matter, books and reviews on chromosomes and cytology should be consulted.

**General Functions of Chromosomes.** The genes of the cell are contained in, and distributed along, the chromosomal threads. The genes are the ultimate units that direct the nature and the activities of the cell. When a cell divides into 2 daughter cells, each of the daughter cells is an exact duplicate of the other and of the mother cell that divided. For the daughter cells to be identical requires that each must have exactly the same complement of genes in their chromosomes. Therefore, before cell division can occur, there must be a

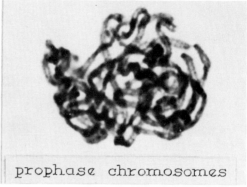

prophase chromosomes

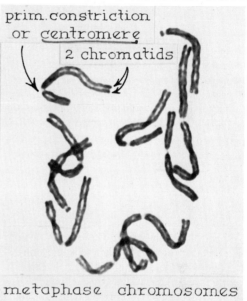

prim. constriction or centromere

2 chromatids

metaphase chromosomes

FIG. 6-8. Oil-immersion photomicrographs of squash preparations of chromosomes from root tips of Trillium. Feulgen stain. These illustrations show that both prophase and metaphase chromosomes each contain 2 chromatids. A careful inspection of the lower picture will enable the student to match the 10 chromosomes shown into 5 pairs. (Preparation by Dr. K. H. Rothfels)

duplication of the genes so that there will be a set for each of the 2 daughter cells that form. It is now known that the genes are duplicated in the interphase (the chemistry of gene duplication will be described later). Accordingly, each chromosome of a cell that enters the prophase of mitosis has a double set of genes. However, the 2 sets of genes do not lie in the same thread, for *in the interphase each splits longitudinally into 2 threads*

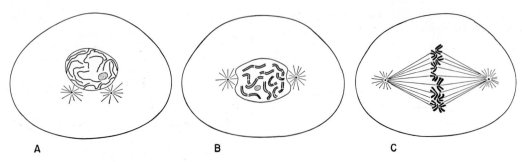

A                                B                                C

Fig. 6-9. Diagrams to illustrate spindle formation.

(A) Represents an early prophase. The 2 centrioles have separated from one another, and astral rays extend out from each. The chromosomes are still somewhat elongated, and at this stage it would be difficult to see that each consisted of 2 chromatids.

(B) Represents a late prophase. The 2 centrioles have now moved to the opposite ends of the nucleus. The chromosomes are shorter than before, and it can be seen that each consists of 2 chromatids.

(C) Represents a metaphase. The nuclear membrane has disappeared, and the rays from the centriole at each pole extend in to the mid-line of the cell where they are attached to the centromeres of the chromosomes. Since the rays diverge from each centriole toward the mid-line of the cell, the appearance given is that of a spindle. The chromosomes have shortened further, and the 2 chromatids of each will soon separate completely from one another.

called chromatids (Fig. 6-8), each of which has one full set of genes. The 2 chromatids of each chromosome remain close to each other along their lengths and firmly attached to each other at one point, the centromere (Fig. 6-8), until, at one step in the process of mitosis, the centromere of each chromosome divides so that its two chromatids become individual entities. When this happens, each chromatid is called a chromosome and so, as division proceeds, the cell comes to have 92 full-fledged chromosomes, 46 for each of the daughter cells that will soon form, and with each of the 46 normally being identical with its representative mate in the other daughter cell.

The chemical components of chromosomes and the chemistry of gene duplication will be considered a few pages further on. Next, we shall consider the histologic changes seen in cell division.

## THE PHASES OF MITOSIS

Mitosis, the process by which nuclei divide, has 4 consecutive phases—prophase, metaphase, anaphase and telophase. When mitosis begins, the process is normally continuous, with each stage merging imperceptibly into the next.

### THE PROPHASE

Before this stage begins, the interphase chromosomes have each become split longitudinally into two chromatids joined only at the centromere of that chromosome (see prophase chromosomes in Fig. 6-8). Furthermore, before the prophase begins, each chromatid is in the form of a drawn-out, very loosely coiled thread over most of its length, but occasionally along its length there are segments where it is tightly coiled in a helical type of coil (the so-called chromatin granules or particles of the interphase nucleus). As the prophase begins, a new process of helical coiling is initiated along the extended portions of the threadlike chromatids and as a result the chromatids shorten. As the new coiling proceeds, the chromatids become dense enough to be stainable along their whole lengths and it becomes increasingly difficult to distinguish the previously coiled (heterochromatic) portions of the chromosomes.

Early in the prophase, the helix formed by the coiling of the chromatids is not as tightly wound or of as great a diameter as it will be later; hence the chromosomes in the prophase are not as short or as thick as they later become. For this reason the chromosomes seen through most of the prophase are longer and not so densely stained as they are in the latter part of the prophase and in the next two phases of mitosis.

In the latter part of the prophase two other important events occur. First, the nuclear membrane dissolves so that there is no formal barrier left between the chromosomes and the cytoplasm of the cell; this fact becomes of importance for the next phase of mitosis to proceed. The breaking up of the nuclear membrane can be seen in Figure 6-7 B; meanwhile the nucleolus seemingly melts away and can no longer be seen as a discrete round body.

### The Metaphase

In order to describe the events that occur here we must discuss one of the components of the cytoplasm, because it is profoundly involved in mitosis.

Those body cells that can divide all contain in their cytoplasm a little spherical area or body called the *centrosphere*, so called because it seemingly tries to take up a position in the center of the cell. Since nuclei generally occupy the central parts of most cells, the centrosphere, which is a cytoplasmic structure, generally cannot attain the center of the cell but is as close to it as possible. Thus, if the nucleus is indented on one of its sides, the centrosphere is commonly seen in the indentation.

With the light microscope and special staining it is possible to see little dots, usually two, in the centrosphere; these are termed *centrioles*. During prophase the centrioles begin to move in opposite directions around the nucleus to take up positions at opposite poles of the cell (Fig. 6-9 A). In certain kinds of cells, for example, sea-urchin eggs, as the centrioles begin to move to opposite poles of the cell, little rays appear in the cytoplasm; these extend out from them like rays of light from stars; this led to the expression *astral (astron = star) rays*; these are illustrated in the diagram (Fig. 6-9). However, these starlike appearances cannot be seen in most kinds of mammalian cells. In mammalian cells the centrioles somehow induce the formation, or themselves form, what were first called *fibers*, but which are seen with the EM to be very fine *tubules*. By the time the nuclear membrane has disappeared, fine tubules radiate out from each centriole; these extend chiefly

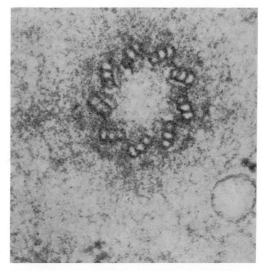

Fig. 6-10. Electron micrograph ($\times$ 125,-000) of a centriole in cross section. (Preparation by S. Dales)

(1) to, and (2) through the region of the nucleus; they can now penetrate into this area because the nuclear membrane has dissolved (Fig. 6-9 C). Before discussing the tubules further, we shall first describe the fine structure of centrioles.

**The Fine Structure of Centrioles.** With the EM the little dots seen with the light microscope are seen to be cylindrical structures about 0.15 microns in diameter (Fig. 6-10) and about 0.3 to 0.5 microns long (Fig. 6-11). The walls of these cylindrical bodies are seen, when they are cut in cross sections, to be composed of bundles of still smaller tubular structures, there being 9 bundles in all (Fig. 6-10). The individual bundles may have up to 3 tubules in them. Furthermore, with the EM 4 centrioles can be seen in the centrosphere at the beginning of prophase. These are arranged in two pairs. In each pair one centriole is arranged at right angles to the other (Fig. 6-11). It seems, therefore, that during the interphase and in preparation for a further cell division, each of the two centrioles of the cell becomes doubled (this is done by means of each centriole giving birth to a daughter centriole), and that the daughter centriole is always arranged at right angles to the parent centriole (Fig. 6-11). At the beginning of the prophase one pair of centrioles begins to move to one pole of the cell and the other pair to

FIG. 6-11. Electron micrograph (approximately × 100,000) of a pair of centrioles at right angles to one another. (Preparation by R. Buck)

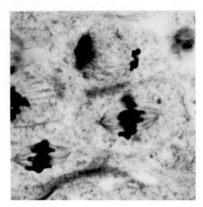

FIG. 6-12. Oil-immersion photomicrograph of cells in the first mitotic metaphase in the rat testis. Spindles appear to advantage because the tissue was fixed in Flemming's solution and stained with iron hematoxylin. (From Y. Clermont and C. P. Leblond)

the other. When they reach the poles, they and their immediate environment constitute centrospheres.

**Fibers (Tubules) Associated With Centrioles.** When seen with the light microscope, the filaments that are seen radiating out from centrioles appear to be delicate fibrils (Fig. 6-12), but instead of being called fibrils they have commonly been termed fibers. With the EM the fibrils that can be seen with the light microscope prove to be very fine *tubules* with a diameter of around 15 to 20 millimicrons (Fig. 6-13). According to their distribution these delicate tubules are classified into two groups: (1) spindle tubules and (2) central continuous tubules. These groups will now be described.

**Spindle Tubules.** At the metaphase, the centromeres of the chromosomes become arranged in a plane that bisects, at right angles, a line drawn between the two centrospheres which are now at the two poles of the cell (Figs. 6-9 C and 6-12). This plane is termed the equatorial plane of the cell, for obvious reasons. The centromeres of the chromosomes

all gather in this plane, but some are near the center of the cell, while others are nearer the periphery of the cell. The limbs of the chromosomes do not lie in the equatorial plane but extend in what seems to be a disorderly way to either side of it. While the chromosomes are becoming arranged in this way their limbs continue to shorten. Tubules from each centrosphere become attached to centromeres of the chromosomes in such a way that each centromere has tubules from one centrosphere attached to one of its sides and tubules from the other centrosphere to the other. Tubules extending from a centriole (Fig. 6-13) reach chromosomes, as can be seen in Figure 6-14, In order to obtain attachments to the centromeres of the chromosomes in the more peripheral regions of the equatorial plane, the tubules must diverge, and this gives a metaphase mitotic figure the appearance of a spindle (Fig. 6-12).

**Central Continuous Tubules.** The central tubules are those that pass from one centrosphere to the other without being attached to chromosomes as they pass through the equatorial plane where the chromosomes are gathered.

The spindle tubules and the central continuous tubules perform somewhat different functions in the latter stages of mitosis as will be described in due course.

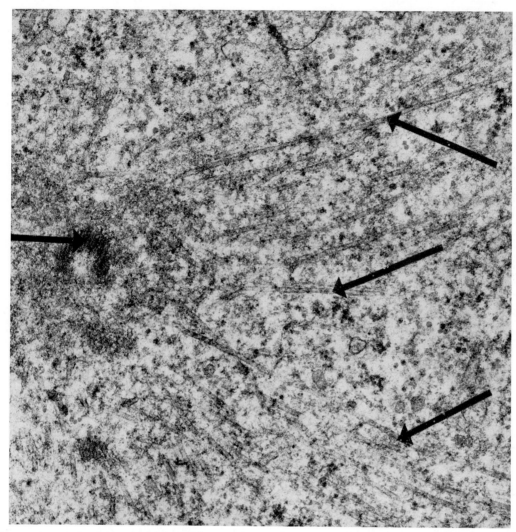

FIG. 6-13. Electron micrograph (× 60,000) of mitotic cell showing centriole (indicated by arrow at left) and spindle tubules (arrows) extending from it to right where they extend to chromosomes (not shown here but in Fig. 6-14). (Preparation by S. Dales)

### THE ANAPHASE

The anaphase is characterized by two events. First, the centromeres of the chromosomes each divide so that the two chromatids of each chromosome become completely separated from each other. Hereafter each chromatid is considered as a chromosome in its own right. Second, when the centromeres divide, the spindle tubules that are attached to the centromeres pull the separated chromatids of each chromosome to opposite poles of the cell. The reason for this movement is not thoroughly understood; one important factor would seem to be that the cell, as can be seen in Figure 6-7 F, has been elongating along a line joining its two poles (at right angles to the equator) and the centrospheres have taken up a position near each pole of the cell; as a consequence, tension has been built up in the spindle tubules so that, when the centromeres separate, the stretched spindle tubules pull the chromatids to their respective ends of the cell. Another factor is that when each centromere divides, the separated halves repel each other.

The continuous tubules—those that extend from a centriole at one pole to the centriole

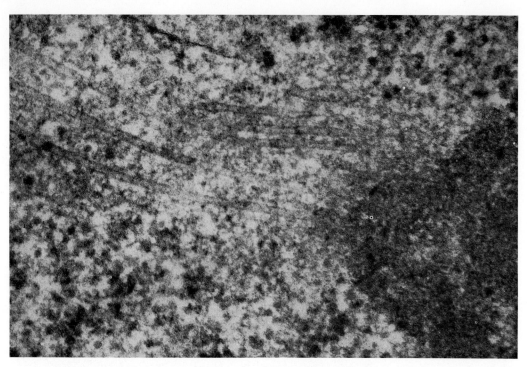

FIG. 6-14. Electron micrograph (× 110,000) showing spindle tubules running from upper left to chromosome (the dark body) at lower right. (Preparation by S. Dales)

at the other pole—are not attached to chromosomes and remain prominent only in the region of the equator where they are associated with an increasing density as seen in the EM (Fig. 6-15). The dense fibrillar structure they form is termed the midbody (Fig. 6-15) and persists into the telophase as will be described next.

### THE TELOPHASE

Toward the end of the anaphase and at the beginning of the telophase a constriction begins to develop at the midpoint of the elongated cell (Fig. 6-7 G); this constriction encircles the cell as a furrow. It is known as the *cleavage furrow* because as it deepens it splits the cell into two daughter cells. At least two mechanisms are probably involved in cleavage. First, it is very probable that the cleavage furrow develops because of an accumulation and contraction of fibrillar material in the cytoplasm immediately beneath, and toward each side of, the cleavage furrow. This material is indicated with arrows in Figure 6-15. With the light microscope, Kallenbach has shown an accumulation of fibrillar material in this site by the use of the tannic acid, phosphomolybdic acid and amido black technic of Puchtler and Leblond, which is so useful in staining the cell and terminal web of cells as will be described in Chapter 8. Kallenbach has shown that in many kinds of dividing cells (but not all kinds) this material assumes the form of a ring beneath and a little to each side of the cleavage furrow. It is possible that the filaments of this material may individually be contractile, but what is perhaps more likely is that the fibrillar material becomes contracted as it becomes condensed; this tightens the ring and makes the cleavage furrow deeper and deeper. Another factor that probably plays a part in the cleavage of some kinds of cells is that little membranous vesicles accumulate beneath the cleavage furrow and then fuse, not only together, but also with the cell membrane at the bottom of the furrow, which of course deepens the furrow. While the cleavage furrow is deepening, a bundle of the continuous tubules can still be seen connecting the two cells that are just about to separate (Fig. 6-15); these constitute what is known as the

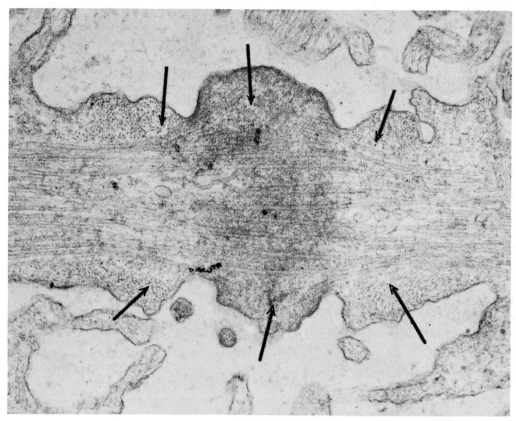

Fig. 6-15. Electron micrograph ($\times$ 60,000) showing cell cleavage in the telophase stage of mitosis. A bundle of continuous tubules still connect the two daughter cells; these constitute the midbody. Fibrillar material that is probably contractile is indicated by arrows. (Preparation by S. Dales)

*midbody* of the dividing cell. When cleavage is complete, the remnants of the midbody are indicated by an increased density along the cell membranes of the two daughter cells at the point where they separated; this increased density is occasioned by what is left of the midbody.

Meanwhile, the chromosomes in each daughter cell have reverted to the elongated state of chromosomes characteristic of interphase nuclei. Nucleoli have re-formed, and a new nuclear membrane has developed in each daughter cell to surround the chromatin, the nucleoli and the nuclear sap of its nucleus.

## A Further Note on Identifying Mitotic Figures in Ordinary Sections

It may take some time for a student to become proficient at identifying mitotic figures in sections that are prepared by ordinary methods from tissue in which mitosis is occurring frequently. Most of the appearances that will be seen in such a preparation are illustrated in Figure 6-7. It should be emphasized that much of the wealth of detail that can be elicited by special technics and described in the preceding pages is not apparent in ordinary sections, and hence, students, to identify mitotic figures, should not look, for example, for centrioles or spindles. In looking over an ordinary section of tissue in which interphase nuclei are of the open-face type, a mitotic figure stands out because of the *deep staining* of its coiled chromosomes. If a clump of deeply staining material is seen on close inspection to be lying *free in cytoplasm*, often with a *pale halo around it* and *not to be surrounded by a nuclear membrane*, and to have *a spiky appearance* due to individual chromosomes projecting from it at various angles,

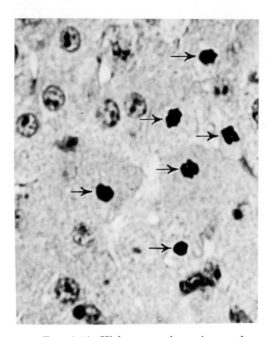

FIG. 6-16. High-power photomicrograph of an H and E section of a chick embryo tissue obtained about 15 hours after a suitable dose of colchicine was administered (through the shell). At least 6 dividing cells have been arrested at the metaphase stage; these are indicated by arrows.

and the group of his patients who suffer from gout, because colchicine exerts a remarkable curative effect, as yet not understood, on gouty inflammations of joints. The second effect is of more interest to biologists, histologists, cytologists and geneticists because colchicine arrests the process of mitosis at the metaphase stage. In arresting mitosis at this stage it seems to act chiefly by interfering with the formation of spindle fibrils (tubules) and also by retarding the division of the centromere. Under the influence of colchicine the chromatids do not separate from one another on time, as it were, and so they have a longer time to keep on coiling; hence metaphase chromosomes seen after colchicine treatment are shorter than normal.

The finding that mitosis can be arrested by the use of colchicine has been put to two very important uses in relation to histology.

First, if a suitable amount of colchicine is given to an animal, or is added to a culture of cells in which cell multiplication is occurring, any cells of the animal or in the culture that enter mitosis after the time when colchicine takes effect only reach the metaphase, and as a result metaphase mitotic figures accumulate until such time as the dose wears off. Hence, sections or stained cell preparations made a given period after colchicine has been given will reveal many metaphase mitotic figures (Fig. 6-16). If these are counted, the number obtained will be, for all practical purposes, the number of cells in that tissue or cell culture under study that entered the process of mitosis over the period of time allowed for the experiment. In those structures and organs in the body where cell multiplication is matched by cell loss or death, it is therefore possible to estimate the turnover rate of the cell population by determining the proportion of cells that enter mitosis over a given period of time. Using this method, Leblond and several associates and students were pioneers in determining the turnover rate of the cell populations in most of the important structures and organs of the body.

Secondly, if colchicine is given an animal or is added to cultures of cells that are growing in solutions of nutritive media, and then, after a given period of time, cells are obtained from the animal or drawn off the cultures and spread out on glass slides in special ways and

the chances are excellent that the object in view is a mitotic figure. The easiest kind of mitotic figure for the beginner or anyone else to identify is one in the anaphase stage, *providing it is sectioned in a plane parallel to that joining the two poles of the dividing cell,* as is shown in Figure 6-7 E. But the chances of any anaphase being sectioned in this plane are not as great as they are of its being sectioned in some other plane. It may take a lot of time and patience and the use of several sections to find mitotic figures illustrating various stages of mitosis that are sectioned in the plane which shows them to best advantage.

## EFFECTS OF COLCHICINE ON MITOSIS

An alkaloid, *colchicine,* extracted from the corm or seed of a fairly common plant, *Colchicum autumnale,* has two and seemingly unrelated remarkable biological properties. The first is of interest to the medical practitioner

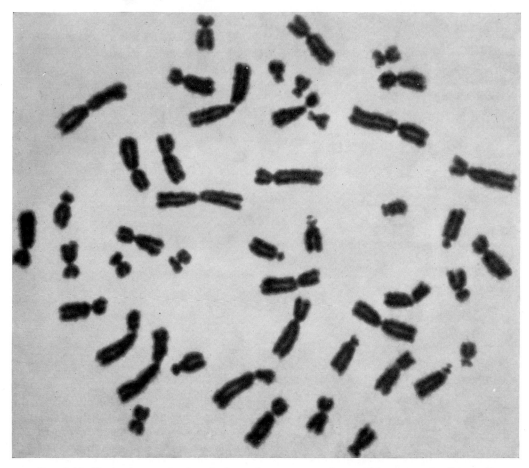

FIG. 6-17. Photomicrograph of metaphase chromosomes of normal human male. Preparation made from blood cells that were cultured as described in text. (Preparation by Charles E. Ford)

appropriately stained, the chromosomes of those cells in which mitosis was arrested at the metaphase by colchicine are so beautifully spread out and delineated (Fig. 6-17) that they can be counted and most of the different individual chromosome pairs identified. Photomicrographs can be taken to show all of the chromosomes of an individual body cell, as is shown in Figure 6-17. The chromosomes can then be counted, and afterward the photomicrograph can be cut up, and the pairs of identical chromosomes in the preparation can be matched up as is shown in Figure 6-18. This is called a *karyotype* (*karyon*—a nut = a nucleus) of the particular chromosomes of the individual from whom the cells were taken. The karyotype or map so constructed can be studied to see if any abnormalities exist with regard to the number or the form of the chromosomes of that individual.

## THE MORPHOLOGY OF METAPHASE CHROMOSOMES AND THEIR CLASSIFICATION

As already noted, the body cells of man normally contain 46 chromosomes, and of these 44 are autosomes. Twenty-two autosomes of each body cell are derived from the mother and 22 from the father. Although the autosomes derived from one side of the family may carry different genes from those derived from the other side, the respective autosomes derived from either side of the family, as seen at the metaphase of mitosis, are practically identical in appearance; this means that body cells have 22 *pairs* of autosomes with the 2 members of each pair having an identical or almost identical appearance; this appearance is generally slightly or considerably different from that of other pairs of autosomes. The 2 sex chromosomes in body cells,

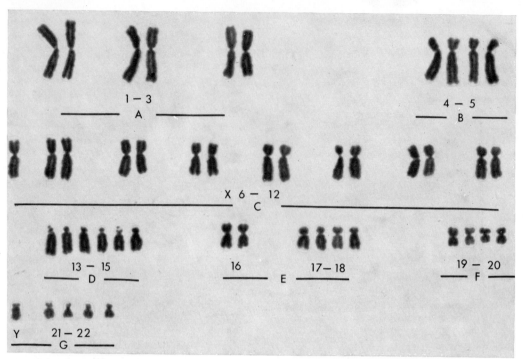

FIG. 6-18. Karyotype of chromosomes of normal human male. (Preparation by Charles E. Ford)

as they appear at the metaphase of mitosis, while they have identical appearances in the body cells of females, do not, of course, have the same appearance in the body cells of males, because the metaphase appearance of a Y chromosome is very different from that of an X chromosome (Figs. 6-17 and 6-18).

As has already been described, the appearances of the chromosomes change at different stages of cell division. At the metaphase stage of mitosis, the chromosomes have become tightly coiled, and thus each has become as short as it can become. Hence, at this stage, with the proper means of preparation, they can be seen in a cell as individual bodies distinct from each other and all lying in the same plane, without overlapping as is shown in Figure 6-17. Therefore, it is at this stage that they can be most readily studied and photographed. A useful way in which to examine the metaphase chromosomes of any individual is to construct a chromosome "map" or karyotype, in which the chromosomes are neatly arranged in pairs, in linear array, and set off in groups according to definite morphologic criteria as is shown in Figure 6-18.

The technics for obtaining preparations of cells of an individual that contain cells in the metaphase of mitosis and which ensure that the metaphase mitotic figures are or can be flattened on slides so that the chromosomes are separated have advanced considerably. One of the first ways in which this was done was by obtaining cells from the skin of an individual and putting these in culture fluid where some of them would undergo mitosis. Another method entailed drawing off bone marrow cells (which are constantly dividing) from the sternum and placing these in culture fluid with some colchicine; such cells in the preparation as were beginning to divide would be arrested at the metaphase stage, and preparations could then be made of these and studied. But a far easier way to obtain preparations of metaphase chromosomes of any individual became available when it was discovered that if some of the white cells of the blood were separated from blood and placed in culture medium to which a substance known as phytohemagglutinin was added, some of the white cells of the blood, which otherwise would not have divided in cultures, were, in the presence of phytohemagglutinin, stimulated to undergo several divisions; then, by using colchicine, the division of these cells could be arrested at the metaphase stage. Stained preparations made of cells obtained in this way proved to be admirable for study. The chromosome spread shown in Figure 6-17 was made from a cell in a culture of blood cells obtained from a normal human male.

**Some Preliminaries to Making a Karyotype.** After obtaining a good photomicrograph (or accurate drawing) of a good stained spread of metaphase chromosomes, the image of each chromosome is cut out and trimmed, and the individual chromosomes of the spread are arranged as will now be described. But first we have to comment briefly on terminology.

Since the two chromatids of metaphase chromosomes have not yet separated completely from one another, the structure that consists of two chromatids is still called a chromosome. As such it is said to have two "arms" that extend more or less in *opposite* directions from the centromere. Each arm of the chromosome of course is itself a paired structure, consisting of parallel portions of two chromatids. As we shall see, the centromere is at the midpoint of some chromosomes, and hence the two arms of such chromosomes are of equal lengths. But in other chromosomes the centromere is nearer one end of the chromosome than the other, and hence the two arms of a chromosome of this type are of unequal lengths.

The identification of an individual chromosome is based primarily on its total length and secondly on the position of its centromere; the latter of course determines the relative lengths of its two arms.

A metaphase chromosome whose centromere is situated approximately at the midpoint (called *the median*) of its length is called a *metacentric* chromosome (*meta* = between); such a chromosome has 2 arms of about equal length. A chromosome whose centromere is situated *between* its midpoint and one of its ends is termed a *submetacentric* chromosome; it has one shorter and one longer arm. A chromosome whose centromere is very near one end is referred to as an *acrocentric* chromosome (*acro* = at the end); it has one *very short* arm and one long arm.

**Making a Karyotype.** The first criterion used to arrange the cut-out chromosomes from the photomicrograph or drawing into a karyo-

type is their total lengths. So the first procedure is provisionally to arrange the chromosomes in a descending order according to their total lengths and with their centromeres along a horizontal line (Fig. 6-18). In the instances of those chromosomes which have one arm longer than the other, each chromosome is oriented with its shorter arm upward and its longer arm downward (Fig. 6-18). The chromosomes may then be divided up into groups, the members of which manifest approximately the same ratios between their arm lengths (Fig. 6-18). This criterion of arm-length ratio sometimes can take precedence over the total length of a chromosome in establishing the position of the chromosome in the karyotype, for it will be found, after arranging them into groups according to relative arm lengths, that sometimes the first member of a later group may be somewhat longer than the last member of the preceding group. By arranging the chromosomes according to their lengths and then re-arranging them into groups according to the relative lengths of their two arms it becomes obvious that there are 2 identical autosomes of each type (but not identical pairs of sex chromosomes if the preparation is from a male). The identical autosomes are, of course, paired in the karyotype (Fig. 6-18).

Within the groups, classification is not so easy, and even the experts are unable to identify every member of the human chromosome complement with assurance. But further criteria such as secondary constrictions (gaps or attenuated regions in characteristic positions along the chromosome), and also the presence of satellites (little dots of chromatin that appear off the end of a chromatid arm with only an indistinct connection to the end) are often helpful in distinguishing individual pairs in a group. More criteria already developed are sometimes used, and others are under study for identifying individual pairs within groups more precisely.

In a karyotype, the individual pairs of human chromosomes that are arranged primarily in a descending order of length are numbered serially 1 to 22 (Fig. 6-18). The further criteria described above permit the 22 pairs to be arranged into 7 groups. These 7 groups are referred to as the 1-3 or A group, the 4-5 or B group, the 6-12 or C group,

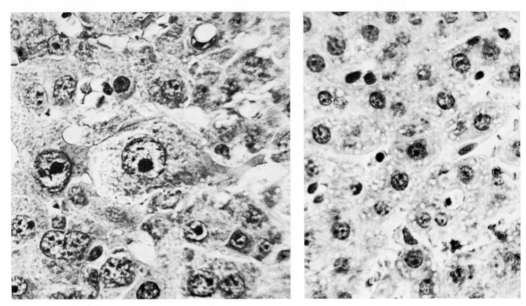

FIG. 6-19. (*Left*) A high-power photomicrograph of a section of regenerating liver obtained from a rat which previously had sustained liver injury. Notice the huge liver cells with large nuclei and hypertrophied dark-staining nucleoli; these result from polypoidy. (*Right*) A photomicrograph of normal rat liver at the same magnification.

the 13-15 or D group, the 16-18 or E group, the 19-20 or F group, and the 21-22 or G group. Group A, for example, consists of chromosome pairs 1 to 3 which are the longest metacentrics, and group G includes pairs 21 and 22, which are the shortest acrocentrics. In males, group G also contains the Y chromosome, which is an acrocentric chromosome like the others but is usually the longest in the group. The X chromosome is very similar to certain members of the 6-12 (C) group (Fig. 6-18) and cannot always be distinguished as a separate entity from certain members of that group.

**Anomalies Involving Autosomes.** In recent years it has been found that many anomalies of man are associated with chromosome abnormalities. Two anomalies dependent on abnormalities in the number of sex chromosomes have already been described in connection with the sex chromosomes. Brief mention will now be made of an anomaly involving an abnormality of the autosomes.

The first autosomal chromosome abnormality to be discovered in human beings was the existence of an extra chromosome #21 of group G, in children with what is known as Mongolism or Down's syndrome. Normally,

as explained before, each autosome is represented twice in the body cells of an individual. In these children with Down's syndrome, each body cell contains chromosome #21 in triplicate, and their cells are thus spoken of as being trisomic for that chromosome; all their other autosomes are in the usual duplicate condition.

Most of these children (who are abnormal from birth both physically and intellectually) owe their difficulties to an error in the distribution of chromosomes to daughter cells when the germ cell of the mother divides just after it has been fertilized. The most likely time for this error to occur is at the second division of meiosis (meiosis is described in the chapter on Reproductive Systems), and in women this happens just after the fertilization of the ovum which will develop into an embryo. The chances of such an accident occurring increases with the age of the mother. Although a man goes on making fresh spermatozoa (male germ cells) every day until he is quite old, a woman has all the ova she is ever going to have at the time when she is born. So, while an older man's spermatozoa are still young, an older woman's ova may be over 40 years old before she stops being able to have children. It is believed that as the ovum ages it becomes more difficult for its chromosomes to be accurately distributed at division.

One kind of Mongolism is known to run in certain families. Here, again, the condition is related to the individual's getting 3 doses of the genes of chromosome #21 instead of 2, but in this instance, gene imbalance results from an extra piece of chromosome #21 becoming attached to, and being carried along with, another chromosome (usually in the D or the G group), instead of the imbalance being caused by an extra and complete chromosome #21. Several other trisomic conditions of autosomes in man are known; these are associated with severe and complex anomalies which are often lethal in that the fetus dies before it is born.

Other autosomal lesions are known but are rare, which probably signifies that most autosomal gene imbalances are incompatible with life.

## POLYPLOIDY

Body cells, also called *somatic* (*soma* = body) cells, are to be distinguished from mature germ cells by the fact that they each have 46 chromosomes while mature germ cells each have only 23. Because each body cells has 46 chromosomes, which is double the number possessed by a germ cell, it is said to have a *diploid* (*diplos* = double) number of chromosomes. Body cells are therefore characteristically *diploid*. Single mature germ cells do not have a double complement of chromosomes; they are said to have a *haploid* (*haplos* = single) number of chromosomes.

Body cells, for reasons that will be explained presently, sometimes have multiples of the usual number of chromosomes; this phenomenon is termed *polyploidy*. This word is derived from *polys* = many, *ploos* = fold and *eidos* = form. The key to its meaning is to understand that "fold" is used here with the meaning it has in 2-fold; in other words, it refers to multiplication. So, just as a diploid cell has 2-fold or 2 times the number of chromosomes of the haploid germ cell, a cell is said to manifest polyploidy if it has a *further multiple* of the chromosome number of haploid cells. For example, a *tetraploid* (*tetra* = 4) cell has 4 times the haploid number of chromosomes—this is twice the diploid number.

Polyploidy is not uncommon in certain cell families under normal conditions; indeed, some cells manifest it regularly and others only occasionally, and such cells seen in the interphase are characterized by large nuclei (Fig. 6-19). The first and probably the most common way that it occurs is for a cell to pass through the prophase and the metaphase of mitosis but then, after the chromosomes have each separated into their 2 chromatids, which thereupon become chromosomes, the 2 sets do not pull apart to opposite ends of the cell but remain in the region of the equatorial plate until a new nuclear membrane forms to enclose them all in the same nucleus. Another way polyploidy can occur is by the chromosomes of a nucleus all splitting into chromatids without the nuclear membrane dissolving; as a consequence, the nucleus comes to contain a double number of chromosomes. Still another way is more indirect and takes place in 2 stages. First, mitosis occurs and results in 2 nuclei. But the cytoplasm does not divide and, as a result, a binucleated cell is formed. Then it may happen that both nuclei in the binucleate cell enter mitosis at the same time, and that when the nuclear membranes disintegrate the chromosomes of both cells become caught in the same spindle and pulled together again. Therefore, when division is complete there would be only 2 cells, but each would have a tetraploid content of chromosomes because the original nucleus has divided twice. An example of 2 sets of chromosomes caught in a single spindle is illustrated in Figure 6-20 (*right*).

**Aneuploidy.** If the number of chromosomes in a body cell is either (1) more than the diploid number but not a multiple of the haploid number, or (2) less than the diploid number, the cell is said to have an *aneuploid* (*a* = not, *eu* = well, *ploos* = folded, *eidos* = form) number, that is a not well-folded (multiplied) number of chromosomes. Two conditions in which aneuploidy is caused by abnormal numbers of sex chromosomes are described on page 71 and aneuploidy resulting from extra autosomes has been described on page 84. It should be mentioned here that aneuploidy is common in the cells of cancers, even though the cells in the rest of the body

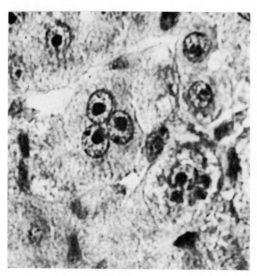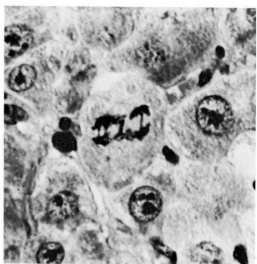

FIG. 6-20. (*Left*) High-power photomicrograph of an H and E section of regenerating rat liver, showing a trinucleated cell. (*Right*) A similar preparation showing double the usual number of anaphase chromosomes arranged in a common spindle which is just visible above them.

of the same individual may have a normal chromosome complement. The abnormalities in cancer cells may involve the number and/or the structure of the chromosomes. No two cancers seem to be alike in this respect. However, there is one kind of cancer which is associated with a *specific* chromosome lesion. In the malignant cells of patients with chronic myelogenous leukemia (a cancer of the cells which produce the granular white cells of the blood), part of the long arm of one of the small acrocentric chromosomes #21 is lost. Because this abnormality was first found in Philadelphia, this little chromosome is called the *Philadelphia chromosome* and is symbolized as Ph. A frequent feature of chronic myelogenous leukemia is the deficiency of an enzyme known as alkaline phosphatase in the white cells. It is therefore believed that the gene responsible for the manufacture of this enzyme normally resides in the part of chromosome #21 which is lost in these patients, but whether the loss of the enzyme is related to the cause of this form of malignancy is still unknown.

## CHEMISTRY AND HISTOCHEMISTRY OF CHROMATIN AND CHROMOSOMES

Both the chromatin and the nucleoli of the interphase nucleus, and the chromosomes of the mitotic nucleus, have an affinity for basic dyes; this is due to the nucleic acids they all contain. Two kinds of nucleic acid are present in the nucleus, as will now be described.

**Two Types of Nucleic Acid in Nuclei, DNA and RNA.** The chief nucleic acid present in chromosomes (and hence in the chromatin of interphase nuclei) yields, on hydrolysis, a particular sugar, D-2-deoxyribose; thus, this type of nucleic acid, because it contains D-2-deoxyribose, is called *deoxyribose nucleic acid*. The term is commonly abbreviated to DNA.

A second nucleic acid that is found sparingly in chromatin but abundantly in nucleoli and in cytoplasm (as will be described when cytoplasm is considered) on hydrolysis yields the sugar D-ribose. This type of nucleic acid is called *ribonucleic acid*, commonly abbreviated to RNA.

**The Feulgen Reaction for DNA.** Feulgen and Rossenbeck, in 1924, described a method for staining nuclear material, particularly chromosomes. This method is now regarded as a histochemical test for DNA.

The Feulgen reaction utilizes an old-established test for aldehydes known as the Schiff reaction; although this has already been described in connection with the staining of certain carbohydrates by the PAS method, for convenience it will be described again here.

There is a dye, basic fuchsin, which is of a magenta (red-blue) color. If hydrochloric acid and sodium bisulfite are added to a suitable solution of it in the order named, sulfurous acid is liberated, bleaching the dye so that it becomes colorless. In this form it is termed *leuko* (*leukos* = white) basic fuchsin (or the Schiff reagent). Aldehydes restore the magenta color to the bleached dye, and this is how the Schiff reaction tests for them.

Next, if sections are subjected to a mild hydrolysis, first with a warm and then with a cold, normal solution of hydrochloric acid, aldehydes are liberated from the D-2-deoxyribose of DNA. The mild hydrolysis employed does not liberate aldehyde from the ribose of RNA. Consequently, if slides are subjected to this mild hydrolysis with hydrochloric acid and then washed and immersed in leuko-basic fuchsin, the aldehydes liberated from the sugar of DNA react with the dye to restore its color. Since this occurs only where there is DNA, the DNA is colored magenta. Because both DNA and RNA are basophilic, the Feulgen reaction makes it possible to decide which basophilic material in a cell is DNA. DNA is confined to chromatin, so the Feulgen reaction is an excellent specific stain for chromatin granules or chromosomes (see Fig. 6-4).

**Other Ways of Distinguishing DNA from RNA.** Nucleic acids strongly absorb ultraviolet light in the 260 millimicron band. Therefore, by photographing slides with ultraviolet light, the sites of nucleic acid in cells can be determined. However, this procedure does not permit the separate localization of DNA or RNA but only of nucleic acids in general. On the other hand, the method can be made specific for DNA or RNA by combining it with another procedure, as will now be described. The enzyme *deoxyribonuclease*, which can be extracted from certain tissues, specifically digests DNA; another enzyme, *ribonuclease*, specifically digests RNA. Since fixation makes cells permeable to these enzymes, if sections cut from fixed tissue are treated with deoxyribonuclease, the DNA is dissolved away. Then, if an ultraviolet photomicrograph is taken of the section and compared with one taken before the enzyme treatment, and if

further but similar sections are correspondingly photographed before and after ribonuclease treatment, when all are compared, it will be shown that DNA is confined to the chromatin granules or chromosomes of the nucleus and that RNA is present in the nucleolus and in the cytoplasm. (A little RNA is also present with much DNA in the chromosomes, and a little DNA is present with much RNA in the nucleolus.)

The DNA content of individual cells can be determined by chemical means provided that the number of cells in the sample that is assayed is known. Furthermore, the DNA content of individual cells can be determined by *microspectrophotometry*. The latter method, though complex, depends essentially on staining sections by the Feulgen technic so that the DNA is specifically colored magenta, and then using a photoelectric cell to measure the amount of light of the magenta wavelength that is absorbed when light is passed through several different and representative interphase nuclei in the section. From the amount of light absorbed, the DNA concentration in the nucleus can be calculated.

By all these various methods it has been possible to determine the DNA content of cells of different types. In general, it has been found that the *amount of DNA in normal diploid body cells is identical* and double that of the haploid germ cells. Of course there are some cells of the body that normally demonstrate polyploidy; here the amount of DNA is some multiple of the normal content. Aneuploidy, which often occurs in cancer cells, can also be detected by this means, as has been shown by Stich.

**The Protein Component of Chromosomes.** The fact that the DNA of chromosomes accounts for their usual and characteristic basophilia, and furthermore, as we shall describe shortly, is of such great biologic significance, tends to detract emphasis away from the protein constituents of chromosomes. That the chromosomes have a considerable protein component is strikingly illustrated by the fact that the DNA can be removed from mitotic chromosomes by the enzyme DNAse, and the protein component that is left behind can then be stained; in such a preparation, chromosomes have much the same appearance under the light microscope as they have when their DNA content is intact. Furthermore, there are indications that the protein component of chromosomes serves more functions than simply acting to hold molecules of DNA in place. As will become apparent, the genes of chromosomes have their chemical basis in DNA. However, in any particular kind of cell only some of the genes are allowed expression: those related to the specialized functions that particular cell performs. There is now some reason to believe that the protein component of chromosomes may be concerned in the mechanisms responsible for some genes in the chromosomes of cells expressing themselves while the expression of others is suppressed.

The proteins of chromosomes are mostly histones; these are relatively simple basic proteins. Because the protein of chromosomes is basic, it stains only with acid dyes, and, since in the usual section or other type of preparation of chromosomes, the DNA with which the protein is associated is so basophilic that it stains deeply with basic dyes, any staining of the protein of chromosomes in preparations stained with both basic and acid stains is overshadowed by basic dyes combining with DNA.

Although histones are the most abundant and probably the most important proteins in chromosomes, other proteins are present; these probably help in providing structural support for the chromosomes. It would seem that some DNA is normally conjugated with histones so as to be present in the form of a nucleoprotein, but that some DNA is not.

## INTRODUCTION TO CHEMISTRY OF GENETIC MATERIAL; HOW INFORMATION IS STORED IN DNA

It has already been explained that if a cell is to divide into two identical cells there must be some mechanism whereby the genes of the chromosomes of that cell are duplicated so that there will be a complete set of identical genes for each daughter cell that results from the division. However, until approximately a decade ago, the possibility of relating different genetic functions to specific chemical configurations in the chromosomes seemed remote, as did also the possibility of under-

standing how the almost innumerable genes in chromosomes could each be duplicated precisely by chemical reactions. About all that was known about the chemistry of genes was that DNA must be involved somehow in their structure, for DNA was known to be a consistent component of chromosomes and was not found anywhere else. In the last decade this great void has been largely filled because of a tremendous development of knowledge relating to an understanding of the chemical nature of genes, the mechanism by which they are duplicated, and how they determine and direct the nature and the function of cells. This new knowledge constitutes one of the most impressive chapters in the history of biologic science.

The first important step in the development of the new knowledge about the chemical basis of genes was obtaining proof that DNA was indeed the hereditary material of cells. This fact was first established from studies on bacteria in which it was shown that if *pure DNA*, extracted from a particular strain of bacteria that was characterized by a special feature, in this instance, a sugar-containing capsule, was added to a culture of another strain of bacteria that lacked this feature, a few members of the second strain acquired a typical sugar-containing capsule. Furthermore, the members of the second strain that acquire this special feature forever after transmit it to their progeny. The alteration in genetic properties of the recipient cells could therefore be explained only by some of the pure DNA from the donor cells becoming incorporated into the genetic material of the recipient cells, which thereafter duplicated this DNA along with their previous DNA. This experiment, called a transformation experiment, demonstrated unequivocally that DNA is the carrier of hereditary characteristics. Other types of experiments, which need not be explained here, substantiated this conclusion.

After it was established that genetic activity had its chemical basis in DNA, it was inevitable that certain questions would be asked, and that answers would be sought to these questions. For example, to more or less serve as a guide for the subsequent discussion, we shall list three questions that could be asked.

1. How could genetic information be stored in a chemical compound?

2. How could a chemical compound housing genetic information be duplicated in such a way that each of the two chromatids that separate in the anaphase would have precisely the same genetic information?

3. How could information stored in a chemical compound, DNA, be transmitted to the various parts of the cell where the enzymes that determine the functions of the cell are located, and by what means would the transmitted information be implemented?

As will be described in the following sections, a great deal of information in relation to answering these questions is now available.

## THE CHEMICAL BASIS OF GENES

Fundamental to developments in this area was the concept of the DNA molecule proposed by Watson and Crick in 1953. The introduction of this concept, now generally adopted, marked the beginning of a new era of research in biology. For their original and continued research on the chemistry of heredity both Watson and Crick were recipients of a Nobel prize in 1962.

In order to facilitate gaining an insight into the mechanism by which information is given by the DNA molecule, it is helpful to consider briefly how information is given by words. Words are composed of letters. Words give different information not only because they are composed of different letters but also because the same letters can be used in words in *different sequences*. When we consider the DNA molecule we will find that it has an alphabet of only 4 chemical "letters" with which words that convey different information are written and arranged into long sentences. We shall find, moreover, that this 4-letter alphabet is used to write only 3-letter words. Now we know that with 4 letters, for example, a, e, p and r, it is possible to write several different 3-letter words that convey different information, for example, ear, par, are, pea, per, ape and pep. If it were not for the fact that words have to be pronounced, which requires that attention be paid to the placement of vowels and consonants, there would be 64 possible 3-letter code words that could be written with a 4-letter alphabet, and, of

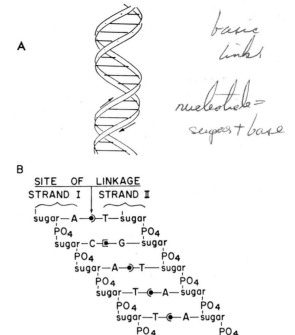

FIG. 6-21. (A) Diagram of a portion of a double-stranded DNA molecule according to the model prepared by Watson and Crick. (B) Portion of a double-stranded DNA molecule showing how deoxyribonucleotides of one strand are joined to those of the other strand through their bases; by adenine being joined to thymine or cytosine being joined to guanine.

course, each 3-letter alphabet and each 3-letter word could code for a different meaning. As will be explained later, no more than 20 code words need be spelled out by the chemical letters of the DNA molecule, because all that is needed is that there be a different code word for each of the 20 amino acids which, as was described in Chapter 2, are variously fitted together to form proteins.

The 4 chemical letters in the 4-letter alphabet of the DNA molecule are 4 bases, *adenine*, *cytosine*, *guanine* and *thymine*. These will be represented in the illustrations by using A for adenine, C for cytosine, G for guanine and T for thymine. In order to explain how these 4 bases are arranged in DNA molecules to code information, we must comment on the DNA molecule in some detail.

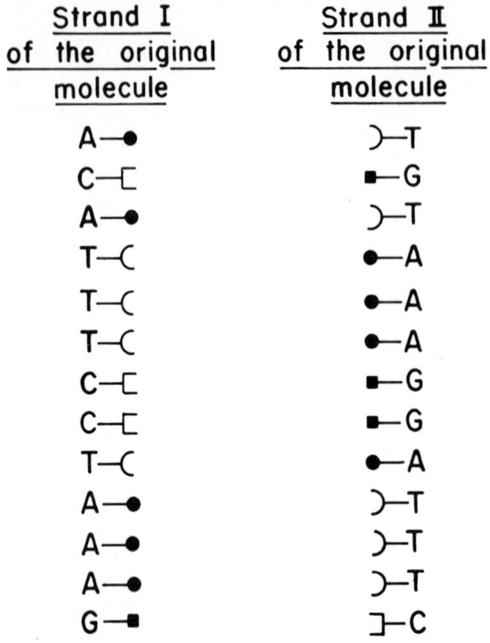

| Strand I of the original molecule | Strand II of the original molecule |
|:---:|:---:|
| A—● | )—T |
| C—⊏ | ■—G |
| A—● | )—T |
| T—( | ●—A |
| T—( | ●—A |
| T—( | ●—A |
| C—⊏ | ■—G |
| C—⊏ | ■—G |
| T—( | ●—A |
| A—● | )—T |
| A—● | )—T |
| A—● | )—T |
| G—■ | ⊐—C |

FIG. 6-22. The first step in the duplication of a DNA molecule is the separation of its two strands.

The DNA molecules of mammalian chromosomes each consist of 2 long thin strands that are wound together in the form of a double helix (Fig. 6-21 A). Each strand is composed of a linear assembly of smaller molecules known as deoxyribonucleotides (Figs. 2-4, and 6-21 B). Each of the latter molecules is composed of 1 of the 4 bases mentioned above, plus a sugar, deoxyribose and phosphate. Adjacent individual molecules of deoxyribonucleotides are linked together to form a strand through the sugar of one being joined to the phosphate of the next (Fig. 6-21 B). There may be as many as 40 million deoxyribonucleotide residues strung along one strand of a single DNA molecule.

In each deoxyribonucleotide molecule, the base on one strand is linked with the base of the neighboring deoxyribonucleotide molecule of the other strand. A very important feature of this bonding between the bases of the two strands is that adenine bonds only with thymine, and cytosine bonds only with guanine. *Hence, as is shown in Figure 6-21 B, wherever there is an A on one strand there must be a T on the other, and where there*

*is a C on one strand there must be a G on the other.*

The genetic information contained by any DNA molecule depends on the number and the order of 3-letter words that are written by the 4-letter chemical alphabet, A, C, G and T, along its strands. A single gene has its basis in a sequence of many consecutive 3-letter words. As will be explained presently in more detail, the long DNA molecules act as templates or patterns for long molecules of messenger RNA which form beside them and on which are imprinted the sequences of 3-letter words that are written along the DNA molecules. The information on the DNA molecule is thus inscribed on molecules of messenger RNA which then move to sites of protein synthesis where the instructions they carry regarding the way amino acids are to be strung together into protein macromolecules are implemented. At first thought it may seem incredible, but the only way that genes seem to be able to act is by determining the kinds and the number of protein macromolecules that are synthesized in cells.

## HOW DNA MOLECULES ARE DUPLICATED

As has been described, the two chromatids of each chromosome separate in the anaphase of mitosis, and the separated chromatids are then known as chromosomes in their own right; each has a full complement of genes. In the past it was believed that the duplication of genes occurred during mitosis, but it is now known that genes are duplicated in the interphase, in preparation for mitosis. Since genes have their chemical basis in DNA, this means that all the DNA molecules of the chromosomes are duplicated during the interphase, and that half of the doubled molecules take their place in one chromatid of each chromosome and half in the other chromatid of that chromosome.

As a prelude to considering the mechanism of duplication of DNA molecules, it is important to realize that the two strands of a DNA molecule each carry different information. A glance at Figure 6-21 will show this fact; it is obvious that the sequences of letters along one strand is different from that of the other, and this, of course, has to be so because wherever there is an A on one strand there is a T on the other, and wherever there is a C on one strand there must be a G on the other. Although this arrangement prevents the two strands from carrying the same genetic information, it does ensure that the two strands of any DNA molecule are *complementary* to one another, and this fact is of great importance with regard to the duplication process, as we shall see.

In order for DNA molecules to duplicate, they must first unwind (this does not mean that they must be unwound along their whole length at any given time; the process about to be described could proceed from one end of a molecule toward the other with unwinding occurring immediately ahead of the advancing duplication process). In any event, as the two strands unwind, they separate along the line of their former attachment between adjacent bases. Hypothetical portions of two unwound and separated strands are shown in Figure 6-22.

Each strand of the original molecule now serves as a template against which a new strand of DNA is synthesized. In forming the new strands, adenine is always formed beside thymine and vice versa, and guanine is always formed beside cytosine and vice versa (Fig. 6-23). *Since the two strands in the original molecule were complementary to one another,*

*the new strand that forms against strand I of the original molecule is an exact duplicate of strand II of the original molecule. Likewise, the new strand that is synthesized against strand II of the original molecule is an exact duplicate of strand I of the original molecule,* as is apparent by inspection of Figure 6-23. Because of this, both of the two new double-stranded molecules are exact duplicates of the original molecule, as may be seen by comparing Figure 6-23 with Figure 6-21 B.

## THE STUDY OF DNA SYNTHESIS BY THE USE OF A RADIOACTIVE LABEL AND RADIOAUTOGRAPHS

The two new strands of DNA that are formed when a DNA molecule is duplicated must be synthesized out of simpler ingredients. Obviously, if one of these ingredients could be labeled with a radioactive isotope, the synthesis of new DNA could be studied by the radioautographic method. In choosing a precursor of DNA for labeling purposes, the important consideration is finding a precursor that is not incorporated into any other product synthesized by cells, for if a specific precursor were available, all the labeling seen in cells after such a labeled precursor was used would be in DNA. It so happens that the only product in which thymine is found in the body is

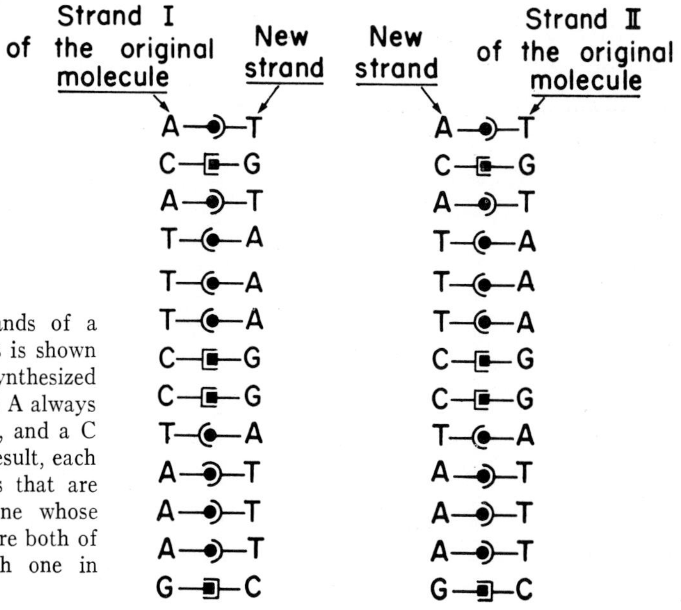

Fig. 6-23. After the two strands of a DNA molecule have separated, as is shown in Figure 6-22, a new strand is synthesized beside each of the two strands. An A always forms beside a T, and vice versa, and a C beside a G, and vice versa. As a result, each of the double-stranded molecules that are formed is identical with the one whose strands become separated. Compare both of these with each other and with one in Figure 6-21 B.

DNA, so obviously thymine would seem to be an ideal product to label for the study of DNA synthesis. However, labeled thymine is of no value in studying DNA synthesis, for pure thymine is not incorporated into DNA molecules. Thymine is incorporated into DNA molecules only when it is attached to sugar, and sugar does not become attached to thymine that is given an animal; sugar must be attached to thymine as thymine is being synthesized by an animal. But if thymine which is attached to sugar (and this is called thymidine) is labeled and given an animal, the thymidine will be incorporated into such new DNA as is being synthesized, just as thymine that was being synthesized and attached to sugar in the cell would be incorporated into newly forming DNA. So thymidine labeled with tritium is universally used to specifically label new DNA that is synthesized.

Since both of the original strands of a DNA molecule serve as a template against which a new strand is synthesized (Figs. 6-21 and 6-22), each one of the two double-stranded molecules of DNA that result when DNA synthesis is completed has one old strand and one new strand, as is shown in Figure 6-23. If labeled thymidine is available during the period of DNA synthesis, the thymine that was synthesized in each of the new strands is labeled; this is shown in Figure 6-24 by putting a star beside the T that represents

thymine that carries a label. The pre-existing thymine on the old strands would of course *not* be labeled.

An important point to appreciate from the foregoing is that if labeled thymidine was sufficiently abundant, every new 2-stranded molecule of DNA formed under the conditions described above would carry a label. But, the label would be present only in the *new strand* of each DNA molecule and not in the strand that was part of the previous DNA molecule. Hence, when a cell divides, after having doubled its DNA content under conditions where label was available, *all* the chromosomes of both daughter cells will carry a label, because every molecule of the DNA of which they are composed would carry some label in *one of its* two strands (the recently formed strand that was synthesized in the presence of label), as is shown in Figure 6-24. And, even though labeled thymidine is incorporated only into newly forming strands of DNA molecules, it labels DNA very satisfactorily for radioautographic studies of DNA synthesis, as is shown in Figure 6-25. Figure 6-25 is a photomicrograph showing the way the "grains" appear over chromosomes in a radioautograph of a mitotic cell in which DNA synthesis took place in the preceding interphase in the presence of labeled thymidine.

Labeled thymidine is not incorporated into any other substance that forms in the body

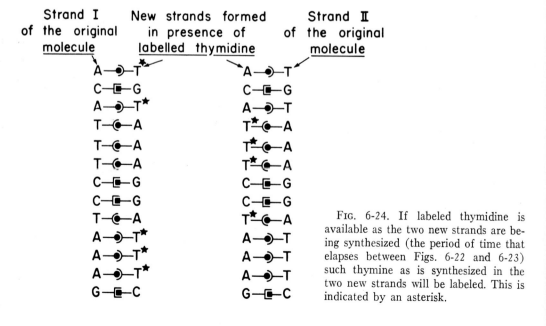

FIG. 6-24. If labeled thymidine is available as the two new strands are being synthesized (the period of time that elapses between Figs. 6-22 and 6-23) such thymine as is synthesized in the two new strands will be labeled. This is indicated by an asterisk.

except DNA, and it is incorporated only into forming DNA molecules. It is not incorporated into newly forming RNA because, as will be explained later, RNA differs from DNA in the respect that instead of having thymine as one of its nitrogenous bases, it, instead, has uracil.

## SOME MATTERS THAT HAVE BEEN CLARIFIED BY LABELING NUCLEI WITH RADIOACTIVE THYMIDINE

**1. It can sometimes be used to trace cell lineages.** It is often a problem in histology to be sure about the kinds of stem cells that differentiate into certain types of specialized cells. Direct evidence can often be obtained about this matter by giving a group of animals some radioactive thymidine and then killing the animals at suitable intervals afterward. Radioautographs made from sections taken from animals shortly after the label was given will reveal label in various cells that were duplicating their DNA during the period when label was available; such cells are generally of the less differentiated or stem cell type. Sections taken at different periods of time afterward may now show the label in highly differentiated cells and, taking proper precautions, it can be assumed that cells that were labeled immediately after the labeled thymidine was given have in due course differentiated into the type of cell in which the label is now seen. By experiments of this kind it is often possible to use a radioactive label to trace the development and differentiation of certain kinds of cells. For example, if soon after label is given to a growing animal the label is found in relatively undifferentiated cells that cover the surface of a bone, but no label is seen in cells that are within the substance of the bone, and then if after a week or so the bone is seen to have increased in width and label is now seen in cells that are within the bone, surrounded by intercellular substance, but only a short distance from the bone surface, it can be assumed that the cells that were seen to be labeled shortly after giving the labeled thymidine have in the next week or so turned into bone-forming cells and surrounded themselves with intercellular substance so that they are now buried in the bone substance that they have made.

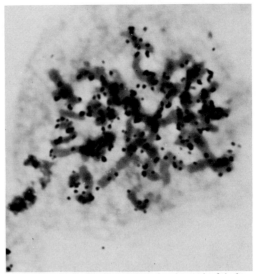

Fig. 6-25. Radioautograph of an air-dried preparation of an L cell from a culture that was given a 16-hour exposure to tritium-labeled thymidine. The labeled thymidine was taken up as the DNA was being duplicated, and enough time elapsed for the cell to enter mitosis; this cell was obtained when it was in the metaphase. The dark grains that are seen over the chromosomes are due to the short tracks of beta particles from the tritium causing ionization in the overlying photographic emulsion. (Stanners, C. P., and Till, J. E.: DNA synthesis in individual L-strain mouse cells, Biochim. biophys. acta *37*:406)

**2. It gives information about the formation of chromatids and their behavior in mitosis.** Let us suppose next that the cells that are labeled immediately after giving labeled thymidine do not differentiate but, instead, continue to divide. Under these conditions they cannot be followed for long because their label becomes diluted for reasons which will now be explained.

If label is taken up during the period when DNA is being duplicated, all the DNA molecules that result from the duplication of DNA will be labeled, but only in one of their strands, as is shown in Figure 6-24. What happens if no more label is given and the labeled cells continue to divide? What actually happens, as has been shown by Taylor and his associates, is that after labeled cells divide in the absence of label only one half

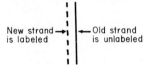

When DNA duplication occurs in the presence of label, the new strand of every DNA molecule of every chromatid is labeled as in the molecule illustrated below

New strand →| |← Old strand
is labeled     | |    is unlabeled

If next duplication of DNA occurs in the absence of label, both the old strand and the new strand act as templates for still newer strands, neither of which is labeled

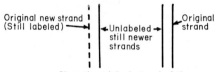

Original new strand |            |Original
(Still labeled) ——→|  ←Unlabeled→| strand
                   |   still newer |
                   |   strands     |

Since the original strand of the molecule on the right is older than the labeled strand of the molecule on the left, and since the two new strands are of the same age, the double-stranded molecule on the right is on the whole the older molecule

After DNA duplication is complete, each chromosome separates into two chromatids. One of these can be thought of as the mother chromatid and the other as the daughter chromatid. The older DNA molecules all stay in mother chromatids, and the newer molecules all go to the daughter chromatids as shown below, using, as an example, only one molecule in each chromatid.

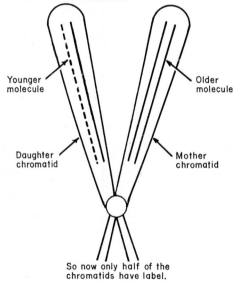

Younger                      Older
molecule                     molecule

Daughter                     Mother
chromatid                    chromatid

So now only half of the chromatids have label.

FIG. 6-26. Diagrams showing newer DNA molecules going to daughter chromatids.

of the chromatids of the cells that enter the next mitosis carry label. To explain this phenomenon it is helpful to remember that each

time a double-stranded DNA molecule is duplicated, one of the two resulting double-stranded molecules will have *one* strand that is *older* than either strand in the other molecule. This can be seen by studying Figure 6-26. The molecule at the top has one strand (indicated by a broken line) that was synthesized in the presence of label, so it is the newer strand of that molecule. The unlabeled strand (indicated by a continuous line) is the older. Then, when duplication of this 2-stranded molecule occurs in the absence of label, as is illustrated in the middle diagrams, each strand of the former molecule gains a new unlabeled strand beside it; both of these new strands are unlabeled, and of the same age, being the youngest of all 4. So now each of the two molecules has a new strand and an older strand, but the older strand in the molecule on the right is older than the older (labeled) strand in the molecule on the left because it served originally as the template for the labeled strand. So, the complete molecule on the left can be considered to be as a whole younger than the one on the right. Next, as the interphase chromosomes each begin to divide into two chromatids, in preparation for the next mitosis, these "younger" DNA molecules all go to the daughter chromatid; and the "older" molecules all stay in the original mother chromatid. As a result of this, all the labeled DNA molecules (the younger ones) end up in the daughter chromatids. It would be easier to understand how this could happen if there were only *one* double-stranded DNA molecule in each chromosome, but there is no assurance that each chromosome of mammalian cells has only one DNA molecule; the size of mammalian chromosomes would suggest that each contains several DNA molecules, and, if so, it would seem that they must all face the same way when a mother chromatid gives rise to a daughter chromatid so that what we have termed the younger DNA molecules, formed as a result of DNA duplication, all go to the daughter chromatid.

**Why Label Becomes Diluted on Continued Cell Division.** It might be thought from the previous discussion, since the labeled DNA all goes to the newer chromatids, that the newer chromatids would, in turn, all go to the same daughter cell and that as a result one daughter cell from each division would continue to be

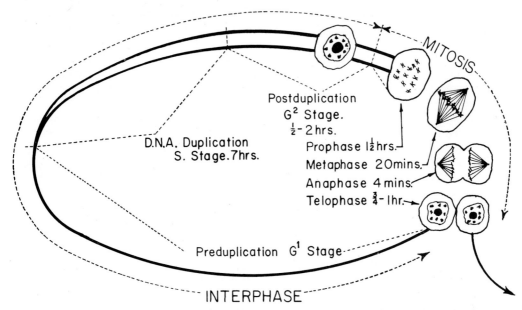

Postduplication
$G^2$ Stage.
$\frac{1}{2}$- 2 hrs.
Prophase $1\frac{1}{2}$ hrs.
Metaphase 20 mins.
Anaphase 4 mins.
Telophase $\frac{3}{4}$- 1 hr.

D.N.A. Duplication
S. Stage. 7 hrs.

MITOSIS

Preduplication $G^1$ Stage

INTERPHASE

Fig. 6-27. Diagram illustrating stages of cell cycle.

labeled indefinitely. But this is not what happens, for at the metaphase, when the chromosomes that have one labeled chromatid and one unlabeled chromatid line up in the region of the equatorial plane, the direction they face is a matter of chance. Accordingly, the labeled chromatid of one chromosome may face one pole of the cell and the labeled chromatid of another chromosome the other pole of the cell. Hence, when the centromeres of the chromosomes separate, half of the labeled chromatids (on the average) are pulled toward one pole and become chromosomes of one daughter cell and half are pulled toward the other pole and become the chromosomes of the other daughter cell. Accordingly the label in each daughter cell is diluted on the average by 50 per cent with each cell division. The same thing happens on subsequent divisions of daughter cells, so the label becomes diluted again with each subsequent division of daughter cells by 50 per cent, and soon there is so little label left in dividing cells that it can no longer be detected.

#### The Cell Cycle and the Three Stages of the Interphase

Cells that continue to divide pass consecutively through interphase, mitosis, interphase, mitosis, and so on. One complete passage through the interphase and mitosis is termed

a *cell cycle* (Fig. 6-27). Provided that all the cells of a culture are of an identical kind, and all are multiplying at the same rate, the time taken for them to complete a full cell cycle can be determined easily by making numerous cell counts from the culture and establishing the average time that it takes for the cell population to double. The time taken for any given kind of cell to complete a full cell cycle is termed its *generation time*.

Let us now consider how it is known that the interphase consists of three stages and how the lengths of time taken for cells to pass through each of these stages can be determined in cell cultures. It would be easier to do this if all the cells in a culture were synchronized so that each and every one was in the same stage of the interphase or mitosis at the same time. Although progress is being made toward achieving synchronized cell cultures, the times taken for various stages of the interphase are generally calculated by making studies on cultures of cells which at any given moment are in different stages of the cell cycle, and this makes the study somewhat difficult.

The common procedure is to add some labeled thymidine for a very brief period of time to a culture of the type described above. It is important to remember that the exposure to labeled thymidine is momentary. Thereafter, samples are taken from the culture at regular periods of time and examined by the radioautographic technic. It will be helpful to consult Figure 6-27 frequently while reading the following.

Cell samples that are taken from the culture *immediately after the exposure to labeled thymidine* show, first, that no mitotic figures that are then seen in the culture are labeled. Label will be seen only in interphase nuclei, and, furthermore, it will be seen in only a certain percentage of interphase nuclei. Since label is seen in only some interphase nuclei, it is obvious that at any given time only a percentage of the cells in the culture are in the DNA duplication stage, and since a sample will show unlabeled interphase cells, there must be other stages besides a DNA duplication stage in the interphase. The percentage of interphase nuclei that reveal label in a sample taken immediately is therefore the percentage of cells that were in the stage of DNA duplication when the label was momentarily made available. The unlabeled interphase cells in the sample could have been in either a stage preceding DNA duplication (the preduplication or G1 stage) or following it (the postduplication or G2 stage).

The fact that there is a postduplication and a preduplication stage can be ascertained very readily if certain further observations are made on the cells of the culture. It is now necessary to point out that those cells that take up label when they are exposed momentarily to labeled thymidine will range all the way from those that are just beginning the stage of DNA duplication to those that have almost completed it. In due course label will be seen in *mitotic* chromosomes, and the first labeled cells to arrive at the prophase of mitosis will be those that had almost completed the process of DNA duplication when they were exposed to label. So, if samples are taken regularly from the culture, a time will come when label will be seen over the chromosomes of a few cells that have entered the prophase of mitosis. Since the cells in which label is *first seen* over prophase chromosomes are cells that were labeled just as they were finishing the duplication of their DNA, the time taken between the time when label was made available and the time when label is first seen over prophase chromosomes is the time of the postduplication or G2 stage.

Next, although the existence of the postduplication stage can be established, and the time it takes roughly estimated by making the above-described observations, it should be said that it is not as easy to identify mitotic figures in the prophase stage as it is to identify, and look for labels in, metaphase chromosomes. So we shall now transfer our attention to metaphase chromosomes and look for label over those. If this is done it will be found, as might be expected, that as successive samples are taken from the culture, more and more metaphase mitotic figures show label, until a time comes when *all* the metaphase mitotic figures are labeled. Then, as time continues to pass, samples taken will show that the percentage of labeled metaphase mitotic figures will begin to fall, and before long samples will show no metaphase mitotic figures with label. The fact that the number of labeled metaphase mitotic figures first increases and then decreases is to be explained as follows.

The first labeled metaphase mitotic figures are seen in cells that were almost at the end of their DNA duplication stage; after they finished their postduplication stage they entered mitosis, and then label was seen over their chromosomes. But, the percentage of cells in the culture that were near the end of the DNA duplication stage when label was made available would be small. The percentage of cells that were somewhere between the beginning and the end of their DNA duplication stage when label was made available would be very much larger. Since the metaphase lasts only about 20 minutes, there would be a time when the cells that were labeled in the midpoint of the DNA duplication stage were all passing through the metaphase, and so 100 per cent of metaphase mitotic figures seen at this time would be labeled. But then, as these labeled cells in the metaphase pass on through mitosis, the percentage of labeled metaphase mitotic figures would fall off because now only the cells that were just beginning their stage of DNA duplication when the label was given would be reaching mitosis, and since the metaphase takes about 20 minutes or so, these would be mixed with others that were about to begin, but had not yet begun their DNA duplication when label was made available. The unlabeled mitotic figures seen at this time would represent cells that were in the *preduplication* stage when the

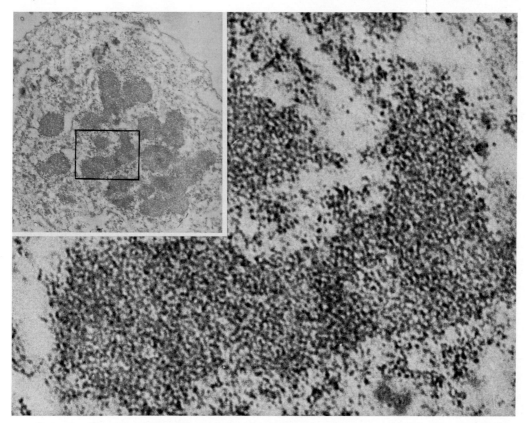

FIG. 6-28. Electron micrograph of section of a dividing L cell fixed in formalin. The magnification of the inset is 8,000, and that of the main picture 53,000 times. As seen in the latter, the sectioned chromatid has a granular appearance which is probably due to curving microfibrils 5 to 20 millimicrons in diameter, being cut generally in cross and oblique section but occasionally, for short distances, in longitudinal section. (Preparation by Dr. Samuel Dales)

label was available, and presently all of the cells in mitosis would be this type.

The time taken for the DNA duplication stage is determined as follows. First, the time is noted when 50 per cent of metaphase mitotic figures in samples are found to be labeled. After this, as described, the percentage increases until 100 per cent of metaphase mitotic figures show label. Then, by taking further samples, a time arrives when the percentage of labeled metaphase mitotic figures falls off to 50 per cent. The time that elapses between the time when 50 per cent first become labeled and when 50 per cent are last seen to be labeled is the time for the DNA duplication stage of the interphase (averages are used).

The time taken for the preduplication stage can be determined as follows. The figure obtained by adding the time taken for the process of mitosis, the time taken for the postduplication stage, and the time taken for DNA duplication, is substracted from the time taken for a complete cell cycle (the generation time); this gives the time for the preduplication stage. The time taken for the preduplication stage varies with different cell lines; it is not nearly as constant as the times taken for mitosis or the other stages of the interphase.

## THE FINE STRUCTURE OF CHROMOSOMES

Sections used for light microscopy are thick enough to contain whole chromosomes but those used for electron microscopy are not; hence, in thin sections of mitotic chromosomes, all that can be seen are thin slices of chromosomes.

Thin sections of dividing cells studied with the electron microscope reveal no nuclear membrane. The region ordinarily occupied by the nucleus contains irregular granular dark patches; there are several of these in the inset in Figure 6-28. Each patch probably represents a slice cut through a chromatid. Each patch has a relatively homogeneous appearance, and there is no suggestion that the chromatids of somatic cells of mammals have central cores that are different from their peripheral regions, or that they have a limiting membrane.

On superficial examination the dark patches seem to be composed of dark granules that measure between 5 and 20 millimicrons in width but vary in length and lie on a lighter background (Fig. 6-28). Any granule that demonstrates much length is generally curved. Granules measuring up to 1 micron in length can sometimes be observed. The picture seen in a single slice cut through a chromatid is what might be expected if the chromatid contained threads of material that had a diameter of 5 to 20 millimicrons and pursued curving courses along the chromatid and were separated from one another by a lighter amorphous material; the latter may be the protein of the chromosome.

However, it has been difficult to determine whether the DNA in the chromosomes is represented by the dark threads that appear as granules or by the amorphous-appearing material that is disposed between the granules. Doubt has been expressed as to whether osmium tetroxide, the usual fixative used for preparing tissues for electron microscopy, is suitable for studying DNA; it has been suggested that it may make the protein of the chromosomes electron-dense instead of the DNA. However, dark granular material can be seen in sections of material fixed in formalin (which does not act as an electron stain), as is shown in Figure 6-28, and the granules appear much the same as in osmium-fixed material. Furthermore, Dales has shown that sections from material fixed in acetic alcohol and then treated with deoxyribonuclease and examined under the electron microscope do not show the dark granules seen in Figure 6-28. Hence, there appears to be reason to believe that the dark granular material seen in sectioned chromatids represents cross, oblique and sometimes short longitudinal sections through threads that contain DNA. The DNA molecule is probably around 2 millimicrons in diameter. Therefore, the 5 to 20 millimicron threads cannot be single DNA molecules cut in section; the threads must contain either several molecules or a very considerable amount of some other material which is probably the protein.

## EFFECT OF RADIATION ON CHROMOSOMES AND MITOSIS

The biological effect of x- or gamma rays is exerted by means of the high energy photons of the rays, which knock electrons out of some of the atoms of the cell. Atoms which lose an electron by this means are intensely reactive and instantaneously enter into some new chemical combination in their immediate environment. Of course, this alters the chemical composition of the material with which they react. A minor chemical change resulting from this cause in any part of an interphase cell except a gene is probably of no more than temporary significance, because the cell either has many duplicates of the altered component or, if it has none, it still has the proper gene or genes to direct the replacement of the injured cell component.

However, if atoms of, or in, DNA are ionized, the results can be more serious, for, in the process by which DNA is duplicated in the interphase, each strand of a molecule serves as a model for each new strand that is synthesized. Accordingly, if the chemical basis of a few genes is altered, they will, when the genes are duplicated, model the formation of similarly altered genes. If the alteration in the genetic material as a whole is not too great, the cell may still be able to perpetuate its kind by mitosis, but all the descendants of this cell will lack not only the normal genes of the type that were altered but also the normal qualities imparted to the cell by normal genes of this type. Moreover, altered genes may impart some new qualities to the cells. This is the way that radiation, in doses that are not lethal to a cell, may induce a cell mutation.

Interphase cells subjected to more severe radiation may (with the light microscope)

FIG. 6-29. Oil-immersion photomicrograph of a squash preparation of an L cell in mitosis following 5,000 r of x-rays that was given to the culture in which this cell was growing. The radiation has interfered with the normal process of cell division in that (1) the spindle in this cell has 3 poles instead of 2; (2) many of the chromosomes are lagging and, as a result, they form *chromosomal bridges*; and (3) many are of an abnormal form. (Till, J. E., and Whitmore, G. F.: Effects of x-rays on mammalian cells in tissue culture *in* Proc. 3rd Canadian Cancer Res. Conf., New York, Acad. Press)

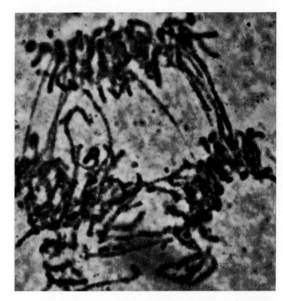

seem to be unaffected as long as they remain in the interphase, but when the cell attempts to pass through a cycle of mitosis, it will become apparent that serious damage has been done to its mitotic apparatus. Indeed, the cell may not be able to complete a single division, but if it manages this, it will fail and die on attempting some subsequent one. This is the chief basis for using radiation in the treatment of cancer; it acts to prevent the cancer cells from continuing their mitotic cycles and hence their growth. The damage to the mitotic apparatus of the radiated cell—which becomes apparent when the cell attempts division—is manifested in several different ways. (1) The chromosomes may be seen to be altered in form, or broken-up or joined together in abnormal ways. (2) The spindle may show abnormalities; for example, it may have 3 poles instead of 2, with the result that chromosomes are drawn to 3 points instead of 2 (Fig. 6-29). (3) The chromosomes act as if they were sticky and, in the anaphase, the chromatids do not pull apart from one another evenly. Some may lag and form bridges between the 2 groups of chromosomes (Fig. 6-29). (4) The chromosomes may divide without the nucleus dividing: this gives rise to large nuclei with more than the normal number of chromosomes, or the nuclei may divide without the cytoplasm dividing. In both these latter instances, the cells affected become much larger than normal and are called *giant cells*.

As we shall describe later, the turnover of the cell population varies greatly from one part of the body to another. Since the effect of radiation on cell division is much the same in all kinds of cells that divide, it can be understood easily that if a whole animal body is radiated, the effects of the radiation will be related primarily to the rate of cell division in various parts of the body. Hence those parts of the body where there is a great deal of mitosis will be most seriously affected. Since the rate of cell turnover is great in the blood-forming organs and in the lining of the intestinal tract, these 2 tissues are said to be very *sensitive* to radiation. On the other hand, there is no turnover of nerve cells; hence, they are said to be *relatively insensitive* to radiation.

## HOW GENETIC INFORMATION IN THE CHROMOSOMES IS MADE OPERATIVE IN THE CELL

As was noted previously, certain questions were raised when it was definitely shown that DNA was the genetic material of the cell. The first of these related to the means whereby genetic information could be recorded in a chemical compound. The answer to this question was the finding that this was accomplished by the sequences in which 3-letter chemical code words are inscribed along the strands of DNA molecules, the letters of the chemical code words being the 4 bases, adenine, cytosine, guanine and thymine. The second question that was asked related to how the information stored in genes could be duplicated as a prelude to cell division, and this was explained as being dependent on the fact that DNA molecules are double-stranded, with the two strands complementary to one another, and that each strand serves as a model for another strand in the duplication procedure. The third question that was asked related to how the information stored in the DNA molecules of chromosomes could be transmitted to, and made operative at, the sites in the cell where proteins are synthesized. This question will be considered now.

**Why the Proteins Formed in Cells Are All-important.** The major reason for the cells of man being different from the cells of any other species is that the proteins of the cells of man differ from those of other animals. Furthermore, except in the instance of identical twins, many of the proteins of the cells of one person are different from those of the cells of any other individual. Next, the various *kinds* of cells that exist within any individual differ from one another mainly because they have different organizations of protein macromolecules within them; this enables them to perform different functions because their enzymatic constitutions which, in turn, depend on their particular organizations of protein macromolecules differ. So, whether a cell is to be a cell of a plant or an animal, a mouse or a man, or a blood cell or a cell of the skin in any given individual depends on its protein constitution. It therefore follows that since cells reproduce their own kind, and since their own kind is dependent on their having a particular protein constitution, genes must act through controlling the protein constitution of cells. Indeed, it is now known that a single gene consists of a long sentence of 3-letter chemical words with each word of the sentence coding for a particular amino acid, and the sentence as a whole—the gene—thus coding for a particular kind of protein macromolecule (not all genes code for only a single protein; recent evidence indicates that one gene may control the synthesis of more than one). Thus genes act by controlling the proteins that are to be formed in cells. The intermediary between genes and protein formation in cells is the second kind of nucleic acid that is found in

cells—ribonucleic acid (RNA), and we shall now discuss its various roles.

Macromolecules of RNA have much the same chemical structure as those of DNA with three main exceptions. First, most kinds are single-stranded, but some are double-stranded. Secondly, although they have 4 bases, only 3 of these are the same as those of DNA molecules, namely, adenine, cytosine and guanine. The fourth base in RNA molecules is uracil, not thymine, and this is the reason RNA does not incorporate labeled thymidine when this labeled material is available. Thirdly, the sugar in RNA is ribose instead of deoxyribose, and because of this RNA does not give a positive Feulgen reaction.

It has now been established that there are at least 3 functional types of RNA and that all 3 are concerned in the mechanism whereby information stored in the DNA of the chromosomes is made operative at the sites of protein synthesis. The three types are respectively termed (1) messenger RNA, (2) ribosomal RNA, and (3) transfer RNA. The evidence now available suggests that all 3 kinds are formed in the nucleus.

Messenger RNA, in the living cell, is synthesized along the course of only one of the two strands of a DNA molecule, probably in much the same way that a new strand of DNA is formed beside an old strand in the duplication of DNA molecules. There is a difference, however, because in the formation of messenger RNA, although an A is always formed in the RNA molecule beside a T in the DNA molecule, and a C beside a G, and a G beside a C, a U (for uracil) (and not a T) is always formed in the RNA molecule wherever there is an A on the DNA molecule (Fig. 6-30). Macromolecules of messenger RNA therefore carry an inscription of the sequences arranged along the DNA molecule but with 3-letter words written from an alphabet of A, C, G and U. Molecules of messenger RNA, carrying the inscription of DNA molecules, then travel to the sites of protein synthesis—the ribosomes. Ribosomal RNA will therefore be discussed next.

Ribosomal RNA occurs in the form of granules that are around 15 millimicrons in diameter and hence are large enough to be seen in the electron microscope (Figs. 7-1 and 7-7). Their appearance in this instrument was first

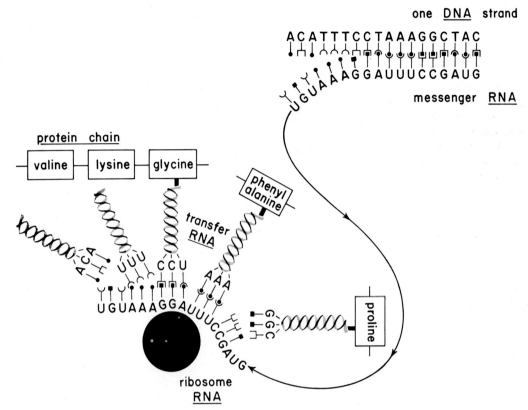

FIG. 6-30. Diagram to show how information coded on one strand of a DNA molecule in the nucleus (*upper right*) is transferred to a strand of messenger RNA which forms beside it (*upper right*) and how the latter peels away from the DNA molecule (*upper right*) and moves (*arrow on right side*) to the cytoplasm to a ribosome (*lower left*). Here the strand of messenger RNA is surrounded by a pool of amino acids, each of which is identified (so far as the messenger RNA is concerned) by a particular 3-letter code word of transfer RNA; thus valine is identified by ACA, lysine by UUU, glycine by CCU, phenylalanine by AAA and proline by GGC. The first 3-letter code word inscribed along the strand of messenger RNA (*bottom left*) fits ACA so that the amino acid valine is the first selected by the messenger RNA. The next 3-letter code word selects UUU so that lysine is added to valine as the construction of a protein molecule is begun. The next word selects glycine which is added to the protein chain. The diagram shows that phenylalanine and proline will be added next (*right side*) and that the transfer RNA responsible for identifying valine and lysine (*left side*), having done its work, has become detached both from the messenger RNA and from the amino acids they identified. The code words for all the amino acids are not yet known.

described by Dr. George Palade of the Rockefeller Institute, and for a time they were called Palade granules in his honor. When it was found that they were rich in RNA, they came to be more generally termed RNA granules, and then when biochemists began to extract them from cells and study them, the term granule, which is primarily a descriptive histologic term, was superseded by the term *ribosomes*, which means, of course, that they are ribose-containing bodies (*soma* = body).

They are now almost universally termed ribosomes.

Ribosomes are distributed in both the nucleus and the cytoplasm. The granules with a diameter of around 15 millimicrons that are so prominent in the nucleolus and which largely account for its granular appearance under the electron microscope are, in all probability, ribosomes, and hence the nucleolus is generally believed to represent a localized aggregation of ribosomes. In the nucleus, ribosomes are also scattered about in the nuclear sap. In the cytoplasm they are distributed in two general ways, first, along the outer surfaces of intracytoplasmic membranous vesicles that will be described in due course, and second, as free granules scattered about in the remainder of the cytoplasm. The cytoplasmic content of ribosomes varies greatly with kinds and states of activity of cells.

The role of ribosomes in protein synthesis is not as thoroughly understood as it doubtless will be in due course. However, from what is now known, ribosomes seem to be essential to serve as sites where the 3-letter words along molecules of messenger RNA become specifically attached to 3-letter code words of transfer RNA with which they fit and which, in turn, are each attached to the respective amino acids for which they code, as will be explained shortly. This fitting together of 3-letter code words inscribed along messenger RNA molecules and the 3-letter code words of transfer RNA that are in turn attached to their respective amino acids, and which results in amino acids being joined together to form macromolecules of protein, does not occur in the absence of ribosomes. The function that ribosomes perform in serving as sites where messenger and transfer RNA code words are fitted together seems to be nonspecific so far as cell types and even species are concerned, for ribosomes from one species introduced in artificial systems permit the messenger RNA and transfer RNA derived from another species to become fitted together and hence for protein synthesis to occur.

Transfer RNA, like the other two types of RNA, is made in the nucleus, and it too passes out to sites of protein synthesis. There is a separate kind of transfer RNA for each of the amino acids. However, each kind acts the same way, namely, by becoming attached to its respective amino acid which either has come to the cell by way of the bloodstream or has been synthesized inside the cell. The specific type of transfer RNA which becomes attached to each of the 20 amino acids identifies that amino acid, by a 3-letter word, and there is a different 3-letter word to identify each of the 20 or so amino acids. Many of the 3-letter words that identify specific amino acids are now known (Fig. 6-30). Each of these 3-letter words of transfer RNA fits with one of the 3-letter words that are strung along a molecule of messenger RNA. So what happens, very roughly, is that as a long molecule of messenger RNA is formed from DNA it moves to a site where there are ribosomes and where it becomes attached. Here it is in the midst of a pool of 20 amino acids, each of which carries a distinguishing label of transfer RNA. The messenger RNA, as it were, calls out the first 3-letter word at the end of its molecule, and the 3-letter word of transfer RNA that is attached to a particular amino acid, and that fits the 3-letter word on the messenger RNA, responds to the call and becomes attached to the messenger RNA at this site (Fig. 6-30). Then the next word along the molecule of messenger RNA is called out, as it were, and the 3-letter word of messenger RNA and the amino acid attached to the transfer RNA become linked with the amino acid that has just been attached to the messenger RNA by its transfer RNA. The process continues so that one by one the amino acids specified by the code along the messenger RNA are linked both to the messenger RNA and together in the proper order. After their work is done and the protein macromolecule is completed, the messenger and the transfer RNA are probably broken down.

Now that we have finished describing the first important component of the nucleus, namely, chromatin and chromosomes, and have given a brief account of the functions of the different types of RNA in the cell, we are in a better position to discuss the second component of the nucleus, namely, the nucleolus, because it is a very important depot of RNA.

## NUCLEOLI

With the light microscope a nucleolus or nucleoli is/are seen, in interphase nuclei of the open-face type, as one or two or even more rounded and generally basophilic bodies that are larger than particles or clumps of chromatin (Figs. 6-1 and 6-3, upper nucleus). Although present in most interphase nuclei of the condensed chromatin type, nucleoli may be so obscured by densely packed chromatin in ordinary preparations that they cannot be seen, and in order to show that such nuclei have nucleoli, it may be necessary to study fresh preparations with the phase microscope, or specially thin sections with the light microscope, or ultrathin sections with the electron microscope.

**Numbers and Formation of Nucleoli.** As already mentioned, nucleoli disappear in the latter part of prophase and begin to form again in the telophase, where they make their appearance at certain sites along only certain pairs of autosomes. The particular segments of the autosomes that give rise to nucleoli are termed *nucleolar organizers*. The number of pairs of autosomes that can organize the formation of nucleoli is limited and varies in different species. In the body cells of man there are probably 5 pairs of autosomes that possess nucleolar organizers; hence, the maximum number of nucleoli that can form in the body cells of man is 10. However, only one or two nucleoli are commonly seen because: (1) the nucleolar organizers of several autosomes may cooperate in forming the same nucleolus, and (2) nucleoli tend to fuse. Shea, working in Leblond's laboratory, has shown that the total amount of nucleolar substance that develops in one type of body cells of mice is always the same, whether the cells contain only one or several nucleoli. Under conditions of polyploidy, the amount of nucleolar substance is increased in the same ratio as the number of chromosomes. For example, in tetraploid cells, which are sometimes seen in the normal liver, and which have double the number of chromosomes of diploid cells, the nucleolar volume is twice that of the nucleolar volume of diploid cells.

**Chemical Composition.** About 5 per cent of the nucleolus consists of RNA. The remainder is chiefly protein. There is also a little DNA in nucleoli; this is probably because of the fact that those portions of the threadlike chromosomes that organize the formation of nucleoli remain embedded in or at least intimately associated with the nucleoli that they organize. Using suitable methods it is possible to break up nuclei and then, by differential centrifugation, to separate out a fraction that consists almost entirely of nucleoli; such fractions always contain a little DNA along with the greater content of RNA.

**Staining Reaction.** This is affected by three factors. First, the nucleic acid is strongly basophilic. Second, the protein component of the nucleolus is chiefly of the basic variety and

hence acidophilic. Third, there is often some condensation of chromatin around the periphery of the nucleolus and this so-called nucleolus-associated chromatin may account for a basophilic shell around a nucleolus. In general nucleoli are basophilic. However, if some of the RNA of the nucleolus is washed out during the processing of a section, or if the section is treated with the enzyme ribonuclease, which dissolves out the RNA, the nucleolus is then colored by acid stains because the protein portion of the nucleolus which still remains is basic.

**The Fine Structure of the Nucleolus.** Perhaps the first point that should be made is that the EM has shown that the nucleolus is not surrounded by any kind of a membrane (Fig. 6-31); this is a point that could not be established with certainty with the light microscope.

Next, information on the components of nucleoli has come from studies on both plants and animals. Lafontaine and Chouinard in an EM study of growing root-tip cells of *Vicia faba* (broad bean) have observed two main components in the dense material of the nucleolus. The first component is granular with the individual granules appearing dark in sections treated with uranyl acetate and lead hydroxide and measuring around 150 Å in diameter. These granules appear to be identical with the ribosomes of the cytoplasm, as can be seen in one of their illustrations, which is Figure 6-31. The other component of the dense material of the nucleolus, in sections treated with lead hydroxide, appear to be fibrillar in nature, with the individual fibrillar structures being between 60 and 100 Å in diameter (Fig. 6-31).

**The Question of Nucleolonemata.** Some years ago, from light microscope studies, Estable and Sotelo described an arrangement seen within nucleoli that appeared under the microscope something like a thick filament wound loosely into a ball and which they termed the *nucleolonema*. Nucleoli seen in the EM often show electron-dense granular and fibrillar components distributed so as to surround irregular spaces filled with much less dense material, as may be seen in both the inset and the main picture in Figure 6-32. The less dense material that fills the irregular spaces has been termed the *pars amorpha* of

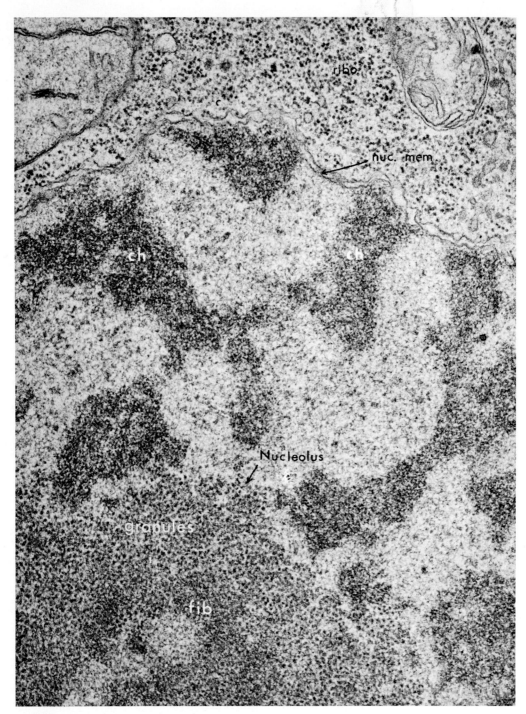

Fig. 6-31. Electron micrograph (× 47,000) of portion of preprophase of cell of *vicia faba*. The nuclear membrane (nuc. memb.) runs across the upper part of the illustration, and above it ribosomes (ribo.) may be seen in the cytoplasm. All the material below the nuclear membrane is nuclear. Several chromosomes (ch.) are cut in section. Approximately the lower left third of the illustration represents nucleolar material (the arrow that runs from *nucleolus* indicates the edge of the nucleolus). Granules from around 150 to 300 Å occupy most of the space in the nucleolus, but it also shows areas where there is a fibrillar component (fib.). (Lafontaine, J. G., and Chouinard, L. A.: J. Cell Biol. *17*:167)

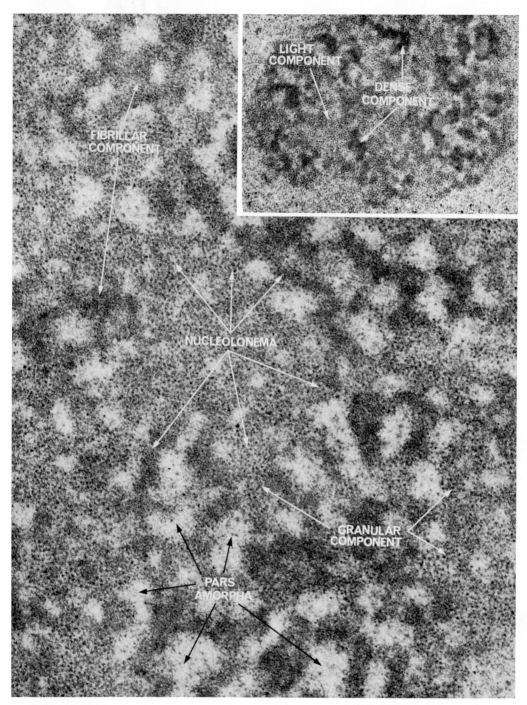

Fɪɢ. 6-32. Electron micrograph (*inset*, × 21,000, *main picture*, × 40,000) of the nucleolus of an interphase rat liver cell. The inset shows that the nucleolonema consists of light and dark components (which are labeled) and has pale areas of pars amorpha (which are not labeled) in its interstices. The higher magnification shows the spongelike structure of the nucleolus. The spongy framework consists of nucleolonema. Parts of this are fibrillar (these parts correspond to the dark areas in the low-power micrograph that are labeled dense component), and parts are granular (these parts correspond to what is labeled light component in the inset). The interstices of nucleolonemal framework are filled with a less electron-dense material called the *pars amorpha* of the nucleolus; this is probably nuclear sap. (Miyai, K., and Steiner, J. W.: The fine structure of interphase liver cell nuclei in subacute ethionine intoxication, Exp. Mol. Path., in press)

the nucleolus. The fact that the denser components are distributed so as to surround spaces containing *pars amorpha* might seem to suggest that the denser components of the nucleolus (the granules and the filaments) are arranged in the form of a long cordlike structure that is twisted upon itself and greatly convoluted, so as to constitute the nucleolonema seen with the light microscope. However, if the dense material of the nucleolus was in the form of a convoluted cord that wound and twisted about in the nucleolus, there should be many examples of dark material in a single section being completely surrounded by *pars amorpha;* instead, what is more commonly seen is areas of *pars amorpha* surrounded by dense material. Accordingly, it seems much more probable from the appearance seen in the EM that the electron-dense material of the nucleolus is not arranged in the form of a continuous cord but in the form of a continuous mass that is permeated by channels and holes filled with *pars amorpha*. Hence, it would seem more likely that if a reconstruction were made from thin sections, the dense material of the nucleolus would be found to be arranged in a 3-dimensional mass that was riddled with holes and channels filled with *pars amorpha;* so it probably would resemble a rounded piece of sponge more than a ball of yarn.

**The Arrangement of the Electron-Dense Components of the Nucleolus.** According to Steiner, one of whose illustrations appears as Figure 6-32, the granules which are around 100 to 150 Å in diameter are (1) in some sites aggregated by themselves in fairly loose arrangements, and (2) in other sites mixed with the fibrillar component of the nucleolus in denser arrangements (see Fig. 6-32). Accordingly, in the nucleolonema, granules are found either in aggregates by themselves or together with the fibrillar components of the nucleolus. The granules, as already noted, give every evidence of being ribosomes. The nature of the fibrillar component of the nucleolus is less certain.

Although it can be shown by histochemical methods combined with electron microscopy that the granules contain RNA, there are difficulties associated with determining the type of nucleic acid and/or protein of which the fibrillar material is composed. There are rea-

sons for thinking that at least some of it may be messenger RNA. On the other hand, some of it may be chromosomal material with DNA. It is perhaps possible that it contains no nucleic acid but consists only of protein. It is to be expected that more definite information on the nature of the fibrillar component of the dense material of the nucleolus will be forthcoming shortly.

*The Pars Amorpha.* The *pars amorpha* of the nucleolus presents an appearance in the EM similar to that of the nuclear sap which fills the parts of the interphase nucleolus that are not occupied by condensations of chromatin. As will be described shortly, the condensations of chromatin that can be seen in the nucleus probably represent coiled and hence inactive segments of chromosomes. The extended portions of chromosomes, which are the parts of the chromosomes that are active in giving off information to messenger RNA, cannot be distinguished with any certainty in an interphase nucleus with the EM, and in all probability these are represented by fine threads cut in various planes throughout the nuclear sap; undoubtedly, some extend into the nucleolus via the *pars amorpha*. The precise distribution of the substance of the chromosomes that act as nucleolar organizers in the nucleoli of interphase nuclei is not known.

**Sites of Synthesis and Storage of RNA.** The synthesis of RNA in cells has been studied by applying the radioautographic technic to sections or other types of cell preparations made from animals or cell cultures in which RNA has been synthesized in the presence of RNA precursors that have been labeled with suitable radioactive tracers (see reference for details of procedures.)

As is shown in an illustration (Fig. 6-33) supplied by C. P. Leblond, a labeled precursor of RNA is seen first over the nucleus, and later the label is seen over the cytoplasm. This is interpreted as meaning that RNA that is labeled in the nucleus subsequently migrates to the cytoplasm. At the time of writing, the bulk of the evidence that is available indicates that RNA is synthesized only in the nucleus.

Next, when labeled precursors of RNA are given, label appears both over the chromosomes and over the nucleolus quickly enough to indicate that RNA is synthesized in both sites. It is logical to believe that messenger

FIG. 6-33. As was explained under Radioautography in Chapter 4, it is possible to label a precursor of both DNA and RNA and then remove DNA with DNAse. When this procedure is followed, it is found that a labeled precursor is found in RNA only in the nucleus where it is seen over both chromatin and the nucleolus in the first hour (*left picture*). Forty-eight hours afterward, the labeled RNA is found only in the cytoplasm (*right picture*). (Photomicrographs from C. P. Leblond)

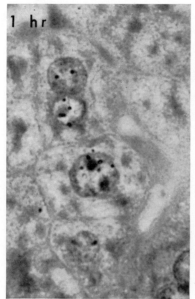
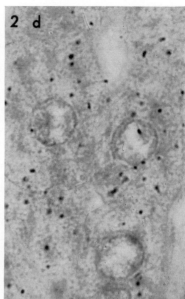

RNA is necessarily synthesized along extensive lengths of chromosomes in the nuclear sap where the code on the DNA would serve as a template and so print its code on messenger RNA. It seems possible that the ribosomes (which are nonspecific) are synthesized in nucleoli. A question arises, however, as to whether the template that serves as a model for their formation resides in the DNA of those portions of chromosomes that enter and leave nucleoli or whether ribosomes themselves can act as templates for the formation of further ribosomes. Experiments with nucleoli that have been separated from cells by differential centrifugation indicate that if all DNA is removed from nucleoli by deoxyribonuclease, the synthesis of RNA in the preparations almost stops. Accordingly, it seems most probable that chromosomal DNA serves as a template for the formation of the ribosomal RNA that appears in the nucleolus. The same is probably true for transfer RNA.

**Nucleolar Hypertrophy.** It has been shown also by using radioautographs and labeled amino acids that little protein is synthesized in the nucleolus; hence its chief role would seem to be that of serving as a site of production or assembly of ribosomes that subsequently migrate to the cytoplasm where they serve as sites of protein synthesis. It also probably serves as a depot for messenger RNA. Therefore, it seems reasonable that nucleoli should become somewhat larger in cells that are actively synthesizing protein and so require more ribosomes than quiescent cells. Before the role of RNA in cells was understood, many investigators through the years observed that nucleoli seemed to be larger than usual in cells that were active, and in particular when they were actively synthesizing protein. There now seems to be a functional basis for this belief.

## THE NUCLEAR MEMBRANE (ALSO TERMED THE NUCLEAR ENVELOPE)

With the light microscope the nuclear membrane appears as a single basophilic line (Fig. 6-1). The EM shows it has 2 layers separated by a space which measures between 200 and 300 Å, and is termed the *perinuclear space* (Fig. 6-34, *bottom*). The two layers of the nuclear membrane are of somewhat different densities. The outer is less dense and often is studded on its outer surface with particles that are around 150 Å in diameter and are considered to be ribosomes. The outer layer of the nuclear membrane, in cells that are actively proliferating, is seen at some sites to connect, and so to be continuous with, certain intracytoplasmic membranes which will be described in the next chapter; these con-

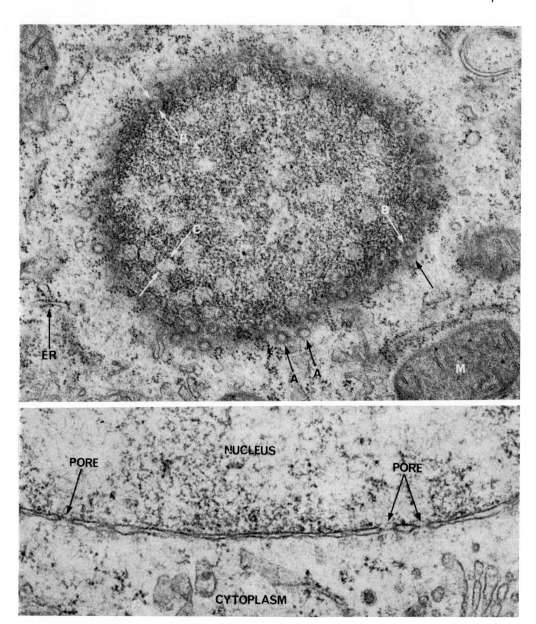

Fig. 6-34. Electron micrograph ($\times$ 35,000) of interphase nucleus of rat liver cell. (*Top*) Slightly oblique section across part of the nucleus showing nuclear pore complexes. Where pore complexes are sectioned through their cytoplasmic portion (A), they lie within the cytoplasm, some distance from the chromatin of the nucleus. When sectioned through the intranuclear channel (C), the pore complex lies within the peripheral chromatin. Pores designated as (B) are seen in sections between levels A and C. (M = mitochondria; ER = endoplasmic reticulum). (*Bottom*) Electron micrograph (*bottom*, $\times$ 56,000) of section cut at right angles to the nuclear envelope showing nuclear pores. The outer and the inner membranes of the nuclear envelope fuse at the periphery of the nuclear pores. Note the appearance of a diaphragm across the pore opening on the right of the micrograph. (Miyai, K., and Steiner, J. W.: The fine structure of interphase liver cell nuclei in subacute ethionine intoxication, Exp. Mol. Path., in press)

stitute what is termed the rough-surfaced endoplasmic reticulum of the cytoplasm. The inner layer of the nuclear membrane is not studded with ribosomes. The perinuclear space is filled with an amorphous material of about the same electron density as cytoplasm.

**Nuclear Pores.** The new knowledge of the biochemical interactions which take place between nuclear and cytoplasmic components would in itself suggest that there must be a means for the ready passage of macromolecules of a considerable size between nucleus and cytoplasm. A pathway between nucleus and cytoplasm would seem to be provided by little circular gaps in the nuclear membrane which are too small to be seen with the light microscope but which the EM has shown to exist (Fig. 6-34, *bottom*). These gaps are termed *nuclear pores*. In most cells they are fairly evenly distributed and numerous, being generally separated from one another by only 0.1 to 0.2 microns. Around the edge of each pore the outer and the inner layers of the nuclear membrane fuse. The diameter of pores varies somewhat; it ranges from around 300 to 1,000 Å. Thin sections cut more or less parallel with the surface of nuclei show that pores are roughly circular (Fig. 6-34, *top*). Detailed studies of pores have led to the designation of a *pore complex* which is essentially a channel that passes through the pore at right angles to it and projects for a short distance to either side of the pore, into the nucleus at one end of the channel and into the cytoplasm at the other end of the channel. Within the nucleus the channel is bounded by a zone of condensed chromatin (Fig. 6-34, *top*). On the cytoplasmic side of the nuclear membrane the channel is surrounded by cytoplasm of slightly increased density; this is termed the cytoplasmic cuff of the pore complex. The content of the channel is termed the channel material, and it contains filaments of low electron density.

There has been some question as to whether the channel of a pore is completely open or whether or not a very thin diaphragm extends across a pore. Although the evidence seems to indicate that pores are sometimes completely closed with thin diaphragms, the evidence also indicates that some pores are open. Furthermore, it seems probable that some of the appearances seen with the EM which are inter-

preted as diaphragms closing off pores are due to the sections having been cut at right angles to the surface of the nucleus, passing through the edges of pores so that the thin edge of the pore (where the outer and the inner nuclear membranes are fused) is included in the section.

**Behavior on Mitosis.** The nuclear membrane melts away in the prophase and is re-formed in the telophase (Fig. 6-7).

## NUCLEAR SAP

So far we have considered 3 of the 4 components of the nucleus—(1) chromatin and chromosomes, (2) nucleolus and (3) nuclear membrane or envelope. We shall now consider briefly the 4th component of the nucleus, the substance in which the chromatin and the nucleolus lie. From light microscopy this clear material was termed nuclear sap (Fig. 6-1). It was believed to be a colloidal solution, perhaps varying between a sol and a gel, and it was shown to contain some protein that demonstrated some enzyme activity.

The study of this material with the EM has led to the introduction of another term, for electron microscopists often refer to the nuclear sap of light microscopy as *interchromatinic substance*. In order to discuss this term and describe what is seen in it we must comment again on chromatin and in particular on the fine structure of chromatin as it appears in the interphase nucleus.

**The Fine Structure of Chromatin in the Interphase Nucleus.** As was explained in the first part of this chapter, the chromosomes in an interphase nucleus are mostly extended, and only coiled sections of chromosomes constitute dense enough bodies to become visible as chromatin granules or particles with the light microscope. When interphase cells are fixed with the newer aldehyde fixatives for electron microscopy, what is termed chromatin (which is probably heterochromatin, representing coiled sections of chromosomes) becomes aggregated in 3 different sites. As is shown in Figure 6-35, there are (1) condensations of chromatin along the inner surface of the nuclear membrane, (2) condensations of chromatin around the nucleolus (this is the nucleolus-associated chromatin) and (3) little islands of condensed chromatin scattered about in the nuclear sap.

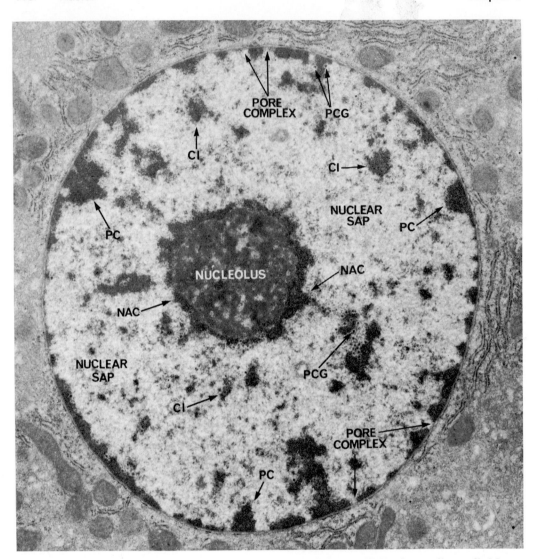

Fig. 6-35. Electron micrograph (× 14,000) of the interphase nucleus of a rat liver cell. Material was fixed in glutaraldehyde and post-fixed in osmium tetroxide. This procedure allows a clear visualization of the condensed parts of chromosomes, forming peripheral chromatin (PC), chromatin islands (CI) and nucleolus-associated chromatin (NAC). The intranuclear channel of a pore complex can be seen as a pale area of nuclear sap between two adjacent masses of peripheral chromatin. Careful inspection shows perichromatin granules (PCG). (Compare with higher magnification of these granules in Fig. 6-36, *left.*) (Miyai, K., and Steiner, J. W.: The fine structure of interphase liver cell nuclei in subacute ethionine intoxication, Exp. & Mol. Path., in press)

The appearance presented in the EM (in sections of material fixed in glutaraldehyde) by the chromatin in these sites where it is condensed is much the same as is seen in mitotic chromosomes with the EM and fits with what would be seen if coiled or curving filaments were cut in various planes. These curving filaments have been described as being of different diameters and can be followed for different, though generally very short, lengths in any given section. The narrowest filaments seen are probably around 50 Å in diameter, and it would seem that these may become aggregated to form filaments of greater diame-

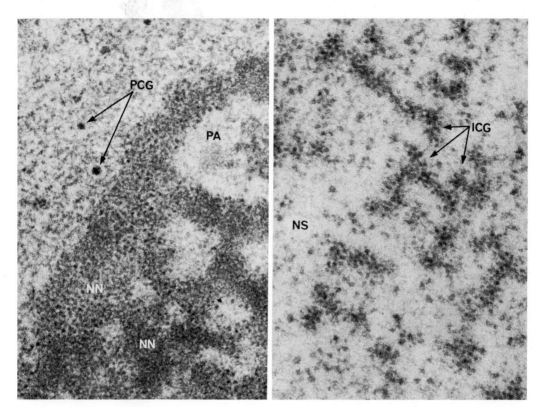

Fig. 6-36. Electron micrograph ($\times$ 58,800) of interphase nucleus of a rat liver cell. (*Left*) Two perichromatin granules (PCG) surrounded by halos are located within the nuclear sap adjacent to a portion of nucleolonema (NN) of the nucleolus. (The pars amorpha is seen at the marker [PA]). This section was taken from tissue fixed in osmium tetroxide. (*Right*) Electron micrograph ($\times$ 72,900) of aggregation of interchromatin granules (ICG) located in the nuclear sap. Note the tendency of the granules to form chains. (Miyai, K., and Steiner, J. W.: The fine structure of interphase liver cell nuclei in subacute ethionine intoxication, Exp. Mol. Path., in press)

ter. The precise distribution of DNA and histones in chromatin is not well established; it seems probable that the curving or coiled filaments described above contain DNA.

**The Term "Interchromatinic Substance."** The extended portions of chromosomes of an interphase nucleus probably lie mostly in the nuclear sap that exists between the various condensations of chromatin. So, if the nuclear sap is termed interchromatinic substance, the word chromatin would have to be defined, not as the material out of which chromosomes are made (for extended portions of chromosomes are in the nuclear sap) but as condensed portions of chromosomes that constitute masses large enough to be seen as such with either the light or the electron microscope. If chromatin is so regarded, it can then be said that

there are two types of granules found in the interchromatinic substance or nuclear sap; these have been termed *perichromatinic* and *interchromatinic granules* respectively.

The perichromatinic granules, as their name suggests, are seen close to masses of chromatin. They are round and large, measuring 300 to 350 Å in diameter. They are generally surrounded by a clear halolike zone that is about 250 Å wide as is seen in Figure 6-36. They can also be seen if one looks carefully in Figure 6-35.

The interchromatinic granules vary from 150 to 500 Å in diameter. They are very electron dense and may occur singly or, more often, in chains or angular clusters in the nuclear sap (Fig. 6-36, *right*).

The chemical nature of perichromatinic or

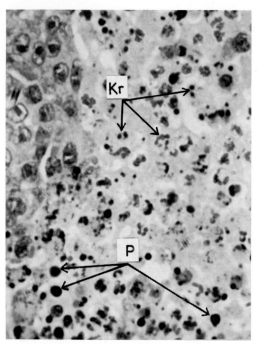

FIG. 6-37. High-power photomicrograph of a section of a malignant tumor. The cells at the left side were still alive and growing (notice their large nucleoli) when the specimen was taken, but those on the right side had died previously and, as a consequence, their nuclei had undergone changes which are indicative of these cells having died. Some nuclei have shrunken into rounded dark-staining bodies (P); this is termed *pyknosis*. Other nuclei have become broken up into fragments (Kr); this is termed *karyorrhexis*. Areas of tissue in which the cells die during life are described as constituting areas of necrosis (*nekros* = corpse). See also karyolysis (Fig. 6-38).

interchromatinic granules has not yet been definitely established. One probability is that they both represent nuclear ribosomes.

## NUCLEAR CHANGES INDICATIVE OF CELL DEATH

It is obvious that all the cells in a section cut from fixed materials are dead. When histologists or pathologists speak of seeing "dead cells" in a section they do not refer to these but to cells which died while the body in which they were contained was still alive.

Dead cells are encountered in a living body for two main reasons. First, in some tissues it is normal for cells to die and be replaced by others; this occurs, for example, in the outer layer of the skin. Likewise, certain of the white cells of the blood have only a short life span and die within the body. Accordingly, in tissue removed from a healthy body, it is normal to see nuclear changes that are indicative of cell death in sites where it is normal for cells to die. Secondly, dead cells may be present as a result of disease. For example, an artery supplying some limited area of tissue may, as a result of disease, become plugged and, as a consequence, the cells in the area supplied by the artery die from lack of oxygen and food. In such areas, the nuclei of the cells at some time variously demonstrate the various changes described below. Rapidly growing cancers are prone to contain areas of dead tissue, probably because the blood supply to the rapidly growing cells is inadequate (Fig. 6-37).

Although the cytoplasm changes greatly in dead cells, the most positive indication that cells are dead is given by their nuclei. The changes here that indicate cell death are of 3 kinds. The commonest change is called *pyknosis* (dense mass). This consists of a shrinkage of the nuclear material into a homogeneous hyperchromatic mass (Fig. 6-37, P). The student must take care not to confuse a pyknotic nucleus with a normal nucleus of the condensed chromatin type or with a poorly fixed mitotic figure. If difficulty is encountered in any instance, it is advisable to examine the cytoplasm of the cell, for if the nucleus is dead, the cytoplasm will become altered also in some way so that it no longer has a normal appearance, as may be seen in Figure 6-37. However, in other instances, death is indicated by the nucleus breaking up into fragments. This is termed *karyorrhexis*. When many nuclei break up in this fashion, nuclear "dust" may be formed (Fig. 6-37, Kr). In still other instances, cell death is indicated by dissolving of the nucleus. This is termed *karyolysis* (Fig. 6-38).

**Postmortem Degeneration.** In the previous section we have described the changes that occur in the appearances of nuclei of cells that die while they are in a living body. When the body as a whole dies, the same kind of changes begin in the cells of the whole body;

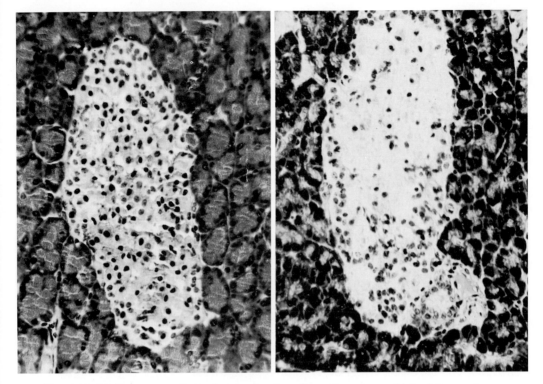

Fig. 6-38. Medium-power photomicrographs of sections of pancreas obtained from rats some hours after they had been given alloxan, a material which destroys many of the cells of the islets of Langerhans. (*Left*) The nuclei of the cells in the oval islet may be seen; there are some examples of pyknosis. (*Right*) The nuclei have mostly dissolved away; this picture illustrates karyolysis.

this is why it is so important, in procuring tissue for histologic study, to obtain and fix tissue as soon as possible after death. The changes that occur in tissues after death are generally classified under the heading of postmortem (after death) degeneration. The changes seen under the microscope involve not only the nuclei, which either become pyknotic, fragmented or dissolved, but are evident in cytoplasm as well. As will be described in subsequent chapters, the cytoplasm of different kinds of cells differs. In postmortem degeneration the normal characteristics of the cytoplasm of various kinds of cells become decreasingly obvious. In some cells the cytoplasm becomes granular and broken up; in others it assumes a melted-down appearance, and in the end it dissolves away. Much of this change is probably brought about by hydrolytic enzymes that are normally in little membranous containers in the cytoplasm from which they cannot escape during life but

are able to do so when cells die. These will be considered in the next chapter under the heading *lysosomes*.

Postmortem degeneration occurs much more quickly in some organs than in others. It begins immediately after death in the lining of most of the intestine; in this instance the breakdown of cells is brought about by the digestive enzymes that are present in the lumen of the intestine, enzymes which, in the normal course of events, digest food in the lumen of the intestine and not the living cells that line the intestine. However, when the lining cells die they are digested just as food is normally digested. At the other end of the scale are intercellular substances; many of these resist postmortem degeneration for a long time.

The rate at which postmortem degeneration occurs is related to temperature; that is why it is desirable, if postmortem examinations of bodies must be postponed for any length of

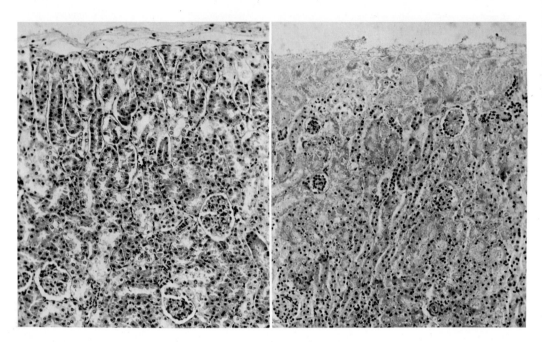

FIG. 6-39. (*Left*) Low-power photomicrograph of section of the cortex of the kidney of a mouse. The tissue was fixed immediately after the death of the animal. (*Right*) Similar photomicrograph of a section of similar tissue which was not fixed until the animal had been dead for many hours. Notice that no cellular detail can be seen near the surface where postmortem change has been greatest. Below the surface pyknotic nuclei and degenerating cytoplasm indicate that extensive postmortem degeneration has taken place.

time, to refrigerate the bodies until the autopsy can be performed.

The left and the right sides of Figure 6-39 represent the same kind of tissue, but the section on the right was made of tissue that was not fixed immediately after death as was the tissue on the left, but only after many hours had elapsed. Note that all detail is lost in the upper part of the section on the right; this is where postmortem degeneration has proceeded the farthest. Deeper in the section there is enough detail left to allow an experienced person to recognize the section as one of kidney, but many cells here have already lost their characteristic appearances.

The student must realize that evidences of postmortem degeneration will be seen in many of the sections of human tissue studied in the histology and histopathology laboratory. This is almost unavoidable because postmortem degeneration begins so quickly after death. Even though autopsies are performed very shortly after death, tissues obtained at autopsies will show signs of postmortem degeneration in many types of cells. One reason for including many sections of tissues taken from animals in the usual histology class set is that tissue can be obtained from animals immediately after death and fixed promptly, and hence postmortem degeneration in sections prepared from these tissues is not apparent.

## REFERENCES

References for Chapter 6 are combined with references for Chapters 5 and 7 and appear at the end of Chapter 7.

# 7    The Cytoplasm

The nucleus directs the work of the cell, but the cytoplasm does most of this work. Since cells are specialized to perform different kinds of work, and since most of this is done by the cytoplasm, the cytoplasm of different kinds of cells exploit different properties of protoplasm to different extents. Specialization of cytoplasm for different functions is reflected in cells having different appearances; for example, it is to be expected that those cells that are specialized for contractility would have a different-appearing cytoplasm from those specialized for secretion and that this would enable the histologist to tell them apart. Hence, although some kinds of cells can be distinguished from each other by their nuclei, *most kinds of cells are identified by the appearance and the amount of their cytoplasm.*

There is a division of labor within the cytoplasm as well as in the cell as a whole. Cytoplasm is not a homogeneous substance of uniform composition; instead, it has a complex organization and contains structures and bodies of various shapes and sizes and of different compositions. The contents of many of the structures within cytoplasm must be kept segregated, for if all the chemical substances in cytoplasm were allowed to mix freely they would interact in a haphazard way and the work of the cell could not go on. One of the greatest contributions of electron microscopy to the study of the cell was that it permitted the elucidation of the means by which segregation within cytoplasm is achieved; it showed that, within the cytoplasm, membranes were employed to prevent various constituents of cytoplasm from mixing, while at the same time often permitting useful chemical reactions to proceed between materials on different sides of the membranes.

Before the existence of intracytoplasmic membranes was known, the various little structures and bodies that could be seen within cytoplasm with the light microscope were classified into two groups, as *organelles*

or *inclusions*. The electron microscope has shown that many of the organelles are membranous structures. The basis on which organelles and inclusions have been distinguished from one another will now be described.

## ORGANELLES AND INCLUSIONS

**Definition.** The term *organ* (*organon* = an instrument or implement) is used with regard to animals to designate a part of the body that is composed of several tissues and is adapted to the performance of some special function or functions. The heart, the lungs and the kidney are all examples of organs. The term *organelle* means *little organ* and has been used for many decades for classifying structures that could be seen within the cytoplasm with the light microscope and which were believed to perform some special function related to the metabolism or function of the cell. Organelles, through the years, have been distinguished from a second class of things that could be seen in at least certain cells with the light microscope and which were termed *inclusions*. Inclusions were regarded as aggregations of material that do not play any part in the metabolism of the cell and which come to be present in a cell for various reasons. As we shall see, some kinds of inclusions are taken into the cell from their environment, but others are formed within the cell. Inclusions of the latter variety have been distinguished from organelles by the fact that they are not part of the metabolic machinery of the cell in which they exist. However, they may be products of the metabolic functions of the cell.

It was perhaps easier and more worthwhile in past years to make a distinction between organelles and inclusions than it is today. With the advent of electron microscopy and the use of other special methods, new structures have been found within cells, and a much more precise knowledge has been gained about the structure and the function of others that had been identified and named by light microscopy alone. This new knowledge has confused more than it has clarified the problem of distinguishing between organelles and inclusions. For example, it is now known that lysosomes and zymogen granules are both membranous vesicles filled with enzymes. Zymogen granules have always been classified as inclusions; this was justified by the fact that the enzymes they contain do not serve any function within the cell in which they are made. The enzymes in lysosomes, however, can serve a function in the cell in which the lysosomes are formed. This then is the only basis for classifying zymogen granules as inclusions and lysosomes as organelles, for both have the same kind of structure. But this criterion is not used for other cell components. For example, pigments are classified as inclusions. But pigment can serve a useful purpose inside the cell in which it is formed; for example, melanin can protect the nuclei of epithelial cells of the skin from ultraviolet light. Should then melanin pigment be not classed as an organelle because it serves a useful purpose inside the cell in which it is formed? Let us consider another example. The cell web is not a very lively structure metabolically, but it is made by the cell and provides structural strength for the cell in which it is made and so it serves a useful purpose. It is therefore classified as an organelle. But melanin pigment would seem to possess the same qualifications of being made by a cell and serving a useful purpose. All this is said in order to suggest that the important matter is to learn all the different structures or components of cells that can be identified by various histologic methods and to understand so far as is possible how these are formed and what functions they perform. This is much more important than trying to classify these various cell components as organelles or inclusions.

A Classification of Cell Components Commonly Classed as Cytoplasmic Organelles

1. **Cytoplasmic RNA—Ribosomes.** As will be described shortly cytoplasmic RNA, which the EM has shown to be chiefly in the form of ribosomes, can be seen with the light microscope in stained sections. The role of RNA in

protein synthesis has been described in part in Chapter 6 and will be considered further here.

2. **Various Organelles Constituted of Membranes.** These are concerned essentially with segregating different chemical materials from one another and yet permitting certain chemical reactions to occur at the interfaces that they present. They also act by being selective with regard to diffusion processes. The membranous organelles are:

A. *The cell or plasma membrane;* this is the membrane that encloses the cell as a whole.

B. *The endoplasmic reticulum*—an intracellular system of membranous vesicles* and tubules

C. *The Golgi apparatus*—another system of membranous vesicles*

D. *Mitochondria.* These are little membrane-covered structures that are concerned in cell respiration and energy production.

E. *Lysosomes.* These are membranous vesicles* that contain hydrolytic (destructive) enzymes.

3. **The Centrosphere and Centrioles.** These have already been described as playing a part in the process of mitosis (p. 75).

4. **Various fibrils, filaments and tubules** that serve structural or contractile functions within the cell; those performing structural functions, most notably those of the *cell* and *terminal web*, will be described in the next

---

* The terminology in use regarding the various membranous structures in the cytoplasm varies a good deal. The word vesicle, which is much used in anatomy, means a bladder. A bladder is a distensible fluid-containing structure that in the human body is generally a closed cavity. Alternate terms for vesicles are (1) sacs and saccules, (2) cisternae and (3) vacuoles. The chief criticism that could be offered for using the terms sac or saccule is that the term sac means a bag, and a bag is commonly either opened or closed. Hence the terms sac or saccules require an adjective to indicate whether it is open or closed. The term cisternae is often used to describe vesicles that are somewhat distended, but this term, from its origin, refers to a cistern or a well, and both cisterns and wells have open tops. The term vacuole in our opinion is not a desirable alternative to vesicle even if the vesicle is rounded, because the term vacuole refers to a space, not a structure. A cytoplasmic vesicle is a structure because it has a membranous wall. For the reasons given above, we shall hereafter use the term vesicle with reference to certain membranous structures found in cytoplasm.

chapter, and those that perform contractile functions will be described in Chapter 20.

## 1. CYTOPLASMIC RNA—RIBOSOMES

**Terminology.** After the chromatin of the nucleus was seen and described, numerous histologists in different parts of the world noticed that the cytoplasm of at least some cells of the body contained an appreciable content of a material that had the same affinity for stains as had nuclear chromatin (Fig. 7-6). These various observers, who were not always familiar with each other's observations, gave this material different names. It was natural, since this material in the cytoplasm stained similarly to nuclear chromatin, that it should be named *chromidial* (chromatinlike) *substance* (Fig. 7-6). Also, since it demonstrated a *love* for stains, it was logical that it should be called *chromophile substance*. When dyes became better understood, and it was learned that some were acid and some basic, it was noticed that this material had an affinity only for basic dyes, and since the remainder of the cytoplasm had an affinity for acid dyes, it came to be referred to as the *basophilic component of cytoplasm*. Garnier, whose findings have been described in some detail in English by Haguenau, made a remarkable study of this material in 1900. He noticed that it was related to the work of the cell, so he termed it *ergastoplasm* (*ergon* = work).

**Histochemistry.** Although the organelle we are discussing reacts similarly to chromatin with most basic stains, it was shown (after the Feulgen reaction came into use) that it was not identical with nuclear chromatin because it proved to be Feulgen-negative. When the enzymes ribonuclease and deoxyribonuclease became available, it was found that it was dissolved by the former and not by the latter. Therefore, it was concluded that the substance contained RNA. As a result of this, it gained still another name—*the cytoplasmic RNA*, and this, we think, is the best of the terms to use for this organelle as it appears with the light microscope because this term is the most specific, relating as it does to its chemical nature. However, all the terms mentioned are firmly entrenched in the literature, and many are still widely used, so the student should be familiar with all of them.

**Terminology in Relation to Diffuse and Localized Basophilia in Cytoplasm.** From the studies made with the light microscope on cells stained with basic stains, it was apparent that the basophilia of the cytoplasm of some kinds of cells was diffuse and in other cells localized to certain of their parts. In particular, as was described by Garnier, the basophilia in the cytoplasm of certain secretory gland cells was localized in the more basal parts of the cells, and he termed this basophilic material localized in the bases of certain gland cells ergastoplasm (Fig. 7-6). In certain other kinds of cells basophilic material was found to be arranged in clumps, scattered about in the cytoplasm as, for example, in nerve cells (Fig. 21-17). Since the arrangement of the basophilic material in the cytoplasm of nerve cells was first described by Nissl, the clumps of basophilic material seen in the cytoplasm of nerve cells are commonly referred to as *Nissl bodies*. Hence, the two terms, ergastoplasm and Nissl bodies are used with special reference to basophilic material that is localized in a characteristic way in special cell types. The other terms, basophilic component of cytoplasm, chromidial substance, chromophile substance, and cytoplasmic RNA are used in a more general way, to depict either basophilic material in cytoplasm that is in a diffuse arrangement or basophilic material localized to some part or parts of the cytoplasm of cells.

### The Study of Cytoplasmic Basophilia With the EM

The development of knowledge about the fine structure of the basophilic material in cytoplasm involved changing concepts and a changing terminology, but in a few years resulted in establishing that the basophilia that can be seen in cytoplasm with the light microscope is due to the presence of tiny bodies of nucleoprotein around 15 millimicrons in diameter. The nucleic acid of these is RNA. As has been mentioned these little bodies were first termed Palade granules, then RNA granules and are now universally termed *ribosomes* (Figs. 7-1, *inset*, and 7-7).

Since it is now known that there are two other kinds of RNA in cytoplasm besides ribosomal RNA, namely, messenger and transfer RNA, it might be asked if these can be identified with the EM and if they play any

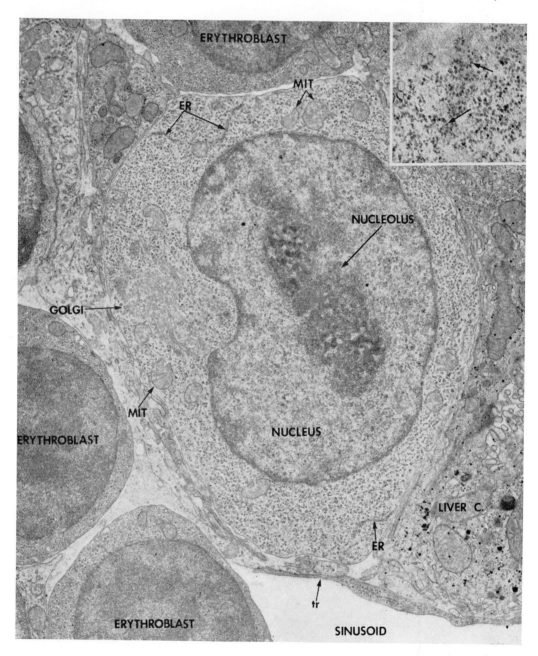

FIG. 7-1. Electron micrograph ($\times$ 28,000) showing blood cell formation in the liver of a 5 day old mouse. The cytoplasm of the central cell contains an abundance of free ribosomes. The inset ($\times$ 50,000) shows free ribosomes to advantage (arrows) and it can be seen that they tend to be arranged in little clusters which, as is described in the text, are known as polysomes. The abundant ribosomes in the cytoplasm of the 3 erythroblasts (which are labeled) are to be explained by their role in the synthesis of the protein hemoglobin, as is explained in the text. The abundant free ribosomes in the cytoplasm of the central large cell may be due in part to this relatively undifferentiated cell synthesizing more protoplasm in preparation for a division and in part by the fact that its progeny are going to differentiate into erythroblasts and synthesize hemoglobin. This cell contains a very few flattened vesicles with attached ribosomes (labeled = ER). (Preparation by A. M. Jézéquel)

part in accounting for cytoplasmic basophilia seen with the light microscope. Recent work, which will be described very shortly, suggests that, using special methods, it is possible, with the EM, to demonstrate messenger RNA in the form of delicate threads in extracts of cytoplasm (Fig. 7-2). It is probable that transfer RNA, which has a molecular weight of only 20,000, is too small to be identified as as entity with the EM. However, neither messenger nor transfer RNA are in the form of large enough bodies, or abundant enough, to contribute to such basophilia of cytoplasm as can be seen with the light microscope.

### Arrangements of Ribosomes in Cytoplasm That Explain Diffuse and Localized Basophilia and Their Significance

The ribosome content of cytoplasm is related to cytoplasmic activity with regard to synthesizing protein. It follows, therefore, that the amount of cytoplasmic basophilia seen in cells with the light microscope is a rough guide to the amount of work that the cell is doing, or is just about to do, in connection with synthesizing protein.

**Free and Attached Ribosomes.** Ribosomes either lie free in the cytoplasm, as is shown in the inset in Figure 7-1, or they may be attached to membranous vesicles, as are most of those shown in Figure 7-7. There can be enough of either free or attached ribosomes in cytoplasm to account for the cytoplasm of a cell being basophilic when it is examined in stained preparations in the light microscope.

Speaking generally, ribosomes that are attached to membranous vesicles are concerned in the synthesis of protein that is destined for secretion, as will be described in detail later. Free ribosomes are concerned with the synthesis of protein that is not destined for secretion but which serves some purpose in the cell in which it is formed.

Protein that is synthesized in cytoplasm and not destined for secretion may be of two general categories (1) the proteins of which cells are made or (2) a protein that is not secreted but which becomes abundant in the cytoplasm to serve some special purpose in special types of cells. First, we shall consider free ribosomes and synthesis of the proteins out of which cells are made.

As has already been described, there is a

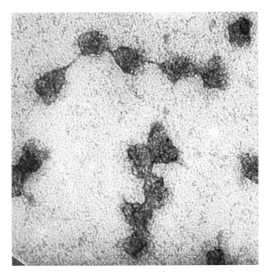

Fig. 7-2. Electron micrograph ($\times$ 400,-000) of reticulocyte polyribosomes stained with uranylacetate. Note the thread of messenger RNA connecting the 5 ribosomes in the upper part of the picture. (Preparation by Henry S. Slater, supplied by Dr. Alexander Rich)

continuous turnover of the proteins in interphase cells with catabolism and anabolism proceeding in them in harmony. However, the synthesis of only enough protein to maintain the structure of an interphase cell does not seem to require an abundance of free ribosomes, not enough to make their cytoplasm basophilic in the light microscope. So, when a cell manifests cytoplasmic basophilia that is due to free ribosomes making new protoplasm it suggests that the cell is of a type that is multiplying fairly often and hence must be constantly synthesizing protoplasm so that there will be enough protoplasm to provide for the two daughter cells that result from each division. Hence, cells that are multiplying, such as many of the cells of embryos, or cells engaged in repair, or cells of malignant tumors (cancer), may contain enough free ribosomes in their cytoplasm for their cytoplasm to appear basophilic in the light microscope.

Cytoplasmic basophilia due to free ribosomes is also seen in certain cells that are synthesizing a good deal of protein that is neither essential for the life of the cell that contains it nor protein destined for secretion but which, instead, is a special protein product that lies free in the cytoplasm to serve some special function. This phenomenon, which will be considered in more detail in Chapter 16, occurs in connection with the cells that become red blood cells. Red blood cells are literally stuffed with the protein hemoglobin which readily takes up and releases oxygen, and for this reason the red blood cells serve as carriers of oxygen to all parts of the body. In order to synthesize this protein, the precursor cells which differentiate into red blood cells, and which are generally called erythroblasts, possess large numbers of free ribosomes in their cytoplasm during the time when the hemoglobin is being synthesized. Parts of 3 erythroblasts are shown in Figure 7-1, and it is seen that their cytoplasm is heavily sprinkled with free ribosomes. As is shown in the color plate (Fig. 16-5, basophilic erythroblast), the free ribosomes in basophilic erythroblasts account for their cytoplasm being basophilic in stained preparations seen in the light microscope.

Although free ribosomes, as will be described under Polysomes, are grouped in clusters (Fig. 7-1, *inset*), the clusters are distributed fairly evenly throughout cytoplasm (except in the Golgi area as will be described later). Hence, such basophilia as is imparted to cells by free ribosomes is generally diffuse. So, as a general rule, diffusely basophilic cytoplasm seen in suitably stained preparations in the light microscope indicates a relative abundance of free ribosomes in that cytoplasm.

**Localized Basophilia.** As will be explained when the next organelle (the endoplasmic reticulum) is described a little later in this chapter, there are membranous vesicles in the cytoplasm to which ribosomes become attached (Fig. 7-7). This arrangement permits protein that is destined for secretion to be segregated from the cytoplasm by its being kept within these membranous vesicles until it is secreted. By this means proteins, whose enzymatic activity might destroy cytoplasm, can be synthesized in cells and yet prevented from mixing with the cytoplasm. The membranous vesicles, studded with ribosomes, and in which protein destined for secretion is synthesized, are generally localized to some part of a cell or distributed in little groups here and there throughout the cell. Cyto-

plasmic basophilia that is accounted for by membrane-attached ribosomes is therefore generally localized as in the acinar cells of the pancreas (shown in Fig. 7-6) or it has a spotty distribution throughout a cell, as it has in nerve cells, shown in Figure 21-17. In a few instances, as we shall learn in connection with plasma cells, almost all the cytoplasm can be filled with membranous vesicles with attached ribosomes, and the cytoplasm under these conditions may appear both deeply and diffusely basophilic. Accordingly, the final analysis as to whether diffuse basophilia is due to free or membrane-attached ribosomes in some cells can be made only with the EM.

**Polysomes.** Warner, Rich and Hall used special and delicate methods for extracting free ribosomes from reticulocytes, which cells, as we shall see when we discuss blood cells, have free ribosomes that are concerned with the synthesis of hemoglobin, and found that the ribosomes that they extracted were arranged in little aggregates rather than as single units. They term these aggregates polyribosomes or polysomes. The most common number to aggregate together in reticulocytes was 5 (Fig. 7-2); however, it has been shown that aggregates of greater numbers of ribosomes are associated with the synthesis of protein molecules larger than hemoglobin. By making special preparations for study with the EM, Warner, Rich and Hall sometimes observed ribosomes disposed along the course of little threads, which they suggest could be threads of messenger RNA (Fig. 7-2). There is, therefore, reason to believe that for the synthesis of hemoglobin, units of 5 ribosomes may be distributed in such a way as to provide proper sites for the code on threads of messenger RNA to be read and acted upon.

## 2. THE MEMBRANOUS ORGANELLES OF THE CYTOPLASM

There are 5 membranous structures in cells that each deserve special consideration: A, the cell or plasma membrane; B, the endoplasmic reticulum; C, the Golgi apparatus; D, mitochondria; and E, lysosomes. We shall first describe the cell membrane.

### A. *The Cell Membrane*

Many physiologic studies in the past established that the contents of a cell are separated

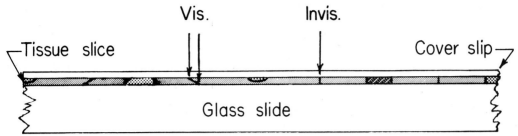

Vis.             Invis.

Tissue slice                                  Cover slip

Glass slide

FIG. 7-3. Diagram to show why a stained cell membrane which is too thin for its cross section to be resolved (invis.) can be seen in a section if it passes through the section at an angle other than a right angle, for then its stained side is seen over a large enough area for it to be visible (vis.).

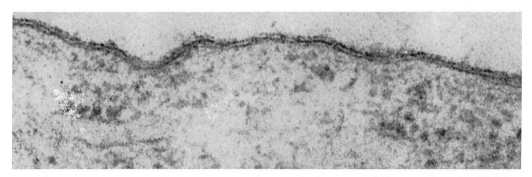

FIG. 7-4. Electron micrograph (× 160,000) of section of mouse kidney embedded in Epon and stained with lead hydroxide and showing the 3 layers of the cell membrane that extends from one side of the illustration to the other. Outer and inner layers of the cell membrane are dark, and the middle layer is light. (Preparation by A. F. Howatson and J. D. Almeida)

from its fluid environment by a membrane that discriminates with regard to what shall pass through it. Microdissection studies also have indicated the existence of a membrane, because substantial tears made through the surface of suitably large cells result in some of the contents of the cell running out through the wound. It might be thought that direct proof of the existence of a membrane around cells could be provided with the light microscope and that indirect proof for its existence was not required. But the cell membrane is too thin for a cross section of it to be resolved with the light microscope, even if it could be specifically stained. However, in the ordinary and relatively thick sections used for light microscopy, cell membranes, since they enclose rounded objects, are almost always cut at angles other than right angles (Fig. 7-3, *left*) and since a section is relatively thick, a cell membrane, in passing from the top to the bottom of a section, pursues a curving path and occupies a wide enough expanse of the section to be seen as is shown in Figure 7-3 (vis.). But where it passes through a section at right angles to the surface, as shown in Figure 7-3, *right*, it would not occupy enough space to be visible (Fig. 7-3, invis.). However, although this explanation probably accounts for it being possible to see stained cell membranes with the light microscope, it is also very probably that shrinkage artefact, condensations of stains and diffraction phenomena assist in indicating the borders seen between cells in the usual sections studied with the light microscope.

Physiologic experiments not only provided indirect evidence for the existence of cell membranes, they also established that the relative solubility of materials in lipids is an important factor with regard to their passage through membranes. Hence lipid has entered largely into the structure of models of cell membranes that have been suggested over the years, and it is now generally agreed that cell membranes are lipid-protein complexes.

**Fine Structure.** With the EM the cell membrane can now be shown to have 3 layers (Fig. 7-4). However, in the usual electron micrograph the cell membrane is seen as a single dark line 6 to 7 millimicrons thick (Fig. 7-26). There are probably two reasons that explain why in the past it usually appeared as a single line. First, osmium, which was so commonly used for fixation, could be expected to have an affinity for both the protein and the lipoid components of the membrane, and hence different layers, containing different percentages of the two, could be expected to have similar electron densities. Secondly, in the past, most material for electron microscopy was embedded in methacrylate, and since this tends to sublime in the electron beam, it does not effectively hold layers of finely layered structures apart, and so layers that are close together can come together and hence not be individually distinguished. With certain other fixatives that came into use, for example, $KMnO_4$, and by using some of the newer embedding materials, it has been possible to resolve the cell membrane in sections to much better advantage than in the past, and when this is done it reveals 3 layers, 2 dark ones, each around 25 Å in thickness, separated by a light layer of about the same thickness (Fig. 7-4). The evidence suggests that the two dark layers are chiefly protein, while the light middle layer has a high content of lipid.

The fine structure of the cell membrane will be considered further in connection with the formation of the myelin sheaths of nerve fibers in Chapter 21 (see Fig. 21-46). Special arrangements of the cell membrane such as those that increase the absorptive area of free surfaces will be considered more thoroughly in the next chapter.

**Derivatives of the Cell Membrane: Pinocytotic Vesicles.** Little membranous vesicles that are derived from the cell membrane are sometimes seen close to it in the cytoplasm (Fig. 22-10). Furthermore, little invaginations of the cell membrane, which look as if they might become pinched off to become such smooth-surfaced vesicles, also are often seen. It seems probable that the smooth-surfaced vesicles in this location are formed in this way, and that one function they perform is pinocytosis.

Pinocytosis has been mentioned already,

and there is much evidence indicating that one method by which a cell can take up fluid is by the formation of fluid-filled vesicles at the cell surface. Such vesicles may pass across the cell to the other surface where the fluid is released. It seems also that the mechanism may operate in another way in that adsorption of certain substances may occur on a segment of the cell membrane, with this segment of the cell membrane then becoming infolded and pinched off to become an intracytoplasmic vesicle. The bounding membrane of the vesicle then may disappear, thus delivering the material to some appropriate region in the cytoplasm.

Vesicles also form from the cell membrane to enclose phagocytosed materials; these will be discussed along with lysosomes in this chapter and in connection with macrophages in a subsequent chapter.

It can be demonstrated with the light microscope, particularly by using the PAS technic, that the membranes of at least some kinds of cells are coated with a layer of carbohydrate-containing material. With the EM this layer can be distinguished in many kinds of cells.

Robertson, who has made many important contributions to the study of the cell membrane and the membranes of the membranous organelles of the cytoplasm (soon to be described) has found a 3-layered structure making up not only the cell membrane described above, but also the membranes of the endoplasmic reticulum, the Golgi apparatus and mitochondria. There has been much discussion about the membranes of these various organelles having a common origin and of their being variously connected with, or related to, one another. It is of interest that Sjöstrand had recently pointed out that the thickness of the membranes in different organelles differs to some extent; for example, he finds that mitochondrial membranes have a thickness of about 50 Å and the membranes of the Golgi apparatus and other smooth-surfaced vesicles in the cytoplasm have a thickness of around 60 Å. Both, therefore, are thinner than the cell membrane.

There is as yet little knowledge about the formation of the membrane of the cell or the membranes of the various membranous organelles.

FIG. 7-5. Diagram-
matic drawings illus-
trating in 3 dimen-
sions various forms
assumed by cytoplas-
mic membranous vesi-
cles. The cut surface
of each vesicle shows
how it would appear
in a section.

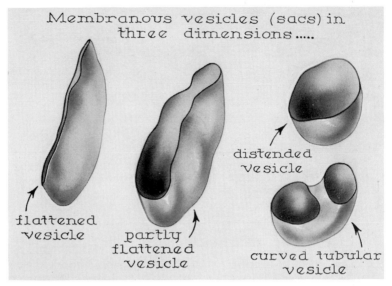

Membranous vesicles (sacs) in three dimensions.....

distended vesicle

flattened vesicle

partly flattened vesicle

curved tubular vesicle

## B. The Endoplasmic Reticulum

Before it became possible to cut sections thinly enough for effective study with the EM, Porter, Claude and Fullam, in 1945, took advantage of the fact that the cytoplasm of cells growing in tissue culture will spread out very thinly, so thinly that after being fixed and mounted, some detail can be seen in it with the EM. In such preparations they observed that cytoplasm contained a lacelike network of what appeared to be, in this type of preparation, strands and vesicles. They named this the *endoplasmic reticulum* (the cytoplasm of the peripheral parts of cells is sometimes termed ectoplasm and that of the more central parts of cells, the endoplasm. Since the network—the reticulum—seen in the preparations described above was not seen to extend into the peripheral cytoplasm—the ectoplasm—it was designated as endoplasmic. When good thin-sectioning methods became available, it was found that what they had described as endoplasmic reticulum consisted of a system of interconnected membrane-lined spaces and that the membrane of which these intracytoplasmic structures was composed was similar to the cell membrane. Although the study of thin sections revealed that the endoplasmic reticulum was not always confined to the endoplasm but could extend to the periphery of the cytoplasm into the so-called ectoplasm as well, the term "endoplasmic reticulum" is still widely used for this system of intracytoplasmic membrane-lined spaces. The vesicular and the tubular components of the endoplasmic reticulum should be visualized in 3 dimensions (see Fig. 7-5). The vesicular components of the system are often termed *cisternae*.

There are two main divisions of the endoplasmic reticulum and in at least one instance they have been shown to connect with each other. The first kind is called the granular or rough-surfaced type of endoplasmic reticulum because the interconnecting membranous vesicles (cisternae) and tubules of which it is composed are studded on their outer surface with ribosomes. The second kind of endoplasmic reticulum consists of membranous tubules and vesicles that are free of ribosomes, so this type is called the agranular or the smooth-surfaced type of endoplasmic reticulum. We shall now consider these two types in turn.

**The Rough-surfaced Type of Endoplasmic Reticulum.** In a previous section, it was pointed out that the basophilia that is imparted to cytoplasm by ribosomes can be either diffuse, as it generally is in rapidly multiplying cells, or localized to some part of the cell, and that the latter state of affairs often exists if the protein that is being synthesized is to be delivered from the cell as a secretion. In such sites the ribosomes are mostly attached to the outer surfaces of membranous vesicles (Fig. 7-7). It was briefly noted also that protein that is synthesized

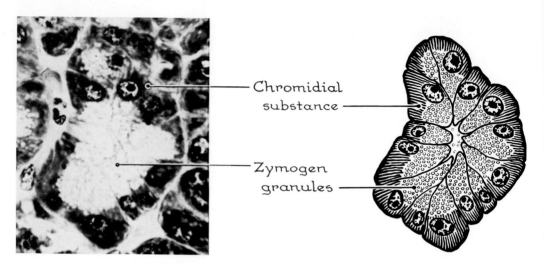

Fig. 7-6. (*Left*) H and E section of dog's pancreas. Note that the cytoplasm in the basal part of the cells stains deeply with hematoxylin similarly to the chromatin of the nucleus. The basophilic material in the cytoplasm was therefore called *chromidial substance*. It was also termed ergastoplasm and now is known to be RNA. (*Right*) A diagram to provide orientation.

within the cell in association with ribosomes that are studded along membranous vesicles, making them rough surfaced, and destined for secretion, can be, for example, the precursor of a potent digestive enzyme. Therefore, if the synthesized protein were permitted to mix freely with the cytoplasm, it might institute chemical reactions which would destroy the cytoplasm. Accordingly, protein destined for secretion is kept segregated in membranous structures as it is synthesized at the sites of ribosomes that stud the surface of the membrane. The membrane component of the rough-surfaced vesicles functions by segregating protein from the cytoplasm as it is synthesized at the ribosomes. Since the vesicles are interconnecting, they also provide a route by which secretion is channeled toward the Golgi apparatus from which it will pass to the cell surface.

**Light Microscope Appearance of Sites of Rough-surfaced Vesicles.** The secretory cells of the pancreas provide a good example of aggregations of rough-surfaced vesicles being concentrated in a part of a cell. The basophilia imparted to such regions chiefly by membrane-attached ribosomes can be seen with the light microscope. The appearance seen in such a cell with the light microscope will now be described.

The pancreas will be described in detail in later chapters; at this time, it is only necessary for the student to learn enough of its microscopic structure to study intelligently the cells of the pancreas that synthesize protein that is destined for secretion; this consists of enzymes important in the digestion of food. These enzymes are delivered into the intestine by means of a duct. The cells that synthesize the protein enzymes are arranged in little clusters in the gland; each cluster is called an *acinus* because it resembles a grape. In a section cut through an acinus the cells are seen to be arranged so as to encircle a tiny central lumen (Fig. 7-6, *right*), and they deliver their secretion into this central lumen which drains into the duct system. A cross section cut through an acinus resembled a pie that has been cut into pieces but has not yet been served (Fig. 7-6, *right*). The individual cells of the acinus appear as individual pieces of pie. Each has a broad base and a narrow apex. The secretion is delivered through the apex of each cell, as is indicated on the right side of Figure 7-6, into the central lumen of the acinus (see also Fig. 25-3).

Each cell in an acinus manufactures a protein (enzyme-containing) secretion. The final product that is to be secreted is seen in the form of rounded bodies termed *zymogen gran-*

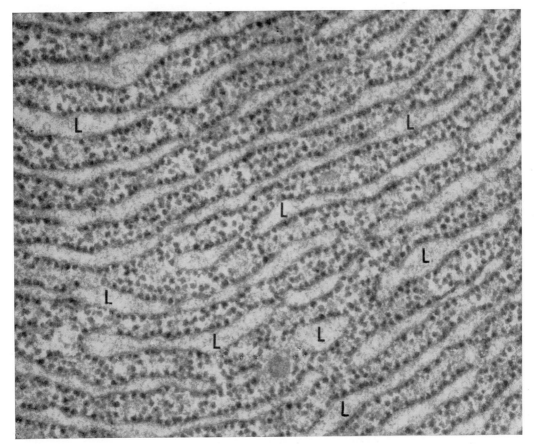

Fig. 7-7. Electron micrograph ($\times$ 66,000) showing rough-surfaced vesicles of endoplasmic reticulum in the basal part of an acinar cell of the rat pancreas. The lumen of several vesicles is marked with an L; the lumens contain recently synthesized protein that is destined for secretion. The outer surfaces of the vesicles are studded with dark granules; these are ribosomes. There are also some free ribosomes between adjacent vesicles. (Preparation by George E. Palade)

*ules* (Figs. 7-6, *right*, and 7-18) which are seen to best advantage toward the apices of the cells.

With the light microscope the cytoplasm close to the base of each cell of an acinus is seen to be dark blue (Fig. 7-6, *left*). This is due to a very substantial amount of cytoplasmic RNA that is concentrated in the basal part of each cell. It was basophilic material in this type of secretory cell that was given the name *ergastoplasm* by Garnier, many years ago.

With the EM, the material (ergastoplasm, cytoplasmic RNA) contained in these heavily stained basal parts of the secretory cells of the pancreas is seen to consist of ribosomes that are attached to, and free between, almost

countless flattened and semiflattened membranous vesicles or cisternae that are often arranged in parallel array (Fig. 7-7). It is the great concentration of ribosomes, both those that are adherent to the vesicles, and those that are free in the cytoplasm between vesicles, that accounts for the basophilia seen with the light microscope in this part of the cytoplasm.

With the light microscope, zymogen granules are not seen in the basal parts of these cells but, instead, toward their apices (Figs. 7-6, *right*, and 7-18). However, the synthesis of the protein that will eventually be secreted in the form of zymogen granules occurs in the basal part of the cell. The secretion in the vesicles (cisternae) of the endoplasmic reticu-

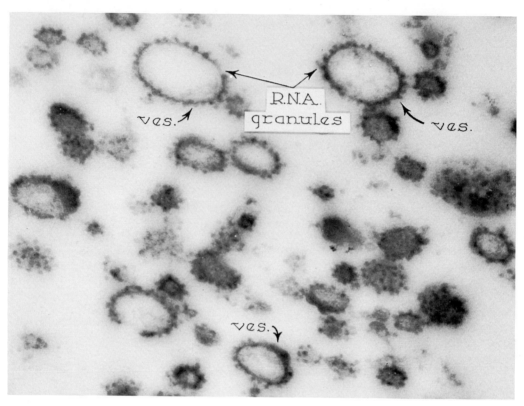

Fig. 7-8, A. Electron micrograph (× 80,000) of a section of a pellet obtained from a microsome fraction obtained by the differential centrifugation of homogenized cells of the pancreas. The illustration shows that the microsome fraction consists chiefly of small vesicles, some of which form from larger vesicles. Most of the vesicles in this fraction have ribosomes (labeled RNA granules in the illustration) attached to their outer surfaces. (Palade, G., and Siekevitz, P.: J. Biophys. Biochem. Cytol. 2:671, labeling added)

lum in this part of the cells of pancreatic acini of most species appears to be of a fluid consistency, and it slightly distends the vesicles that contain it, and hence the lumens of the rough-surfaced vesicles are easy to see (Fig. 7-7, *left*).

The newly synthesized protein material segregated in rough-surfaced vesicles, and destined for secretion will, as is described a few pages farther on, reach and be modified in another membranous organelle, the Golgi apparatus, before it is extruded from the cell.

**Microsomes and Microsome Fractions.** By centrifugation, different fractions can be separated from homogenized cell preparations. One fraction, isolated before EM inspection of fractions was possible, had been termed the *microsome fraction*, and this gave rise in some minds to the erroneous impression that microsomes were a type of cell organelle. When it

became possible to study cell fractions in the EM it was found that the so-called microsome fractions, separated from homogenized cells by centrifugation, were composed chiefly of rough-surfaced membranous vesicles of the cytoplasm (Fig. 7-8, A). The larger vesicles, of course, become broken up into smaller ones as a result of the technics employed, but many smaller ones seem to remain intact. It is of interest that in these fractions the ribosomes tend to remain adherent to the rough-surfaced vesicles throughout the whole procedure (Fig. 7-8, A); this is the reason for microsome fractions containing RNA. Some vesicles in the microsome fraction, of course, are of the smooth-surfaced type. So, the microsome fraction was shown by the EM to consist chiefly of the broken-up rough-surfaced membranous vesicles of the cytoplasm, and no evidence was found to indicate that microsomes

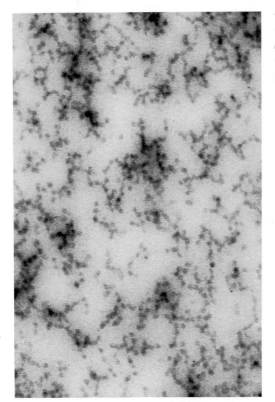

Fig. 7-8, B. Electron micrograph (× 80,-000) of a section of a pellet of a fraction obtained by differential centrifugation from a homogenate of pancreas cells. The micrograph shows this fraction to be a very pure preparation of ribosomes. (Palade, G., and Siekevitz, P.: J. Biophys. Biochem. Cytol. 2:671)

are discrete bodies that exist in cytoplasm as independent structures.

As is shown in Figure 7-8, B, it is now possible to fractionate the microsome fraction into subfractions, which are composed either almost exclusively of ribosomes (see Palade and Siekevitz) or almost exclusively of membranes. It is obvious that at this time anyone who discusses a microsome fraction must define his meaning lest confusion arise.

**The Smooth-surfaced Components of the Endoplasmic Reticulum—Agranular Reticulum.** There are, in only some kinds of cells, large numbers of smooth-surfaced membranous and generally tubular structures, which are part of the endoplasmic reticulum, and distinct from the smooth-surfaced membranous structures of the Golgi apparatus (Fig. 7-9).

The function of these is not definitely known. Those seen in the liver cells after fasting may conceivably be what is left of rough-surfaced vesicles after starvation, for in the liver connections can be seen between smooth- and rough-surfaced components of the endoplasmic reticulum, and it may be that in starvation the ribosomes that formerly studded vesicles are metabolized so that the membranous structures became smooth surfaced. However, since some smooth-surfaced vesicles are also seen in the liver cells of well-fed animals, it is possible, as Porter has suggested, that they may play a role in the conversion of glucose to glycogen and its storage in cells.

Smooth-surfaced components of the endoplasmic reticulum are very prominent in the interstitial cells of the testis (Fig. 30-11); these cells produce a steroid hormone as will be described in a later chapter, and the agranular reticulum of these cells may be concerned with the production or elaboration of this hormone.

Smooth-surfaced tubules of endoplasmic reticulum are seen in skeletal muscle where they probably play a very important role in conducting impulses into the substance of the muscle cells (Fig. 20-15). Thus agranular reticulum is found in cells with very different natures and functions.

## THE GOLGI APPARATUS

**Historical Introduction.** In 1898, Camillo Golgi, of whom we shall learn more when nervous tissue is considered, noticed in some brain tissue that had been fixed in a bichromate solution and then impregnated with a silver salt, that the nerve cells showed little dark networks in their cytoplasm (see Fig. 21-20). He named this dark network the *internal reticular apparatus* of the cell. Later it became customary to term it the *Golgi apparatus* in honor of its discoverer. However, for some time some investigators hesitated to designate it as an apparatus and referred to the *Golgi complex* or *Golgi region* of the cell. Soon after it was noticed in nerve cells, Golgi and others showed that a similar structure could be demonstrated in many kinds of cells by the same technic (chrome-silver impregnation). In 1902, Kopsch showed that the same type of structure could be demonstrated in the cells of tissue that had been subjected to

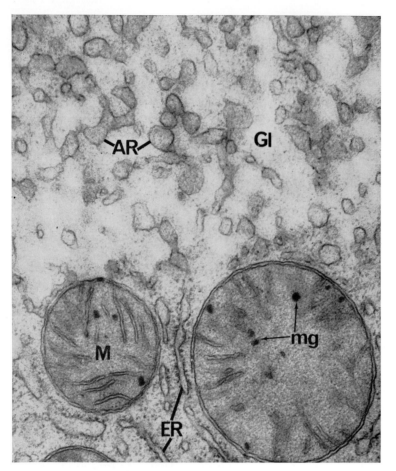

Fig. 7-9. Electron micrograph of liver cell of normal mouse showing smooth-surfaced (agranular) endoplasmic reticulum (AR) and glycogen (Gl) between the tubules and the vesicles of agranular reticulum, and mitochondria (M) and mitochondrial granules (mg). (Trump, B. F.: Lab. Invest. *11*:986)

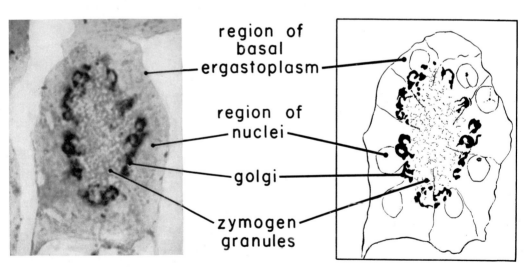

FIG. 7-10. (*Left*) A pancreatic acinus stained to demonstrate the Golgi apparatus in the acinar cells. (*Right*) A diagram for orientation. Note that the Golgi apparatus is between the nuclei and the aggregations of zymogen granules that are toward the apical parts of the cells. (Preparation of C. P. Leblond and H. Warshawsky)

prolonged immersion in 2 per cent osmium tetroxide.

By using both types of technics described above, it was shown that in different kinds of cells the Golgi apparatus assumed somewhat different forms. In nerve cells it seemed to consist of tortuous strands that tended to encircle the nucleus (Fig. 21-20). In certain other types of cells it was found to assume a spherical shape, in others a conical shape and in still others a cylindrical shape. Perhaps of more importance than its shape was the position it was found to occupy in cells, for in secretory cells it was always found between the nucleus and the surface through which the cell elaborated its secretion as is shown in Figure 7-10 which illustrates a pancreatic acinus, a structure with which the student is now familiar from the preceding section and Figure 7-6. When it became possible to study thin sections with the EM, it became possible to demonstrate that it had 3 main components; these will soon be described.

**Early Views on Function.** Through the years when the study of the Golgi apparatus was limited to ordinary light microscopy and sections stained by various technics, there was much speculation about its function. The most common belief that emerged was that the Golgi apparatus played some role in the process of secretion. In view of what has been shown recently by radioautography and electron microscopy (soon to be described), it is of interest that Bowen in the twenties and Hirsch in the thirties, and others, concluded that the Golgi apparatus functioned as a site of aggregation and condensation of secretory products that were formed elsewhere in the cell.

**Negative Golgi Images.** The student may think, because special and more or less empirical technics are required to demonstrate the Golgi apparatus in sections, that there would be no sign of this organelle in sections or spreads of cells stained by ordinary methods. However, it is often possible in ordinary sections stained with H and E (Fig. 7-11) or in cell spreads stained with ordinary blood stains (Fig. 11-10), to detect a clear area in the cytoplasm at the site of the Golgi apparatus. These clear areas seen in ordinary preparations are termed *negative Golgi images.* They are prominent in certain cells that are

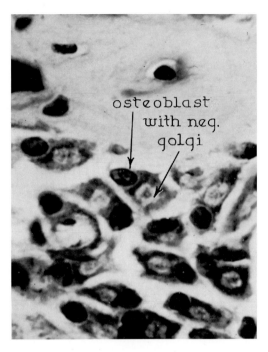

Fig. 7-11. Medium-power photomicrograph of a section of decalcified bone stained with azure-eosin-hematoxylin. It shows osteoblasts beginning to lay down bone near the site of a fracture. The osteoblasts show pale areas (negative Golgis) in their basophilic cytoplasm.

elaborating secretions. For example, they are clearly obvious in the cells shown in Figure 7-11; the cells illustrated here are osteoblasts that are synthesizing and elaborating materials that will become the organic intercellular substance of bone. Negative Golgi images are characteristic of plasma cells—the cells that synthesize, and elaborate into body fluids, the protein antibodies that combine with foreign invaders, such as viruses, as is shown in Figure 11-10. However, it should not be assumed that what is termed the negative Golgi image, and which is seen in some cells in ordinary sections, is in effect a true negative image of the components that we now know to comprise the Golgi apparatus. The negative Golgi image is more in the nature of an unstained area of cytoplasm which surrounds and contains the Golgi apparatus, as well as the centrioles (Fig. 11-11). The reasons for this region being pale, in contrast to darker cytoplasm about it, are that as well as containing the components of the Golgi apparatus (which themselves stain

Distended   peripheral   portions of vesicles which
become   secretory  vesicles

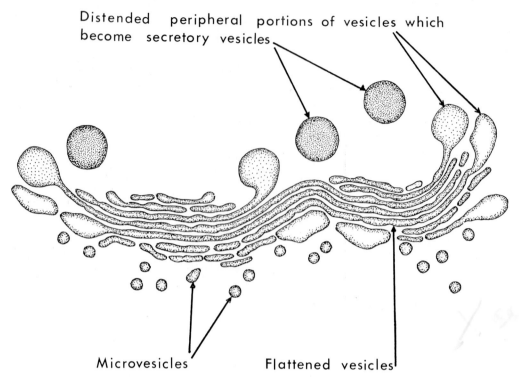

Microvesicles                          Flattened vesicles

FIG. 7-12. Diagram showing the 3 components of the Golgi apparatus, microvesicles, flattened vesicles and secretory vesicles.

poorly in ordinary preparations) the cytoplasm that immediately surrounds the components of the Golgi apparatus is deficient in cytoplasmic RNA. The cytoplasm that in turn surrounds this pale area often does contain RNA and hence is basophilic, and there is therefore a contrast between the area of cytoplasm that contains the Golgi apparatus and the surrounding cytoplasm in cells that are actively synthesizing protein.

## THE FINE STRUCTURE OF THE GOLGI APPARATUS

**Terminology.** The EM has revealed 3 components in the Golgi apparatus; all of the nature of membranous vesicles (Fig. 7-12). The term *saccule* is often used for some of these membranous structures, but we think, as has already been pointed out, that *vesicle* is preferable, first, because vesicle is used so commonly in anatomy and in clinical medicine to refer to a distensible cavity that is enclosed by a wall, and secondly, because the end of a sac or bag can be either *open* or *closed*, and

hence the use of the term saccule (small sac or bag) requires qualification if it is to be precise. The three components of the Golgi apparatus will now be described.

1. **Flattened Vesicles.** The most prominent vesicles in the Golgi apparatus are flattened so that each is wide and thin (Figs. 7-12 and 7-13). They are commonly stacked one upon the other, much like a stack of hot cakes. In a longitudinal section cut through a stack of them it might at first be thought that one was looking at longitudinal sections of tubules, but this possibility is ruled out, first, by the fact that it would be most improbable for so many tubules to lie parallel with, and in, a thin section; and secondly, the same type of appearance is seen in sections cut in different planes. Along most of their lengths the two walls of each flattened vesicle are separated from each other only slightly by the contents of the vesicle. As is shown in Figures 7-12 and 7-14, the portions of flattened vesicles near their periphery may become distended by their contents and then bud off from the flattened vesicles of which they were formerly a part.

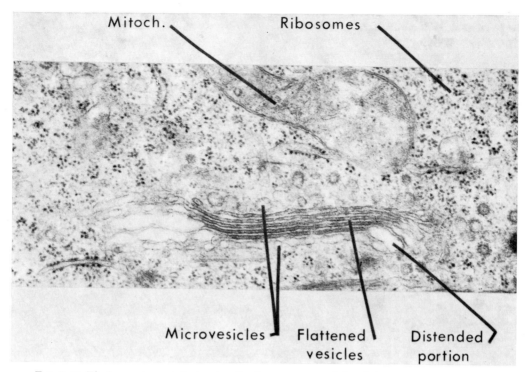

Mitoch.    Ribosomes

Microvesicles    Flattened    Distended
vesicles    portion

FIG. 7-13. Electron micrograph showing the 3 components of the Golgi apparatus in section of intestinal epithelial cell. (Preparation by J. McNabb)

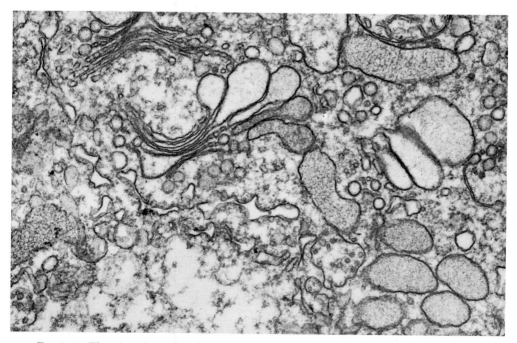

FIG. 7-14. Electron micrograph ($\times$ 34,000) of section of an outer root cap of the primary root of *Zea mays* L., showing Golgi apparatus producing secretory vesicles. Fixation in osmium tetroxide and embedding in a mixture of Epon and Araldite epoxy resins. (Preparation by H. H. Mollenhauer)

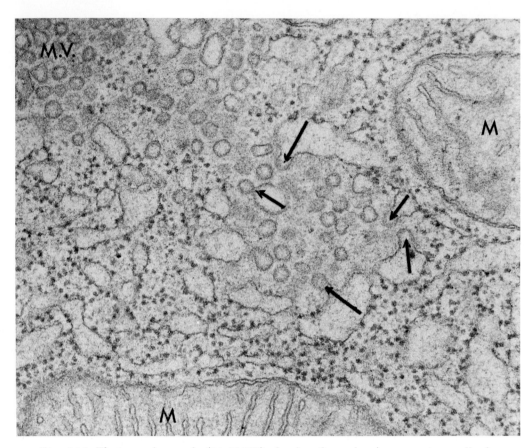

Fig. 7-15. Electron micrograph (× 70,000) showing the region in a secretory cell where rough-surfaced vesicles of endoplasmic reticulum abut on the periphery of the Golgi apparatus. Microvesicles of the Golgi apparatus are prominent in the center of the picture and also at the upper left corner where they are labeled M.V. In several sites, some of which are indicated by arrows, smooth-surfaced microvesicles are fused with, or perhaps are originating from, rough-surfaced vesicles of endoplasmic reticulum. It is because of these microvesicles becoming filled with secretion from rough-surfaced vesicles that protein secretion can be transported from rough-surfaced endoplasmic reticulum to the Golgi apparatus. (Palade, G. F.: Proc. Nat. Acad. Sci. *52*:613)

The distended portions that bud off from the edges of flattened vesicles constitute the second component of the Golgi apparatus, and we shall term them *secretory vesicles*.

**2. Secretory Vesicles.** The ovoid-to-round distended vesicles that bud off from flattened vesicles were first termed vacuoles. However, since it is established that each is surrounded with a membranous wall and hence that they are not merely holes in the cytoplasm, it seems better to term them vesicles, and since it can be shown that in some kinds of cell their contents represent materials that will be elaborated from a cell surface as a secretion, it seems permissible at least provisionally to

term them secretory vesicles, thus qualifying their anatomic structure by an adjective relating to their function.

The fluid content of secretory vesicles that begin to swell and take form at the edge of a flattened vesicle does not at first show up to advantage with the EM. But as the secretory vesicles mature and become separated from their parent flattened vesicles—and maturation probably involves a concentration of their contents—their contents become increasingly electron dense (Fig. 7-12). It is now known from radioautographic studies, to be described presently, that protein material destined for secretion is synthesized in the rough-surfaced vesicles of the endoplasmic reticulum (in the more basal parts of the acinar cells of the pancreas) and that later the secretory vesicles of the Golgi apparatus come to contain this secretion. Furthermore, it has been shown that in these secretory vesicles of the Golgi apparatus the secretion, which was formerly a sol, becomes more or less gelled into a semisolid body known as a zymogen granule. Hence, in the acinar cells of the pancreas, it is in the secretory vesicles of the Golgi apparatus that a secretion, produced in another part of the cell, is consolidated into semisolid zymogen granules that will be carried to a cell surface, each still surrounded by a membrane, and then discharged from that cell surface.

We must next inquire into how a protein secretion that is synthesized in rough-surfaced vesicles in another part of the cell reaches the flattened vesicles of the Golgi apparatus and that leads us to consider the third component of the Golgi apparatus, the *microvesicles.*

3. **Microvesicles.** As their name implies the microvesicles are small, having a diameter of around 40 millimicrons (Figs. 7-12, 7-13, 7-14 and 7-15). Their membranous walls, like the other vesicles of the Golgi apparatus, are smooth; no ribosomes are attached to them. Their content is not very electron dense. In some cells microvesicles were found to be sufficiently numerous in the region between the rough-surfaced vesicles of the endoplasmic reticulum and the flattened vesicles of the Golgi apparatus, as they are in Figure 7-15, to suggest that the microvesicles serve as carriers of protein material from rough-surfaced vesicles of the endoplasmic reticulum to the larger vesicles of the Golgi apparatus; and indeed, that they serve this function now seems to be definitely established.

Caro and Palade have shown by autoradiographic studies that protein material, labeled as it is synthesized in rough-surfaced vesicles of the endoplasmic reticulum, makes its appearance in the microvesicles of the Golgi apparatus before it appears in other parts of the apparatus. This finding strongly supports the concept that the microvesicles provide a shuttle service to convey secretion from the rough-surfaced vesicles of the endoplasmic reticulum to the larger vesicles of the Golgi apparatus. However, a question, as yet unsettled, arises as to where the microvesicles are formed.

The appearances seen in Figure 7-15, where smooth-surfaced microvesicles seem to be budding off from vesicles of endoplasmic reticulum, which over the rest of their surfaces are covered with ribosomes could be interpreted in either of two ways: (1) that microvesicles from the Golgi apparatus move to, and fuse with, adjacent rough-surfaced vesicles where they become filled with the protein secretion contained by the rough-surfaced vesicles, and then after they are filled they become detached from the rough-surfaced vesicles and move toward and fuse with the larger vesicles of the Golgi apparatus, into which they deliver their cargoes of secretion, or (2) that microvesicles of the Golgi apparatus have their origin from rough-surfaced vesicles of endoplasmic reticulum: if so, this would require that portions of the membrane of a rough-surfaced vesicle would become granule-free and that these portions would bulge outwardly so as to present appearances indicated by the arrows in Figure 7-15. The explanation of this appearance which is given under (1) would require that microvesicles shuttle back and forth between the larger vesicles of the Golgi apparatus and vesicles of rough-surfaced endoplasmic reticulum while the explanation given under (2) would require the constant formation of new microvesicles and their movement in only one direction in the shuttle service they provide.

### *How the Process of Secretion Has Been Clarified by Electron Microscopy and Radioautography*

By utilizing the technics of radioautography and electron microscopy it has become possible to gain much new and precise knowledge about the formation and the elaboration of secretions by cells and about the parts that different cell organelles play in the process.

Although, as will be pointed out in various following chapters, there are many different kinds of secretions formed by various cells of the body, we shall limit our description and discussion in this chapter to a consideration of two fundamental types of secretion—the two main types of secretions that are delivered into the lumen of the small intestine.

The first kind of secretion consists of enzymes which act to bring about the digestion of food in the intestine. As already noted, en-

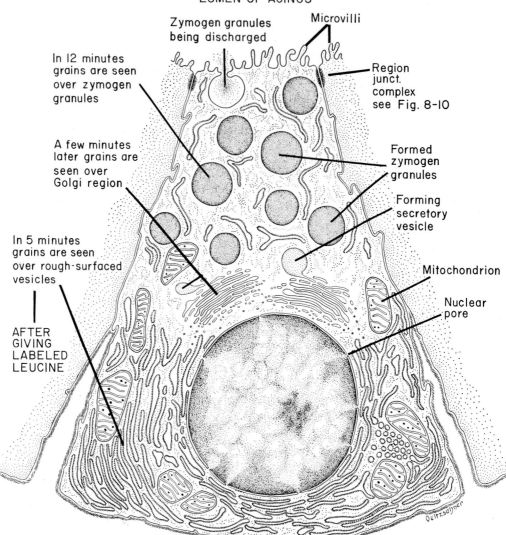

LUMEN OF ACINUS

Zymogen granules being discharged

Microvilli

In 12 minutes grains are seen over zymogen granules

Region junct. complex see Fig. 8-10

A few minutes later grains are seen over Golgi region

Formed zymogen granules

Forming secretory vesicle

In 5 minutes grains are seen over rough-surfaced vesicles

Mitochondrion

Nuclear pore

AFTER GIVING LABELED LEUCINE

BASE OF ACINAR CELL OF PANCREAS

FIG. 7-16. Diagram of acinar cell of pancreas showing sites where grains are seen in radioautographs at different times after giving an animal labeled leucine. (Diagram from C. P. Leblond)

zymes are proteins. Hence the study of the formation and the elaboration of this kind of secretion, which is almost all protein, containing only a little carbohydrate, involves the study of the synthesis of protein within secretory cells and the migration of the synthesized protein to the surface of the cell through which the secretion is elaborated, and finally its transport via a duct to the intestine. It is obvious that the study of this type of secretion

by the radioautographic technic would involve giving animals labeled precursors of proteins, that is, labeled amino acids such as leucine labeled with tritium.

The other main kind of secretion that is elaborated into the intestine is the slippery substance *mucus*, that adheres to, and protects, the surfaces of the cells that are exposed to the digesting contents of the intestine. Mucus is a glycoprotein. Its protein component exerts no enzymatic activity in the intestine. Since glycoproteins have a great carbohydrate content, it is obvious that a study of the synthesis of this type of secretion within cells should provide information about the site where the carbohydrate component of secretions is formed. It follows, moreover, that the way to study the sites of synthesis and the movement of this type of secretion by the radioautographic technic would be to give animals labeled precursors of carbohydrate, for example, glucose labeled with tritium.

**The Study by Radioautography of the Synthesis and Movement of Secretions That Are Primarily Protein.** The secretory units of the pancreas, called *acini*, have already been described and illustrated (Figs. 7-6 and 7-10). Zymogen granules represent the packaged secretory product, and zymogen granules are delivered from the surface of the cell that abuts on the tiny lumen that is roughly in the center of the acinus (Fig. 7-16). We might now ask how fluid secretion, synthesized in rough-surfaced vesicles, becomes zymogen granules, and how much time is required for each of the various steps concerned in the formation and elaboration of secretion, and what part the Golgi apparatus plays in the process, and how radioautography has contributed information on these points.

To investigate these problems, Warshawsky, Leblond and Droz injected labeled leucine into rats and then killed them at various intervals of time afterward and prepared radioautographs from sections of the pancreas. They found grains over the region of rough-surfaced vesicles of the endoplasmic reticulum in the animals that were killed 5 minutes after the labeled leucine was given (Fig. 7-16); this was the only place grains were seen over acinar cells at this short time. This finding showed that the precursor leucine had become incorporated into a product in this site in as short a time as 5 minutes.

In radioautographs prepared from the pancreas of animals killed more than 5 minutes after the labeled leucine was injected, grains were found over the general area of the Golgi apparatus (Fig. 7-16) as well as over the rough-surfaced vesicles of the endoplasmic reticulum. The grains over the Golgi region seen at this time could be explained either (1) by protein synthesis occurring in this

region but more slowly than protein synthesis occurs in the rough-surfaced vesicles toward the bases of the cells, or (2) by protein that was synthesized and labeled in the more basal part of the cell migrating to the Golgi region. Warshawsky, Leblond and Droz have presented evidence which indicates that when labeled amino acids are used as precursors, the appearance of label over the Golgi region is due to protein synthesized and labeled in the more basal part of the cell migrating to the Golgi region. Studies by Caro and Palade and by van Heyningen also provide evidence for this conclusion. The migration of the protein is rapid, for it takes only a few minutes after label is seen over the rough-surfaced vesicles where the protein is synthesized before label is seen over the Golgi region.

As has already been described in connection with the microvesicles of the Golgi apparatus, it now seems clear that they provide a shuttle service to convey secretion that is synthesized in rough-surfaced vesicles of endoplasmic reticulum to the larger vesicles of the Golgi apparatus. The sequence of events here would most probably seem to be that microvesicles, filled with secretion, fuse with and empty their contents into flattened vesicles of the Golgi apparatus. Once the protein secretion has been delivered into a flattened vesicle, it soon begins to accumulate at some point around the edge of the vesicle, and this peripheral part of the vesicle then begins to dilate into an ovoid body which soon becomes detached from the vesicle to constitute a secretory vesicle (Fig. 7-16). At first the contents of these expanded portions of vesicles are not very electron dense, but immediately before or after they are detached they very quickly become dense (this suggests that concentration of the secretion occurs here) and when this happens, the detached vesicle, filled with secretion, has the typical appearance of a zymogen granule (Fig. 7-16). It takes only 12 minutes from the time when label is first seen over the Golgi region for label to be seen in typical zymogen granules, so the processes involved are rapid (Fig. 7-16).

**The Study by Radioautography of the Formation of Carbohydrate Components of Secretion.** The next problem to consider is what happens in the Golgi apparatus which results in a fluid secretion that is brought to it being

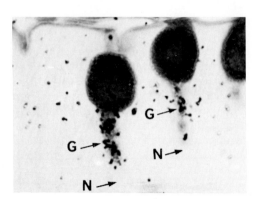

FIG. 7-17. Radioautograph of duodenal epithelium of rat made from tissue removed 5 minutes after the last of 4 systemic injections of glucose labeled with tritium. PAS stain. Illustration shows grains over the Golgi region (labeled G) of the goblet cells. The nuclei of the goblet cells are not stained; their location is indicated by N. (Peterson, Marian, and Leblond, C. P.: J. Cell Biol. *21*:143)

consolidated into a semisolid zymogen granule. In considering this matter it is important to note that although the secretion elaborated by the acinar cells of the pancreas is mostly protein, it contains also a little carbohydrate (2% in one of its enzymes, ribonuclease).

Suggestive information on what may happen in the Golgi apparatus in addition to concentration to make fluid protein secretion into semisolid zymogen granules has come from the study of the secretory process in other kinds of cells. At the beginning of this section we noted that the second type of secretory cell that we would consider in this chapter is the type that makes the glycoprotein mucus. Mucus is produced and secreted by cells of different shapes and form; here we shall consider a particular but common type of mucus-secreting cell that is termed a *goblet cell*.

As will be described in detail later, the small intestine is lined by a single layer of cells that are taller than they are wide and are arranged side by side (Fig. 8-5). Some of these cells are specialized to absorb the products of digestion, others to secrete mucus to protect the naked surfaces of the absorptive cells. The cells that are specialized to secrete mucus commonly have the shape of a goblet (Figs. 8-4, 8-5 and 8-6). This shape is due (1) to the fact that the basal part of the cell,

which contains the nucleus, is narrow and hence appears as the stem of the goblet, and (2) the part of the cell which is disposed between the stem and the free surface swells out, as it were, so that it is much wider than the stem and, then, near the free surface of the cell it narrows down again (Figs. 8-4 and 8-5). The resemblance to a goblet is made even more striking by the fact that the widened part of the cell is seen to be filled with bubble-like globules of mucus (Fig. 8-6). As a result, a goblet cell resembles a goblet which has a thick stem (which contains the nucleus and just above the nucleus the Golgi apparatus), and then above the stem the cell is expanded from within by its content of droplets of mucus so that the cell as a whole looks like a goblet, the bowl of which is filled with a bubbly fluid, which can often be seen to be flowing out through the open end of the goblet (the free surface) onto the surface of adjacent cells.

Clues indicating that the Golgi apparatus might have some function with regard to furnishing the carbohydrate component of secretions came from several sources. For example, the PAS technic (which colors certain carbohydrates magenta) often revealed PAS-positive material in the Golgi region of various types of cells. Badinez *et al.* showed that the Golgi region stains with the colloidal iron technic; this technic detects acid mucopolysaccharides. Revel and Hay, using the EM, showed that the latter reaction for mucopolysaccharides occurred in the content of the distended portions of the flattened vesicles of the Golgi apparatus of cells that produce the intercellular substance of cartilage (which contains much carbohydrate). Peterson and Leblond then showed that when radioactive glucose was injected into the intestine of animals, and radioautographs were prepared from tissues containing goblet cells, grains could be detected over the Golgi region of goblet cells in less than 5 minutes after the radioactive glucose was given (Fig. 7-17). This latter finding indicates that almost immediately after labeled glucose is given it is incorporated into carbohydrate macromolecules in the Golgi region. The labeled material subsequently entered the goblet portion of the goblet cell and later still was eliminated through the free surface of the cell.

**Some Conclusions About the Secretory**

**Process.** The use of labeled amino acids for the study of the protein components of secretion show that the synthesis of the protein components of secretions occurs in the rough-surfaced vesicles of the endoplasmic reticulum and that the protein thus formed migrates to the Golgi region where it is consolidated into zymogen granules. The study of the synthesis of the carbohydrate component of mucus by means of a labeled precursor of carbohydrate macromolecules shows that the precursor is incorporated into carbohydrate macromolecules in the Golgi region, and this indicates that it is in the Golgi region that the carbohydrate macromolecules of secretions are synthesized. Very recently Peterson and Leblond have obtained radioautographic evidence for carbohydrate synthesis occurring in the Golgi region in acinar cells of the pancreas. Accordingly, it would seem from such knowledge as is now available, that the protein component of secretions is synthesized in the rough-surfaced vesicles of the endoplasmic reticulum and the carbohydrate component in the Golgi apparatus. It would seem therefore that the most probable explanation for the fact that secretions that are primarily protein become consolidated into zymogen granules in the Golgi apparatus is that they become concentrated there and also that some carbohydrate macromolecules are added to protein material by the Golgi apparatus and that this somehow stiffens the mix, as it were, so that the granules become semisolid.

**Mechanism of Discharge of Granules.** From his EM studies, Palade has shown that the zymogen granules are segregated from the cytoplasm by smooth-surfaced membranes not only up to, but also *during*, the time that they are secreted. When a granule, enclosed by a membrane, reaches the free surface of the cell, its surrounding membrane becomes continuous with the cell membrane that covers the free surface of the cell. The granule then breaks through the fused membrane and thereby gains entrance to the lumen of the acinus. However, this does not result in a break in the continuity of the cell membrane at the free surface, for the membrane around the deeper part of the granule remains intact, and since it is fused with the cell membrane around the edges of the departing granule, the remaining contents of the cell are always enclosed by a continuous membrane (see Fig. 7-16).

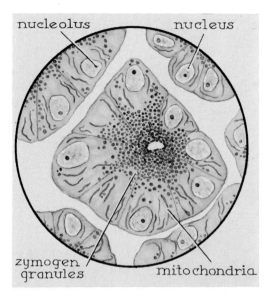

Fig. 7-18. Drawing of a section of the pancreas (high-power). Tissue was fixed in an acetic-osmic-bichromate mixture and stained with aniline acid fuchsin and methyl green. A cross section of an acinus fills most of the field. Mitochondria are present in the outer parts of the cells of the secretory unit, and zymogen granules are numerous in the parts near the lumen of the unit. (Preparation by S. H. Bensley)

## MITOCHONDRIA

*Mitochondria* (*mitos* = thread, *chondrion* = granules) appear with the light microscope as delicate rods, filaments or granules that are present in the cytoplasm of all animal cells (Fig. 7-18). In some cells they are unbelievably numerous; for example, the cytoplasm of a normal liver cell contains at least 1,000 mitochondria (see Fig. 4-12, *right*).

Although mitochondria can be seen with the light microscope, they are not visible in H and E sections. For classroom study, mitochondria can be demonstrated in fresh tissue with darkfield illumination or with the phase microscope, or with the ordinary light microscope by staining them by the supravital technic with Janus green B and certain other stains. They are difficult to fix because pinching or other mishandling of tissue easily results in their breakdown into granules. After fixation with the usual fixatives they are not

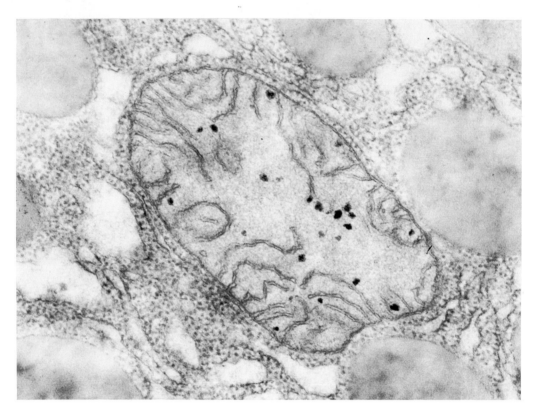

FIG. 7-19. Electron micrograph showing the appearance of a mitochondrion in a section. (Preparation by H. van Heyningen)

readily stained, but after fixation with osmic acid, chromic acid or potassium dichromate, they can be stained in sections. However, only certain stains color them to advantage; iron hematoxylin demonstrates them fairly well, and so does acid fuchsin (Fig. 7-18).

For many decades after the light microscope disclosed their presence in cells, their function remained a mystery. Two developments contributed to elucidating their function: (1) the development of differential centrifugation technics whereby whole cells can be broken down in a homogenizer and their different parts centrifuged from the homogenate, and (2) electron microscopy.

From biochemical studies made on mitochondria isolated by differential centrifugation, it became apparent that they are agents of the greatest importance in cell respiration and hence in providing energy for many of the metabolic processes that occur in cells. Respiration, it will be recalled, is a basic property of protoplasm and is the process whereby *food* and *oxygen* taken into the cells react to pro-

duce energy. In order to explain the function of mitochondria it is necessary to comment further on cell respiration.

**Cell Respiration.** Although respiration is the most important source of energy for life processes, it should be mentioned that oxygen is not always necessary for the life of cells. For example, Pasteur showed that yeast could live and flourish in sugar solutions in the total absence of oxygen. Under such conditions, yeast cells must obtain energy for life and growth from the chemical process whereby sugar is changed to alcohol, a process called *fermentation*. Cells of a human body also obtain energy by this primitive and basic mechanism. In mammalian cells, however, the process is termed *glycolysis*, and the product of the reaction is not alcohol as it is with yeast but, in the absence of oxygen, lactic acid. Although fermentation (glycolysis) occurs in all body cells, the glycolytic mechanism by itself is used to support the life of only very unspecialized embryonic cells and perhaps some cells in postnatal life which have a poor blood supply, for example, cartilage cells. Curiously enough, cancer cells utilize glycolysis as a source of energy more than their normal counterparts. The glycolytic anaerobic mechanism is relatively inefficient for obtaining energy, and as we shall see, most cells have improved on it because in them an oxidative process is superimposed on, and so follows, the glycolytic process. The oxidative process requires that enzymes be segregated by membranes, and this is accomplished in mitochondria.

In most animal cells both glycolysis and oxidation takes place. For example, glucose absorbed by the cell enters into the glycolytic series of reactions, and the product of this then enters into the oxidative set of reactions. The glycolytic reactions take place in the cytoplasm outside *mitochondria*. If glycolysis occurs in the absence of oxygen, glucose is broken down to lactic acid, and a certain amount of energy is made available to the cell from the process. If oxygen is available, however, glycolysis produces not lactic acid but pyruvic acid; this then diffuses into mitochondria where it is subsequently oxidized with the production of much more energy.

**Fine Structure of Mitochondria.** Mitochondria, under the EM are seen to be membranous organelles. They each possess two surrounding membranes, an outer and an inner (Figs. 7-9 and 7-19). Folds of the inner membrane project like shelves into the interior of the mitochondria (Figs. 7-19 and 7-16); these are shown in a 3-dimensional diagram in Figure 7-20 and are termed *cristae mitochondriales*. Obviously, in thin sections, the mitochondria will be cut only infrequently in longitudinal section throughout their whole lengths. Most will be cut in cross and oblique section; hence, deciding on their size, shape and structure from thin sections provides an exercise in 3-dimensional visualization. Typical mitochondria are of cylindrical form, but some may branch, and usually they vary in size in any one cell type. For example, Palade found they varied from 0.35 micron to 0.74 micron in diameter in liver cells. In different cell types the extent of development of the cristae (internal shelves) varies, the cristae being short and extending only about halfway across the mitochondria of liver cells, but in some cell types, the cristae extend completely

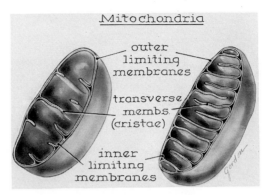

Fig. 7-20. Diagrammatic drawings to illustrate the structure of mitochondria in 3 dimensions.

across the mitochondria. If a section passes longitudinally through a mitochondrion close to the periphery, relatively short cristae may *appear* to extend all the way across the mitochondrion.

The interior of each mitochondrion is filled with a fluid which usually is denser than the surrounding cytoplasm and structureless in appearance. Occasional spherical or ovoid dark granules are sometimes seen in it (Figs. 7-9 and 7-19).

**The Function of Mitochondria in Relation to Their Fine Structure.** As has been noted already, glycolytic processes, catalyzed by enzymes outside the mitochondria, result in pyruvic acid being formed from glucose, with some energy being liberated from the process. The pyruvic acid so formed, plus fat and amino acids that have been broken down to acetic acid, are then fed to the mill of enzymes that comprise what is known as the Kreb's citric acid cycle; this mill is contained in the fluid content of the mitochondria. The function of the Kreb's citric acid cycle is to provide, from substances fed into the mill, suitable breakdown products that can be oxidized. Oxidation depends on oxygen diffusing into mitochondria and then being utilized in reactions catalyzed by another set of enzymes which are housed in mitochondria and termed *respiratory enzymes*. There are two kinds of these respiratory enzymes, flavoproteins and cytochromes; the latter, like hemoglobin, contain iron. The respiratory enzymes are arranged in the inner membranes of mitochondria, and they use certain products of the Kreb's citric acid cycle as substrates. The

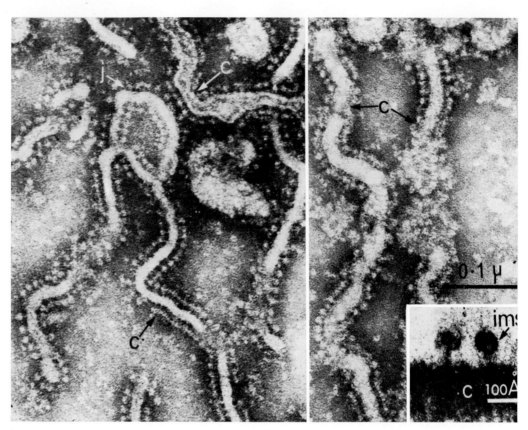

Fig. 7-21. Electron micrographs (× 192,000) of negatively stained preparations showing mitochondrial cristae. Cristae, covered on both their surfaces with subunits, are labeled C. The inset in the right lower corner is a reversed print (× 770,000) showing 2 subunits (labeled IMS). (Parsons, D. F.: Science *140*:985)

oxidative reactions they catalyze provide energy for what is termed *oxidative phosphorylation*. This latter process depends on still another group of enzymes which act to add a third phosphate group to a substance known as adenosine diphosphate (ADP) which has only 2 phosphate groups, and thus convert it to adenosine triphosphate (ATP), which has 3 phosphate groups. The energy needed for the phosphorylating enzymes to add this extra phosphate group to ADP, so that it becomes ATP, is provided by the reactions catalyzed by the respiratory enzymes. The energy-rich ATP is made available to the cytoplasm outside the mitochondria where it provides, by again becoming ADP, the energy required for many of the metabolic processes that proceed in the cytoplasm. *The chief function of mitochondria is therefore that of providing energy-rich ATP to the remainder of* *the cell* and it is by losing the energy imparted to it by its possessing a third phosphate group that it is able to provide energy required for life processes. It is for this reason that mitochondria are often described as the powerhouses of the cell.

**Location of the Enzymes.** Most of the enzymes of the citric acid cycle, except some of the dehydrogenases, are housed in the fluid content of the mitochondria. The respiratory enzymes (flavoproteins and cytochromes) and the phosphorylating enzymes are bound to the membranes of the mitochondria. At the time of writing, the fine structure of mitochondrial membranes is being studied in detail to learn more about the location and the arrangements of these enzymes, using the technic of negative staining. To study mitochondria by this technic a thin layer of the cellular material is dried down on an electron microscope specimen grid, together with some potassium phosphotungstate solution. The potassium phosphotungstate forms a dense background that sharply outlines structural elements in the specimen. A high-magnification picture of the cristae of a liver mitochondrion as it appears in a specimen prepared this way is shown in Figure 7-21. The surface of a crista is seen to be covered with toadstool-like objects called "inner membrane subunits" which have heads 90 Å in diameter and stems 35 Å wide. Britton Chance, D. F. Parsons and G. R. Williams have shown, by stripping the inner membrane subunits from the cristae, that the cytochrome respiratory enzymes are not present in the subunits but instead are in the membrane on which the subunits stand. The function of the subunits is not yet understood, but there are indications that they are concerned with oxidative phosphorylation.

**Nucleic Acid in Mitochondria.** Long ago, soon after mitochondria were first seen in cells, there was some doubt as to whether they were true organelles. One theory then held was that they were intracellular parasites which had become symbionts of cells. In due course, mitochondria became accepted as true organelles. However, as matters have turned out, although this does not affect the concept of their being true organelles of cells, mitochondria, in at least some kinds of living things, recently have been shown to possess some of the requisites for independence that have hitherto been considered to be the sole perquisite of the nucleus, for they have been shown to possess some DNA and to reproduce this DNA. There is also some indication (but it is not yet proved) that RNA may be synthesized in association with their DNA and that this RNA may be used to control a limited amount of protein synthesis in mitochondria. It thus appears that some mitochondria, in at least some forms of living cells, may be shown to account for the synthesis of a few of their enzymatic components, although they are by no means independent of the cells they inhabit.

## LYSOSOMES

Lysosomes, the most recently discovered type of cytoplasmic organelle, are membranous vesicles filled with hydrolytic enzymes. Although numerous in some kinds of cells, they are not numerous in others. When *inac-tive* they are rounded-to-ovoid bodies about 0.4 micron in diameter. Each is surrounded by a smooth-surfaced membrane. Often the interior of inactive lysosomes is sufficiently electron dense to make lysosomes show up under the EM as darker bodies than mitochondria. Unlike mitochondria, inactive lysosomes reveal little or no internal structure with present methods.

Novikoff and his associates took advantage of the fact that one of the enzymes contained by lysosomes is acid phosphatase, and were able to show that lysosomes could be identified in thin sections by a combination of the histochemical test for acid phosphatase and electron microscopy. The histochemical test results in a ring of electron-dense precipitate forming in association with the membrane that surrounds each lysosome (Fig. 7-22). Precipitate is also seen at least in some instances within the lysosome. As will be described, *active* lysosomes present many different appearances because to become active they fuse with, or incorporate into themselves, certain materials with which they come into contact.

The enzymes of lysosomes are potent enough to bring about the lysis of the cells that they inhabit. However, under ordinary circumstances the enzymes do not destroy the cells that contain them because the enzymes can neither escape through the membranous walls of the lysosomes into the cytoplasm nor can the substrates in the cytoplasm, on which the enzymes could act, penetrate through the membranous walls of the lysosomes to reach their contents. Lysosomes therefore provide a further example of membranes being employed in cells to segregate reactive substances from one another.

Because lysosomes represent bags of hydrolytic enzymes that could, under certain circumstances, destroy the cells that contain them, lysosomes are sometimes referred to, somewhat dramatically, as "suicide bags."

**Functions of Lysosomes.** Although it is very probable that the enzymes contained in lysosomes are liberated when cells die, or even when cells are near death, and that this accounts for the lysis and other changes that occur in cells as they undergo postmortem degeneration (Fig. 6-37), it is becoming increasingly obvious that lysosomes may serve

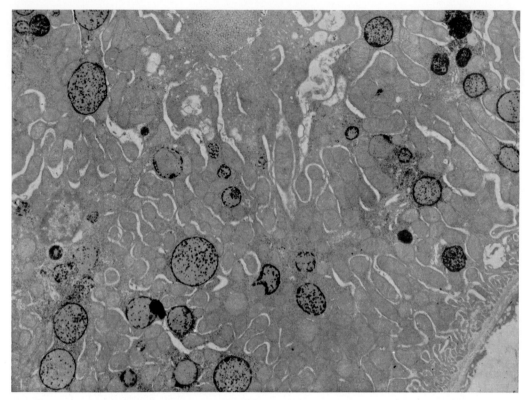

FIG. 7-22. Electron micrograph ($\times$ 7,600) of section of kidney of male rat. This section illustrates how lysosomes can be identified by, and hence shown to contain, acid phosphatase. The enzyme is demonstrated here by the Gomori technic. The end result of this histochemical procedure leads to the deposition of lead salts where acid phosphatase was present. Since lead salts are very electron dense, the sites of their deposition are black in this illustration. (Novikoff, A. B.: Ciba Symposium on Lysosomes, p. 36, Boston, Little, 1963)

important and helpful functions in cells during life as well.

The general function that lysosomes serve during life is sometimes described by saying that they act as the digestive apparatus of the cell. This thought requires some qualification lest it be incorrectly assumed that most food that is taken into cells requires digestion. The usual food that is used by cells for the production of energy (glucose) and the food required for protein synthesis (amino acids) is absorbed by cells from body fluids and metabolized by enzymatic systems that are different from those in lysosomes. However, particularly in some kinds of cells, substances, generally particulate, may be taken into the cytoplasm by means of phagocytosis or pinocytosis. These latter substances cannot be utilized directly by the cell. The breakdown of ingested particular substances may require the

cooperation of lysosomes, and yet the breakdown of ingested particulate substance must be accomplished without the enzymes from lysosomes being released into the cytoplasm as a whole. The way this is accomplished is by the whole process occurring within an enlarged membranous vesicle which forms as follows:

Particulate or other complex substances that gain entrance to cells are engulfed at the cell surface by means of the cell membrane forming a membranous vesicle around the phagocytosed substance. The membranous vesicle containing the engulfed substance which is to be digested (such a vesicle is often termed a *phagosome*) migrates through cytoplasm until it meets a lysosome. When this occurs, it seems that the membranous walls that surround each structure fuse, and as a result the contents of the two vesicles become mixed,

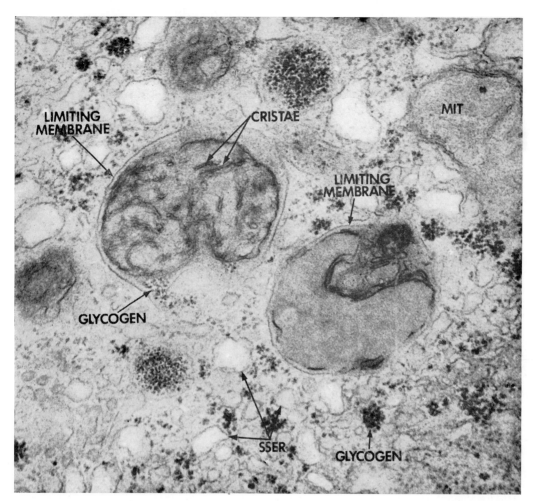

FIG. 7-23. Electron micrograph ($\times$ 57,000) of part of the cytoplasm of a hepatocyte of a rat 3 days after partial hepatectomy. In the center are 2 cytolysomes. They are each surrounded by an incomplete membrane. The incompleteness of the membrane may be due to a tangential section through the membrane. It could also be interpreted as indicating that the cytolysomal contents are in the process of being enclosed by a membrane. The cytolysome on the left contains a clearly recognizable, though markedly altered, mitochondrion, and some glycogen. The organelloid contents of the cytolysome on the right are no longer clearly recognizable. The cytolysomes are thought to be specialized lysosomes in which obsolete cytoplasmic components are undergoing degradation. (Preparation by A. M. Jézéquel)

and as a result the substance taken in at the cell surface is digested by the hydrolytic enzymes of the lysosomes without these escaping into the cytoplasm as a whole.

While the above-described mechanism may be important in ridding many kinds of cells of various materials that may sometimes be taken into them, and which, without the help of lysosomes, might accumulate and interfere with the function of the cells, a similar mechanism is very important in the defense of the body against bacteria that gain entrance to it. Certain cells of the blood (neutrophilic leukocytes, which will be described in Chapter 10) leave the bloodstream and assemble in areas where a bacterial infection has begun and here the blood cells phagocytose the bacteria which by this time are multiplying in the tissue (Fig. 12-8). For example, neutrophils, to be described in Chapter 12, contain granules which appear to be of the same general nature as lysosomes (Fig. 12-7), and when bacteria are phagocytosed by these special blood cells, the lysosomelike granules of the cell meet and fuse with the ingested bacteria and as a result the ingested bacteria are destroyed. The process is violent, which probably accounts for the fact that blood cells of this type are themselves destroyed along with the bacteria they have destroyed.

Lysosomes also help to rid a cell of certain of its parts that have worn out or become altered for some other reason. Such parts of cells do not remain free in the cytoplasm but become surrounded by a membrane which suggests that cells can phagocytose particulate matter that arises within cells as well as particulate matter that has its origin outside the cell. Since the vesicles that contain bits and pieces of parts of cells within the cytoplasm, for example broken-down mitochondria (Fig. 7-23), can be shown by histochemical methods to contain enzymes characteristic of lysosomes (Fig. 7-22), it is possible that lysosomes act in these instances as intracellular phagocytes. Another possibility is that the breaking-down cell component is first surrounded with a membrane from some other source and the vesicle so formed then fuses with a lysosome. Lysosomes that are digesting broken-down mitochondria or other structures that were once part of the cell are termed *cytolysomes* (Fig. 7-23).

Enough has probably been said to indicate that lysosomes in various states of activity, for example, before and after fusion with membrane-surrounded particulate matter of various sorts will present many different appearances in the EM. Before discussing this matter further we shall comment briefly on how lysosomes were discovered, because this illustrates how they can be identified in sections of cells by histochemical means.

**Development of Knowledge About Lysosomes.** The existence of lysosomes was first postulated by Christian de Duve and his associates in 1955. Shortly before this time, de Duve and his associates were examining, by biochemical methods, the enzyme content of various fractions that could be separated from homogenates of rat liver cells by differential centrifugation. They were interested particularly in investigating the enzymes of mitochondrial fractions, and by refinements of the centrifugation procedures they managed to obtain two different mitochondrial fractions, one termed the light and the other the heavy. In the light fraction they unexpectedly found a number of hydrolytic enzymes including acid phosphatase; all were characterized by a low pH optimum. They then performed a number of biochemical experiments which led them to postulate that the hydrolytic enzymes that they had found in the light mitochondrial fraction must be contained in particulates around 0.4 micron in diameter and also that the particles must be each surrounded by a membranous wall which kept the enzymes from reacting with substrates in the cytoplasm. They proposed the name lysosomes for the organelles whose existence they postulated from their biochemical experiments.

Subsequently, the fractions which gave biochemical evidence of containing these particles were examined in the EM by Novikoff, Beaufay and de Duve, and the particles whose existence were postulated by de Duve and his collaborators were seen. Since that time Novikoff, Holt and others have studied lysosomes in a great variety of cells by means of combining the histochemical test for acid phosphatase with electron microscopy. Although lysosomes contain several other hydrolytic enzymes, acid phosphatase is the most easily tested for by a histochemical technic (see Fig. 7-22). It will be recalled from Chapter 4 that the presence of phosphatase in a cell can be located by a procedure which indicates the presence and the site of the enzyme in a cell by the deposition of a black precipitate which is electron dense and hence shows up as black material in an electron micrograph (Figs. 7-22 and 7-24).

Meanwhile EM studies revealed what came to be called *pericanalicular* dense bodies in liver cells more electron dense than mitochondria and showed no evidence of cristae. In due course, de Duve and his associates obtained evidence indicating that the dense pericanalicular bodies that had been described in liver cells were lysosomes.

As already noted, it seems probable that lysosomes can occur in forms that are not active. When lysosomes meet and fuse with membrane-surrounded particulate matter from outside or from inside the cell, the fused structures so formed, which might be termed active lysosomes, demonstrate a great variety of appearances. In their final form, when un-digested products accumulate in them, they are termed residual bodies; these, in some in-stances, may be excreted by the cell. One in-teresting appearance presented by residual bodies is a content of undigested lipid which may take the form of what are termed myelin figures (Fig. 7-24) because such figures have a lamellated appearance similar to the myelin sheaths of nerves.

**Formation of Lysosomes.** The way that lyso-somes are formed in cells is not known. How-ever, lysosomes are so similar to zymogen granules (both are membranous vesicles filled with enzymes) that it seems very probable that both are formed in much the same man-ner. If so, the enzymes of lysosomes, neces-sarily being proteins, would be synthesized in rough-surfaced vesicles of the endoplasmic reticulum and from there would be taken up by microvesicles, and perhaps taken to the flattened vesicles of the Golgi apparatus, where the enzymes would come to be con-tained in an expanded portion of a flattened vesicle at one of its edges, which would bud off to constitute a membrane-surrounded ves-icle filled with enzymes. In other words, the main difference between zymogen granules and lysosomes would seem to be that in the former the enzymes are destined to break down pro-teins outside the cell, while those of the latter are designed to digest materials inside the cell.

**Terminology.** Since much of the work on lysosomes is relatively new, its description has led to the use of both old terms and new terms in designating the various structures that are seen and the processes that account for their formation. Since it is very probable that many of the terms that have been intro-duced recently in this field will change over the years, the preceding account has been written using as few as possible of them. How-ever, it should perhaps be mentioned that in the special literature dealing with lysosomes, the process by which material is ingested at the cell surface is often referred to as *endocy-tosis*; the ingested material surrounded by a membrane is often termed as a *phagosome*; what we have referred to as an inactive lyso-some is sometimes termed a *primary lyso-some*; a fused lysosome and phagosome is termed a *digestive vacuole*, and what is left after digestion has proceeded for some time

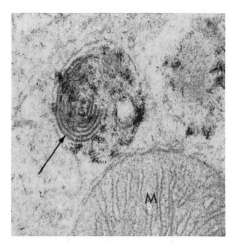

FIG. 7-24. Electron micrograph ($\times$ 41,000) showing myelinlike figure in lyso-some that is identified by histochemical re-action. (Goldfischer, S., Essner, E., and Novikoff, A. B.: J. Histochem. Cytochem. *12*:72)

in one of these latter structures is termed a *residual body*. It is obvious that this terminol-ogy is not consistent for structures of the same general order (in that they are membra-nous vesicles) are thus variously termed bod-ies, granules and vacuoles, and it may be hoped that in due course when more is known, a more consistent terminology will be evolved.

### 3. THE CENTROSPHERE, CENTRIOLES AND SPINDLE TUBULES

These cytoplasmic organelles have all been dealt with in connection with the description of mitosis in the previous chapter.

### 4. VARIOUS FIBRILS, FILAMENTS AND OTHER STRUCTURES THAT SERVE SUPPORTING OR CONTRACTILE FUNCTIONS WITHIN CELLS

The supporting organelles, in particular the cell and the terminal web, will be considered in the next chapter in connection with Epi-thelial Tissue. Contractile fibers and filaments will be considered in a subsequent chapter on Muscular Tissue.

## CYTOPLASMIC INCLUSIONS

The term *cytoplasmic inclusion* is generally used for bodies or materials which, although they may be products of metabolic activity, are not part of the metabolic machinery of the cell. Three main types are generally distinguished.

1. Stored foods
2. Secretion granules and globules
3. Pigments

### STORED FOODS

A healthy man may withstand starvation for weeks. During the time he takes no food, his metabolism, though somewhat altered, continues. This requires a constant supply of fuel. Since he obtains no food from outside sources, he must draw on his internal stores. These consist mostly of foods that have been stored in the cytoplasm of certain of his cells as inclusions.

There are 3 basically different types of foods that can be used by the body for energy; carbohydrates, fats and proteins. Two of these (carbohydrates and fats) are stored by cells as cytoplasmic inclusions. Carbohydrates and fats are not stored to the same degree by all types of cells; as might be expected, some cells have become specialized to serve as food stores for the body. Carbohydrates are stored chiefly in the cells of the liver and in the cells of muscle. Fat is stored chiefly by special cells called fat cells that are distributed widely throughout the body but particularly in the fat depots (for example, over the belly). Protein is not stored in the form of a specific inclusion, for cytoplasm itself is composed chiefly of protein, but in times of need cells may catabolize their own protoplasm. In a sense, a degree of protein storage is achieved by having large healthy cells.

Since the cells of the liver normally store carbohydrate, they may be studied to advantage to learn the appearances conferred on cells by their storing carbohydrate as an inclusion.

**Carbohydrate** is absorbed from the intestine in the form of glucose, and this is brought to the liver by the bloodstream. To store it, the cells of the liver convert it into macromolecules of animal starch. This is called *glycogen*. Glycogen is not stained in H and E sections. However, a fairly good idea of the glycogen content of liver cells can be obtained from an H and E section, because ordinary aqueous fixatives harden the cyto-

plasm of cells more quickly than they dissolve out its glycogen; hence, the glycogen content of a cell acts more or less as a "mold" around which the cytoplasm "sets" on fixation. Then, as the glycogen dissolves away, open spaces are left in the hardened cytoplasm which indicate the sites that were formerly occupied by glycogen. The pattern of open spaces left in the cytoplasm of liver cells by the dissolving away of glycogen is fairly characteristic: the open areas are irregular in shape and have ragged borders (Fig. 7-25, *left*). A cell that contained almost no glycogen when it was fixed has cytoplasm of a more even texture than one that had even moderate amounts of it. A considerable amount of glycogen in a cell (Fig. 7-25) does not tend to displace the nucleus to one side of the cell and flatten it to the same extent as does a great deal of fat in a cell (Fig. 7-27).

Glycogen in cells can be demonstrated beautifully by the histochemical method known as the PAS technic as was described in Chapter 4. This technic colors the glycogen magenta (Fig. 7-25, *right*).

**Fine Structure.** Accumulations of glycogen in cytoplasm appear in unstained electron micrographs as pale amorphous areas, as is illustrated in Figure 7-26. It is of interest that mitochondria and membranous vesicles retain their close association to one another as glycogen accumulates in liver cells; hence, areas of cytoplasm, containing both mitochondria and membranous vesicles, may become widely separated from one another by extensive areas of amorphous material (Fig. 7-26). That the material labeled glycogen in Figure 7-26 was actually glycogen was indicated by the fact that other sections obtained from the same liver and stained by the PAS technic revealed similar areas. See Chapter 26 for details about the fine structure of glycogen.

**Fat** is stored mostly in fat cells, but it may also accumulate in liver cells, particularly under conditions of dietary deficiency.

How is stored fat in cytoplasm recognized? Fat dissolves away in the preparation of the usual section, in the clearing agents, in which it is very soluble. It can be fixed by a special fixative, osmic acid, so that it does not dissolve out of a section so readily with clearing agents; hence, osmic-acid fixation permits fat to be demonstrated (Fig. 21-15). It can also

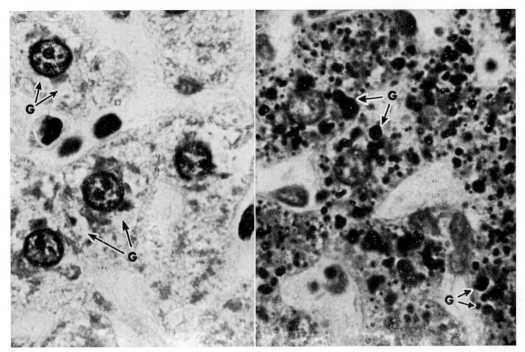

FIG. 7-25. Photomicrographs of sections of liver of well-fed rat. (*Left*) An H and E section, and the sites of glycogen in the cytoplasm are indicated by irregular ragged clear areas (G). (*Right*) A similar section stained by the PAS technic which colors the glycogen magenta; this appears black in the photograph (G).

be demonstrated by cutting frozen sections and, without subjecting them to either dehydrating or clearing agents, staining them with special fat stains (for example, Scharlach R., which colors the fat droplets a bright red).

In most instances, however, a useful appreciation of the amount of fat that has been present in cells can be obtained by studying the pattern of the cytoplasm that is left behind after the fat has dissolved away. Like glycogen, fat in cytoplasm forms a mold around which cytoplasm sets on fixation. Fat first accumulates in cells in the form of small droplets (Fig. 7-27), which tend to fuse to form larger droplets. If a droplet is very large, the cell becomes little more than a thin shell around the fat droplet (Fig. 7-27); when this is sectioned, it gives the cell a "signet-ring" appearance, the nucleus forming the bulge or "signet" (Fig. 7-27). Hartroft has shown that under certain conditions liver cells take up more fat than they can contain subsequently in their cytoplasm. As adjacent cells continue to take up fat their thin walls, at the sites

where they touch one another, first fuse and then, as the process continues, they rupture. The fat globules formerly contained in single cells then coalesce into a single pool, and the large globule so formed is surrounded by the crescentic segments of the original cells that still persist about the periphery of the large globule (Fig. 7-27, *right*). The surrounding cells, although they form a continuous membrane around the large globule, do not actually fuse; so as a result the fat of the large globule is actually extracellular, being contained, as it were, in the cavity of an epithelial cyst. Such structures that form in the liver or in other fat-containing tissues are termed fatty cysts (Fig. 7-27, *right*).

The pattern of open spaces left in liver cells by the dissolving out of fat droplets is different from that left by the dissolving out of glycogen. The spaces left by dissolved fat are spherical and have smooth outlines (Fig. 7-27). These differ from the jagged outlines of the spaces left by dissolved glycogen (Fig. 7-25). Furthermore, as already noted, fat tends to displace the nucleus of the cell to one

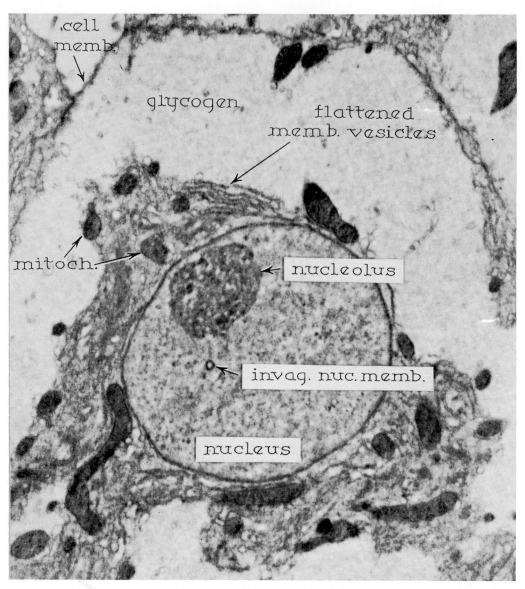

Fig. 7-26. Electron micrograph ($\times$ 11,000) of a section of the liver of a rat fetus in a late stage of development. The membranous vesicles and the mitochondria are closely associated, and areas of cytoplasm containing each are separated by structureless appearing material, most of which is probably glycogen. The nucleus shows a large nucleolus as well as an invagination of the nuclear membrane that has been cut in cross section. (Preparation by A. Howatson)

side and flattens it more than glycogen does.

**Proteins** are not stored as inclusions. Cytoplasm itself is chiefly protein, and in starvation, cells may, up to a point, consume their own cytoplasm. In this sense, there is a normal reserve of cytoplasm which can serve as stored protein.

## SECRETION GRANULES AND GLOBULES

Cells that are specialized to secrete the various digestive juices and other special potent fluids needed by the body must synthesize these products in their cytoplasm from raw materials brought to them by the blood and tissue fluid. The synthesis, the transport, the

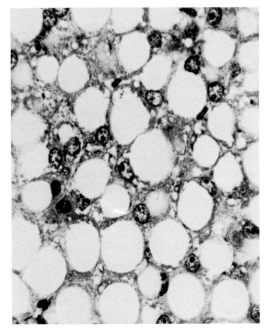 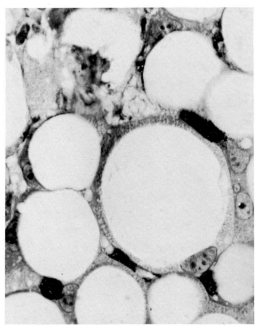

FIG. 7-27. (*Left*) Photomicrograph of a section of liver from a rat which had experienced a choline deficiency for 12 days. (McGregor stain, × 600.) The liver cells that are distended with fat are almost twice as wide as normal cells. (*Right*) A similar preparation from a rat that experienced the same kind of deficiency for 45 days. Observe that individual cells have liberated their fat into a cyst which is surrounded by several cells. The black structures seen are capillaries that have been injected with India ink. (Hartroft, W. S.: Anat. Rec. *106*:61)

delivery and the fine structure of secretion granules already has been described and illustrated in this chapter in the section dealling with the Golgi apparatus.

### PIGMENT

The need for the medical student to become interested in the color of tissues cannot be emphasized too strongly. A most important factor and sometimes the chief one in the clinical diagnosis of some diseases is the changed color of some part of the body. Color is of even greater importance to the pathologist than to the clinician. A good part of the description of the gross appearance of diseased organs at operation or at autopsy relates to their changed color. Therefore, the student is advised to learn the causes of the different normal and abnormal colors of the various parts of the body.

Color in any tissue is due chiefly to its content of pigment. Moreover, pigments are usually present in tissues as cytoplasmic inclusions in cells. Fortunately, there are only a few broad groups of pigments with which the student should become familiar. Much is known about some of these, but relatively little about others.

It is important to realize what constitutes a pigment. There are many ingredients of cells that, while colorless in life, take on brilliant colors after they are treated with stains. These are *not* pigments. To qualify as a pigment a material must possess color in life; hence, a pigment, to be seen, does not need to be treated with stains. However, pigments are sometimes colored further or differently by stains.

**Classification of Pigments.** Pigments are usually divided into two groups, *exogenous* and *endogenous*. Exogenous pigments are those that have been *generated* as such *outside* the body and subsequently taken into it by one route or another. Endogenous pigments are *generated inside* the body from nonpigmented ingredients.

**Exogenous Pigments.** There are several kinds of these, and they may be taken into the body in various ways. An important group consists of various vegetable pigments, par-

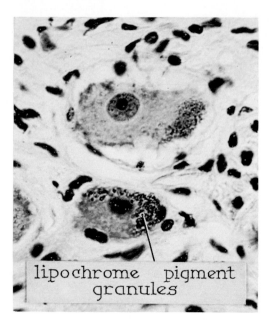

lipochrome pigment granules

FIG. 7-28. High-power photomicrograph of a human nerve ganglion. Two ganglion cells may be seen in the picture; their cytoplasm contains numerous granules of lipochrome pigment.

ticularly those of the *carotenoid* group. *Carotin,* the pigment of carrots but contained also in other vegetables, is a very important one. Under normal conditions, enough vegetable pigment is absorbed to color only certain cells of the body, but when carrots or certain other vegetables are eaten to excess, enough carotin may be absorbed and retained to color a great deal of the body; indeed, even the skin and the body fluids may become tinged with it (carotinemia), and a patient demonstrating this condition may, until suitable tests are made, be thought to have jaundice.

LIPOCHROMES. Yellow pigments which are relatively soluble in fat solvents are found in several types of cells, particularly as individuals become older. The precise nature of lipochrome pigment is not known. It is generally conceded that lipochrome pigments form as a result of "wear and tear"; in other words, that they are a product of prolonged activity on the part of the cells that contain them. They are most easily seen in ganglion and liver cells and muscle cells of the heart. Recently it has been shown that lipochrome pigment in cytoplasm is contained within lysosomes. Lipochrome pigment will be discussed and illus-

trated further in connection with the fine structure of liver cells where the lipochrome pigment is generally referred to as *lipofuchsin.*

DUSTS. A second important group of exogenous pigments is provided by the various kinds of dusts that gain entrance to the respiratory system through inspired air. Pigmentation of parts of this system by this means is of course pathologic. But there is so much particulate matter in the air in towns and cities where coal is used that it is a usual, if not normal, condition. Coal dust in the tissues of the lungs is termed *anthracosis* (*anthrax* = coal; *osis* = increase, invasion) and it is of very common occurrence (Fig. 7-29).

Coal dust is not as harmful to the lungs as certain other particles that may be inhaled by unprotected workers in certain trades. Silica particles, for example, when present in lung tissue in sufficient amounts (silicosis), may lead to serious complications, as will be explained in the study of pathology.

MINERALS. Certain minerals taken by mouth or absorbed through the surface of the body may lead to pigmentation. For example, too much silver applied to body surfaces in the treatment of certain diseases may lead to an accumulation of silver and hence a gray pigmentation of the body. Lead can be absorbed to give a blue line on the gums.

Tattoo marks are due to pigments being driven deep into the skin by needles.

**Endogenous Pigments.** The most important one is *hemoglobin,* the iron-containing coloring matter of red blood cells. This serves as the great oxygen carrier of the body. It will be discussed in detail in Chapter 13, so further comment on it will be omitted here. Certain altered forms of hemoglobin, of a different color from the normal, will also be discussed in the same chapter. Here we shall content ourselves with a brief discussion of a group of pigments that result from the normal destruction of hemoglobin in the body.

**Pigments From the Destruction of Hemoglobin.** Under normal conditions, red blood cells do not survive for more than a few months in the circulatory system. As they wear out, they are phagocytosed by certain large cells in the spleen, the liver and the bone marrow. In the cytoplasm of these, the iron-containing hemoglobin is broken down into an iron-containing pigment called *hemosiderin* and a non-iron-containing one called *hematoidin* or *bilirubin*.

*Hemosiderin* is golden brown and is disposed in the cytoplasm of phagocytes in the form of granules or small irregular masses. By suitable chemical tests hemosiderin can be shown to contain iron; this permits it to be distinguished from the other golden and brown pigments of the body.

The normal human body is very economical of iron, and that of the hemoglobin of old red blood corpuscles is mostly used over again in the synthesis of hemoglobin for new ones. It is not known if all the iron liberated from the breakdown of hemoglobin is converted to hemosiderin before being used over again. Furthermore, little is known about how the iron from hemosiderin goes back into solution to allow its subsequent use in building new hemoglobin.

Whereas hemosiderin is normally present to some extent in the phagocytes of the spleen, the liver and the bone marrow, it becomes greatly increased in these sites in diseases in which red blood corpuscles are broken down much more rapidly than usual. It may even appear in large quantities in certain other cells under certain pathologic conditions.

*Hematoidin and Bilirubin.* Bile is a yellow-to-brown fluid secreted by the liver, stored and concentrated in a bag termed the gallbladder, and eventually passed into the intestine where it plays an important role in absorption and digestion. Its coloring matter is *bilirubin*, a yellow-to-brown pigment which is easily oxidized to *biliverdin*, a green pigment. In some animals (birds), a considerable amount of biliverdin is present normally in their bile, hence their bile tends to be green, but in man only a little biliverdin is normally present, so human bile is yellow to brown.

For many years it was believed that bilirubin was manufactured by the liver cells that secrete it. But with further studies it became apparent that bilirubin, like hemosiderin, is a breakdown product of hemoglobin and hence formed in the sites where old, worn-out red blood corpuscles are destroyed. Unlike hemosiderin, however, bilirubin contains no iron and is more soluble; hence it does not tend to remain in the cytoplasm of the phagocytes that destroy red blood cells but instead dissolves into the blood, from which it is con-

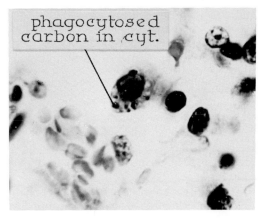

FIG. 7-29. High-power photomicrograph of a section of a rat's lung. A large alveolar phagocyte may be seen in the center of the picture; its cytoplasm contains granules of phagocytosed carbon derived from smoke.

tinuously removed by the cells of the liver to be transferred into the bile.

It took a great many observations and experiments to prove that bilirubin originated from hemoglobin. The first tangible lead was given by Virchow, the originator of the cell-state concept, about 100 years ago. He observed that crystals of pigment tended to form in tissues of the body that were the sites of former internal hemorrhages. He named the pigment that crystallized out among the old breaking-down red blood corpuscles in such areas *hematoidin* and concluded that it was derived from hemoglobin. Not content with microscopic examinations alone, he subjected deposits of this pigment to chemical tests and made the remarkable discovery that hematoidin, so far as these tests would demonstrate, was the same thing as the pigment that colors bile (bilirubin), and said "this was of special interest from its being supposed that the colored constituents of bile are products of the decomposition of the coloring matter of the blood."

However, for many years afterward, hemoglobin was not accepted as the origin of bile pigment, and it is only in the last few decades that the idea has gained general acceptance. For further reading the student is advised to consult Rich's most admirable review.

**Melanin** is usually a brown-to-black pigment found chiefly in the skin and its appendages and in the eye. In white races it appears in skin in appreciable amounts after exposure to sunlight (suntan). Melanin accounts for the dark color of the Negro; here too, however, the degree of pigmentation is increased by sunlight. The color of eyes is due to melanin. Deep in the eye melanin is used as a light-proofing material much in the same way as photographers use black paper, black curtains and black paint. Melanin appears in the body in the form of granules or clumps of granules in the cytoplasm of cells as inclusions (Fig. 23-17, *right*).

Melanin is a nitrogenous substance that in pure form contains no sulphur or iron. For a time it was suspected that melanin, like hemosiderin and bilirubin, originated from breaking-down hemoglobin, but this theory has long been discredited. The modern theory owes much to studies made on plants. These were found to contain enzymes that, given the opportunity, oxidize certain colorless chromogens (substances that can generate color) of the plant into pigment. The phenomenon can easily be studied by slicing a raw potato. When the fresh-cut surface is exposed to air (oxygen), the enzymes of the potato oxidize certain colorless chromogens of the potato into a brown-to-black pigment. Cooks who peel potatoes in advance of a meal keep them in water away from oxygen to prevent them from darkening.

The problem of melanin formation will be considered in detail in connection with skin in Chapter 23; for the present, it is enough to say that melanin probably forms inside certain body cells by a mechanism somewhat similar to that described for plants. Cells that make melanin are termed *melanocytes*. They contain an enzyme capable of acting on a colorless chromogen brought to the cell by the blood and tissue fluid, and converting it into melanin.

## SIGNIFICANCE OF THE NEWER KNOWLEDGE ABOUT CELLS TO THE PROBLEM OF CELL DIFFERENTIATION

In Chapter 6 we discussed the present-day state of knowledge about the chemical nature of genes and chromosomes, and how DNA is duplicated preparatory to mitosis, and how the information that is present in DNA is transmitted by means of messenger RNA to sites of protein synthesis in cells and how the message results in certain amino acids being linked together in certain sequences to form specific proteins. In this present chapter further details of protein synthesis in cells have been given. With these various facts fresh in our minds this would seem to be an appropriate time to consider the significance of this new knowledge of the chemistry of heredity and the control of protein synthesis to a most important histologic problem, that of cell differentiation, a problem already discussed in a very general way in Chapter 5.

The process of differentiation concerns the phenomenon of cells that arise from a single mother cell becoming different from one another. Furthermore, when they become different from one another, they give rise to different cell families the members of which thereafter transmit their special nature to their progeny. It would *seem* therefore that differentiation results in body cells being changed genetically.

If we recall the way in which DNA molecules are duplicated, it is obvious that the mechanism is such as to ensure that daughter cells always have exactly the same set of genes as each other and, of course, the same as the mother cell that divided. The way that DNA is duplicated explains why each two cells that result from a division should always have *exactly the same set of genes*. The mechanism of DNA duplication therefore explains why species should remain the same, for the DNA of one species differs from the DNA of other species. It explains why identical twins should be identical. But the mechanism of DNA duplication in itself does not explain how or why body cells should become so different from one another during differentiation; on the contrary, it explains why they should all have the same genes.

The fact that body cells *seem* to become genetically different during the process of differentiation, so that the different cell families that arise thereafter breed cells of only their specific family type, might seem to suggest that the DNA of the cells of the different family types does become different. For this to happen—for the DNA of differentiating cells to become different in different cell types—would require that mutations occur, that parts of DNA molecules were lost or transposed or otherwise affected so that the information contained in the cell's DNA was no longer the same as before. And indeed, one explanation of differentiation that was at least contemplated in the past was that differentiation depended on a succession of mutations occurring in body cells during the developmental process. But this concept flies in the face of what is known about mutations. Mutations are haphazard events. Differentiation is an orderly process, and, furthermore, it is in many instances clearly directed by environmental factors. It is inconceivable that it could be due to thousands of particular and different mutations occurring in an orderly way.

If differentiation is not due to changes occurring in the DNA of cells during development we are left with the concept of the body cells of any individual, except those that normally manifest polyploidy, all having precisely the same DNA. It is known from quantitative chemical studies that they all have the same absolute content of DNA. But since cells become different from one another, we are faced with the fact that there must be some mechanism that operates in the differentiation process to keep certain parts of the DNA molecules of cells blocked off so that they cannot act as templates for messenger RNA, and that as differentiation occurs different sequences along DNA molecules are blocked off, and others unblocked, in different kinds of cells. Furthermore, since many families of cells in the body reproduce only their own family type of cell, the blocks placed on parts of the DNA molecule must in effect become irreversible at some stage of development. The concept of some genes becoming *permanently* suppressed during development could explain the results of the well-known experiments of Briggs and King. These investigators devised methods whereby they could remove the nucleus from the fertilized egg of a frog, and then transplant into the enucleated egg, a nucleus which they removed from a somatic cell of a frog embryo. They found that the nuclei of somatic cells obtained from very young embryos would permit normal frogs to develop from enucleated eggs into which they were transplanted, but if they transplanted into enucleated eggs,

nuclei from somatic cells obtained from embryos in which differentiation had proceeded to a substantial degree, complete embryos would not form.

Recently there has been considerable interest with regard to the possibility that the information on any part of a DNA molecule can be blocked from being transcribed onto messenger RNA molecules by that part of the DNA molecule being combined firmly with histones. Histones, as has been noted previously, are important protein constituents of chromosomes. It has been shown, for example, in experimental systems, that removal of histones from DNA facilitates the synthesis of messenger RNA by the DNA. It has also been shown that the addition of histones to DNA inhibits the synthesis of messenger RNA by that DNA. It is therefore possible that the mechanism by which genes are blocked off from giving information to messenger RNA is by histone being combined with the DNA of these genes, in the form of a nucleohistone, and that genes that are functional in any body cell are represented by sites along DNA molecules where combination with histone is not of this type. Indeed, there is evidence that the problem may be more complicated still, in that studies by Allfrey, Faulkner and Mirsky suggest that gene expression or suppression may not be due to whether or not histones are combined with DNA, but instead whether or not the histone is in its natural state, for they have shown that if the histone with which DNA is combined is acetylated, it does not inhibit RNA synthesis by the DNA.

Histones are synthesized in the interphase probably in the same period during which DNA is duplicated. However, the synthesis of histones is not dependent on the process of DNA duplication, for it has been shown that histones are synthesized if DNA duplication is experimentally blocked. It is thought that there may be hundreds of different histones in a single cell type, but there do not seem to be nearly as many different histones as there are genes. Furthermore, different histones seem to move and undergo re-arrangements readily as they form, all of which suggests that individual histones are not as specific as genes.

Therefore, in our present state of knowledge it is generally conceded that all the body cells of an individual have the same base sequences in the DNA of their chromosomes but as development proceeds some genes are expressed while others are suppressed. At the moment, a good deal of attention is being paid to the possibility of histones being involved in determining whether genes in a cell are expressed or suppressed.

The next problem to consider in differentiation is how environmental, or more specifically, factors outside the nucleus, determine which genes are to be expressed and which ones are to be suppressed so as to account for different kinds of cells developing in different parts of the body.

First, from the study of bacterial systems, mechanisms are known that explain how the expression of a particular gene can be stimulated by an environmental factor. For example, if certain strains of E. coli (a variety of bacteria), are grown in a medium that contains no galactoside, the bacteria produce only traces of the enzyme (a specific protein) that can break down galactosides. But, if galactosides are added to the medium, the enzyme is produced by the bacterial cells in quantities. Since the production of this enzyme is known to be under the control of a special gene, the findings show that a factor external to the nucleus can stimulate the expression of a gene. This phenomenon is known as the induction of an enzyme. Attardi has shown that the induction of an enzyme increases the rate of synthesis of messenger RNA that directs the synthesis of the enzyme concerned.

It might next be asked if mechanisms similar to the above could act in differentiation. It is known that in the early cleavages of the fertilized ovum, the components of the cytoplasm (stored food, for example) become divided unequally in the first few generations of daughter cells, and hence it is not impossible that substrates that could induce different enzymes are allocated to different daughter cells in different quantities, and that as a result of this the expression of different genes is stimulated in different daughter cells which thereupon come to have different protein constitutions.

The next point to consider is that an environmental factor which might induce the differentiation of a cell at a particular stage of development of the embryo does not necessarily induce its differentiation at an earlier stage of development. Unless this generalization were true, most of the cells of the developing fetus would differentiate prematurely. There must be a time during development when certain cells become responsive to certain agents which affect their differentiation and until cells reach this stage of development they are not affected by these particular environmental factors. For example, if one injects hydrocortisone into an adult animal, it causes glycogen to accumulate in the cells of the liver. If one injects the same hormone into chick embryos in the later stages of development, it exerts this same effect. But, if the hormone is injected into younger chick embryos, it does not cause glycogen to accumulate in their liver cells, probably because the enzymes through which it exerts its effects have not yet appeared; this could be explained by the genes that determine the formation of these particular enzymes not yet having become operative. Likewise, the injection of female sex hormones into newborn mice has very different effects on cells of the reproductive system than it has if it is injected into older animals. In other words, it seems that extranuclear factors that lead to the expression of different genes act in a successive manner during development, with one preparing cells for the effect of another, and so on.

There is one interesting example of a factor that at one stage of development seems to act as a suppressor of gene function and at another stage as an excitor of gene function. If enough of a foreign antigen is injected into a fetus before birth, the cells of the family that ordinarily make antibodies (antigens and antibodies were discussed on p. 37) are generally in later life *inhibited* with regard to making antibodies against that antigen. If, however, the same antigen is injected into another animal of the same kind, but this time into an animal that is a few weeks old the cells of the antibody-forming family respond very differently because now, instead of being made unable to make antibody, they become differentiated and produce a specific protein antibody in abundance which combines with the antigen that was given.

Possible mechanisms of gene suppression have been much studied by Jacob and Monod in bacterial systems and from their studies they have suggested possible mechanisms that might be involved in cell differentiation in higher species. They visualize, in addition to genes that are operative and transcribe their base sequences onto molecules of messenger RNA, genes that they term regulator genes and which direct the formation of products that can block operative genes from transcribing their base sequences onto messenger RNA. They describe how activities dependent on the two types of genes could be interrelated so that feedback mechanisms from one set of activities could exert influence on the other. Their imaginative and penetrating studies and concepts should be read by those desiring to examine this problem in depth.

In an attempt to sum up the foregoing briefly, certain points might be made. Present-day opinion is that all body cells have the same complement of DNA and hence the same complement of genes. Differentiation involves the activation and suppression of different genes. The combination of DNA with histones, or the chemical state of the histones with which DNA is combined, may be involved in gene expression or suppression. The suppression of genes that occurs when definite cell families are established in the body seems to be irreversible. Which genes will be expressed and which genes will be suppressed in differentiating cells seems to be dependent on extranuclear factors, and this, of course, means that environment can affect cell differentiation. However, the ability of different extranuclear factors to affect gene expression is dependent on the cells on which they act being in a proper stage of development. Mechanisms are known, such as the induction of enzymes, that could explain how the expression of certain genes could be stimulated. Mechanisms are also known in bacterial systems that could account for gene suppression. Why gene suppression should be irreversible, when cell families are established, is not well understood. The further elucidation of the mechanisms involved in cell differentiation is at the moment one of the greatest challenges in modern biology. The new knowledge about the chemistry of heredity has not explained cell differentiation but has provided a basis for its investigation by the technics of molecular biology.

In subsequent chapters many examples of differentiation will be described and discussed in relation to different tissues and organs.

## REFERENCES FOR CHAPTERS 5, 6, AND 7: CELL STRUCTURE AND CELL BIOLOGY

First, some books that deal with at least some aspects of cell structure and cell biology are listed. Most of these books provide comprehensive bibliographies for further reading.

Secondly, those who wish to keep up to date on any particular matter in this field should consult the more recent numbers of the several journals which deal with cell structure and cell biology. A list of these journals that are published in English is provided.

Thirdly, only a few of the enormous number of individual papers that have been written about cell structure and cell biology can be listed in a textbook which deals with the broad subject of histology. In general, an attempt has been made to list (1) papers mentioned in the text, (2) important papers of historical interest and significance, and (3) comprehensive articles or reviews which include extensive bibliographies. The order followed in listing these references will be the same order as that in which various aspects of cell structure and cell biology are discussed in the text of Chapters 5, 6 and 7. Accordingly, references will be found under approximately the same headings that distinguish these different parts of the text.

### Books

Brachet, J., and Mirsky, A. E. (eds.): The Cell, vols. 1-6, New York, Acad. Press (the different volumes have been published at different dates from 1959 on).

DeRobertis, E. D. P., Nowinski, W. W., and Saez, F. A.: General Cytology, ed. 3, Philadelphia, Saunders, 1960.

Engström, A., and Finean, J. B.: Biological Ultrastructure, New York, Acad. Press, 1958.

Loewy, A. G., and Siekevitz, P.: Cell Structure and Function, New York, Holt, Rinehart and Winston, 1963.

McElroy, W. D., and Glass, B. (eds.): The Chemical Basis of Development, Symposium, Baltimore, Johns Hopkins Press, 1958.

Palay, S. L. (ed.): Frontiers in Cytology, New Haven, Conn., Yale University Press, 1958.

Waddington, C. H. (ed.): Biological Organization: Cellular and Sub-cellular, New York, Pergamon Press, 1959.

### Books of the Atlas Type Illustrating Fine Structure

Porter, K. R., and Bonneville, M. A.: An Introduction to the Fine Structure of Cells and Tissues, ed. 2, Philadelphia, Lea & Febiger, 1964.

Rhodin, J. A. G.: An Atlas of Ultrastructure, Philadelphia, Saunders, 1963. (N.B.: Rhodin's *Atlas* contains an extensive bibliography relating to the fine structure of cells, tissues and organs.)

### JOURNALS

A list of journals published in English, in which important articles relating to cell structure and cell biology commonly appear. The journals listed in *italics* have special reference to histology.

Acta Anatomica
*American Journal of Anatomy*
*Anatomical Record*
Blood, Journal of Hematology
Cancer Research
Developmental Biology
Endocrinology
Experimental and Molecular Pathology
*Experimental Cell Research*
Fertility and Sterility
*Journal of Anatomy*
*Journal of Cell Biology*
Journal of Comparative Neurology
Journal of Histochemistry and Cytochemistry
Journal of Morphology and Experimental Biology
Journal of the National Cancer Institute
*Journal of Ultrastructure Research*
Laboratory Investigation
Nature
Proceedings of the National Academy of Sciences
Proceedings of the Society of Experimental Biology and Medicine
Science

### 1. CELL POPULATIONS. THE EFFECTS OF DIFFERENTIATION ON THE REPRODUCTIVE CAPACITY OF CELLS. CELL FAMILIES. STEM CELLS

Enesco, M., and Leblond, C. P.: Increase in cell number as a factor in the growth of organs and tissues of the young male rat, J. Embryol. Exp. Morphol. 10:530, 1962.

Ford, C. E., Micklem, H. S., and Gray, S. M.: Evidence of selective proliferation of reticular cell clones in heavily irradiated mice, Brit. J. Radiol. 32:280, 1959.

Leblond, C. P.: Classification of cell populations on the basis of their proliferative behaviour,

National Cancer Institute Monograph #14, p. 119, 1964.

Leblond, C. P., and Walker, B. E.: Renewal of cell populations, Physiol. Rev. 36:255, 1956.

Siminovitch, L., Till, J. E., and McCulloch, E. A.: Decline in colony-forming ability of marrow cells subjected to serial transplantation into irradiated mice, J. Cell. Comp. Physiol. 64:23, 1964.

Till, J. E., McCulloch, E. A., and Siminovitch, L.: A stochastic model of stem cell proliferation based on the growth of spleen colony-forming cells, Proc. Nat. Acad. Sci. 51:29, 1964.

### Cells In Vitro

Hayflick, Leonard: History of the development of human diploid cell strains *in* Proceed. Human Diploid Cell Strains, p. 37, 1963.

Merchant, D. J., and Neel, J. V.: (Preface) Approaches to the Genetic Analysis of Mammalian Cells, Ann Arbor, Univ. Michigan Press, 1962.

Parker, R. C.: Methods of Tissue Culture, ed. 3, New York, Hoeber, 1961.

Puck, T. T.: Quantitative studies on mammalian cells *in vitro*, Rev. Modern Physics 31:433, 1959.

Puck, T. T., Cieciura, S. J., and Fisher, H. W.: Clonal growth *in vitro* of human cells with fibroblastic morphology, J. Exp. Med. 106:145, 1957.

### 2. THE CHROMATIN OF INTERPHASE NUCLEI, INCLUDING DIFFERENCES IN APPEARANCE DUE TO DIFFERENT SEX CHROMOSOMES

Barr, M. L.: The sex chromatin and its application to errors in sex development *in* Modern Trends in Obstetrics and Gynaecology, London, Butterworth, 1960.

———: The significance of the sex chromatin, Internat. Rev. Cytol. in press, 1965.

———: Sexual dimorphism in interphase nuclei, Am. J. Human Genet. 12:118, 1960.

———: Nuclear sex, Science 126:1187, 1957.

Barr, M. L., and Bertram, E. G.: A morphological distinction between neurons of the male and female, and the behaviour of the nucleolar satellite during accelerated nucleoprotein synthesis, Nature 163:676, 1949.

Barr, M. L., Bertram, L. F., and Lindsay, H. A.: The morphology of the nerve cell nucleus, according to sex, Anat. Rec. 107:283, 1950.

Davidson, W. M., and Smith, D. R.: A morphological sex difference in the polymorphonuclear neutrophil leucocytes, Brit. M. J. 1:6, 1954.

Klinger, H. P.: The fine structure of the sex chromatin body, Exp. Cell Res. 14:207, 1958.

Lyon, M. F.: Sex chromatin and gene action in

the mammalian X-chromosome, Am. J. Human Genet. *14*:135, 1962.

Moore, K. L.: Smears from the oral mucosa in the detection of chromosomal sex, Lancet *2*:57, 1955.

———: Sex reversal in newborn babies, Lancet *1*:217, 1959.

Moore, K. L. (ed): Sex Chromatin, Philadelphia, Saunders, in press, 1965.

### 3. THE PROCESS OF MITOSIS. EFFECTS OF COLCHICINE

Bertalanffy, F. D.: Tritiated thymidine vs. colchicine technique in the study of cell population cytodynamics, Lab. Invest. *13*:871, 1964.

Buck, R. C.: The central spindle and the cleavage furrow *in* Levine, L. (ed.): The Cell in Mitosis, p. 55, New York, Acad. Press, 1963.

Carrière, R., Leblond, C. P., and Messier, B.: Increase in the size of liver cell nuclei before mitosis, J. Exp. Cell Res. *23*:625, 1961.

Eigsti, O. J., and Dustin, P.: Colchicine in Agriculture, Medicine, Biology, and Chemistry, Ames, Iowa State College Press, 1955.

Levine, L. (ed.): The Cell in Mitosis, New York, Acad. Press, 1963.

Mazia, Daniel: Mitosis and the physiology of cell division *in* Brachet, J., and Mirsky, A. E. (eds.): The Cell, vol. 3, p. 77, New York, Acad. Press, 1961.

### 4. MORPHOLOGY OF METAPHASE CHROMOSOMES. KARYOTYPES. POLYPLOIDY

A Proposed Standard of Nomenclature of Human Mitotic Chromosomes, Cerebral Palsy Bull. (Suppl.) *2*(3):1, 1960.

Beams, H. W., and King, R. L.: The origin of binucleate and large mononucleate cells in the liver of the rat, Anat. Rec. *82*:281, 1942.

Burdette, W. J.: Methodology in Human Genetics, p. 436, San Francisco, Holden-Day, 1962.

———: Methodology in Mammalian Genetics, p. 646, San Francisco, Holden-Day, 1963.

Montagu, M. F. Ashley (ed.): Genetic Mechanisms in Human Disease (Human Chromosome Bibliography to 1961—Classical Papers), p. 592, Springfield, Ill., Thomas, 1961.

Rothfels, K. H., and Siminovitch, L.: The chromosome complement of the Rhesus monkey (Macaca mulatta) determined in kidney cells cultivated *in vitro*, Chromosoma *9*:163, 1958.

Sachs, L., and Shelesnyak, M. C.: The development and suppression of polyploidy in the developing and suppressed deciduoma in the rat, J. Endocrinol. *12*:146, 1951.

Stich, H. F.: The DNA content of tumor cells. II. Alterations during the formation of hepa-tomas in rats, J. Nat. Cancer Inst. *24*:1283, 1960.

———: Chromosomes and carcinogenesis, Canad. Cancer Conf. *5*:99, 1963.

Tjio, J. H., and Puck, T. T.: The somatic chromosomes of man, Proc. Nat. Acad. Sci. *44*:1229, 1958.

White, M. J. D.: The Chromosomes, New York, Wiley, 1961.

Wilson, J. W., and Leduc, E. H.: The occurrence and formation of binucleate and multinucleate cells and polyploid nuclei in the mouse liver, Am. J. Anat. *82*:353, 1948.

### 5. CHEMISTRY AND HISTOCHEMISTRY OF CHROMATIN AND CHROMOSOMES. DNA

Kurnick, N. B.: Histochemistry of nucleic acids, Internat. Rev. Cytol. *4*:221, 1955.

Lessler, M. A.: The nature and specificity of the Feulgen nucleal reaction, Internat. Rev. Cytol. *2*:231, 1953.

Mazia, D.: Some problems in the chemistry of mitosis *in* McElroy, W. D. and Glass, B. (eds.): The Chemical Basis of Development, Symposium, Baltimore, Johns Hopkins Press, 1958.

Thomson, R. Y., and Frazer, S. C.: The desoxyribonucleic acid content of individual rat cell nuclei, Exp. Cell Res. *7*:367, 1954.

### 6. THE CHEMISTRY OF HEREDITY. THE CHEMICAL BASIS OF GENES. THE DUPLICATION OF DNA

Cairns, J.: The form and duplication of DNA, Endeavour *22*:141, 1963.

Crick, F. H. C.: Genetic code, Science *139*:461, 1963.

Ochoa, Severo: The chemical basis of heredity—the genetic code, Bull. N. Y. Acad. Sci. Med. *40*(5):387, 1964.

———: Synthetic polynucleotides and the genetic code, Canad. Cancer Conf. *5*:37, 1963.

Siminovitch, L.: The chemical basis of heredity in viruses and cells, Canad. M. A. J. *86*:1137, 1962.

Watson, J. D., and Crick, F. H. C.: Genetical implications of the structure of deoxyribonucleic acid, Nature *171*:737, 1953.

### 7. FOLLOWING LABELED CHROMOSOMES. THE CELL CYCLE

Messier, B., and Leblond, C. P.: Cell proliferation and migration as revealed by radioautography after the injection of thymidine H[3] into male rats and mice, Am. J. Anat. *106*:247, 1960.

Stanners, C. P., and Till, J. E.: DNA synthesis in individual L-strain mouse cells, Biochem. biophys. acta *37*:406, 1960.

Taylor, J. H.: Chromosome reproduction *in* International Reviews of Cytology, vol. 13, p. 39, 1962.

———: The time and mode of duplication of chromosomes, Am. Naturalist *91*:209, 1957.

## 8. THE FINE STRUCTURE OF CHROMOSOMES

Bennett, H. S.: Fine structure of cell nucleus, chromosomes, nucleoli and membrane in biophysical science *in* Oncley, J. L., *et al.* (eds.): A Study Program, p. 297, New York, Wiley, 1959.

Dales, S.: A study of the fine structure of mammalian somatic chromosomes, Exp. Cell Res. *19*:577, 1960.

Locke, M.: Role of chromosomes in development, 23rd Symposium on the Study of Growth, New York, Acad. Press, 1965.

Ris, H.: Chromosome structure *in* McElroy, W. D., and Glass, B. (eds.): Chemical Basis of Heredity, p. 23, Baltimore, Johns Hopkins Press, 1957.

———: Ultrastructure and molecular organization of genetic systems, Canad. J. Genet. Cytol. *3*:95, 1962.

## 9. EFFECTS OF RADIATION ON CHROMOSOMES

Elkind, M. M., and Whitmore, G. F.: Radiobiology of Cultured Mammalian Cells, Washington, D. C., Am. Inst. Biol. Sci., 1965.

Evans, H. J.: Chromosome aberrations induced by ionizing radiations, Internat. Rev. Cytol., vol. 13, 1962.

Whitmore, G. F., and Gulyas, S., and Botond, J.: Radiation sensitivity throughout the cell cycle and its relationship to recovery, 18th Ann. Symp. Fundamental Cancer Research, Houston, Texas, University of Texas Press, 1964.

Wolff, S. (ed.): Radiation Induced Chromosome Aberrations, New York, Columbia Univ. Press, 1963.

## 10. HOW GENETIC INFORMATION IN THE CHROMOSOMES IS MADE OPERATIVE IN THE CELL. INTRODUCTION TO RNA AND PROTEIN SYNTHESIS

Jacob, F., and Monod, J.: Genetic regulatory mechanism in the synthesis of proteins, J. Molec. Biol. *3*:318, 1961.

*See also* references in Sections 6, 15, 16 and 21.

## 11. NUCLEOLI. THE SYNTHESIS OF RNA

Amano, M., Leblond, C. P., and Nadler, N. J.: Radioautographic analysis of nuclear RNA in mouse cells revealing three pools with different turnover times, Exp. Cell. Res. (in press) 1965.

Lafontaine, J. G., and Chouinard, L. A.: A corre-

lated light and electron microscope study of the nuclear material during mitosis in *Vicia faba*, J. Cell Biol. *17*:167, 1963.

Marinozzi, V.: Cytochimie ultrastructurale du nucléole—RNA et protéines intranucléolaires, J. Ultrastruc. Res. *10*:433, 1964.

Miyai, K., and Steiner, J. W.: The fine structure of interphase liver nuclei in subacute ethionine intoxication, Exp. Molec. Path. (in press) 1965.

## 12. THE NUCLEAR MEMBRANE AND NUCLEAR PORES

Miyai, K., and Steiner, J. W.: The fine structure of interphase liver nuclei in subacute ethionine intoxication, Exp. Molec. Path. (in press) 1965.

Watson, M. L.: The nuclear envelope; its structure and relation to cytoplasmic membranes, J. Biophys. Biochem. Cytol. *1*:257, 1955.

———: Further observations of the nuclear envelope of the animal cell, J. Biophys. Biochem. Cytol. *6*:147, 1959.

———: Further observations on the nuclear envelope of the animal cell, J. Biophys. Biochem. *6*:147, 1959.

## 13. NUCLEAR SAP. INTERCHROMATINIC AND PERICHROMATINIC GRANULES

Brown, G. L., Cullan, H. G., and Leaf, G.: Chemical nature of nuclear sap, Nature *156*:600, 1950.

Miyai, K., and Steiner, J. W. (see Section 12)

Watson, M. L.: Observations on a granule associated with chromatin in the nuclei of cells of rat and mouse, J. Cell Biol. *13*:162, 1962.

## 14. THE CELL MEMBRANE

Locke, M. (ed.): Cellular Membranes in Development, New York, Acad. Press, 1964.

Robertson, J. D.: The ultrastructure of cell membranes and their derivatives, Biochem. Soc. Symposia, No. 16, 1959.

Sjöstrand, F. S., and Elfvin, L. G.: The layered, asymmetric structure of the plasma membrane in the exocrine pancreas cells of the cat, J. Ultrastruct. Res. *7*:504, 1962.

## 15. RIBOSOMES AND POLYRIBOSOMES. MESSENGER RNA. PROTEIN SYNTHESIS

Alfrey, V. G.: Nuclear ribosomes, messenger RNA and protein synthesis, Exp. Cell Res., Suppl. 9, p. 183, 1963.

Fawcett, D. W.: Changes in the fine structure of the cytoplasmic organelles during differentiation *in* Radmik, D. (ed.): Development Cytology, p. 161, New York, Ronald Press, 1959.

Garnier, C.: Du role de l'ergastoplasme dans la sécrétion, J. Anat. et physiol. *26*:22, 1900.

Haguenau, F.: The ergastoplasm: its history, ultrastructure and biochemistry, Internat. Rev. Cytol. *7*:425, 1958.

Howatson, A. F., and Ham, A. W.: Electron microscope study of sections of two rat liver tumors, Cancer Res. *15*:62, 1955.

Palade, G. E.: A small particulate component of the cytoplasm, J. Biophys. Biochem. Cytol. *1*:59, 1955.

Rich, Alexander: Polyribosomes, Sci. Am. *209*(6): 44, 1963.

Warner, J. R., Rich, A., and Hall, C. E.: Electron microscope studies of ribosomal clusters synthesizing hemoglobin, Science *138*:1399, 1962.

16. The Endoplasmic Reticulum. Rough-surfaced Endoplasmic Reticulum and the Synthesis of Protein Destined for Secretion

Palade, G. E.: Studies on the endoplasmic reticulum. II. Simple disposition in cells *in situ,* J. Biophys. Biochem. Cytol. *1*:567, 1955.

———: Functional changes in the structure of cell components *in* Hayashi, T. (ed.): Subcellular Particles, p. 64, New York, Ronald Press, 1959.

Palade, G. E., and Siekevitz, P.: Liver microsomes; an integrated morphological and biochemical study, J. Biophys. Biochem. Cytol. *2*:171, 1956.

Porter, K. R.: Electron microscopy of basophilic components of cytoplasm, J. Histochem. *2*:346, 1954.

Porter, K. R., Claude, A., and Fullam, E. F.: A study of tissue culture cells by electron microscopy, J. Exp. Med. *81*:233, 1945.

Warshawsky, H., Leblond, C. P., and Droz, B.: Synthesis and migration of proteins in the cells of exocrine pancreas as revealed by specific activity determination from radioautographs, J. Cell Biol. *16*:1, 1963.

Weiss, J. M.: The ergastoplasm: its fine structure and relation to protein synthesis as studied with the electron microscope in the pancreas of the Swiss albino mouse, J. Exp. Med. *98*:607, 1953.

17. The Golgi Apparatus

Badinez, O., Gasic, G., Loebel, F., and Baydak, T.: Examination of the Golgi zone using Hale's procedure, Nature *193*:704, 1962.

Baker, J. R.: New developments in the Golgi controversy, J. Roy. Micro. Soc. *82*:145, 1963.

Caro, L. G., and Palade, G. E.: Protein synthesis, storage and discharge in the pancreatic exocrine cell. An autoradiographic study, J. Cell Biol. *20*: 473, 1964.

Dalton, A. J., and Felix, M. D.: A study of the Golgi substances and ergastoplasm in a series of mammalian cell types *in* Fine Structure of Cells, p. 170, New York, Interscience, 1954.

———: A comparative study of the Golgi complex, J. Biophys. Biochem. Cytol. *2*:79, 1956.

Farquhar, M. G., and Wellings, S. R.: Electron microscopic evidence suggesting secretory granule formation within the Golgi apparatus, J. Biophys. Biochem. Cytol. *3*:319, 1957.

Florey, H. W., Wright, R. D., and Jennings, M. A.: The secretions of the intestine, Physiol. Rev. *21*:36, 1941.

Glegg, R. E., Clermont, Y., and Leblond, C. P.: The use of lead tetraacetate, benzidine, o-dianisidine and a "film test" to investigate the significance of the "periodic acid-fuchsin sulfurous acid" technique in carbohydrate histochemistry, Stain Technol. *27*:277, 1952.

Hirsch, G. C.: Die Flieszbandarbeit in der exokrinen Pankreaszelle bei der Produktion von Enzymen mit einem Exkurs über Ergastoplasma und Golgi-Körper, Natureissensch. *2*:25, 1960.

Hokin, L. E.: Isolation of the zymogen granules of dog pancreas and a study of their properties, Biochem. biophys. acta *18*:379, 1955.

Kallenbach, E., Sandborn, E., and Warshawsky, H.: The Golgi apparatus of the ameloblast of the rat at the stage of enamel matrix formation, J. Cell Biol. *16*:629, 1963.

Leblond, C. P., Glegg, R. E., and Eidinger, D.: Presence of carbohydrates with free 1,2-glycol groups in sites stained by the periodic acid-Schiff technique, J. Histochem. Cytochem. *5*: 445, 1957.

Mollenhaurer, H. H., and Whaley, W. G.: An observation on the functioning of the Golgi apparatus, J. Cell Biol. *17*:222, 1963.

Nadler, N. J., Young, B. A., Leblond, C. P., and Mitmaker, B.: Elaboration of thyroglobulin in the thyroid follicle, Endocrinology *74*:333, 1964.

Novikoff, A. B., Esner, E., and Quintana, N.: Golgi apparatus and lysosomes, Fed. Proc. *23*: 1010, 1964.

Palade, G. E., Siekevitz, P., and Caro, L.: *In* Ciba Symposium on the Exocrine Pancreas, p. 23, London, Churchill, 1962.

Peterson, Marian, and Leblond, C. P.: Synthesis of complex carbohydrates in the Golgi region as shown by radioautography after injection of labeled glucose, J. Cell Biol. *21*:143, 1964.

Revel, J. P., and Hay, E. D.: An autoradiographic and electron microscopic study of collagen synthesis in differentiating cartilage. Z. Zellforsch. mikr. Anat. *61*:110, 1963.

Sjöstrand, F. S., and Hanzon, V.: Ultrastructure of Golgi apparatus of exocrine cells of mouse pancreas, Exp. Cell Res. *7*:415, 1954.

Van Heyningen, H. E.: Secretion of proteins by the acinar cells of the rat pancreas, as studied by electron microscopic radioautography, Anat. Rec. *148*:485, 1964.

Warshawsky, H., Leblond, C. P., and Droz, B.: Synthesis and migration of proteins in the cells of the exocrine pancreas as revealed by specific activity determinations from radioautographs, J. Cell Biol. *16*:1, 1963.

Young, B. A., and Leblond, C. P.: The light cell as compared to the follicular cell in the thyroid gland of the rat, Endocrinology *73*:669, 1963.

### 18. MITOCHONDRIA

Bensley, R. R., and Hoerr, N.: The preparation and properties of mitochondria, Anat. Rec. *60*: 449, 1934.

————: Studies on cell structure by the freezing-drying method. VI. The preparation and properties of mitochondria, Anat. Rec. *60*:449, 1934.

Chance, B., and Parsons, D. F.: Cytochrome function in relation to inner membrane structure of mitochondria, Science *142*:1176, 1963.

Chance, B., Parsons, D. F., and Williams, G. R.: Cytochrome content of mitochondria stripped of inner membrane structure, Science *143*:136, 1964.

Claude, A., and Fullam, E. F.: Electron microscope study of isolated mitochondria, J. Exp. Med. *81*:51, 1945.

Cowdry, E. G.: The mitochondrial constituents of protoplasm, Contrib. Embryol. *271*:39, 1918.

Fernandez Moran, H., Oda, T., Blair, P. V., and Green, D. E.: A macromolecular repeating unit of mitochondrial structure and function, J. Cell Biol. *22*:63, 1964.

Goldfischer, S., Essner, E., and Novikoff, A. B.: The localization of phosphatase activities at the level of ultrastructure, J. Histochem. Cytochem. *12*:72, 1964.

Lehninger, A. L.: The Mitochondrion, New York, W. A. Benjamin Inc., 1964.

Luck, D. J. L., and Reich, E.: DNA in mitochondria of *Neurospora crassa*, Proc. Nat. Acad. Sci. *52*:931, 1964.

Palade, G. E.: An electron microscope study of the mitochondrial structure, J. Histochem. *1*: 188, 1953.

————: The fine structure of mitochondria, Anat. Rec. *114*:427, 1952.

————: Functional changes in the structure of cell components *in* Hayashi, T. (ed.): Subcellular Particles, p. 64, New York, Ronald Press, 1959.

Parsons, D. F.: Mitochondrial structure: Two types of subunits on negatively stained mitochondrial membranes, Science *140*:985, 1963.

————: Recent advances correlating structure and function in mitochondria, Internat. Rev. Exp. Path. (in press) 1965.

### 19. LYSOSOMES

deDuve, Christian: The lysosome, Sci. Am. *208*(5):64, 1963.

deReuck, A. V. S., and Cameron, M. P. (eds.): Lysosomes, Ciba Foundation Symposium, London, Churchill, 1963. (This publication contains articles by deDuve, Novikoff and many others.)

Novikoff, A. B., and Esner, E.: Cytolysomes and mitochondrial degeneration, J. Cell Biol. *15*: 140, 1962.

Novikoff, A. B., Esner, E., and Quintana, N.: Golgi apparatus and lysosomes, Fed. Proc. *23*: 1010, 1964.

### 20. CYTOPLASMIC INCLUSIONS

#### *Secretion Granules*

See references in Sections 16 and 17.

#### *Stored Foods*

See references on liver, Chapter 25.

#### *Bile Pigment*

Rich, A. R.: The formation of bile pigment, Physiol. Rev. *5*:182, 1925.

*See also* references on liver, Chapter 25.

#### *Melanin Pigment*

See references for Chapter 23.

#### *Carotenoids*

Karrer, P., and Jucker, E.: Carotenoids, Princeton, N. J., Van Nostrand (Elsevier), 1950.

### 21. CELL DIFFERENTIATION

Alfrey, V. G., Faulkner, R., and Mirsky, A. E.: Acetylation and methylation of histones and their possible role in the relation of DNA synthesis, Proc. Nat. Acad. Sci. *51*:786, 1964.

Attardi, G.: Stimulation of the rate of synthesis of specific messenger RNA after enzyme induction in *E. coli in* Harris, R. J. C. (ed.): Biological Organization at the Cellular and Supercellular Level, p. 43, New York, Acad. Press, 1963.

Bloch, D. P.: The histones: Syntheses transitions and functions *in* Levine, L. (ed.): The Cell in Mitosis, p. 205, New York, Acad. Press, 1963.

Brachet, J.: The Biochemistry of Development, New York, Pergamon Press, 1960.

Fell, H. B.: Histogenesis in tissue culture *in* Cytology and Cell Physiology, London, Oxford, 1951.

————: Recent advances in organ culture, Sc. Prog. *162*:212, 1953.

Flickinger, R. A.: Cell differentiation: Some aspects of the problem, Science *141*:608, 1963.

Huang, Ru-Chih, and Bonner, James: Histone

suppressor of chromosomal RNA synthesis, Proc. Nat. Acad. Sci. *48*:1216, 1962.

Jacob, François, and Monod, Jacques: On the regulation of gene activity, Sympos. Quant. Biol. *26*:193, 1961.

————: Elements of regulatory circuits in bacteria *in* Harris, R. J. C. (ed.): Biological Organization at the Cellular and Supercellular Level, p. 1, New York, Acad. Press, 1963.

————: Genetic repression, allosteric inhibition and cellular differentiation *in* Cytodifferentiation and Macromolecular Synthesis, 21st Symposium, p. 30, New York, Acad. Press, 1963.

King, T. J., and Briggs, R.: Changes in the nuclei of differentiating gastrula cells, as demonstrated by nuclear transplantation, Proc. Nat. Acad. Sci. *41*:321, 1955.

————: The transplantability of nuclei of arrested hybrid blastulae (*R. pipiens* ♀ X. *R. Catesbiana* ♂), J. Exp. Zool. *123*:61, 1953.

————: Transplantation of living nuclei of late gastrulae into enucleated eggs of *Rana pipiens*, J. Embryol. Exp. Morph. *2*:73, 1954.

McElroy, W. D., and Glass, B. (eds.): The Chemical Basis of Development, Baltimore, Johns Hopkins Press, 1958.

Monod, Jacques, and Jacob, François: General conclusions: Teleonomic mechanisms in cellular metabolism, growth, and differentiation, Sympos. Quant. Biol. *26*:389, 1961.

Needham, J.: Biochemistry and Morphogenesis, London, Cambridge Univ. Press, 1942.

Sonneborn, T. M.: Beyond the gene, Am. Sci. *37*:33, 1949.

Waddington, C. H.: Organizers and Genes, London, Cambridge Univ. Press, 1940.

Waddington, C. H. (ed.): Biological Organization, Cellular and Sub-cellular, New York, Pergamon Press, 1959.

PART THREE

# The Four Primary Tissues and Their Subdivisions

# 8   The Four Primary Tissues; Epithelial Tissue

## INTRODUCTION

There are only 4 basic types of tissue in the human body; everything in it is built of these. Each has a characteristic and distinguishing appearance. Hence, when a student views an unknown section, to recognize the tissues he sees therein does not require that a thousand possibilities be considered, but only 4, and if he knows the fundamental differences between the 4 basic types well, he can decide with ease which of the 4 is represented. It is true that each of the 4 basic types contains subtypes, but the way a subtype of any one tissue varies from its basic plan will not be found to be very great. It cannot be emphasized too strongly that the most important step toward histologic and histopathologic competence is understanding the nature and knowing the appearance of the 4 basic tissues. They are:

1. Epithelial tissue
2. Connective tissue
3. Muscular tissue
4. Nervous tissue

## A SUGGESTION ON HOW TO STUDY THE TISSUES

The student will find it helpful, as he proceeds through the study of the four basic tissues and their various subdivisions, to construct, step by step, on a large piece of paper, a chart of the tissues, similar to that shown on the next page. The sheet of paper should be large enough for the student to make little drawings beside each subdivision in the classification of the microscopic appearance of the particular kind of tissue listed. By the time a student has made *his own* classification of the tissues and understands it, and knows the typical appearance of every subtype in it, he will be admirably equipped to begin the study of the last part of the course which deals with the microscopic anatomy of different organs and other structures, for these are all assembled from the kinds of tissue he already knows.

## EPITHELIAL TISSUE

**Origin of the Term "Epithelium."** The term *epithelium* is derived from *epi* = upon and *thele* = nipple. It was first used with regard to the translucent membrane that covers the lips. Under this epithelium are little nipples or papillae of connective tissue which are rich in capillaries and which project into the epithelial membrane but not through it. Lips appear red because the epithelium of the lips is translucent and the red blood in the capillaries of the nipples or papillae of connective tissue that project into the epithelium is thus visible.

**How the Meaning of the Term Broadened.** From the beginning described above, the meaning of epithelium came to be used for all the cellular membranes, whether they were translucent or opaque, that cover and line surfaces on or in the body. It should be noted here that the terms "covering" and "lining" are not synonymous. For example, a tennis ball is covered with felt, but is lined with rubber. Hence one says that the body is *covered* with epithelium, but the tubes of the body such as the intestine or trachea are *lined* with epithelium.

As microscopy developed, the meaning of epithelium came to include more than covering and lining membranes, for it was found out in embryologic studies that during development the cells of epithelial covering and lining membranes often grew into the body substance that was deep to the membranes to form structures called *glands*. These and their development will be described in the next

A MORPHOLOGIC CLASSIFICATION OF THE TISSUES

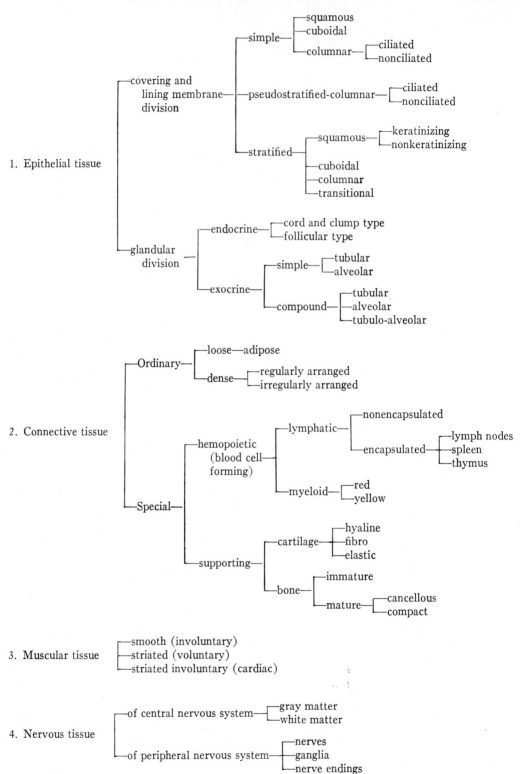

chapter. So there are two broad divisions of epithelial tissue:

Epithelial tissue:
1. Covering and lining membranes
2. Glands that develop from covering and lining membranes

In this chapter we shall consider only covering and lining membranes.

## EMBRYOLOGIC ORIGIN OF EPITHELIUM

At one early stage of development, the embryo is shaped something like a tube, the lumen of which is destined to become the intestinal canal. The embryo, at this time, is covered with a layer of cells termed the *ectoderm*. The tube is lined by another layer of cells, the *endoderm*, that is destined to form the lining of the intestine and certain glands. Between the ectoderm and the endoderm is the *mesoderm*. These 3 layers are referred to as the 3 primary germ layers.

Since the ectoderm *covers*, and endoderm *lines* the embryo, both ectoderm and endoderm are epithelial membranes; indeed, they serve as the origin for most of the epithelium that arises in subsequent development. Because of these facts, it becomes a temptation to use the word epithelium as if it had embryologic significance, inferring an origin from ectoderm and endoderm. But the fact is that a not inconsiderable amount of epithelium in the body (that of most of the urinary and the genital systems and that of the adrenal cortex) and which is in the form of lining membranes or glands similar in appearance to those that develop from ectoderm and endoderm, is derived from mesoderm. Therefore, the tissue that is termed epithelium in postnatal life is called epithelium because of its appearance, position and function and *not* because of its embryologic origin.

**"Endothelium" and "mesothelium" are exceptions to the rule.** Having said that epithelium is a term that is defined by structural, positional and functional criteria, and not because of its developing from any particular germ layers, we now have to say that there are two important exceptions to this rule. The cells that line the tubes of the blood vascular

and lymphatic systems, which in structure, position and function are typically epithelial, develop from mesoderm and are generally referred to as endothelial cells, and the membrane they constitute, an endothelial membrane. The cells that line the great body cavities and cover the organs that occupy these cavities also are typical of squamous epithelial cells in their structure, position and function, but are termed *mesothelial* cells, and the membrane they constitute is termed *mesothelium.*

The chief reason for these special names is that both endothelium and mesothelium, under certain pathologic conditions, behave more like connective tissue cells than epithelial cells (for example, malignant tumors that arise from endothelium or mesothelium are classed as sarcomas and not as carcinomas).

**General Function of Epithelial Membranes.** Since epithelium covers or lines body surfaces, it is obvious that one of its functions is that of *providing protection*. But it has others. The epithelium that lines the intestine must, in addition to providing protection, absorb certain products of digestion into the body. Hence *selective absorption* is a second function of some kinds of epithelial membranes. Furthermore, the inner surfaces of many of the tubes in the body that are lined by epithelium must be kept wet and more or less lubricated. In order to satisfy this requirement, certain cells of some epithelial membranes must possess *secretory functions* by which they exude certain fluid materials onto the surface that they line to keep it wet.

**Reasons for There Being Different Types of Epithelial Membranes.** Since the kind and the extent of protection required by epithelium membranes differs greatly in different parts of the body, it is only to be expected that the histologic structure of various epithelial membranes will differ in relation to the amount and the kind of protection they have to provide in various locations. Furthermore, since epithelial membranes in some sites have to perform absorptive and/or secretory functions, as well as providing protection, it is to be expected that in these sites the histologic structure of the membranes will be different from that where these other functions are not required. But since there are features which

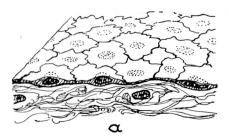

a

Simple squamous

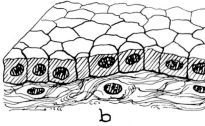

b

Simple cuboidal

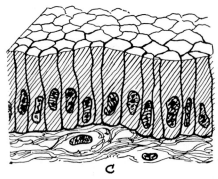

c

Simple columnar

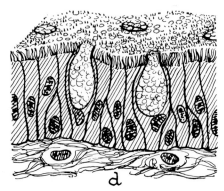

d

Pseudostratified
columnar ciliated

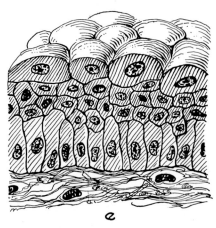

e

Transitional

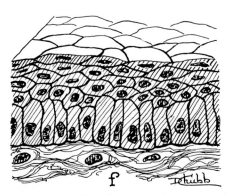

f

Stratified squamous
(nonkeratinized)

FIG. 8-1. Three-dimensional diagrams illustrating the different types of epithelial membranes found on wet surfaces.

all epithelial membranes have in common, we shall describe these first and then later take up, one by one, the different kinds of epithelial membranes that serve special purposes in various parts of the body.

**Some Features That Epithelial Membranes Have in Common.** Epithelial membranes consist entirely of cells; various types to be described later are shown in Figure 8-1. The cells are fitted together so closely that epithelial membranes are true continuous membranes. The structural components of epithelial cells that are involved in holding them close together will be considered in detail later in this chapter.

*Epithelial membranes in themselves contain no capillaries.* Hence the cells of epithelial membranes must obtain their nourishment from the capillaries of connective tissue. The latter tissue is always found beneath an epithelial membrane. The ways in which epithelial cells are nourished from the capillaries of connective tissue will be considered in detail in Chapter 10.

The connective tissue on which epithelial membranes always rest provides, in addition to nourishment, support for the epithelial membranes. Since epithelium consists only of cells, epithelial membranes, though continuous, are not strong. In general they are bound firmly to the connective tissue by which they are supported. The binding of epithelial membrane to connective tissue is aided by the fact that there is generally, between the epithelial membrane and the underlying connective tissue, a very thin layer of nonliving material called a basement membrane (Fig. 8-2, B.M.) which, though very permeable, serves an adhesive function. Recent information suggests that basement membranes are synthesized jointly by the epithelium and connective tissue. Basement membranes will be described and discussed in more detail in connection with connective tissue.

All epithelial membranes are subjected to a certain normal amount of wear and tear, and some, such as the epithelium of the skin, are not infrequently subjected to injuries which disrupt their continuity, sometimes over considerable areas, as for example occurs in thermal burns. At least some of the cells of epithelial membranes must therefore be capable of division so as to provide new cells for those that are lost from normal wear and tear and also to regenerate areas of membrane that are destroyed through accidents. The various phases of mitosis illustrated in Figure 6-7 are all examples of mitosis occurring in the cells of an epithelial membrane.

Having given this general introductory account of epithelial membranes we shall now consider how epithelial membranes differ from one another because of the special require-

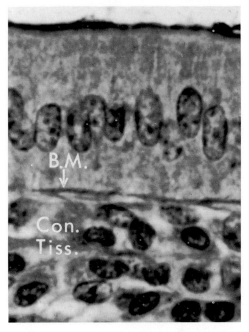

Fig. 8-2. Photomicrograph of section of mouse intestinal epithelium stained by the PAS method. Mucus on the free surfaces of the cells is stained by this method, as is the basement membrane (B.M.) that is seen between the bases of the epithelial cells and the connective tissue (con. tiss.) on which the epithelial membrane rests.

ments that must be fulfilled in various parts of the body.

**Simple and Stratified Epithelium.** Epithelial membranes are adapted to the functions they must perform in various parts of the body, as will be described presently. Here, however, it should be mentioned that the functions of some epithelial membranes are performed by, and indeed require, a membrane that consists of only a single layer of cells; such a membrane is termed a *simple* epithelial membrane. The function performed by epithelium in other parts of the body requires that membranes be two or more cells in thickness; such epithelium is termed *stratified*.

**The Differences Between Epithelial Membranes That Cover Wet and Dry Surfaces.** There is an extremely important difference between the epithelial membranes of *wet* and *dry* surfaces. It is possible for the surface cells of any stratified epithelial membrane to re-

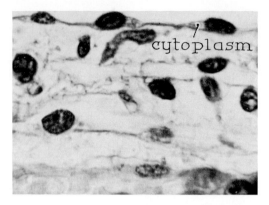
cytoplasm

Fig. 8-3. Simple squamous epithelium runs across the top from one side to the other. This is how it appears in sections cut at right angles to its flat surface. Note how the nuclei bulge to form small bumps on its free surface and that the cytoplasm is very thin.

main alive if the surface at which they are situated is always kept wet with a suitable fluid. For example, the surface cells of the epithelial membrane that lines the cheek remain alive because the inside of the mouth is always kept wet with saliva. If the student draws his finger across the inside of his cheek (it is not necessary to scratch it, the surface cells wipe off readily) and dabs the material so obtained on a glass slide and stains it, he will see surface cells complete with reasonably healthy appearing nuclei (Fig. 6-6).

However, in any stratified epithelial membrane that covers the exterior of the body and hence is exposed to air, the cells of the outermost layer cannot remain alive because they would become dehydrated. Hence, the surface cells of dry epithelial membranes do not remain alive, but fuse together and become converted into a horny material called *keratin* (Fig. 8-20). Since this is an *albuminoid* (a tough type of protein) and relatively insoluble and impermeable, it forms a protective sheet of waterproof material which preserves the fluid environment of the epithelial cells of the deeper layers of the membrane (Fig. 8-20). Since the deeper, living epithelial cells constantly reproduce themselves, new cells are constantly pushed toward the surface, and as they approach it they become converted into keratin to replace that which is worn

away. So the process of keratinization is a continuous one.

Not all the epithelial surfaces that are in contact with air become keratinized, and very ingenious arrangements exist to keep such nonkeratinized external surfaces wet. For example, if the outer layers of the membrane covering the front of the eye, through which one sees, became keratinized, the eye could not function, because keratin does not transmit light readily. The surface of the eye is covered with epithelial cells that do not become keratinized; therefore, these must be kept wet with a thin film of moisture. This is accomplished by glands associated with the eye secreting small amounts of the same fluid that is seen more obviously when its secretion is stimulated by weeping. The right amount of this fluid, secreted normally, is kept spread over the surface of the eye by the frequent blinking of the eyelids that occurs automatically in a normal individual.

## TYPES OF EPITHELIUM FOUND ON WET SURFACES

### SIMPLE EPITHELIUM

Simple epithelium is only 1 cell thick. Simple squamous (squamous means scalelike) epithelium consists of a single layer of *thin flat* cells of irregular outline that fit together to form a continuous, thin membrane. A 3-dimensional view of simple squamous epithelium is given in (Fig. 8-1, a). If the simple squamous epithelium is not too thin, it appears in sections cut at right angles to the surface, as in Figure 8-3. If it is very thin, the cytoplasm is not visible, and all that can be seen are the flattened nuclei of the cells scattered at intervals along the surface.

**Simple squamous epithelium** is adapted to performing a dialyzing or filtering function. It is not adapted to withstanding wear and tear. As previously noted, the endothelium that lines the blood-vascular and lymphatic systems is morphologically simple squamous epithelium. So is the mesothelium that lines the great body cavities. The EM has shown that there is a continuous membrane of very thin simple squamous epithelium present in, and lining, the air spaces in the lung. Oxygen, to enter blood, must pass through it and the endothelium of the lung capillaries. It is dif-

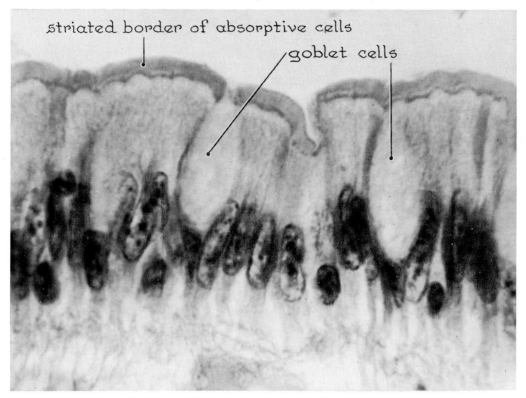

striated border of absorptive cells

goblet cells

FIG. 8-4. A very high-power photomicrograph of a section of the jejunum of a dog. The basement membrane is indistinct. A well-marked striated border is present on the absorptive cells. Two goblet cells opening through the striated border may be seen in this illustration.

ficult to suggest examples of this type of membrane, other than endothelium and mesothelium, that the student can find and study with ease with the light microscope. The photomicrograph appearing in Figure 8-3 was taken from the lower portion of a descending loop of Henle in the kidney. The student is perhaps best advised to postpone searching for simple squamous epithelium in this site until the kidney is studied.

**Simple Cuboidal Epithelium.** This is of a somewhat stouter character than simple squamous (Fig. 8-1, b). It is used in only a very few sites in the body; perhaps the student can find an example of it most easily in a section of the ovary, for it forms a covering for that organ. The cells of simple cuboidal epithelium are actually not cubes, as may be seen in Figure 8-1, b; the name "cuboidal" refers to the side appearance of cells when they are sectioned at right angles to the surface that they cover.

**Simple Columnar Epithelium.** This type of

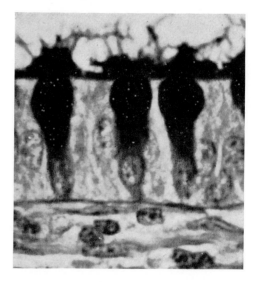

FIG. 8-5. Intestinal epithelium of mouse stained by the PAS technic. Three goblet cells are evident, with their secretion flowing over the free surfaces of adjacent cells. The basement membrane also can be seen.

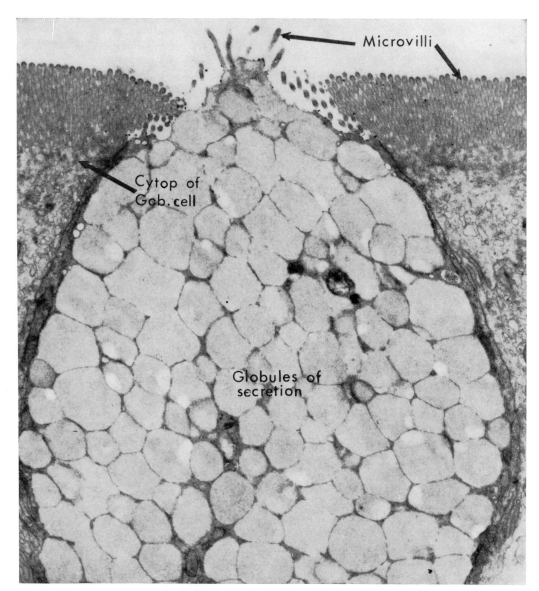

Microvilli

Cytop of
Gob. cell

Globules of
secretion

FIG. 8-6. Electron micrograph showing the bowl portion of a goblet cell. Arrow, upper left, *crosses* thin cytoplasm of bowl. (Preparation by R. Buck)

epithelium is composed of epithelial cells that are taller than they are wide and which are more or less hexagonal in cross section. When fitted together side by side they constitute a relatively thick epithelial membrane (Fig. 8-1, c). The nuclei of the columnar cells are disposed toward the bases of the cells.

Although there are a few examples of simple columnar epithelial membranes in the body, which seem to serve no particular function except that of protecting the underlying tis-

sue, the cells of nearly all simple columnar epithelial membranes are specialized for the performance of some specialized function in addition to that of providing protection. The first of these other functions that we shall consider is that of secretion.

All or only some of the cells in a simple columnar epithelial membrane may perform a secretory function. The material that they commonly secrete is *mucus*; this is a slippery protective material, chemically a sulfate-containing glycoprotein. In some simple columnar epithelial membranes all of the cells secrete mucus; examples of this are to be found in the surface epithelium of the stomach (Fig. 24-27) and the lining of the cervical canal (Fig. 27-29). In other sites, simple epithelial membranes contain two types of columnar epithelial cells that are interspersed with one another. Those of one type are specialized to secrete mucus, and those of the other to perform one of two other functions, either that of selective absorption or that of moving mucus along the free surface of the membrane by ciliary action. The most prominent example of the first combination is seen in the lining of the small and the large intestines. The simple columnar epithelial membranes found in both of these sites are composed of two kinds of cells: goblet cells (Fig. 8-4, goblet cells) specialized to secrete mucus, and columnar absorptive cells that act to absorb selectively the products of digestion and/or water (Fig. 8-4). A good example of an epithelial membrane in which some of the cells are specialized to secrete mucus and others to move the mucus along the free surface of the membrane is to be found in parts of the upper respiratory tract where some of the lining cells are goblet cells specialized to secrete mucus, while the other kind of cells present have cilia, which are little hairlike projections from their free surface (Fig. 8-17). The cilia beat in unison and so move the mucus secreted by goblet cells along the free surface of the epithelial membrane. We shall consider this type of membrane after we have dealt with membranes that consist of a mixture of goblet cells and absorptive cells.

*Goblet cells* have already been described in connection with the discussion of the mechanism of secretion in the previous chapter. Even in H and E sections (one is illustrated in Fig. 8-4) it can be seen that the cells that are specialized to secrete mucus deserve the term "goblet cells" because even though the accumulating secretion, which distends the supranuclear portion of a cell is not stained specifically, but remains pale, it is sufficiently obvious to appear like the contents of a goblet. The mucus that is within goblet cells, and that which has been secreted and lies on the surface of adjacent absorptive cells, is colored

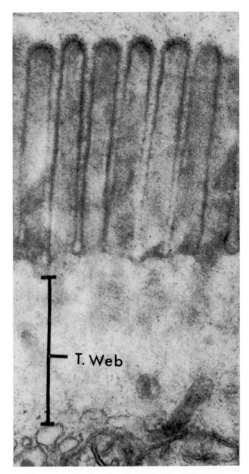

Fig. 8-7. Electron micrograph ($\times$ 52,000) of section of mouse intestine, showing microvilli projecting from surface of absorptive cells. The terminal web is also seen clearly. (Preparation by A. F. Howatson)

brilliantly by the PAS technic (Fig. 8-5). There are other stains which also demonstrate mucus to advantage.

*Fine Structure.* Palay has shown the free surface of a nonsecreting goblet cell is covered with microvilli; the latter will be described presently (Fig. 8-7). When the goblet cell is discharging its secretion the microvilli tend to disappear, only a few remain in the electron micrograph of a secreting goblet cell shown in Figure 8-6. This electron micrograph of a goblet cell (Fig. 8-6) shows only the supranuclear portion of the cell; this portion of the cell is distended by globules of mucus within the bowl of the goblet. The cytoplasm of the

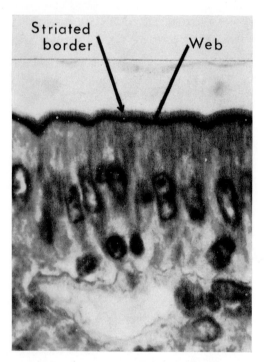

**Striated border**    **Web**

FIG. 8-8. Photomicrograph of section of mouse intestine stained by the tannic acid, phosphomolybdic acid and amido black technic. The terminal web is deeply stained and can be seen extending across the free ends of the cells just below the striated border.

absorptive cells was believed to be of the nature of a protective cuticle. However, with improved methods it became possible, with the light microscope, to demonstrate fine striations that roughly paralleled the long axes of the underlying cells in this border, and so it was termed a striated border, and different theories were suggested for its nature. When thin-sectioning methods improved to the point where this border could be studied with the EM, it was shown first by Granger and Baker, and by Dalton, that the appearance of striations was due to the cytoplasm, at the free surface of the cells, being arranged into multitudinous adjacent and very minute fingerlike projections; these are termed *microvilli* (Fig. 8-7).

Microvilli are each from 80 to 100 millimicrons in diameter and somewhat more than half a micron in length. Each is covered with cell membrane and has a core of cytoplasm which is continuous with the cytoplasm of the main part of the cell. The cytoplasm in the cores appears to be somewhat denser than cytoplasm as a whole, and the denser cytoplasm of the cores of villi can be seen to be filamentous and to extend into the region of the terminal web (as is shown in Fig. 8-9), which also has a filamentous content, as will be described presently.

It is generally considered that the purpose of microvilli is to increase the surface area through which absorption can occur. Granger and Baker have estimated that a single cell may have 3,000 microvilli and that in a square millimeter of intestinal lining there may be 200,000,000 microvilli. Although it seems most reasonable to consider that microvilli serve in providing extra surface for absorption, they are found on many kinds of cells that are not noted for absorptive functions, and so they may have other functions as well.

cell in which some flattened rough-surfaced vesicles can be seen is thinned out around the edge of the bowl, like the thin glass of a goblet.

Although all phases of the formation of mucus are not known, it seems probable that the protein components of the glycoprotein are synthesized in the rough-surfaced vesicles of the endoplasmic reticulum below and to the sides of the nucleus, and that the carbohydrate component of the glycoprotein is formed in the Golgi region as was described in the previous chapter.

**Absorptive Cells, Striated Borders and Microvilli.** In a well-fixed H and E section the absorptive cells that occupy the areas between the goblet cells of the simple columnar epithelium of the intestine are seen to be covered with a thin layer of some material of a different refractive index from that of the underlying cytoplasm (Fig. 8-4). When first noticed many years ago this superficial layer on the

## THE INTERNAL SUPPORT IN EPITHELIAL CELLS AND HOW EPITHELIAL CELLS ARE HELD TOGETHER IN MEMBRANES

**The Cell Web.** Before considering other types of epithelial membranes we cannot further postpone discussing the problem of how the cells in a membrane are held together.

In order to do this we must first consider another organelle of cytoplasm, the structure of which has been elucidated chiefly in Leblond's laboratory. This organelle is fibrillar in nature, serves a supporting role in many kinds of cells, and is known under the general term of the *cell web*. The distribution of this fibrillar material that serves more or less as a skeleton for cells differs in different kinds of cells. In the absorptive cells of the intestinal epithelium, however, it is concentrated beneath the free surface of the cell (just beneath the microvilli), and in this position it is referred to as the *terminal web* of the cell. If sections of the simple columnar epithelium of the intestine are stained by any one of several special staining methods but, in particular, by the tannic acid, phosphomolybdic acid and amido black technic developed in Leblond's laboratory, a heavy dark line is apparent at the free borders of absorptive cells, just below the microvilli (Fig. 8-8). This is the terminal web of the cell. It extends across the free end of the cell much as the skin of a drum extends across a drum. However, instead of being like a skin, the terminal web is more like a lacework of delicate fibrils.

In electron micrographs of intestinal epithelium, the terminal web of the cell appears as an area of fibrillar cytoplasm, which extends across the free end of the cell directly below the microvilli and contains no mitochondria or vesicles of the endoplasmic reticulum (Figs. 8-7, 8-9 and 8-12). The very delicate filaments in this region probably provide necessary internal support for the free end of the cell and serve as anchorage for the cytoplasmic cores of microvilli (Fig. 8-9) (and for the rootlets of cilia in ciliated cells). The terminal web connects all around the circumference of the cell with the cell membrane, which becomes involved in, and part of, what is termed the junctional complex and which will be described presently. The individual filaments of the terminal web have a diameter of about 70 Å and, therefore, are beyond the resolving power of the light microscope, so such fibrils as are visible with the light microscope in epithelial cells, such as *tonofibrils* that will be described in connection with skin later in this book, must be aggregates or bundles of these filaments. A corollary of this interpretation is that, when-

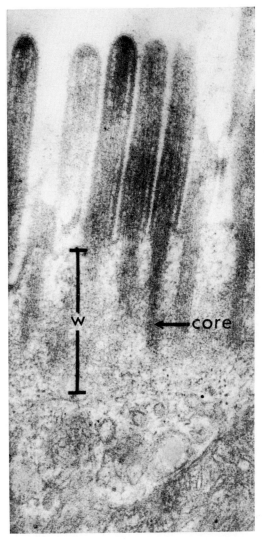

Fig. 8-9. Electron micrograph ($\times$ 52,000) of section of intestinal epithelium of mouse, showing microvilli and their cores of fibrillar material which are seen here to extend into the region of the cell web. Preparation by A. F. Howatson)

ever filaments are widely dispersed in the cytoplasm of a cell, they may escape observation by light microscopy. Bundles of filaments visible in the light microscope are referred to as cellweb fibrils; they can be seen for example in transitional epithelium in suitable preparations (Fig. 8-10). Many other kinds of cells contain bundles of filaments which are in a different position from those of the terminal web of absorptive cells. Thus, the goblet

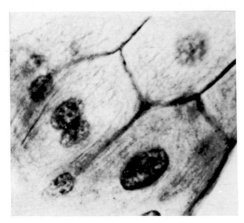

FIG. 8-10. Fibrils of the cell web can be seen in sections cut parallel to the inner surface of the transitional epithelium that lines the bladder when sections are stained by the technic described in the caption for Figure 8-8. Preparation by E. Kallenbach, Y. Clermont and C. P. Leblond)

cells of the rat's intestine have no terminal webs (Fig. 8-13). Instead, goblet cells possess fibrils, called vertical fibrils, that extend along their edges from their free surfaces past the nuclei toward the bases of the cells.

Leblond, Puchtler and Clermont have described *cell webs* in many different kinds of cells; and in these it may assume different forms, as will be described when these other types of cells are considered, later in the book.

The filaments of a terminal or cell web commonly converge on, and are anchored to, little bodies seen along the edges of contiguous cells and which are known as *desmosomes* and function in holding cells together.

**Desmosomes.** This word (derived from *desmos* = bond or fastening, and *soma* = body) has emerged from relative obscurity into common use as a result of the studies with the EM on the attachments between cells. These studies have shown that there are little bodies that are often scattered along adjacent cell membranes of contiguous cells (Fig. 8-11) and which are concerned with holding the cells tightly together. With the light microscope and special staining technics, dark dots could be seen at some of the sites where desmosomes can now be identified with the EM; indeed, for many years the appearances seen with the light microscope (illustrated in Fig. 23-4) were interpreted to indicate that at the sites

where epithelial cells remained adherent to one another, tiny fibrils (tonofibrils) crossed from the cytoplasm of one cell into the cytoplasm of the other. The EM, however, has shown that at these sites there is no cytoplasmic continuity between adjacent cells; what is seen with the EM will now be described.

In a desmosome the cell membranes of adjacent cells neither fuse nor come into direct contact with one another. Next, if a desmosome is seen in a section cut at right angles to the plane of the adjacent cell membranes, it shows, as may be seen in the central desmosome in Figure 8-11, and in the desmosomes illustrated in Figure 23-5, three fine dark parallel lines with lighter lines between them, running from one end of the desmosome to the other. Farther out, on each side, there is a coarse dark line and farther out still on each side a good deal of dark fibrillar material. We shall now describe what seems to account for these various appearances.

First, the fine middle line is called either the *intermediate* line or the *intercellular contact layer*. It is labeled ICI in the diagram (Fig. 23-5 B) accompanying Figure 23-5 A. It would seem that this line is to be accounted for by each of the cell membranes that approach each other in a desmosome being coated with some very finely granular material. The site along which the *coatings* on the two cell membranes come into contact becomes electron-dense and accounts for the middle dark intermediate line (the intercellular contact layer). The coatings themselves, however, do not seem to be electron-dense (except where these come into contact) and hence there is a light line to either side of the middle dark line.

To interpret the two fine dark lines that lie one to either side of the middle fine dark line, it is necessary to recall that a cell membrane consists of three layers, two dark ones and a middle light one (Fig. 7-4). The fine dark lines on each side of the middle dark line are thought to represent the outer layers of the membranes of the two contiguous cells (O.C.M. in Fig. 23-5 B). Next, the fine light line that is to be seen on the outer side of each of these two fine dark lines, is thought to represent the middle layer of the membrane of the cell on that side. To the outer side of each of these there is a thick dark band (i.c.m.);

these are to be accounted for by the inner layers of the membranes of the contiguous cells plus an adjacent plate consisting of an accumulation of electron-dense material on their cytoplasmic sides (Figs. 8-11 and 23-5 A and B). This dense plate may represent condensed fibrillar material similar to that of the cell web and in which closely packed filaments run more or less parallel to the cell membrane. Certainly, from these plates of dense material, bundled filaments of the cell web can be seen extending into the cytoplasm. Many of these filaments that extend into the cytoplasm run in a direction almost parallel with the plate and are tightly apposed to it. From the plate most of the filaments run more or less parallel to the cell membrane. Bundles of filaments that extend from desmosomes and which can be seen in the light microscope with appropriate stains may be called tonofibrils.

**Junctional Complexes.** The epithelial membrane that lines the intestine represents a barrier between the contents of the intestine and the internal environment of the body. The contents of the intestine are outside the body, and it is of the greatest importance that only certain substances that are present in the intestine be absorbed and that other substances be prevented from gaining entrance to the body proper. The ability to select and reject is a property of the epithelial cells. It is therefore of the greatest importance that no separations should occur between the individual cells of the single layer that constitutes the membrane. A separation that began between the free margins of adjacent cells could soon become complete, for it would act much as a wedge that is driven into a log to split it apart. It is therefore important that the strongest adhesion between epithelial cells should be at their free margins. In times past it was believed that adhesion between them at this site was provided by a special cement substance that was placed between their everted free edges, much as caulking is put between the outer edges of the seams between the individual planks of a wooden boat. Only recently has the fine structure of the junctions between the edges of contiguous epithelial cells been resolved clearly enough with the EM to reveal that instead of there being crevices filled with cement between the free edges of contiguous cells, the mem-

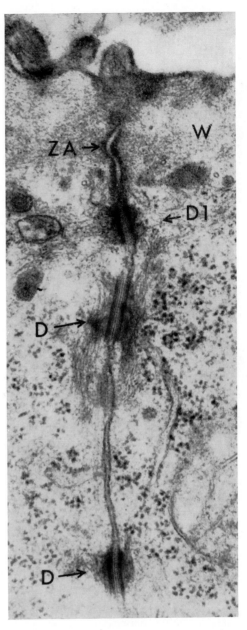

FIG. 8-11. Electron micrograph (× approx. 50,000) of section that passes through the line along which two epithelial cells of a rat's intestine are attached to each other. Three desmosomes labeled D1, D and D are seen; their structure is described in the text. The desmosome labeled D1, also termed the macula adhaerens of the junctional complex is also seen. The terminal web is labeled W. (From the thesis of J. D. McNabb, Dept. of Anatomy, McGill Univ., 1964)

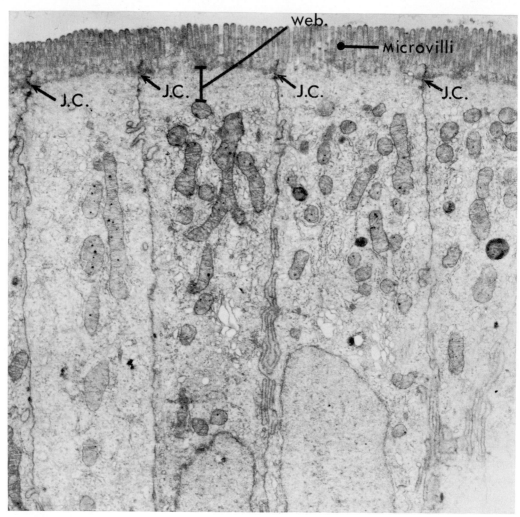

FIG. 8-12. Low-power electron micrograph of section of rat intestine showing several contiguous cells. The arrows labeled J.C. point approximately to the mid-point of junctional complexes which extend above the arrows as dark heavy lines for a short distance and below the
arrows to a point near the bottom of the terminal web. The terminal web is labeled, as are the
microvilli. (Preparation by R. Buck)

branes of contiguous cells are actually fused
in this important area. This fact and other
features of the arrangements which hold cells
together near their free margins have been
described recently by Farquhar and Palade,
under the terms of *junctional complexes*. The
sites occupied by junctional complexes are
indicated in Figure 8-12.

Junctional complexes have 3 segments
which succeed one another passing from the
free edges of cells toward their bases. The
first and most superficial segment is termed

by Farquhar and Palade the *zonula occludens*
(Fig. 8-13). As has already been explained in
the previous chapter, the cell membrane has
3 layers (two dark layers with a lighter layer
between them). In the zonula occludens the
outer layers of the cell membranes of two contiguous cells fuse to form what appears in a
micrograph as a single faint dark line. This
single dark line can be seen to advantage in
Figure 8-14, which is an electron micrograph
taken at a magnification of close to a quarter
of a million times. To each side of the single

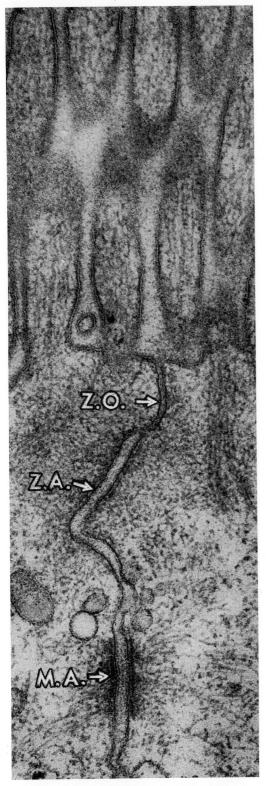

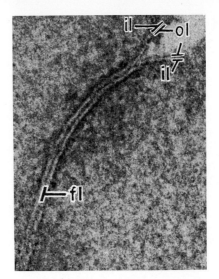

FIG. 8-14. Electron micrograph ($\times$ 230,000) of section passing through zonula occludens of a junctional complex between two cells of the gastric mucosa. The line of fusion between the outer layers of the cell membranes of the two contiguous cells is marked fl; this appears as a dark line that is continuous along this portion of the complex. Near the top of the illustration the cell membranes of the two cells diverge. The outer layer of the cell membrane of each cell is here marked ol and the inner layer, il. (Farquhar, M. G., and Palade, G. E.: J. Cell Biol. *17*:375)

dark line which is seen in the middle of the zonula occludens is a lighter line; these lighter lines represent the middle layers of the respective cell membranes of the contiguous cells. The dark lines seen on the outer (cytoplasmic) aspects of the lighter lines represent the inner layers of the cell membranes of the two contiguous cells.

Accordingly, at the most important site for a strong and effective seal between adjacent cells, the cell membranes of contiguous cells are fused.

The second, and deeper section, of the junctional complex is termed by Farquhar and Palade, the *zonula adhaerens*. Here the ad-

FIG. 8-13. Electron micrograph showing junctional complex between two contiguous cells in the intestinal epithelium of the rat.

The zonula occludens (Z.O.), the zonula adhaerens (Z.A.) and the macula adhaerens (M.A.) are each indicated by arrows. For a description of these three parts of the complex see text. (Farquhar, M. G., and Palade, G. E.: J. Cell Biol. *17*:375)

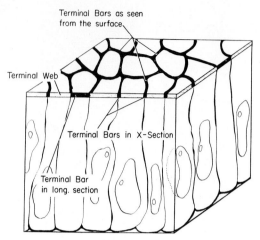

FIG. 8-15. Diagram to illustrate a few columnar epithelial cells and the appearances that led to the concept of terminal bars of cement substance between the free edges of contiguous cells.

jacent cell membranes are not fused; indeed, they are slightly separated by a space of around 200 Å which is filled with a homogenous material of low electron density (Fig. 8-13). The fibrillar material of the terminal web of each of the contiguous cells seems to be condensed along the inner surface of that part of the cell membrane of each cell that participates in forming this part of the complex.

The first two sections of the junctional complex are termed *zonula* because they encircle cells (zonula means a little encircling band, belt or girdle). While the two first segments of the junctional complex are constant, the third is not, and consists of desmosomes frequently present below the zonula adhaerens. These have been referred to by the name *macula adhaerens* because they do not form a continuous structure around each cell but are distributed in a spotty way (*macula* = spot), here and there, around the cells. In a macula adhaerens that is seen in a section, the membranes of the contiguous cells are separated by a space about 240 Å wide (Fig. 8-13). The space contains denser material than that seen in the similar space in the zonula adhaerens. Furthermore, there is dense material on the cytoplasmic side of each of the two cell membranes in a macula adhaerens; this dense material lies beside the

cell membrane as if a plate of dense material had been formed close to the cell membrane in this position, but separated from it slightly. On the cytoplasmic side of each plate of dense material there is fibrillar material of the terminal or cell web; this fibrillar material of the terminal or cell web of contiguous cells is anchored at the plates of dense material. From this description, which is that of a desmosome, it is obvious that a macula adhaerens is in effect a desmosome, but in a special location. Further desmosomes, scattered along the borders of the contiguous cells, but deeper from the surface (see Fig. 8-11) are not considered part of the junctional complex.

The zonula occludens extends from the free surface of the cell for a distance of from around 0.2 to 0.5 micron (Fig. 8-13). The zonula adhaerens extends from the bottom of the zonula occludens in a basal direction for between 0.3 to 0.5 micron (Fig. 8-13). The macula adhaerens or desmosome of the junctional complex lies at least 0.2 micron below the bottom of the zonula adhaerens (Fig. 8-13). Desmosomes may also be found along the adjacent membranes of the contiguous cells, deeper than this first one, but they are not considered to be part of the junctional complex, which is the arrangement that binds cells together directly beneath their free surfaces.

The junctional complex does not extend below the region of the terminal web, and, as

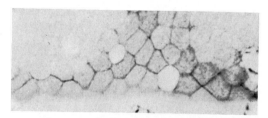

FIG. 8-16. Section of rat intestine cut parallel and close to the free surfaces of the columnar cells, so that it passed through the terminal webs of the cells. Note that the goblet cells appear as empty spaces because they have no terminal webs and that the webs of the absorptive cells stain deeply at the cell edges, giving the appearance of terminal bars. Tannic acid, phosphomolybdic acid and amido black technic. (Preparation by E. Kallenbach et al.)

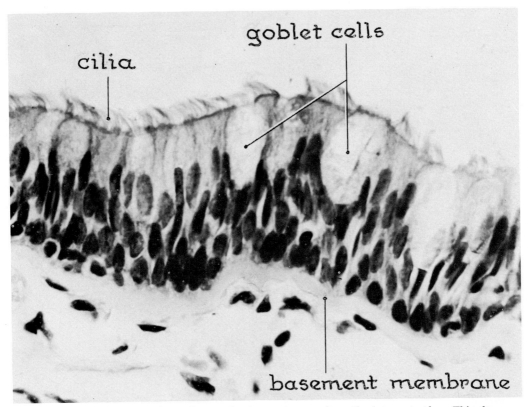

F IG. 8-17. High-power photomicrograph of a section cut from the human trachea. This shows pseudostratified ciliated columnar epithelium with goblet cells.

already noted, the fibrillar material of the terminal web extends to, and is presumably firmly attached to, all three components of the complex.

**Terminal Bars.** The easiest way to deal with terminal bars would be to say that in the light of knowledge resulting from modern electron microscopy there are no such things. However, there is something that stains with, say, iron hematoxylin, that outlines the edges of the free surfaces of columnar epithelial cells (Fig. 8-15), and whatever it is that stains by this technic in this position has the cross section appearance of a bar or a rod (Fig. 8-15). This appearance must be explained.

It was once believed that the material that could be stained in this position was cement substance disposed in the form of bars that were interposed between the edges of the free surfaces of contiguous cells. Now that the nature of junctional complexes has been elucidated by electron microscopy, the ques-

tion arises as to what component of the junctional complex or the terminal web that joins it stains so as to give an appearance of bars of cement substance between the free edges of contiguous cells.

Lest it be assumed that the material in the space between the membranes of adjacent cells in the zonula adhaerens and also in the macula adhaerens, and which could be thought of as a cement substance, is responsible for the appearance of terminal bars, it should be pointed out that even though the material in these spaces stained with iron hematoxylin it would be a line only 200 Å wide which could not possibly account for the appearance of terminal bars which are many times wider. Accordingly, the appearance of terminal bars cannot be explained by a cement or any substance *between* the edges of contiguous cells.

The tannic acid, phosphomolybdic acid and amido black technic stains the fibrillar material of the terminal web, but in sections

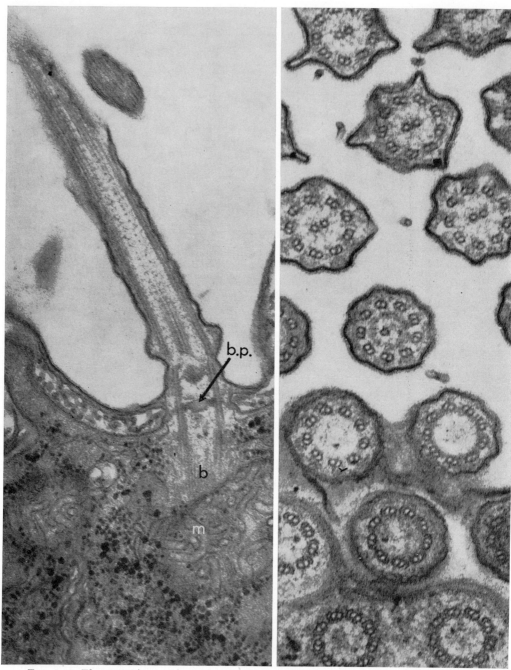

Fig. 8-18. Electron micrographs of longitudinal (*left*) and cross sections (*right*) of cilia of paramecium (× 100,000). On the left the free portion of the cilium is covered with cell membrane. Central filaments do not extend into the basal corpuscle (b), but terminate before reaching the basal plate (b.p.). The basal corpuscle (b) resembles a centriole. The cross sections on the right differ from each other because those near the top are cross sections of the free portions of cilia, whereas those near the bottom are cross sections of the portions of cilia that project into the cytoplasm to become the basal corpuscle. Passing from the cross sections at the top to those at the bottom, it will be observed that the central filaments disappear and that the double filaments become triple filaments. The structure below the basal corpuscle (*left*) is a mitochondrion (m). (Preparation by Dr. K. R. Porter)

cut more or less parallel to, and at, the free
surface of columnar epithelium (so that the
superficial parts of the cells are cut in cross
section) it is seen that the web at the adjacent *edges* of cells stain more deeply than
the main portion of the terminal web that
crosses from one side of the cell to the other
(Fig. 8-16). Accordingly, it would seem that
the sites where the fibrillar material of the
terminal web is *condensed* as it meets the
junctional complex are the sites that are
stained by iron hematoxylin to give the appearance of "terminal bars," and that the
substance of what have been known as terminal bars is chiefly condensed fibrillar material of the terminal web, and hence is *inside
cells and not between them.*

Interdigitations of the cell membranes of
contiguous cells also help to hold cells together; some may be seen in Figure 8-12.

**Ciliated Epithelium.** In the foregoing discussion of simple columnar epithelium we
have dealt with a type that is composed of
absorptive cells with striated borders and cells
which secrete mucus and have the form of
goblets. This type of epithelium lines the intestine. Another combination of cells in a
simple columnar epithelial membrane is that
of goblet cells intermixed with ciliated cells;
the latter are characterized by little hairlike
processes called cilia, which project from
their free surfaces (Figs. 8-1 d, 8-17 and
8-18). The cilia beat in harmony with one
another and so move mucus along the membrane. This type of epithelium is found in
some parts of the upper respiratory tract, but
it is not as common here as another type
which is called pseudostratified ciliated epithelium, and so we shall describe cilia later
in connection with this.

**Pseudostratified Columnar Epithelium.**
Stratified epithelium is defined as consisting
of two or more layers of cells. Pseudostratified
epithelium does not quite fill this requirement.
Some of the cells in contact with the basement membrane do not reach the surface
(Figs. 8-1, d and 8-17), but many do. It appears stratified because sections cut at right
angles to its surface show nuclei at two levels:
the nuclei of the shorter cells that do not reach
the surface are closer to the basement membrane than the nuclei of the longer cells that
reach the surface. So, because the two rows of
nuclei make this membrane *appear to be*

*stratified,* and yet it is not, it is called *pseudostratified.* Pseudostratified columnar epithelium forms the lining for most of the
upper respiratory tract, and it is to be seen
to advantage in a section cut from the
trachea (Fig. 8-17).

In this type of epithelium the cells that
reach the surface are either ciliated or goblet
cells. The mucus, secreted by the latter, forms
a film on the inner surface of the respiratory
passages, and this serves as a dust-catcher to
prevent dusts being inhaled into the lungs; it
also moistens the dry air that is inspired. The
cilia serve a very useful function by moving
the mucus that contains the dust particles upward to where it can be swallowed or otherwise eliminated from the body.

**The Fine Structure of Cilia.** With special
staining methods it was shown with the light
microscope that cilia were hairlike processes
that protruded from the cell surface and
seemed to be anchored in the cytoplasm to
dark-staining bodies called *basal corpuscles.*
The latter, it was noted, bore resemblances to
centrioles. With the EM much more detail has
become available; perhaps the most striking
thing that it has revealed about cilia is that
their fine structure, which is complex, is
identical throughout the plant and the animal
kingdoms. Some of the findings made with
the EM will now be described.

The EM made it possible to count the
number of cilia possessed by a single cell; for
example it was shown that each of the ciliated
cells of the trachea possesses around 270 cilia.

The EM has confirmed that each cilium is
an individual structure that has a free part or
shaft that projects outwardly from the free
surface of the cell and a part that extends into
the superficial part of the cytoplasm. The free
part is covered with the cell membrane; the
part within the cell is not.

The shaft portion of a cilium cut in cross
section (Fig. 8-18, upper right) reveals in its
center 2 longitudinally disposed and adjacent tubular filaments. These 2 central filaments are ringed by 9 paired filaments, each
of which in cross section presents a figure-8
appearance (Fig. 8-18, upper right). The ring
of 9 double filaments is located about halfway between the central filaments and the
cell membrane that ensheathes the shaft of
the cilium (Fig. 8-18, upper right).

The core of the cilium extends into the

substance of the cell for a short distance, and, over what is termed the *transition zone*, certain structural changes in the core become evident. First, the central axial filaments (Fig. 8-18, left) terminate. Second, just below the site where they terminate there is a diaphragmlike structure which is called the *basal plate* (Fig. 8-18, b.p.). The portion of the cilium below the basal plate is known as the basal corpuscle. The 9 pairs of double filaments, on reaching the basal corpuscle, each gain another filament so that instead of being double filaments they become triple filaments (Fig. 8-18, lower right).

An important feature of the basal corpuscle is the so-called basal foot. It is a conelike group of very fine filaments extending from the basal corpuscle in the direction of the stroke of the cilium. This structure (not shown in Fig. 8-18) probably anchors the cilium firmly into place, thus allowing a vigorous beat. In addition to the basal foot, similar fine filaments extend from each triple filament of the basal corpuscle into the surrounding cytoplasm. All these fine filaments seem to be part of the cell web. Some of them connect the basal corpuscles with one another as well as with the junctional complexes.

As already mentioned, the basal bodies seen with the light microscope seemed to resemble centrioles. With the EM the resemblance is much more striking. It will be recalled (Chap. 6, Figs. 6-9 and 6-10) that centrioles are tubular structures, the walls of which contain 9 pairs of longitudinally disposed double filaments similar to those observed in the basal bodies of cilia.

The mechanisms that accounts for the beating of cilia and their synchronized action are not understood. However, it seems very probable that the filaments of cilia are contractile, and a beating motion could be explained by filaments on one side contracting while those on the other side relax, and vice versa.

## STRATIFIED EPITHELIAL MEMBRANES

Stratified epithelial membranes can withstand more wear and tear than simple membranes. But because they are stratified, they cannot serve efficiently as absorptive mem-

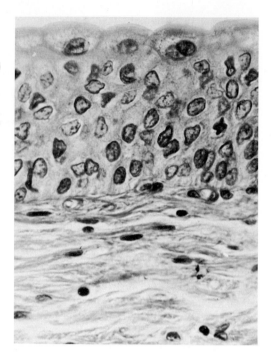

FIG. 8-19. Medium-power photomicrograph of a section cut from the bladder of a dog. Transitional epithelium, when contracted, is characterized by the innermost cells; these show rounded, free borders which give the surface a scalloped appearance.

branes; furthermore, their stratified structure makes them ill-adapted to performing secretory functions. Hence, such secretion as is found on stratified membranes is provided by glands that are situated below the epithelial membrane. Therefore, stratified membranes serve chiefly to protect, and the different ones of the body are dissimilar only because different kinds and degrees of protection are needed in different places.

**Stratified Squamous Nonkeratinizing Epithelium.** This type of membrane is found on wet surfaces that are subjected to considerable wear and tear, surfaces where absorptive function is not needed. The fluid required to keep such a surface wet is not provided by cells of the membrane. The inside of the mouth and the esophagus are both lined with this type of epithelium, where it is kept wet by saliva and provides protection from coarse foods. Part of the epiglottis is covered with it, and

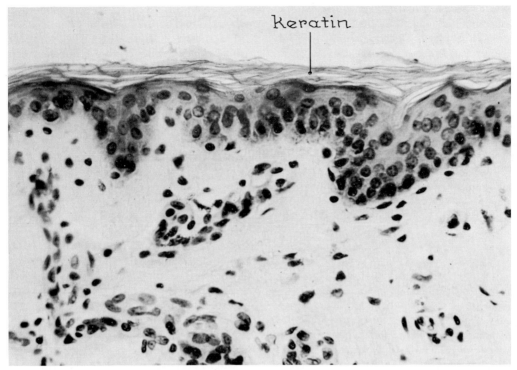

Keratin

FIG. 8-20. Low-power photomicrograph of a section of skin cut from the abdomen. The stratified squamous epithelium of thin skin, such as exists on the abdomen, is only a few cells thick. It runs across the upper part of the illustration, and at the surface the epithelial cells undergo a metamorphosis into keratin, which is labeled. The pale tissue on which the epithelium rests is connective tissue; this is what the deeper layer of the skin, the dermis, is composed of.

the vagina is also lined with it. It is illustrated in Figure 8-1, f.

Stratified squamous nonkeratinizing epithelium is not, as its name implies, composed of successive layers of squamous cells. The deepest cells in such a membrane (the basal layer that abuts on the basement membrane) are columnar. Just above these the cells are *polyhedral* (many-sided), and it is only toward the surface that the cells assume a squamous shape (Fig. 8-1, f), So *only the more superficial cells in stratified squamous nonkeratinizing epithelium are actually squamous.*

**Stratified Columnar Epithelium.** This type of epithelium is found on a few wet surfaces in the body that need more protection than that afforded by simple columnar epithelium but not as much as that provided by stratified squamous nonkeratinizing epithelium. For example, whereas ducts of moderate size are usually lined with simple columnar epi-

thelium, the larger ducts of glands are commonly lined by stratified columnar epithelium.

**Transitional Epithelium.** This is very much like stratified squamous nonkeratinizing epithelium except that unless it is stretched, the more superficial cells of transitional epithelium tend to be large and rounded rather than squamous in shape (Figs. 8-1 and 8-19). This allows such a membrane to be stretched without the superficial cells breaking apart from one another; they merely become drawn out into squamouslike cells (Fig. 27-21). Hence, transitional epithelium is well adapted to lining tubes and hollow structures that are subjected to being expanded from within, such as the urinary bladder.

It was observed some years ago that such mitotic figures as were seen in the surface cells in the transitional epithelium of rodents were very large. Subsequently, Leuchtenberger, Leuchtenberger and Davis found that the nuclei of the surface cells of the transitional epithelium in the urinary bladder of man contained multiple amounts of DNA; in other words, these cells demonstrated polyploidy. Walker has studied the development of this condition in the mouse and has found that at around the 16th to the 17th day of embryonic life both binucleate cells and polyploid nuclei become obvious in the superficial layers of the urinary bladder. Walker suggests that the chromosomes of binucleated cells entering division become grouped together, and as a result each of the two daughter cells that results has double the previous number of chromosomes.

## STRATIFIED MEMBRANES ON DRY SURFACES

Stratified squamous keratinizing epithelium resembles stratified squamous nonkeratinizing epithelium except for the fact that the more superficial cells of the membrane undergo a metamorphosis into a tough nonliving layer of *keratin* which is tightly attached to the underlying living cells of the epithelial membrane. The outer layer of the skin provides a good example of stratified squamous keratinizing epithelium (Fig. 8-20). In skin, keratin serves several purposes. It is relatively waterproof; hence, it prevents fluid from evaporating from the living cells that lie beneath it; likewise, it keeps the body from imbibing water when one has a bath. Since it is tough and resilient, it protects the underlying living epithelial cells from being injured by the ordinary wear and tear to which skin is exposed. It is relatively impervious to bacteria and hence is a first line of defense against infection. Over the soles of the feet and the palms of the hands the stratified squamous epithelium of the skin becomes thicker and, in particular, the keratin becomes very thick; this enables it to withstand the great wear to which these particular surfaces are exposed.

A further description of stratified squamous keratinizing epithelium and of the process of keratinization will be given in Chapter 23, which deals with skin.

**Some Features That Stratified Epithelial Membranes Have in Common.** The cells of stratified epithelial membranes commonly exhibit desmosomes along contiguous borders; these will be described in more detail in connection with the stratified squamous keratinizing epithelium of thick skin in Chapter 23.

The surface cells of all kinds of stratified epithelial membranes wear off, and hence there must be a mechanism for cell renewal in these membranes. Studies made in Leblond's laboratory show that in general, except for very thick stratified epithelial membranes, only the cells of the deepest layer of cells in a stratified membrane duplicate their DNA and subsequently divide. In very thick stratified epithelial membranes such as those that cover the palms of the hands and the soles of the feet, the cells of layers adjacent to the deepest layer of the membrane also undergo mitosis. New cells from the deepest, or the few deepest layers, depending on whether the stratified membrane is thin or thick, are squeezed from the deepest or the deeper layers into more superficial layers where they begin to differentiate; the continued generation of new cells below them gradually forces them into the most superficial layer of the membrane from which they are sooner or later lost.

**Interdigitations of Contiguous Cell Surfaces.** The EM has shown that in many types of epithelial membranes, the borders between adjacent cells may be extraordinarily complex, with ridges or other protrusions of each cell extending into grooves or other types of depression on the surface of the other. A complex one can be seen in the center of Figure 8-12. Desmosomes are found along some of interdigitating membranes but not along others.

## REFERENCES

### Mesothelium

Odor, D. L.: Observations of the rat mesothelium with the electron and phase microscopes, Am. J. Anat. *95*:433, 1954.

### Goblet Cells

Freeman, J. A.: Fine structure of the goblet cell mucous secretory process, Anat. Rec. *144*:341, 1962.

Hollman, K. H.: The fine structure of the goblet cells in the rat intestine, Ann. N. Y. Acad. Sci. *106*:545, 1963.

Jennings, M. A., and Florey, H. W.: Autoradiographic observations on the mucous cells of the stomach and intestine, Quart. J. Exp. Physiol. *41*:131, 1956.

## STRIATED BORDERS

Brandt, P. W.: A consideration of the extraneous coats of the plasma membrane, Circulation 26: 1075, 1962.

Fawcett, D. W.: Structural specifications of the cell surface *in* Palay, S. L. (ed.): Frontiers in Cytology, p. 19, New Haven, Conn., Yale Univ. Press, 1958.

Granger, B., and Baker, R. F.: Electron microscope investigation of the striated border of intestinal epithelium. Anat. Rec. 107:423, 1950.

## CELL WEB

Kallenbach, E., Clermont, Y., and Leblond, C. P.: The cell web in ameloblasts of the rat incisor, Anat. Rec. (in press) 1965.

Leblond, C. P., Puchtler, H., and Clermont, Y.: Structures corresponding to terminal bars and terminal web in many types of cells, Nature 186:784, 1960.

Palay, S. L., and Karlin, L. J.: An electron microscopic study of the intestinal villus, J. Biophys. Biochem. Cytol. 5:363, 1959.

## DESMOSOMES, JUNCTIONAL COMPLEXES AND TERMINAL BARS

Farquhar, M. G., and Palade, G. E.: Junctional complexes in various epithelia, J. Cell Biol. 17:375, 1963.

Fawcett, D. W.: Structural specifications of the cell surface *in* Palay, S. L. (ed.): Frontiers in Cytology, p. 19, New Haven, Conn., Yale Univ. Press, 1958.

## CILIA

Fawcett, D. W.: Structural specifications of the cell surface *in* Palay, S. L. (ed.): Frontiers in Cytology, p. 19, New Haven, Conn., Yale Univ. Press, 1958.

Fawcett, D. W., and Porter, K. R.: A study of the fine structure of ciliated epithelia, J. Morphol. 94:221, 1954.

Gibbons, I. R.: The relationship between the fine structure and direction of beat in gill cilia of a lamellibranch mollusc, J. Biophys. Biochem. Cytol. 11:179, 1961.

## TRANSITIONAL EPITHELIUM

Richter, W. R., and Moize, S. M.: Electron microscopic observations on the collapsed and distended mammalian urinary bladder, J. Ultrastruct. Res. 9:1, 1963.

Walker, B. E.: Electron microscopic observations on transitional epithelium of the mouse urinary bladder, J. Ultrastruct. Res. 3:345, 1960.

### *Stratified Squamous Keratinizing Epithelium*

See references for Chapter 23.

### *Cell Renewal in Epithelial Membranes*

See particularly references for Chapter 24.

# 9    Epithelial Tissue

## (Continued)

### EPITHELIAL GLANDS

In the previous chapter the various types of epithelial covering and lining membranes of the body are described, and it is shown that in different locations these membranes must provide different amounts and types of protection and that, in addition, in some locations they must perform absorptive and/or secretory functions as well. It should now be reiterated that epithelial membranes are better adapted to performing protective and absorptive functions than they are to secretory ones. A cell highly specialized for secretion can scarcely be a sturdy protective cell. Furthermore, for its efficient functioning, the body needs so much secretion that its covering and lining membranes are not sufficiently extensive to accommodate within them the vast number of secretory cells required. In sites where secretion over and above that which can be provided by cells in a membrane is needed, it will be found that cells from the membrane of the part have turned inward and, during development, grown from the surface into the supporting connective tissue, there to form epithelial structures highly specialized to provide the full secretory requirements of the part. These epithelial structures are called *glands* because some of the first ones studied were shaped like acorns (*glans* = acorn).

### CLASSIFICATION

The glands of the body are classified as *exocrine* or *endocrine*. The *crine* that appears in both these words is derived from *krino,* which means "I separate" and, in regard to glands, is taken to mean "secrete." So exocrine glands are those that secrete "out of" the body, and endocrine blands those that secrete into (within) the body. Both kinds, of course, are situated within the substance of connective tissue in the body. So exocrine glands, to secrete "out of" the body, must be provided with *ducts*, which are tubes that collect the secretion formed by the secreting cells of the gland and convey it to a surface where it can

be delivered out of the substance of the body. Endocrine glands, because they secrete directly into the substance of the body (into capillaries), need no ducts, and for this reason they are commonly called *ductless glands*.

### THE DEVELOPMENT OF GLANDS

The way in which both exocrine and endocrine glands develop is illustrated in Figure 9-1. Both kinds originate as a result of epithelial cells from a surface membrane growing, in the form of either a cord or a tubule, into the connective tissue beneath the membrane. The epithelial cells that thus invade the connective tissue, by means of their further proliferation and their subsequent differentiation, come to constitute a gland. In the instance of exocrine glands, the epithelial connection between the gland and the surface is retained (Fig. 9-1, *bottom, left*). The epithelial cells that thus connect the gland to the surface become somewhat differentiated to form the lining of a duct, which allows the secretion manufactured in the gland to be conveyed to and emptied upon the surface from which the gland originally developed. In the instance of endocrine glands, however, the epithelial cells that connect the gland to the surface and mark the path by which the gland developed disappear to leave the gland an epithelial island surrounded entirely by connective tissue (Fig. 9-1, *bottom, right*). Occasionally, however, little isolated groups of these epithelial cells that once connected the gland to the surface from which it developed persist, and later in life they may begin to secrete fluid in such a fashion that they come to surround the fluid they secrete; they form the covering for a sphere that is full of fluid. Such a structure is called a *cyst* (*kystis* = a bladder). Cysts, then, may sometimes form along the paths by which endocrine glands developed. There are, of course, other kinds of cysts that develop for other reasons and in other ways.

### EXOCRINE GLANDS

Although all the epithelial cells of an exo-

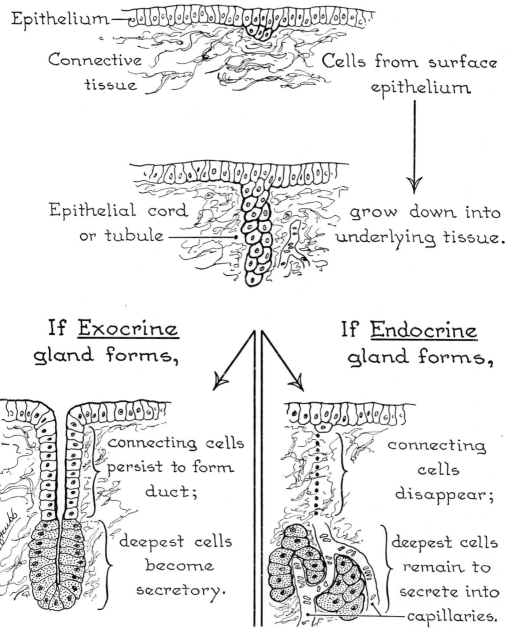

Epithelium

Connective tissue

Cells from surface epithelium

Epithelial cord or tubule

grow down into underlying tissue.

If <u>Exocrine</u> gland forms,

If <u>Endocrine</u> gland forms,

connecting cells persist to form duct;

deepest cells become secretory.

connecting cells disappear;

deepest cells remain to secrete into capillaries.

FIG. 9-1. Diagram showing how exocrine and endocrine glands develop.

crine gland belong to the same family, and hence are closely related to one another, they are not all differentiated to the same degree or along quite the same lines. The more highly differentiated cells are those that are specialized to secrete, and the less highly differentiated cells those that line the duct or ducts which carry the secretion to the surface.

In the development of a gland, the cells near the termination or terminations of the epithelial growth that invades the connective tissue differentiate into secretory cells, and those between the secretory cells and the surface, into duct cells (Fig. 9-1, *bottom, left*). Therefore, the secretory cells are to be found at the termination of the duct or, if it is a branching duct, at the end of each branch. In this site, or in each of these sites, they are

If secretory portion is:

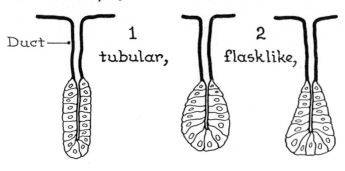

1
tubular,

Duct

2
flasklike,

3
both,

it is a tubular
exocrine gland.

it is an alveolar or
acinous gland.

it is a tubulo-
alveolar gland.

If duct doesn't branch:

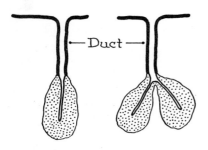

Duct

it is a simple gland.

If duct branches:

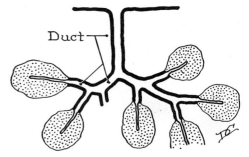

Duct

it is a compound gland.

FIG. 9-2. Diagram showing the different kinds of secretory units of exocrine glands and the difference between simple and compound glands.

arranged to form a little cluster of secretory cells, which we shall call a *secretory unit*. Each secretory unit possesses some sort of central cavity or lumen into which the secretion of the cells that compose it can be liberated. This lumen or cavity of the secretory unit is continuous with the lumen of the duct to which the secretory unit is attached (Fig. 9-1, *bottom, left*).

Secretory cells wear out from time to time; hence, they must be replenished. There are two possible sources for new cells: (1) other secretory cells and (2) the cells of the duct to which the secretory unit is attached. As noted previously, differentiation usually entails some loss of reproductive capacity. And, as the cells of the ducts are not so highly differentiated as

the highly specialized secretory cells, it is only natural that they should be able to reproduce themselves more readily, and that those nearest the secretory unit should differentiate into secretory cells and take the place of those that wear out. Hence, duct cells, particularly those nearest the secretory unit, serve as a source of new secretory cells. In some glands, however, it is not unlikely that secretory cells can reproduce themselves, to some extent at least, and so provide more secretory cells without the duct cells having to contribute all the new ones that are necessary.

**Classification of Exocrine Glands.** Exocrine glands may be classified several different ways. According to a classification made on one basis, an exocrine gland may be said to be a tubular gland; according to a classification made on another basis, a compound gland, and so on. In stating the type of any particular gland, attention is usually paid to all the different bases for classification so that a gland may be called, for example, a compound, tubular, mucous gland. The various bases on which classifications are made and the types therein will now be considered.

**Tubular, Acinous and Alveolar Glands.** If the clusters of cells that constitute the secretory unit or units of a gland are tubular in shape (Fig. 9-2), the gland is said to be a tubular gland. But if the secretory units are more rounded in shape, the gland is said to be an *acinous* (*acinus* = grape, berry) or an *alveolar* (*alveolus* = a little hollow, a little hollow vessel) gland. For many years it was customary to distinguish between acini and alveoli, and hence between acinous and alveolar glands, the term acinous being used for secretory units that are rounded and somewhat resemble Florence flasks, and alveolus for those that are more conical and roughly resemble Erlenmeyer flasks (Fig. 9-2). But in the recent past it has become usual practice not to insist on this distinction and to call both acinous and alveolar glands by the latter name. However, there are a few exceptions to this rule, most notably the secretory units of the pancreas which are still commonly called acini. If glands contain both tubular and alveolar secretory units, or units that have some characteristics of each, they are called tubulo-alveolar glands (Fig. 9-2).

**Simple and Compound Glands.** Any exocrine gland in which the secretion formed by the secretory unit or units is collected and conveyed to a surface by an unbranched duct is said to be a *simple gland* (Fig. 9-2, *bottom, left*). If the duct branches, so as to form a duct system, the gland is known as a *compound gland* (Fig. 9-2, *bottom, right*).

As the trunk of a tree branches first into a few fairly large branches and then into increasingly smaller and more numerous ones, eventually to supply twigs for the leaves, so the main duct branches into increasingly smaller and more numerous branches to supply all of the almost innumerable secretory units of large compound glands. Large glands, then, all characteristically have extensive branching duct systems.

Large compound glands, being epithelial structures, need the support of connective tissue. This is provided by a capsule of connective tissue which surrounds the gland and also by partitions of connective tissue which divide the substance of the gland up into areas, which are thus "fenced off" in 3 dimensions by connective tissue. In some glands large areas so fenced off, particularly if cleavage has occurred in the partition so that the fenced-off areas are somewhat separated from one another, are termed *lobes;* but if the fenced-off areas are not very large and are close to one another, they are called *lobules* (little lobes).

A connective tissue partition of the sort described above is termed a *septum*. Hence, connective tissue partitions between lobes are termed *interlobar septa,* and those between lobules, *interlobular septa* (Fig. 9-4).

The septa in some glands converge toward the point at which the main duct enters the gland. Hence, they provide an excellent means whereby the main branches of the duct may be conveyed and supported as they pass toward the gland's interior. As the larger branches of the duct system are thus conveyed in interlobular septa, they are termed *interlobular ducts* and they are easily recognized because they are large, have a thick epithelial lining and are surrounded by the connective tissue of the partition which conveys them (Fig. 9-4). Branches from interlobular ducts leave the partitions to enter the substance of lobules, and, being *inside* rather than *between* lobules, are called *intralobular ducts*. They are smaller than interlobular ducts and are lined by epithelium that is not as thick as that of the corresponding interlobular ducts. Furthermore, they are not surrounded by as much connective tissue as are the interlobular ducts because they do not run in partitions. However, they may be surrounded by a certain amount of connective tissue, because the partitions usually send out prolongations of connective tissue into the substance of the lobules to afford them some support (Fig. 9-4).

**Holocrine, Merocrine and Apocrine Glands.** These terms refer to the manner in which the secretory cells of the glands elaborate their secretion. In holocrine glands the process is very drastic. A cell, to secrete, first accumulates secretory products in its cytoplasm and then dies and disintegrates. Thereupon the

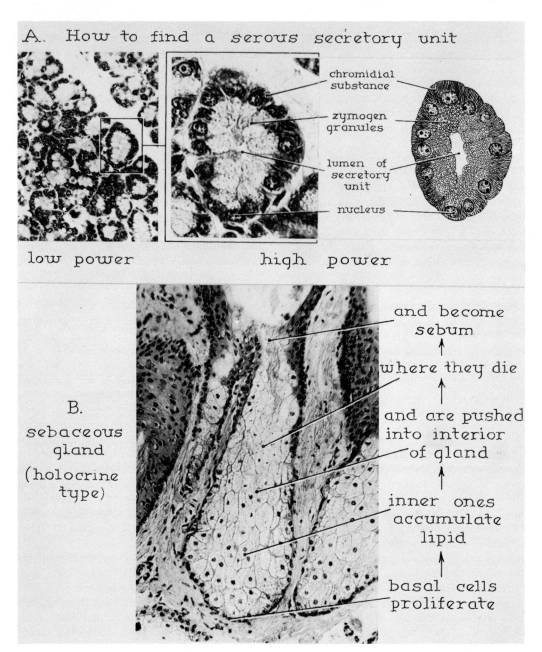

A. How to find a serous secretory unit

chromidial substance

zymogen granules

lumen of secretory unit

nucleus

low power                    high power

and become sebum

where they die

and are pushed into interior of gland

B. sebaceous gland (holocrine type)

inner ones accumulate lipid

basal cells proliferate

FIG. 9-3. (A) The way that a section of pancreas (which contains serous secretory units) appears under low power is illustrated at the left. The pictures at the right show how individual secretory units appear under higher powers. (B) A medium-power photomicrograph of a sebaceous gland of the skin. These glands generally open into hair follicles and they make the fatty secretion, sebum. For details of structure see Chapter 23.

dead cell is discharged to constitute the secretion (Fig. 9-3, *bottom*); in holocrine glands (*holos* = all), all of the cell is secreted. Holocrine glands are not common in the body. The sebaceous glands of the skin (Fig. 9-3) are convenient ones to study. It is obvious that, for a holocrine gland to maintain its full complement of cells, the less highly differentiated cells of the gland must constantly reproduce so as to provide a steady supply of cells which

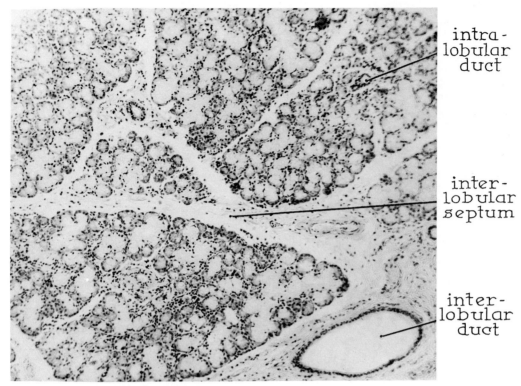

intra-
lobular
duct

inter-
lobular
septum

inter-
lobular
duct

Fig. 9-4. Low-power photomicrograph of a salivary gland of the mixed type. This illustration shows interlobular septa, interlobular and intralobular ducts and secretory units.

can differentiate into secretory cells. Merocrine glands are the opposite of holocrine glands in that, although *meros* means a part, they secrete without any part of the cell being lost. It is to be recalled that secretory granules are in the nature of cytoplasmic inclusions; hence, although they are manufactured by the cytoplasm, they are not actually part of the cytoplasm. (Probably this was not understood when the name merocrine originated.) In merocrine glands, formed secretory products, such as secretory granules, are passed through the free surfaces of secretory cells into the lumen of a secretory unit without any of the secretory cells' cytoplasm being lost in the process. In apocrine glands (*apo* = from), the process is much the same except that a little of the cytoplasm along the free secretory borders of the secretory cells is supposed to be lost as the formed secretory products are passed through them. However, these classifications were made from observations with the light microscope, and it is quite possible that from observations with the EM which show secretion granules to be sur-rounded with a membrane that becomes continuous with the cell membrane as the secretion is delivered (see Fig. 7-16) that at least some glands, believed to be apocrine, will have to be reclassified.

### Serous, Mucous and Mixed Glands

This classification is not applicable to all exocrine glands but only to some. It is used particularly in classifying the salivary glands, those glands whose ducts open into the oral cavity and supply it with saliva.

This classification is based on the character of the secretion made by the gland. The word *serous* means "wheylike," and as whey is a clear, watery fluid, those glands in which secretion is of this nature are termed *serous glands*. Mucus is a slightly more viscid fluid. The glands that secrete mucin, the glycoprotein which, when mixed with water becomes mucus, are termed *mucous glands*. Any gland that produces a mixture of serous and mucous fluids is called a *mixed gland*.

However, the histology student will not be called upon to classify these glands from an

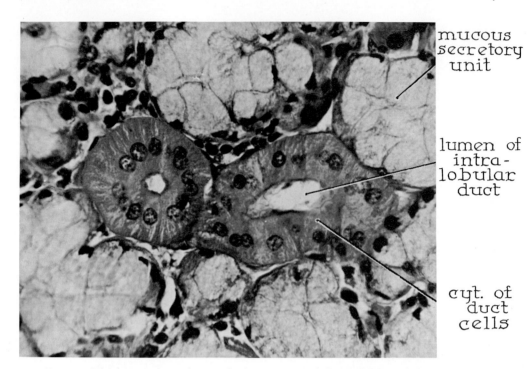

mucous
secretory
unit

lumen of
intra-
lobular
duct

cyt. of
duct
cells

Fig. 9-5. High-power photomicrograph of a mucous gland, showing two ducts cut more or less in cross section.

investigation into the character of their secretion but from the appearance that sections cut through them present under the microscope. And since cells that make serous and mucous secretions, respectively, differ considerably from one another in appearance, the identifications of sections cut from serous, mucous and mixed glands (in which both types are present) is a relatively easy matter.

A section cut through a highly specialized gland, such as one of the salivary glands, is at first a puzzling picture for the student to interpret, because secretory units and ducts are packed together, with only a slight amount of supporting connective tissue, in almost any way that allows the greatest number of secretory units, with their ducts, to be fitted into a limited amount of space. This is accomplished only by both secretory units and ducts being disposed in almost every conceivable plane; hence, a section through the substance of a gland cuts both ducts and secretory units in a vast variety of planes. The interpretation of such a section requires some thought.

With the low-power objective, the student, when he first studies a section of one of the salivary glands or of the pancreas (which is

similar to the salivary glands in its general plan of construction but different in certain of its secretory functions), will be able to make out the outlines of lobules (Fig. 9-4). It is noted that lobules are not always complete, that is, lobules are not always, in any given section, completely surrounded by partitions of connective tissue. In glands, moreover, shrinkage often occurs along the line of the partitions between lobules; this is an artefact. With the low-power objective a few intralobular ducts (Fig. 9-5) may be seen within a lobule. These may be cut at right angles to their long axes, obliquely, or more or less longitudinally. (If necessary refer back to the section dealing with the appearance of tubes cut in different planes.)

When the section is examined with the high-power objective, secretory units may be seen (Fig. 9-3, *top*). In attempting to identify these, however, the student should remember that in every section they are cut in almost every conceivable plane, many of them obliquely. A search will soon reveal some cut approximately in cross section, and the diameter of one so cut is roughly comparable with that of one of the larger intralobular ducts

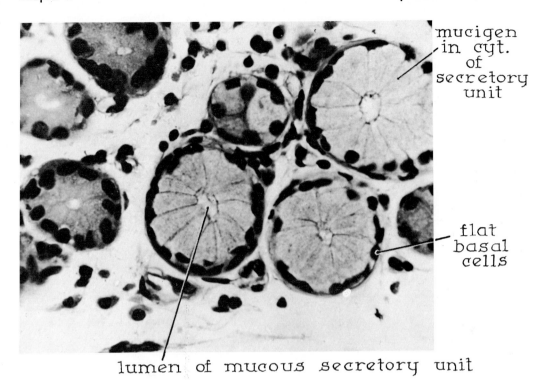

mucigen
in cyt.
of
secretory
unit

flat
basal
cells

lumen of mucous secretory unit

FIG. 9-6. High-power photomicrograph of a section of trachea, showing mucous secretory units cut in cross section.

(Fig. 9-5). Secretory units are separated from one another and from intralobular ducts by a minimal amount of delicate connective tissue (Fig. 9-6) which brings capillaries and nerves close to them.

Before examining secretory units in a section, it is perhaps helpful to visualize the appearance of the surface of a pie that has been cut into several pieces but not yet served. The individual pieces of pie are roughly triangular in shape, and their apices meet in the center. A cross section of a secretory unit presents a similar appearance, the individual cells of the unit, like the individual pieces of pie, presenting a more or less triangular appearance with their apices almost meeting in the center of the unit (Fig. 9-6). The apices of the different cells do not quite meet, because this region constitutes the lumen of the secretory unit. Often, however, the lumen cannot be seen because shrinkage causes the cells to obliterate it.

**Serous Secretory Units.** The nucleus of a serous secretory cell is usually rounded and lies toward, rather than at, the base of the cell (Fig. 7-16). (Although all secretory cells contain nuclei, all do not exhibit them in a single thin section, since the slice may miss the nucleus.) At the base of the cell the cytoplasm (Figs. 7-6 and 9-3 A) is very basophilic because of its considerable content of cytoplasmic RNA, which, as has already been noted in Chapter 7, is variously termed *chromidial substance, chromophil substance* or *ergastoplasm.*

The details of serous secretory cells—their fine structure and the mechanism of secretion —are given in Chapter 7.

*Zymogen* granules (*zym* has come to refer to enzyme and *gen* means "I produce"), are the forerunners of the enzymes that are present in the secretions of serous glands. In fixed tissue preparations these granules appear as small spheres of solid substance (Fig. 7-18), provided that the fixative and the stain employed in making the section are designed to present a "positive" picture of the granules (with a combination of some fixing and staining methods a "negative" picture of the granules is seen (Fig. 7-6, *left*); they are represented only by unstained spaces of the same size and distribution as granules).

Zymogen granules are secreted through the

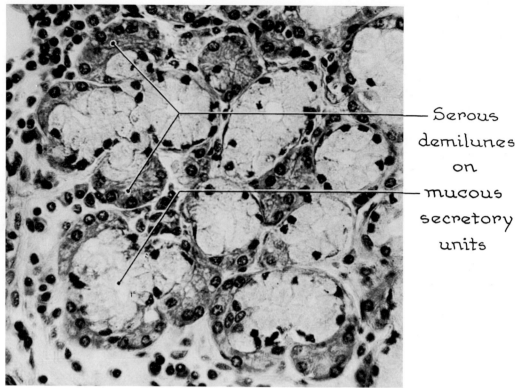

Serous demilunes on mucous secretory units

FIG. 9-7. Medium-power photomicrograph of a mixed gland, showing mucous secretory units with serous demilunes.

apical region of secretory cells into the lumen of the secretory unit. This is very minute. When the granules enter the lumen of the secretory unit they dissolve and so lose their form.

**Mucous Secretory Units.** The appearance of a cross section of mucous secretory unit exhibits certain differences from that of a serous secretory unit. The nuclei are of a different shape and they occupy a different position in the cells. In serous cells they are rounded and situated near, but not at, the bases of the cells. In mucous cells they are flattened, almost to the point of becoming disks; furthermore, they are crowded against the bases of the cells that contain them (Fig. 9-6). The cytoplasm of mucous cells is also different from that of serous cells. There is less cytoplasmic RNA at the bases of the cells than there is in serous cells. That portion of the cytoplasm situated between the nucleus and the apex of a mucous cell contains, not zymogen granules, but a variable number of mucigen (mucigen is the forerunner of mucin) droplets which, in the

usual preparation, present a negative picture and hence impart a vacuolated appearance to the very light-staining cytoplasm that contains them (Fig. 9-6). For an electron micrograph of mucigen droplets, see Figure 8-5.

Mucins from different sources vary in composition, but they all contain carbohydrate and are of the order of glycoproteins. Their carbohydrate component is responsible for their staining brilliantly in suitably fixed tissue with the P. A. Schiff technic (Fig. 8-4).

**Radioautographic Studies.** Bélanger has shown that after giving subcutaneous injection of $S^{35}$-labeled $H_2SO_4$, radioactive sulfur enters and can be demonstrated by radioautographs in many tissues. Of interest to us here is the fact that the secretory cells of mucous glands take up the labeled sulfur in considerable amounts; indeed, in low-power radioautographs mucous glands stand out as a sprinkling of black ink drops on a white page. The uptake of radioactive sulfur by cells that secrete mucus is due to the fact that the mucoprotein that they synthesize has sulfur as one of its components; mucus probably contains some mucoitin sulfate. Radioautographic studies on the formation of the glycoprotein secretion of goblet cells by the use of glucose labeled with tritium are described in Chapter 7.

**Mixed Glands.** Some glands, to be enumerated later, are of the mixed variety and so deliver both serous and mucous secretions through their ducts. This is accomplished by the glands possessing both serous and mucous units (Fig. 9-7) or by combinations of the two. Combinations usually consist of mucous units capped by crescent-shaped aggregations of serous cells called *serous demilunes* (half moons) (Fig. 9-7). Obviously, there must be passageways for the secretion of these serous cells to gain entrance between the mucous cells which separate them from the lumen of the mucous unit. These passageways are probably in the nature of tiny intercellular canals situated between adjacent cells of the mucous secretory unit and are not evident in the ordinary preparation.

**Myoepithelial Basket Cells.** Secretory units of either the mucous or the serous type can be shown by special technics to be cradled in a loose basket made of the cytoplasmic processes of special cells that lie between the bases of the secretory cells and the basement membrane. These cells have a central cell body and many long cytoplasmic processes that encircle and so grasp the secretory unit (Fig. 9-8). Although these cells are of epithelial origin, it seems very probable that their cytoplasm is contractile, not only because of their shape and position, but also because myofibrils have been seen in them with the EM. Therefore, it is assumed that these cells function in some way to encourage the expression of secretion from secretory units into ducts. Leeson has shown that these cells are selectively demonstrated to advantage by the histochemical method employed for the demonstration of alkaline phosphatase (Fig. 9-8), which enzyme they contain in abundance.

### ENDOCRINE GLANDS

The structure of endocrine glands is considerably simpler than that of exocrine glands because they possess no ducts. As their secretory cells discharge their secretions into capillaries, the secretory cells must be arranged in

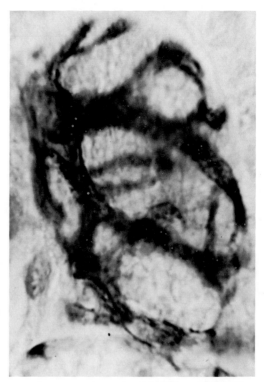

Fig. 9-8. Photomicrograph (× 2,250) of myoepithelial (basket) cell in submaxillary gland of rat. The material was fixed in acetone and stained by the Gomori method for alkaline phosphatase. The cytoplasmic arms of the cell appear black in the illustration. (Leeson, C. R.: Nature *178*:858)

such a fashion that all abut on capillaries. This is accomplished by the secretory cells being disposed in either straight or irregular cords, separated from one another by capillaries, or in little clumps surrounded by capillaries (Fig. 9-1, *bottom, right*).

**Intracellular Storage.** All endocrine glands store their secretion to some extent. This is accomplished in most of them by intracellular storage. For example, the endocrine cells that make insulin, the hormone so important in preventing an individual from having the disease diabetes, normally store within their cytoplasm enough of the hormone or its immediate forerunner to kill a person if it were all secreted at one time.

**Extracellular Storage.** If it is desirable for an endocrine gland to store secretion over and above that amount that can be accommodated by intracellular storage, another expedient is

# ENDOCRINE GLANDS

## How a clump of cells can become a follicle

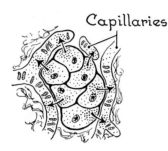  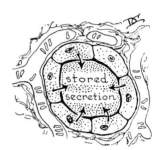

Endocrine cells commonly secrete into capillaries,

but, to store secretion, cells may secrete in opposite direction.

Then they expand the clump into a follicle.

FIG. 9-9. Diagram showing how different types of endocrine glands store secretion and how a clump of cells can become a follicle.

adopted. The cells of a clump secrete inwardly and so give rise to a pool of stored secretion (or precursor of secretion), which is extracellular but completely surrounded by the cells (Fig. 9-9). Such an arrangement of cells surrounding a little sphere of stored secretion is termed a *follicle* (a small bag).

**Secretion Granules.** The immediate forerunner of the secretion of some endocrine glands is evident in the cytoplasm of secretory cells as secretion granules (Fig. 9-9). These usually require very special histologic technics for their demonstration. Some endocrine glands that secrete fat-soluble hormones reveal droplets of fatty material in the cytoplasm, and these, in the usual paraffin section, appear as vacuoles (Chap. 28). It is not entirely clear how these are related to the secretory process of the gland concerned.

Endocrine glands are enclosed by capsules of connective tissue, and usually some projections from these extend into the substance of the gland as *trabeculae* (little beams) to provide it with internal support and to carry blood vessels and nerves into it. These trabeculae account for the lobulated appearance that sections of some endocrine glands present under the microscope.

## GLANDS THAT ARE BOTH EXOCRINE AND ENDOCRINE

The pancreas provides an excellent example of such a gland. This gland arises from an epithelial ingrowth that comes from the epithelial lining of the intestine. This epithelial ingrowth branches and branches to become a duct system, but also it gives rise to two kinds of secretory units: serous ones, in which the lumina of the secretory portions remain connected with the end branches of the duct system, and little groups of cells, called islets of Langerhans, that do not develop a lumen but become arranged into irregular cords and clumps richly provided with capillaries. These islands of cells which arise from the same source as the developing duct system may remain in contact with it, but there is no continuity of the lumen of the duct system with them; hence, they must secrete directly into the many capillaries with which they are provided. They thus constitute the endocrine element of the pancreas.

The pancreas, then, contains numerous islands of endocrine tissue scattered through its substance, which is chiefly composed of serous secretory units that empty their secretion into its duct system. Therefore, it is both an endocrine and an exocrine gland, with different types of specialized cells to perform its two different functions.

## REFERENCES

Bélanger, L. F.: Autoradiographic visualization of $S^{35}$ incorporation and turnover by the mucous glands of the gastro-intestinal tract and other soft tissues of rat and hamster, Anat. Rec. *118*:755, 1954.

Bensley, R. R.: Studies on the pancreas of the guinea pig, Am. J. Anat. *12*:297, 1911.

Leeson, C. R.: Localization of alkaline phosphatase in the submaxillary gland of rat, Nature *178*:858, 1956.

Leeson, C. R., and Jacoby, F.: An electron microscopic study of the rat submaxillary gland during its postnatal development and in the adult, J. Anat. (Lond.) *93*:287, 1959.

Montagna, W., and Noback, C. R.: Histochemical observations on the sebaceous glands of the rat, Am. J. Anat. *81*:39, 1947.

Palay, S. L. (ed.): The morphology of secretion *in* Frontiers in Cytology, p. 305, New Haven, Conn., Yale Univ. Press, 1958.

References dealing with the synthesis and the movements of secretions in cells are given in Chapter 7. References are given regarding particular glands in the chapters in which these glands are considered; this can be ascertained by consulting the index.

# 10   Connective Tissue

## INTRODUCTION

The second of the 4 basic tissues is called connective tissue because it serves the very important function of connecting the other tissues together and to the skeleton. The skeleton itself is built of a special kind of connective tissue. As we shall see, however, connective tissue has functions in addition to that of connecting and providing support; these will be described in due course.

The connecting and supporting role of connective tissue hinges on the fact that certain of the cells of connective tissue produce materials known as intercellular substances which are so called because they occupy a position *between* the cells of connective tissue. The intercellular substances are nonliving materials, and some of them are very strong. It is due to the strong ones that connective tissue is able to provide support for other tissues and hold them together.

Cells in general are jellylike, and if it were not for intercellular substances a body could be no more than a jellylike mass. It is the intercellular substances of connective tissue that give the body form. It is not too much to say that the body is an edifice of intercellular substance in which cells live as residents.

Although some of the cells of epithelial, muscular and nervous tissue can produce a little intercellular material for special and local purposes, they do not contribute significantly to the production of intercellular substances of the body. Accordingly, the production of intercellular substance is allotted almost exclusively to the second of the 4 basic tissues. Hence, one important aspect of the study of connective tissue is the study of the formation, the nature and the function of intercellular substances.

Having emphasized the importance of the intercellular substances of connective tissue we should now add that there is much more to the study of the connective tissues than the study of intercellular substances, for the cells of connective tissue serve many and very important functions besides that of making intercellular substance. Indeed, there is one important variety of connective tissue—the hemopoietic tissues, which are the tissues that make the blood cells (*hemo* = blood, *poiesis* = making)—which consist almost entirely of cells. So we shall find that there are different kinds of connective tissue. At one extreme there are kinds, for example, bone and cartilage, that consist chiefly of intercellular substance. At the other extreme is the hemopoietic tissue which, as already noted, makes the cells of the blood, and this kind contains very little intercellular substance but does contain a vast cell population with most of the cells specialized to make blood cells. In between the two extremes is what is termed *loose ordinary* connective tissue which, in general, is a representative mixture of cells and intercellular substances. Some of the cells of loose ordinary connective tissue are specialized to make intercellular substance but, as we shall see, other cells of loose ordinary connective tissue perform other functions. Since loose ordinary connective tissue has a good representation of both the cells and the intercellular substances of connective tissue, it is more or less of a prototype of all kinds, and we shall therefore consider it first. After this is done we shall consider the kinds of connective tissue that are more specialized to serve less general but more specific functions.

The easier order to follow in studying loose ordinary connective tissue is to deal first with the form and the functions of the intercellular substances of loose connective tissue and then with the cells of loose connective tissue. We shall follow this order.

## LOOSE ORDINARY CONNECTIVE TISSUE

This kind of connective tissue is called loose because its intercellular substances are arranged so that the tissue is somewhat flexible and can be stretched to some extent in various directions without damage. It is called

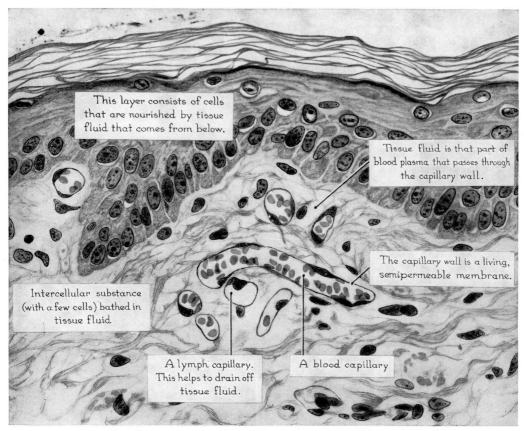

This layer consists of cells that are nourished by tissue fluid that comes from below.

Tissue fluid is that part of blood plasma that passes through the capillary wall.

The capillary wall is a living, semipermeable membrane.

Intercellular substance (with a few cells) bathed in tissue fluid

A lymph capillary. This helps to drain off tissue fluid.

A blood capillary

FIG. 10-1. High-power photomicrograph, lightly retouched, of a section cut through the outer part of the skin of a pig. This illustration shows the cellular epidermis above and capillaries surrounded by intercellular substance below. It shows how tissue fluid must migrate from capillaries to nourish adjacent cells. Wavy collagenic fibers of various diameters, but generally slightly narrower or wider than the red blood cells in the capillaries, pass in various directions through the intercellular substance.

ordinary because it is so widely distributed throughout the body. It is found immediately beneath most epithelial membranes. It also provides a delicate wrapping for the secretory units and ducts of glands. It permeates various epithelial organs. It extends into muscles and nerves; indeed, loose connective tissue extends almost everywhere in the body. It is important that it should, because in addition to its holding other tissues together, it serves two other important functions which also require that it should permeate almost everywhere.

### THREE IMPORTANT FUNCTIONS OF LOOSE ORDINARY CONNECTIVE TISSUE

In order to visualize and appreciate 3 important functions of loose ordinary connective tissue reference should be made to Figure 10-1. Extending across the upper half of this illustration is a layer of stratified squamous keratinizing epithelium, a tissue with which the reader is already familiar. Immediately beneath the epidermis is a layer of relatively loose connective tissue (this is all that shows in this illustration; deeper still the connective tissue of the skin becomes dense). Although a few nuclei of cells can be seen scattered throughout this latter tissue, most of it consists of intercellular substance; this reveals little structure, composed seemingly of strands of fibrillar material, which are scattered here and there with what seem to be empty spaces between them. Close to the center of the illustration is a prominent blood capillary; the dark objects in it are red blood cells.

**Interpretation of the Appearance of Intercellular Substance Seen in Fig. 10-1.** In order to understand why the intercellular substance appears in an ordinary H and E section as is illustrated in Figure 10-1, as bundles of fibrillar material mixed with seemingly empty spaces, it should be explained that there are two main kinds of intercellular substances. The first kind is protein in nature and exists in tissues in the form of *fibrils* or *fibers*. The proteins concerned are either collagen or elastin, and the fibers that are made of these proteins are termed collagenic and elastic fibers respectively. Since it generally requires special staining to demonstrate elastic fibers in a tissue preparation, it can be assumed that the fibrillar material seen in Figure 10-1, which represents a section stained with H and E, is collagen. Both collagenic and elastic fibers are strong; they are responsible for the connecting and supporting function of loose connective tissue. The respective special properties of collagenic and elastic fibers will be described presently.

In order to explain the seemingly empty spaces between the bundles of collagenic fibrils, it must be explained that there is a second main kind of intercellular substance. This second kind is essentially carbohydrate in nature and exists in loose connective tissue as a jellylike material. Since this kind of intercellular substance does not assume any special form, but merely exists as a jelly that fills in all the interstices between cells, fibers and capillaries, it is termed an amorphous (without form) kind of intercellular substance. It is also termed the ground substance of connective tissue. Chemically, this material is mostly the acid mucopolysaccharide known as hyaluronic acid, although some sulfated mucopolysaccharides, other carbohydrates and even dispersed protein macromolecules may be present in it to varying extents in different locations. The macromolecules of acid mucopolysaccharides, as was described in Chapter 2, are difficult to fix and stain; they tend to wash out of tissue as a section is prepared, and hence the spaces they occupied may look empty in sections.

Since this jellylike amorphous intercellular substance has no tensile strength it does not function primarily, as do the protein (collagen and elastin) fibrils and fibers of intercellular substance, in connecting other tissues together. However, it does serve an important role in another function that must be performed by loose ordinary connective tissue and which becomes obvious if Figure 10-1 is studied again, for as this figure shows, blood capillaries are not present in the epithelium to nourish epithelial cells directly. Instead, capillaries are distributed in the intercellular substance of the loose connective tissue that lies beneath the epithelium and are often separated from the epithelium by appreciable distances. It is obvious that oxygen and nourishment brought to the tissue by the capillaries must have to pass somehow through the intercellular substances to reach the epithelial cells. Likewise, waste products from the metabolism of epithelial cells must have to pass in the reverse direction through intercellular substance to reach and be absorbed by capillaries and carried away. The transfer of dissolved materials between the blood in capillaries and cells that are distant from capillaries is facilitated by the amorphous ground substance of loose connective tissue, because this soft jelly-like material holds cells and other materials apart and at the same time *permits the diffusion of dissolved materials to occur readily through* its substance. Furthermore, as will be described presently, fluid is exuded from capillaries and absorbed back again into capillaries, and so that there is often a movement of fluid back and forth between capillaries and cells; in all probability this fluid passes back and forth either through spaces in semisolid types of ground substance or directly through it when it is not firmly gelled. Accordingly, the second important function of the amorphous intercellular substance is concerned with permitting the ready transmission of nutriment and fluid from capillaries to cells. This second important function of loose ordinary connective tissue, like the first function (that of connecting cells and tissues together), demands that it must have a very wide distribution, penetrating almost everywhere.

A third very important function of loose ordinary connective tissue is in connection with the defense of the body against infecting organisms. As is shown in Figure 12-8, and explained in more detail a little farther on, a break in the epithelium that covers or lines any exposed part of the body permits harmful bacteria to gain entrance through the break to the loose and nutritive connective tissue.

In this environment the bacteria begin to multiply and elaborate harmful substances. A bacterial infection (as well as other types of injury to tissues) induces a response that is known as *inflammation*. As will be explained in more detail later, many things happen in the inflammatory process that are designed to overcome the bacteria and repair the damage that they cause. The blood capillaries become dilated and congested, and certain blood cells that are phagocytic emigrate through the capillary walls out into the intercellular substance where they phagocytose and destroy the bacteria (Fig. 12-8). Bacterial products serve as antigens and incite the formation of antibodies which react against the bacteria and their poisons. In short, a whole chain of events is set in motion when some part of the body becomes infected, and it is the loose connective tissue of that part of the body that is the chief *arena* in which the battle between infection and the defenses of the body is fought.

We shall now begin a more detailed study of loose ordinary connective tissue with the thought that it serves at least 3 important functions: (1) that of connecting tissues together and providing flexible support for them, (2) a nutritive role because it carries the capillaries and permits the exchange of dissolved substances between capillaries and cells, and (3) an important role in the defense of the body against infection.

We shall begin by presenting a more detailed account of the intercellular substances of loose connective tissue. We shall then consider the capillaries and the mechanisms whereby the fluid content of intercellular substance is regulated and then, in the next chapter, we shall consider in some detail the various kinds of cells of connective tissue, particularly those that make the intercellular substances and the processes by which they are made.

## THE INTERCELLULAR SUBSTANCES OF LOOSE CONNECTIVE TISSUE

As has been noted already, there are 2 main kinds of intercellular substance: (1) the kind that is in the form of fibers and (2) the kind that is amorphous. We shall first consider the fibrous kinds in some detail.

### THE FIBROUS KINDS OF INTERCELLULAR SUBSTANCE

The two main kinds of fibers in loose connective tissue are termed *collagenic* and *elastic,* respectively. The first are made of the protein *collagen;* the second of the protein *elastin.* In addition to collagenic and elastic fibers, a third kind of fiber is often found where loose connective tissue abuts on epithelial structures and in certain other sites; these are termed *reticular* fibers because they are arranged in the form of networks (*rete* = a net). As we shall see, reticular fibers also contain collagen, but, for certain reasons to be described later, they bind stain differently from the more usual type of collagenic fiber. We shall consider collagenic fibers and then, elastic and reticular fibers.

## COLLAGENIC FIBERS

In the loose connective tissue that is disposed beneath the epithelial membrane in Figure 10-1, interlacing strands of wavy pink-staining material are apparent. These wavy strands are collagenic fibers; similar strands can be seen in sections prepared from most parts of the body because connective tissue is found almost everywhere. Collagen is the commonest protein in the body.

**Terminology.** The term fiber is not a term used exclusively in histology; it is used in many other fields as well, such as the textile industry, to refer to slender threadlike structures that can be woven or twisted into useful commodities. There is no precise definition regarding how thick or how long a threadlike structure should be in order for it to be called a fiber. In histology, and with regard to collagen, the term *fiber* is generally used to describe threadlike structures that vary between 1 and 12 microns in diameter; hence, on the average, collagenic fibers are roughly about the same diameter as red blood cells. (Compare the red blood cells in the capillaries in Fig. 10-1 with the wavy collagenic fibers.) In loose connective tissue, collagenic fibers are commonly woven loosely (Fig. 10-1) and, hence, a section cut through loose connective tissue cuts fibers that run in different directions so that some are cut more or less longitudinally, others in cross section, and still others at various angles (Fig. 10-1).

elastic    collagenic
fiber    fibers

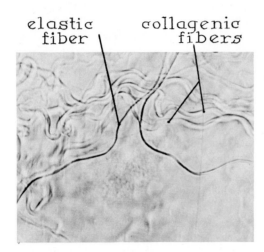

FIG. 10-2. Collagenic and elastic fibers as seen in a fresh, unstained, teased preparation of areolar tissue with the light cut down. The elastic fibers are more refractile than the collagenic.

**Collagenic Fibrils and Microfibrils.** With advances in light microscopy it became obvious that collagenic fibers were themselves made up of much finer threadlike structures that were bundled together side by side to constitute fibers (Fig. 10-3). These finer threadlike structures are around 0.3 and 0.5 microns in thickness and are termed *fibrils*. Finally, with the advent of the EM, it was found that fibrils were in turn made up of still finer threadlike structures about 400 Å in diameter; these are invisible with the light microscope and are generally termed *microfibrils*. These will be considered after we describe collagenic fibers further.

THE STUDY OF FRESH COLLAGENIC FIBERS

It is usual for students in the laboratory to begin the light microscope study of collagenic fibers in fresh loose connective tissue. This is easily done by reflecting the skin and the subcutaneous tissue from the muscles of the thigh of a mouse, rat or rabbit, and then cutting tiny pieces of the loose connective tissue that is torn apart along the plane of cleavage. (Loose connective tissue disposed in thin layers between various structures that are commonly separated from one another as a body is dissected in the gross anatomy laboratory was termed *areolar tissue* by anatomists many years ago, because, as the two struc-

tures which have a layer of loose connective tissue between them are pulled apart, the loose connective tissue is stretched before it is torn apart, and as it stretches it sucks little bubbles of air into its substance which thereupon occupy *areola* [little spaces] within the loose connective tissue.)

Having cut a tiny piece of loose connective tissue (areolar tissue) from a cleavage plane, the little piece is placed on a glass slide in saline, teased apart to some extent and then covered with a coverslip. In viewing it with the light microscope the condenser diaphragm should be closed enough to obtain enough contrast to see collagenic fibers. These appear, as may be seen in Figure 10-2, as wavy structures that pass in various directions in the preparation. A little practice may be required to make a preparation that shows collagenic fibers clearly. Care should be taken in cutting the tiny piece of tissue to avoid fat, for if there is much fat in the preparation, the globules of fat (which are inside cells) will obscure such collagenic fibers as are present. Air bubbles may also gain entrance to the preparation if care is not used in making sure that no air enters the preparation as the coverslip is placed onto the saline that covers the tissue.

The refractive index of fresh collagenic fibers is so similar to the fluid in which they are embedded that they do not show up in a preparation of this kind to as great advantage as might be wished. Thinner darker fibers of a more constant diameter than collagenic fibers can be seen much less frequently than collagenic fibers in a preparation of this type; these are elastic fibers (Fig. 10-2).

**Fresh Preparations of Fibrils.** If a fresh preparation of collagenic fibers is studied, preferably with a phase microscope, and particularly after treating the preparation with a little alkali, the individual fibrils that are assembled together to make collagenic fibers can be seen under the higher powers of the microscope (Fig. 10-3). The fibrils are around 0.3 to 0.5 micron in diameter. Collagenic *fibers* vary in diameter more than fibrils because in different connective tissues fibers range from being only a few fibrils thick to a dozen or more microns in diameter.

**Flexibility of Loose Connective Tissue.** Since collagenic fibers have great tensile

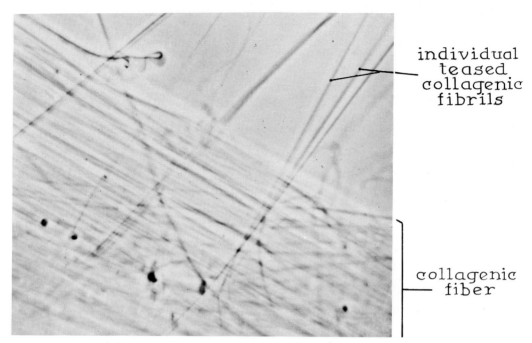

individual
teased
collagenic
fibrils

collagenic
fiber

Fɪɢ. 10-3. Oil-immersion photomicrograph, taken with the phase microscope, of collagenic fibers which had been treated with a mild alkali and then teased apart. Individual collagenic fibrils may be seen (*upper right*), and in the lower part of the photograph a collagenic fiber, having a longitudinally striated appearance due to its fibrils, is present.

strength, it might be thought that loose connective tissue would not be as flexible as it is. The reason for its flexibility is that such collagenic fibers as it contains are generally disposed in various directions as in a weave; hence loose connective tissue can be stretched slightly just as a woven cloth can be stretched slightly without stretching any of its fibers longitudinally. Moreover, it seems probable that in their natural state, at least some collagenic fibers in loose connective tissue are wavy, and these, of course, could be stretched longitudinally until they were straight. The elastic fibers in loose connective tissue help to restore it to its usual state when a stretching force is removed from the tissue, for, unlike collagenic fibers, straight elastic fibers can be stretched longitudinally, after which they will snap back like rubber bands to their original state.

**Color of Fresh Fibers.** Fresh collagenic fibers are white and so are termed *white fibers*. Fresh elastic fibers are slightly yellow and hence are termed *yellow fibers*. Since collagen is such a tough protein, a considerable content of it in meat makes meat tough. If collagen is boiled in water it becomes hydrated, and this makes it into gelatin which is soft; this is one reason for cooking tough meat for a long time. Glue is made from collagen. Collagen is also made into leather; this is done by digesting off the epithelium from the hides of animals and then treating the connective tissue of the hide (which is the part left) with tanning agents which make the collagen even more resistant to chemical change than before.

**Staining Reactions.** Collagen stains with acid dyes, but after treatment with phosphotungstic acid it may stain with basic dyes. In ordinary stained sections little detail can be seen in collagen. In H and E sections it is colored pink to red. Special stains may be used to color it more or less specifically if there is a question about whether or not something that is seen in a section is collagen or not. Collagen is colored red with Van Giesson's picrofuchsin stain, and collagen is stained with the aniline dyes in Mallory's connective tissue stain and Masson's trichrome stain. Another test that may be used for collagen is that collagenic fibers are birefrigent when examined in polarized light.

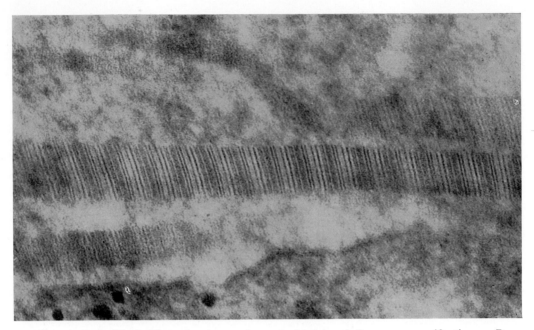

FIG. 10-4. A (*Top*). Electron micrograph, approximately of the same magnification as B, showing the appearance presented by a microfibril of collagen in a thin section. Although traversed by finer cross banding, the gap and overlap regions illustrated in B can be identified. For an explanation of the finer cross banding, the article by Hodge and Petruska should be consulted. (Preparation from H. Warshawsky)

B (*Below*). Electron micrograph (× 175,000) of an isolated negatively stained collagenic microfibril showing alternating light and dark regions. One dark and one light segment represents one 640 Å period. The diagram below is based on the arrangement of tropocollagen molecules suggested by Hodge and Petruska to account for the 640 Å periodicity (see explanation in text). (Electron micrograph by A. F. Howatson and J. D. Almeida)

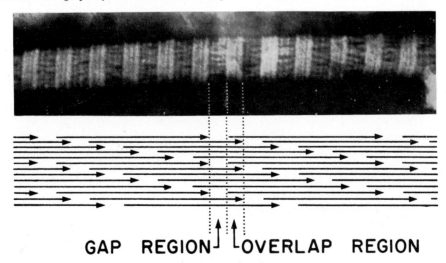

## GAP REGION┘ └OVERLAP REGION

Collagen is digested by an enzyme, collagenase. It is of interest in connection with the study of certain diseases that collagenase can be produced by certain bacteria.

**The Fine Structure of Collagen.** With the advent of the EM it became obvious that the fibrils seen under high magnification with the light microscope (Fig. 10-3) are not the finest fibrils present in collagen. The EM disclosed fibrils that are much narrower, being in general around 400 Å in diameter and hence much too fine to be seen with the light microscope. These very fine fibrils, seen only in the EM, are commonly called microfibrils, and they are bundled together, side by side, to form the fibrils of light microscopy.

Microfibrils, in the EM, reveal a very interesting type of structure in that they exhibit axial periodicity. In particular, they demonstrate along their lengths little units of structure that repeat themselves every 640 Å (Figs. 10-4 A and B). Ever since this periodicity was observed it has been of great interest to find an explanation for it, but only recently has a suitable explanation been forthcoming, as will now be described.

To understand how microfibrils of collagen could be formed, it must first be emphasized that, as was described in Chapters 6 and 7, proteins are synthesized inside cells. The cells in loose connective tissue that are responsible for the synthesis of collagen are termed *fibroblasts,* and they and their fine structure will be dealt with in the next chapter. Here, it is enough to say that since fibrils and fibers of collagen are infinitely longer than cells, the basic molecules of which collagen is composed must be small enough to be secreted by fibroblasts and then polymerized, outside cells, into fibrils and fibers.

The study of the nature of the basic molecules of collagen that are synthesized inside cells and then secreted outside cells where they become polymerized into microfibrils that show an axial periodicity of 640 Å was greatly facilitated when it was found that (1) collagen could be dissociated biochemically into the molecules of which fibrils and fibers are composed, and (2) the basic molecules of collagen could then be reassembled by biochemical procedures into microfibrils that showed the same axial periodicity as natural collagen. The basic molecules into which collagen could be dissociated were termed *tropocollagen* molecules. An interesting question then arose, namely, how molecules of tropocollagen were assembled so as to account for the 640 Å periodicity of collagenic microfibrils.

Perhaps the first thought about this matter was to suspect that tropocollagen molecules were themselves 640 Å long and that they

became arranged side by side in bundles along the length of collagen microfibrils with the ends of the molecules of one bundle joining the ends of the molecules of the next bundle every 640 Å along the microfibril. But then some experiments were performed in which it was shown that if collagen were dissociated into tropocollagen macromolecules and then reconstituted a different way from before, by a special procedure, the microfibrils that formed had a periodicity of 2,800 Å instead of 640 Å. This finding and other evidence indicated that tropocollagen macromolecules must be around 2,800 Å in length. The question then arose as to how macromolecules 2,800 Å in length could be bundled together in a microfibril so that they would account for a crossbanding appearance repeating itself every 640 Å. It was first suggested that the 640 Å periodicity could be accounted for if the 2,800 Å molecules in a microfibril were staggered, each one overlapping the one beside it by one quarter of its length. However, if staggered macromolecules were joined end-to-end without any overlapping, the result of this arrangement would be a periodicity of around 700 Å. So, the hypothesis relating to staggered tropocollagen macromolecules by itself did not quite solve the problem. However, a modification of the staggered hypothesis proposed by Hodge and Petruska does explain how molecules 2,800 Å in length could be fitted together side-by-side in a staggered fashion in a microfibril so that they cause the microfibril to have a 640 Å periodicity. Their explanation is that the staggered tropocollagen macromolecules in the microfibril do not meet end-to-end; instead, there is roughly half of one period between their ends. To explain further how they are arranged, we shall say that along the length of a negatively stained microfibril there are light and dark segments (Fig. 10-4 B) which repeat themselves. One dark plus one light segment accounts for one period. Each light segment accounts for slightly more than half a period, and each dark segment for slightly less than half a period. Next, the tropocollagen macromolecules are assembled side-by-side and in a staggered arrangement, but they are staggered in such a way that the gaps between the ends of tropocollagen macromolecules always fall in a dark segment. Hence, the dark segments are not as dense

FIG. 10-5. Electron micrograph (× 37,000) of an elastic fiber from the aorta of a rabbit, showing the essentially amorphous nature of elastic fibers which is in sharp contrast with the highly ordered structure of collagenic fibrils illustrated in Figure 10-4. (Gross, J.: J. Exp. Med. *89*:699)

as the light segments, for each light segment has 5 macromolecules passing through it to every 4 that pass through a dark segment. By this arrangement, each 2,800 Å tropocollagen macromolecule extends over approximately 4½ periods, always over 5 light segments and over only 4 dark segments (see Fig. 10-4 B).

The longitudinal striations that can be seen in the negatively stained microfibril illustrated in Figure 10-4 B probably represent small (and perhaps unit) bundles of tropocollagen molecules.

Still finer crossbanding can be seen in the 640 Å units (Fig. 10-4 A). We shall not attempt to explain these.

## ELASTIC FIBERS

These consist of the protein *elastin*. This albuminoid is probably the most resistant of all the body proteins to chemical change. Even in mummies thousands of years old the elastic fibers of arteries are often sufficiently well preserved to allow some conclusion to be drawn about the arterial diseases suffered by the Egyptians of that era.

**Histologic Structure of Fibers.** Although fresh elastin is said to be yellow, Lansing says this is not true of fibers from the young. Elastic fibers are highly refractile in contrast with collagenic and reticular fibers (Fig. 10-2). They are long and narrow, ranging from less than a micron to a few microns in thickness. With the EM, elastic fibers give no indication of being made up of fibrils or microfibrils but instead seem homogeneous (Fig. 10-5).

**Histologic Structure of Membranes.** Elastin is not uncommonly disposed as membranes or plates in the body, particularly in the walls of blood vessels (Figs. 22-2 and 22-5). Elastic membranes are commonly fenestrated, probably because elastin is not very permeable and fenestra are required to permit the passage of nutrients and waste products through them. If sections of normal elastic fibers are incinerated, the fibers are seen to contain no mineral elements (Fig. 4-4); they do, however, become calcified in certain types of degenerative arterial diseases. Elastic fibers are mildly acidophilic, but their staining with eosin is erratic. They are stained more or less selectively by certain dyes—for example, dark brown by orcein and dark blue by resorcin fuchsin.

As their name implies, elastic fibers, on being stretched and then released, tend to snap back, like rubber bands, to their original state, to help impart a diffuse elasticity to tissue they commonly branch.

**Regeneration.** It is commonly said that elastic fibers that are destroyed are not regenerated. However, the author has observed the formation of new elastin in the repair of arteries damaged experimentally.

## RETICULAR FIBERS

Since reticular fibers examined in the EM reveal the periodicity of collagen, they do not represent a special kind of protein fiber.

Reticular fibers are put in a special category because of their arrangement and staining reactions.

Reticular fibers are commonly seen in loose connective tissue where it abuts on epithelial structures, particularly in association with basement membranes (Fig. 8-2). In such sites delicate fibers are arranged in networks, and this is the reason for their name (*rete* = a net). However, there is something more than their arrangement that has led to their having special consideration; this is that they can be stained by special technics which do not stain collagenic fibers. One way that they were more or less specifically stained in the past was by means of silver impregnation technics (Fig. 10-6). However, reticular fibers also stain by the PAS technic (Fig. 8-2), and it seems probable that this is to be accounted for by the fact that the fibers in reticular nets are generally associated with a special carbohydrate type of amorphous intercellular substance which is the material that stains. So, we shall postpone further discussion of reticular fibers and their staining reactions until we have considered the amorphous intercellular substances.

## THE AMORPHOUS INTERCELLULAR SUBSTANCE OF LOOSE CONNECTIVE TISSUE

For many years it was uncertain whether or not loose connective tissue contained any amorphous material—any ground or background substance in which the fibers and the cells were embedded. That there was a *ground substance* in loose connective tissue, in which the cells and fibers were embedded, was first proved by Sylvia Bensley in 1934. She showed that if fluid was injected into the intercellular substances of loose connective tissue the fluid was absorbed by *something* that became swollen as a result; the fluid did not form a bleb or flow away as might be expected if there were no amorphous material present. She also showed that there was something that presented an obstacle to the movement of certain little organisms that were introduced into tissue of this type. From these and further observations it became clear that there was a ground substance in which the cells and fibers of loose connective tissue were em-

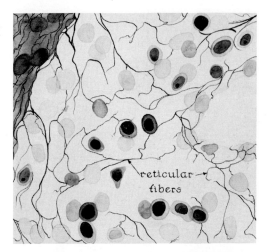

Fig. 10-6. Drawing of a section of spleen stained by the Bielschowsky technic for reticular fibers (high-power). By this method, silver is precipitated on the reticular fibers, which makes them stand out as fine black lines.

bedded, and that this material was most elusive when ordinary histologic methods were used in attempts to demonstrate its presence.

Around this time another discovery was made which proved to have an important bearing on this matter.

In 1928 Duran-Reynals discovered that when he injected rabbits' skins with an extract that had been made from a testis infected with a certain disease virus, the disease *spread* very rapidly in the infected skin. Further study showed that the rapid spread was due to something that could be extracted from normal testis tissue, because an extract of normal testis tissue was found to make dyes that were injected into the connective tissue of the skin spread rapidly (Fig. 10-7). From these experiments Duran-Reynals postulated the existence of something that he called "spreading factor" that could be extracted from testicular tissue. For many years the nature of this effect remained a mystery. Then Karl Meyer began a series of studies on the chemistry of the amorphous intercellular substances. Before his work, the amorphous intercellular substances were usually described as belonging to a chemically ill-defined group of substances called *mucoids*. These were supposed to be glycoproteins, that is, proteins with

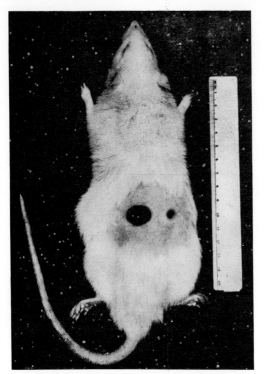

FIG. 10-7. The back of a rat, showing the spreading phenomenon. Two dark spots may be seen. The one at the right is the result of the injection of 0.1 ml. of saline and India ink into the site; the spot at the left is due to the injection of 0.1 ml. of India ink and an aqueous extract of rat testicle. The extract of testicle contains a spreading factor which permits the India ink to spread much more widely and much more quickly in the tissues than occurs when India ink is injected by itself. (W. R. Harris)

a carbohydrate prosthetic group. Meyer's illuminating researches resulted in a reclassification of these materials. Meyer suggested that they should be called *mucopolysaccharides,* a term which suitably emphasizes the fact that they are essentially of a carbohydrate nature and this has been treated more fully in Chapter 2.

The mucopolysaccharides of intercellular substance are classified into 2 main groups according to whether or not they are esterified with sulfuric acid on the hexosamine part of the molecule. Hyaluronic acid and chondroitin (an isomer of hyaluronic acid) are representa-

tives of the nonsulfated types, while chondroitin sulfates (chondroitin sulfuric acid) are representatives of the sulfated types.

Hyaluronic acid, the chief type of amorphous intercellular substance of loose connective tissue, is a viscid material when it is polymerized into molecules of considerable size; this is important in relation to the next point to be considered.

The next discovery in this area was made when Meyer found that certain kinds of bacteria produced an enzyme that depolymerizes hyaluronic acid, thus making it less viscous. He named this enzyme *hyaluronidase.* Then in 1939, two British workers, Chain and Duthie, observed that the spreading factor of testicular extract decreased the viscosity of synovial fluid, which was known by this time to contain hyaluronic acid. This, of course, raised the suspicion that the spreading factor discovered by Duran-Reynals some years before was the enzyme hyaluronidase, and indeed it was soon shown that testicular extract does contain hyaluronidase.

This discovery of hyaluronidase was important for several reasons. Whereas it is of interest that certain bacteria can make hyaluronidase which, in infections, could act to reduce the viscosity of the intercellular substance being invaded by the bacteria and so perhaps be a factor in the spread of infection, it is of much greater interest that hyaluronidase can be produced by the normal tissues of the body, for this suggests that it has a physiologic function. How great this is has not yet been ascertained. The discovery of hyaluronidase has also had very practical results; for example, it is now used when it is desirable to increase the spread throughout tissue of a substance injected into tissue, for example, local anesthetics.

## THE STAINING OF THE GROUND SUBSTANCE OF LOOSE CONNECTIVE TISSUE (HYALURONIC ACID)

As has been observed already, ground substance (hyaluronic acid) is very difficult to fix and stain. In H and E sections the observer sees only relatively clear areas in the sites where it was present during life (Fig. 10-1). Special methods which assist in staining by hyaluronic acid will now be described.

**Metachromatic Staining Methods.** Muco-polysaccharides stain metachromatically (*meta* = beyond; *chroma* = color). This means that when tissues containing them are treated with dyes of a certain type, they take on a color different from that of the dye employed. Only some dyes give this kind of reaction. Metachromasia was first ascribed to sulfate but it was shown that hyaluronic acid in tissues also stained metachromatically even though hyaluronic acid contains no sulfate group. Nevertheless, the sulfated types are demonstrated to better advantage by metachromatic stains than hyaluronic acid.

Another staining method for acid muco-polysaccharides, the colloidal iron technic, is described in Chapter 4 under Histochemistry.

**Other Components of Ground Substance.** The amorphous intercellular substance of loose connective tissue—the ground substance in which the protein fibers are embedded—probably consists chiefly of hyaluronic acid, but this is accompanied to different extents in different situations by sulfated mucopoly-saccharide. As will be described in due course in connection with reticular networks and basement membranes, it seems very probable that there are further kinds of carbohydrate components in ground substance, in at least some locations. Furthermore, apart from the protein that is in the form of fibers in loose connective tissue, there is protein that is in the form of a sol type of colloidal solution also present in ground substances; this is sometimes referred to as the soluble protein of loose connective tissue. This latter constituent of amorphous intercellular substance is derived from two main sources. Some of it consists of protein molecules that have been synthesized by connective tissue cells, but have not yet been polymerized into fibrils. However, there is also a considerable amount of protein in the ground substance that is derived from the blood (the extravascular pool of blood proteins is considerable—see review by Mancini). As will be described in the next section, blood plasma contains macromolecules of protein, and some of these normally leak through the walls of blood capillaries to enter the ground substance of loose connective tissue; indeed, they may circulate to some extent through the ground substance and enter lymphatic capillaries by which they return to the blood circulatory system. And, finally, since the amorphous intercellular substance is a colloid, the various molecules that are dispersed in it must be dispersed in an aqueous medium; the ground substance in effect is a hydrophilic colloidal solution which would normally seem to be in the form of a soft gel. The indications are that within certain limits this gel can bind varying quantities of water. The aqueous dispersion medium of the ground substance is derived from capillaries as a fluid known as tissue fluid. This component of amorphous intercellular substance will be described next.

## TISSUE FLUID

### GENERAL CONSIDERATIONS

The blood of the body is contained by a system of tubes called *blood vessels*. These form a circuit through which blood is pumped in one direction by the heart (Fig. 22-1). The vessels that lead away from the heart have relatively thick and strong walls because they carry blood under considerable pressure; these vessels are called *arteries*. Arteries branch and rebranch and finally empty their blood, under low pressure, into capillaries which are narrow tubes with thin delicate walls (Figs. 10-1 and 10-8). The capillaries generally pursue a curving course through the intercellular substance (hence the term capillary loops) after which they drain into veins which carry the blood back to the heart (Fig. 10-8). Blood in the veins is not under much pressure; hence, the walls of veins are not as thick as those of arteries.

As has already been illustrated in Figure 10-1, nutritive substances and oxygen dissolved in the blood must leave the blood and pass through the walls of blood vessels and then through the intercellular substances of tissues to reach the cells that they nourish (Fig. 10-8). The waste products formed by cells must make the same journey in an opposite direction.

The walls of arteries are much too thick to permit food substances or oxygen to pass through them. Arteries do not nourish tissues directly; their function is to carry blood to the very thin-walled capillaries and empty it into capillaries through narrow arterioles which

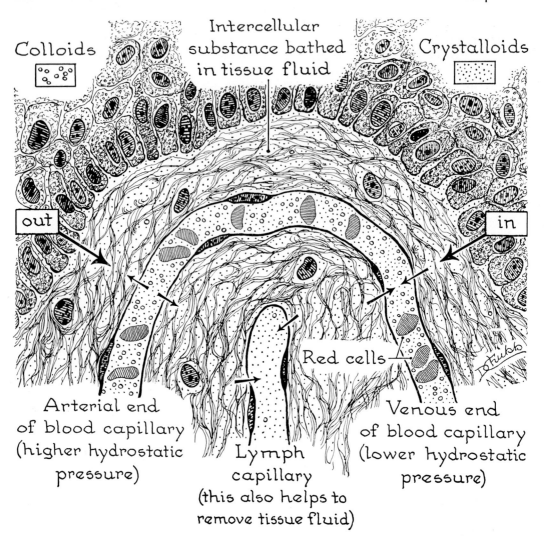

Colloids          Intercellular          Crystalloids
              substance bathed
                in tissue fluid

out                                              in

Arterial end                              Venous end
of blood capillary                        of blood capillary
(higher hydrostatic      Red cells        (lower hydrostatic
      pressure)                                 pressure)
                     Lymph
                   capillary
                (this also helps to
               remove tissue fluid)

Fig. 10-8. A diagram to show how tissue fluid is formed by capillaries and absorbed by capillaries and lymphatics. The colloids of the blood are represented as small circles and the crystalloids of blood and tissue fluid as dots. Under normal conditions only a very little colloid escapes
from most capillaries, and such colloid as escapes is returned to the circulation by way of the
lymphatics.

reduce pressure; as a result, blood enters the
thin capillaries under a very low pressure.

The walls of capillaries are thin enough to
permit water and substances dissolved in water
to pass through them. The walls of capillaries
are composed of very thin platelike cells similar to the squamous epithelial cells illustrated
in Figure 8-1 A, but which are called endothelial cells for reasons explained at the beginning of Chapter 8. Moreover, the thin endothelial cells that constitute the walls of

capillaries are curved in one direction so that
they fit together to form a tube. In small capillaries a single endothelial cell may be enough
to completely encircle a lumen, but in larger
capillaries it may take 2 or even more endothelial cells to encircle the lumen. The endothelial cells of capillaries each have a flattened nucleus, but over most of their extents
they consist only of cytoplasm. Hence capillaries are in effect very thin cytoplasmic tubes.
For fluid to pass through their walls requires

that the fluid need only pass through cytoplasm, and this is so thin that it is sometimes seen only with difficulty with the light microscope.

The capillaries shown in Figure 10-1 are particularly large. It should be noted that an occasional dark flattened ovoid nucleus of an endothelial cell can be seen both in the longitudinal and the cross section views of capillaries that appear in this illustration.

Although the fine structure of capillaries will be described in a later chapter dealing with the circulatory system, the student at this time should inspect Figure 22-10 which is an electron micrograph of a cross section of a capillary. The capillary in this illustration is of a size that required 2 endothelial cells to encircle its lumen; this is indicated because two sites of attachments between the edges of endothelial cells can be seen; these are marked *end. cell boundaries* in this illustration. At the boundaries between the cell membranes of adjacent endothelial cells that abut on each other an increased density is obvious; this is similar to some of the appearances seen at sites of attachment between epithelial cells which were described in Chapter 8. Another feature to notice in this illustration is that the cytoplasm of the endothelial cells is seen with the EM to contain many pinocytotic vesicles. These are concerned with the transport of fluid and substances dissolved in fluid into and/or through the capillary wall. Under normal conditions probably some of the tissue fluid that emerges from capillaries is due to vesicles of fluid developing at, and becoming pinched off from, the inner surfaces of the endothelial cells of the capillaries and then moving to the outer surface of the endothelial cells where their content of fluid is released into the adjacent intercellular substance. But fluid from the blood also passes through capillary walls more directly because of other factors that will be described very shortly. In order to describe the chief mechanism by which fluid in capillaries passes through their walls we must describe what is meant by tissue fluid.

**What Is Tissue Fluid?** Blood is a fluid that contains cells, parts of cells (called platelets) and sometimes tiny fat droplets (called chylomicrons) in suspension. The fluid part of blood is called *plasma*. Blood plasma is a *hydrophilic*

colloidal solution for it contains macromolecules of protein which *like* the state of solution. The fluid of blood also contains many substances such as glucose, salts and oxygen which are in true solution. It is usual to refer to the substances that are in true solution in plasma as *crystalloids* in order to contrast them with the proteins that are in *colloidal* solution.

The walls of capillaries hold back the cells and parts of cells that are in blood (Fig. 10-8). Furthermore, under normal conditions, the walls of capillaries hold back most of the protein macromolecules that are in plasma (Fig. 10-8). However, the walls of capillaries are permeable to the water of the blood and the crystalloids (and gases) that are dissolved in the water. Hence the fluid that is normally exuded through the walls of capillaries to provide a dispersion medium for the intercellular substances is primarily a watery solution of crystalloids and gases. This fluid is called *tissue fluid*, and under normal conditions it is a dialysate of blood plasma. It is probable that its composition is similar to that of the sea water in which life originated, but which has now become a more concentrated solution. The factors that are concerned with the elaboration of tissue fluid into intercellular substances and its resorption from intercellular substances will now be described.

## HYDROSTATIC PRESSURE AND THE FORMATION OF TISSUE FLUID

Anyone who has seen a pressure filter in operation readily understands that increasing the hydrostatic pressure on a fluid drives it through a filter faster. The hydrostatic pressure generated by the pumping action of the heart is an important factor in driving tissue fluid out through the endothelial walls of capillaries.

It might be thought that arteries would be the chief source of tissue fluid in the body because the hydrostatic pressure in them is much greater than in other vessels. But the thick and closely knit walls of arteries—and these are necessary to prevent their bursting because of the high hydrostatic pressure within them—do not permit tissue fluid to diffuse through them; indeed, the tissue fluid that diffuses through the endothelial lining of a large artery does *not even effectively penetrate the outer zone of its walls,* which must be fed by tissue fluid from an outside source. Arteries, then, are of practically no use in directly providing tissue fluid for the tissues through which they pass.

The hydrostatic pressure in capillaries is very slight compared with that in arteries, because arterial blood is fed into capillaries through tiny arterioles that have narrow lumens and here act as do pressure reduction valves. Furthermore, the hydrostatic pressure decreases as blood moves along the length of capillaries, because they are such very narrow tubes and blood is viscous. Nevertheless, because the walls of capillaries are so thin, the hydrostatic pressure within them at their arterial ends is sufficient to force tissue fluid out through the endothelium. The arterial ends of capillaries, then, constitute the most important source of tissue fluid in the body (Fig. 10-8).

There is, of course, some slight hydrostatic pressure in the venous ends of capillaries and also in most veins. We shall find that certain veins even serve as a source of tissue fluid, but this is the exception rather than the rule, because most veins have too thick walls and too little hydrostatic pressure within them to produce tissue fluid. However, the venous ends of capillaries are not handicapped by thick walls, and there is a slight hydrostatic pressure within them. Why they do not produce tissue fluid, but instead, absorb it, will now be discussed.

## ABSORPTION OF TISSUE FLUID

If tissue fluid were only produced and not absorbed, the tissues of the body would become increasingly swollen with it. Two mechanisms operate under normal conditions to absorb it at the same rate at which it is produced.

1. **Absorption at the Venous Ends of Capillaries.** In forcing fluid out through the endothelial walls of capillaries, the hydrostatic pressure within a capillary must be sufficient to overcome the effects of another factor which is always seeking to draw tissue fluid back into the capillary. This other factor is the attraction of blood for tissue fluid that is due

to the osmotic pressure of blood being somewhat greater than that of tissue fluid. We shall elaborate.

Both blood and tissue fluid contain crystalloids. These impart the same osmotic pressure to both solutions. But, blood contains more colloid than tissue fluid. And, although colloidal solutions do not exert very great osmotic pressures, the greater colloid content of blood is sufficient to make its osmotic pressure somewhat greater than that of tissue fluid. Hence, when blood (under no hydrostatic pressure) is separated from tissue fluid by a membrane that allows the passage of crystalloids but not that of colloids, blood attracts tissue fluid through the membrane into itself. Hence, the colloids of blood, although they do not exert a very great absolute osmotic pressure are, nevertheless, very important because such osmotic pressure as they do exert is of a marginal nature.

Whether tissue fluid moves in or out through the endothelium at any site along a capillary depends, then, on whether or not the hydrostatic pressure within the capillary at that particular site is greater or less than the difference between the osmotic pressures of blood and tissue fluid. It is generally believed that the hydrostatic pressure at the arterial ends of capillaries is greater than the difference between the osmotic pressures of blood and tissue fluid, so that tissue fluid is formed at this site (Fig. 10-8). But as the hydrostatic pressure gradually falls as the viscous blood courses along narrow capillaries toward their venous ends, it sooner or later becomes insufficient to overcome the attraction that blood, by virtue of its greater osmotic pressure, possesses for tissue fluid, with the result that tissue fluid returns into the capillary. This allows for a circulation of tissue fluid (Fig. 10-8).

2. **Absorption by Lymphatics.** In most, but not all, parts of the body there is a second mechanism to assist in the absorption of tissue fluid. This second mechanism employs a second set of capillaries called lymphatic capillaries to serve as absorptive organs. Lymphatic capillaries permeate the tissue between the blood capillaries. They originate in the tissue, frequently from blind ends (Fig. 10-8), and because they branch freely they com-

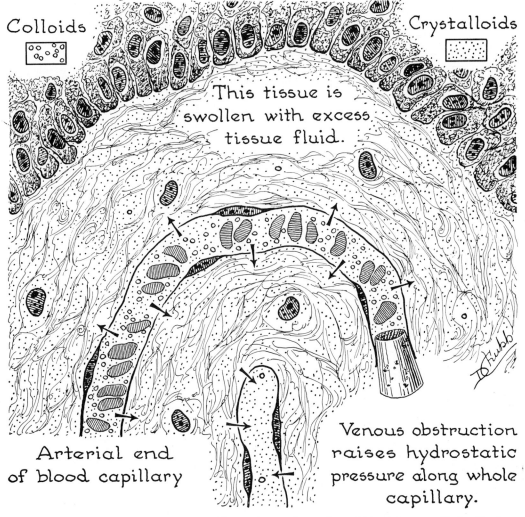

Colloids

Crystalloids

This tissue is swollen with excess tissue fluid.

Arterial end of blood capillary

Venous obstruction raises hydrostatic pressure along whole capillary.

FIG. 10-9. Diagram to show how an obstruction to the outflow of blood from capillaries (back pressure on veins) can cause an increased amount of tissue fluid to form from the capillaries and also interfere with its absorption.

monly form networks of great complexity. That part of the tissue fluid not absorbed by blood capillaries diffuses through their endothelial walls, and once it has gained entrance to them is called *lymph* instead of tissue fluid. Lymphatic capillaries drain into larger lymph vessels to be described later, and these, connecting with still other lymph vessels, eventually form two chief lymphatic trunks that return the lymph collected from the whole body into large veins near the heart. Hence, that part of the tissue fluid absorbed by lym-

phatic capillaries eventually reaches the confines of the blood circulatory system again, but by a somewhat circuitous route.

Lymphatic capillaries are useful in regulating the quality of the tissue fluid as well as its quantity. At present, it is generally agreed that the endothelium of blood capillaries normally allows a little blood protein to escape into intercellular substances. It is also generally agreed that the escaped protein macromolecules cannot diffuse back into blood capillaries. However, it would seem that macromolecules of protein can pass from intercellular substances back through the endothelial walls of lymphatics. The studies of Drinker and his associates have shown that if it were not for the lymphatic drainage of tissue fluid, blood protein would accumulate in tissue fluid and by virtue of its osmotic pressure would tend to hold increasing amounts of water in the tissue. By more or less continually draining away colloid from tissue fluid, lymphatic capillaries exert a profound effect on the quality, as well as the quantity, of tissue fluid.

## EDEMA

The many factors concerned in the production and the absorption of tissue fluid all represent possible causes for the mechanism to be disrupted. Although it is conceivable that a disrupted mechanism could lead to there being too little tissue fluid, as for example might occur in tissues that have received enough radiation to inhibit the growth of capillaries, the common example of a disrupted mechanism is the swelling of tissue by an excess. A swelling of tissue, caused by its containing excess tissue fluid is termed *edema* (*oedema* = a swelling), and it is a very common clinical condition. If edematous tissue is examined under the microscope, the cells and the structures within it are seen to be spread apart more widely than is usual (Fig. 10-9), and if it is extreme, pools of fluid may be seen lying in the intercellular substance.

The amount of tissue fluid that can accumulate in tissues varies in relation to the type of tissue affected. Some tissues offer little resistance to being spread apart from within; others, because they are firmly knit together, offer more. In most sites edema tends to be self-limiting because the more the tissue becomes swollen, the more resistance it offers to becoming stretched further. When a certain point is reached, the hydrostatic pressure of the fluid in the stretched tissue is almost as great as that within the capillaries, and as a result the production of tissue fluid in the part almost ceases.

It might be thought that the increased hydrostatic pressure of the tissue fluid in swollen tissue would cause the collapse of its lymphatic vessels and so interfere with lymph drainage. However, the studies of Pullinger

and Florey indicate the opposite. The walls of lymphatic vessels are attached to fibers of intercellular substance that extend throughout the tissue. As tissues become spread apart by fluid, these fibers are put on the stretch with the result that they pull on the walls of lymphatic vessels in various directions and so hold them open.

## SOME CAUSES OF EDEMA

1. **Increased Hydrostatic Pressure in Blood Capillaries.** Theoretically, the hydrostatic pressure in blood capillaries would be raised either if blood were delivered to capillaries under increased pressure or if the free drainage of blood from capillaries into veins were impeded. Arterial pressures high enough to raise capillary pressures sufficiently to cause edema are seldom encountered and, indeed, such pressures are scarcely compatible with life. Hence, increased hydrostatic pressure in capillaries is almost always due to some obstruction to the free drainage of blood into veins and back to the heart.

If a vein becomes obstructed, that portion of it between the obstruction and the capillaries soon becomes distended with blood, and the hydrostatic pressure within it rises. The increased hydrostatic pressure in the vein is transmitted back to the venous ends of those capillaries that drain into it and, as a result, the hydrostatic pressure at their venous ends becomes almost as great as at their arterial ends. Under these conditions, the whole capillary exudes tissue fluid, and none of the capillary absorbs it (Fig. 10-9).

There are many different ways in which the venous return of blood may be obstructed sufficiently to cause edema. The heart may be so diseased that it cannot pump away all the blood that is returned to it; hence, blood backs up in the veins to increase the hydrostatic pressure within them. Edema caused by such a mechanism is often said to be "dependent" because it tends to occur in the lowest parts of the body. Again, certain diseases cause certain individual veins to become obstructed; the edema in this instance is roughly localized to the area normally drained by the affected vein.

2. **Lymphatic Obstruction.** Since part of the tissue fluid produced at the arterial ends of

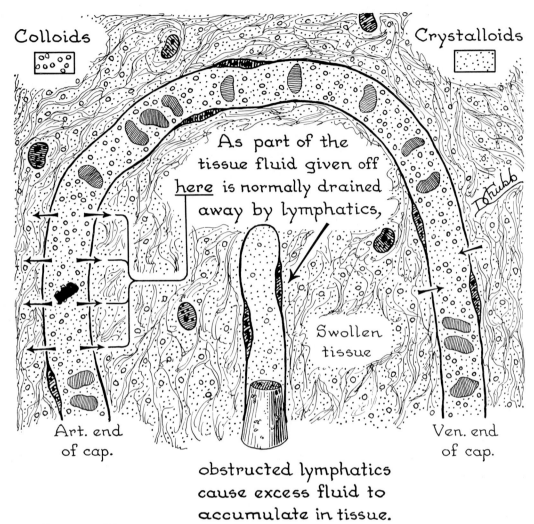

Colloids                                                    Crystalloids

As part of the tissue fluid given off <u>here</u> is normally drained away by lymphatics,

Swollen tissue

Art. end of cap.                                            Ven. end of cap.

obstructed lymphatics
cause excess fluid to
accumulate in tissue.

Fig. 10-10. Diagram to show how the obstruction of lymphatics may cause an increased amount of tissue fluid to be present in the tissues they normally drain. It should be observed also that the amount of colloid in the tissue fluid becomes increased when lymphatics are obstructed because such colloid as normally escapes from capillaries is normally drained away by the lymphatics.

capillaries normally is drained away by lymphatic capillaries, any obstruction to the drainage of lymph tends to lead to an increase of tissue fluid. Moreover, since lymphatics normally drain away blood colloid that escapes into tissue, the tissue fluid that accumulates when lymphatics are obstructed comes to contain an increasing amount of colloid, and this gradually raises its osmotic pressure. This contributes further to the edema (Fig. 10-10).

Lymphatic obstruction can be caused by several different disease processes. However, the most dramatic one is seen in the tropics and is due to a small parasite that, on gaining entrance to the body, tends to occlude lymphatics. So, great persistent swelling of parts of the body (elephantiasis) may result.

3. **Insufficient Colloid in the Blood.** The absorption of tissue fluid at the venous ends of blood capillaries depends on the fact that the osmotic pressure of blood is greater than that of tissue fluid. This extra osmotic pressure possesed by blood depends on its colloid content. Therefore, a depletion of blood col-

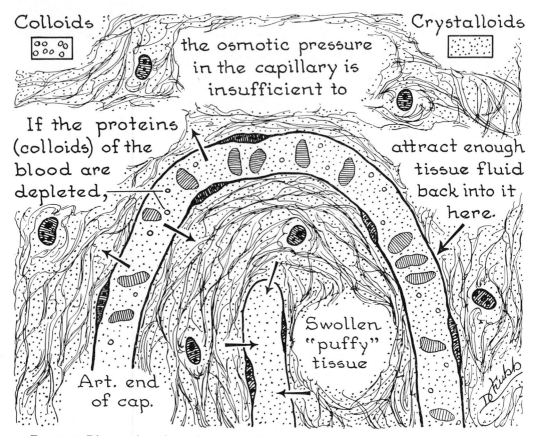

Colloids                                Crystalloids

the osmotic pressure
in the capillary is
insufficient to

If the proteins
(colloids) of the
blood are
depleted,

attract enough
tissue fluid
back into it
here.

Swollen
"puffy"
tissue

Art. end
of cap.

FIG. 10-11. Diagram shows how a lack of colloid in the blood increases the amount of tissue fluid.

loid diminishes the attraction of blood for tissue fluid and hence causes edema (Fig. 10-11).

The colloids of blood are proteins. Proteins, of course, are a most important and essential dietary ingredient; as noted previously, protoplasm consists chiefly of protein. So starvation, particularly protein starvation, can deplete the proteins of the blood with resulting edema. But more commonly, in countries where food is relatively abundant, a depletion of blood protein occurs when proteins are lost from the blood in some fashion faster than they can be replaced. This may happen, for example, in some kinds of disease of the kidneys. Normally, the capillaries in the kidney which act as filters in connection with the formation of urine retain protein. But when injured in certain ways, they lose their ability to hold back protein, which thereupon escapes into the urine. Testing the urine for albumin—a very common procedure—gives information as to whether or not proteins are being lost this way. A low level of blood protein caused by

the persistent escape of blood proteins from diseased kidneys can cause edema. Another way by which the blood proteins can become seriously depleted is by their seeping away from large, denuded areas of injured tissue (weeping wounds).

4. **Increased Permeability of Blood Capillary Endothelium.** The ability of endothelium to act as a semipermeable membrane and to hold back colloidal particles while permitting the passage of crystalloids in solution depends on endothelial cells remaining alive and healthy. If the endothelial cells of capillaries are injured, they no longer hold back the colloidal particles of the blood; if enough capillaries are injured the consequences can be serious, for injured capillaries can permit a great deal of plasma to leak into the intercellular substance surrounding them (Fig. 10-12). Since plasma is the fluid in which blood cells are suspended, it is obvious that if a great deal of plasma leaked through capillaries at a site of extensive injury, that there

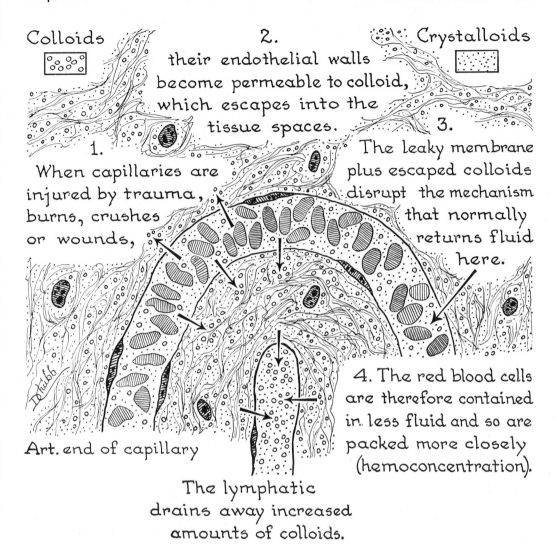

Colloids

Crystalloids

2. their endothelial walls become permeable to colloid, which escapes into the tissue spaces.

1. When capillaries are injured by trauma, burns, crushes or wounds,

3. The leaky membrane plus escaped colloids disrupt the mechanism that normally returns fluid here.

4. The red blood cells are therefore contained in less fluid and so are packed more closely (hemoconcentration).

Art. end of capillary

The lymphatic drains away increased amounts of colloids.

FIG. 10-12. Diagram shows how plasma escapes when the endothelial walls of capillaries are injured by burns, crushes, near-by wounds or other means. Notice that as plasma leaks away from the capillary the number of red blood cells in relation to plasma in it becomes increased. This is called hemoconcentration. Observe also how, under conditions of this sort, increased amounts of colloid are drained away by the lymphatic capillaries.

might not be enough fluid left in the circulatory system for the heart to maintain a proper circulation. The situation would be much like that which occurs when much whole blood is lost from severed blood vessels with the result that there is not enough left in the circulatory system for the heart to fill properly between contractions. However, plasma loss is somewhat different from a true hemorrhage, because in hemorrhage both plasma and blood cells are lost, whereas when capillaries are damaged they still manage to hold back the cells of blood fairly well so that only the plasma

is lost (Fig. 10-12). Consequently, in plasma leakage due to injured capillaries, the proportions of cells to plasma in the blood increases, not because there are more cells in the blood but because there is less plasma to suspend them. This condition is termed *hemoconcentration* and it can be diagnosed readily, for example by counting the number of red blood cells present in each cu. mm. of blood. A steadily increasing number of red blood cells per cu. mm. of blood indicates increasing hemoconcentration.

A lack of plasma (hemoconcentration) to

suspend the cells in the circulatory system results, like hemorrhage, in what is termed *surgical shock*. This condition is treated or, still better, prevented, by giving plasma intravenously to individuals who are experiencing plasma leakage from extensive capillary damage, so as to restore the fluid content of their circulatory systems.

Extensive capillary damage can result, for example, from a considerable body surface being burned or from a limb or some body part being crushed by a great weight, or for several other reasons which will be described when the student studies clinical medicine and surgery.

### The PAS Technic and the Staining of Intracellular Substances

The PAS technic described in Chapter 4 under Histochemistry is widely used to specifically stain certain carbohydrate macromolecules that are retained in sections (see Fig. 27-13). We shall now consider briefly how much application this widely used technic has to the staining of intercellular substances.

First, it does not usually stain either collagenic or elastic fibers, although it has been claimed that it stains elastic fibers in a few parts of the body.

Secondly, it sometimes seems to be assumed that it does stain the amorphous intercellular substances—the acid mucopolysaccharides. This assumption is based on the fact that the intercellular substance of cartilage (which contains much sulfated mucopolysaccharide) is sometimes faintly PAS positive. However, both Davies, and Glegg, Clermont and Leblond have provided convincing evidence to the effect that pure hyaluronic acid is PAS negative, and the latter investigators have also provided evidence for thinking that this also is true for the sulfated mucopolysaccharides. Accordingly, the reason for intercellular substances sometimes staining faintly with the PAS technic is very probably that they contain some other carbohydrate macromolecules besides acid mucopolysaccharides. Evidence for this will be given later.

Finally, although collagenic fibers, elastic fibers and acid mucopolysaccharides all seem to be PAS negative, reticular fibers commonly stain with the PAS method. Since reticular fibers in the EM show the same periodicity as collagen, it creates a puzzling problem as to why they should be PAS positive when collagenic fibrils are not.

**The Components of Basement Membranes.** One of the complications in trying to ascertain why reticular fibers and not collagenic fibers are PAS positive is due to the fact that reticular fibers are so commonly studied in sites where loose connective tissue abuts on epithelial membranes. As has already been described, at these sites there are basement membranes which are PAS positive (Fig. 8-2). It was formerly believed that basement membranes represented condensations of the intercellular substances of loose connective tissue, being more or less of a complex of acid mucopolysaccharides and reticular fibers. However, in recent work, basement membranes have been studied by the immunofluorescence technic (see Midgley and Pierce). This technic has shown that the antigens of the amorphous material of basement membranes are related, not to any antigens found in connective tissue, but to antigens that are present in epithelial cells. Furthermore, Revel and Hay have shown by radioautography that epithelial cells play a major role in the secretion of basement membranes. Accordingly, it seems very probable that the amorphous material of basement membranes that abut on epithelial cells is produced by the epithelial cells and hence is not a part of the underlying connective tissue. It also seems very probable that this amorphous material that is derived from epithelial cells contains carbohydrate macromolecules that stain with the PAS technic.

The study of basement membranes by means of silver impregnation technics, particularly those in the kidney (which will be described in a later chapter) leave no doubt about the fact that reticular nets are also present at or in basement membranes. It would seem, therefore, that what have been termed basement membranes generally represent a complex of an amorphous permeable material derived from epithelial cells and a supporting network of reticular fibers. Since the epithelium-derived amorphous component of basement membranes probably contains a type of carbohydrate that is PAS positive, it probably accounts for at least some of the PAS-positive reaction that has been attributed to the reticular fibers that are present in these locations. However, this is probably not the only reason for reticular fibers being PAS positive. Leblond and his group hydrolyzed reticular and collagenic fibers obtained from several different parts of the body and found by means of paper chromatography that these materials yielded certain sugars, namely, galactose, fucose, mannose and glucose. Material from reticular fibers yielded more of these sugars than material from collagenic fibers, particularly more glucose. They concluded that it is this carbohydrate material that is responsible for such PAS staining as is exhibited by fibers and that it is because reticular fibers have more carbohydrate that they are PAS positive. However, it is difficult to be certain that the carbohydrate responsible for the PAS staining of reticular fibers is actually a component of the reticular fibers themselves or a carbohydrate that is bound to them.

Another unsolved problem arises from the fact that there are basement membranes in the body, for example those that surround capillaries, that do not abut on ectodermal- or endodermal-derived epithelial membranes. Midgley and Pierce found that these basement membranes do not possess the antigens of epithelial cells. How these basement membranes are formed is as yet not understood.

## INTERCELLULAR SUBSTANCES AND AGING

Houses do not last forever, and the edifice of intercellular substance which houses the cells of the body is no exception to this rule. The passing of the years is inevitably associated with a deterioration of the intercellular substances of the body. The cells that produce intercellular substances can be most ingenious, on occasion, at patching up old intercellular substance with new, but a continuous renewal of *all* the intercellular substances of the body, with the old being completely removed and with new being substituted for it, seems to be beyond the capacities of the organism. In particular, much of the fibrous type of intercellular substance seems to persist through life, and it deteriorates with the years.

Perhaps the most obvious age change that occurs in intercellular substance is the gradual diminution of the amount of the amorphous kind that it contains. The tissues of a fetus

are jellylike because of their high content of amorphous intercellular substance, and those of a newborn infant have proportionately much less fibrous intercellular substance and much more of the amorphous kind than those of an adult. But as the years pass, the fibrous elements are built up, and thereafter the amount of amorphous intercellular substance gradually becomes lessened. The tissues of the aged contain so little that dyes spread through them more readily than they do in the tissues of the young; in the latter, the free passage of dyes is impeded by the amorphous material that is present.

There is some difference of opinion as to the effects of aging on collagenic fibers. However, there is indication that the average size of collagenic fibers and bundles is increased, and their substance becomes more basophilic.

Pronounced changes occur in elastic fibers and laminae as an individual ages. Normal ones, obtained from the young, evidence no content of mineral by the micro-incineration method (Fig. 4-4), but they commonly contain mineral in the aged. Lansing (who should be read for details) has studied the structure of elastic fibers and laminae in great detail and has shown that there are various types of elastin in the body and that the elastin of the old is not the same as the elastin of the young. With the electron microscope, elastin fibers appear to be amorphous. With age, elastic fibers fray and fragment and develop an increased affinity for calcium salts. This, of course, is of the greatest importance in connection with the "hardening of arteries" (Fig. 22-3). It is probable that the sagging and the general lack of tone of the skin of the aged are due more to age changes in its elastic fibers than to changes in its collagenic fibers.

The relative proportion of amorphous and fibrous elements in intercellular substance, as well as the density and the size of collagenic fibers, is, at least in some parts of the body, greatly influenced by certain hormones, as will be described when the endocrine glands are considered.

## REFERENCES

### COLLAGEN, COLLAGENIC FIBERS, FIBRILS AND MICROFIBRILS

(For the formation of these, see references under fibroblasts in next chapter.)

Angevine, D. M.: Structure and function of normal connective tissue *in* Ragan, C. (ed.): Connective Tissues, p. 13, New York, Macy Foundation, 1950.

Astbury, W. T., and Bell, F. O.: Molecular structure of the collagen fibres, Nature *145*:421, 1940.

Bear, R. S.: The structure of collagen molecules and fibrils, J. Biophys. Biochem. Cytol. *2*: 363, 1956.

Cooper, Z. K.: Aging of the skin *in* Lansing, A. J. (ed.): Cowdry's Problems of Aging, ed. 3, p. 764, Baltimore, Williams & Wilkins, 1952.

Gross, J., and Schmitt, F. O.: The structure of human skin collagen as studied with the electron microscope, J. Exp. Med. *88*:555, 1948.

Hodge, A. J., and Petruska, J. A.: Recent studies with the electron microscope on ordered aggregates of the tropocollagen macromolecules *in* Aspects of Protein Structure, p. 289, New York, Acad. Press, 1964.

Hodge, A. J., and Schmitt, F. O.: The tropocollagen macromolecule and its properties of ordered interaction *in* Edds, M. V., Jr. (ed.): Macromolecular Complexes, pp. 19-51, New York, Ronald Press, 1961.

Jacobson, W.: Histological survey of the normal connective tissue and its derivatives *in* Randall, J. T., and Jackson, S. F. (eds.): Nature and Structure of Collagen, p. 6, New York, Acad. Press, 1953.

Keech, M. K.: The effect of collagenase and trypsin on collagen; an electron microscopic study, Anat. Rec. *119*:139, 1954.

Kramer, H., and Little, K.: Nature of reticulin *in* Randall, J. T., and Jackson, S. F. (eds.): Nature and Structure of Collagen, p. 33, New York, Acad. Press, 1953.

Porter, K. R.: Repair processes in connective tissues *in* Ragan, C. (ed.): Connective Tissues, p. 126, New York, Macy Foundation, 1951.

Schmitt, F. O., Hall, C. E., and Jakus, M. A.: Electron microscope investigations of the structure of collagen, J. Cell. Comp. Physiol. *20*: 11, 1942.

————: The ultrastructure of protoplasmic fibrils *in* Hoerr, N. L. (ed.): Frontiers of Cytochemistry, p. 261, Lancaster, Cattell, 1943.

Wassermann, F.: The intercellular components of connective tissue: origin, structure and interrelationship of fibers and ground substance, Ergebn. Anat. Entwicklungsges. *35*:240, 1956.

Wassermann, F., Roth, L. E., and Minick, O. T.: The fine structure of native collagen in thin sections, Exp. Cell Res. *13*:407, 1957.

Woessner, J. F., and Gould, B. S.: Collagen biosynthesis. Tissue culture experiments to ascertain the role of ascorbic acid in collagen formation, J. Biophys. Biochem. Cytol. *3*:685, 1957.

Wyckoff, R. W. G.: The fine structure of connective tissues *in* Ragan, C. (ed.): Connective Tissues, p. 38, New York, Macy Foundation 1952.

Zawisch, C.: Die Morphogenese der kollagenen Fibrille, Acta anat. *29*:143, 1957.

ELASTIN AND ELASTIC FIBERS

Gross, J.: The structure of elastic tissue as studied with the electron microscope, J. Exp. Med. *89*:699, 1949.

Lansing, A. I.: Aging of elastic fibers, J. Nat. Cancer Inst. *12*:217, 1951.

————: Chemical morphology of elastic fibers *in* Ragan, C. (ed.): Connective Tissues, p. 45, New York, Macy Foundation, 1951.

THE AMORPHOUS INTERCELLULAR
SUBSTANCES—MUCOPOLYSACCHARIDES—
METACHROMASIA

Bensley, S. H.: On the presence, properties and distribution of the intercellular ground substance of loose connective tissue, Anat. Rec. *60*:93, 1934.

Bergeron, J. A., and Singer, M.: Metachromasy: an experimental and theoretical re-evaluation, J. Biophys. Biochem. Cytol. *4*:433, 1958.

Chain, E., and Duthie, E. S.: Identity of hyaluronidase and the spreading factor, Brit. J. Exp. Path. *21*:324, 1940.

Davies, D. V.: Specificity of staining methods for mucopolysaccharides of the hyaluronic acid type, Stain Technol. *27*:65, 1952.

Day, T. D.: The nature and significance of the cementing substance in interstitial connective tissue. J. Path. Bact. *95*:567, 1947.

Dempsey, E. W., Bunting, Henry, Singer, Marcus, and Wislocki, G. B.: The dye-binding capacity and other chemohistological properties of mammalian mucopolysaccharides, Anat. Rec. *98*:417, 1947.

Duran-Reynals, F.: Some remarks on the spreading reaction *in* Asboe-Hansen, G. (ed.): Connective Tissue in Health and Disease, p. 103, Copenhagen, Munksgaard, 1954.

Edds, M. V., Jr.: Origin and structure of intercellular matrix *in* McElroy, W. D., and Glass, B. (eds.): The Chemical Basis of Development, p. 157, Baltimore, Johns Hopkins Press, 1958.

Hale, C. W.: Histochemical demonstration of acid polysaccharides in animal tissue, Nature *157*: 802, 1946.

Hoffman, D. C., and Duran-Reynals, F.: Influence of testicle extract on intradermal spread of injected fluids and particles, J. Exp. Med. *53*: 387, 1931.

McManus, J. F. A.: Histochemistry of connective

tissue *in* Asboe-Hansen, G. (ed.): Connective Tissue in Health and Disease, p. 31, Copenhagen, Munksgaard, 1954.

Mancini, R. E.: Connective tissue and serum proteins, Internat. Rev. Cytol. *14*:193, 1963.

Meyer, Karl: The biological significance of hyaluronic acid and hyaluronidase, Physiol. Rev. *27*: 335, 1947.

———: The chemistry of the ground substances of connective tissue *in* Asboe-Hansen, G. (ed.): Connective Tissue in Health and Disease, p. 54, Copenhagen, Munksgaard, 1954.

———: Mucoids and glycoproteins *in* Advances in Protein Chemistry, vol. 2, New York, Acad. Press, 1945.

———: The chemistry of the mesodermal ground substance, Harvey Lectures, Ser. 51, p. 88, 1955.

Strauss, J., and Necheles, H.: Variations in dermal absorption with age, J. Lab. Clin. Med. *33*:612, 1948.

Wassermann, F.: The intercellular components of connective tissue: origin, structure and interrelationship of fibers and ground substance, Ergebn. Anat. Entwicklungsges. *35*:240, 1956.

Wislocki, G. B., Bunting, H., and Dempsey, E. W.: Metachromasia in mammalian tissues and its relationship to mucopolysaccharides, Am. J. Anat. *81*:1, 1947.

(*See also* "Reticular Fibers—Basement Membranes—The PAS Technic.")

### RETICULAR FIBERS—BASEMENT MEMBRANES—THE PAS TECHNIC

Gersh, I., and Catchpole, H. R.: The organization of ground substance and basement membrane and its significance in tissue injury, disease and growth, Am. J. Anat. *85*:457, 1949.

Glegg, R. E., Clermont, Y., and Leblond, C. P.: The use of lead tetraacetate, benzidine, o-dianisidine and a "film test" to investigate the significance of the "periodic acid sulfurous acid" technique in carbohydrate histochemistry, Stain Technol. *27*:277, 1952.

Glegg, R. E., Eidinger, D., and Leblond, C. P.: Some carbohydrate components of reticular fibers, Science *118*:614, 1953.

———: Presence of carbohydrates distinct from acid mucopolysaccharides in connective tissue, Science *120*:839, 1954.

Hotchkiss, R. D. A.: Microchemical reaction resulting in the staining of polysaccharide structures in fixed tissue preparations, Arch. Biochem. *16*:131, 1948.

Leblond, C. P.: Distribution of periodic acid-reactive carbohydrates in the adult rat, Am. J. Anat. *86*:1, 1950.

Lillie, R. D.: Connective tissue staining *in* Connective Tissues, p. 11, New York, Macy Foundation, 1952.

———: Further exploration of the HIO₄ Schiff reaction with remarks on its significance, Anat. Rec. *108*:239, 1950.

———: Histochemistry of connective tissues, Lab. Invest. *1*:30, 1952.

McManus, J. F. A.: Histological and histochemical uses of periodic acid, Stain Technol. *23*:99, 1948.

———: The periodic acid routine applied to the kidney, Am. J. Path. *24*:643, 1948.

Midgley, A. R., Jr., and Pierce, G. B., Jr.: Immunohistochemical analysis of the basement membranes of the mouse, Am. J. Path. *43*:929, 1963.

Puchtler, Holde, and Isler, H.: The effect of phosphomolybdic acid on the stainability of connective tissues by various dyes, J. Histol. Cytochem. *6*:265, 1958.

Robb-Smith, A. H. T.: The nature of reticulin *in* Connective Tissues, p. 92, New York, Macy Foundation, 1952.

Wislocki, G. B., Bunting, H., and Dempsey, E. W.: Metachromasia in mammalian tissues and its relationship to mucopolysaccharides, Am. J. Anat. *81*:1, 1947.

### TISSUE FLUID AND LYMPH

Cowdry, E. V.: Ageing of tissue fluids *in* Lansing, A. J. (ed.): Cowdry's Problems of Ageing, ed. 3, Baltimore, Williams & Wilkins, 1952.

Drinker, C. K., and Field, M. E.: Lymphatics, Lymph and Tissue Fluid, Baltimore, Williams & Wilkins, 1933.

Pullinger, B. D., and Florey, H. W.: Some observations on the structure and function of lymphatics, Brit. J. Exp. Path. *16*:49, 1935.

———: Proliferation of lymphatics in inflammation, J. Path. Bact. *45*:157, 1937.

Rouvière, H.: Anatomy of the Human Lymphatic System, translated by M. J. Tobias, Ann Arbor, Edwards Bros., 1938.

(*See also* textbooks of physiology and pathology. For capillaries, see references for Chapter 22.)

# 11 The Cells of Loose Ordinary Connective Tissue

In order to understand the relationship between the cells that develop in loose connective tissue, and which we shall soon describe, it is helpful first to consider how loose ordinary connective tissue develops.

## THE DEVELOPMENT OF CONNECTIVE TISSUE

That the embryo, at one stage of its development, consists of 3 primary germ layers— ectoderm, mesoderm and endoderm—already has been noted in Chapter 8, as has the fact that most, but not all, of the epithelium of the body arises from ectoderm and endoderm. The connective tissue of the body, as might be assumed, develops from the middle layer of the embryo, the mesoderm. In particular, it develops from a subdivision of mesoderm called *mesenchyme* (middle infusion).

Mesenchyme is typically a loose, soft tissue that infiltrates between the various structures in the body that are developing from sources other than mesenchyme. It consists of both cells and intercellular substances. Its cells possess delicate, wavy cytoplasmic arms that extend out into the intercellular substance in which they lie (Fig. 11-1). Some think that there is cytoplasmic continuity between the arms of adjacent cells; tissue culture studies suggest that cell continuity comes and goes. Tiny fibrils, the forerunners of fibrous types of intercellular substance, may be demonstrated at the tips of some of the cytoplasmic arms by special methods. But the great bulk of the intercellular substance of mesenchyme is of the amorphous type.

Mesenchyme illustrates well the capacity of amorphous intercellular substances to permit diffusion over considerable distances, for, in embryonic life, when the vascular system is developing, there may be considerable stretches of tissue which contain no small blood vessels. Yet the cells in mesenchyme thrive.

**Potentiality and Differentiation of Mesenchymal Cells.** When they first develop in the embryo and are as yet undifferentiated, mesenchymal cells have great potentiality, for they have the capacity to differentiate along any one of several lines that lead to the formation of the many different kinds of cells in connective tissue.

From the studies of Maximow, who contributed so much to our knowledge of the connective tissues, a very important concept arose, namely, that in the development of any kind of adult connective tissue all of the undifferentiated mesenchymal cells of the part do not differentiate. Therefore, in any adult connective tissue we might expect to find a few *undifferentiated mesenchymal cells*, and it could be expected that they could serve as stem cells of great potentiality. The continuing presence of undifferentiated mesenchymal cells in various connective tissues explains metaplasia sometimes occurring in adult connective tissues as will now be described.

**Metaplasia in Ordinary Connective Tissue.** It sometimes appears under certain pathologic conditions as if one specialized type of connective tissue turns into another kind, for example, very occasionally, after an abdominal operation, a piece of bone may form in the operation scar. This phenomenon is called *metaplasia*. It should be understood that although undifferentiated mesenchyme can develop into any specialized type of connective tissue, any of the specialized adult types of connective tissue, once they have formed, cannot actually change into any other specialized type. As Adami pointed out so clearly many years ago, there is no metamorphosis of one adult type of tissue into another adult type. What really happens when this *seems* to occur as, for example, when bone appears in the abdominal wall, is that there is a replacement of the old type of tissue by a new type that is born within it. The new type of tissue arises from cells that have never completely differ-

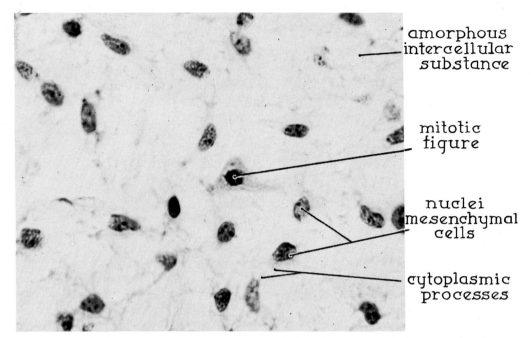

amorphous
intercellular
substance

mitotic
figure

nuclei
mesenchymal
cells

cytoplasmic
processes

FIG. 11-1. High-power photomicrograph of a section cut through developing connective tissue (mesenchyme) of an embryo. This tissue is characteristically soft because the cells are separated by a jellylike, amorphous type of intercellular substance.

entiated and so have retained much of their original mesenchymal potentiality. In understanding how this could occur, it is helpful to remember that the environment of cells plays a very important role in affecting their differentiation. So, if some new, potent environmental influence appears in a special kind of connective tissue, it may induce the undifferentiated cells that remain in that tissue to differentiate along a different pathway from their customary one, and the new cells of a different type that arise in this way may gradually replace those of the former tissue, thus giving the impression that the previous type of tissue has changed into another type. Actually, it has been replaced by another.

## THE CELLS OF LOOSE ORDINARY CONNECTIVE TISSUE

### 1. Persisting Undifferentiated Mesenchymal Cells

From observations such as those that are provided by the phenomenon of metaplasia occurring in ordinary connective tissue, it is assumed that a few of the mesenchymal cells from which loose ordinary connective tissue

develops do not differentiate, but instead remain, endowed with all their original potentiality. It is thought that such cells generally occupy a position along small blood vessels. It seems very probable that in most instances undifferentiated mesenchymal cells in loose connective tissue serve as a very primitive type of stem cell and that when any begin to differentiate under ordinary circumstances they differentiate in a direction so as to become stem cells for some family of cells that is normally found in loose ordinary connective tissue. But, as noted above, under extraordinary circumstances they can differentiate into stem cells for a family of cells (for example the family concerned in making bone) that is not ordinarily found in loose connective tissue. So, the first kind of cell that we shall list as a normal component of loose connective tissue is the undifferentiated mesenchymal cell.

It is doubtful if undifferentiated mesenchymal cells in loose ordinary connective tissue could be identified by their appearance, for they probably would resemble young fibroblasts. Accordingly, it is mostly from evidence relating to what they sometimes do that makes us list, as the first (but probably the

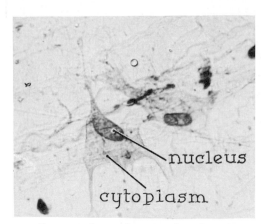

FIG. 11-2. A teased preparation of areolar tissue stained lightly with methylene blue, and showing 2 fibroblasts.

rarest) cell of loose ordinary connective tissue, the undifferentiated mesenchymal cell.

We shall assume then, that in an area of mesenchyme that is situated where some loose ordinary connective tissue is to develop, a few undifferentiated mesenchymal cells do not differentiate. Most do, and we shall now deal with the various kinds of cells that they become and the kinds of cell families that are thus established.

### 2. ENDOTHELIAL CELLS OF CAPILLARIES

In the loose connective tissue illustrated in Figure 10-1 there were several blood, and some lymph, capillaries. In the early development of the mesenchyme some of its cells become the endothelial cells of the capillaries that form in this area. At some later stage of development, mesenchymal cells seem to stop differentiating along this pathway, and after this time endothelial cells themselves serve as the stem cells for more endothelium. So, later in development, new capillaries are formed in the body by the endothelial cells of capillaries budding off from pre-existing capillaries to form new capillaries. The endothelial cells of capillaries have already been described in Chapter 10.

### 3. FIBROBLASTS

The third line of differentiation we shall consider is that along which mesenchymal cells become the *fibroblasts* that make the intercellular substances of loose ordinary connective tissue. This name, which means fiber-

forming cells, was given before it was known that there were amorphous intercellular substances as well as the fibrous kinds; otherwise a name might have been selected which would indicate that these cells make both the amorphous and the fibrous kinds of intercellular substance, for "fibroblasts" probably make both kinds.

In the laboratory it is desirable to study fibroblasts in teased preparations of areolar tissue, similar to those used for the study of fresh collagenic fibers. To see fibroblasts in such preparations, the teased tissue should be stained lightly with a basic stain such as methylene blue. In such a preparation cells can be found which have an appearance similar to the two illustrated in Figure 11-2. The cytoplasm of these cells is probably drawn out by the teasing procedure and so appears more extensive than it would be in life. Characteristically, it extends from the main cell body in prolongations. The cytoplasm is pale. The nuclei of such cells are generally ovoid, the chromatin is fine, and a nucleolus generally can be seen in each nucleus.

When fibroblasts are studied in H and E sections prepared from various tissues that are in different states of activity or development, it becomes apparent that the cells termed fibroblasts can present different appearances. Although it is customary to term both young cells of this type, that are just beginning their work, and old cells that have finished their work, by the same term, fibroblast, it seems better to term the latter fibrocytes.

Fibrocytes (old fibroblasts), as seen in stained sections, are commonly surrounded by intercellular substance that they made some time ago. It is very difficult to see any cytoplasm in these old cells; all that can often be seen is a pale ovoid nucleus with a little chromatin (Fig. 11-3, *right*). The nuclei are more or less flattened ovoids, and so, if cut in some planes, they appear much thinner than they do in others, and if they are cut in cross section they appear smaller than if they are cut in longitudinal section.

A young fibroblast in H and E sections has an appearance that differs from an older fibroblast (a fibrocyte) first because it has an abundant amount of *basophilic cytoplasm* surrounding its nucleus and, from its main body

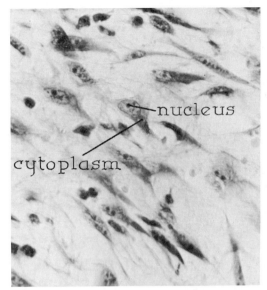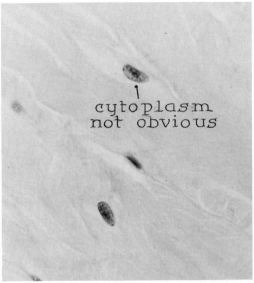

Fig. 11-3. (*Left*) A medium-power photomicrograph of a section cut through a healing wound, where young fibroblasts are growing rapidly. Observe that the cytoplasm of young, actively growing fibroblasts is apparent in H and E sections. (*Right*) Picture taken from a section of mature connective tissue in the deeper part of the skin. Most of the tissue in this illustration consists of collagenic fibers. Only the nuclei of the old fibroblasts present in such tissue can be seen to advantage.

of basophilic cytoplasm, less basophilic processes that extend off for considerable distances (Fig. 11-3, *left*). Secondly, the nucleus of a young active fibroblast can generally be seen to have a prominent nucleolus (Fig. 11-3, *left*). The appearance of a (young) fibroblast as seen under the light microscope is that of a cell that is actively synthesizing protein. The protein that is synthesized by active fibroblasts could be either protein for growth (for the formation of more fibroblasts) or protein destined for secretion (the production of protein intercellular substances), or both. In this connection it seems very probable that during growth the least differentiated fibroblasts serve as stem cells for cells of this lineage and that these provide a supply of fibroblasts that differentiate to make intercellular substances, and that after a fibroblast has made its quota of intercellular substances it becomes a nonactive fibrocyte.

**The Formation of Fibers by Fibroblasts.** For many years there was controversy as to whether or not fibrils of collagen were formed within the cytoplasm of fibroblasts and secreted as such or polymerized outside of fibroblasts chiefly from precursor materials that were thought to be available in the tissue fluid. This was a difficult problem to settle by light microscopy, although, in 1939, Stearns, in a very ingenious study, actually watched the formation of collagenic fibrils among cells that had grown into a transparent chamber that was sewn into a rabbit's ear. She found that fibers developed at sufficient distances from fibroblasts, and sufficiently rapidly, to rule out the necessity of fibrils all being formed within fibroblasts and then excreted as such as was previously believed by many histologists. When it became possible to study the problem of fibril formation with the EM it became established that although microfibrils of collagen were observed to form so close to the cell membranes of fibroblasts as to make it sometimes uncertain as to whether they formed inside or outside cells, there was much proof of collagenic microfibrils being polymerized in intercellular spaces that were clearly apart from cells and, furthermore, that microfibrils outside cells can become larger with the passage of time (see Fig. 11-5). Accordingly, it is now generally agreed the microfibrils with the axial periodicity of collagen are polymerized outside fibroblasts; not,

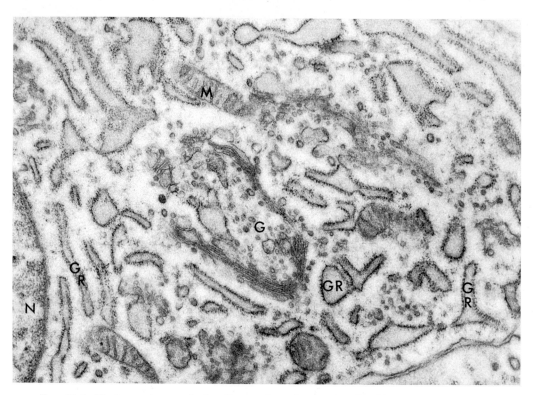

Fig. 11-4. Electron micrograph showing portion of an active fibroblast. A small portion of the nucleus is evident (*lower left*—N). The cytoplasm constitutes the remainder of the illustration and contains very numerous rough-surfaced vesicles of endoplasmic reticulum (labeled GR for granular reticulum); the presence of so many indicate the synthesis of much protein destined for secretion. A well-developed Golgi (G) is seen in the central region; here a group of flattened smooth-surfaced vesicles are arranged in the shape of a horseshoe. Mitochondria are present; one is labeled M. (Movat, H. Z., and Fernando, N. V. P.: Exp. Mol. Path. *1*:509)

however, from materials available in tissue fluids but from tropocollagen molecules secreted by fibroblasts.

**The Fine Structure of Fibroblasts.** Figure 11-4, taken from Movat and Fernando, is an electron micrograph of part of an active fibroblast and shows the character of its cytoplasm. The latter contains an abundance of rough-surfaced vesicles of endoplasmic reticulum (labeled gr for granular reticulum) which, as was explained in Chapter 7, indicate activity with regard to the synthesis of protein materials destined for secretion. Moreover, the illustration shows a well-developed Golgi apparatus (G), which, as was also explained in Chapter 7, is related to secretion.

**The Study of Collagen Formation by Radioautography.** The formation of protein intercellular substances has been investigated by the radioautographic technic in Leblond's laboratory, by studying the formation of dentin in the developing tooth. The study of the formation of dentin offers peculiar advantages for studying the formation of collagen. The process of dentin formation will be described in detail in Chapter 24; for our purpose here it is enough to observe that the cells that make the dentin of the tooth are called *odontoblasts* and that they are very similar to fibroblasts in many respects. Odontoblasts are more or less columnar in form and are lined up beside each other around the inner surface of the shell of the tooth; the latter becomes steadily thicker because collagen and other intercellular substances are laid down at the ends of the odontoblasts that abut on the inner surface of the shell. Since collagen appears at only

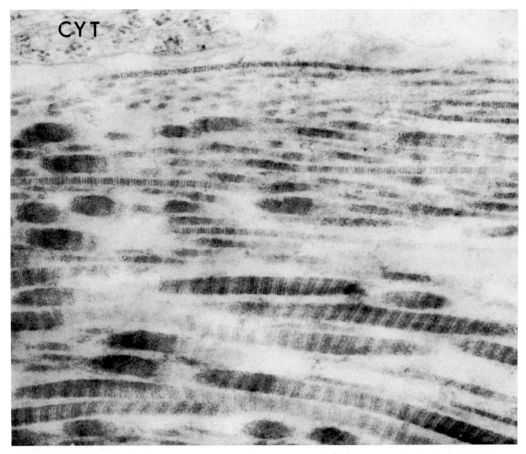

FIG. 11-5. Electron micrograph ($\times$ 76,000) of newly polymerized microfibrils of collagen beside a fibroblast the edge of whose cytoplasm is seen at the top (CYT). Note that the microfibrils closest to the cytoplasm are finer than those that are farther away, showing how microfibrils can increase in diameter after they are first polymerized outside of fibroblasts. (Fernando, N. V. P., and Movat, H. Z.: Lab. Invest. 12:214)

one end of each odontoblast (the end that abuts on the dentin), its formation is relatively easy to follow, and Carneiro and Leblond have taken advantage of this fact and have studied its formation by giving young mice labeled glycine, an amino acid that enters into the composition of collagen. They followed the labeled glycine in radioautographs prepared from animals at different times after the labeled glycine was given and found that it appeared in the cytoplasm of the odontoblasts in 30 minutes. By 4 hours the label was seen outside the cell in the site where collagen was forming, and in 35 hours it was out in the organized intercellular substance of the dentin proper. The findings strongly support the concept that some pre-cursor substance in which glycine is incorporated (probably tropocollagen molecules) is synthesized in the cytoplasm and secreted through the end of the cell where it becomes polymerized into collagen.

As noted in the previous chapter, present-day opinion is to the effect that the precursor substance of collagen that is synthesized in fibroblasts and secreted through the cell surface consists of molecules of tropocollagen which are around 2,800 Å in length and around 15 Å in diameter and that these are polymerized into microfibrils of collagen at the cell surface or just outside the cell by becoming fitted together side-by-side and end-to-end in the staggered arrangement described in Chapter 10 (see Fig. 10-4). As the secretion of tropocollagen molecules is continued, new microfibrils are formed close to the cell, and the previously formed microfibrils, which are by now slightly farther away from the cell, continue to increase in length and width by reason of more tropocollagen molecules being added to them (Fig. 11-5).

It is probable that tropocollagen or its precursor is delivered from the rough-surfaced vesicles of the endoplasmic reticulum into vesicles of the Golgi apparatus as has been shown to occur in the instance of other protein sections in other secretory cells, and from what is known of other secretory cells it would also seem probable that the Golgi apparatus is concerned with the formation or secretion of the carbohydrate (mucopolysaccharide) content of intercellular substances. Precise information on these points will doubtless be forthcoming over the next few years.

The formation of the carbohydrate-containing amorphous components of intercellular substance has not been studied as yet as effectively as the formation of the protein fibrils. However, it seems very probable that at least part of it is synthesized simultaneously with fibrils. Some of it acts to cement fibrils together so that they can become fibers. In loose connective tissue it could be assumed that amorphous material made by fibroblasts would also act as a ground substance in which the fibers would lie.

**Growth and Repair of Ordinary Connective Tissue: The Proliferative Capacity of Fibroblasts and Fibrocytes.** The easiest way to obtain information on whether or not fibroblasts that have differentiated into fibrocytes retain any proliferative capacity is to study the repair of ordinary connective tissue that is of the dense variety such as that which is seen in a tendon (to be described later). In *dense* ordinary connective tissue, most of the cells that were fibroblasts when it was being made have become mature fibrocytes by the time its structure is completed and show little or no proliferative activity when repair of an injury has to be effected. Repair is effected because young fibroblasts materialize in the area of the injury and form new intercellular substance.

It is of course of the greatest importance

that new young fibroblasts should materialize in sites where connective tissue has been injured, otherwise it would not become repaired. Every time a surgeon uses a scalpel he counts on lots of young fibroblasts appearing around the edges of the incision. He also counts on the fibroblasts soon forming enough new intercellular substance to constitute a good strong scar that will permanently bind the two edges of the incision together. However, it is one thing to know that fibroblasts will appear and do the work that is required of them with regard to the healing of incisions or the repair of other types of connective tissue injury; it is another matter to know where they all come from.

**Local and Hematogenous Sources of Fibroblasts.** Much of the difficulty associated with determining the source of all the fibroblasts that appear at the site of a connective tissue injury is that whenever connective tissue is injured, a certain amount of inflammation ensues, even in aseptic wounds. The reason for this is that injured tissue constitutes or liberates toxic substances that not only stimulate such young fibroblasts as are in the area to proliferate, but also cause capillaries in the area to dilate and leak a certain amount of plasma. The circulation in these dilated capillaries becomes slowed, and certain of the white cells of the blood (to be described in detail in a following chapter) migrate through the walls of the capillaries to perform various essential tasks in the injured tissue. It seems very probable that some of the white cells of the blood that enter the area can become fibroblasts and help to repair the injury. It is very difficult to obtain positive direct information on cell changes which occur rapidly in such an area, for there are so many cells and what seems to be so many transition forms between different cell types that interpretation is hazardous. However, in the opinion of the author there is strong indirect evidence of there being a hematogenous source of cells that can become fibroblasts in the repair of connective tissue wounds, because preoperative radiation is sometime given over areas on which operations for cancer are to be performed and the doses that are employed are large enough for it to be expected that the mitotic capacity of cells in the irradiated area would be greatly impaired. The fact that the

surgeon can count on incisions made through
connective tissue in such sites healing readily
suggests very strongly that cells from nonirradiated sites are delivered into the area by
the bloodstream and there multiply and differentiate into fibroblasts. The most likely can-
didates for this function would seem to be a
white cell of the blood, and, in turn, the most
likely white blood cell to serve this function
would seem to be the monocyte which, it is
generally believed, can form both macrophages and fibroblasts.

**Granulation Tissue.** Sizeable defects in connective tissue are repaired by a combination
of young fibroblasts and capillary buds proliferating together to cover or fill in the defect; such a combination of fibroblasts and
capillaries is known as *granulation tissue*. It
is at first pink-to-red in color because of its
numerous capillaries. However, as time passes
the fibroblasts of granulation tissue have time
to make more and more intercellular substance which squeeze the capillaries so that
not so much blood flows through them. Hence
as granulation tissue gradually becomes a
scar it becomes paler.

### 4. Macrophages

The word macrophage means "large eater"
and suitably designates a large phagocytic cell
found normally in loose connective tissue and
which can ingest certain kinds of bacteria in
infections and also help to rid loose connective
tissue of bits of debris of one sort or another
that may result from the breakdown of cells
or their products. These same cells by some
authors are termed *histiocytes* or *clasmatocytes*. Perhaps one reason for there being different names for these cells is that macrophages may assume different appearances.
When they are more or less free, they tend to
have an ovoid shape, but when they are in
positions where they are crowded by other
tissue components they may be drawn out
and have angular contours.

The prefix *macro* distinguishes these cells
from smaller phagocytic cells that are found
in the blood but which enter loose connective
tissue that is the site of an inflammatory
process. These smaller phagocytic cells, which
are normal residents of blood, were long ago
called *micro*phages, However, "microphages"
are now universally termed neutrophilic

Fig. 11-6. Drawing of a group of macrophages (under oil-immersion) which have
phagocytosed trypan blue in an area of
loose connective tissue into which trypan
blue and some bacteria were injected. Observe that the nuclei of macrophages tend
to be indented, smaller and more deeply
stained than those of fibroblasts.

(polymorphonuclear) leukocytes. They will
be described in the next chapter along with
the other cells of the blood.

**Reticuloendothelial Cells.** While commenting on terminology it is important to note
that macrophage is the name given to the
large phagocytic cell that is a normal inhabit-
ant of loose connective tissue. In hemopoietic
tissues, which will be considered shortly, it is
customary to term similar large phagocytic
cells *reticuloendothelial cells*. The reason for
this is that in the hemopoietic tissues and in
a few other sites in the body, phagocytic cells
that are identical functionally with the
macrophages of loose connective tissue become arranged to form a somewhat imperfect
lining of blood passages that are wider than
capillaries. In this position they can phagocytose undesirable material from the blood
that passes slowly by them. But since large
phagocytic cells, in these sites, are held in
place in reticular fibers, and since the phagocytic cells serve as endothelial cells by lining
a type of blood vessel, these cells, which are
essentially the same as macrophages in this
particular position, are termed *reticuloendothelial* cells. As reticuloendothelial cells, their

shape is modified variously by factors that hold them in position.

To sum up: the large phagocytic cells of loose connective tissue are commonly called macrophages, but the same kind of cell that lines blood passages in certain organs are called reticuloendothelial cells. In loose connective tissue macrophages tend to assume an oval shape but, particularly in denser types of ordinary connective tissue, macrophages can be drawn out and angular because of their environment determining their shape.

A macrophage that is not impinged upon by any tissue constituent that distorts its shape is typically ovoid (Fig. 11-6). Another distinguishing feature is its nucleus which generally has the form of an oval indented on one side so that it is more or less bean- or kidney-shaped. Furthermore, the nucleus generally lies toward one end of the cell with its convex border facing that end of the cell. The nucleus of a macrophage is slightly more condensed than the nucleus of a fibroblast in a section, and hence it differs from the nucleus of a fibroblast in 3 ways, by being slightly smaller and darker and by being indented on one of its sides.

**The Vital Staining of Macrophages.** Although a few macrophages can generally be found in normal loose areolar tissue, the easiest way to see lots of them and to identify them with certainty is to take advantage of their phagocytic abilities and inject the areolar tissue of a living animal with a suspension or a solution of some material that will be phagocytosed and therefore will come to lie within their cytoplasm and hence identify them. They readily phagocytose certain colloidal dyes termed *vital stains*. Trypan blue is one of these, and if a freshly made 1 per cent solution of this dye is injected into the arealor tissue of an experimental animal, sections cut from the site of injection a day or two afterward will reveal large numbers of macrophages in the area, with their cytoplasm containing accumulations of the injected trypan blue (Fig. 11-6).

If trypan blue is injected into the areolar tissue of a normal animal, as described above, the injected material generally incites some inflammatory reaction in the areolar tissue and results in an increase in the number of macrophages in and about the injured area. Some

of the extra macrophages that appear in inflammatory reactions have a local, and others a hematogenous, origin. It is generally believed that some develop locally as a result of cell division of the pre-existing macrophages of the part. However, many have a hematogenous origin, developing from monocytes, soon to be described. Monocytes pass through the walls of capillaries and the venules of tissue that is the seat of an inflammatory reaction and in the tissue develop into macrophages (and probably also into fibroblasts).

**Fine Structure.** The EM has revealed interesting detail in macrophages, particularly with regard to the configuration of the cell membrane; this is probably of significance with regard to the mechanism of the phagocytosis.

As is shown in Figure 11-7, the cell membrane of a macrophage characteristically is not smooth; it presents an uneven contour, projecting outwardly in the form of little pseudopodia and inwardly in the form of depressions and clefts. Phagocytosis probably occurs as follows: the particle that is to be phagocytosed comes to lie in the bottom of a groove between two pseudopodia. Next, either one of two things can happen, or, what is more probable, a combination of the two happens. Either the pseudopodia meet and fuse over the particle, or the bottom of the groove in which the particle lies sinks deeply into the cytoplasm, and the edges of the groove about the particle meet and fuse. By either mechanism, or by a combination of the two, the particulate matter comes to lie in the cytoplasm surrounded by a membrane which shortly before was cell membrane (see ppt in Fig. 11-7). As was suggested in Chapter 7, membrane-surrounded phagocytosed material in the cytoplasm may require the cooperation of lysosomes for its digestion.

**Foreign Body Giant Cells.** Any foreign material that gains entrance to loose connective tissue and does not consist of particles small enough to be phagocytosed by individual macrophages may incite the formation of *foreign body giant cells*. These, as their name implies, are very large and contain from 2 to a great many nuclei (Fig. 11-8). There is no evidence to suggest that they form as a result of the repeated division of the nucleus of a macrophage without the cytoplasm subsequently dividing, because mitotic figures are

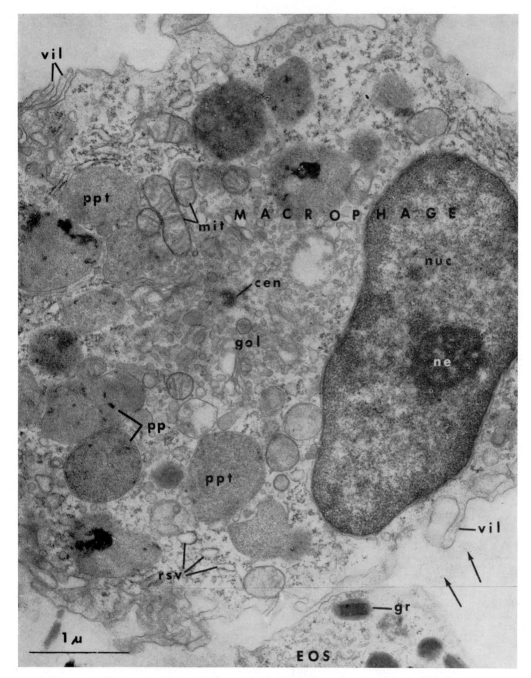

Fig. 11-7. Electron micrograph ($\times$ 26,000) of section of macrophage which has phagocytosed some ferritin-antiferritin precipitate. Rounded masses of precipitate enclosed in
membranous sacs derived from the cell membrane are labeled *ppt*. Villi projecting from the
surface are labeled *vil*. The nucleus is labeled *nuc* and the nucleolus *ne*. The Golgi apparatus
is labeled *gol* and a centriole *cen*, mitochondria *mit* and rough-surfaced vesicles *rsv*. Part
of an eosinophil shows at *lower right*. (Preparation by H. Z. Movat)

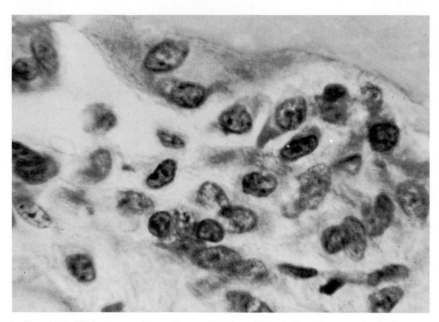

FIG. 11-8. High-power photomicrograph of an H and E section cut from the sub-cutaneous tissue of a rabbit at the site where some fragments of dead bone had been implanted. A portion of a fragment may be seen at the top of the illustration. Young connective tissue cells are multiplying beneath the fragment, and at the upper left some have fused to form 2 small giant cells. The cells to the right of the middle are preparing to fuse. Note that any intercellular substance that would lie between them would be incorporated into the giant cell that would result from the fusion.

not seen in them. The usual view is that they originate from the fusion of monocytes or macrophages, and indeed this phenomenon has been observed in tissue cultures. Their purpose would seem to be that of providing a cell large enough to enclose or wall off masses of debris that cannot be incorporated into a single phagocyte.

It is very easy to produce these cells experimentally by injecting foreign material, such as agar-agar, into the loose connective tissue of an animal. Foreign body giant cells soon form around the margins of the larger masses of injected foreign material and completely surround the smaller masses. If this procedure is performed in animals that are being given vital stains such as trypan blue, the vital stain can be found later in some of the foreign body giant cells. Sometimes this is taken as an indication that foreign body giant cells are phagocytic. The finding of vital stain in them could be an indication, not that they themselves are actively phagocytic, but that the cells that fused to form them were phagocytic and had accumulated some vital

stain in their cytoplasm before they fused. In our opinion, foreign body giant cells, once they have formed, are not very active, except with regard to functions dependent on the actions of the hydrolytic enzymes of their lysosomes, and these actions of course would not be conducive to the cell's continuing its normal metabolic function to advantage.

**Fine Structure of Developing Foreign Body Giant Cells.** From some thin sections that we have studied with the EM, there is evidence to suggest that, as a prelude to fusion, the cytoplasmic processes of adjacent macrophages may become sheetlike and interdigitate with each other in a very extensive manner (Fig. 11-9). Hence, in a sense, giant cell formation may be an expression of the cells acting toward each others' processes as they would toward material that they try to phagocytose.

5. Cells That Function Immunologically; Plasma Cells and Graft Rejection Cells

It has been known for a long time that the

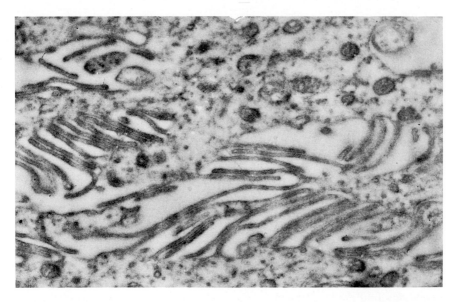

Fig. 11-9. Electron micrograph (× 24,000) of a section cut from tissue adjacent to where agar-agar had been injected into the subcutaneous tissue of a rabbit. This picture shows the cell borders of macrophages that, in all probability, are fusing to form a giant cell. Note the thin platelike processes that extend from the surfaces of the macrophages and how they interdigitate with one another. (Preparation by A. F. Howatson)

postnatal body reacts to various disease organisms and other antigens by producing antibodies that combine specifically with the particular antigens that induce their production. Recently, antibodies have been seen in the EM, and an electron micrograph of antibody combining with an antigen (the virus that induced its formation) is shown in Figure 4-13; this illustration also shows that antibody is specific, because it does not combine with another virus in the same preparation that has a similar appearance but which is different antigenically.

In 1948 Fragraeus had assembled and published convincing evidence to the effect that certain cells (that may be present either in loose connective tissue or more commonly in hemopoietic tissue) called plasma cells (Fig. 11-10), were responsible for the production of antibodies. That plasma cells indeed produce antibodies was established directly by Coons and his associates in 1955 by employing the immunofluorescence technic as was described in Chapter 4.

The antibodies whose source was traced to plasma cells are protein macromolecules (gamma globulins) that can be recovered

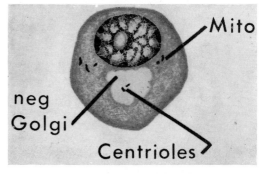

Fig. 11-10. A mature plasma cell as it appears in a stained section under oil-immersion. Note the large negative Golgi; this area is sometimes crescentic. Compare Fig. 11-11. (Preparation from C. P. Leblond)

from the blood in which these macromolecules circulate. They are therefore referred to as *circulating* or *humoral* antibodies. When plasma cells came to be studied with the EM it became obvious that their structure, as will soon be described, is typical of secretory cells that are concerned with manufacturing a protein type of secretion such as gamma globulins.

**Graft Rejection Cells.** It soon became apparent that plasma cells and circulating anti-bodies do not account for all the immunologic reactions that occur in the body. In particular it was found that when transplants of tissue such as skin were made from one individual to another, the donor tissue is soon rejected because of immunologic reactions occurring locally at the site to which it was transplanted. It was found that a transplant of foreign tissue and the bed to which it was trans-planted soon became infiltrated with cells which are somewhat different from plasma cells. It was found, moreover, that the rejec-tion of transplants of foreign tissue was com-monly achieved without there being any, or any substantial amount of, circulating anti-body in the bloodstream. It therefore became obvious that cells could develop in the body which exerted immunologic effects without secreting antibody into the bloodstream. Cells of this type are now commonly called "graft rejection cells."

From what is now known, there would seem to be two types of cells that can func-tion immunologically: (1) plasma cells that produce and secrete circulating or humoral antibodies, and (2) cells of the graft rejection type that exert immunologic effects by direct contact. Although they may act some other way, it seems probable that they do not se-crete antibody into body fluids and so have to act immunologically by coming into close contact with the antigens that induce this function in order for them to exert their im-munologic effects.

In this chapter we shall describe and discuss plasma cells, and in the next chapter we shall describe and discuss graft rejection cells. However, much of what we say in introducing the subject of plasma cells applies to both plasma cells and graft rejection cells, so in the following preliminary section we shall refer to both.

*Introductory Comment.* Before describing the light microscope appearance and the fine structure of plasma cells and graft rejection cells it is of interest to raise the question of whether or not strictly normal tissue contains any of either type. Certainly it is usual for plasma cells to be present both in loose con-nective tissue and in hemopoietic tissue. But it could be argued that if we lived in a disease-free world we would have no plasma cells. The

only reason for suggesting that there could be an argument about this matter is to em-phasize that the reasons for plasma cells (or graft rejection cells) being present in tissue are not as simple as those that explain the presence of the other cells of these tissues. We shall now comment briefly on some of the factors that determine whether or not func-tioning immunologic cells of either type de-velop in tissue.

**When Functioning Immunologic Cells Ap-pear in the Body.** Plasma cells do not nor-mally make their appearance in most species until roughly around the time of birth. The reason for their differing from almost every other kind of cell in this respect is that their antibodies represent a *response* to the pres-ence of some antigen in the body. Now here we must be very careful to explain further and clearly what is meant by an antigen. An antigen is defined as a macromolecule of over a certain size that on gaining entrance to a body induces a response (*anti* = against, *gen* = something that generates) against it. The production of a specific antibody that combines with the antigen is a very important aspect of the response to an antigen.

Any given body abounds in macromolecules to which that body does not respond by mak-ing antibodies; these are the macromolecules of which that particular individual body is composed. Although the macromolecules of a given body do not act as antigens in the body of which they are a part, many of them would act as antigens if they were injected into some other body. So, for any type of macromole-cule to be an antigen in a particular body, it must be a kind of macromolecule that is not a normal constituent of that body.

However, there is a further qualification about macromolecules acting as antigens. Even if macromolecules are of a kind that are not normal constituents of a body, they will not act as antigens and invoke responses unless they are *recognized* by that body as being foreign to it. The next and very im-portant fact is that an animal body does not acquire the ability to distinguish between its own and other kinds of macromolecules, that is, to recognize any macromolecules as being foreign, until around the time of birth (the precise time varies in different species and with regard to different antigens). Until this time it accepts all the macromolecules that develop normally in it *or are injected into it in sufficient quantities* as its own, and it remembers and recognizes them all thereafter as its own, and so does not react against them. So, in order for any kind of macromolecule to act as an antigen in a given body, it must not only be foreign to that body; it must also be *recognized* as being foreign.

Functioning immunologic cells do not develop in a body until it acquires the ability *to recognize* macromolecules as being foreign to it, and that is why functioning immunologic cells are not constituents of the body before, roughly, the time of birth.

**Natural and Acquired Immunologic Tolerance.** Since the base sequences along the DNA molecules of the cells of different individuals differ to some extent, many of the proteins that are synthesized in one individual are slightly different from those of other individuals and considerably different from those synthesized by members of other species. Accordingly, although the macromolecules of one individual do not act as antigens in that individual, many will act as antigens if they are injected into another individual of the same species, and still more will act as antigens in other species. This is why tissue such as skin cannot be successfully grafted from one person to another; the donor skin contains macromolecules that are different from those of the host, and hence the host reacts against these and this causes the grafted skin to be rejected. However, there are two interesting and informative natural exceptions to this generalization about not being able to graft tissue from one individual to another without the donor tissue inducing an immunologic response in its new host.

First, identical twins have the same genes, and hence the macromolecules that are synthesized in one are exactly the same as those synthesized in the other. For this reason the tissues of one twin may be grafted to the other without the transferred tissues containing any macromolecules that are recognized as foreign by the host, and for this reason there is no immunologic reaction when tissue is grafted from one identical twin to the other. This may be stated by saying that identical twins are naturally *tolerant* to each other's macromolecules.

**Acquired or Induced Immunologic Tolerance.** The second natural exception to one individual always reacting to another's macromolecules was also observed in twins but, in this instance, in unlike twins, and it was this discovery that led to our present-day knowledge of what is known as *induced immunologic tolerance.*

In 1945 Owens found examples of non-identical twin cows, each of which had the other's type of red blood cells in its circulation as well as its own, and neither showed any immune reaction to the presence of its unlike twin's blood antigens. It became apparent that the reason for this is that unlike twins, in cattle, commonly share the same placenta, and this permits blood and blood-forming cells from one to gain entrance to the other during fetal life. Some of the blood-forming cells from each twin take up residence in the other, and since this happens before the time the fetus develops the capacity to recognize macromolecules as being foreign, the cells from the unlike twin are accepted as part of the normal constitution of the animal in which they have taken up residence. The animal in which they thereafter reside is said to have *acquired immunologic tolerance* to the antigens possessed by the cells from the unlike twin.

Over the succeeding years, Billingham, Brent and Medawar showed that skin could be transplanted between unlike twin cows that had shared a common circulation before birth, and so it appeared that such animals were not only tolerant to each other's blood antigens but also to all the antigens in each other's skin. From the extensive research performed in this field since Owen's discovery it has become apparent that if enough of any of a great variety of antigens is given to a fetus before it is born, or in many instances immediately after birth, the animal, during at least much of its later life, will be tolerant to that antigen —that is, it will not react to it immunologically and produce antibodies against it.

Only a little thought is required to realize how important it is that a body, through the period of time through which it develops, should *not* be able to recognize macromolecules as being new and different. The development of a body is associated with, and dependent on, the formation of thousands of different macromolecules. These do not all appear simultaneously, for new macromolecules that are needed by the body are synthesized at different periods during its development. A fetus would never live if each new kind of macromolecule that was made in its body induced the formation of plasma cells that made antibodies that were specific for that type of macromolecule. It is not until development is completed and after all the kinds of macromolecules that are to be made in a body have been made, that the body develops the ability to recognize new macromolecules to which it is exposed as being foreign and hence antigens.

The next question is of course how does a body remember each and every kind of macromolecule which appeared in it naturally during development (or was injected into it) so that it will thereafter not respond to the presence of these various macromolecules by the development of plasma or graft rejection cells. It would seem logical to think that such memory as is involved must reside in the cells that after birth serve as precursors for plasma cells (or graft rejection cells) that could react against the antigens, and that during prenatal life the stage of development of precursor cells is such that each new type of macromolecule that appears in the body acts not to induce them to make antibody but instead to permanently block off the genes that could direct the synthesis of an antibody that would be specific for each of these types of macromolecules. By the time of birth the precursors of cells destined to function immunologically would seem to have developed to the point where exposure to new macromolecules act, not to block genes, but to *activate* genes in the precursor cells—the genes that can direct the synthesis of a specific antibody to each new macromolecule that appears in the body.

We shall now consider plasma cells in detail.

## FEATURES OF PLASMA CELLS

**Where They Develop in Loose Connective Tissue.** The kind of loose connective tissue in which plasma cells are seen most commonly is that which supports the wet epithelial membranes that line the respiratory and the intestinal tracts. The reason for plasma cells developing here is that these wet epithelial membranes are not perfect barriers, and they are both exposed to a great many antigens and some of these penetrate through them. Another factor that accounts for plasma cells developing here is that the precursor cells (to be described later) which can form plasma cells are numerous in this tissue. Plasma cells developing in this site represent more or less a local response to a local antigen. Plasma cells develop also in the lymph nodes, the spleen and the bone marrow of an individual; this occurs when antigens become disseminated from their site of entry as will be described when we consider the hemopoietic tissues. The development of plasma cells in these tissues that may be far off from the site of entry of an antigen represents a more general response to an antigen than do the development of plasma cells in loose connective tissue.

**Microscopic Appearance of Plasma Cells.** Plasma cells are easily distinguished in sections stained by ordinary methods. To recognize a plasma cell, the student should look for a rounded cell that has an eccentrically placed spherical nucleus (Fig. 11-10). The latter contains coarse, angular, densely staining flakes of chromatin that sometimes (but only sometimes; too much has been made of this) are arranged in the nucleus like the hours on the face of a clock or like the spokes of a wheel; accordingly, the nucleus is said to have sometimes a clockface or cartwheel appearance. The cytoplasm generally is strongly basophilic and reveals a pale area in the region where the centrioles and the Golgi apparatus are located (Fig. 11-10). The pale area sometimes is rounded with ill-defined edges, but it may be crescentic, following the curved border of the nucleus but removed from it by a very short distance.

The pronounced basophilia of the cytoplasm of plasma cells is due to its great content of RNA which is mostly in the form of membrane-attached ribosomes. Pyronin is commonly used to stain RNA (although it is not specific for RNA) and is much used to detect cells that exert immunologic effects and are said to be *pyroninophilic*.

Little rounded bodies or droplets of acidophilic material are sometimes seen in mature plasma cells with the light microscope. These are termed Russel bodies. They probably represent condensations or aggregations of the

## MATURE PLASMOCYTE

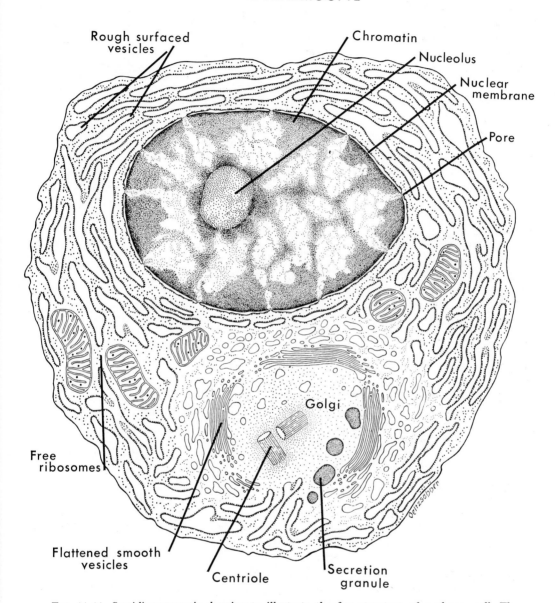

FIG. 11-11. Semidiagrammatic drawing to illustrate the fine structure of a plasma cell. The abundance of rough-surfaced vesicles of endoplasmic reticulum is characteristic and indicates the synthesis of protein destined for secretion. The extremely well developed Golgi region suggests that the secretion is delivered via this organelle. (Drawing supplied by C. P. Leblond)

secretory product of plasma cells. Their function in the cytoplasm will be described under Fine Structure.

Many plasma cells *seen in sections* may be crowded against each other; if so, they may be pressed out of a spherical shape into other shapes (Fig. 11-12). Furthermore, the nucleus may not have the classic eccentric position in the cell but may lie more toward its center, and the pale area in the cytoplasm may not be very obvious.

**Fine Structure.** Antibody activity is found

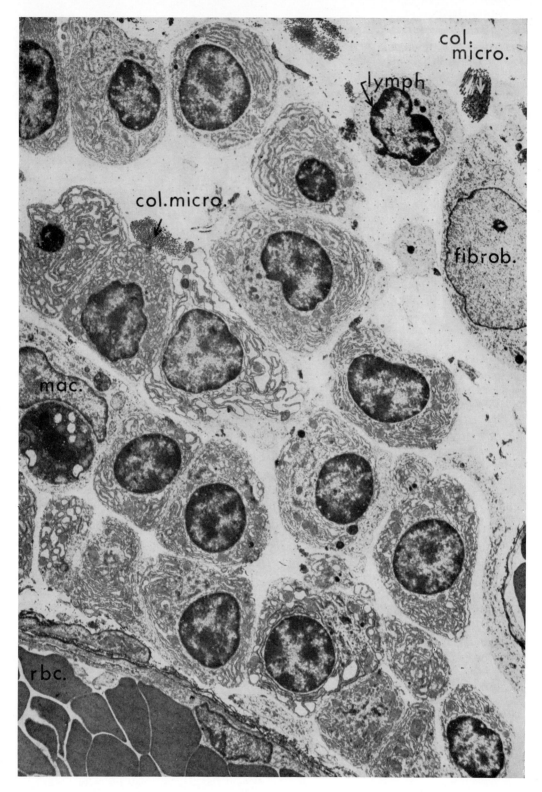

FIG. 11-12. Low-power electron micrograph ($\times$ 3,200) of a section of mesentery from a rabbit which had received several injections of an antigen (horse serum). A venule containing red blood cells is present at the lower left corner (rbc). Most of the cells in the rest of the pic-

mostly in the gamma globulin fractions of tissue extracts and blood, and hence it can be assumed that antibodies have their structural basis in macromolecules of gamma globulin (which is a type of protein). Plasma cells are essentially secretory cells which produce and secrete gamma globulins with specific affinities for particular antigens. As might be expected their cytoplasm shows a great specialization for the production of a protein secretion, being replete with rough-surfaced vesicles of endoplasmic reticulum (Fig. 11-11). The rough-surfaced vesicles may be flattened or somewhat dilated (Fig. 11-12). According to Movat and Fernando, the dilated vesicles may contain a fine floccular substance, small dense bodies (which are probably the Russel bodies that can sometimes be seen with the light microscope) and crystals.

The Golgi region of plasma cells is customarily very large (Figs. 11-11 and 11-12). Centrioles can be demonstrated in it (Fig. 11-11). The apparatus itself consists of the usual three components, flattened smooth-surfaced vesicles, microvesicles and secretory vesicles. The latter would seem to originate in the same manner as they do in the acinar cells of the pancreas, namely by secretion first accumulating at the edge of a flattened vesicle so that a localized expanded vesicular structure is formed at this site which then buds off from the edge of the flattened vesicle to become a *free* secretory vesicle. The great development of the Golgi apparatus in plasma cells suggests strongly that the globulins which are synthesized in rough-surfaced vesicles of endoplasmic reticulum pass to the Golgi apparatus and are delivered from the cell via secretory vesicles reaching and delivering their contents through the surface as occurs in connection with the secretion of zymogen granules (Fig. 11-11). Rounded dark bodies suggestive of secretory vesicles can be seen with

the EM in the Golgi region of plasma cells (Fig. 11-12), and Movat and Fernando remark that these bodies are smaller than the Russel bodies which are sometimes seen in rough-surfaced vesicles of the endoplasmic reticulum. Accordingly, Russel bodies seen with the light microscope would seem to represent abnormally large accumulations of secretion in rough-surfaced vesicles.

The other features of plasma cells, as seen by the EM, are not unusual except that the cell membrane of plasma cells often extends from the cell in fingerlike processes.

**The Formation of Plasma Cells.** The plasma cells of loose connective tissue probably are formed the same way as they are in lymphatic tissue, and this will be described in detail in Chapter 15. As will become apparent, it is helpful, before dealing with the formation of plasma cells, to deal first with lymphocytes, which will be done in the next chapter, for it now seems very probable that lymphocytes, under antigenic stimulation, can give rise to the precursor cells which in turn give rise to cells of the plasma cell series.

**The Specificity of Plasma Cells.** The evidence indicates that any given plasma cell that develops in the postnatal body does not make a thousand different kinds of antibody that would specifically react with a thousand different antigens but, instead, that each plasma cell is highly specialized with regard to making a specific antibody for a particular antigen. Accordingly, an individual who has been subjected in postnatal life to a great variety of antigens will have in general just as great a variety of groups or families of plasma cells with the members of each group or family specialized to make antibody that combines with a particular antigen.

**Committed and Uncommitted Cells.** The production of plasma cells in the body is thus involved with a complication. As soon as pre-

ture are plasma cells and can be recognized by their abundant content of rough-surfaced vesicles. Note that the vesicles show various degrees of distention and that the shape of plasma cells is affected by their being packed closely with one another. Some of the solid globules seen in the cytoplasm probably represent accumulations of secretion and would probably stain as Russel bodies and be visible in the light microscope. A few other cells are present. At the left middle there is a macrophage (mac.) with a large rounded phagocytosed mass in its cytoplasm immediately below its nucleus. A lymphocyte (lymph) is seen at the upper right and a fibroblast (fibro) just below it. Two bundles of collagenic microfibrils are seen (col. micro.). (Movat, H. Z., and Fernando, N. V. P.: Exp. Mol. Path. *1*:535)

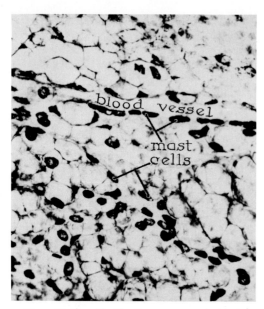

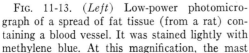

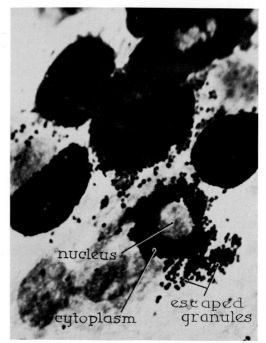

Fig. 11-13. (*Left*) Low-power photomicrograph of a spread of fat tissue (from a rat) containing a blood vessel. It was stained lightly with methylene blue. At this magnification, the mast cells show as dark-blue blotches. It is to be observed that many of them are distributed along the blood vessel, which courses across the tissue. (*Right*) Oil-immersion photomicrograph of a spread of areolar tissue (from a rat) stained with methylene blue. Several dark-stained mast cells may be seen. Granules are so densely packed in most that no details can be seen. However, the lowermost one is broken up, and some of its granules can be seen to have escaped into the adjacent area. Its nucleus is also apparent.

cursor cells are induced by a particular antigen to differentiate into cells that will produce antibodies to that antigen, they are thereafter permanently *committed* to produce only antibodies that are specific for that particular antigen. Hence cells of the plasma cell series that are thus committed are of no use to the body with regard to responding to new antigens that may enter the body. Cell division in precursor cells is of course essential for keeping up the supply of functioning cells that are required to combat the antigen which induced their origin. But, in order for the body to respond to new antigens, there must also be a supply of *uncommitted* cells available that can differentiate into cells of the plasma cell series to form a new family of cells of the plasma cell type that will become committed to make antibody to the new antigen. The question therefore arises as to what cells in the body remain uncommitted, and which are always available to become committed and

form cells of the plasma cell series when a new antigen comes along.

It seems probable from recent work which will be described when we consider lymphocytes that at least some small lymphocytes are *uncommitted* stem cells which can form cells of the plasma cell series when a new antigen appears somwhere in the body, and hence that it is because a population of uncommitted lymphocytes is maintained in the body that an individual always can develop new families of antibody-forming cells when he is subjected to new antigens. Furthermore, it seems probable that the thymus gland serves as a source of uncommitted lymphocytes, as will be explained when the thymus is described.

### 6. MAST CELLS

The word mast, which is derived from the German and relates to feeding, was applied by Ehrlich in 1879 to certain connective tissue cells that he observed and which he thought represented overnourished kinds of connective tissue cells because they were large and stuffed with granules.

Mast cells, for many decades, did not receive the attention they deserved. One reason for this was that their granules, which are their chief distinguishing feature, do not show up well in the H and E sections that are so commonly used for histologic studies, and hence the number of mast cells in connective tissue was not generally appreciated. A second reason for their neglect was that there were literally no interesting hypotheses, or any information, about their possible functions. As will be described presently, interest and information began to develop about mast cells along with knowledge about sulfated mucopolysaccharides.

The easiest way for students to see mast cells in abundance is to study some teased preparations of areolar tissue of a rodent into which some 1 per cent methylene blue (or some toluidine blue) has been injected. Bits of fatty areolar tissue that contain small blood vessels show many mast cells scattered along the blood vessels (Fig. 11-13). Under low power the mast cells in such a preparation appear as large dark oval cells (Fig. 11-13). Nuclei can be seen only occasionally in these cells in this type of preparation (Fig. 11-13) because in the whole cells that are seen there is cytoplasm overlying nuclei, and the cytoplasm is so stuffed with granules that the nuclei are generally obscured. Nuclei, of course, can be seen in mast cells in sections (Fig. 11-14), because sections are slices, and mast cells are so large that what is seen in sections of tissue in which mast cells are present, are slices cut through mast cells and if the slices pass through the nuclei of mast cells the nuclei are not obscured.

Mast cells are often ruptured in making preparations of areolar tissue, and as a consequence, the granules of mast cells can often be seen streaming from cells and scattered about in the tissue (Fig. 11-13, *right*). To consider mast cells and their granules further we must first discuss heparin.

**Heparin.** In 1916, in some experiments in Howell's laboratory, McLean discovered that a particular extract of liver, obtained by the use of certain solvents and procedures, would delay the clotting of blood. Howell and Holt

then succeeded in preparing extracts of liver that had a very potent and anticoagulant effect. They named the active principle in this extract *heparin* (*hepar* = liver). Subsequently, it was found that heparin can be extracted from many different organs and tissues; also, that the relative amount in different organs and tissues varies considerably with regard to species.

Since many deaths are caused by thrombosis (thrombosis is caused by platelets aggregating, as will be described in a following chapter) occurring in the arteries and the veins of man, the discovery of heparin aroused hopes that it might find a use in preventing thrombosis and, indeed, this hope was realized, for it was shown that, in addition to acting as an anticoagulant, it also helps in keeping platelets from agglutinating, and the administration of heparin to individuals threatened with fatal thrombosis has saved many lives. It also introduced the present-day era of blood-vessel surgery. It is to be realized that operations on blood vessels involve a great risk of thrombi forming at the sites where the cut ends of vessels are sutured together and this greatly limited what could be done before heparin was discovered. Other anticoagulants also are now available.

Another action of heparin has been discovered recently; if it is injected into animals it acts to clear the blood of fat.

**Relation of Heparin to Mast Cells.** What we now term sulfated mucopolysaccharides were first referred to by several European workers as sulfuric acid esters of great molecular weight. In 1936, Lison discovered that these substances stained metachromatically; for example, toluidine blue colored them red. A year or so later Jorpes found that heparin exhibited metachromasia, and this, with further work on his part, together with the studies of Charles and Scott, have shown that heparin is one of these substances now termed a *sulfated mucopolysaccharide*. Since the cytoplasmic granules of mast cells were known to be metachromatic, it is not surprising that they soon came to be suspected as the source of such heparin as could be extracted from the liver or other organs and tissues. Holmgren and Wilander, and later Wilander alone, made studies in this connection and showed that the amount of heparin that could be ex-

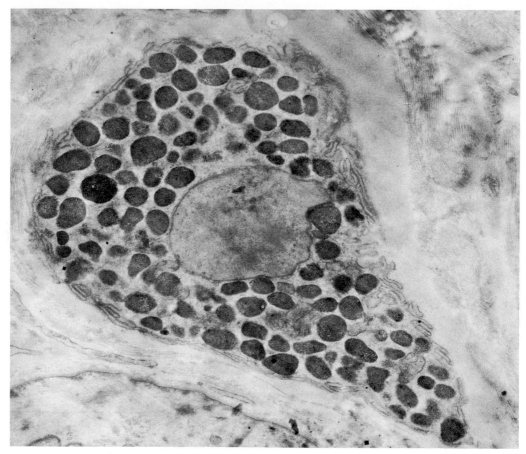

Fig. 11-14. Electron micrograph (× 12,000) of a mast cell in a section of a rat's tongue. The cytoplasm is well filled with specific granules. (Fernando, N. V. P., and Movat, H. Z.: Exp. Mol. Path. 2:450)

tracted from an organ or a tissue was related to the number of mast cells it contains; for this reason, in addition to the fact that both mast-cell granules and heparin are metachromatic, these workers suggested that mast cells manufacture heparin.

The fact that mast cell granules were shown to be largely composed of heparin did not of course prove that the mast cells produce heparin. Another hypothesis that had to be considered was that fibroblasts made heparin and secreted it into the amorphous intercellular substance from which it was phagocytosed by mast cells. However, two solid pieces of evidence are available to indicate that mast cells actually produce the heparin they contain. The first comes from the study of mast cell tumors which are not uncommon in dogs. Bits of mast cell tumors have been grown in tissue cultures and transferred from one culture to another many times and all the while the cells of the tumors continue to produce heparin. The second type of evidence has come from radioautographic studies in which radioactive sulfur, given animals, was shown to be taken up very quickly by mast cells which indicates that the mast cell itself is the site where the precursor sulfur becomes integrated into macromolecules of sulfated mucopolysaccharide.

**Fine Structure of Mast Cells.** There is nothing unusual about the nuclei of mast cells (Figs. 11-14 and 11-15). The cytoplasmic granules are around 0.5 micron in diameter and of a granular texture (Figs. 11-14 and 11-15). It has been a problem to know whether these granules are or are not surrounded by a membrane. In well-preserved

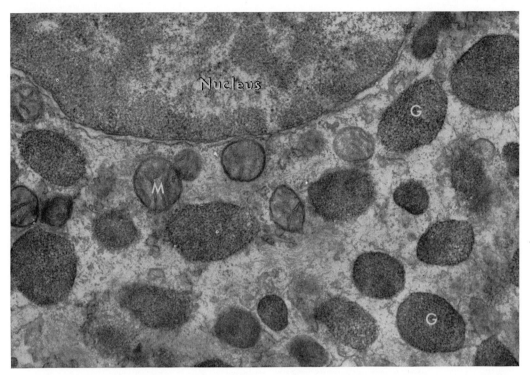

FIG. 11-15. Electron micrograph (× 28,000) of portion of a mast cell from the cheek pouch of a hamster, showing details of cytoplasmic granules, labeled G. (Fernando, N. V. P., and Movat, H. Z.: Exp. Mol. Path. 2:450)

specimens it is difficult to detect a membrane around the granules, but in less well fixed material, in which granules are somewhat shrunken, there is some indication, according to Movat, of a membrane being present, and from which the granule has partly withdrawn. It would be unusual for bodies such as mast cell granules which are synthesized in cells to lie free in cytoplasm without each being surrounded by a membrane. According to Fernando and Movat, whose electron micrographs are shown here, the mitochondria of mast cells are relatively inconspicuous. These authors also did not find much in the way of ribosomes or rough-surfaced vesicles of endoplasmic reticulum in mast cells. However, this might be expected because the secretory product of mast cells (heparin) is a mucopolysaccharide. They did find a Golgi apparatus in mast cells, but it was not very extensively developed, which is perhaps somewhat surprising because it might be thought that, since heparin is a mucopolysaccharide and hence essentially carbohydrate, the Golgi apparatus would be concerned with its synthesis, and therefore well developed.

**Function of Mast Cells With Regard to Secretion of Heparin.** Since it has not been shown that there is enough heparin in blood for heparin to serve any normal function with regard to preventing circulating blood from clotting, it becomes a problem to know what purpose mast cells serve with regard to producing heparin. One possible function that occurs to us is in connection with the fact that some blood protein continually escapes through the walls of capillaries to enter the intercellular substances of loose connective tissue. This protein, as has been mentioned, is returned to the blood circulatory system, via the lymphatic capillaries, which seem to be permeable to it. Among the proteins of the blood that escapes into intercellular substance is fibrinogen, which, as will be explained in a subsequent chapter, becomes converted to a solid material called fibrin in the clotting process. If the process which converts fibrinogen (which is a sol) into fibrin, were set into motion in the intercellular substances of the body under normal conditions, it could be visualized that the intercellular substances of the body would become cluttered up with fibrin, and hence it is possible that the role of mast cells is to keep up a supply of heparin, in, but confined to, the intercellular substances which prevents the fibrinogen that is constantly escaping through capillaries into the intercellular substances from clotting in this local environment under normal conditions.

## MAST CELLS, HISTAMINE, ANAPHYLAXIS AND ALLERGY

It became obvious a long time ago that those who recovered from certain infectious diseases were immune from further attacks of the same disease. When the causative organisms of various diseases were identified, it was therefore only natural that attempts would be made to produce immunity in people to the organisms that caused these diseases by injecting people, before they were exposed to the diseases, with the causative organisms, modified in some way so that they could not multiply in the injected individual and cause disease but not modified sufficiently to prevent their acting as antigens and inducing the formation of antibodies against the disease organisms. As we all know, this approach has been successful in many instances. Procedures such as this that are designed *to prevent* disease are said to be *prophylactic*, which word from its origin means "to be on guard."

Late in the last century, however, it was found that complications could arise in connection with injecting antigens. Sometimes the second injection of an antigen given to an animal had a deleterious effect, and indeed it could be fatal. Richet, in 1893, gave a name to the phenomenon that was observed; he termed it *anaphylaxis* because he thought it was the opposite of prophylaxis. As matters turned out, anaphylaxis is not a good term for the phenomenon, for the individual is put very much "on guard" by the first injection.

Anaphylaxis is easily demonstrated in guinea pigs. If a guinea pig is injected say with some horse serum (which is an antigen because it contains proteins foreign to guinea pigs) and then after 10 to 14 days injected with a second dose of horse serum, the guinea pig manifests difficulty in breathing and a rapid pulse rate and may die from an inability to breathe. The reason for its respiratory failure is that the smooth muscle cells that encircle the tubes through which it draws air into its lungs become contracted to such an extent that the lumens of these tubes become too narrow to permit air to enter and, in particular, to leave the lungs. The same kind of phenomenon occurs but to a lesser extent in the common condition, asthma, for the air tubes that lead into the lung of individuals who suffer from asthma also become so constricted that it is difficult for them to draw air into and to force air out of their lungs.

Another effect observed in anaphylactic phenomena is that blood capillaries become dilated, congested and leaky, so that plasma escapes from them. This is particularly noticeable in the skin of people who experience anaphylactic phenomena, because in man there are capillaries close to the epidermis, and plasma that leaks from the capillaries below the epidermis accumulates locally to form blebs of fluid, as are seen for example in people with hives (urticaria).

People differ greatly with regard to their tendency to manifest anaphylactic phenomena on second or more exposures to an antigen. However, many people are affected in their every-day life by suffering from these phenomena. All of us absorb some protein macromolecules through little breaks in the epithelium of our respiratory tracts or intestine. Pollens, dusts and so on, absorbed this way can act as antigens with the result that further absorption of these antigens may set off anaphylactic phenomena. Those people who react to antigens that are absorbed into the body in normal life by manifesting some signs of anaphylactic phenomena are said to be sensitive to these antigens, or allergic to them, and in general such people are said to be hypersensitive. Hay fever is a common manifestation of an allergy; people who suffer from hay fever are commonly sensitive to the pollen from ragweed which is prevalent in the air at the time of year when hay is cut. There are literally hundreds of possible antigens to which people may be exposed in every day life and which may be the cause of an allergy.

To sum up the above: In some individuals an antigen which gains entrance to the body may result in that body thereafter being hypersensitive or allergic to that antigen so that further exposures to that antigen are associated with some manifestations of anaphylactic phenomena which in general involve some contractions of smooth muscle and some congestion of, and leakage from, capillaries. Now what has all this to do with mast cells?

The second line of investigation that threw light on the nature of anaphylactic phenomena resulted from researches by Sir Henry Dale, who between 1911 and 1914 showed that most but not all of anaphylactic phenomena exhibited by pigs could be caused by giving guinea pigs a substance that had just been discovered and which was called histamine. Histamine is a base derived from the amino acid histidine, and it exerts a profound effect on most smooth muscle, causing it to contract; it also, in most species, causes blood capillaries to dilate and leak plasma.

The third line of investigation involved in clarifying the mechanisms involved in anaphylactic phenomena dates from 1955 when West and Riley introduced the concept of mast cells containing histamine as well as heparin. Many of the same kinds of experiments were done with regard to histamine as were done with regard to heparin, to show that mast cells are the chief repositories of histamine in tissue. For example, Riley and West found that there was a correlation between the histamine content and the mast cell content of various tissues in various animals. By means of certain procedures it became possible to separate fractions from mast cells that contained the granules, and these were shown to contain histamine. Certain chemicals which can be injected into animals cause the liberation of histamine, and it was found that giving these caused mast cells to more or less disintegrate and liberate their granules into the tissues. It was shown that mast cells have enzymes that would be involved in producing histamine from its precursor and that the content of histamine in the cells of mast cell tumors that were transferred many times became increased instead of becoming decreased as it would if mast cells did not synthesize the histamine that they contain.

The evidence described to date suggests that anaphylactic phenomena are due to mast cells releasing histamine, and that when histamine

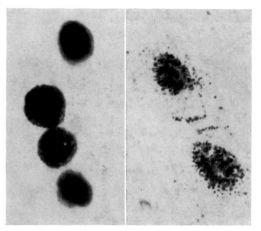

FIG. 11-16. Mast cells from a rat (*left*) before and (*right*) after an antigen-antibody reaction. Toluidine blue stain. Note that the mast cells on the right are disrupted and their granules scattered. The process is accompanied by the release of histamine. (Humphrey, J. H., and White, R. G.: Immunology for Medical Students, Oxford, Eng., Blackwell, 1963)

is released it acts to bring about the contraction of smooth muscle, and the dilation, and an increased permeability, of blood capillaries. The next question for consideration is therefore related to how a second injection of an antigen could cause the release of histamine from mast cells.

Of interest in this connection are in-vitro experiments. If a strip of smooth muscle is removed from an animal and placed in a suitable solution it does not contract if an antigen is added to the medium. If, however, the strip of muscle is taken from a suitable animal that was given an injection of that antigen 10 days before, the addition of antigen to the medium in which the strip of muscle is bathed will cause it to contract. Experiments of this type and other experiments which need not be recounted here indicate that in animals that exhibit an anaphylactic phenomenon, the antibody that is produced in response to the first injection of antigen is adsorbed onto body cells and perhaps particularly onto mast cells. The reason that mast cells release histamine on a second exposure to the antigen (even in vitro) would seem to have something to do with the antigen reacting with the antibody that is on mast cells; somehow this triggers the release of histamine (see Fig. 11-16).

It should be explained next that the antibody that is made in response to an antigen is not all of the same kind or quality. Those animals or people who develop hypersensitivity to certain antigens readily are probably characterized by a disposition to produce a kind of antibody that becomes adsorbed onto tissue cells, including mast cells, and which may not combine strongly with the antigen that caused its formation. Conversely, those animals and individuals who do not so readily experience hypersensitivity reactions probably make relatively more of a type of antibody that combines firmly with antigen and blocks it from reaching the kind of antibody that might have been adsorbed onto mast cells.

It seems very probable that people who suffer from allergy, who exhibit hypersensitivity to many of the antigenic substances that abound in the air or diet, are disposed to make the kind of antibody that seeks out and hides on tissue cells, and not enough of the kind of antibody which probably circulates in blood and can combine firmly with antigens so that they are blocked from reaching and being adsorbed onto mast cells. The treatment of allergies by desensitization procedures is based on the concept that if very minute and then increasing doses of antigens are injected into patients who are allergic to those antigens, the patients will eventually produce more and more of the kind of antibody that blocks any antigen to which they are exposed so that the minute quantities of antigen they absorb from the outside world will never reach and react with the kind of antibody that is present on mast cells.

Mast cells are believed to contain most of the histamine in the body. Certain other cells may contain a little; in particular, the blood platelets of some species contain appreciable amounts of histamine. Mast cells at least in some species may contain other substances which on being released act something like histamine. One of these is serotonin; this acts like histamine in many respects but differently in others. It is found in the mast cells of some species (but not in man) but is a more usual constituent of blood platelets. Its release from platelets can be triggered by antigen reaching antibody on the platelets.

**Origin and Maintenance of the Mast Cell Population.** There is general agreement that mitotic figures are not seen in mast cells, or if they are, very rarely. Therefore, mast cells must develop from less differentiated stem cells that can divide and so maintain a population of cells from which mast cells can differentiate. There is no universal agreement as to which cells of the mesenchymal family serve as a source of mast cells; it could be that they form from the undifferentiated mesenchymal cells of loose connective tissue, but their origin has not been definitely established. There is normally a very slow turnover of the mast cell population.

## 7. FAT CELLS AND ADIPOSE TISSUE

Fat cells are a normal constituent of loose connective tissue where they occur singly or as small groups. When a great many fat cells are present in loose connective tissue, organized into lobules, the tissue is termed *adipose tissue*. Adipose tissue represents a specialized variant of loose connective tissue.

Like so many of the other kinds of cells that develop from mesenchyme, fat cells are most easily distinguished after they begin to manifest their particular specialized function. Hence, fat cells are most easily distinguished from other kinds of cells that develop from the mesenchyme when they begin to store fat. Fat cells probably represent a separate cell lineage in the mesenchymal family, for if fat is transplanted from some site in the body where much fat is normally stored to some site where fat does not ordinarily accumulate, the transplanted fat cells that survive the transplantation continue to store fat in their new location. It would seem therefore that the reason fat tends to accumulate, for example, over the belly and the buttocks, is because the mesenchymal cells of the part differentiated in such a way as to provide for a generous supply of cells in these locations that would have a special ability to store fat.

The first indication that can be seen with the light microscope of a fat cell beginning to store fat is the appearance of tiny fat droplets in the cytoplasm. Soon the tiny droplets begin to fuse together to form larger droplets. As further small droplets appear in the cytoplasm, these too fuse with the larger droplets and finally the cell comes to contain only one large droplet which so greatly expands the cell that its cytoplasm becomes reduced to a thin

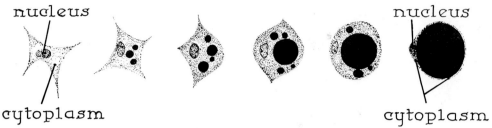

nucleus                                                    nucleus

cytoplasm                                            cytoplasm

FIG. 11-17. Diagrams showing the changes in appearance caused by a cell's taking in globules of fat until it finally becomes a typical fat cell with a "signet-ring" appearance.

film which surrounds the fat droplet (Fig. 11-17). The nucleus, which can be seen at some site around the periphery of the cell, becomes stretched so that it is thin and crescent-shaped (Figs. 11-17, *right*, and 11-18). The appearance seen in a section in which a fat cell is cut in cross section is therefore like that of a signet ring because the cytoplasm of the cell is thinned out so that it resembles a ring and the nucleus bulges slightly from one place around the ring as would the signet.

As was described in Chapter 2, fat is dissolved during the preparation of a paraffin section so all that can be seen in paraffin sections are the rounded holes it occupied during life. It can be fixed in position so that it can be seen in paraffin sections as blackened droplets if the tissue is fixed in osmium tetroxide. Commonly, fat is studied in tissues by using frozen sections stained with Scharlach R or Soudan III, which color it red.

Fats from different sources differ. One way they differ and which is generally conceded to be of importance with regard to dietary fat is with regard to the degree to which the fatty acid of a fat is saturated or unsaturated. There is much present-day opinion to the effect that modern diets tend to contain too much fat and particularly too much saturated animal fat and that this may be a factor in causing much atherosclerosis, a condition in which lipid material is deposited in the inner layers of arteries.

The nature of the fat contained in the fat cells of any individual is derived from two sources. First, fat cells, under the influence of the hormone insulin (to be described later), can synthesize fat from carbohydrate. The kind of fat formed in this way is characteristic of the fat of the species to which the individual belongs. Since mammalian fat is

generally saturated, such fat as we synthesize from carbohydrate is mostly saturated fat. However, the fat cells of an individual also synthesize fat from fatty acids that reach the cells by way of the bloodstream from the intestine and are derived from the breakdown of dietary fat. Dietary fat may be saturated or unsaturated depending on the particular diet of the individual. The fat in corn oil, for example, is largely unsaturated, and hence a person who (wisely in our opinion) substitutes unsaturated fat, for example, corn oil, for saturated (animal) fats in his or her diet absorbs much unsaturated fatty acid from the intestine, and this, on reaching his or her fat cells, may be resynthesized into fat which contains much unsaturated fatty acid. The fact that the fat in fat cells is synthesized in

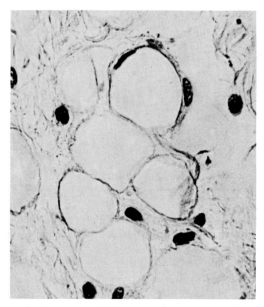

FIG. 11-18. High-power photomicrograph of a section of areolar tissue that contained several fat cells.

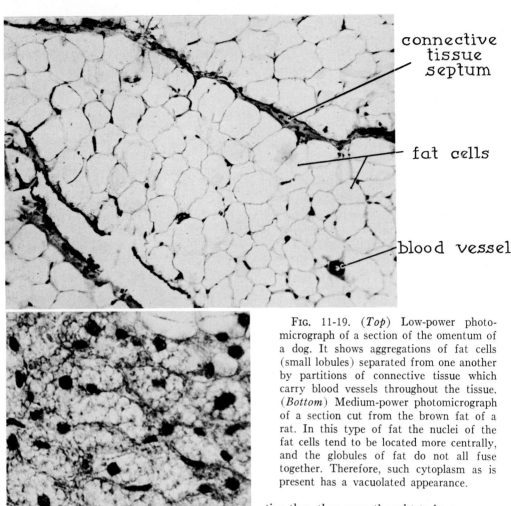

connective
tissue
septum

fat cells

blood vessel

Fig. 11-19. (*Top*) Low-power photomicrograph of a section of the omentum of a dog. It shows aggregations of fat cells (small lobules) separated from one another by partitions of connective tissue which carry blood vessels throughout the tissue. (*Bottom*) Medium-power photomicrograph of a section cut from the brown fat of a rat. In this type of fat the nuclei of the fat cells tend to be located more centrally, and the globules of fat do not all fuse together. Therefore, such cytoplasm as is present has a vacuolated appearance.

tive than they were thought to be many years ago when they were viewed as relatively quiescent storage depots. Fatty acids come and go from fat cells; accordingly, they require an excellent blood supply which is provided by means of capillary beds which border on all the fat cells in a depot.

As has been mentioned already, single or groups of fat cells are normal constituents of loose ordinary connective tissue. When, however, connective tissue consists primarily of fat cells, it is generally termed *adipose tissue*, and in this the fat cells are organized into lobules by partitions of collagenic and elastic fibers (Fig. 11-19, *top*). The individual fat cells within lobules are supported by reticular fibers and are supplied by abundant capillaries which, as noted, are essential because of the constant metabolic activity that proceeds in fat cells.

part from fatty acids obtained from dietary fat and the fact that unsaturated fats tend to be soft, accounts for the fact that animals fed unsaturated vegetable fats (and not all vegetable fats are unsaturated) come to have fat that is soft. Such fats as they would synthesize from carbohydrate would, of course, be hard if saturated fat was characteristic of the species to which they belong.

Fat cells are metabolically much more ac-

Adipose tissue serves more purposes than that of providing a storehouse for food. It acts as a cushion in many sites where weight must be born. It serves as insulation. It provides essential packing to keep various structures in their proper position. Finally, it is chiefly responsible for the human form presenting curves instead of angles.

**Transplantation of Adipose Tissue.** Peer has studied the fate of free transplants of adipose tissue. He found that adipose tissue from one person transplanted to another always atrophies and, in the end, all that remains is a fibrous scar. On the other hand, he found that adipose tissue transplanted from one part of a person to another part of the same person survived in part. The circulation in the free transplants became connected with vessels of the transplant, which thereupon functioned again; this is the same method of revascularization that we observed occurring in full-thickness skin transplants (Fig. 23-21). Peer found that, on the average, the transplants became reduced in size to approximately one half their original bulk, so it would seem that roughly half of the cells of the transplant survive transplantation. Peer believes that if the transplant later increases in size it is due to the cells accumulating more fat and not to their multiplying.

**Brown Fat.** In rodents in particular, fat cells of a special character are present in certain sites. In these, the individual fat droplets in the cytoplasm do not become confluent (Fig. 11-19, *bottom right*). This type of fat is termed *brown fat,* and it makes up the so-called hibernating glands of these animals. The reason for its color is not known.

## 8. CELLS FROM THE BLOOD

As will be described in the next three chapters, there are two main kinds of cells in the blood, red and white. The red cells are non-nucleated cells of the nature of end-products and are concerned in the transport of oxygen. The white cells are nucleated. Unlike the red cells, which perform their function in the blood, the white cells, although they are described as blood cells, do not function to any extent in blood—they perform their chief functions when they leave the blood by migrating through the walls of capillaries and enter the loose connective tissues of the body.

The white cells of blood, on entering loose connective tissue, perform two kinds of function. One kind of white cells, the neutrophilic leukocytes, or as they are commonly termed, polymorphonuclear leukocytes, act as phagocytes. Certain other white cells achieve function in loose connective tissue not as they are but by serving as stem cells for connective tissue cells. For example, monocytes from the blood, on entering loose connective tissue, can become macrophages and, probably, also fibroblasts. Recent evidence indicates that lymphocytes from the blood can serve as cells in loose connective tissue that give rise to cells that function immunologically.

It is apparent, therefore, that we cannot complete a study of the cells of loose connective tissue without considering the white cells of the blood, for their functions are performed primarily in the loose connective tissue of the body. So, after dealing with dense connective tissue, we shall continue our study of the cells that appear and function in loose connective tissue by considering the white cells of the blood.

## DENSE ORDINARY CONNECTIVE TISSUE

Having discussed the intercellular substances and the cells of loose ordinary connective tissue, which, as has already been mentioned, is more or less of the prototype of all connective tissues, we can now deal with the second kind of ordinary connective tissue, the dense variety.

**Relationship Between Loose and Dense Ordinary Connective Tissue.** In discussing loose ordinary connective tissue it was pointed out that it had more than one function; that some of its functions were performed by its intercellular substances and some by its cells. Dense ordinary connective tissue differs from the loose kind because its chief function is performed by its intercellular substances, and such cells as it contains are mostly those that are concerned with producing intercellular substance. In most kinds of dense ordinary connective tissue the abundant intercellular substance is mostly collagen, but in a few places in the body there is a good deal of elastin.

Since dense ordinary connective tissue con-

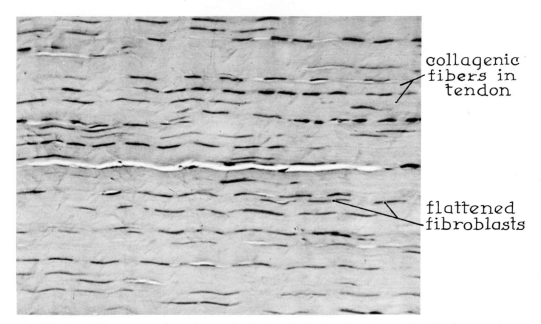

collagenic fibers in tendon

flattened fibroblasts

FIG. 11-20. Low-power photomicrograph of a longitudinal section of a tendon. Tendons consist chiefly of collagenic fibers and bundles of collagenic fibers which run in one direction, with rows of flattened fibroblasts between them. Notice that this tissue is chiefly intercellular substance.

sists mostly of collagen, which is a nonliving material, and hence metabolically inactive, dense ordinary connective tissue does not require many capillaries to be distributed throughout its substance, and indeed it is sparingly supplied with capillaries. In this respect it differs from the loose variety.

There is no sharp line of demarcation in the body between loose and dense ordinary connective tissue. Commonly, one type merges into the other, and even in sites where there is only one kind, it may be of a type that is neither very dense or very loose, and hence impossible to classify.

**Classification.** Dense ordinary connective tissue is commonly classified into two main types, the regularly arranged and the irregularly arranged. The word "arranged" is used with reference to the collagenic fibers of the tissue. In the regularly arranged kind, the collagenic fibers all run more or less in the same plane and more or less in the same direction. Hence structures built of regularly arranged dense connective tissue have great tensile strength and can withstand tremendous pulls exerted in the plane and the direction of their fibers without stretching. It is obvious that dense regularly arranged connective tissue would be ideal for tendons and

ligaments which join muscles to bones and bones to bones and where pull is exerted in one general direction.

In the irregularly arranged type, the collagenic fibers are disposed either mostly in the same plane but in different directions, or in different planes. In the more or less thin flat sheets of dense irregularly arranged connective tissue that are seen in aponeuroses and sheaths of various sorts, the fibers are more or less in the same plane but run in different directions. Such sheets of dense irregularly arranged connective tissue can thus withstand stretching in different directions by stretching forces applied in the plane of the fibers. In other sites, however, such as in the reticular layer of the dermis of the skin (which comprises most of the substance of the skin) the collagenic fibers run both in different directions and in different planes (Fig. 23-7), and hence dermis can withstand stretching in any direction.

As we shall see, the capsules of many organs are composed of thin dense irregularly arranged connective tissue and this often branches from the capsule to extend into organs as septa. Dense connective tissue is often seen as an outer wrapping for tubes of various sorts in the body, as well as for muscles and nerves. It forms a sheath in which the central nervous system (brain and spinal cords) is enclosed. In short, it is a very common tissue and will be seen in many of the sections that will be studied in the laboratory. Here we shall study only one example of it, the dense regularly arranged connective tissue of tendons.

### Some Details About Tendons

**Development.** Tendons, as they develop in the embryo, first appear as dense bundles of fibroblasts that are oriented in the same plane and packed closely together. The fibroblasts proliferate to permit the growth of the tendon. But, as development proceeds, more and more fibers appear between the fibroblasts which become arranged into rows (Fig. 11-20), and eventually the character of the structure changes from being primarily cellular to being primarily intercellular substance.

**Blood Supply.** During development, when tendons are cellular, they have a reasonably good blood supply; it is obvious that intercellular substances cannot be built from nothing, and the materials for the construction of the fiber bundles must be brought to the fibroblasts by capillaries. But when the fiber bundles of collagen become built up, the capillary blood supply within the tendon bundles almost entirely disappears. The fibroblasts which lie between the fiber bundles become dormant fibrocytes and, of course, the intercellular substance itself requires no nourishment.

**Tendon Sheaths.** Some tendons, in certain sites, where they otherwise might rub against bone or other friction-generating surfaces, are enclosed in sheaths. Actually, a tendon sheath consists of two sheaths. The outer one is a connective tissue tube, and its exterior is attached to the structures that surround it. The inner sheath directly encloses the tendon and is firmly attached to it. There is a space between the inner and the outer sheaths, and this is filled with ground substance diluted with tissue fluid; this makes a slippery sol. This is termed *synovial fluid*, and it is discussed in detail in Chapter 19.

The inner surface of the outer tendon sheath and the outer surface of the inner sheath do not possess a continuous lining of cells, so the surfaces that glide over one another are mostly surfaces of intercellular substances, chiefly collagen, along which, how-

ever, some cells are scattered (Fig. 19-11). The synovial fluid between the two sheaths is an excellent lubricant.

**Regeneration of Tendons.** The severance of tendons is of common occurrence in accidents, and it is fortunate that, if they are properly treated, they heal excellently and in due course become as strong as before. Soon after a tendon is cut, fibroblasts from the inner tendon sheath or, if the tendon has no proper sheath, from the loose connective tissue around its periphery, grow into the gap, proliferating all the while. Gradually, they become orientated in the axis of the tendon. Here they re-enact the same scenes that are to be witnessed when a tendon develops. At first they have a good capillary blood supply and produce much collagen which becomes deposited in bundles between them, and so arranged in the long axis of the tendon. Some of the cells grow into the cut ends of the tendon and cement the new collagen that is being formed to the old. As more and more collagen is deposited between the fibroblasts, the capillary blood supply diminishes, and the site of the repair eventually becomes almost free of capillaries. It is not generally believed that the fibroblasts between the fiber bundles of the original tendon contribute very much to the repair process; most of the fibroblasts that repair the tendon, as noted before, come from the inner tendon sheath, or if there is no sheath, from the loose connective tissue at the periphery of the tendon. We shall find that broken bones are repaired in much the same way.

**Tendon Insertions.** Near tendon insertions, the fibroblasts between the fiber bundles of a tendon are somewhat different from ordinary fibroblasts in that they exhibit certain of the properties of the cells that produce cartilage or bone. Hence, at their points of insertion, some tendons consist of a tissue which has the properties of both dense regularly arranged fibrous tissue and cartilage; this is called *fibrocartilage* (Fig. 17-5). The way that tendons are inserted into bones by means of *Sharpey's fibers* is illustrated in Figure 24-17 and into cartilage in Figure 19-10, but it is described more conveniently after we have studied cartilage and bone.

**The Transplantation of Fascia and Tendon.** Fascia and tendon consist chiefly of the intercellular substance collagen, and the fibroblasts that each contains are mostly of a mature type, having completed their work of producing the intercellular substance that surrounds them. The question arises as to whether or not the fibroblasts of fascia and tendon live after free transplantation. Also, there is the question of whether or not they can divide, with the daughter cells they produce manufacturing new intercellular substance.

The evidence obtained from experimental studies in this field is very conflicting. In many studies, healthy appearing cells have been seen in transplanted autogenous fascia and tendon, but it is difficult to know whether these represent the original cells of the transplanted tissue or new ones that have invaded it from the region into which the tissue was transplanted. Perhaps it is not very important to settle this point, because the value of these transplants hinges chiefly on the persistence of their intercellular substance. It seems more probable that the cells that produce the new intercellular substance which cements the transplant to whatever it is attached come from younger fibroblasts in the region rather than from the transplant itself.

The problem of transplanting tendon to bone is an involved one because this requires that the fibers of the transplanted tendon either become buried in bone substance or attached to something that is already well anchored in bone. A subsequent discussion on Sharpey's fibers will be informative on this matter.

Homogenous transplants of fascia and tendon sometimes are used. The cells of these would not survive, but the intercellular substance could persist, and it is possible that it could be replaced gradually by new intercellular substance made by cells of the host. Since even foreign intercellular substances can act as antigens, it would seem that, even if the cells of autogenous transplanted fascia and tendon do not survive, it would be better to employ autogenous transplants whenever this is possible.

Peer gives a comprehensive review of the controversial literature on this subject.

## REFERENCES

### FIBROBLASTS AND FORMATION OF INTERCELLULAR SUBSTANCES

Asboe-Hansen, G. (ed.): Connective Tissue in Health and Disease, Copenhagen, Munksgaard, 1954.

————: Hormonal effects on connective tissue, Physiol. Rev. 38:446, 1958.

Bloom, W.: Fibroblasts and histiocytes in Downey's Handbook of Hematology, vol. 2, p. 1335, New York, Hoeber, 1938.

Carneiro, J., and Leblond, C. P.: Role of osteoblasts and odontoblasts in secreting the collagen of bone and dentine as shown by radioautography in mice given tritium-labelled glycine, Exp. Cell Res. 18:291, 1959.

Fernando, N. V. P., and Movat, H. Z.: Fibrillogenesis in regenerating tendon, Lab. Invest. 12:214, 1963.

Jackson, S. F.: Connective tissue cells in Brachet, J., and Mirsky, A. E. (eds.): The Cell, vol. 6, p. 387, New York, Acad. Press, 1964.

Lewis, M. R.: Development of connective tissue fibers in tissue culture of chick embryos, Contrib. Embryol. 6:45, 1917.

Maximow, A.: The development of argyrophile and collagenous fibers in tissue cultures, Proc. Soc. Exp. Biol. Med. 25:439, 1928.

Movat, H. Z., and Fernando, N. V. P.: The fine structure of connective tissue. I. The fibroblast, Exp. Molec. Path. 1:509, 1962.

Revel, J. P., and Hay, E. D.: An autoradiographic and electron microscopic study of collagen synthesis in differentiating cartilage, Z. Zellforsch. 61:110, 1963.

Ross, R.: Collagen formation in healing wounds in Montagna, W., and Billingham, R. E. (eds.): Advances in Biology of Skin: Wound Healing, p. 144, London, Pergamon Press, 1964.

Porter, K. R., and Pappas, G. D.: Collagen formation of fibroblasts of the chick embryo dermis, J. Biophys. Biochem. Cytol. 5:153, 1959.

Stearns, M. L.: Studies on the development of connective tissue in transparent chambers in the rabbit's ear, Am. J. Anat. 66:133, 1939; 67:55, 1940.

Wassermann, F.: Fibrillogenesis in the regenerating rat tendon with special reference to growth and composition of the collagenous fibril, Am. J. Anat. 94:399, 1954.

Wolfe, J. M., Burack, E., Lansing, W., and Wright, A. W.: The effect of advancing age on the connective tissue of the uterus, cervix, and vagina of the rat, Am. J. Anat. 70:135, 1942.

### MACROPHAGES AND FOREIGN BODY GIANT CELLS

Clark, E. R., and Clark, E. L.: Relation of monocytes of the blood to tissue macrophages, Am. J. Anat. 46:149, 1930.

Evans, H. M.: The macrophages of mammals, Am. J. Physiol. 37:243, 1915.

Evans, H. M., and Scott, K.: On the differential reaction to vital dyes exhibited by the two great groups of connective tissue cells, Contrib. Embryol. *10*:1, 1921.

Felix, M. D., and Dalton, A. J.: A comparison of mesothelial cells and macrophages in mice after the intraperitoneal inoculation of melanin granules, J. Biophys. Biochem. Cytol. (Supp.) *2*: 109, 1956.

Haythorn, S. R.: Multinucleated giant cells with particular reference to the foreign body giant cell, Arch. Path. Lab. Med. *7*:651, 1929.

Maximow, A.: Development of nongranular leucocytes (lymphocytes and monocytes) into polyblasts (macrophages) and fibroblasts *in vitro*, Proc. Soc. Exp. Biol. Med. *24*:570, 1927.

————: The macrophages or histiocytes *in* Cowdry's Special Cytology, ed. 1, p. 425, New York, Hoeber, 1928.

————: Relation of blood cells to connective tissue and endothelium, Physiol. Rev. *4*:533, 1924.

Palade, G. E.: Relations between the endoplasmic reticulum and the plasma membrane in macrophages, Anat. Rec. *121*:445, 1955.

Sampaio, M. M.: The use of thorotrast for the electron microscopic study of phagocytosis, Anat. Rec. *124*:501, 1956.

## PLASMA CELLS

(*See also* references for Chapter 15.)

Coons, A. H., Leduc, E. H., and Connolly, J. M.: Studies on antibody production: I. A method for the histochemical demonstration of specific antibody and its application to a study of the hyperimmune rabbit, J. Exp. Med. *102*:49-60, 1955.

dePetris, S., Karlsbad, G., and Pernis, B.: Localization of antibodies in plasma cells by electron microscopy, J. Exp. Med. *117*:849, 1963.

Fagraeus, A.: Antibody production in relation to development of plasma cells; *in vivo* and *in vitro* experiments, Acta med. scandinav. *130*: Suppl. *204*, 3-122, 1948.

Humphrey, J. H., and White, R. G.: Immunology for Students of Medicine, ed. 2, Oxford, Blackwell, 1964.

Leduc, E. H., Coons, A. H., and Connolly, J. M.: Studies on antibody production: II. The primary and secondary responses in the popliteal lymph node of the rabbit, J. Exp. Med. *102*: 61-71, 1955.

Movat, H. Z., and Fernando, N. V. P.: The fine structure of connective tissue. II. The plasma cells, Exp. Molec. Path. *1*:535, 1962.

Rifkind, R. A., Osserman, E. F., Hsu, K. C., and Morgan, C.: The intracellular distribution of gamma globulin in a mouse plasma cell tumor as revealed by fluorescence and electron microscopy, J. Exp. Med. *116*:423, 1962.

Sainte-Marie, G.: Study on plasmocytopoiesis. I. Description of plasmocytes and of their mitoses in the mediastinal lymph nodes of ten-week-old rats, Am. J. Anat. *114*:207, 1964.

### SOME REFERENCES ON INDUCED IMMUNOLOGIC TOLERANCE

Billingham, R. E.: Actively acquired tolerance and its role in development *in* McElroy, W. D., and Glass, B. (eds.): The Chemical Basis of Development, p. 575, Baltimore, Johns Hopkins Press, 1958.

Billingham, R. E., and Brent, L.: A simple method for inducing tolerance of skin homografts in mice, Transplan. Bull. *4*:67, 1957.

Billingham, R. E., Brent, L., and Medawar, P. B.: Quantitative studies on tissue transplantation immunity, III. Actively acquired tolerance, Phil. Tr. Roy. Soc. London, Ser. B *15*:357, 1956.

Billingham, R. E., Lampkin, G. H., Medawar, P. B., and Williams, H. L.: Tolerance to homografts, twin diagnosis, and the freemartin condition in cattle, Heredity *6*:201, 1952.

Burnet, Sir MacFarlane: The Clonal Selection Theory of Acquired Immunity, Nashville, Tenn., Vanderbilt University Press, and Cambridge, Eng., University Press, 1959.

Humphrey, J. H., and White, R. G.: Immunology for Students of Medicine, ed. 2, Oxford, Blackwell, 1964.

Medawar, P. B.: A discussion of immunological tolerance—introductory remarks. Proc. Roy. Soc., Series B, Nov. 1956.

Owen, R. D.: Immunogenetic consequences of vascular anastomoses between bovine twins, Science *102*:400, 1945; Fed. Proc. *16*:581, 1957.

### MAST CELLS

(For references on heparin see textbooks of physiology.)

Asboe-Hansen, G.: The mast cell, Internat. Rev. Cytol. *3*:399, 1954.

Bloom, F.: Spontaneous solitary and multiple mast cell tumors (mastocytomata), Arch. Path. *33*:661, 1942.

Fawcett, D. W.: An experimental study of mast cell degranulation and regeneration, Anat. Rec. *121*:29, 1955.

Fernando, N. V. P., and Movat, H. Z.: The fine structure of connective tissue. III. The mast cell, Exp. Molec. Path. *2*:450, 1963.

Humphrey, J. H., and White, R. G.: Immunology for Students of Medicine, ed. 2, Oxford, Blackwell, 1964.

Mota, Ivan: The behaviour of mast cells in anaphylaxis, Internat. Rev. Cytol. *15*:363, 1963.

Padawer, J.: Studies on mammalian mast cells, Trans. N. Y. Acad. Sci., Ser. II, *19*:690, 1957.

Paff, G. H., and Bloom, F.: Vacuolation and the

release of heparin in mast cells cultivated *in vitro*, Anat. Rec. *104*:45, 1949.

Paff, G. H., and Mergenthaler, D. D.: Vacuolation in normal mast cells and in mast cells treated with protamine sulfate, Anat. Rec. *121*:579, 1955.

Riley, J. F.: The Mast Cells, Edinburgh, Livingstone, 1959.

Smith, D. E.: The tissue mast cell, Internat. Rev. Cytol. *14*:327, 1963.

## FAT CELLS

Clark, E. R., and Clark, E. L.: Microscopic studies of the new formation of fat in living adult rabbits, Am. J. Anat. *67*:255, 1940.

Hausberger, F. X.: Quantitative studies on the development of autotransplants of immature adipose tissue of rats, Anat. Rec. *122*:507, 1955.

Menschik, Z.: Histochemical comparison of brown and white adipose tissue in guinea pigs, Anat. Rec. *116*:439, 1953.

Napolitano, L., and Fawcett, D.: The fine structure of brown adipose tissue in the newborn mouse and rat, J. Biophys. Biochem. Cytol. *4*:685, 1958.

Peer, L. A.: Loss of weight and volume in human fat grafts, Plast. Reconstruct. Surg. *5*:217, 1950.

——: Transplantation of Tissues, vol. 1, Baltimore, Williams & Wilkins, 1955.

Wassermann, F., and McDonald, T. F.: Electron microscopic study of adipose tissue (fat organs) with special reference to the transport of lipids between blood and fat cells, Z. Zellforsch. *59*:326, 1963.

Wells, H. G.: Adipose tissue, a neglected subject, J.A.M.A., *114*:2177, 1940.

## DENSE CONNECTIVE TISSUE

Buck, R. C.: Regeneration of tendon, J. Path. *66*:1, 1953.

Ingelmark, B. E.: The structure of tendons at various ages and under different functional conditions, Acta anat. *6*:193, 1948.

Jackson, D. S.: Chondroitin sulfuric acid as a factor in the stability of tendon, Biochem. J. *54*:638, 1953.

Peer, L. A.: Transplantation of Tissues, vol. 1, Baltimore, Williams & Wilkins, 1955.

# 12 The Cells of Blood

## LEUKOCYTES

Blood is a fluid in which whole cells and fragments of cytoplasm are suspended. The fluid portion is called *plasma*. The cells are of two main types, called red and white, respectively. The fragments of cytoplasm are derived from certain special cells in the bone marrow, and because they are shaped like little disks they are called *platelets*.

The red cells of blood are so called because they are responsible for blood being red. However, isolated fresh unstained red blood cells seen under the microscope are straw-colored and only when many accumulate do they appear red. Red cells are commonly called *erythrocytes* (*erythros* = red). The white cells of the blood are commonly termed *leukocytes* (*leukos* = white). However, individual white cells are actually colorless when isolated; it is only when many are packed together that they appear white.

Erythrocytes are from 500 to 1,000 times more numerous than leukocytes in normal blood which means that the student will have to hunt for leukocytes if he is to study them in the usual preparations of blood cells provided for laboratory work. However, even though they are much rarer than erythrocytes, leukocytes are relatively easy to find in blood cell preparations because the erythrocytes of man (and other mammals) do not possess nuclei, whereas leukocytes do possess nuclei. Hence, in stained preparations, leukocytes can be found readily by looking for blue-to-purple nuclei.

The erythrocytes perform their function in the blood. But as was noted at the end of the previous chapter, the chief functions of most leukocytes are not performed while they are in the blood but only when they leave blood to enter the loose connective or other tissues of the body. Leukocytes are blood cells chiefly in the sense that they use the blood as a means of transport between the time they enter the bloodstream and leave it to perform their work. Therefore, we shall consider leukocytes next, more or less as a continuation of the study of the cells of loose connective tissue, and then afterward consider erythrocytes and platelets.

### How Leukocytes From Blood Are Studied

1. **Preparation of a Blood Film.** Both leukocytes and erythrocytes are commonly studied in the laboratory in preparations termed "blood films" or "blood smears." To be useful, a film must be prepared understandingly and with great care. It is necessary to use a very clean slide. It was a time-tested procedure to wash new slides with soap and water and then, after rinsing them in several changes of clean water, to dry them with an old lint-free towel or rag that has been previously washed and rinsed many times and is kept for this purpose only. In drying them, slides should be held by the edges so that their flat surfaces remain uncontaminated. However, it is now generally possible to purchase slides that are clean enough to use as they are.

The cleaned ear or finger is punctured lightly, and the first drop or two that well up are wiped away with sterile gauze. And then, as a *tiny* drop (the first drops are too large) wells up from the puncture, one surface of a clean slide, held by its edges, is applied to this (avoiding contact of the slide with the skin), so that most of the drop adheres to the slide midway between its sides and a short distance from one end (Fig. 12-1, *top*). A second slide, hereafter called the *spreader*, is now put in the position indicated in Figure 12-1 (many consider that a spreader should be at an angle of 30° to the slide). The edge of the spreader that touches the first slide should not be pressed against it firmly, but rather lightly. The spreader is now drawn back until the edge that is in contact with the first slide touches the drop of blood, which thereupon spreads quickly along the line of contact between the slides. The spreader is then pushed steadily forward, still without putting more than light pressure upon it, and by this means the drop of blood is spread out into a thin film.

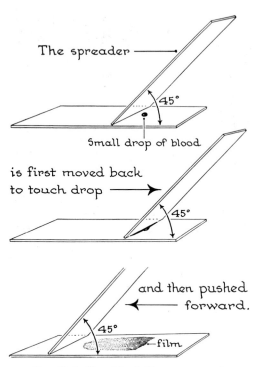

The spreader ——

45°

Small drop of blood

is first moved back
to touch drop ——→

45°

and then pushed
←—— forward.

45°

film

Fig. 12-1. How blood films are spread.

The angle at which the spreader is held in relation to the first slide determines the thickness of the film to some extent. The greater the angle the thicker the film. Furthermore, the film is usually thicker toward the end of the slide from which the film is spread.

After a film has dried in air, it is generally stained with what is often called a "blood stain." Although there are different varieties of these, each commonly exists as a single solution. Enough blood stain is added to a slide to cover the film, and then after a very short time twice as much distilled water, adjusted to a pH 6.4 to 6.6 with a phosphate buffer, is added to dilute the stain. After the diluted solution has been allowed to act for a few minutes, the slide is rinsed in tap water and dried in air. Then it can be studied with the oil-immersion objective, through oil, without a coverslip.

To stain blood films properly, the student must know something about the history and the nature of blood stains.

**Blood Stains.** It will be recalled from Chapter 2 that most stains are classified as acid or basic and that these stain acidophilic and basophilic components, respectively. In 1891,

Romanovsky tried the effect of mixing an acid stain (eosin) with a basic stain (methylene blue). Curiously enough, the mixture acted as a better stain for blood than did the ingredients applied separately. With this mixture he was able to stain malarial parasites particularly well; indeed, one part of the parasite was colored a violet shade, which could not be attributed directly to eosin or methylene blue. He realized that the two dyes must have interacted chemically to produce still another dye. At about the same time, Unna discovered that if he treated methylene blue with alkali and heat, it would impart a violet color to tissues which was not obtained with untreated methylene blue; hence, he decided that a new dye had formed as a result of the partial decomposition of methylene blue. Methylene blue treated to produce this new dye (or dyes) was said to be *polychromed*. Next, since Romanovsky had obtained such success with his mixture in which the polychroming of methylene blue occurred as a result of its being mixed with eosin, it was thought that mixing polychrome methylene blue and eosin might give still better results than Romanovsky's mixture and, when this was tried, it did.

However, there were so many practical disadvantages with regard to the use of the improved Romanovsky stain that it could scarcely be used except by an expert. The ingredients had to be mixed very exactly each time the stain was to be used, and even then they tended to react with each other very quickly to form a precipitate. These difficulties that restrained its common use were largely overcome by a further advance. The ingredients, mixed by experts, are allowed to precipitate. The precipitate is then dissolved and bottled in methyl alcohol, in which it keeps well. This is what is usually contained in the bottle of blood stain kept in the laboratory. Of course, in this form it is not an effective stain. But when water is added to it *on the slide,* the compound previously in solution in methyl alcohol partly passes into aqueous solution and some dissociation occurs into anions and cations and both carry color. So, for a brief period, the stain acts as if the ingredients had just been freshly mixed. Later on, of course, it tends to form a precipitate again, but by this time staining has been completed.

Leukocytes are studied in stained blood films for two main purposes. First, in connection with the diagnosis of certain diseases, it is very important to determine whether or not the leukocytes of a person have a normal or an abnormal appearance; the presence of abnormal leukocytes is associated with various disease states. Secondly, it is important to determine the relative percentages of the different kinds of leukocytes that are present in an individual's blood, for certain shifts in the percentages of the different kinds are also of diagnostic significance. The determination of the relative percentages of the kinds of leukocytes in blood is known as making a *differential count;* the way this is done will be described presently.

It is also of great importance in connection with the diagnosis of many different diseases to know whether or not the total number of leukocytes in blood is increased or decreased. The number of leukocytes in blood cannot be determined from the study of a stained blood film but only by making a leukocyte count.

**Making a Leukocyte Count.** Since medical students do not commonly learn the technic of making leukocyte counts until they have begun clinical courses, perhaps because to make either leukocyte or erythrocyte counts the student must first purchase a hemocytometer and the pipettes which go with it, only elementary information will be given here. A hemocytometer is essentially a glass slide that has certain areas on its upper surfaces ruled into squares of a certain size (Fig. 12-2). The glass slide is so arranged that a coverslip fits over the ruled areas with a space of a known distance separating the coverslip and the ruled glass beneath. To make a leukocyte count, a little blood, from a drop obtained as described for making a blood film, is drawn up into a special pipette, and then a much larger but known quantity of leukocyte counting fluid is drawn up in the pipette which fills its bowl. The leukocyte counting fluid is slightly acid so that it destroys the erythrocytes in the bowl of the pipette but not the leukocytes; indeed, the fluid contains a little stain which stains the nuclei of the leukocytes so that they can be seen easily. A few drops of the mixture are then forced out of the pipette so that the mixed blood and fluid in the bowl can reach its tip; the

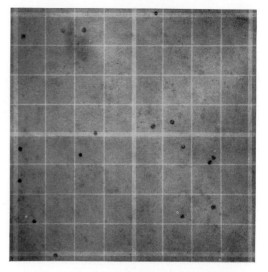

FIG. 12-2. The appearance presented by leukocytes in a counting chamber. Leukocytes are counted in representative squares enclosed by triple lines. When erythrocytes (not seen here) are counted, they are counted over the smaller squares at higher magnification. (Photomicrograph from R. Hasselback)

latter is placed against the edge of ruled areas of the hemocytometer that are covered with a coverslip and the fluid is then drawn by surface tension into the space between the coverslip and the ruled squares. The hemocytometer is then placed on the stage of the microscope and the average number of leukocytes seen over several squares (see Fig. 12-2) is determined and when this figure is known a calculation can be made to estimate the number of leukocytes per cubic millimeter of blood that was present in the sample.

## THE BASIS FOR CLASSIFYING LEUKOCYTES

Although there are 5 kinds of leukocytes, they are the representatives of only 2 families of cells. The distinguishing trait of one family is *granular cytoplasm;* that of the other, *nongranular cytoplasm*. Hence, the leukocytes are classed as either granular or nongranular.

There are 3 kinds of granular leukocytes. Although they are similar in certain respects, they differ in others, most notably in the affinity of their respective granules for acid and basic stains. In fact, their difference in

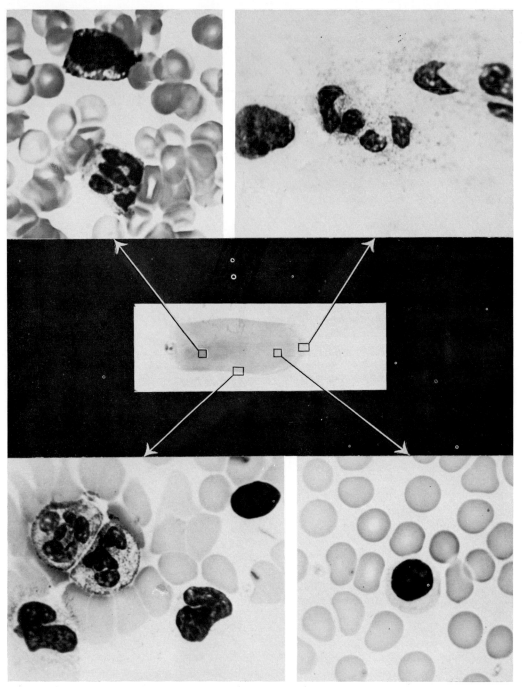

Fig. 12-3. The 4 photomicrographs in this figure show the way that leukocytes appear in different parts of a blood film. (*Upper left*) Picture taken from an area of the film in which the cells are thickly spread. The erythrocytes are seen to be superimposed on one another; leukocytes in such an area stain very poorly and are shrunken. Leukocytes should not be studied in such an area. (*Upper right*) Picture taken from the tail end of the film, where the leukocytes are pulled apart and their granules spread. This is not a good area for their detailed study. (*Lower left*) Picture taken from the edge of the film. Here the leukocytes tend to be crowded together and poorly stained. (*Lower right*) Picture taken from a thinly spread central part of the film and, although leukocytes are not numerous in this area, those seen are well stained and intact. This is the best place to study the cytology of leukocytes.

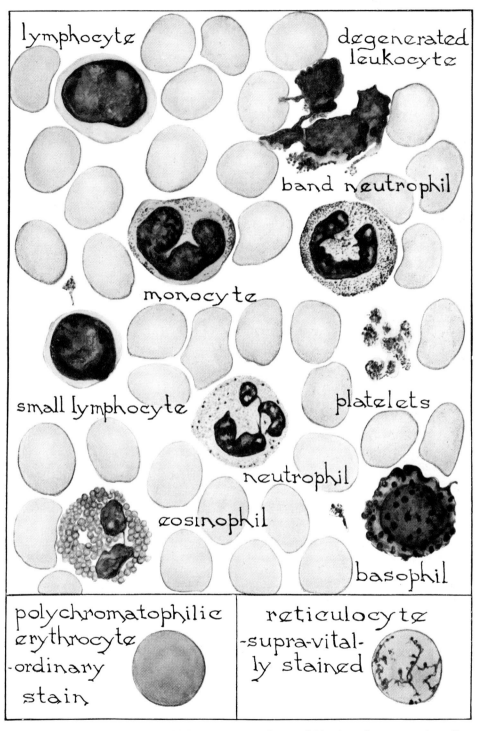

FIG. 12-4. The erythrocytes and the leukocytes of normal blood as they appear in a film stained with Hastings' stain.

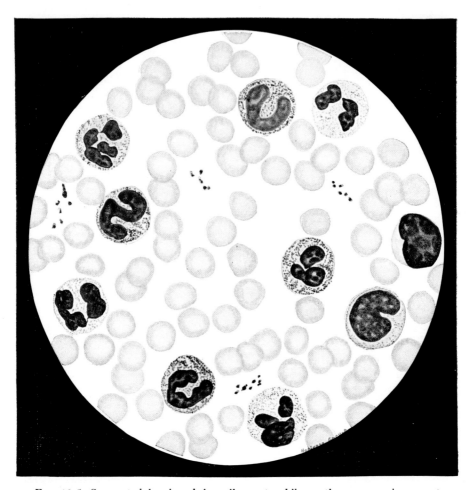

Fig. 12-5. Segmented band and juvenile neutrophils as they appear in a neutrophilic leukocytosis. A juvenile neutrophil may be seen at about 4 o'clock. Band neutrophils may be seen at 6:30, 9:30 and 12:30, respectively. With the exception of a lymphocyte present at 3 o'clock, the remaining leukocytes are segmented neutrophils. Several of the neutrophils in this illustration show toxic granulation. (Kracke, R. R.: Diseases of the Blood, ed. 2, Philadelphia, Lippincott)

this respect accounts for their names. Those with granules that stain avidly with acid stains are called *acidophilic,* or more commonly *eosinophilic granular leukocytes.* Those with granules that stain avidly with basic stains are called *basophilic granular leukocytes.* Those with granules that do not stain well at the point of neutrality with either acid stains or basic stains are called *neutrophilic granular leukocytes.* Since these are long terms, neutrophilic granular leukocytes are generally referred to as *neutrophils.* They are also called *polymorphs,* for reasons which will be given when their nuclei are described. Acidophilic granular leukocytes are called *acidophils* or, more commonly still, *eosinophils,* because eosin is the usual acid stain employed to color their granules. Basophilic granular leukocytes are generally referred to as *basophils.* There are 2 kinds of nongranular leukocytes. The more numerous and usually smaller ones are called *lymphocytes* because they are to be found in lymph as well as in blood, for reasons to be explained later. The larger and less numerous ones are called *monocytes,* a term which is not very meaningful.

Therefore, the leukocytes seen in stained smears of normal blood may be tabulated as follows:

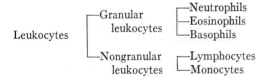

Leukocytes
- Granular leukocytes
  - Neutrophils
  - Eosinophils
  - Basophils
- Nongranular leukocytes
  - Lymphocytes
  - Monocytes

## THE STUDY OF LEUKOCYTES IN A STAINED BLOOD FILM

**Some General Instructions.** Often the things that are most desirable require the greatest amount of work for their realization. This is certainly true with regard to finding good examples of all 5 kinds of leukocytes in a blood film. The method of making a film usually results in the film's being thicker at the end to which it is spread (Fig. 12-3). Leukocytes are more numerous and easier to find in the thicker part of the film. But wherever the film is thick (and this is indicated by erythrocytes being superimposed on one another to a great degree), the leukocytes do not stain sharply

and hence are difficult to study (Fig. 12-3, *top, left*). They appear to much better advantage in the thinner part of the film. But here they are not as numerous as might be anticipated, because, being somewhat larger than erythrocytes, they tend to be drawn to the edges of the film (Fig. 12-3, *bottom, left*), as well as toward the very end of it (Fig. 12-3, *top, right*). In either of these positions (the edge or the end), they may become distorted, and their cytoplasm may even be broken and scattered about them. Therefore, it is best to learn the appearance of normal leukocytes from the regions where they are most difficult to find (Fig. 12-3, *bottom, right*), and in order to find here good examples of each kind the student may have to study not only one film but several.

If a film is provided with a coverslip, it may be examined with low-power, high-power and oil-immersion objectives. If it has no coverslip, the high-power objective does not reveal a clear image.

Leukocytes are conveniently detected with the low-power objective and centered with it, after which each should be studied with the oil-immersion objective.

When the student first searches a stained normal blood film for good examples of the 5 kinds of leukocytes, he can save much time by avoiding the following:

1. *Examining a Degenerating Leukocyte.* In every blood film there are many examples of partly broken-down leukocytes (Fig. 12-4), and it is a waste of time to try to identify their nature. So examine only well-formed and well-stained examples.

2. *Confusing Clumps of Platelets With Leukocytes.* In every film there are many little bodies, called *platelets,* that commonly clump together. Most of each platelet is pale blue, but its central part may contain a dark-staining granule or granules (Fig. 12-4). Platelets will be considered in detail in the next chapter.

3. *Examining Cells That Are Difficult to Classify.* At first the student should examine only leukocytes that are easily recognized and disregard those that seem difficult to classify.

In the following description of the 5 kinds of leukocytes the student will learn that both the nuclei and the cytoplasm give important information that is useful in identifying any particular cell that is seen in a blood film.

## GRANULAR LEUKOCYTES

### Neutrophils (Polymorphs)

**Numbers.** In a film of normal blood, neutrophils constitute from 60 to 70 per cent of the leukocytes. In absolute numbers, 3,000 to 6,000 is considered a normal range. Therefore, they are the first kind of leukocyte that the student generally sees in a normal film.

**Appearance.** Neutrophils, as will be described in a subsequent chapter, develop in myeloid tissue (the bone marrow). In myeloid tissue they go through many developmental changes before they finally assume their mature form, and then they are liberated into the bloodstream. In health, only an occasional neutrophil is released into the bloodstream before it is mature. Under conditions of disease, however, many immature ones may be released and so are seen in films made from peripheral blood. Therefore, it is necessary for the student to learn the appearance of both mature and immature neutrophils, so now both will be described, the mature type first.

**Mature Neutrophils.** These are from 10 to 12 $\mu$ in diameter, so they are slightly more than half as wide again as the erythrocytes in a film.

The nucleus of a mature neutrophil is divided into from 2 to 5 or more lobes (Fig. 12-4, *neutrophil*). The term "lobe" refers to a mass of nuclear material that is either completely separated from all other masses or connected to others by no more than *very delicate* strands (Figs. 12-4 and 12-5). The substance of the lobes is made up of coarse chromatin flakes that are rather densely packed (Fig. 12-4). As a consequence, the nuclear material stains fairly deeply with basic dyes, being colored a blue or blue-purple in the usual preparation. No nucleoli can be seen.

Since the nuclei of neutrophils may exhibit different numbers of lobes, neutrophils are commonly called *polymorphonuclear leukocytes* because their nuclei exhibit many forms (*morphi* = form). Since this is a long term, the abbreviation polymorph is often used in its place.

In 1954, Davidson and Smith demonstrated that it was possible to identify the chromosomal sex of an individual by the examination of blood films. It seems that the Barr body in the female, while it generally is contained in one of the lobes of the nucleus of a mature neutrophil, where it is very difficult, if not impossible, to identify because the chromatin is so packed, sometimes forms a separate tiny lobe which has the form of a drumstick (Fig. 12-6). According to Davidson and Smith this happens in about 1 out of every 38 neutrophils of females. Accordingly, to identify chromosomal sex from blood films, many neutrophils must be examined, and several examples of drumsticks must be found. Somewhat similar little bodies very occasionally are seen in the neutrophils of males but, on close scrutiny, most of these can be ruled out as examples of typical drumsticks. Furthermore, as many as 6 never are seen in a series of 500 neutrophils, and at least 6 always can be seen in 500 neutrophils obtained from females.

The cytoplasm of mature neutrophils occupies more space than the nucleus and reveals little structural detail except that it is fairly evenly and heavily sprinkled with very fine granules (Fig. 12-4). The true neutrophilic granules in many preparations are so fine that they are difficult to resolve with the light microscope; hence, all that may be seen is that the cytoplasm has a granular appearance. Commonly, the granules either have, or impart to the cytoplasm, a lavendar (lilac) color. Occasionally, neutrophils contain granules that are larger than the specific neutrophilic granules; these larger granules are reddish-purple in color. Since this color is imparted to them by the methylene azure, which is one of the basic dyes in a blood stain, they are called *azurophilic granules*. A sprinkling of these can be seen in the neutrophil illustrated in Figure 12-4. The presence of these or somewhat similar large granules in the cytoplasm of neutrophils is sometimes referred to as toxic granulation. As we shall see when we study the formation of granular leukocytes further, the first granules that appear in cells of this lineage are of the azurophilic type; only later do true neutrophilic granules appear, and when they do appear they are first seen in the Golgi region of the developing cells. The azurophilic granules would seem to represent a more primitive or less specific type of granule than the neutrophilic granules, and their persistence in what otherwise appear to be mature neutrophils would indicate that the neutrophils that contain them are perhaps not as mature as they otherwise seem. Such neutrophils might well appear in the blood during infections which cause less than fully matured neutrophils to be liberated from bone marrow; this possibly accounts for azurophilic granules being considered an indication of "toxic granulation."

**Immature Neutrophils.** In order to describe immature neutrophils it is necessary to describe briefly how neutrophils develop in myeloid tissue. Here younger forms of neutrophils can be identified because, instead of having lobulated nuclei, they have nuclei that are in the form of indented ovoids (Fig. 12-5). At this stage of development the cell is called a neutrophilic metamyelocyte (or a *juvenile neutrophil*, Fig. 12-5, *4 o'clock*). As this cell develops further, its nucleus becomes increasingly indented until it becomes frankly horseshoe-shaped, and at this stage of development it is termed a *band* or a *stab neutrophil* (Fig. 12-4, *band neutrophil*, and Fig. 12-5). Under normal conditions, the horseshoe-shaped nucleus of the band form becomes segmented to divide the nucleus into 2 or more lobes before the cell is released into the bloodstream, for under normal conditions not more than 1 or 2 per cent of band forms are seen in films But if there is a great need for neutrophils in the blood, as will be explained under function, some band and even some juvenile forms are released into the bloodstream, so these are seen in blood films.

The nuclei of juvenile neutrophils do not stain as deeply as those of band forms (Fig. 12-5), and those of band forms do not stain as deeply as those of mature forms. Both juvenile and band neutrophils have cytoplasmic granules similar to those of mature neutrophils (Fig. 12-5) and both may contain some azurophilic granules in addition to their specific neutrophilic granules.

From the above it is evident that *the maturity of a neutrophil is revealed chiefly by the shape of its nucleus* and to a lesser extent by how heavily the nucleus stains.

**Fine Structure.** Films of leukocytes cannot be studied with the EM because whole flat-

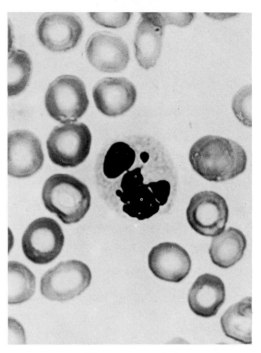

FIG. 12-6. Photomicrograph ($\times$ 1,750) of a stained film of the blood of a human female. The neutrophil in the center illustrates a characteristic "drumstick." (Davidson, W. M., and Smith, D. R.: Brit. M. J. *2*:6).

tened leukocytes are too thick to be penetrated by electrons. Accordingly, for the EM, leukocytes must be cut into thin sections. In examining electron micrographs of leukocytes it is important to remember that one is looking at very thin slices cut through them, and not at whole cells, as one does when examining a blood film with the light microscope.

Leukocytes are obtained for sectioning in different ways. One way is to obtain tiny pieces of bone marrow from a puncture made into the sternum. The little pieces so obtained can be fixed and sectioned in the usual way. Sometimes it is helpful to drain the blood from the little pieces of bone marrow before fixing them. In sections prepared from bone marrow by these methods there are, of course, many immature cells of various kinds, but there are also most kinds of mature leukocytes, and a sufficient search will reveal them. It is also possible to obtain sections of leukocytes from blood; if whole blood is allowed to settle, or if it is centrifuged in a tube, the erythrocytes go to the bottom of the tube, and the leuko-

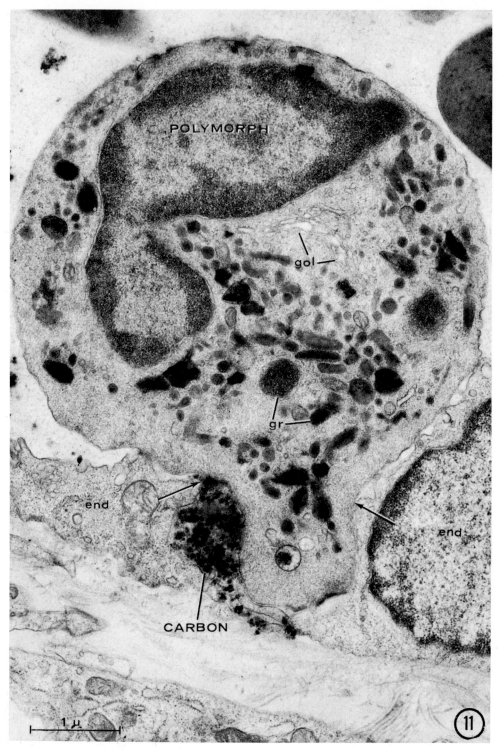

Fig. 12-7. Electron micrograph (× 23,500) showing a rat polymorph (neutrophil) beginning to migrate between two endothelial cells (*end*) in early inflammation. The nucleus is labeled *polymorph*, the Golgi apparatus *gol*, and the specific granules of the polymorph *gr*. Inflammation was produced before giving carbon particles intravenously; a clump of these can be seen to the left of the pseudopodium of the neutrophil that is projecting downward through the site of attachment between two endothelial cells in the lining of this small blood vessel. Notice the variation in size of the specific granules of the neutrophil. (Movat, H. Z., and Fernando, N. V. P., Lab. Invest. *12*:895)

cytes form a layer (called the buffy coat) just above them. Bits of this can be fixed and sectioned for electron microscopy. Another way is to cut sections of the tissues of an animal where has been the kind of injury that makes neutrophils migrate through capillary walls into the tissues; this is the way Figure 12-7 was obtained.

It is obvious that a thin section cut through a mature neutrophil would pass through only some of the lobes of the nucleus and that in all likelihood it would not pass through any of the strands that connect lobes. Hence, in electron micrographs neutrophils do not reveal as many lobes as they do in ordinary blood films. The nuclei, in sections, appear granular (Fig. 12-7), but of course the structures that appear as granules may be threads cut in section. The granules are more closely packed near the nuclear membrane, although some densely packed areas may be present in the more central parts of nuclear lobes. No nucleoli are visible in mature cells.

The cytoplasm, viewed with the EM, reveals not only the usual organelles: a few mitochondria, a few membranous vesicles and ribosomes and, in favorable sections, a Golgi apparatus (Fig. 12-7, gol), but also prominent inclusions which are the specific granules.

The specific granules, that in ordinary blood films are colored lilac, are round-to-ovoid in shape and mostly around 0.1 to 0.2 $\mu$ in diameter; most are therefore somewhat smaller than mitochondria (Fig. 12-7), and so it is not surprising that most granules are very difficult to see clearly with the light microscope. However, some granules are larger (Fig. 12-7). The variation in size of granules in electron micrographs is due not only to some granules being sliced through their greatest diameters and others through one side or the other, but is also real. Recent work suggests that the specific granules are in effect lysosomes—tiny smooth-surfaced vesicles containing hydrolytic enzymes.

Neither free ribosomes nor rough-surfaced vesicles of endoplasmic reticulum are very numerous in neutrophils. The Golgi apparatus is relatively more prominent than endoplasmic reticulum. The formation of the specific granules has not yet been investigated thoroughly. The nature of azurophilic granules is not known.

## THE FUNCTION OF NEUTROPHILS

Almost everyone has had personal experience with a cut in his skin that has become "infected." While an unbroken skin surface keeps disease organisms from gaining entrance to the underlying tissues, a cut in the surface opens the door to them. So, if a cut is not treated properly, bacteria are prone to invade the loose connective tissues and, in this new environment, grow and multiply, but usually only for a short time. During this time the margins of the cut become red and swollen, and the infected area may feel hot and painful. In the language of pathology, the cut has become a site of inflammation. But then, instead of becoming worse, it is more likely that the redness and the swelling begin to decrease, and before long the cut has healed. Obviously, something happens to repel the bacterial invasion, first to localize it to the tissue immediately adjacent to the cut and then to overwhelm it completely.

For many years the significance of the changes occurring at the site of such an injury (redness, swelling, etc.) was not understood. John Hunter (1728-1793) was the first to understand that there was something purposeful about them—that they were the manifestations of the reaction of the host to injury and of a sort disposed to restore the part to normal. But beyond that little was known. However, as histologic methods improved, their precise nature was revealed by the microscope. Cohnheim (1839-1884), in particular, showed that the swelling of inflamed tissue is due to the endothelium of its capillaries leaking plasma because it is injured. Therefore, the swelling of inflamed tissue can be described as an inflammatory edema. The redness of inflamed tissue is due to the dilatation of its smaller blood vessels, allowing the tissue to contain an increased amount of blood (Fig. 12-8). Cohnheim made many other accurate observations on the changes that occur in inflamed tissues. He observed, for example, that certain blood leukocytes migrated through the walls of injured capillaries and small venules to take up their residence in the tissue spaces (Fig. 12-8). However, the significance of this phenomenon was determined at a later date by Elie Metchnikoff (1845-1916), a Russian zoologist.

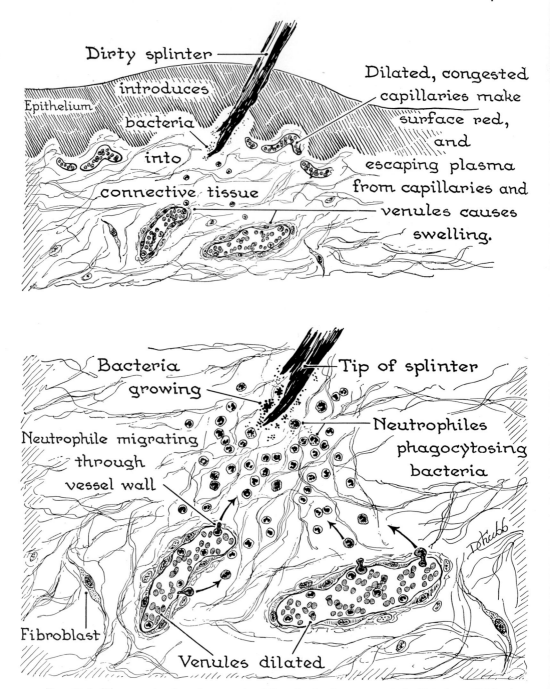

FIG. 12-8. Diagrams to show how neutrophils migrate from congested, dilated small blood vessels to combat bacteria introduced into the tissues by means of an injury.

Metchnikoff's contribution to the study of inflammation in man was the outcome of a long series of investigations made on a great variety of simpler living creatures. He noted, for example, that unicellular organisms can ingest particulate matter and digest it within their cytoplasm and that any mildly noxious properties of certain particles seemed to disappear as the particles were digested by the chemical activity of the cytoplasm. When he then studied simple types of multicellular organisms wherein the cells had become variously specialized to perform different functions, he found that there were certain roving cells that were very adept at devouring and destroying particulate matter that gained entrance to their tissues; indeed, they could deal even with living particles such as yeast cells and bacteria. He termed these special cells *phagocytes* (*phago* = I eat), and their ability to engulf matter became known as *phagocytosis* (*eosis* = increase, i.e., phagocytes have increased ability in this respect). When he studied organisms with circulatory systems, and the circulatory system evolves in the middle layer, he found that most of the phagocytes came to be contained in the blood, an arrangement that increases their mobility tremendously.

Metchnikoff's studies made the significance of many of the phenomena associated with inflammation much clearer. Because leukocytes are present in blood, they can be mobilized rapidly at any point of bacterial attack, make their way through the injured endothelium of the capillaries and the venules of that part and act to destroy the bacterial invader by phagocytosis, as is illustrated in Figure 12-8. Metchnikoff observed that all the 5 kinds of leukocytes were not good phagocytes but only 2, the neutrophil and the monocyte, and that these seemed to be called into the tissues by different kinds of injuries.

Since infections constitute the largest single kind of human disease and since two kinds of leukocytes are such important agents in combating them, it is obvious that the study of leukocytes deserves our closest attention. It must not be thought, however, that phagocytosis is the only way in which the body copes with disease organisms. Although Metchnikoff's thesis has stood the test of time and it is agreed that phagocytosis is an extremely important mechanism of defense, there are other important mechanisms involved in our defenses; in particular, antibodies which are produced by the body and which react against disease agents. As we shall see one of the other kinds of leukocytes (the lymphocytes), when they leave the bloodstream to enter the tissues can serve as stem cells for forming the kinds of cells that make antibodies. So, all in all, leukocytes are of tremendous importance to the defenses of the body.

The neutrophils of the blood serve as a mobile defensive force of cells that can migrate through capillary walls in any part of the body where inflammation has been set up by a bacterial invasion or by some other damaging agent. Neutrophils, in general, are called out of the bloodstream and into the tissues by *acute* bacterial infections. Since they are mobile cells, they can move through the tissues; and since they are phagocytic, they can engulf bacteria in their cytoplasm and destroy them.

The migration of neutrophils (polymorphs) into loose connective tissue occurs more through the walls of the tiny venules into which capillaries empty than through capillary walls themselves. There has been doubt as to whether or not the neutrophils penetrate through the cytoplasm of the endothelial cells that line the venules and the capillaries or whether they penetrated through the sites where endothelial cells come into contact. In instances of severe damage it seems probable that many endothelial cells may become injured and broken up so that there are many openings through which neutrophils could gain entrance to the tissues. But the most recent evidence indicates that in less severe injuries the sites where individual endothelial lining cells come into contact with each other are the sites through which neutrophils penetrate when they leave the bloodstream to enter the tissues. Movat and Fernando, in their study of acute inflammation with the EM, injected fine carbon particles into the bloodstream of animals. Certain tissues were then injured by various irritants, and they found, as is shown in their illustration (Fig. 12-7), that gaps developed between the edges of adjacent endothelial cells of small venules and that carbon particles often accumulated in these gaps. Moreover, the cytoplasm of neutrophils bulged into gaps of this type and in due course the whole cells would leave the circulation by this means. Movat and Fernando found, moreover, that this was the way that eosinophils and monocytes also left the bloodstream to enter loose connective tissue.

The mechanism by which neutrophils destroy the bacteria that they phagocytose has become much more understandable in the light of the discovery of lysosomes. It would seem that the process of the phagocytosis of bacteria by neutrophils involves bacteria being enveloped at the cell surface by the cell membrane and that bacteria-containing membranous vesicles formed in this manner migrate into the cytoplasm where they come into contact and fuse with granules which are essentially membranous vesicles filled with hydrolytic enzymes (lysosomes). The enzymes then digest the bacteria. However, it would seem that the various activities set in motion by neutrophils phagocytosing and digesting bacteria are so extensive and relatively violent or widespread in the cells that they result in the death of the neutrophils concerned.

A severe infection in any part of the body results in a chemical message (the nature of this has been investigated by Menkin) being sent to the bone marrow, and the reception of the message results in the bone marrow liberating more neutrophils into the bloodstream. Accordingly, in severe infections there is generally a *leukocytosis,* and a differential count will show that this is due to a great increase in the number of neutrophils in the blood. Therefore, a leukocyte and differential count can be used to help to establish the presence of infection in the body. An examination of blood films from individuals who have severe infections also provides further information. If the infection continues to progress, the bone marrow sends out an increasing number of immature cells, neutrophils of the band type and even some juvenile neutrophils, as in Figure 12-6. (Some hematologists now term both types metamyelocytes.) Accordingly, if in any patient, the examination of regularly obtained blood films shows that the percentage of immature cells is increasing, it is said that a shift to the left is occurring. If, however, it is found in regularly obtained films that the percentage of immature forms is decreasing, it is said there is a shift to the right. So, in a very general way, a shift to the left indicates that an infection is progressing, and a shift to the right indicates that it is subsiding.

## EOSINOPHILS

**Numbers.** Eosinophils constitute from 1 to 3 per cent of the leukocytes seen in a film of normal blood. In absolute figures, 150 to 450 per cu. mm. of blood is considered normal.

**Appearance.** Eosinophils are from 10 to 15 microns in diameter; they tend to be slightly larger than neutrophils.

The nuclei of eosinophils commonly are composed of only 2 lobes (Fig. 12-4), and these may or may not be connected with a strand of nuclear material. The coarse clumps of chromatin are not so densely packed in the nuclei of eosinophils as they are in neutrophils; hence, eosinophil nuclei do not stain as deeply (Fig. 12-4).

The cytoplasm of eosinophils characteristically is packed with large refractile granules that in well-stained blood films are colored red or orange (Fig. 12-4). In poorly stained films their color may veer toward pink or a muddy blue. Even in poorly stained preparations they can be distinguished from the granules of neutrophils because they are more numerous—the cell seems to be packed with them—and because they are distinctly larger and more refractile (Fig. 12-4).

**Fine Structure.** The EM reveals no special features in the nuclei. The cytoplasm contains specific granules in addition to the usual organelles.

The specific granules of the eosinophil, seen with the EM, have a striking appearance, being dense and from 0.5 to 1 $\mu$ in diameter (Fig. 12-9). In immature eosinophils they are composed of a homogeneous material of considerable density. In mature eosinophils some of the granules are seen to contain still denser bodies in their more central parts (Fig. 12-9). These bodies, as seen in a section, may have the form of rough squares or rectangles. They sometimes occupy more and sometimes less than half of a granule.

Eosinophils, with the EM, reveal well-developed Golgi regions (see center of Fig. 12-9).

**Functions of Eosinophils.** Anaphylactic phenomena, allergy and hypersensitivity have been described in connection with mast cells. It seems that eosinophils are somehow concerned in anaphylactic phenomena because they are more numerous in both the tissues that are the sites of allergic reactions and also in the blood of people who suffer from allergies. Curiously enough, the hormone hydrocortisone, which depresses allergic reactions, causes eosinophils to disappear from the blood. Indeed, the number of eosinophils in

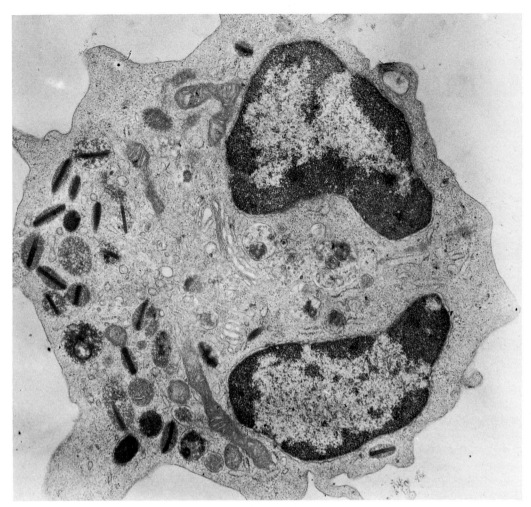

Fig. 12-9. Electron micrograph (× 18,500) of eosinophil of mouse. Note the bilobed nucleus. Flattened smooth-surfaced vesicles of the Golgi apparatus can be seen slightly left of the center as well as some free rounded vesicles filled with pale secretory material. The specific granules in the cytoplasm vary in size; many show the dark disks that characterize the specific granules of eosinophils. Only a few mitochondria are visible. (Preparation from A. F. Howtson)

blood varies over each 24-hour period, probably because the secretion of hydrocortisone of the adrenal gland varies over the same period. In some species eosinophils have been shown to contain histamine, and so it has been thought that they might either liberate histamine or perhaps absorb histamine that has been released from mast cells. The number of eosinophils in the blood becomes increased in individuals who are infected with certain parasites.

In addition to their as yet ill-understood role in allergic phenomena, eosinophils also can act as phagocytes, but their function in this respect is not comparable with that of the neutrophils.

### BASOPHILS

Basophils comprise only about 0.5 per cent of the blood leukocytes; hence, to find a good example of one, it may be necessary to examine several hundred leukocytes and perhaps several different blood films. Basophils are usually from 10 to 12 $\mu$ in diameter; they are of about the same size as neutrophils (Fig. 12-4). About half the cell consists of

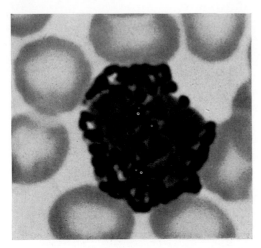

FIG. 12-10. Oil-immersion photomicrograph of a basophil from human blood. Prominent granules are darker than the nucleus and tend to obscure it. (Preparation from C. P. Leblond and Y. Clermont)

nucleus, which may be segmented and, in any event, often presents a very irregular shape. It is colored much less intensely than the nucleus of the neutrophil or the eosinophil and is overshadowed by the large, dark, blue-stained granules of the cytoplasm, which may be seen lying over the paler nucleus (Fig. 12-10). The granules of basophils are similar in many respects to those of mast cells, and like them are metachromatic, which suggests that they, like those of mast cells, contain heparin. Basophils are said to contain about half of the histamine that is present in blood. Furthermore, basophils, like eosinophils, tend to leave the bloodstream under the influence of certain hormones of the adrenal gland. In many respects they seem to be involved in allergic and stress phenomena in much the same way as eosinophils.

## NONGRANULAR LEUKOCYTES

### LYMPHOCYTES

**Numbers.** Next to neutrophils, lymphocytes are the commonest leukocytes seen in a film of normal human blood. In absolute numbers there are 2,000 plus or minus 1,000 per cu. mm. of blood. In relative numbers, from around 20 to 30% of the leukocytes seen in a normal film are lymphocytes.

The percentage of lymphocytes in the blood of many experimental animals differs considerably from that in man; those beginning experimental work can obtain precise information about the normal range of leukocytes in different species from Albritton's *Standard Values in Blood.*

**Appearance.** The usual lymphocyte is the smallest of all the 5 kinds of leukocytes (Fig. 12-4). The small size of lymphocytes is due to two factors; first, their nuclei are condensed, and secondly, they have very little cytoplasm. Even in films, where their cytoplasm is spread out, and so makes the most of itself, it is no more than a narrow rim of material that stains a pale blue with blood stains (Fig. 12-4). In sections, where the normal globular shape of the lymphocyte is preserved, the rim of cytoplasm is so thin, and stains so poorly, that it can be seen only with difficulty.

The nucleus of a lymphocyte is its most prominent feature. The nucleus is rounded or ovoid and generally exhibits a little indentation on one of its sides (Fig. 12-4, *upper left*). The chromatin is in the form of coarse clumps and stains deeply with basic stains.

Nucleoli are not seen in the nuclei of lymphocytes that are examined in films stained with blood stains. Moreover, they are not readily seen in the nuclei of lymphocytes in the usual section because they are obscured by the densely packed chromatin. If *thin* sections are prepared of lymphocytes, so that individual slices are cut through nuclei, nucleoli can be demonstrated in every one of them.

The cytoplasm of about 10% of lymphocytes contains reddish-purple granules called *azurophilic granules*; the significance of these is not known.

**Lymphocytes of Two Sizes.** Although most lymphocytes are small, as described above, it becomes obvious from the careful examination of a blood film that there are some that are larger, having both somewhat larger nuclei and somewhat more cytoplasm than the usual ones (Fig. 12-4, *upper left corner*). However, in deciding that some lymphocytes are larger than others, it is necessary to be very careful lest one be misled by the fact that the size of cells seen in films depends to a considerable extent on how thinly the cells are spread, and this differs in different parts

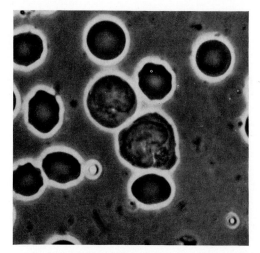 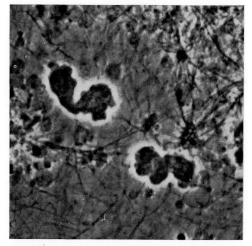

Fig. 12-11. Oil-immersion phase photomicrographs of living lymphocytes in cell cultures. The two at the left are resting, and the two on the right are moving. (Preparation from D. M. Whitelaw)

of a film. Figure 12-3, *lower right,* shows a thinly spread lymphocyte. However, it is sometimes possible in a film to find two lymphocytes close together, with one being of the usual kind and the other obviously larger; if they are close together, it can generally be assumed that they have been spread to the same extent and hence some lymphocytes are larger than others. Nevertheless, the safest way to draw conclusions about lymphocytes being of different sizes is to study them in sections, where they are not spread out but retain their globular form. When this is done, it will be found that the nuclei of most lymphocytes are about 5 microns in diameter, while those of around 8 per cent of the total number of lymphocytes have nuclei that are around 7 microns in diameter. If an example of these two types were seen side by side in a blood film, where it could be assumed that they were both spread to the same extent, the smaller would have an over-all diameter of around 7 to 8 microns and the larger a diameter of around 12 microns.

**Terminology.** The fact that around 8 per cent of the lymphocytes in blood are of a larger size than the other 92 per cent requires that they have a special name to distinguish them from the ordinary kind. One way this has been, and is still done, is by terming the usual lymphocytes of the blood *small* lymphocytes and the others *large* lymphocytes. The difficulty

with this terminology is that the term *large* lymphocyte is used by several authors to designate not any lymphocytes in the blood but instead the precursor cells of lymphocytes, which reside in lymphatic tissue, and which do not enter the blood under normal conditions. These latter cells that exist in lymphatic tissue are not the same as the "large lymphocytes" seen in the blood. To get around this difficulty, those who describe the large precursor cells in lymphatic tissue as large lymphocytes generally designate the larger lymphocytes of blood as medium-sized lymphocytes. However, since it is such a common and useful practice to use the suffix *blast* for indicating cells of the precursor type that serve as the mother cells for some particular cell family, we think, along with many others, that the cell that resides in lymphatic tissue, and serves as the mother cell for the lymphocytes that appear in blood, should be termed a *lymphoblast,* and that the suffix *cyte* should be used only for the cells of this series that appear in blood. If this is done, the two kinds of lymphocytes in the blood can be termed *small* and *large lymphocytes,* respectively.

Another terminology that is used to distinguish between the two cells found in blood has resulted from a growing tendency to designate the immediate precursor of a cell by adding the prefix *pro* to the name of the cell. Since it can be shown that cells, identical

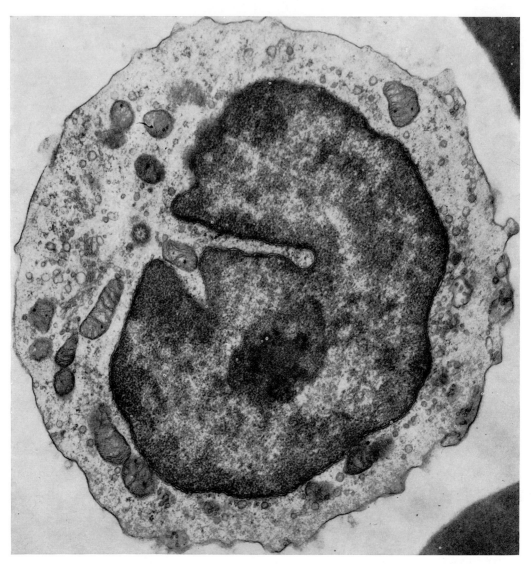

FIG. 12-12. Electron micrograph (approximately × 30,000) of section of small lymphocyte from thoracic duct lymph. Note the deep indentation of the nucleus, below which can be seen the nucleolus. Close to the open end of the indentation is a centriole cut in cross section; to its left, components of the Golgi apparatus are visible. About a dozen mitochondria can be seen. Note that free ribosomes are only sparsely distributed in the cytoplasm. (Preparation by Dorothea Zucker-Franklin)

with the larger lymphocytes of the blood, give rise to smaller lymphocytes in lymphatic tissues, the larger lymphocytes in this location are often termed *prolymphocytes*. If this term is used for the larger lymphocytes of the blood, the others do not have to be qualified by the adjective small.

**Motility of Lymphocytes in Cell Cultures.** In cell cultures lymphocytes manifest a very characteristic type of motion. When they move, the nucleus, preceded by a thin fringe of cytoplasm, leads the way and the bulk of the cytoplasm that contains the mitochondria and a small sphere of lipoid material that can be seen in the living cell, termed a *Gall body*, follows afterward. As a result they assume shapes that are very different from that of a resting lymphocyte. (Compare left and right of Fig. 12-11.)

**Fine Structure.** As will be described, there

has been much speculation in the past about possible functions of lymphocytes. The study of lymphocytes with the EM has been helpful in this regard, not so much by indicating possible functions that the cell could perform but by showing that the cytoplasm of lymphocytes as they exist in blood is ill-equipped to perform any specialized function. This finding fits in with the concept that if lymphocytes are to perform any specialized function, they would have to differentiate into cells that would have, in the EM, a very different appearance from blood lymphocytes. As they exist in blood (Fig. 12-12), they have only a few mitochondria, perhaps not more than 25, which suggests that their metabolic rate is low. Their cytoplasm is only sparsely provided with either free or membrane-attached ribosomes. A Golgi apparatus is evident in them (Fig. 12-12). Since lymphocytes have often been considered to be possible producers of antibody, perhaps the most important point to make is that their cytoplasm gives no indication of possessing the equipment required for actively synthesizing protein and hence, in this respect, their fine structure is different from that of plasma cells, which have already been described in detail, and of graft rejection cells which will be described in detail shortly.

## THE LIFE SPAN AND THE FUNCTIONS OF LYMPHOCYTES

During the past few years there has been a remarkable development of knowledge about lymphocytes. In order to understand much of this new work, the reader must know something about the circulation of the fluid lymph, so although this matter receives more detailed consideration in later chapters, we shall give a very brief account of it here.

**The Circulation of Lymph—Thoracic Duct Lymph.** It has been explained already how tissue fluid is formed (Fig. 10-8). It has also been explained that much of the tissue fluid that is forced out through the walls of the arterial ends of capillaries is sucked back into the blood capillaries through their walls at their venous ends because of osmotic phenomena (Fig. 10-8). However, some tissue fluid and such blood protein as escapes from blood capillaries into tissue spaces is returned to the blood circulatory system by a more

devious route; it percolates through the walls of the lymphatic capillaries which are found in close association with blood capillaries in many parts of the body (Fig. 10-8). As soon as tissue fluid penetrates into lymphatic capillaries it is called *lymph*. Therefore, normal lymph *as it is formed* is tissue fluid plus a little protein, and it contains few if any cells. We shall now consider the route that it follows in order for it to return to the blood vascular system and how lymphocytes are added to it as it passes along this route.

Lymphatic capillaries begin from blind ends (Fig. 10-8) in and about blood capillaries that are producing tissue fluid. As the lymphatic capillaries pass inwardly and centrally in the body, they join together to form larger vessels that are called *lymphatics* which are very similar to small veins except that they contain lymph instead of blood. Sooner or later along their course the lymphatics reach little organs called *lymph nodes*. As can be seen in the top illustration in Figure 15-3, which should be referred to briefly here, lymphocytes enter the convex surface of the beanshaped lymph nodes as *afferent* lymphatics; the lymph they contain percolates through the passageways of a netlike kind of tissue which fills the lymph nodes and contains both many phagocytic cells of the macrophage type and little nodules in which lymphocytes are formed from lymphoblasts. The lymph, as it percolates through this tissue (which also contains many blood capillaries), washes away many lymphocytes, so that when the lymph leaves the lymph node, by means of *efferent* lymphatics, which drain away from the concave surface of the node (Fig. 15-3), it contains many lymphocytes in suspension. The afferent lymphatics from one node may join with lymphatics from other nodes and may again empty as afferent lymphatics into nodes farther along the lymph stream. Eventually, however, lymph from the lower part of the body empties into a main lymphatic duct called the *thoracic duct*. The thoracic duct conveys all the lymph that is formed in association with the intestine and which has drained perhaps through several lymph nodes before it reaches the thoracic duct. The thoracic duct and another large lymph duct which drains lymph from the rest of the body (mainly the upper right part of the body) both empty into large veins near the heart and so by the means of these two large lymph ducts all the lymph that is formed in the body is emptied back into the blood circulatory system. *The lymph that is returned* to the bloodstream differs from the lymph that forms in association with capillaries because it contains lymphocytes.

The thoracic duct, in an experimental animal, is large enough to permit a cannula to be inserted into it, and by this means the lymph that flows along it may be collected and studied. As already noted, this lymph contains lymphocytes. Both prolymphocytes and lymphocytes are represented. So by obtaining thoracic duct lymph it is possible to obtain fairly large numbers of lymphocytes for study. It is also possible to inject cells into the thoracic duct of an animal so that in due course they appear in the blood. With this information in mind we can now describe some of the experiments that have been performed in connection with the thoracic duct and the cells it contains.

By counting the numbers of lymphocytes that were carried by the thoracic duct back to the blood circulatory system over given periods of time, Yoffey and his associates found that literally enormous numbers of lymphocytes were added to the bloodstream every day by the thoracic duct, so many that it would be impossible for them to remain in the bloodstream for more than part of a day without causing the numbers of lymphocytes in blood to increase rapidly. Since the lymphocyte count in the blood remains fairly constant, the only conclusion to draw was that lymphocytes must leave the blood at the same rate at which they enter it, and this would mean that on the average, lymphocytes emptied into the blood stay there less than a day before they leave it.

This finding of course created the problem of explaining what happens to the lymphocytes that leave the blood. One early and widely held assumption was that lymphocytes must have a very short life span and that they die or are lost from the body almost as quickly as they are made. And, indeed, examples of lymphocytes undergoing pyknotic and other changes indicating that they are dying can generally be found in areas in the body where lymphocytes are numerous. Furthermore, lymphocytes are commonly seen migrating through the lining of the epithelium of the intestine to enter its lumen. Washings of the gut lumen show many lymphocytes. Lymphocytes exhibit a remarkable ability to penetrate between, and even sometimes into, cells such as those that line the intestine. So there was evidence to the effect that many lymphocytes die within the body or are lost from the body each day. Nevertheless, it seemed that even though there was a loss of lymphocytes by mechanisms such as these, the loss was not sufficient to explain the fate of all the lymphocytes that were emptied into the blood each day. So for many decades the problem of what happened to all the lymphocytes that were poured into the bloodstream every day remained an enigma.

Most of the thinking about this matter was of course based on the assumption that the enormous number of lymphocytes that entered the blood via the thoracic duct each day were new lymphocytes that had been produced in the lymph tissue through which the lymph passed on its way to the thoracic duct. But gradually it came to be questioned if all these lymphocytes were new lymphocytes. There was, it was suggested, another possibility; namely, that lymphocytes, as they circulated through the blood capillaries and small venules in lymph nodes, might migrate through the walls of these small blood vessels to enter the spaces of the netlike tissue of the lymphatic tissue through which lymph was passing. If they did this, it would mean that lymphocytes could recirculate back from the bloodstream into the lymph stream. The concept of lymphocytes recirculating from bloodstream to lymph stream of course would explain why the number of lymphocytes in blood remained relatively constant even though enormous numbers were added by the thoracic duct every day, the explanation being, of course, that almost as many left the bloodstream every day to enter the lymph as would be returned to the bloodstream by the lymph of the thoracic duct. This concept, moreover, raised another question. As has already been noted, most previous thinking was based on the idea of at least most lymphocytes having a very short life span. If the theory of recirculation could be proved, there would no longer be any good reason for assuming that lymphocytes must have only a very short life span. Here then there were two problems that were bound up together, whether or not there was recirculation of lymphocytes and whether or not they had a short or a long life span.

Experiments of Gowans first proved that there is a considerable recirculation of lymphocytes. He showed that as lymph was continuously drained away from the thoracic duct the number of lymphocytes in it became less and less. This showed that the lymphocytes in the thoracic duct were not all newly formed lymphocytes, for if they were, their numbers in the thoracic duct would remain constant even if the lymph was being drained away. He showed, moreover, that the numbers of lymphocytes in the lymph that flowed along the thoracic duct was restored to normal when he reinjected the lymphocytes collected from the duct back into the bloodstream. Furthermore, he used a radioactive tracer to label lymphocytes as they formed in one animal and then injected the labeled lymphocytes into the bloodstream of another identical animal, and found that the labeled cells appeared in the thoracic duct lymph of the animal into whose bloodstream they had been injected. These experiments showed that lymphocytes recirculated back and forth between the blood and the lymph streams.

The other question—the life span of lymphocytes—was also investigated by modern methods. First, it was found by Hamilton that if the lymphocytes that formed in people suffering from chronic lymphatic leukemia were labeled with labeled adenine over a short period, labeled cells could be found in the circulation as long as 300 days afterward. This would seem to show that at least some lymphocytes lived as long as 300 days. However, these experiments did not prove that the labeled cells that were seen at 300 days were necessarily the cells that were labeled at the time when the labeled adenine was administered; it was just possible that cells labeled at that time might have died, with the result that their label was taken up by new cells that were forming. To rule out the possibility that it was not cells but only label that persisted in the animal, Little, Brecher, Bradley and Rose performed an experiment in which they continuously infused animals with labeled thymidine for 90 days so that all the lymphocytes that

formed during the 90 days would be labeled. They found that at the end of 90 days there were still some circulating lymphocytes that were not labeled, and hence must have been formed before the experiment was begun, more than 90 days before. As a result of all these experiments it was obvious that at least some lymphocytes have a long life span and that they live out much of this long life span by circulating back and forth between the lymph stream and the bloodstream.

## THE FUNCTIONS OF LYMPHOCYTES

Through the years many theories have been offered about the possible functions of small lymphocytes. Some of these are still entertained to some extent. The multiplicity of theories is perhaps to be explained by the fact that it was difficult to obtain satisfactory proof for any of them. Only recently has satisfactory proof become available to establish a function for small lymphocytes, and even now such proof as is available leaves some questions unanswered. We shall now deal briefly with new information that has been obtained about at least a portion of the small lymphocytes of blood and lymph in both in-vivo and in-vitro experiments.

In order to explain the in-vivo experiments, we must first describe a very curious condition called *runt* or *wasting disease* that can be produced in experimental animals of inbred strains.

**Inbred Strains.** It is possible to inbreed mice, rats and other experimental animals by brother-to-sister matings through so many generations that for all practical purposes the members of the inbred strain all come to have exactly the same genes. In this way the members of an inbred strain resemble identical twins. Animals that have been inbred through a sufficient number of generations for them to all have the same genes in their cells are termed *isologous* in relation to one another. Since their genes are all alike, and since their genes control the proteins that are formed in their bodies, their proteins are all alike. Hence, when tissue, for example skin, is transplanted from one animal to another within any inbred strain, the transplanted skin has no antigens that are foreign to those of the animal onto which the skin is transplanted.

The animal that receives the skin graft is of course tolerant to all the proteins of an isologous animal because these are the proteins to which it became tolerant when its own proteins were formed in prenatal life.

**Crossing Inbred Strains.** Next, if a male animal from one inbred strain is mated with a female of the same species but of a different inbred strain, their offspring, called F1 hybrids, will have derived half of their genes from their mothers and half from their fathers. But since all their body cells will contain one *full set of chromosomes* from their mothers and one full set from their fathers, the body cells of the F1 hybrids will have *all* the genes that directed the formation of proteins in both their mothers and their fathers. Hence, tissue from either their mother or their father will not contain any proteins that seem foreign to the F1 hybrids because the F1 hybrids have all the same genes that directed the formation of these proteins in their mother and in their father. Hence, even though the mother and the father come from different inbred strains, their tissues will not be regarded as foreign by their immediate offspring. It should be emphasized here that the above statement holds only for inbred animals. For reasons described a little farther on, the genes of fathers or mothers in anything but inbred strains can be different from those of their immediate offspring, and hence tissue transplanted from mothers or fathers to offspring in anything but inbred strains may contain some foreign antigens.

**Runt and Wasting Disease.** Whereas an F1 hybrid from two inbred strains that receives a transplant from a father or mother will recognize no foreign antigens in the transplant and so permit the transplanted cells to live, the cells of the transplant will find foreign antigens in the host into which it has been transferred. This is because the host (the F1 hybrid) has genes *from both* its father and mother, and so, if the transplant is from the father, the cells of the transplant will find the mother's genes of the hybrid, and the proteins whose formation they control, foreign to it. This can cause trouble for the hybrid, for if the transplant contains any immunologically competent cells (cells which have the ability to become or form immunologically functioning cells), these cells in the transplant will be induced to develop and then react against the host into which they have been transplanted. This is strikingly illustrated if lymphatic tissue from either the mother or the father is injected into an F1 hybrid when it is still young. The F1 hybrid accepts the injected cells and does not react against them, so they continue to grow and differentiate, and as a result, they begin to react immunologically against some of the proteins of their new host (those determined by the genes from the mate of the donor) with the result that cell multiplication and function is so affected in the injected animal that it does not grow properly and is termed a *runt*. If the same experiment is done with older F1 hybrids, at least in rats, the reaction produced by the transplant causes what is termed "wasting disease."

**Lymphocytes as Immunologically Competent Cells.** It was, of course, a problem to know which cells of the lymphatic tissue that is injected into F1 hybrids in experiments such as this were the cells that developed into immunologically functioning cells in their hosts. To see if lymphocytes were immunologically competent cells, Gowans, using inbred rats, collected lymphocytes from the thoracic duct of fathers or mothers of hybrids such as we have described, and injected these into the hybrids and found that wasting disease occurred. Gowans' work, moreover, showed that it was the small lymphocytes of thoracic lymph that were responsible for the production of wasting disease in the hybrids, and labeling experiments which he also performed showed that the small lymphocytes that were injected into the hybrids could form much larger cells which had abundant basophilic cytoplasm, and that this could occur in as short a time as 24 hours.

The result of these and other experiments with the cells of thoracic duct lymph were of course not in accord with a previous and widely held concept to the effect that circulating lymphocytes were end products, incapable of further division or differentiation. Evidence to the effect that blood lymphocytes could divide and differentiate also came from in-vitro experiments.

Lymphocytes, obtained from blood or thoracic lymph, had been much studied in cell cultures through the years. Since they would live for some days in suitable culture fluids, their motility could be investigated by this means (Fig. 12-11). In ordinary cultures they were not observed to divide or differentiate. However, Nowell discovered that the addition of a substance known as phytohemagglutinin to cultures of blood leukocytes caused certain of the leukocytes to undergo mitosis. Which of the blood leukocytes manifested this property was duly investigated by several workers. There was general agreement to the effect that neutrophils, eosinophils and basophils quickly deteriorated in the cultures and hence were not responsible for the mitotic figures that were seen. Moreover, no evidence was found for the division of monocytes in the cultures. It was therefore concluded that it must be the lymphocytes that are stimulated to divide by phytohemagglutinin, and this raised the problem as to whether mitosis occurred only in the much scarcer large lymphocytes (prolymphocytes) or whether mitosis occurred also or even exclusively in the much more numerous small lymphocytes. The evidence available indicates that the number of mitotic figures seen in the cultures could be accounted for only by mitosis occurring in the small lymphocytes. (This is the technic used to obtain representative mitotic figures for making karyotypes of individuals from blood cells as was explained in Chap. 6.)

At first, when it was discovered that phytohemagglutinin would stimulate lymphocytes to divide in vitro, it was thought that phytohemagglutinin must act in some specific way to stimulate mitosis. But then it was noticed that if leukocytes from two different individuals were mixed in a cell culture, the lymphocytes would divide without any phytohemagglutinin being added. It was also noticed that if leukocytes from identical twins were mixed, no mitosis occurred without phytohemagglutinin being added. Finally, it was shown that the factor that stimulated lymphocytes to divide in cultures was an antigen of some sort, for many kinds of macromolecules foreign to the body from which the lymphocytes had been obtained were found to stimulate their division in cell cultures.

All the above described evidence led to the general conclusion that lymphocytes are not end products, as was believed by many in the past, but instead they are capable of both division and differentiation. The present view on this matter is that some or perhaps all circulating small lymphocytes are *immunologically competent cells,* that is, they are *capable* of multiplying and forming cells with immunologic properties. The stimulus required to set a lymphocyte off on this kind of career is an antigen to which it is not tolerant.

It should be mentioned that two widely opposed views had been held about lymphocytes through the years; (1) the view originally espoused by Maximow to the effect that they were mesenchymal cells of such potentiality that they could serve as the mother cells for all kinds of blood cells, and (2) that they were end products. The new work shows that they can divide and become functioning immunologic cells and hence that they are not end products. However, new work shows that their potentiality is more limited than was suggested by Maximow because it has been shown that if thoracic duct lymphocytes or lymphocytes from lymphatic tissues are injected intravenously into animals whose hemopoietic system has been destroyed by radiation, the bone marrow, with its capacity for producing erythrocytes, granular leukocytes and platelets, is not regenerated from lymphocytes.

The above-described evidence indicates that at least some cells that satisfy the morphologic criteria for small lymphocytes can respond to antigens by developing into cells that exert immunologic functions. The question of whether or not they can serve as precursor cells of the plasma cell series, that produce and secrete circulating antibody, will be discussed in Chapter 15. Here we shall discuss how they develop into cells that act immunologically in a somewhat different way from that of secreting circulating antibody. In order to examine this matter we must discuss homograft reactions.

**Lymphocytes, Homografts and the Transplantation of Tissues.** The transplantation of tissue from one site to another in the same individual (autogenous transplantation) is a common surgical procedure. This practice involves certain technical problems as will now be described.

First, in transplanting tissue from one part of the body to another in the same individual,

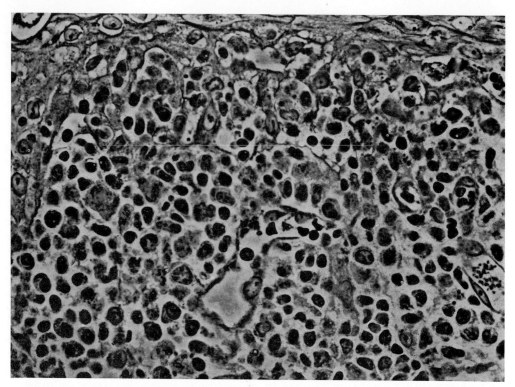

Fig. 12-13. Phase contrast photomicrograph of section of site of implantation of homograft of epidermis in a rabbit. The transplanted epidermis can be seen extending across the top of the picture. The bed of the transplant which is host tissue is heavily infiltrated with mononuclear cells, many of which have pyroninophilic cytoplasm and are graft rejection cells. Some of the latter have infiltrated into the epidermal transplant. This picture illustrates what is known as a homograft reaction. (Weiner, Joseph, Spiro, David, and Russel, P. S.: Am. J. Path. *44*:319)

the main problem is that of ensuring that the cells of the transplanted tissue will be adequately nourished in their new position and live so that the transplant will become a true graft that "takes." Provided that tissue is permeable, thin slices or bits of it can be transplanted to a new position with some confidence that the cells of the transplant will be nourished by means of diffusion mechanisms operating through tissue fluid long enough for the transplant to become vascularized. The vascularization of a transplant can be accomplished by new capillaries growing into it or by means of blood vessels in the transplant becoming connected to capillaries in the bed of the graft. Illustrations showing that the blood vessels of transplanted skin grafts become connected with capillaries in the bed of the graft and used again are shown in Chapter 23 in connection with the discussion

there on skin grafts. Secondly, if attempts are made to transplant large amounts of tissue, for example an organ, there is no hope of the transplanted tissue living by means of diffusion mechanisms until it is vascularized. Accordingly, if organs are transplanted, the blood vessels of the organ must be connected surgically and immediately to blood vessels at the site to which the organ is transplanted. When this is done successfully, as it can be, the cells of the transplanted organ can live because they receive nourishment from the blood circulating in capillaries just as it did in its former position.

Transplants that are made from one part of the body to another part of the same individual are termed autologous or autogenous (*auto* = self) transplants. Since autologous transplants do not induce immunologic responses, they are widely used with success.

However, the scope of tissue transplantation would be much greater if it were possible to transplant tissues and organs from one person to another, and this involves immunologic problems, except in the instance of identical twins, as will now be described.

It has been observed already that as a result of random breeding, the DNA molecules that dictate the arrangements of amino acids in protein molecules are slightly different in different individuals of the same species. As was explained earlier in connection with our discussion of lymphocytes, it is possible by means of inbreeding over many generations to rear strains of experimental animals which for all practical purposes are identical, and in such strains it is possible to transplant tissue from one (isologous) animal to another without invoking immunologic reactions. It is also possible to cross males and females from two *different* inbred strains and transplant tissue from either the mother or the father to the offspring (without the host reacting against the transplant) because, as was explained earlier in this section on lymphocytes, the F1 hybrids possess all the genes of both their father and their mother so that the hybrids, on receiving a transplant from either the father or the mother, recognize no new proteins and hence do not react against the transplant; as has been explained, however, cells of the transplant may react against the host. If the father and the mother are not derived from inbred strains, the offspring of a mating will not necessarily possess all the genes that are possessed by the father or the mother, and, moreover, the genes in different offspring will be different from those of their brothers and sisters. Accordingly, there is no assurance in man that transplants from a mother or a father to an offspring or from one offspring to another will not invoke immunologic reactions in their hosts. Because of this heterogeneity, attempts to transplant tissue from one individual to another in man are almost always unsuccessful because the transplants contain macromolecules that are different from those of the host, and the host reacts against them by means of what is termed a *homograft reaction* (*homos* = same [species]).

The homograft reaction is commonly studied in transplants of skin. Skin transplanted from one individual to another in anything but an isologous situation lives for a short time by means of diffusion phenomena. But after several days the bed of the transplant and the transplant itself both become infiltrated with cells, many of which demonstrate pyroninophilic cytoplasm (Fig. 12-13). Such cells, because they have pyroninophilic cytoplasm, differ from ordinary lymphocytes (or monocytes) and yet, even though they have pyroninophilic cytoplasm, they do not have enough to present the typical appearance of plasma cells. They have recently been studied with the EM by Wiener, Spiro and Russel who term them *graft rejection cells.* In contrast with plasma cells, the EM appearance of which is characterized by an abundance of rough-surfaced vesicles, the basophilia of the graft rejection cells was found to be due to a profusion of free ribosomes (Fig. 12-14). Few rough-surfaced vesicles were found in the cytoplasm of graft rejection cells.

Cytoplasmic basophilia due to free ribosomes could be interpreted in two ways. First, it might be thought that after acquiring an abundance of free ribosomes the cell would subsequently develop membranous vesicles on which the ribosomes would take up residence and as a result the cell would become a plasma cell. In other words, it might be thought that graft rejection cells in due course might become plasma cells and *secrete* antibody. On the other hand, they may represent a different line of cells from plasma cells, being specialized, not to *secrete* antibody that gains entrance to the circulation, but instead to produce antibody of some sort which they do *not* secrete, but which exerts an effect only when the cell is in direct contact with antigen. In support of this view is the fact that the rejection of homotransplants is often accomplished without any antibody to the transplant being detectable in the blood. Therefore, it is very possible that antibody can reach antigens in the body by two different mechanisms: (1) by plasma cells secreting antibody into body fluids by which it is carried to the antigen and (2) by cells of the graft rejection type producing antibody (using the term antibody in a very broad sense); since they lack the facilities for secreting antibody, graft rejection cells have to develop in, or move to, sites

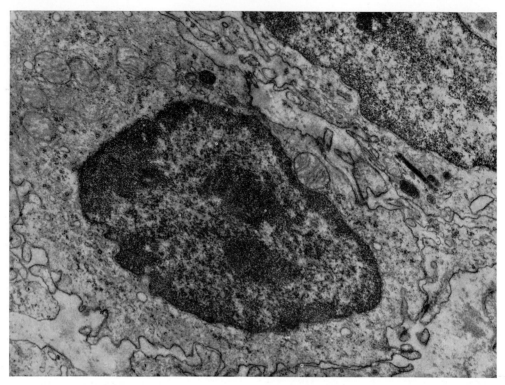

FIG. 12-14. Electron micrograph ($\times$ 20,000) of a graft rejection cell in a homograph reaction. The cytoplasm is characterized by the presence of many free ribosomes. Unlike plasma cells, the cytoplasm contains only a very few rough-surfaced vesicles. (Weiner, Joseph, Spiro, David, and Russel, P. S.: Am. J. Path. 44:319)

of antigen where they come into contact with the antigen and hence apply their product (perhaps by disintegrating) directly to the agent which induced the formation of the product.

At the time of writing, the evidence suggests that at least some of the small lymphocytes of blood or thoracic lymph can serve as the precursors for the formation of graft rejection cells and that the same or other lymphocytes can serve as the precursors for plasmablasts as will be described in Chapter 15. Just how closely graft rejection cells and plasmablasts are related is not yet clear.

Using Lymphocytes to Test for Incompatibilities between Transplants and Hosts. It has been noted already that there is no assurance that the proteins of children born of the same mother and father will be alike. However, they are less likely to be different from one another than the proteins of individuals selected randomly, and, furthermore, it is pos-

sible that one member of a family may have proteins which are almost all represented in another and hence to which the other is tolerant. Recently Brent and Medawar devised a test employing lymphocytes which might provide useful information as to whether or not a given individual will react strongly or weakly to transplants from any other given individual. Lymphocytes from the would-be recipient of a homotransplant are injected into the skin of a would-be donor of a transplant. If the lymphocytes find antigens in the would-be donor, they react (as they would in a homograft reaction) at the site where they were injected, and in due course an immunologic reaction can be detected at this site. If, on the other hand, they find no antigens in the would-be donor, they do not react and this of course indicates that this would-be donor's tissues will at least be much less likely to invoke a homograft response than tissue chosen from a random donor. So far, the test employed on guinea pigs gives helpful information. Experience will show how useful this test or other tests based on the same principle will be in man and how much it or they will contribute to solving some of the present-day problems of homografting.

### Sensitivity of Lymphocytes to Radiation and Radiomimetic Drugs

In discussing the effects of radiation on cells in Chapter 6 it was pointed out that the chief effects of radiation on body cells were observed in those tissues in which there was a rapid turnover of the cell population and that this was due to the fact that radiation damages the hereditary apparatus of the cells in such a way that the cells thereafter either become unable to continue to divide, or if they do continue they may have some hereditary defect due to their DNA having been chemically altered because of ionization produced by the radiation in their DNA molecules. However, the damage that radiation does to lymphocytes in vivo seems to be of an additional kind, and is reflected, not in their remaining alive and becoming unable to divide, but instead by their almost immediately undergoing pyknosis. This effect is produced on lymphocytes by much less radiation than is required to block mitosis in other cell types. Lymphocytes are similarly sensitive to certain drugs whose actions more or less mimic the effects of radiation and which are called radiomimetic drugs. Curiously enough, the adrenal hormone hydrocortisone, which will be described in later chapters, in doses which are not harmful to other cells, likewise brings about the pyknosis of lymphocytes.

### Monocytes

**Numbers.** Monocytes constitute only from 3 to 8 per cent of the leukocytes of normal blood; hence, a student may have to examine a great many leukocytes before a good example of a monocyte is found. A typical monocyte can be distinguished without undue difficulty. However, there are some difficulties associated with deciding whether some cells are monocytes or large lymphocytes and whether others are monocytes or juvenile neutrophils, as will be described.

**Appearance.** Although not all monocytes

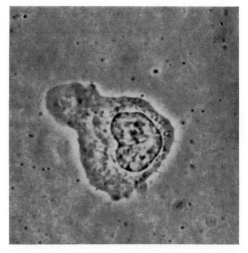

Fig. 12-15. Oil-immersion (phase) photomicrograph of a monoctye in a cell culture. (Preparation by D. M. Whitelaw)

are larger than other kinds of leukocytes, the largest leukocytes seen in blood films are generally monocytes (Fig. 12-3). They are from 12 to 15 microns in diameter when suspended in fluid (Fig. 12-15) and permitted to assume a more or less spherical shape. When they are flattened, as they are in dried films, they measure up to 20 microns in diameter.

The nuclei of monocytes vary from being slightly indented ovals to kidney-shaped structures (Fig. 12-3). In some instances the indentation becomes great enough to give the nucleus a horseshoe-shaped appearance. Sometimes nuclei, particularly of the latter type, appear as if they had been twisted or folded in preparing the film. The chromatin of the nucleus is disposed in a network of granules and flakes; the network is of a finer texture than that in lymphocyte nuclei. The chromatin is colored a blue-violet shade in the usual preparation, and since it is finer and more spread out than that of lymphocytes it does not stain as intensely as that of lymphocytes. Nucleoli are not visible in the usual stained film but can be seen in monocytes examined with the phase microscope. There are often two in each nucleus.

The cytoplasm of monocytes is relatively abundant; it comprises the larger part of the cell. In blood films it is colored a pale gray-blue (Fig. 12-3). Fine lilac granules are sometimes present in the cytoplasm of mono-

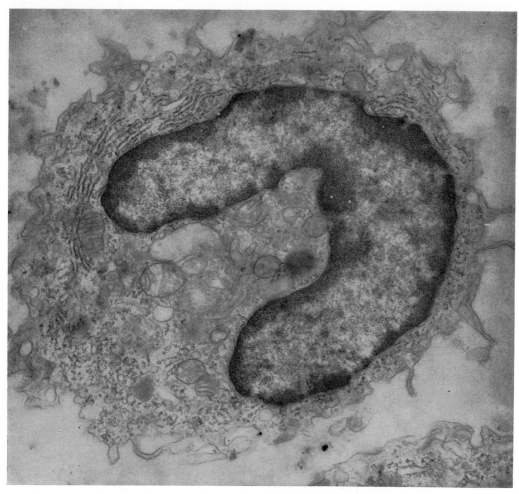

Fig. 12-16. Electron micrograph (approximately $\times$ 18,000 as printed) of a monocyte. Note the horseshoe-shaped nucleus. Some distended vesicles of the Golgi apparatus and some mitochondria can be seen in the concavity of the nucleus. The cytoplasm above the nucleus shows some flattened rough-surfaced vesicles of endoplasmic reticiulum. The ragged cytoplasmic border is a feature of monocytes. (Preparation by H. Z. Movat)

cytes (Fig. 12-3). These are called azurophilic granules because they have an affinity for the methylene azure of blood stains.

**Monocytes Are Motile Cells.** One feature of their motility is their ability to extend from and withdraw to their ordinary boundaries, pseudopodia of cytoplasm. With supravital staining technics, which have been used extensively in the study of monocytes, a rosette can be demonstrated surrounding the centrosome. This rosette is due to vacuoles concentrating the supravital stain, and it occupies the same position as the Golgi apparatus when this is demonstrated by other means.

The rosette made visible with vital staining is not specific for the monocyte: a few other kinds of cells may reveal the same appearance if treated by the same technic.

**Fine Structure.** A well-developed monocyte has a horseshoe-shaped nucleus (Fig. 12-16). Sections prepared for electron microscopy are of course so thin that they may miss nucleoli; monocyte nuclei generally have one or two, but none is seen in this illustration. A prominent feature of the monocyte in this illustration is dilated vesicles of the Golgi apparatus which are seen in the concavity of the cytoplasm that fills the nuclear border.

Flattened rough-surfaced vesicles of endoplasmic reticulum are seen to advantage on the left side of the illustration. The mitochondria are not particularly numerous. A few dark bodies about the size of the smaller mitochondria are present in the cytoplasm; these may be lysosomes. It is to be observed that the edge of the monocyte is very ragged because of the pseudopodia extending out from it.

**Function and Length of Life.** The monocyte generally is regarded as a young cell that reaches its full development and attains its full capacity for function only when it leaves the bloodstream and enters the tissues. In the tissues it develops into a somewhat larger cell which has great phagocytic powers. The larger cell generally is known as a macrophage, but it has many other names. Macrophages have been discussed in detail in Chapter 11. Perhaps it should be pointed out here that the macrophages of connective tissue do not all develop from monocytes, for a certain number are born in, and remain as residents of, connective tissue. However, monocytes provide an easily mobilized force of cells that can be easily marshalled from the bloodstream, in any tissue where more macrophages are needed, and in that tissue they develop into macrophages. It seems very probable that monocytes can also serve as a source of fibroblasts, as was described in connection with a hematogenous source of fibroblasts.

The length of time that monocytes stay in the bloodstream is not known.

**Origin of Monocytes.** There is much uncertainty about the origin of monocytes. There is one widely held view to the effect that all transition forms between lymphocytes and monocytes can be found in normal blood, and hence that monocytes develop from lymphocytes. However, there is much evidence that monocyte production and lymphocyte production represent proliferative activity along two different cell lineages. One view that has been suggested is that macrophages and reticuloendothelial cells can serve as stem cells for monocytes, but this seems improbable. Another view widely held by clinical hematologists is that there are stem cells called monoblasts which develop particularly in the spleen and the bone marrow and which serve as mother cells for the production of monocytes.

We shall postpone further discussion of the origin of the various leukocytes until we have considered myeloid tissue.

## SOME PROBLEMS ASSOCIATED WITH IDENTIFYING CERTAIN LEUKOCYTES SEEN IN A BLOOD FILM

We shall discuss first some simple problems that are likely to bother a beginner.

Two have been mentioned already. The student should learn to identify platelets and so learn to distinguish between clumps of platelets and leukocytes. The student also should be aware of the fact that platelets sometimes are superimposed on erythrocytes or even on leukocytes.

The beginner should pay no attention to degenerating or distorted leukocytes. Indeed, at first, the student should pay no attention to any leukocytes that do not closely resemble those seen in good illustrations.

A common mistake made by beginners who are eager to see an eosinophil is that of believing a neutrophil whose granules are a little on the pink side to be an eosinophil. Since there are relatively few eosinophils in normal blood the student must be prepared to examine a great many leukocytes before finding one. Once an eosinophil is seen it is easily recognized and seen to be obviously different from a neutrophil because its cytoplasm is literally stuffed with large, orange-red refractile granules, and its nucleus commonly has only 2 lobes. If in doubt about whether any given cell is a neutrophil or an eosinophil, compare it with other neutrophils and with other eosinophils; the latter may take some time.

Students, in their desire to find the elusive basophil, are likely to consider that some degenerating or poorly fixed cell, or even a neutrophil with a bluish tinge to its granules, is a basophil. When a true basophil is found the student will have no doubts, because it has large blue granules that overshadow its relatively pale nucleus. If the student is in doubt about whether or not any cell is an eosinophil or a basophil, the cell, in all likelihood, is neither.

A more serious difficulty is that of deciding whether certain cells are large lymphocytes or monocytes. As already mentioned, there are different schools of thought about the origin of monocytes. One school believes that they are formed from lymphocytes and hence that in blood there are cells that represent all transitions between the two types. If lymphocytes turn into monocytes, it is obvious that some cells will be seen in blood films that are halfway between the two types and hence impossible to classify definitely as one type or the other. Another school of thought about the origin of monocytes subscribes to the view that monocytes arise from a separate stem cell, the monoblast, and hence that lymphocytes and monocytes represent two different but closely related families of cells. Those who follow this school think that it is possible to distinguish large lymphocytes that otherwise resemble monocytes from monocytes by the character of the chromatin network in their nuclei. In lymphocytes this is a coarse network, and in monocytes it is a fine network. It takes experience to make this distinction.

If juvenile neutrophils are present in any numbers in blood—and this does not occur under strictly normal conditions—there may be difficulty in distinguishing them from monocytes that have granular cytoplasm. Here, again, the character of the nuclear chromatic is probably the most helpful guide, for it is of a coarser character in juvenile neutrophils than it is in monocytes. Moreover, the neutrophils have more granules in their cytoplasm than monocytes.

When abnormal blood is studied, as it will be when the student begins clinical work, other difficulties will be encountered, for in certain disease states immature cells of both the erythrocyte and the leukocyte series may be present in blood. To recognize these it is necessary to learn the appearance of the cells that normally are found only in myeloid and lymphatic tissue—the tissues where the mature cells are found. The appearances of these cells will be described in subsequent chapters, and further comment will be made on this matter.

## REFERENCES

GENERAL REFERENCES ON GRANULAR LEUKOCYTES AND INFLAMMATION

The Acute Inflammatory Response, Ann. N. Y. Acad. Sci. *116*(3):747-1084, 1964.
Movat, H. Z., and Fernando, N. V. P.: Acute inflammation. The earliest fine structural changes at the blood-tissue barrier, Lab. Invest. *12*: 895, 1963.

SPECIAL REFERENCES ON GRANULAR LEUKOCYTES
(See also textbooks on hematology.)

Bierman, H. R., Kelly, K. H., and Cordes, F. L.: The sequestration and visceral circulation of leukocytes in man, Ann. N. Y. Acad. Sci. *59*: 850, 1955.
Bunting, C. H.: The polymorphonuclear leucocytes *in* Downey's Handbook of Hematology, vol. 1, p. 159, New York, Hoeber, 1938.
———: Functions of the leucocytes *in* Downey's Handbook of Hematology, vol. 1, p. 437, New York, Hoeber, 1938.
Cohn, Z. A., Hirsch, J. G., and Wiener, E.: The cytoplasmic granules of phagocytic cells and the degradation of bacteria *in* deReuck, A. V. S., and Cameron, M. P. (eds.): Lysosomes, Ciba Foundation Symposium, p. 126, London, Churchill, 1963.
Davidson, W. M., and Smith, D. R.: A morphological sex difference in the polymorphonuclear neutrophil leucocytes, Brit. M. J. *2*:6, 1954.
De Castro, N. M.: Frequency variations of "drumsticks" of peripheral blood neutrophils in the rabbit in different alimentary conditions, Acta anat. *52*:341, 1963.
Garrey, W. E., and Bryan, W. R.: Variations in white blood cell counts, Physiol. Rev. *15*:597, 1935.
Lillie, R. D.: Factors influencing the Romanovsky staining of blood films and the role of methylene violet, J. Lab. Clin. Med. *29*:1181, 1944.
McCutcheon, M.: Chemotaxis and locomotion of leukocytes, Ann. N. Y. Acad. Sci. *59*:941, 1955.
Menkin, V.: Factors concerned in the mobilization of leukocytes in inflammation, Ann. N. Y. Acad. Sci. *59*:956, 1955.
Pease, D. C.: An electron microscopic study of red bone marrow, Blood *11*:501, 1956.
———: Marrow cells seen with the electron microscope after ultrathin sectioning, Rev. hémat. *10*:300, 1955.
Sheldon, H., and Zetterquist, H.: Internal ultrastructure in granules of white blood cells of the mouse; a preliminary note, Bull. Johns Hopkins Hosp. *96*:135, 1955.
Sieracki, J. C.: The neutrophilic leukocyte, Ann. N. Y. Acad. Sci. *59*:690, 1955.
Speirs, R. S.: Physiological approaches to an understanding of the function of eosinophils and basophils, Ann. N. Y. Acad. Sci. *59*:706, 1955.
Valentine, W. N.: The enzymes of leukocytes, Ann. N. Y. Acad. Sci. *59*:1003, 1955.

Visscher, M. B., and Halberg, F.: Daily rhythms in numbers of circulating eosinophils and some related phenomena, Ann. N. Y. Acad. Sci. *59*: 834, 1955.

Wright, C-S., and Dodd, M. C.: Phagocytosis, Ann. N. Y. Acad. Sci. *59*:945, 1955.

REFERENCES ON LYMPHOCYTES AND THEIR FUNCTIONS; ALSO MONOCYTES
(See also references for Chapter 15.)

Anderson, N. F., Delorme, E. J., and Woodruff, F. A.: Induction of runt disease in rats by injection of thoracic duct lymphocytes at birth, Plast. Reconstruct. Surg. *25*:93, 1960.

Bain, B., Vas, M. R., and Lowenstein, L.: The development of large immature mononuclear cells in mixed leucocyte cultures, Blood *23*: 108, 1964.

Carstairs, K.: The human small lymphocyte: its possible pluripotential quality, Lancet, *1*:829, 1962.

Dougherty, T. F.: Adrenal cortical control of lymphatic tissue mass *in* Stohlman, F., Jr. (ed.): The Kinetics of Cellular Proliferation, p. 264, New York, Grune & Stratton, 1959.

Gesner, B. M., and Gowans, J. L.: The fate of lethally irradiated mice given isologous and heterologous thoracic duct lymphocytes, Brit. J. Exp. Path. *43*:431, 1962.

Gowans, J. L.: The recirculation of lymphocytes from blood to lymph in the rat, J. Physiol. *146*: 54, 1959.

————: The life history of the lymphocytes, Brit. M. Bull. *15*:50, 1959.

————: The fate of parental strain small lymphocytes in F1 hybrid rats, Ann. N. Y. Acad. Sci. *99*:432, 1962.

Gowans, J. L., McGregor, D. D., and Cowen, D. M.: The role of small lymphocytes in the rejection of homografts of skin *in* Wolstenholme, G. E., and Knight, Julie (eds.): The Immunologically Competent Cell, Ciba Foundation Study Group #16, p. 20, London, Churchill, 1963.

Humphrey, J. H., and White, R. G.: Immunology for Students of Medicine, ed. 2, Oxford, Blackwell, 1964.

Little, J. R., Brecher, G., Bradley, T. R., and Rose, S.: Determination of lymphocyte turnover by continuous infusion of tritiated thymidine, Blood *19*:236, 1962.

Marshall, W. H., and Roberts, K. B.: The growth and mitosis of human small lymphocytes after incubation with a phytohemagglutinin, Quart. J. Exp. Physiol. *48*:146, 1963.

McKinney, A. A., Jr., Stohlman, F., Jr., and Brecher, G.: The kinetics of cell proliferation in cultures of human peripheral blood, Blood *19*:359, 1962.

Najarian, J. S., and Feldman, J. D.: Passive transfer of tuberculin sensitivity by tritiated thymidine-labeled lymphoid cells, J. Exp. Med. *114*:779, 1961.

Nowell, P. C.: Phytohemagglutinin: an initiator of mitosis in cultures of normal human leukocytes, Cancer Res. *20*:462, 1960.

Pulvertaft, R. J. V.: Cellular associations in normal and abnormal lymphocytes, Proc. Roy. Soc. Med. *52*:315, 1959.

Rebuck, J. W., and Crowley, J. H.: A method of studying leukocytic functions *in vivo*, Ann. N. Y. Acad. Sci. *59*:757, 1955.

Rosenau, W., and Moon, H.: Lysis of homologous cells by sensitized lymphocytes in tissue culture, J. Nat. Cancer Inst. *27*:471, 1961.

Schooley, J. C.: Preliminary autoradiographic observations of cellular proliferation in lymphoid tissues, using tritiated thymidine *in* Stohlman, F., Jr. (ed.): The Kinetics of Cellular Proliferation, p. 208, New York, Grune & Stratton, 1959.

Schreck, R.: Radiation effects on lymphocytes *in* Rebuck, J. W. (ed.): The Lymphocyte and Lymphocytic Tissue, p. 125, New York, Hoeber, 1960.

Shelton, E.: Prolonged survival of rabbit thoracic duct lymphocytes in a diffusion chamber, J. Cell Biol. *12*:652, 1962.

Tompkins, E. H.: The monocyte, Ann. N. Y. Acad. Sci. *59*:732, 1955.

Trowell, O. A.: The sensitivity of lymphocytes to ionizing radiation, J. Path. Bact. *64*:687, 1952.

Wiener, J., Spiro, D., and Russell, P. S.: An electron microscopy study of the homograft reaction, Am. J. Path. *44*:319, 1964.

Wolstenholme, G. E., and Knight, Julie (eds.): The Immunologically Competent Cell, Ciba Foundation Study Group #16, London, Churchill, 1963.

Yoffey, J. M., and Courtice, F. C.: Lymphatics, Lymph and Lymphoid Tissue, Cambridge, Mass., Harvard Univ. Press, 1956.

REFERENCES REGARDING IMMUNOLOGIC PROBLEMS RELATING TO THE TRANSPLANTATION OF TISSUES

Since 1953 there has been a journal, the *Transplantation Bulletin*, which is devoted to the subject of tissue transplantation; it is published regularly. As well as publishing articles on the subject, this journal, from time to time, publishes extensive bibliographies of articles relating to the transplantation of different tissues.

Billingham, R. E., and Brent, L.: Quantitative studies on tissue transplantation immunity. IV. Induction of tolerance in newborn mice and studies on the phenomenon of runt disease, Phil. Trans. Roy. Soc. London, ser. B *242*:439, 1959.

Converse, J. M. (ed.): Second tissue homotransplantation conference, Ann. N. Y. Acad. Sci. *64*:735-1073, 1957.

————: Fourth tissue homotransplantation conference, Ann. N. Y. Acad. Sci. *87*:1-607, 1960.

Humphrey, J. H., and White, R. G.: Immunology for Students of Medicine, ed. 2, Oxford, Blackwell, 1964.

Medawar, P. B.: Zoologic laws of transplantation *in* Peer, L. A. (ed.): Transplantation of Tissues, vol. 2, p. 41, Baltimore, Williams & Wilkins, 1959.

Merrill, J. P.: Transplantation of normal tissues, Physiol. Rev. *39*:860, 1959.

Peer, L. A.: Transplantation of Tissue, vols. 1 and 2, Baltimore, Williams & Wilkins, 1955, 1959.

Rogers, B. O. (ed.): The relation of immunology to tissue homotransplantation, Ann. N. Y. Acad. Sci. *59*:277-466, 1955.

————: Third tissue homotransplantation conference, Ann. N. Y. Acad. Sci. *73*:539-868, 1958.

————: Fifth tissue homotransplantation conference, Ann. N. Y. Acad. Sci. *99*:335, 1962.

Wiener, J., Spiro, D., and Russell, P. S.: An electron microscopy study of the homograft reaction, Am. J. Path. *44*:319, 1964.

# 13  The Cells of Blood

## (Continued)

### RED BLOOD CELLS (ERYTHROCYTES)

Erythrocytes are from 500 to 1,000 times more numerous in blood than leukocytes.

**Shape.** The normal shape of the human erythrocyte is that of a *biconcave disk* (Fig. 13-1). The animal kingdom presents examples of other shapes. In certain diseases, human erythrocytes of altered shape make their appearance in the circulation (Fig. 13-2, *right*); hence, the determination of the shape of erythrocytes in any given sample of blood is of diagnostic importance.

As will be noted later, there probably is no supporting structural framework inside the erythrocyte to explain its shape, which, therefore, is determined and maintained by other factors. One is probably the molecular constitution of the material in its interior, because when this is abnormal, cells of different shapes are seen. Another is the composition of the fluid in which the cell is suspended, for certain changes in the fluid may lead to the erythrocyte becoming spherical, as will be discussed in more detail when the behavior of erythrocytes in solutions of different osmotic pressure is considered.

**Size.** The diameter of erythrocytes usually is determined by spreading a drop of blood on a glass slide (this is called making a blood film) (Fig. 12-1) and then measuring the dried cells under high magnification by means of a micrometer eyepiece. Dried cells may not be of exactly the same diameter as cells suspended in plasma, but any difference in size is probably not great. If blood is normal the erythrocytes in a film are of an almost uniform diameter, not differing from one another by more than 1 $\mu$ (Fig. 13-4). If the size of each is ticked off on a properly prepared piece of graph paper it will be found that the greatest number are 7.2 $\mu$ wide and that almost all are within half a micron of this either way. If the sizes seen in a large sample are all indicated on graph paper, a curve can be drawn which shows at a glance whether the size range is normal, or whether the size of the cells as a whole is greater or less than normal, or whether the size range within the sample is greater than it should be. Such a curve is called a Price-Jones curve.

Cells smaller than 6 $\mu$ are termed *microcytes* (*mikros* = small) (Fig. 13-2, *right*). Cells moderately larger than the normal, from 9 to 12 $\mu$, are termed *macrocytes* (*makros* = large) (Fig. 13-5, *right*). The shift in size that occurs in certain blood diseases is usually either to the smaller or the larger side; when the average is smaller, the condition is termed *microcytic* (Fig. 13-5, *left*), when larger *macrocytic* (Fig. 13-5, *right*). In some conditions, both microcytes and macrocytes may be present (Fig. 13-2, *right*).

**Structure and Composition.** From the evidence that is available, it does not seem likely that there is any supporting framework within the erythrocyte other than that provided by the molecular constitution of the colloidal complex with which it is filled. This results in the cell being soft and elastic.

More than half of the erythrocyte consists of water (60%), the rest of solids. About 33 per cent of the erythrocyte is the conjugated protein hemoglobin. This is said to be a conjugated protein because it consists of the protein *globin* joined to the pigment *heme*. Although only 4 per cent of hemoglobin actually consists of pigment (heme), its combination with globin results in the combined entity (hemoglobin) being colored; hence, hemoglobin is spoken of as a pigment. A little other protein and some fatty material also exist in the cell along with hemoglobin.

It may seem curious that erythrocytes containing only a soft jelly would maintain their biconcave shape, and that the molecular constitution of the jelly could be such as to be an important factor in making the cell assume this shape. However, the fact is that a change in the chemical constitution of hemoglobin can be responsible for the cells taking on a differ-

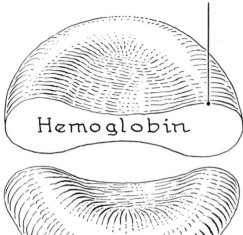

Plasma membrane

Hemoglobin

FIG. 13-1. Diagram of a red blood corpuscle that has been cut in half.

ent shape. For example, there is a curious disease in which the erythrocytes may assume the form of sickles. In this form they are destroyed easily, and so individuals with this disease do not have enough erythrocytes. For many years no one knew what was responsible for the altered form of these cells. In 1949, however, Pauling and his colleagues discovered that the hemoglobin in them was of a slightly different composition from the normal, but the difference was sufficient to make the cells assume a shape different from that of biconcave disks. Hereditary factors are responsible for the condition; hence, this disease provides an example of how an altered sequence in a DNA molecule which results in one amino acid being substituted for the usual one in the hemoglobin molecule can cause a disease.

The substance of the erythrocyte is somewhat modified at its periphery to constitute the *cell* or *plasma membrane*. This is believed to be a lipoid-protein complex. Although its thickness is to be measured in molecules (it is therefore invisible with the light microscope), it normally acts to prevent the escape of the colloidal material of the cell into the plasma. It also exhibits great selectivity with regard to the passage of ions.

**Behavior in Solutions of Different Osmotic**

Pressure. The osmotic pressure of plasma equals that of erythrocytes, and so plasma is said to be *isotonic* (*iso* = equal; *tonos* = tension) with regard to them. In plasma, then, there is no tendency for either the erythrocytes or the plasma to absorb water from each other. It is possible to prepare saline solutions that are isotonic with erythrocytes. If the salt concentration of a saline solution is below that of erythrocytes, it is said to be *hypotonic* (*hypo* = under); if above it, *hypertonic* (*hyper* = above, over).

Erythrocytes respond in somewhat different ways to the kind of solution in which they are immersed.

First, it already has been explained that the molecular structure of hemoglobin is an important factor in determining the biconcave shape of the cell. However, another factor is the nature, as well as the osmotic pressure, of the solution in which the cell is bathed. For example, if erythrocytes are washed and suspended in physiologic saline solution, they become spheres and extend little projections out from them. The biconcave disk form can be restored to such cells by resuspending them in plasma or certain other solutions which are said to possess antisphering properties. Apparently, then, the molecular constitution of hemoglobin needs the help of certain substances which have some effect on the cell surface to bring about and maintain the biconcave shape of erythrocytes.

Secondly, erythrocytes can be shrunken or expanded by varying the osmotic pressure of the solution in which they are suspended. Erythrocytes are fairly resistant to slight changes in the osmotic pressure, but if the solution in which they are bathed is sufficiently hypotonic, they assume a spherical shape and swell. When they become excessively swollen, another phenomenon occurs: their membranes become incapable of retaining hemoglobin, and this escapes into the surrounding fluid, coloring it. This is known as *hemolysis* (*lysis* = solution). Not all the substance of the erythrocyte escapes when hemolysis occurs; enough remains to leave a "shadow" or "ghost" of the cell.

Hemolysis can be induced by means other than hypotonic solutions. Certain chemicals, particularly lipoid solvents, exert a hemolytic effect. Snake venom is a hemolytic agent. The

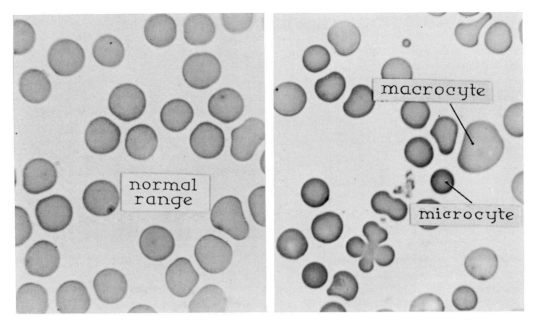

Fig. 13-2. Oil-immersion photomicrographs of stained films of rabbit's blood. (*Left*) Normal blood with the cells varying in size only slightly and, except where they have been pressed upon by other cells in the film, having a normal shape. (*Right*) Blood that was obtained from an animal with TNT poisoning. It shows a great range in the size of the red blood cells, with both microcytes and macrocytes present. It also shows red blood cells of different shapes.

plasma of some species hemolyzes the erythrocytes of others.

The erythrocytes in any given sample of blood are not equally susceptible to hemolysis. For instance, a solution of saline may be prepared of such concentration that it will hemolyze only some cells; for all to be hemolyzed, the strength of the solution must be reduced further. Hence, erythrocytes are said to vary with regard to their *fragility* (their susceptibility to hemolysis). The fragility of erythrocytes becomes altered in certain diseases; hence, fragility tests are of use in diagnosis.

If erythrocytes are immersed in a hypertonic solution, water is drawn from them into the solution. This results in the shrinkage of the erythrocytes and, as they shrink irregularly so that their outlines contain notches and indentations, they are said to be *crenated* (*crena* = a notch).

**Function.** Respiration is the basic metabolic process of life. For it to proceed without fatal interruption, the cells of the body require a continuous and substantial supply of oxygen. This is brought to them from the lungs by the blood in the circulatory system.

Oxygen does not dissolve to any great extent in water, or even in plasma. Hence, if the circulatory system contained only plasma, only a small fraction of the amount of oxygen needed by the cells of the body would dissolve into it as it passed through the lungs. To develop the great avidity that blood has for oxygen, Nature was forced to evolve a mechanism employing some other principle than that on which the ordinary solution of gases in fluids depends. This was accomplished by adding the protein hemoglobin to blood (within the erythrocytes).

Hemoglobin has the very important attribute of being able to combine with oxygen to form the compound *oxyhemoglobin*. A solution of hemoglobin, then, can continue to absorb oxygen until the hemoglobin it contains is converted into oxyhemoglobin, and this, of course, permits much more oxygen to be taken up than could be absorbed by blood plasma alone.

Hemoglobin, fortunately, is, in a sense, fickle in its liking for oxygen. In the lungs, where the oxygen tension (concentration) is high because of fresh air being constantly provided by the respiratory system, hemoglobin combines with oxygen avidly. But when oxygenated blood reaches the various tissues of the body, where the cells are constantly using oxygen so that its tension is low, hemoglobin releases a good part of its oxygen. When oxygen is thus divorced from oxyhemoglobin, the hemoglobin that remains is usually called *reduced hemoglobin* and this, on reaching the lungs, as it continues on its route through the circulatory system is, therefore, prepared to unite with oxygen and become oxyhemoglobin again.

## WHY HEMOGLOBIN IS CONFINED INSIDE ERYTHROCYTES

It is interesting to consider why hemoglobin is confined within the erythrocytes instead of being contained free in the plasma. Although hemoglobin is a protein, and in the nature of a colloid, it is not restrained by the endothelial membranes of the blood-vascular system to the same extent as the other colloids in the blood. Hence, when it is free, it escapes into the tissues and into the urine. This state of affairs occurs in "red-water fever," a disease of cattle in which a minute parasite invades the erythrocytes and so injures them that their hemoglobin escapes first into the plasma and then into the urine, which becomes colored sufficiently to justify the name of the disease. In certain human diseases, for example in "black water fever" which is a virulent type of malaria, enough erythrocytes may be injured to produce a like condition.

The cells that contain hemoglobin also have other uses. For example, as well as serving in the carriage of oxygen from the lungs to the tissues, erythrocytes are involved in the carriage of carbon dioxide from the tissues to the lungs. Their use in this respect is dependent on their containing an enzyme, carbonic anhydrase, which, like hemoglobin, is confined within the erythrocyte (and in other cells as well). There are still other advantages in having hemoglobin confined to cells rather than in solution, and these, together with the details of its function in both oxygen and carbon dioxide transport, are best left to be considered in physiology.

**Structure in Relation to Function.** In addition to transporting large amounts of gases, the erythrocytes, to be efficient, must also absorb and release these gases very quickly. The absorption and the release of gases is a surface phenomenon; it occurs at an interface.

Therefore, it is desirable that the interface between each erythrocyte and plasma should be as great as possible per unit of hemoglobin, and this desirable end is obtained by the biconcave form of the erythrocyte. The biconcave shape gives a surface area from 20 to 30 per cent greater than that of a sphere containing the same amount of hemoglobin. Furthermore, if erythrocytes were spheres, the average distance a gas would have to travel to reach the surface from the interior of the cell would be greatly increased. Hence, the biconcave shape is an ideal one for absorbing and releasing gases quickly.

The non-nucleated state of the erythrocyte is advantageous in that it allows the whole cell to contain hemoglobin and so be more efficient per unit volume.

The rounded edges of the erythrocyte protect it from injury, and its resilient elastic structure allows it to bend rather than break as it strikes bifurcations in capillaries. This phenomenon may be watched under the microscope in the web of a living frog's foot, suitably mounted, or in any thin living tissue possessing a good capillary bed and prepared in the same way. However, when examining such a preparation, it should be remembered that the microscope magnifies the speed of erythrocytes as much as it does their size; their movement is not actually as rapid as it seems.

It is the oxyhemoglobin in the erythrocytes in capillaries below the surface that imparts pinkness to cheeks and varying degrees of redness to lips and mucous membranes. The degree of color so imparted depends on many factors: the number of capillaries in operation, their closeness to the surface, the transparency of the overlying tissue and finally, the percentage of oxyhemoglobin in the blood.

Reduced hemoglobin, on the other hand, is blue rather than red. Normally, as blood passes through capillaries, not enough reduced hemoglobin is formed for the blue color to show. But if the oxygenation of blood in the lungs is seriously impaired so that blood containing a considerable amount of reduced hemoglobin is delivered to capillaries or if the circulation through the capillaries is slowed down so that a great deal of reduced hemoglobin forms and is not carried to the lungs fast enough, sufficient of this reduced hemoglobin (absolute amount—not percentage) may be present to impart a blue color to surfaces of the body that are ordinarily pink or red. This is termed *cyanosis* (*kyanos* = blue) and it is often a very important sign when detected on physical examination.

Hemoglobin is adversely affected by certain drugs and chemicals. Nitrites, for example, tend to cause hemoglobin to alter into a compound known as *methemoglobin*, which does not serve as a carrier for oxygen. Consequently, if this altered hemoglobin is present in the blood to too great an extent, there may not be enough hemoglobin left to support life. Moreover, methemoglobin, like reduced hemoglobin, imparts a dusky blue color to tissues, that is, in sufficient amounts it causes cyanosis.

Hemoglobin has a great affinity for certain other gases beside oxygen, most notably carbon monoxide. This gas forms a firm union with hemoglobin and so is not released to the tissues. Hence, a person breathing air containing even a low percentage of it gradually comes to have more and more of his hemoglobin bound to it and, therefore, valueless for the transport of oxygen. Carbon monoxide hemoglobin is a bright-red color, and the cherry-red lips of the carbon monoxide victim, whose tissues are in reality starved for oxygen, provide a sad paradox.

As the ability of the blood to transport oxygen efficiently is often impaired, an examination of the blood to ascertain its ability in this respect forms an important part of every physical examination.

Two of the procedures commonly employed, making an erythrocyte count and estimating the hemoglobin content of blood are learned about rather than learned thoroughly in the usual histology course. One reason for this is that making these tests requires the use of special equipment which students can scarcely be expected to purchase before they approach clinical work more closely. A third procedure, which is of at least equal importance, the preparation, the staining and the examination of a blood film, requires no special instruments and should be learned thoroughly in a histology course. The way this is done has already been described in the previous chapter on leukocytes. A fourth procedure, the making of a reticulocyte count, can also be learned to advantage at this time.

ERYTHROCYTE COUNT

The same principles apply to making an erythrocyte count as apply to making a leukocyte count; these were described in the previous chapter. While the procedures employed are of the same type, they vary in certain respects, chiefly because erythrocytes are so much more numerous in blood than leukocytes. First, the pipette used for diluting blood for an erythrocyte count has a larger bowl so that the measured amount of blood that is drawn up in the pipette can be diluted with a much greater percentage of counting fluid. Secondly, the counting fluid in which the blood cells are diluted is different from that used for making leukocyte counts, and thirdly, counts are made over smaller squares that are ruled on the hemocytometer slide (Fig. 12-2).

Under normal conditions, the blood of women should contain from 4,500,000 to 5,000,000 erythrocytes per cubic millimeter, that of men 5,000,000 to 5,500,000. However, the method employed in making the count is open to experimental error on many sides; hence, a blood count should always be read with a mental plus or minus reservation, the extent of which should bear a relation to the skill and the experience of the counter. Even under the best of circumstances the experimental error is considerable. For this reason, clinical hematologists commonly depend more on hemoglobin determinations, the examination of blood films, and reticulocyte counts for making diagnoses than they do on erythrocyte counts.

There is some evidence to suggest that counts made from blood obtained from different parts of the body differ and that the normal count varies somewhat throughout the day; it becomes increased after exercise and is somewhat higher in the newborn. The normal erythrocyte count of those who live in high altitudes is greater than that given above; less oxygen in the air is reflected by increased facilities for its absorption and transport.

**Hemoglobin Content.** This may be determined with different degrees of accuracy by several methods. Commonly, it is done by the use of the principle of colorimetry. This method, which is widely used clinically, involves the comparison of the color of blood with the color of a standard. Such a method is applicable when the color of a substance (for example, the hemoglobin in blood) changes in proportion to its concentration. As the amount of hemoglobin in blood becomes decreased or increased the color of the blood changes but its brick-red color is difficult to match. For this reason, blood is usually treated with acid to change its hemoglobin into acid hematin, which is of a reddish-brown color, much easier to match accurately. Similarly, stable pigments which can be readily matched can be produced by alkalies, carbon-monoxide, cyanide and other chemicals. The cyanmethemoglobin method is now very much in favor in clinical laboratories in hospitals. In all these methods the color is compared with a standard, either by diluting the solution until it matches the standard when compared visually or by the use of a fixed dilution, which is examined in a photoelectric colorimeter. From the readings obtained it is easy to calculate the amount of hemoglobin that was present in the original sample of blood. Normal blood is said to contain about 15 Gm. of hemoglobin per 100 ml. In the past, hemoglobin estimations were often given in percentages, but here again it is best to deal in absolute numbers.

**Anemia.** If the amount of hemoglobin in circulating blood is reduced so that oxygen transport is impaired, the condition is said to constitute anemia (without blood). And, although the erythrocyte count and the hemoglobin estimation are of great importance in allowing the diagnosis of an anemia, it is difficult to assert just how great a reduction in either justifies the diagnosis.

There are different causes for anemia, and so there is some justification for saying that there are different kinds of anemia. An examination of the blood by erythrocyte counts, hemoglobin estimation and stained films are all of the greatest importance in establishing the type and the cause of any particular example of the condition. Until the cause is known, rational treatment cannot be given. The investigation of anemia is a clinical problem, which the student will encounter later in his medical course. It is helpful if a few facts learned in histology are remembered well. These are:

Erythrocytes, although in most ways admirably suited to their purpose, are not very substantially constructed. Hence, they disintegrate after a certain length of time. There is a general but not precise agreement on their exact length of service in the bloodstream, for different technics used to determine their life span give figures from 100 to 120 days. A common method for estimating their length of life is to remove some erythrocytes from an individual, label them with some radioactive material and then reinject them into the same individual and follow their length of life by technics which pick up their radioactivity. Another method hinges on the fact that erythrocytes of one individual may sometimes be sufficiently similar to those of another to permit them to live a normal life when they are injected into the bloodstream of the other individual, and yet in this other individual they may retain certain specific properties by which they can be identified by agglutination tests. This latter technic, which does not require labeling the cells with radioactive material, indicates that their life span is about 120 days. After erythrocytes have lived their lives in the circulatory system they must be removed from it to prevent their disintegrating bodies from cluttering up the circulatory system. Worn-out erythrocytes are removed from the bloodstream by certain phagocytic cells in the spleen, the bone marrow and the liver. The details of this process will be presented in later chapters.

It is obvious, of course, that if erythrocytes were constantly removed from the circulation, their numbers in the blood would steadily fall if new ones were not delivered into the blood at a corresponding rate. Indeed, the erythrocyte count must progressively fall or rise if the rate of their removal from blood is not in harmony with the rate of their liberation into blood. Furthermore, a little thought makes it apparent that the erythrocyte count need not be normal just because the rate of their removal from blood equals the rate of their liberation into blood. Such a circumstance would ensure that the count remained stationary, but it might remain stationary with only 2 million instead of 5 million erythrocytes per cubic milliliter of blood. Hence, a normal content of erythrocytes depends on the *level* at which the two processes of removal and liberation come into balance.

It is now easily seen that an anemia could occur as a result of a disturbance of either the rate of removal of erythrocytes from blood or the rate of their liberation into it. In other words, some anemias are due primarily to an increased rate of erythrocyte destruction or loss from the body; others, to a deficient rate of production.

In order to obtain information on either the rate of erythrocyte production or the rate of erythrocyte destruction, further tests must be made. Only the one that deals with the rate of their production will be considered at this time.

If a normal blood film, stained with a neutral blood stain, is examined with the oil-immersion objective, it will be seen that almost all the erythrocytes are of a clear pink color; they are acidophilic. But an occasional erythrocyte—anywhere from 1 out of 100 to 1 out of 1,000—will be slightly different in that, while fundamentally pink, it demonstrates a blue tinge. Such an erythrocyte is said to demonstrate basophilia and to be a *polychromatophilic erythrocyte* (Fig. 12-3) for reasons previously given.

From time to time it was argued that the basophilia of these cells indicated degeneration. This view is no longer accepted. Instead, it is agreed that basophilia in erythrocytes is a sign of youth. The reason for this will now be explained.

The bone marrow cells that give rise to erythrocytes are of a rapidly growing undifferentiated type and, like other cells of this type, they have enough RNA in their cytoplasm to make it basophilic. Normally, the mother cells divide so many times before they become erythrocytes, their cytoplasmic RNA nucleoprotein becomes so divided up that it is lost. But when there is an increased need for erythrocytes, some of the mother cells become erythrocytes before their cytoplasmic RNA is lost, and the erythrocytes that are formed this way are polychromatophilic.

Polychromatophilic erythrocytes in which basophilia is not very pronounced, so that they are only very faintly blue, are extremely difficult to identify in blood films stained with ordinary neutral blood stains. However, there is another way in which preparations may be made to show them much more distinctly. This is done by utilizing the supravital staining method. The dye used is brilliant cresyl blue. This may be employed in several ways but, in our experience, best results are obtained by preparing it in a 1 per cent aqueous solution to which 0.04 per cent potassium oxalate is added. A drop of this is placed in a freshly scooped-out, bowl-shaped depression in a block of paraffin wax and to this a drop of fresh blood, taken with a pipette from a puncture, is added. Another way of doing this is by means of mixing the solution of dye with blood in a pipette or test tube. After thorough mixing, a small drop is then put on a glass slide, and a film is made in the usual manner. Although the polychromatophilic erythrocytes are already stained by the cresyl blue, the film may then be stained with an ordinary neutral blood stain to color the other cells present.

Brilliant cresyl blue reacts with the newborn erythrocyte in freshly drawn and, as yet undried or otherwise affected blood, in a very curious manner: it appears to coagulate and concentrate the basophilic material previously spread through the cell so that this material comes to appear as a threadlike blue structure which, if abundant, may assume the form of a wreath or, if scanty, no more than scattered blue dots (Fig. 13-3). Because of this threadlike network, which was first thought to represent the staining of a previously existing reticular network inside the cell, the cells exhibiting it were termed *reticulocytes*. This name still persists even though it is generally agreed, first, that the network is an artefact due to cresyl blue coagulating and concentrating the basophilic material of the cells, and, secondly, that the reticulocyte is the same cell that would be termed a polychromatophilic erythrocyte if it were stained with an ordinary blood stain (Fig. 12-3).

By determining the percentage of reticulocytes among erythrocytes in a blood film, evidence can be obtained about the rate of erythrocyte production. Under normal conditions, 0.5 to 1.5 per cent of erythrocytes are reticulocytes (40,000—120,000 per cu. mm.).

Although some erythrocytes are born with basophilic material in them, it soon fades away. Exactly how long it lasts has been estimated by different procedures with different results; our experience, derived from making day-to-day reticulocyte counts on animals whose counts were falling from as high as 40

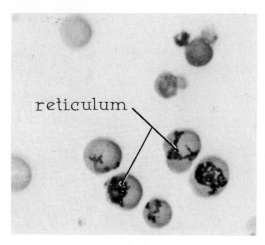

FIG. 13-3. Oil-immersion photomicrograph of a blood film stained with brilliant cresyl blue to show the so-called reticulum of the reticulocytes. The blood used was obtained from an animal which was regenerating large numbers of new erythrocytes.

per cent, is in agreement with those estimates that put the time at one day or, at most, a very few days. Therefore, young reticulocytes show more reticulum than older reticulocytes; however, old reticulocytes are still very young erythrocytes. It is likely that only some erythrocytes, released into the circulation, are released as reticulocytes. Probably under normal conditions many mature and so lose their basophilic material in the bone marrow before they are released into the circulation. But when erythrocyte production is increased, there is a tendency for the bone marrow to liberate erythrocytes in a less mature state than usual, so probably both the fact that more erythrocytes are being made and the fact that more of these are released as reticulocytes contribute to the increased percentage of reticulocytes when erythrocyte production is increased.

Under otherwise normal circumstances, any condition that causes an increased rate of erythrocyte destruction (or loss by hemorrhage) is compensated for, to at least some extent, by an increase in the rate of erythrocyte production. So if, for example, the reticulocyte count remains high day after day with no increase in the total number of erythrocytes in blood, it can be assumed that the rate of destruction is increased or that erythrocytes are being lost from the circulation in some

other fashion. In other words, the reticulocyte count can often be used to deduce information about the rate of erythrocyte destruction or loss.

Although anemias are generally caused by the reduced production or the increased destruction of erythrocytes, it is usual to classify them according to the appearance of the erythrocytes in stained films. For example, sooner or later the student must learn to examine a blood film and say whether it indicates a *hypochromic microcytic anemia* or a *macrocytic anemia* or some other kind designated by this type of terminology. What do these terms mean?

Macrocytes and microcytes have already been defined. If, in any anemia, the erythrocytes tend to be substantially larger than normal, the anemia is said to be macrocytic; if they tend to be smaller than normal, microcytic; and if of normal size, normocytic. The terms "hyperchromic," "normochromic" and "hypochromic" require a more detailed explanation.

As the erythrocyte is a biconcave disk, it is thinner in its central portion than at its periphery. When stained and viewed from above, as is done when a dried film is examined under the microscope, the thinness of its central portion is manifested by lighter staining than that which characterizes the peripheral zone of the cell (Fig. 13-4, *left*). Indeed, if the *proper part of a properly made film* is examined, the normal erythrocyte is seen to contain a central clear area that merges insensibly into the deeper-staining peripheral zone of the cell. In our experience, however, this clear portion is not to be seen in areas on a film where the erythrocytes are spread too thinly (Fig. 13-4, *right*). It is best seen in areas where they are spread fairly thinly but not so thinly that at least occasional cells are not superimposed on others (Fig. 13-4, *left*).

If the central pale area is not wider than a third, or slightly more, of the diameter of the erythrocyte and if the peripheral zone of the cell stains reasonably well, the erythrocytes are said to be *normochromic* (normal color) (Fig. 13-5, *center*). Some anemias are characterized by a reduction in the number of erythrocytes, but such cells as are present are normochromic; hence, they are said to be *normochromic anemias*. However, in a much

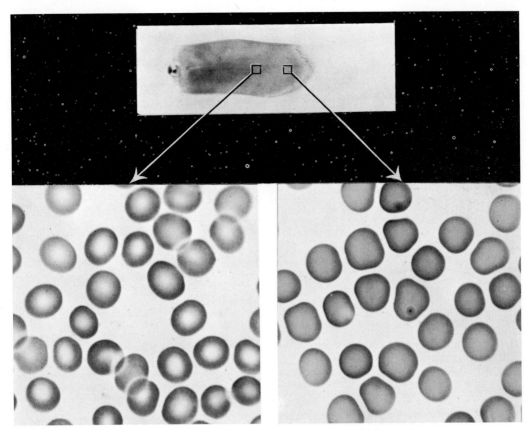

Fig. 13-4. Oil-immersion appearance of the red blood cells at two different sites in a blood film. (*Lower left*) These cells show the pale areas characteristic of normal cells. These pale areas show up only when the film is thick enough for occasional red cells to be superimposed on one another. (*Lower right*) Appearance of red cells at a place in the film where they are spread very thinly. Notice that no cells here are superimposed on one another and that in areas like this the central pale areas, characteristic of the normal red cell, cannot be seen.

more common type of anemia, the erythrocytes exhibit enlarged central pale areas and poorly stained peripheral zones (Fig. 13-5, *left*). The cells so altered are said to be *hypochromic* (undercolored); hence, the anemias with which they are associated, *hypochromic anemias*. In still other anemias there are few cells, and these are well filled with hemoglobin. It is doubtful if red cells can be overfilled, so the reason these anemias have sometimes been called *hyperchromic* is that the cells are generally larger, and since they are well-filled they *appear denser* (Fig. 13-5, *right*).

Films of normal blood usually exhibit an occasional erythrocyte of abnormal shape. The general term for such a cell is *poikilocyte* (*poikilis* = manifold). In the anemias, poi-

kilocytes are more common; hence, anemic blood is often said to exhibit poikilocytosis (Fig. 13-2, *right*). In some anemias, the cells of abnormal shape are named more specifically, for example, the type in which erythrocytes tend to be shaped like sickles, which has already been mentioned.

In any given anemia, knowing whether the hemoglobin is reduced more or less than the erythrocyte count is helpful in indicating the possible cause of the anemia. For example, iron is an essential ingredient of hemoglobin, so when iron is deficient the production of hemoglobin is reduced. However, iron is not so necessary for the production of erythrocytes as it is for hemoglobin, so in iron-deficiency anemias the hemoglobin content of

microcytic
hypochromic

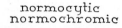

normocytic
normochromic

macrocytic
hyperchromic

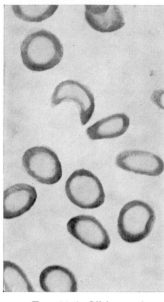
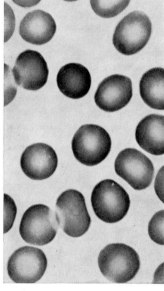
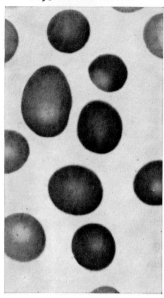

Fig. 13-5. Oil-immersion photomicrographs taken at the same magnification of 3 different films of human blood. (*Left*) This blood was obtained from a patient who had a microcytic hypochromic anemia due to iron deficiency, and the cells are seen to be small and their central pale areas greatly enlarged. (*Center*) Normal blood. (*Right*) Blood obtained from a person with pernicious anemia. In this condition the red blood cells, though fewer than normal, tend to be larger than usual and so they *appear* to be overfilled with hemoglobin.

blood is reduced more than the number of erythrocytes; hence, the cells are poorly filled with hemoglobin, and the anemia is said to be of the hypochromic type (Fig. 13-5, *left*). On the other hand, certain chemicals (vitamin B$_{12}$ and folic acid) seem to be more necessary for permitting erythrocytes to be produced than they are for permitting hemoglobin to be produced, so that when either one of these substances is lacking there is more difficulty in producing cells than hemoglobin; hence, those cells that are produced under these conditions are filled to capacity with hemoglobin, and the anemia is of the *hyperchromic macrocytic* type (Fig. 13-5, *right*). The most important kind of this type is called *pernicious anemia,* and it is caused by an inability to absorb vitamin B$_{12}$ from the stomach and the intestine. If the missing vitamin is injected into individuals they recover, and the condition recurs only if injections are discontinued. There is no point in feeding the vitamin by mouth because those afflicted cannot absorb it. (Vitamin B$_{12}$ is present in liver

extracts, and for those who might be interested it is the substance that, in the past, has been called the extrinsic factor of Castle.)

**Rouleaux Formation.** If fresh blood is placed on a slide and covered with a coverslip, the broad surfaces of erythrocytes often adhere to one another with the result that numbers of erythrocytes may become arranged together like coins in a pile. These arrangements of adherent erythrocytes are termed *rouleaux formations,* and they are probably manifestations of surface tension forces. If circulating blood is examined under the microscope, rouleaux formations are sometimes seen in areas where the circulation is not rapid. Rouleaux formations are not permanent, and the erythrocytes in them can become separated from one another again with presumably no harm having been done to them. This is probably not true of sludges.

**Sludging of Blood.** By using the quartz-rod illuminator to study the circulating blood in laboratory animals and in man, Knisely and his associates were able to show a few years ago that a very curious condition, which they term *sludging*, develops as a result of certain disease conditions and after severe trauma. This condition is manifested by erythrocytes in the circulating blood becoming clumped together in the form of little irregular masses that are large enough to plug and otherwise obstruct the finer blood vessels of the body. It has been explained already that the capillaries near burned skin (or at the site of trauma caused by other means), if they are not entirely destroyed, are injured enough to leak plasma. Moreover, trauma is prone to cause sludging of the blood, so that in addition to causing local damage, trauma may cause general damage because the circulation of blood through the finer blood vessels in distant parts of the body may become impeded by sludges. (See Knisely [1951] for a complete and concise account of the various kinds of damage caused by sludging.)

## REFERENCES

Berlin, N. I., Waldmann, T. A., and Weissman, S. M.: Life span of the red blood cell, Physiol. Rev. *39*:577, 1959.

Haden, R. L.: Factors affecting the size and shape of the red blood cell *in* Moulton, F. R. (ed.): Blood, Heart and Circulation, A.A.A.S. publication #13, Lancaster, Pa., Science Press, 1940.

Harris, J. W.: The Red Cell, Production, Metabolism, Destruction: Normal and Abnormal, Cambridge, Mass., Harvard Univ. Press, 1963.

Isaacs, R.: The erythrocytes *in* Downey's Handbook of Hematology, vol. 1, p. 1, New York, Hoeber, 1938.

Jones, O. P.: The influence of disturbed metabolism on the morphology of blood cells *in* Macfarlane, R. G., and Robb-Smith, A. H. T. (eds): Functions of the Blood, New York, Acad. Press, 1961.

Jordan, H. E.: Comparative hematology *in* Downey's Handbook of Hematology, vol. 2, p. 699, New York, Hoeber, 1938.

(*See also* textbooks of hematology.)

### SLUDGING OF BLOOD

Bigelow, W. G., Heimbecker, R. O., and Harrison, R. C.: Intravascular agglutination of erythrocytes (sludged blood), vascular stasis, and the sedimentation rate of the blood in trauma, Arch. Surg. *59*:667, 1949.

Heimbecker, R. O., and Bigelow, W. G.: Intravascular agglutination of erythrocytes (sludged blood) and traumatic shock, Surgery *28*:461, 1950.

Knisely, M. H.: An annotated bibliography on sludged blood, Postgrad. Med. *10*:15, 1951.

Knisely, M. H., Bloch, E. H., Eliot, T. S., and Warner, L.: Sludged blood, Science *106*:431, 1947.

Knisely, M. H., Eliot, T. S., and Bloch, E. H.: Sludged blood in traumatic shock, microscopic observations and precipitation and agglutination of blood flowing through vessels in crushed tissues, Arch. Surg. *51*:220, 1945.

# 14 Platelets and Fibrin

The next feature of blood that we shall consider are the mechanisms that are set into operation to seal off a cut or a seriously injured blood vessel so that the escape of blood from the circulatory system is limited. Since the mechanisms that are set into operation at the site of an injured or severed vessel bring about a stoppage of blood in the vessel concerned, the mechanisms involved are termed *hemostatic* (*hemo* = blood; *stasis* = a standing) mechanisms.

The vast importance of hemostatic mechanisms is only appreciated when the student sees patients in whom they are deficient. Patients in whom the mechanisms are very defective may bleed to death from a trivial injury. Even those who are not so seriously affected are endangered much more than the normal person when having to undergo surgical operations. Indeed, those of us who are normal in this respect can scarcely visualize the innumerable difficulties that ordinary life, with its bumps, bruises and other ordinary injuries, presents to those who have defective hemostatic mechanisms.

Efficient hemostatic mechanisms, however, are not an unmixed blessing, for particularly in middle and later life they may act so efficiently that they seal off the lumens of blood vessels that, though they may be diseased, would be better left open. Hemostatic mechanism can seal off coronary arteries that supply the muscle of the heart and so accounts for heart attacks of the kind termed "coronaries," which are all too common, and cause similar occlusions of blood vessels supplying the brain to account for what are commonly called "strokes."

Although hemostatic mechanisms are generally triggered by injuries to blood vessels, there are examples of them being set off in blood vessels that are seemingly normal.

## THE TWO BASIC HEMOSTATIC MECHANISMS

The two basic processes that come into operation to seal off cut blood vessels in mammals are (1) agglutination, which term refers to the platelets of the blood sticking together and piling up at the site of the injury so as to plug the open vessel and (2) coagulation or clotting, which process is dependent on fibrinogen (which is one of the normal blood proteins) being acted on locally by an enzyme called *thrombin* which causes the soluble fibrinogen to polymerize into delicate threadlike fibrils of fibrin around the site of the injury. The two processes, though very different from one another, occur more or less in sequence in sites of injury to blood vessels, and some of the factors, for example thrombin, that act in one process also act in the other.

A third factor that assists in bringing about a stoppage of blood flow from a severed vessel is that cut vessels tend to collapse when they are severed, and this makes their lumens smaller.

As Zucker, who has made so many informative studies in this area, has remarked, it is a common error to think that a hole in a blood vessel is closed off (merely) by a clot similar to that which forms when blood is put in a test tube. Although clotting, as we shall see, plays a part in hemostasis, the early and chief feature of the process which results in the sealing off of blood vessels in a living individual is agglutination—the formation of a plug of platelets at and over the site of the injury as will now be described.

## THE FORMATION OF PLATELET PLUGS THAT SEAL OFF BLOOD VESSELS

In the lower vertebrates, the inner surface of an injured blood vessel seems to attract erythrocytes. These cells become sticky and adhere both to the vessel wall and to one another at the site of injury. In birds the mechanism is more specialized and depends chiefly on certain cells called *thrombocytes* that are present in their blood. These are

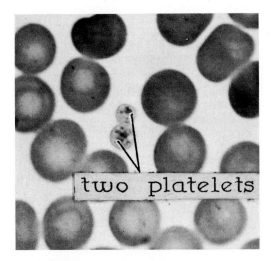

FIG. 14-1. Oil-immersion photomicrograph of a stained film of human blood. Two platelets may be seen adherent to one another in the center of the picture.

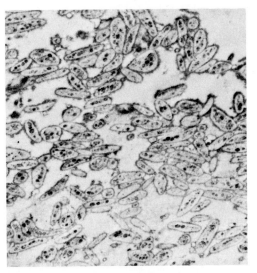

FIG. 14-2. Low-power electron micrograph of platelets beginning to agglutinate in a vessel to form a plug. (Preparation by R. Buck)

shaped something like erythrocytes but are smaller and of a different composition. They are believed to be highly specialized with regard to adhering and accumulating at points of injury along vessels. In mammals a further development of the mechanism is to be observed. Instead of there being specialized cells to perform this adhering function, there are still smaller bodies in circulating blood that are fragments of cytoplasm rather than complete cells. These are called *platelets* (*platum* = a plate, dish) because they look like little plates (Fig. 14-1).

In mammals when an artery, an arteriole, a vein or a venule is injured, the platelets in the blood that flows along past the site of injury or, if the vessel is severed, out through its open end, settle out and adhere to the endothelium of the vessel at the site of injury. The blood in the vessel at the site of injury, at any given second, does not contain enough platelets to completely seal off the vessel, and as a result blood continues to flow through the injured vessel for a minute or so, even though the vessel contracts, and this of course carries more and more platelets to the injured site and as the blood passes through the injured area the platelets in the blood, instead of passing by, continue to settle out and adhere to those already helping to plug the opening (Fig. 14-2). If the cut vessel is

not too large, a somewhat leaky platelet plug forms in and over the cut end of the vessel in around 1 minute. However, a little blood continues to leak through the plug, and this of course contains platelets that also settle out from the blood to plug up any little openings in the platelet plug. At around 2 minutes the plug becomes an effective seal, although it may leak a little now and again for a short while afterward. Very shortly the platelets in the plug become so very tightly drawn together that they seem to lose their individuality and become a cohesive mass; this is described by saying that the platelet clump has undergone a *viscous metamorphosis*.

Platelet plugs do not form at the end of cut capillaries; the endothelium of these tiny tubes in which there is little hydrostatic pressure seems to close off their cut ends spontaneously.

Although platelet plugs, after they have undergone viscous metamorphosis, constitute good seals, they act only temporarily unless they are reinforced by fibrin developing around their borders to provide them with support. So, to continue our discussion of the processes by which blood vessels are sealed off we must next discuss coagulation, which is the name for the process in which fibrin is formed.

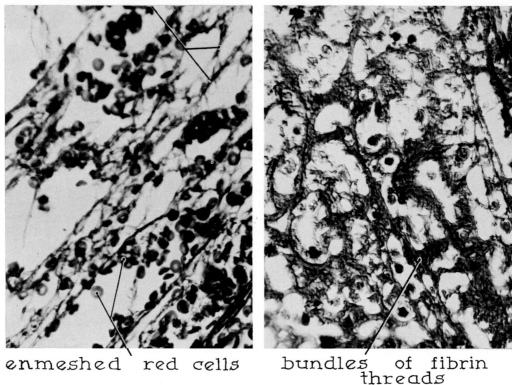

FIG. 14-3. High-power photomicrographs of sections cut through an area into which bleeding has occurred. (*Left*) Fine threads of fibrin which are forming a mesh entangling many cells. (*Right*) Fibrin threads arranged into coarser bundles.

## COAGULATION

The formation of fibrin from the fibrinogen of plasma occurs when fibrinogen is acted upon by an enzyme termed *thrombin*. Obviously, thrombin cannot be a normal component of blood or else clotting would occur in the circulatory system. Therefore, there must be some mechanism which permits thrombin to be formed locally at the site of an injury to blood vessels. Thrombin is formed in sites of injury from a precursor substance which is termed *prothrombin*. Prothrombin is a normal constituent of blood, but in its natural state it does not institute the clotting process. It follows, therefore, that in sites where clotting occurs, prothrombin must change to thrombin. The enzyme that converts prothrombin to thrombin has several names; perhaps the most usual name for it is *prothrombinase*. We next ask why it should appear at sites of injury. The substance that triggers the formation of

prothrombinase at sites of blood vessel injury is a substance called *tissue thromboplastin* which is released immediately from tissue when tissue is injured. However, tissue thromboplastin can only trigger the formation of prothrombinase if sufficient calcium ions are present; its work is also facilitated by the presence of two or three other factors which we will not discuss further here. So the sequence of events in the blood that is more or less pooled in and about the terminal part of a cut vessel is that the injured tissue liberates tissue thromboplastin which, with the help of calcium ions and two or three other factors, triggers the formation of prothrombinase which acts to convert the prothrombin of the blood of the part to thrombin, and the thrombin then brings about the formation of fibrin from the fibrinogen of the plasma. As the threads of fibrin are polymerized in the pooled and stagnant blood they become arranged in a mesh that holds erythrocytes and platelets in their interstices

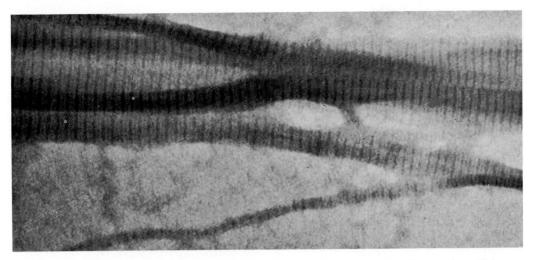

Fig. 14-4. Electron micrograph (× 115,000) of bovine fibrin, clotted in vitro by the addition of thrombin to fibrinogen solution, stained with phosphotungstic acid. (Preparation by C. E. Hall)

(Fig. 14-3). With the EM, fibrin, like collagen, shows axial periodicity, but the repeating periods are shorter, being only about 250 Å (Fig. 14-4).

## COAGULATION AND ITS DEPENDENCE ON EXTRINSIC OR INTRINSIC FACTORS

In the above-described sequence of events, the formation of prothrombinase is described as being triggered by tissue thromboplastin which is not a normal constituent of blood. Since it is not normally present in blood, it is called an extrinsic factor. The reason for making this distinction is that blood can clot as a result of prothrombinase being formed as a result of the interaction of substances all of which are present in blood. These factors together constitute the factors in the intrinsic clotting system. The intrinsic system is triggered by two intrinsic factors interacting to form what is termed an activation product this occurs when blood becomes exposed to some surface which for want of a better name is termed foreign. Blood that is put in a glass test tube finds the glass surface foreign, and this triggers the formation of an activation product which institutes interactions between intrinsic factors which result in the formation of prothrombinase.

As might be expected, when coagulation is brought about by extrinsic factors, the equivalent of foreign surfaces are soon brought into existence with the result that the intrinsic mechanism is also brought into play, so that in the usual clot occasioned originally by the extrinsic mechanism there is generally cooperation between the extrinsic and the intrinsic mechanisms.

Learning about the various factors concerned in blood coagulation has been stimulated and facilitated by the fact that individuals may suffer from inborn deficiencies of one or the other of certain of the factors that are required for the process to reach completion. However, the problem of blood coagulation, and the various diseases resulting from deficiencies of various factors involved in the process, is more properly dealt with in textbooks of physiology, biochemistry, hematology and medicine than here. However, since platelets are structures and so properly dealt with in histology, and since their behavior is affected by certain factors involved in the clotting process, and also since platelets affect clots, it has been necessary to give the above brief description of the clotting process in order to continue our discussion of platelets.

**Role of Thrombin in Platelet Agglutination.** It has been pointed out that thrombin is essential to convert fibrinogen to fibrin. Thrombin is also necessary for platelets to adhere to one another. Thrombin is therefore a factor that is involved in causing platelets to agglutinate at the site of an injury. The amount of thrombin necessary to induce platelet aggregation is much less than that required for inducing coagulation.

**Role of Platelets in Clot Retraction.** After a platelet plug has formed, and the blood around it has clotted, platelets as well as erythrocytes will be found to be entangled in the fibrin meshwork of the clot. Commonly, platelets are found at sites where fibrin threads cross one another, and in these sites they send out relatively long spikelike processes along the threads on which they lie. In due course the extended processes of the platelets contract, and this pulls on the fibrin threads and shortens them. The next result of this operation is that the clot undergoes retraction and this makes it stronger.

**Replacement.** If the formation of a platelet plug is not followed by fibrin formation, because of some defect in the clotting mechanism, the platelet plug may begin to leak within hours after it has formed, and as a result there is secondary bleeding from the injured vessel. If fibrin forms to support the platelet clot as it does normally, the plug is stronger and lasts longer—long enough for fibroblasts to grow into the area and replace the fibrin with connective tissue which makes a permanent seal. The fibrin disappears as it is replaced by connective tissue. It was once thought that fibrin was converted into the intercellular substance of connective tissue, but it is now known that fibrin dissolves under the influence of enzymes known as fibrinolysins.

Having discussed the function of platelets we shall now describe their structure.

## THE STUDY OF PLATELETS IN THE LABORATORY

Platelets are more difficult to study than blood cells. When blood is obtained for a blood film by means of a puncture wound, the platelets tend to stick together. Hence, in an ordinary blood film, clumps of platelets are commonly seen lying among the blood cells (Fig. 12-4). Moreover, their form may change appreciably when blood is removed from the body and spread on a glass slide. There is considerable variation in the way platelets are preserved in different blood films.

Platelets, in circulating blood, are oval-shaped disks, but they frequently appear in dried, stained blood films as rounded disks (Figs. 14-1 and 12-4). They vary somewhat in size. Most of the more rounded ones seen in dried, stained blood films are about one half or slightly less than one half the diameter of the erythrocytes (Fig. 14-1), but they may be much smaller. However, oval ones may be about three quarters of an erythrocyte's diameter in length. In examining a blood film, clumps of platelets are common (Fig. 12-4). However, an adequate search will reveal isolated platelets, so that the appearance of the individual platelet may be learned; thereafter the clumps of platelets will present no difficulty.

It is usual to describe a platelet (as seen in a dried and stained blood film) as having two parts, the *chromatomere* (*meros* = part), the colored part (the colored part is sometimes called the granulomere) and the *hyalomere* (*hyalos* = glass), the clear part. The chromatomere is so named because it is brightly colored after staining with dyes of the Romanovsky type (Fig. 12-4). Its color after this treatment may be red or violet, or even blue-violet. The chromatomere may have the form of what seems to be a fairly solid central body in the platelet or, what is more common, it may be broken up into small granules which tend to occupy a more or less central position in the platelet (Figs. 12-4 and 14-1). The hyalomere comprises the relatively transparent substance in which the chromatomere lies and is colored a very pale blue by the usual Romanovsky stain (Fig. 12-4). When the chromatomere is granular, the hyalomere usually appears plate-shaped, but when the chromatomere is a fairly solid and relatively large central body, the hyalomere (in dried, stained films) may present varied forms; sometimes it is drawn out into spikelike processes. Furthermore, there are all sorts of gradations between these two types. For example, some platelets exhibit a chromatomere that consists of both granules and a larger body of chromatophilic material, and some platelets whose chromatomere is granular may be of a most irregular outline. However, platelets alter so quickly when removed from the bloodstream that it is difficult to know just how much of the appearance they present in dried, stained films is due to artefact.

It may be that certain of the forms de-

FIG. 14-5. Electron micrograph ($\times$ 33,000) of a section of a platelet that was in a capillary of a normal rat. A good example of a mitochondrion, showing cristae, can be seen at the left. Many large, round and ovoid granules are distributed throughout the platelet in the region of the chromomere; these probably account for the staining properties of the chromomere. Some membranous vesicles also can be seen. Note that the platelet is surrounded by a cell membrane and has some pseudopodia covered with the membrane. Only a few ribosomes are to be seen. (Preparation by W. Bernhard)

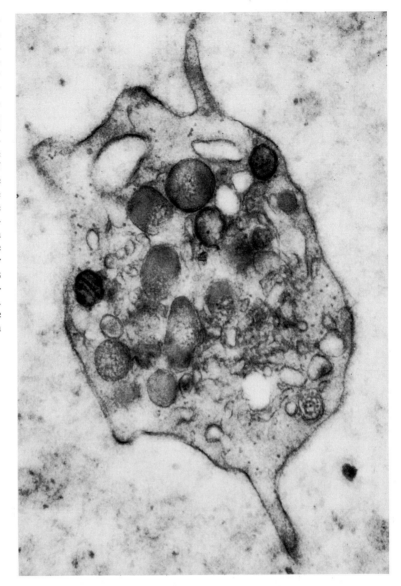

scribed above represent younger types, and other forms older types of platelets. Olef, from studying platelets in wet-fixed films, has proposed ways of distinguishing young from old platelets.

In the examination of a stained blood film it is not uncommon to encounter platelets superimposed on erythrocytes, an appearance that may be puzzling unless it is understood.

**The Fine Structure of Platelets.** In sectioned platelets, the region of the chromatomere is seen to contain mitochondria, distended membranous vesicles (which on the average are somewhat smaller than the mitochondria, although some may be as large) and specific granules of a size comparable with that of the vesicles (Fig. 14-5). The origin of the specific granules has not been settled; probably they are formed in membranous vesicles.

Bernhard observed, in addition to the foregoing, a fine granularity in the region of the chromatomere but found relatively few ribosomes in this region. Pease, however, reports finding ribosomes in abundance.

With the EM, the hyalomere reveals no particular structural features. It is of interest, however, that the platelet as a whole is surrounded with a membrane comparable to the usual cell membrane (Fig. 14-5).

Chemical studies have shown recently that platelets have a very considerable content of ATP, which finding is in concord with their being metabolically active. Furthermore, platelets take up and carry serotonin. It seems probable that the release of serotonin from platelet plugs is not of very great importance in causing contraction of the blood vessel in which the plug forms, because the vessel contracts probably about as much as it can because of the direct effects of the injury it has suffered.

Recently it has been shown that platelets are phagocytic (see Movat, Weiser, Glynn and Mustard for a recent study on this matter).

## HOW PLATELETS ARE COUNTED

The tendency of platelets to clump together and adhere to any surface presented to them as soon as blood is drawn creates technical difficulties with regard to their enumeration. To keep them apart so that they may be seen as individuals and hence counted, it is necessary to mix blood taken from the body with an antiagglutinating fluid immediately. The antiagglutinant now commonly used is EDTA ethylenediamine tetra-acetic acid). The platelets in blood that contain antiagglutinant can be counted in either of two ways, by the indirect or the direct method.

In the indirect method a drop of sterile antiagglutinating solution is placed on the clean skin, and a puncture is made through the drop so that the blood wells up into the antiagglutinant. A film of this mixture is then prepared and stained in the same manner as an ordinary blood film. The platelet count is estimated by noting the number of platelets in relation to the number of erythrocytes counted in several areas of the film; for example, if in one field 100 erythrocytes and 6 platelets are present, and if many other fields give the same ratio, it is assumed that there are 6 platelets for every 100 erythrocytes in that specimen of blood. So, if an erythrocyte count is made, the number of platelets per cubic millimeter of blood can be determined.

With the direct method, no antiagglutinating fluid is placed over the puncture site. Instead, a measured amount of blood is drawn up into a pipette containing a measured amount of antiagglutinant, and they are thoroughly mixed. As a little dye is added to the antiagglutinant to stain the platelets, they may be seen and distinguished from the erythrocytes when some of the mixture is examined in a counting chamber, where both an erythrocyte and a platelet count may be made from the same preparation with the ordinary light microscope.

The phase microscope has proved to be very useful for counting platelets, and probably the best method now available is a direct count made with this instrument.

It is very difficult to state exactly what constitutes a normal or an abnormal platelet count. The methods used in their enumeration are open to experimental error, and counts obtained by the indirect and the direct methods differ from each other considerably. Counts from arterial, venous and capillary blood are said to differ from one another, as are counts made from vessels supplying or leaving different organs and parts of the body. Platelet counts have a seasonal variation; they become altered with exercise and even vary throughout the day. (For details consult Tocantins' review.)

By the indirect method, the normal range is often considered to be between 250,000 and 350,000, or perhaps even between 200,000 and 400,000 per cubic millimeter of blood. By the direct method the normal range is between 150,000 and 350,000.

## THE FORMATION AND LIFE-SPAN OF PLATELETS

Platelets are fragments of cytoplasm that become detached from the cytoplasm of large polyploid cells in the bone marrow termed *megakaryocytes*. On becoming detached they soon enter the bloodstream as will be described in Chapter 16. The feature about platelet formation that should be described here is how the cytoplasm of megakaryocytes can become broken up into fragments which are approximately of the same size and each completely surrounded by a membrane. The way this is accomplished is easily understood. If an electron micrograph of a portion of the cytoplasm of a megakaryocyte (Fig. 14-6) is examined, it shows that much of the cyto-

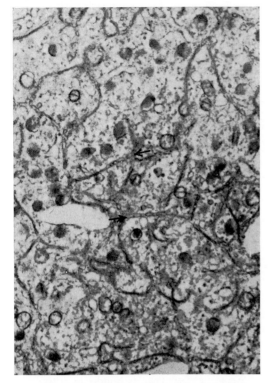

FIG. 14-6. Electron micrograph showing a small area of the cytoplasm of a mega-karyocyte. The rows of tiny vesicles that extend through the cytoplasm to divide it up into platelets are shown diagrammatically in Figure 14-7 and can be seen at sites indicated by arrows in this illustration. (Preparation by R. Buck)

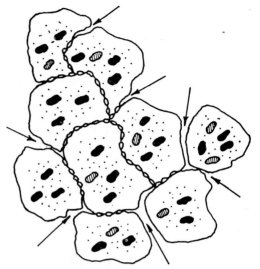

FIG. 14-7. How membranous vesicles develop and extend between tiny fragments of the cytoplasm of megakaryocytes to become detached as platelets and be covered with cell membrane while the sites from which they become detached remain covered with cell membrane. Arrows indicate lines of detachment.

plasm of megakaryocytes is divided up by membranes into areas about the same size as platelets (Fig. 14-6). The way that these intracytoplasmic membranes form is not entirely clear, but it seems probable that they represent infoldings of the cell membrane which, at first, are not necessarily continuous but first appear as strings of vesicles that become arranged along future cleavage planes as is shown diagrammatically in Figure 14-7. When the membranous vesicles that are in any cleavage plane coalesce, two membranes are provided, one to cover the detached surface of the platelet that is leaving and the other to cover the surface of the cytoplasm of the cell where the detachment occurred. By this mechanism platelets can be separated from the main body of the cytoplasm of a megakaryocyte and yet be completely covered

with a membrane similar to the membrane that surrounds the cell as a whole, and with the cytoplasm from which the platelet separates being left with an intact covering membrane.

Studies with radioactive tracers have indicated that platelets have a life-span of from 5 to 9 days.

Worn-out platelets are probably removed from the circulation similarly to worn-out erythrocytes, by phagocytic cells in the spleen, the liver and the bone marrow.

The normal content of platelets in blood, like the normal levels of erythrocytes, depends on the balance attained at a certain level between the liberation of platelets into blood and their removal from it. And, like the erythrocyte level, the platelet level may be depressed primarily because of increased removal of platelets from blood or from their decreased production.

## A FEW EXAMPLES OF DEFECTS IN HEMOSTATIC MECHANISMS

**Hemophilia.** The student will have heard

of hemophilia, a hereditary disease which, although transmitted by females, affects, with a few exceptions, only males. This is because the defective gene responsible for the condition is recessive and is carried on the X chromosomes. As was explained in Chapter 6, females have 2 X chromosomes, 1 from the father and 1 from the mother. Therefore, the chances are very great that even if 1 X chromosome has the defective gene, the other will be normal. The normal one will act as the dominant one, and because it is dominant, the disease does not appear. But males, with their XY combination, have only one X chromosome in their cells. This, of course, comes from the mother, and so if this carries the defect, they, unlike the female, have no normal gene of this type to compensate for the defective one, so they suffer from hemophilia. Individuals who have hemophilia are commonly termed "bleeders." Their blood does not clot promptly, and so they are disposed to bleed from simple cuts or injuries for much longer periods of time than normal individuals. Indeed, there have been many examples of hemophiliacs bleeding to death from having a tooth extracted or from undergoing a simple surgical operation. When the clotting mechanism of blood was understood reasonably well, it became apparent that the defect in hemophiliacs lay in their inability to produce thromboplastin; they lacked the trigger to set off the clotting mechanism. Understanding this helped in their treatment. To stop the bleeding, one commonly employed measure was that of giving them transfusions of blood from normal individuals. However, in 1947, one investigator gave a hemophiliac a transfusion from another person who was also considered to be a hemophiliac and, probably much to his surprise, found that the blood from the second hemophiliac brought the coagulation time of the blood of the first to normal. In 1950 other investigators reported that after mixing blood from what were believed to be two different hemophiliacs the clotting time of the mixed blood had become normal. Soon afterward the reason for this reaction was discovered; it was that more than one factor is concerned in the formation of thromboplastin; and some individuals with bleeding disease lack one, and others the other. If blood from the two types were mixed, it would, of course, have both the factors necessary to make thromboplastin; hence, it would clot. As this type of defect was studied further, it became apparent that more than two factors could be defective and that deficiencies of any of these could account for a defective clotting mechanism.

A deficiency of prothrombin is responsible for a condition called *hemorrhagic disease of the newborn*. This formerly mysterious disease, in which newborn infants were prone to bleed into their tissues and from various internal body surfaces, sometimes fatally, has been found to be due to a deficiency of vitamin K, a vitamin that is necessary for the synthesis of 4 of the plasma factors now known to be essential in the clotting process. Curiously enough, this vitamin is synthesized by bacteria that normally live in the intestine, so the reason that newborn infants are particularly disposed to suffer from a vitamin K, and hence a prothrombin, deficiency is that their intestines have not yet had time to become contaminated with bacteria.

Since prothrombin is made in the liver, certain kinds of liver disease are associated with a defective production and hence with impaired clotting mechanisms.

Another condition in which individuals show an increased tendency to hemorrhage is known as *ideopathic thrombocytopenic purpura* (*purphyreos* = purple), a condition in which affected individuals may exhibit purple patches in their skin caused by hemorrhages into their superficial tissues. These hemorrhages are caused by too small a number of thrombocytes (platelets) in the blood. Lest the student be given a false impression, it should be said that there are other kinds of purpura, resulting from causes other than a deficiency of platelets. In the idiopathic types, however, alleviation is usually obtained by removal of the spleen, an organ which, in this instance, seems to be particularly concerned in removing platelets from the circulation so that the number in the blood is kept at too low a level.

That a deficiency of calcium ions will prevent the clotting process is often taken advantage of for purposes of transfusion by mixing a certain amount of citrate solution with blood. Calcium ions in blood readily unite with the citrate ion to form a complex compound which does not dissociate into calcium ions. Hence, citrate removes calcium *ions* rather than calcium from the blood with which it is mixed.

## REFERENCES

Aschoff, L.: Lectures on Pathology, XI. Thrombosis, New York, Hoeber, 1924.

Biggs, Rosemary, and Macfarlane, R. G.: Human Blood Coagulation and Its Disorders, ed. 3, Oxford, Blackwell, 1962.

Hall, C. E., and Slayter, H. S.: The fibrinogen molecule: its size, shape, and mode of polymerization, J. Biochem. Biophys. Cytol. 5:11, 1959.

Hjort, P. F., and Hasselback, R.: A critical review of the evidence for continuous hemostasis *in vivo*, Thromb. Diath. Haemorrh. 6:580, 1961.

Kerr, C. B.: Modern blood coagulation theory and its clinical application, Med. J. Austr. 49(2):914, 1962.

Pease, D. C.: An electron microscope study of red bone marrow, Blood 11:501, 1956.

Shulman, Irving: Vascular factors in hemostasis, Ann. Rev. Med. 14:339, 1963.

Silberberg, M.: The causes and mechanism of thrombosis, Physiol. Rev. 18:197, 1938.

Tocantins, L. M.: The mammalian blood platelet in health and disease, Medicine 17:155, 1938.

Wislocki, G. B., Bunting, H., and Dempsey, E. W.: Further observations on the chemical cytology of megakaryocytes and other cells of hemopoietic tissues, Anat. Rec. 98:527, 1947.

Wright, J. H.: Histogenesis of the blood platelets, J. Morphol. 21:263, 1910.

Zucker, M. B.: General observations on hemostasis *in* Duyff, J. W., Binet, P., Bornschein, H., Brun, P., Fabre, R., LeMoan, G., and Noble, D. (eds.): XXII International Congress of Physiological Sciences, vol. 1, p. 219, New York, Excerpta Medica Foundation, 1962.

————: Blood platelets, Scient. Am. 204(2):58, 1961.

(*See also* references on Megakaryocytes, Chap. 16.)

# 15 Hemopoietic Tissue

## SOME GENERAL CONSIDERATIONS

Having dealt with the leukocytes, the erythrocytes and the platelets of blood we are now in a position to deal with the specialized tissues in which they are made. The specialized tissues that produce blood cells and platelets are termed hemocytopoietic tissues which means *blood cell making* tissue (*poiesis* = a making). Since the shorter term hemopoietic tissue is generally used to mean the same thing as hemocytopoietic tissue we shall use it hereafter, even though it is not so accurate.

**The 3 Basic Functions of Hemopoietic Tissues.** Although hemopoietic tissues, as their name implies, are concerned with producing blood cells and delivering them into the bloodstream, they are also concerned under strictly normal conditions with removing worn-out blood cells and other debris from the circulation. If hemopoietic tissue did not perform this second function as well as producing blood cells, the blood vessels might become cluttered up and plugged with dead and dying functionless cells. For hemopoietic tissues to perform two different functions requires that there are *2 primary lines* of cell differentiation operating in the development and the maintenance of hemopoietic tissue. One line of differentiation leads to the production of blood cells of some kind or kinds. The other primary line of differentiation leads to the formation of phagocytic cells that are of the order of macrophages but which in hemopoietic tissue are generally called reticuloendothelial cells because (1) most of them are held in position by reticular fibers, and (2) they take the place of endothelium in certain blood or lymph channels as will be described in detail presently. The cells that form from this line of differentiation remove worn-out blood cells and other debris from the circulation.

The third function of hemopoietic tissue is immunologic. Antigens that reach hemopoietic tissues somehow induce the formation of cells that begin to synthesize antibodies that specifically combine with the antigens. All features of this phenomenon are not known. However, there is reason to believe that antigens are removed from the lymph that passes through lymph nodes or the blood that passes through the spleen or marrow by the reticuloendothelial cells, and for many years it was believed that the reticuloendothelial cells that took up an antigen produced the antibodies that combined with that antigen. But then it was shown that plasma cells are the cells that actually produce circulating antibodies. However, it has not been shown that the antigens that manage to gain entrance to the body go directly to plasma cells or their precursors. This has led to the concept of antigens being removed from the fluids of the body by the reticuloendothelial cells of hemopoietic tissue (or macrophages in loose connective tissue) as the first step in the immunologic response. The question then arises as to how reticuloendothelial cells or macrophages that take up an antigen are able to cause plasma cells to develop and make antibody specific for the antigen. Some experiments have shown that a substance, perhaps RNA, extracted from macrophages or reticuloendothelial cells that have been exposed to a given antigen will cause certain free cells of lymphatic tissue to turn into antibody-forming cells and make antibody specific for that antigen. In support of the concept that cells of the macrophage type that take up an antigen can transmit information somehow to cells that can turn into plasma cells are the findings of Schoenberg, Mumaw, Moore and Weisberger, for they have shown by electron microscopy what seems to be cytoplasmic connections between macrophages exposed to an antigen and lymphocytes (Fig. 15-8). Other workers have shown that the reticuloendothelial cells of lymph nodes possess many cytoplasmic prolongations which can touch many lymphocytes. Hence, in the light of such knowledge as is available in this area where knowledge is accumulating rapidly, it would seem that the cells of both lines of differentiation in hemopoietic tissue, particularly in lymphatic tissues—the line of reticuloendothelial cells and the line of free cells—are both involved in the response to an antigen and hence that the close association of cells of these two lines of differentiation in these tissues is not merely fortuitous.

That there should be a division of labor in the antibody response seems reasonable because one type of cell cannot become specialized for too many functions. Since macrophages or reticuloendothelial cells are specialized to phagocytose, it is logical that they should take up antigen. It would seem, however, that reticuloendothelial cells, being specialized for other functions, are not adapted to producing the antibody themselves; their role would seem to be that of delivering some product made in response to the antigen (perhaps messenger RNA) into the cytoplasm of previously *unspecialized uncommitted* immunologically competent cells which possess the synthetic capacity to become plasma cells and make antibody specific for the antigen. Since the immunologically competent cell would receive only a very little messenger RNA (if this is what it receives) from a reticuloendothelial cell or macrophage in the first place, it seems probable that for it to develop into a small antibody factory and make large quantities of antibody it would be necessary for the messenger RNA it receives in the first place to set up processes of some kind that would affect its own DNA so that the cell's own DNA would serve as a template for the formation of more messenger RNA of the same type. Some of the concepts of Jacob and Monod (mentioned briefly near the end of Chapter 6) might have application in attempting to visualize how this could be done.

**The Two Main Kinds of Hemopoietic Tissue.** In man, in postnatal life, there are two fairly clearly defined types of hemopoietic tissue, lymphatic and myeloid. Lymphatic tissue normally produces lymphocytes. Myeloid tissue is found in the marrow cavities of certain bones, and normally it produces erythrocytes, granular leukocytes and platelets. Possibly both tissues produce monocytes. Specialization is not so pronounced in the embryo and the fetus. In prenatal life, erythrocytes

are produced in some of the lymphatic tissues, and in some animals this also occurs in postnatal life.

With these general comments we shall now begin the study of lymphatic tissue and leave our consideration of myeloid tissue for the next chapter.

## LYMPHATIC TISSUE

**Distribution in the Body.** A very important primary function of lymphatic tissue is to defend the body against disease-inducing agents that gain entrance to it. One very important role it performs in this respect is to provide lymphocytes which, in response to antigens, develop into cells that function immunologically. The distribution of lymphatic tissue in the body becomes understandable if its function in this respect is considered, because it is distributed so as to be exposed to: (1) Antigens that penetrate the epithelial membranes that line various tubes in the body that have contact with the outside world. To provide a line of defense behind the wet epithelial membrane, little depots of lymphatic tissue called lymphatic nodules are scattered about in the loose connective tissue that is found beneath the epithelial membranes that line the upper respiratory passages, the intestine and the urinary tract. The association between lymphatic tissue in loose connective tissue and wet epithelium is particularly intimate in what are termed tonsils, which are paired structures disposed in 3 different sites (tongue, pharynx and nasopharynx) where they more or less stand on guard at the entrance of the alimentary and the respiratory tracts. (2) Antigens that gain entrance to lymphatic capillaries anywhere in the body so that they enter the lymph. As has been explained already in connection with the description of the thoracic duct, lymph that begins in lymphatic capillaries flows into larger tubes called lymphatics, which empty into the convex surfaces of encapsulated lymphatic structures termed *lymph nodes (synonym = lymph glands)* where it comes into contact with reticuloendothelial cells and cells of the lymphocyte series which act as precursor cells for the formation of cells that function immunologically. (3) Antigens that gain en-

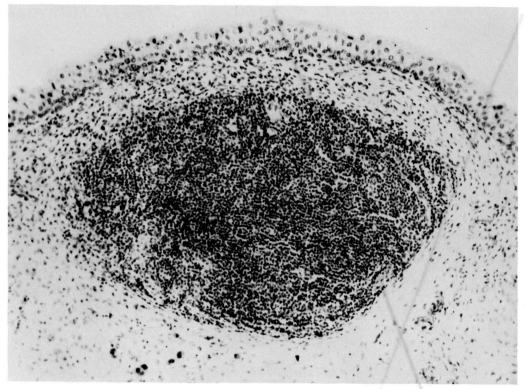

Fig. 15-1. Low-power photomicrograph of a section of the wall of the bladder of a dog. The surface seen at the upper part of the picture is covered with transitional epithelium. In the connective tissue below this there is an ovoid nodule of lymphocytes. Such nodules are called lymphatic, primary or malpighian nodules.

trance to the blood either by the direct invasion of venules in infected tissue anywhere in the body or via the lymph stream. Much blood constantly passes through an organ termed the spleen which also abounds in reticuloendothelial cells and cells of the lymphocyte series that can give rise to cells that function immunologically.

From the foregoing it is obvious that much lymphatic tissue is judiciously distributed in the body so that disease agents that gain entrance to the body or spread in the body soon encounter lymphatic tissue and so set into motion the process of antibody formation. The fact that the function of lymphatic tissue is to combat invaders in the shape of disease organisms is emphasized by the fact that if animals are born and raised in a germ-free environment, their lymphatic tissue in the sites described above is little developed.

Next, although all the lymphatic tissue described above is advantageously located so as to be encountered quickly by any disease organism (antigens) that gain entrance to the body, there is one large depot of lymphatic tissue that is not; this is the thymus gland. When we study this gland shortly we shall find that it is constructed so that lymphocytes can be produced here in, and delivered into blood and lymph from, an environment that is protected from, rather than exposed to, antigens. We shall consider possible reasons for this arrangement when we deal later with possible functions of the thymus gland.

With these preliminary considerations in mind we shall now discuss the 4 subdivisions of lymphatic tissue in turn, namely;

1. Nonencapsulated nodules of lymphatic tissue in loose connective tissue (also called primary or malpighian nodules)

2. Lymph nodes (also called lymph glands)

3. The spleen

4. The thymus (also called thymus gland)

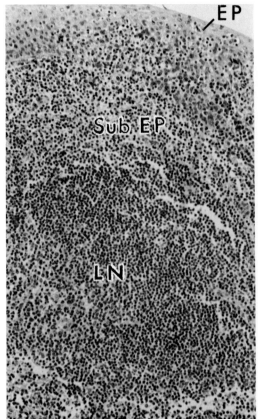

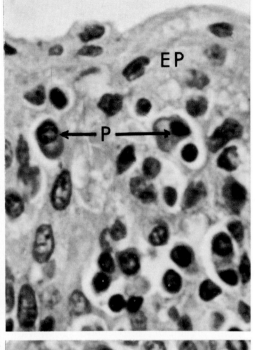

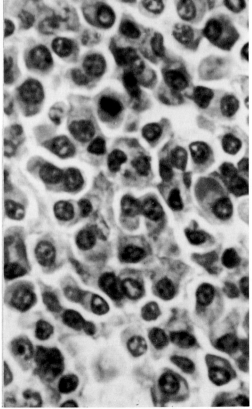

FIG. 15-2. Photomicrographs of sections of tonsil of child. (*Top, left*) Low-power showing a lymph nodule (**LN**) below the epithelium (**EP**). Between the epithelium and the nodule there is loose connective tissue (**Sub. Ep**) containing many lymphocytes and plasma cells. (*Top, right*) Both plasma cells (**P**) and lymphocytes (not labeled) can be seen infiltrating into the lining epithelium (**EP**). (*Bottom, right*) Many plasma cells in the loose connective tissue (**Sub. Ep.**) immediately below the epithelium.

## THE NONENCAPSULATED LYMPHATIC NODULES OF LOOSE CONNECTIVE TISSUE

**Distribution.** As already noted, these are commonly seen in the loose connective tissue that underlies the wet epithelium of the upper respiratory tract, the alimentary tract and the urinary tract (Fig. 15-1.) As noted, lymphatic nodules come into very intimate contact with epithelium in the tonsils (Fig. 15-2). However, nonencapsulated nodules of lymphatic tissue are not limited to the sites mentioned and may be encountered in loose connective tissue in many more deeply located parts of the body.

**Histologic Features.** The primary nodule in loose connective tissue is roughly spherical and may measure from a few hundred microns to a millimeter or more in diameter (Fig. 15-1). In an H and E section, a primary nodule appears, under low power, as a dark blue area (Fig. 15-1). Under higher magnification the blue appearance is seen to be due to the nodule being packed with cells of the lymphocyte series; since these cells have little cytoplasm, there is a great concentration of nuclei in the nodule; and since the densely packed nuclei are all colored blue, the whole nodule stands out as a rounded blue area. Indeed, the dense blue staining of primary nodules is so obvious when a section is inspected with the naked eye that the student can generally detect the presence of lymphatic tissue when he holds a section to the light and does his preliminary inspection of it with the naked eye.

The next point about a primary nodule that should be emphasized is that its periphery is not sharply defined (Figs. 15-1 and 15-2). The reason for this is that the lymphocytes (and plasmablasts) that are produced in the nodules are pushed out from its periphery into whatever loose connective tissue the nodule happens to be in (as in Fig. 15-2), so at the periphery of the nodule the appearance gradually changes from that of a dense concentration of lymphocytes to a decreasing concentration in the adjacent tissue. Another point that should be made is that lymphatic nodules are *not* encapsulated; they lie naked in whatever tissue they are in. To avoid misunderstanding, it should be noted that the *lymph nodes* (which filter lymph) and the *spleen* (which filters blood) *are* enclosed by connective tissue capsules. However, the primary nodules that lie within these organs or elsewhere are not encapsulated.

Whereas most lymphatic nodules that lie in the loose connective tissue of the body are discrete, they may become confluent when they are very close together. This happens particularly in the lower part of the small intestine where confluent nodules form structures called *Peyer's patches* which are large

enough to be seen with the naked eye. Nodules may become confluent also in tonsils.

**The Development of Lymphatic Nodules.** As was noted at the beginning of this chapter, there are two main lines of differentiation in hemopoietic tissue, one to provide phagocytic reticuloendothelial cells and the other to supply free cells of the various types found in blood. Since lymphatic nodules develop from the mesenchyme, it is believed that the cell that gives rise to the two lines of cells that appear in lymphatic tissue is an immediate descendant of an undifferentiated mesenchymal cell and endowed with the potentiality required to form all the kinds of cells that form in lymphatic tissue. This hypothetical mother cell of lymphatic tissue is generally termed a reticular cell or, more specifically, a primitive reticular cell (Fig. 15-4, *top*; its appearance will be described later). This cell can divide, and by this means it is believed that a small pool of primitive reticular cells is maintained in lymphatic tissue. Members of this pool can differentiate probably along either of two different lines.

Along the first line they are thought to differentiate into reticuloendothelial cells. At least some of the cells along this line of differentiation seem to be able to produce reticular fibers to which both the primitive reticular cells and most of the reticuloendothelial cells (which will be described later) are attached. Along the second line of differentiation the primitive reticular cells are believed to form lymphoblasts. Lymphoblasts are said to be free cells (Fig. 15-6, *right middle*) because they are not attached to, and hence not so firmly held in place by, reticular fibers as the primitive reticular and reticuloendothelial cells. Lymphoblasts are merely loosely suspended in the meshes of the net of reticular fibers. Within primary nodules lymphoblasts divide and here maintain a pool of lymphoblasts. Some differentiate into prolymphocytes which also can divide a few times and in turn can differentiate into (small) lymphocytes. The latter may divide a time or two in the nodules before they leave. The lymphoblasts are generally present in the more central part of a nodule and the prolymphocytes and lymphocytes in its more peripheral part from which they may escape into the adjacent tissue. Reticuloendothelial cells, although present, are not prominent in primary nodules.

Lymphatic nodules are not so prominent before birth as they become after birth, and they remain relatively undeveloped in germ-free animals after birth.

Plasma cells may be seen in association with lymphatic nodules in loose connective tissue (Fig. 15-2), and it is probable that they develop from precursor cells that arise in the nodules. However, plasma cells, in at least most species, do not develop in association with lymphatic nodules or elsewhere before birth.

Lymphatic nodules in loose connective tissue sometimes acquire what are termed *germinal centers*. These will be described in detail in connection with lymph nodes in the next section of this chapter. Here it is enough to say that they are rounded areas that appear in the central parts of primary nodules and stain differently from the remainder of the primary nodule. Germinal centers do not develop before birth.

From what has been said in the preceding 3 paragraphs it is obvious that birth is an important factor in bringing about the development of (1) the primary lymphatic nodules themselves, (2) the production of plasma cells and (3) the development of germinal centers in lymphatic nodules. These features of postnatal lymphatic nodules would seem, therefore, to be dependent on new macromolecules gaining entrance to loose connective tissue and on the otherwise relatively dormant lymphatic nodules recognizing these new macromolecules as antigens and responding to the antigen, i.e., stimulus, by (1) developing more extensively, (2) producing plasma cells (Fig. 15-2) and (3) in many instances developing germinal centers. Details of the response in nodules to antigens will be given in the following discussion of lymph nodes.

## LYMPH NODES

As has been described in the section of this book dealing with the formation and the absorption of tissue fluid (Chap. 10), a certain amount of the tissue fluid formed in many parts of the body is drained away by means of lymphatic capillaries (Fig. 10-8). These begin from blind endings and join with one another to form lymphatic vessels of a larger caliber and with thicker walls. Eventually, these all empty into two main lymphatic trunks—the thoracic duct and the right lymphatic duct. The thoracic duct empties and so returns the lymph it carries into the venous system at the point of junction between the left subclavian and the left internal jugular veins. The right lymphatic duct returns the lymph collected by it into the venous system at the point of junction of the right subclavian and the right internal jugular veins. Hence, all the lymph collected in the body is restored to the blood circulatory system to help to maintain the fluid content of the blood.

Most of the lymph collected by the lymphatic capillaries of the body, before being returned to the blood circulatory system by the thoracic or the right lymphatic duct, passes through one or more little round, oval or bean-shaped structures called *lymph glands* or *nodes*. The student should understand that while the word "gland" means "acorn-shaped," it is also used to designate any structure that secretes. Lymph glands may be acorn-shaped, but they do not secrete. Since the word "gland" has gradually come to be defined on a physiologic rather than a morphologic basis, and since many lymph glands are not shaped like acorns, they should not be called glands; therefore, we shall refer to them from now on as lymph nodes. However, the student in using this term must be careful to distinguish between nodes and nodules; the latter have been described already.

Many lymph nodes are situated in the axilla and in the groin. A great many are also distributed along the great vessels of the neck, and a considerable number in the thorax and the abdomen, particularly in association with the great vessels and the mesentery. A few are associated with the popliteal vessels, and also a few are at the elbow. In general, then, lymph nodes are distributed, not where lymph originates (like lymphatic nodules) but rather along the course of the main tributaries that flow into the thoracic and the right lymphatic ducts. Their chief function is to filter the lymph that is picked up by the lymphatic capillaries before it is returned to the bloodstream and to produce antibodies in response to the antigens that reach them.

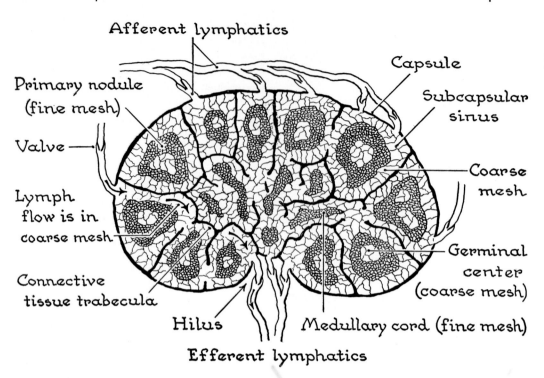

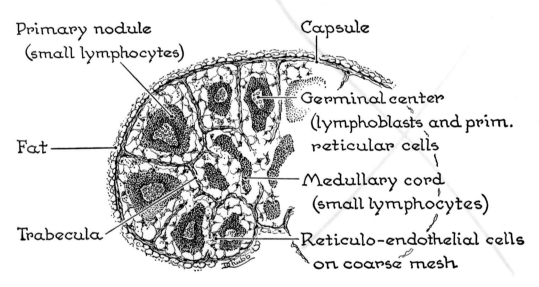

Fig. 15-3. Diagrams showing the structure of lymph nodes. (*Top*) The framework of the node as it would appear if the lymphocytes were removed from it. (*Bottom*) The distribution of lymphatic nodules, with or without germinal centers, in the node and also the distribution of medullary cells.

They also add lymphocytes to the lymph that flows through them. Once it was believed that they also act to concentrate lymph, but the evidence for this view is not convincing. The problem relating to the recirculation of lymphocytes was discussed in Chapter 12.

**The Microscopic Structure of Lymph Nodes.** They may be round, ovoid or bean-shaped. They vary greatly in size; some are as small as seeds; others are as large as almonds. Each is said to consist of two main parts: a cortex and a medulla. The cortex (bark) is the outer part, and the medulla (marrow) the inner. Since bean-shaped nodes are common and facilitate description by possessing convex and concave surfaces, in the following we shall describe the intimate structure of a node of this shape.

A lymph node is surrounded by a connective tissue capsule (Figs. 15-3, *bottom,* and 15-4, *center*). Since lymph nodes commonly lie in fat tissue, some fat usually adheres to the outer part of the capsule (Fig. 15-3, *bottom*) when they are dissected out for sectioning. This provides an aid in distinguishing between a section of a lymph node and one of spleen (which has a somewhat similar microscopic appearance) because the latter has a smooth peritoneal surface. Lymphatic vessels penetrate the capsule covering the convex aspect of the node (Fig. 15-3) and leave from the deepest part of the indentation. This area is called the *hilus.* The lymphatic vessels that bring lymph *to* the node are called *afferent lymphatics,* and those that *bring it out* from the node are called *efferent lymphatics.* Both kinds are provided with valves so that the lymph in them cannot pass backward toward its point of origin. Refer to Figure 15-3 to see these features.

The connective tissue capsule is usually somewhat thicker in the region of the hilus, and in this site it gives rise to trabeculae of connective tissue that extend into the substance of the node to provide support and carry blood vessels (Figs. 15-3 and 15-4). Trabeculae of connective tissue also extend in from the capsule, covering the convex aspect of the node (Fig. 15-3, heavy black lines).

Within the node, a mesh of reticular fibers, on which many reticuloendothelial cells are suspended, extends like a continuous cobweb to fill all the space between the various trabeculae and between them and the capsule. In the cortex, there are rounded areas in which the mesh is finer than it is in the remainder of the cortex (Fig. 15-3, *top*). These areas of fine mesh constitute the sites of *primary nodules* (a fine mesh holds small lymphocytes better than a coarse mesh). In the medulla, also, areas of fine mesh may be seen; these are in the nature of extensions into the medulla of fine mesh from the edges of primary nodules.

However, these are not rounded but have an irregular, elongated form and are called *medullary cords* (Fig. 15-3). Their fine mesh, unlike that of the lymphatic nodules in the cortex, contains more plasma cells than lymphocytes. The cords commonly branch and anastomose with one another as well as connecting with the primary nodules of the node.

The primary nodules of the cortex are separated from the capsule by a coarse reticular mesh on which many reticuloendothelial cells are suspended. This zone of coarse mesh is commonly called the *subcapsular sinus* (Fig. 15-3). It should be realized that this particular sinus, unlike the sinuses of certain other organs, is not in the nature of a tube with a clear lumen; it is merely a zone of coarse mesh through which fluid can percolate easily. Lymph emptied into it by the afferent lymphatics seeps deeper into the gland by way of the coarse mesh situated between the primary nodules and the trabeculae or that between primary nodules that are adjacent but not in direct contact with one another. Because primary nodules have a fine mesh and are packed with lymphocytes, their substance does not offer as easy a passage to lymph as does the coarse mesh that surrounds them. On reaching the medulla of the gland, the lymph, for the most part, passes through the coarse mesh disposed between the medullary cords and the trabeculae and finally enters the efferent lymphatics.

There is some difference between the microscopic appearance of lymph nodes taken from different parts of the body. In some nodes the lymph nodules of the cortex are highly developed, and little medulla is apparent. In a section of a node of this type, the student will have difficulty finding medullary cords and typical coarse-mesh filtering tissue. In nodes taken from other parts of the body, particularly those from the mesentery, the medulla rather than the cortex is well developed. These should be used for the study of medullary cords. The character of the filtering coarse-mesh tissue that lies between them can also be studied to advantage in these.

## THE MICROSCOPIC STRUCTURE OF LYMPH NODES IN RELATION TO THEIR FUNCTIONS

Even a cursory examination of a section of

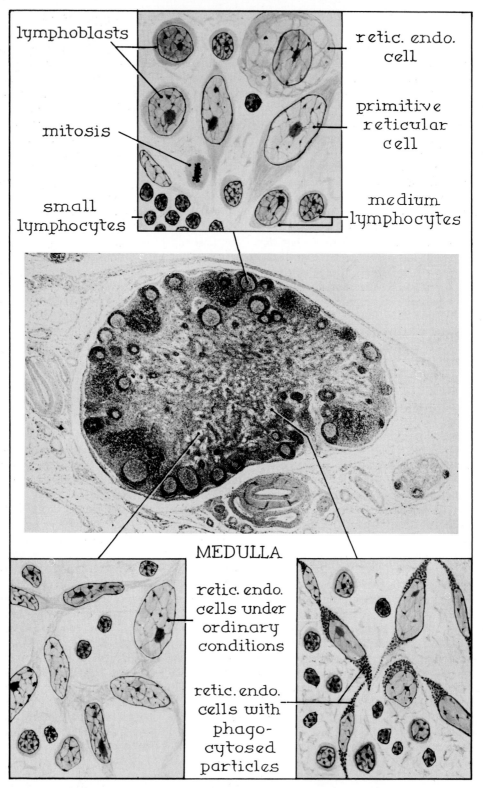

lymphoblasts

retic. endo. cell

mitosis

primitive reticular cell

small lymphocytes

medium lymphocytes

MEDULLA

retic. endo. cells under ordinary conditions

retic. endo. cells with phago- cytosed particles

FIG. 15-4. (*Center*) Low-power photomicrograph of a lymph node. (*Top*) High-power drawing of cells in germinal center. (*Bottom*) High-power drawings of reticuloendothelial cells in mesh of medulla.

primary       germinal
nodule        center

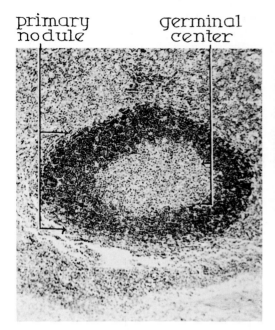

Fig. 15-5A. Low-power photograph of a section of a lymph node of a dog, showing a primary nodule. The central part of this contains a pale germinal center.

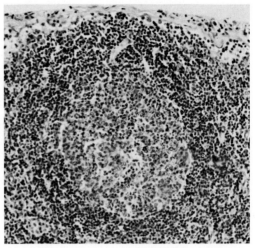

Fig. 15-5B. Low-power photomicrograph of a primary nodule that contains a germinal center which is not pale but basophilic. On close inspection it would be seen to contain many mitotic figures (see Fig. 15-6 for higher-power views of this type of germinal center).

a lymph node suggests that it has two main functions.

**Filtering Lymph.** First, its architectural arrangements are such that lymph, which enters it by way of the afferent lymphatics (Fig. 15-3), would percolate most readily through the node via the coarse mesh of reticuloendothelial cells that exist first in the subcapsular sinus, then between the primary nodules of the cortex and, finally, between the medullary cords of the medulla before it entered the efferent lymphatics that leave the hilus. Since the reticuloendothelial cells are phagocytic (Figs. 15-4, *bottom,* and 15-6, E) it is obvious that particulate matter could be strained effectively from lymph during its passage through the node; and indeed, sections of the lymph nodes that filter that lymph that flows from the lungs of city-dwellers commonly contain large accumulations of carbon (smoke) particles that have been phagocytosed from the lymph that flows through them. Figure 15-4 *(lower right)* illustrates the filtering function of reticuloendothelial cells.

**Producing Cells.** The second important function of lymph nodes is the production of cells. These are of two chief types: lymphocytes and plasma cells. First we shall consider the formation of lymphocytes in lymphatic nodules, and in connection with this matter we shall describe the germinal centers that often develop in lymphatic nodules.

**Germinal Centers.** Beginning only in postnatal life, the more central part of a lymphatic nodule may take on a different appearance from the remainder of the nodule. When this happens, the primary nodule is said to have developed a *germinal center.* Under low-power inspection the germinal center is often paler than the remainder of the nodule (Fig. 15-5, A). However, it often is not; instead, it may be moderately deep blue in color (Fig. 15-5, B). Even when blue, the appearance of a germinal center differs from that of the primary nodule in which it lies because the nuclei within it are *fewer* and *farther apart* than those in the primary nodule. The blue appearance of such a germinal center is due not only to the large blue nuclei that are present in it but also to the fact that many of the cells in the germinal center have considerably more cytoplasm than ordinary lymphocytes, and this cytoplasm is very basophilic.

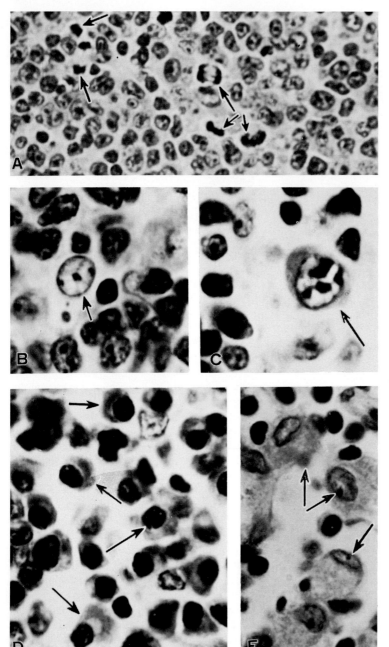

Fig. 15-6. High-power photomicrographs of somewhat different magnifications of different parts of a mediastinal lymph node of a rat.

A. An active germinal center. Arrows indicate cells in mitosis.

B. A germinal center. Arrow indicates the nucleus of a reticular cell. Note that its cytoplasm is very indistinct.

C. Edge of a germinal center. Arrow indicates a large cell with a ring of basophilic cytoplasm that has a sharp edge. This is a free, rounded cell, either a lymphoblast or a plasmoblast.

D. A medullary cord. Arrows indicate some of the plasma cells that are present. Note the negative Golgi areas in their cytoplasm.

E. A medullary sinusoid. Arrows indicate reticuloendothelial cells.

Germinal centers, particularly when they demonstrate the basophilia mentioned above, reveal many mitotic figures (Fig. 15-6, *top*) and so are active sites of formation of cells of the lymphocyte series. However, lymphocytes can be formed in primary nodules that do not have germinal centers. Since it is easier to see the various cells concerned in these lines of differentiation in germinal centers than it is in nodules without germinal centers, it is suggested that the student study a basophilic type of germinal center to see the cell types that are concerned in the production of lymphocytes and which will now be described.

**The Cells of Germinal Centers.** As has been mentioned already, lymphatic tissue develops from mesenchyme, and it is believed that the mesenchymal cell that gives rise to lymphatic tissue is represented in lymphatic tissue in postnatal life by cells termed primitive reticular cells (Fig. 15-6, *left middle*). These cells are recognized in germinal centers because only their nuclei can be seen. Their nuclei are oval, large and pale, and each generally contains only a single nucleolus (Fig. 15-6, B). The cytoplasm of the cell is very faint, and a very important feature of it is that its limits are not defined; this is in contrast with the free cells that are believed to develop from primitive reticular cells, for, as we shall see, the cytoplasm of free cells can be seen with the edges of the cytoplasm of each cell being generally distinct (Fig. 15-6, C).

**The Stem Cell of Lymphatic Tissue.** In the past it was generally conceded among histologists that the mesenchymal cells that give rise to lymphocytes in lymphatic tissue in prenatal life retain their representation later in the lymphatic tissue of postnatal life as *primitive reticular cells*. It has been generally conceded, moreover, that primitive reticular cells divide so as to maintain a pool of primitive reticular cells in lymphatic tissue so that some reticular cells are free to differentiate into lymphoblasts without diminishing the numbers of the pool of primitive reticular cells. Thus, in the past, the latter cells have been generally regarded as the stem cells of lymphatic tissue, and indeed, in a recent study, Sainte-Marie and Leblond have provided evidence indicating that there are large cells that divide so that some of their members can differentiate into lymphoblasts without reducing the numbers of larger precursor cells.

Recently, however, there has been an increasing amount of experimental evidence that indicates that lymphatic tissue that has failed to develop properly because of the thymus being removed in the early days of life (as will be described later) or which has been destroyed by total-body irradiation, can be restored by injecting into the affected animal cells from the thoracic duct lymph of an isologous animal. In other words, mounting evidence shows that there is some cell *that circulates* that can regenerate lymphatic tissue, and to do this it must serve as a stem cell for lymphocyte production. The evidence shows, moreover, that this cell does not regenerate myeloid tissue so that its potentiality is restricted to serving as a stem cell for lymphatic tissue.

The problem that arises from these two types of findings—(1) histologic evidence of large presumably primitive reticular cells dividing in lymphatic tissue and (2) the fact that a circulating cell can regenerate lymphatic tissue—is that the primitive reticular cell has been considered to be a fixed cell and hence does not circulate. Unfortunately, the morphology of the circulating cell that can restore lymphatic tissue is not known. However, if primitive reticular cells give rise to lymphoblasts, it seems possible that there could be a type of free cell formed from primitive reticular cells that retains the great capacity for relatively unlimited proliferation that is believed to characterize primitive reticular cells, and that this free cell occasionally gains entrance to the circulation and can "home out" in lymphatic tissue elsewhere and take on the duties of serving as a stem cell and forming lymphoblasts which then go on to form lymphocytes. At the moment, the cell that is ordinarily described as a lymphoblast is not believed to possess the power of unlimited proliferation that a stem cell must possess. So for the time being we must assume that there is some kind of a cell in lymphatic tissue that has the stem cell properties formerly ascribed to primitive reticular cells alone, but which, unlike a fixed cell, can and does enter the circulation from which it can "home out" in lymphatic tissue elsewhere and serve as a stem cell to provide lymphoblasts in its new location.

Lymphoblasts can be distinguished in germinal centers because they have nuclei that are almost as large as those of reticular cells, and in addition they have basophilic cytoplasm that has a sharply defined edge (Fig. 15-6, C). These cells are mostly lymphoblasts; however, some may be plasmablasts or their immediate precursors. The nucleoli of lymphoblasts are very prominent.

Lymphoblasts divide, and some of the progeny of the lymphoblasts become prolymphocytes (Fig. 15-24). The prolymphocytes sometimes enter the lymph stream and so reach the bloodstream where they constitute around 8 per cent of the lymphocytes of blood. In blood they are sometimes termed large lymphocytes although, as has been noted, prolymphocyte is perhaps a better term. However, most prolymphocytes remain in nodes for further division and then give rise to small lymphocytes; these enter the circulation in larger numbers.

Although some lymphocytes are probably delivered directly into the bloodstream, because they pass through the walls of the capillaries of the node, most lymphocytes that enter the bloodstream from lymph nodes do so by an indirect route; they are, as it were, washed from the node by the lymph that passes through it and hence leave the node by its efferent lymphatics (Fig. 15-3). The lymphocytes that are washed into the lymph stream as lymph percolates through a node are partly newly formed lymphocytes and partly recirculating lymphocytes; the latter migrate from blood through the small venules of the node to enter the lymph-containing spaces of the node. Since the lymphatics eventually drain into the blood circulatory system, the lymphocytes in the lymph from lymph nodes eventually reach the bloodstream. It should be noted that fresh lymph, before it has drained through a lymph node, may not contain lymphocytes; most lymphocytes of lymph are picked up in the nodes through which the lymph drains.

**The Formation of Plasma Cells in Lymph Nodes.** The formation of plasma cells has been studied in lymph nodes that drain sites where an antigen has been injected. Studies have been made by ordinary light microscopy, by immunofluorescence technics and by electron microscopy. The formation of plasma cells has been studied in both what are termed primary and secondary responses. Much has been learned and much remains to be learned about various aspects of the immunologic response in lymph nodes. Here we shall try to give a brief account of some of the facts and some of the problems. First, we shall describe primary and secondary responses.

**Primary and Secondary Responses.** When an animal is given its first injection of an antigen anytime in postnatal life (except in the first few days of postnatal life during which tolerance can be established), it reacts to the antigen by manifesting what is termed a *primary response.* This takes several days to develop; and when it has developed, some antibody to the antigen appears in the circulation.

When an animal that has been given an injection of antigen as described above and has experienced a primary response is, after a suitable length of time, given a second injection of the same antigen, it responds (except in the instance of certain antigens) in a much shorter time than that required for a primary response by producing antibody to the antigen, and it produces much more than it did in the primary response. This response is termed the *secondary response.*

**Immunofluorescence Studies.** Coons (1958), using the immunofluorescence technic, has studied lymph nodes in various stages of primary and secondary responses to an antigen.

First, Coons showed that an hour after an antigen is given it can be detected in thousands of cells in the lymph node draining the region where the antigen is given. Probably much of the antigen is taken up by reticuloendothelial cells.

By the 4th day, in a comparable section of the node, and this time testing for antibody instead of antigen, only about 50 cells can be seen that are producing antibody to the antigen, and their numbers do not appear to increase over the next 4 days. There is, then, a wide exposure of cells to an injected antigen, but only relatively few cells respond by making antibody in the primary response and indeed, it is not likely that the cells in which a response occurs are the kind of cells that originally take up the antigen (see Introduction to this chapter where it is suggested that antigen is taken up by reticuloendothelial cells).

Next, in a secondary response, Coons finds that hundreds of cells demonstrating a little antibody appear by the 2nd day in an area where only about 50 appeared in the primary response by the 4th day (Fig. 15-7). His observations suggest that these cells spring up independently; they do not appear to develop as colonies or clones from the 50 or so cells that could be seen in a comparable area in the primary response. However, later on in the secondary response these cells do form groups and colonies as they proliferate.

How do the histologic findings contribute toward explaining the shorter time taken for

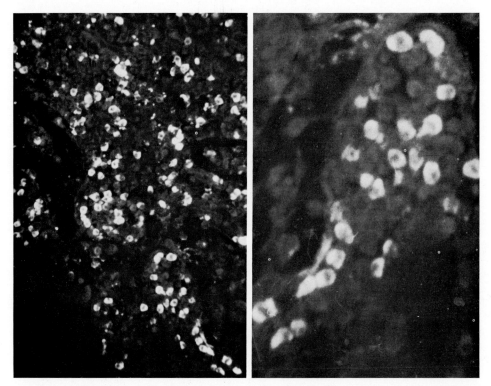

Fig. 15-7. Low-power and high-power photomicrographs of sections of a portion of a popliteal lymph node of a rabbit after it had received a second injection of diphtheria toxoid. The photomicrographs were taken, not from frozen sections as described in the text, but from paraffin sections prepared by a new method devised by G. Sainte-Marie which permits immunofluorescence studies to be made on this type of section. The photomicrographs were taken using an ultraviolet source of light, and sites where antibody was present appear in the photomicrographs as bright areas. Careful inspection of the picture on the right will show that antibody is present in the cytoplasm of cells which have the characteristic structure of young plasma cells. (Preparation by G. Sainte-Marie)

the secondary response and its greater vigor? The findings suggest that one step, which takes a certain amount of time and is not required in the secondary response, must occur in the primary response. This first step is probably that of the antigen being taken up by reticuloendothelial cells which then pass on some substance to the cytoplasm of immunologically competent cells (which are probably uncommitted lymphocytes), probably because of direct cytoplasmic connections with them (see Fig. 15-8), so that a line of cells is established which are committed to develop, on a further antigenic stimulus, into cells that will make antibody against, and only against, the administered antigen. In other words, the first step in the primary response would be in the nature of an induction of a special committed cell type. The second part of the *primary* response would be the differentiation of only relatively few of these cells of the special type into functioning types that actually produce antibody. The evidence suggests further that the rapid and effective response observed on a second exposure to the antigen, when a great many more and widely scattered cells develop quickly into antibody formers, could be explained by cells having been induced in the primary response so that they are able to react specifically and rapidly when they come into direct contact with this antigen (on its second administration) and that they respond by both proliferating and differentiating into functioning plasma cells (Fig. 15-7).

**Where Plasma Cells and Their Immediate**

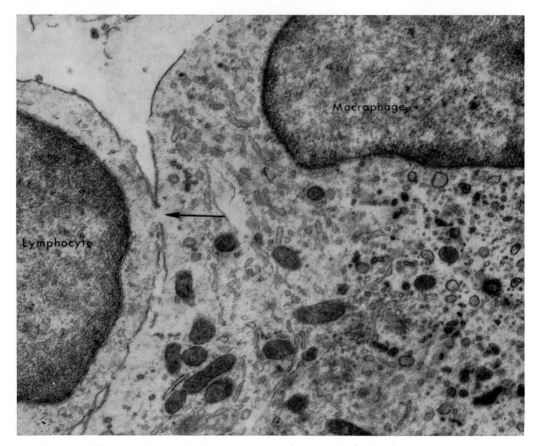

FIG. 15-8. Electron micrograph showing an example of the kind of close relationship that can be seen between lymphocytes and macrophages in the lymph nodes or spleen of immunized animals. The arrow indicates a site where it would seem that there is actual cytoplasmic continuity between the two cell types. (Schoenberg, M. D., Mumaw, V. R., Moore, R. D., and Weisberger, A. S.: Science *143*:964)

**Precursors Are Seen in Lymph Nodes.** Sainte-Marie in Leblond's laboratory made a light microscope study of the mediastinal lymph nodes of rats designed to show the chief sites where plasma cells and their precursors were distributed and also to determine the mitotic behavior of plasma cells, proplasmacytes and plasmablasts. Since they found an abundance of plasma cells in the nodes they studied, and in view of the fact that this is a common finding in laboratory rats, it can be assumed that the lymph that drains through these nodes in rats comes from sites where there is a chronic infection of some sort and that what is seen in the lymph nodes is representative of a persisting secondary response.

These investigators found that the cells of the plasma-cell series, plasmablasts, proplas-

macytes and plasmacytes, were disposed chiefly in the medullary cords of the node where these cells undergo frequent mitoses. Indeed, cells of this series made up about half of the cell population of the medullary cords. They conclude that the medullary cords of lymph nodes represent a site of active plasma cell formation in lymph nodes.

**Histologic Features of Cells of the Plasma Series.** The 3 types of cells they distinguished as being concerned in the formation of plasmacytes and observed in medullary cords are shown in Figure 15-9. The plasmablast has a large nucleus with a prominent nucleolus. The large nucleus is more or less centrally disposed in the cell and is surrounded by a relatively narrow rim of basophilic cytoplasm (Fig. 15-9). It is obvious that the appearance of a plasmablast is very similar to that of a lymphoblast, and, indeed, it is doubtful if lymphoblasts and plasmablasts can be distinguished from one another by light microscopy. There are two ways they may possibly differ slightly; the nucleolus of the plasmablast, in general, may be somewhat larger than that of a lymphoblast and the cytoplasm of plasmablast may be slightly more pyroninophilic. Both of these differences would be dependent on the plasmablast synthesizing more RNA than the lymphoblast.

Proplasmacytes differentiate from plasmablasts and differ from them in appearance in 3 chief ways: (1) the nucleus is smaller (Fig. 15-9); (2) the nucleus assumes more of an eccentric position in the cell; and (3) the cytoplasm becomes more abundant in relation to the total size of the cell and is more basophilic than the cytoplasm of a prolymphocyte. Proplasmacytes in turn differentiate into plasmacytes which, of course, have a smaller eccentrically placed nuclei and a large amount of basophilic cytoplasm. The appearance presented by plasmacytes in both the light and the electron microscope have been described in detail in Chapter 11.

In their study of mitosis in these various cell types Leblond and Sainte-Marie in 1960 suggest that on the average there are 4 generations of plasmablasts, 2 of proplasmacytes and 2 of plasmacytes. They tentatively suggested that the stem cell for plasmacyte formation may be a primitive plasmablast but noted that further work would be required to establish this point. Since their study was made, a great deal of information has become available about lymphocytes being immunologically competent cells, and this has raised the question as to whether or not lymphocytes under antigenic stimulation become plasmablasts. As has been pointed out already in connection with our discussion of lymphocytes in Chapter 12, a good case now can be made for lymphocytes serving as a source of uncommitted cells readily available to differentiate into functioning committed immunologic cells when they are exposed to a specific antigenic stimulation. It might be thought that an EM study of lymph nodes manifesting primary and secondary responses would be informative about whether or not lymphocytes serve as a source of plasma-

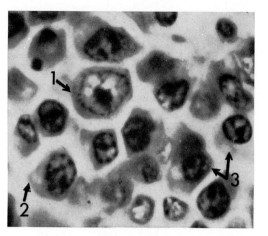

FIG. 15-9. Photomicrograph of a medullary cord of a thoracic lymph node of a rat showing (1) a plasmablast, (2) a proplasmacyte, and (3) mature plasmacytes (plasma cells). (Leblond, C. P., and Sainte-Marie, G.: In Ciba Symposium on Haemopoiesis, p. 152, London, Churchill, 1960)

blasts. Such a study has recently been made by Movat and Fernando, and the author is obliged to these investigators for some of their illustrations from their report as it was going to press. Essentially they found that the administration of either a single dose of an antigen or two doses appropriately spaced was associated in 2 to 3 days, with a considerable development in the cortex of lymph nodes of cells whose light microscope appearance differed from lymphocytes (compare cytoplasm of the two cells at left in Fig. 15-10) in that they are larger and their cytoplasm is very pyroninophilic. With the EM the cytoplasm of these cells (labeled immunoblast) was found to contain a great abundance of free ribosomes and very few rough-surfaced membranous vesicles (Fig. 15-10, immunoblast). Because these cells possessed a great abundance of free ribosomes, they differ from ordinary lymphoblasts. By not possessing many rough-surfaced membranous vesicles, these cells differed from the hitherto known and described appearance of cells of the plasma-cell series. Movat and Fernando found, however, that the character of the cells they observed in these areas rapidly changed and that any time between 2 and 5 days after a single injection of an antigen, there were many cells in these same sites that revealed some rough-surfaced mem-

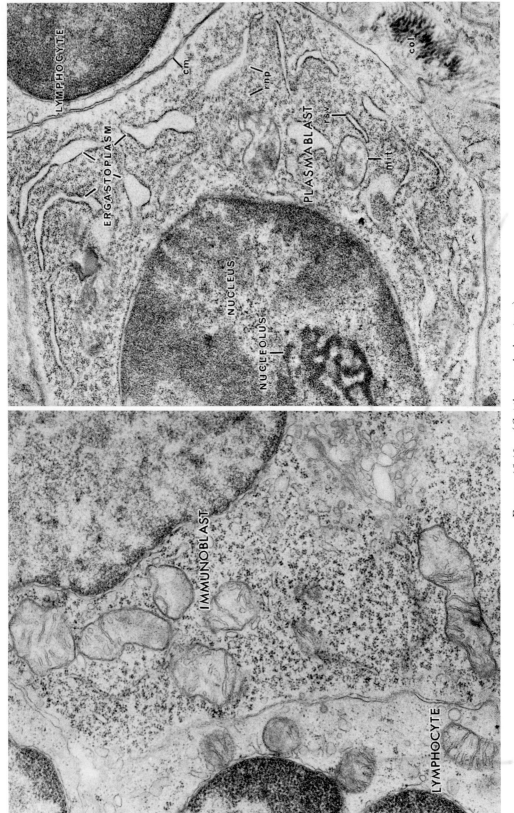

FIGURE 15-10. (*Caption on facing page*)

branous vesicles in their cytoplasm as well as an abundance of free ribosomes (Fig. 15-10, plasmablast). They consider that these latter cells resulted from the cells with the free ribosomes beginning to develop the characteristics of cells of the plasma-cell series and that when the cells began to develop rough-surfaced vesicles in their cytoplasm in addition to their abundant free ribosomes, while still having large nuclei and not overly abundant cytoplasm, they have become plasmablasts. From their light microscope study of the same material, Movat and Fernando found evidence indicating that the plasmablasts migrated from the sites where they were formed into the medullary cords.

To sum up briefly: Movat and Fernando found that the first results of an antigenic stimulus delivered to a lymph node occurred in the lymphatic nodules of the cortex, where lymphocytes were abundant. In 2 to 3 days after the antigenic stimulus, they found a considerable development, among the lymphocytes, of large cells with pyroninophilic cytoplasm. In the EM the cytoplasm of these cells was found to be characterized by a great abundance of free ribosomes. They think that the evidence for these cells developing from lymphocytes is strong. A question arises as to what name should be given to these cells that develop in response to an antigen. Movat and Fernando tentatively suggest that they should be termed immunoblasts (Fig. 15-10); however, until more is known, it may be premature to name them too precisely. The evidence provided by Movat and Fernando strongly suggests that this cell, which at first has only free ribosomes in its cytoplasm, soon begins to acquire rough-surfaced vesicles

of endoplasmic reticulum in its cytoplasm and hence soon becomes recognizable as a member of the plasma-cell series (read left-to-right in Fig. 15-10). At about this time these cells migrate into medullary cords where, as Leblond and Sainte-Marie have shown, plasmablasts divide and give rise to proplasmacytes which in turn divide and give rise to plasmacytes.

It should be noted that what would seem to be an important change that occurs when lymphocytes begin to develop into cells that function immunologically is the development of an abundance of free ribosomes in their cytoplasm, and that this also occurs when graft rejection cells develop from lymphocytes. Whether or not graft rejection cells, like the immunoblasts that develop from lymphocytes in lymph nodes, can develop further into plasmablasts, proplasmacytes and plasma cells is a question not yet settled. Hence, it is not yet known whether or not lymphocytes stimulated by an antigen can differentiate along only one pathway or two.

One approach to the study of this latter problem has been that which has developed from the finding that different kinds of antibodies are made to the same antigen and then by inquiring into the problem of whether or not different types of cells are required to make these different antibodies. In considering this question it should be emphasized that what we are considering is the different molecular forms of antibody that can be made to the same antigen and not the question of different antibodies being made in response to different antigens. To discuss this problem we must discuss briefly the chemistry of antibodies.

---

FIG. 15-10. Electron micrographs of sections of a lymph node a few days after an antigen was injected into a site which drained into this node. (*Left*) This shows a lymphocyte at the left. Its cytoplasm shows a few mitochondria and a few ribosomes. Its cell membrane abuts on a cell to its right, the cytoplasm of which is profusely sprinkled with little groups of free ribosomes. This cell is tentatively labeled an immunoblast, and it is assumed that it developed from a lymphocyte in response to the stimulus of the injected antigen. (*Right*) At the same time as the cells on the left were seen, plasmablasts were found a little closer to the medullary tissue. The plasmablast shown here is characterized by having large numbers of free ribosomes in its cytoplasm together with many rough-surfaced vesicles of endoplasmic reticulum. The further differentiation of this cell will be associated with its having fewer free ribosomes and more rough-surfaced vesicles. It is tentatively assumed that plasmablasts may form because of a further development of the cells described as immunoblasts, one of which is shown on the left. (Electron micrographs from H. Z. Movat)

**The Nature of Antibodies.** The proteins of the blood are constituted of macromolecules of different sizes, and they bear, at a constant pH, different charges, and so they may be separated from one another by electrophoresis. From a well in an agar gel in which a mixture of protein macromolecules is placed, the macromolecules migrate in the electric field with different mobility depending on their charge and become more or less segregated into groups by this movement. By this means blood proteins were shown some time ago to separate into 4 main groups of macromolecules: albumins, alpha globulins, beta globulins and gamma globulins.

**Immuno-electrophoresis.** If electrophoresis is followed by tests based on the precipitin reaction between antigen and antibody in the agar gel, the technic is termed *immunoelectrophoresis*. This can be used two ways.

First, serum proteins from an animal that has been immunized with an antigen are separated in the electrophoresis apparatus. Then a trough is cut along the sides of the agar gel parallel with the direction of the current, and the antigen is placed in the troughs. Arcs of precipitation then appear as antigen and antibody diffuse through the gel to meet each other. Experiments of this type showed that antibody activity was found mostly in the gamma globulins of the serum but since it was not found *exclusively* in the gamma globulins it has become customary to use the term *immunoglobulins* for globulins with antibody activity.

With suitable refinements the immuno-electrophoresis technic brought out more detail, for it showed that within the globulins there were several that differed from one another and yet had antibody activity. It has been shown, moreover, that these different immunoglobulins play somewhat different roles in the immunologic response as will now be described.

**How the Various Immunoglobulins Are Distinguished and Designated.** The immunoglobulins that have been studied differ from one another with respect to the mobility that they demonstrate under the influence of an electric current in the electrophoresis apparatus, and also with regard to the rate at which they sediment in the high-speed centrifuge. They can therefore be classified and named according to their mobility and sedimentation constant. Using these 2 criteria, 3 important kinds of antibody have been demonstrated (there are others as well), and we shall now name these.

First, there are 2 important immunoglobulins that have the same sedimentation constant which is 7. These, therefore, have in the past been designated as 7-S antibodies (the S stands for sedimentation constant). The first, now termed gamma G ($\gamma$ G) is the common type of circulating antibody that precipitates with antigens. The second type, now termed gamma A ($\gamma$ A), does not precipitate with antigens and it seems probable that this is the kind that tends to adhere to mast cells and other kinds of cells, and that the antigen-antibody complex thus formed is concerned in histamine release from mast cells, as was described in Chapter 11.

Another important kind of antibody has a sedimentation constant of 19 and so this kind has been designated S-19. It is now known as gamma M ($\gamma$ M). This kind has a molecular weight of around 1,000,000 and hence is called a *macroglobulin*. It is intermediate in mobility between the first two that are described. It is the type *that appears first* in immune responses. This type is usually the only kind of antibody made in response to antigens that are polysaccharides. There are other antibody globulins, for example 11-S and 13-S, that are of intermediate molecular weight.

The reason for mentioning all the above is that it has been shown by Nossal and his associates that an antibody-forming cell first produces 19-S. Then later the same cell begins to produce also 7-S and finally ends up by producing antibody of only the 7-S type. Although not enough is known to be certain about this matter, it would seem that the first kind of cell that develops from lymphocytes, which we have tentatively termed an immunoblast and which is characterized by free ribosomes in its cytoplasm (immunoblast in Fig. 15-10), produces S-19. Since it would seem that the production of S-19 is associated with free ribosomes, it might be questioned if this is the type of antibody produced by graft rejection cells (Fig. 12-14), for they too possess free ribosomes but have no or few rough-surfaced vesicles. If so, it would suggest that the graft rejection cell represents, not a different cell lineage from plasma cells, but a cell of the same family that tends to remain relatively immature. However, this problem as yet is by no means settled, and we must await further developments.

**Germinal Centers and the Immunologic Response.** It is of interest that Movat and Fernando observed that the development of germinal centers in the lymphatic nodules of lymph nodes subjected to a single antigenic stimulation did not occur until the 6th to the 8th day after the antigen was given. When germinal centers did develop in the stimulated nodes, they contained blast cells and cells of the lymphocyte series as well as macrophages. But, as Movat and Fernando point out, antibody production was well on its way before germinal centers made their appearance. Therefore, germinal centers would not seem to play the leading role in primary immunologic responses. Although they become more prominent in secondary responses, their function would not seem to be altogether a direct immunologic one, but also one of maintaining an adequate population of lymphocytes in nodules.

**The Blood Supply of Lymph Nodes.** Arteries enter and veins leave a lymph node at its hilus. The branches of the arteries are carried to the various parts of the node by the trabeculae that extend into it from the hilus. Arterioles leave the trabeculae and, supported by an ensheathment of condensed reticular tissue derived from the mesh, branch into capillary nets. Capillaries, while present throughout the reticular mesh, are particularly abundant in the peripheral parts of the lymphatic nodules, and in this site some lymphocytes enter the bloodstream by penetrating through the capillaries' rather thick walls. The capillaries empty into venules. These traverse the mesh to open into the veins of the trabeculae which carry the blood back to the hilus.

NATURE AND DISTRIBUTION OF LYMPHATIC TISSUE DESIGNED TO FILTER BLOOD

Most mammals have, in addition to lymph nodes, a much smaller number of structures that are similar except that they are yellow or red instead of gray in color. On section, these structures resemble lymph nodes except that

they have somewhat better-defined channels in their coarse mesh, and either some of these channels or all of them are filled with blood instead of lymph. If only some are filled with blood and others with lymph, the structure is called a hemal *lymph node*. If all the channels are filled with blood, it is called a *hemal node*.

There is some question as to whether hemal lymph nodes or hemal nodes are constant structures in man, but they have often been described as commonly occurring in the prevertebral peritoneal tissue, in the root of the mesentery, near the rim of the pelvis and occasionally in other sites. There are not enough of them in man to filter very much blood, but it is important to know of them, lest, on being discovered at operation or at autopsy, they be mistaken for pathologically altered tissue.

THE SPLEEN

With the possible exception of a few hemal and hemal lymph nodes, all the lymphatic tissue of the body that is specialized to filter blood is concentrated in one organ, the spleen.

Galen described the spleen as an organ full of mystery. A student who reads all the accounts of those who have tried to determine the precise course by which blood circulates through it might come to the same conclusion. But much has been learned about the spleen. It removes most of the worn-out red blood cells of the body from the circulatory system. From the hemoglobin of these worn-out cells it manufactures bilirubin (bile pigment), which it liberates into the blood, from which the liver collects it. It also extracts the iron from the hemoglobin of the worn-out cells and liberates this into the bloodstream in a form that permits it to be used over again in the manufacture of new red blood cells in the red bone marrow. The spleen, because of its ability to form plasma cells, produces antibodies that give protection from various disease organisms. It also produces many of the lymphocytes and possibly many of the monocytes that are present in blood. It also acts to some extent like an automatic transfusion bank in that, particularly in animals that are called on for great bursts of activity, it can quickly liberate stored blood into the circulatory sys-

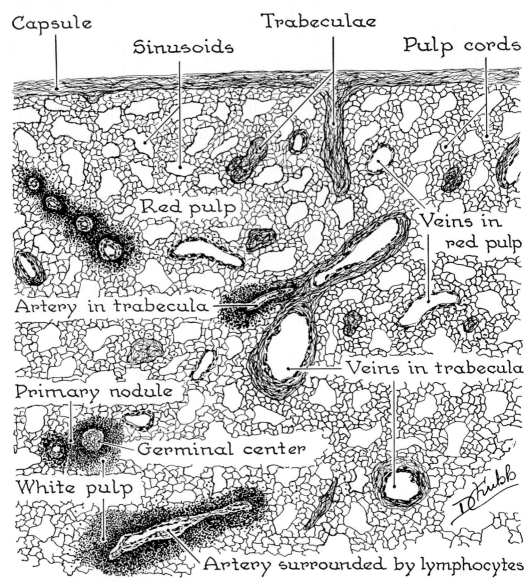

Capsule    Trabeculae

Sinusoids    Pulp cords

Red pulp

Veins in red pulp

Artery in trabecula

Veins in trabecula

Primary nodule

Germinal center

White pulp

Artery surrounded by lymphocytes

FIG. 15-11. Diagram of a section cut at right angles to the surface of a distended spleen. Notice that the white pulp (*left lower corner*) consists of nodules and aggregations of lymphocytes and that the red pulp is an open mesh with sinusoids running through it. A trabecula with veins may be seen in the central part of the illustration.

tem. Yet, with all these functions, the spleen is not essential to life. This is not because its functions are not valuable but because most of them are taken over by the other hemopoietic tissues when the spleen is removed.

**Gross Characteristics.** The spleen is roughly the size and the shape of a clenched fist. It lies in the shelter of the left 9th, the 10th and the 11th ribs, with its long axis parallel with them. Its purple color is due to its great con-

tent of blood. It is soft in consistency and more friable than most organs. A long fissure may be seen close to its medial border; this is termed the hilus. On approaching this, the splenic artery divides into several branches that enter the substance of the spleen separately at different points along the elongated hilus. Veins leave the spleen in association with the arteries that enter it and later unite to form the splenic vein.

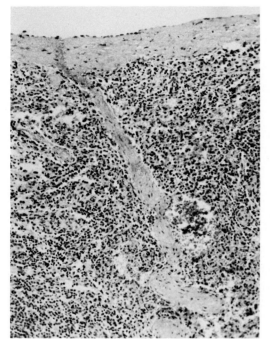 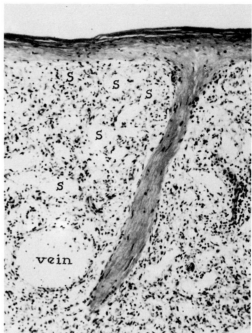

FIG. 15-12. Low-power photomicrographs of 2 sections cut at right angles to the capsule of the spleen. (*Left*) Picture taken from a section of collapsed spleen. The capsule and also a trabecula extending in from the capsule may be seen. (*Right*) Picture taken from a spleen that was distended with fixative through its veins. Notice that the red pulp has been opened up by this procedure and that the sinusoids (S) are apparent.

Before beginning the microscopic study of this organ, the student should examine, with the naked eye or a magnifying glass, the surface of a slice cut through the spleen. The spleen will be seen to be surrounded by a connective tissue capsule (the capsule has smooth muscle fibers in it also, but these cannot be seen with the naked eye). Trabeculae of the same material as the capsule will be seen extending into the substance of the organ both from the hilus and to a lesser extent from the capsule. The remainder of the interior of the spleen is filled with what is called splenic pulp. Two kinds of pulp can be seen with the naked eye: white and red. The white pulp is distributed as tiny little firm gray islands, somewhat less than 1 mm. in diameter, among the soft, red pulp that fills all the remaining space.

**General Microscopic Structure.** If sections cut from a block of splenic tissue, cut at right angles to the capsule, are examined with the microscope, it will be obvious that the little nodules of gray pulp observed on the cut surface of the spleen with the naked eye are lymphatic nodules (Fig. 15-11). These, then, are the chief sites of lymphocyte production in the spleen. Moreover, it will be seen that the red pulp (Fig. 15-11) that surrounds the lymphatic nodules contains vast numbers of red blood cells in its mesh and so represents the part of the lymphatic tissue of the spleen that is designed to act as a filter. In the spleen then, as in lymphatic tissue in general, the two functions—lymphocyte production and filtering—tend to be segregated from one another; the white pulp makes the lymphocytes, and the red pulp filters.

Before studying the white and the red pulp in more detail, the student should examine the capsule of the organ (Figs. 15-11 and 15-12). This consists of collagenic and elastic fibers in which fibroblasts and some smooth muscle cells are distributed. In some animals there is much more smooth muscle in the capsule of the spleen than in man, and its contraction can materially assist the smooth muscle of the trabeculae in contracting the spleen and so forcing the blood it contains into the circulatory system in times of emer-

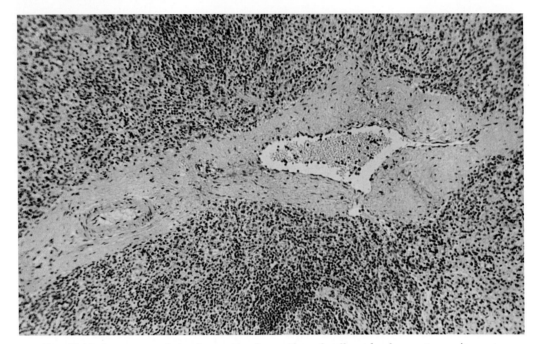

Fig. 15-13. Low-power photomicrograph of a section of collapsed spleen cut near its center. The picture shows a large trabecula containing an artery on the left and a vein on the right.

gency. It is doubtful if there is enough smooth muscle in the capsule of the spleen of man to function very efficiently in this respect.

The capsule is covered with a serous (peritoneal) coat of mesothelium; this consists of a single layer of squamous cells. The cytoplasm of the mesothelial cells is too scant to be seen in sections, but their nuclei may be seen occasionally.

Next, the student should examine the trabeculae that are scattered through the substance of the spleen (Figs. 15-11, 15-12 and 15-13). Since these extend in from the hilus like a branching tree and pass in various directions to connect with those that extend in from the capsule (though not all do), they will be cut, in any section, in almost every plane. Most of them, of course, will be cut obliquely. They consist, like the capsule, of dense connective tissue in which there is a fairly high percentage of elastin. They also contain a few muscle cells, but, as is true of the capsule, the amount of smooth muscle in them is not as great in man as in certain other animals.

In the trabeculae both arteries and veins, as well as nerves, may be seen. In general, the largest trabeculae are seen near the hilus,

and these contain the largest vessels. Although the detailed microscopic structure of arteries and veins will not be considered until a later chapter, it should be said here that arteries have thicker walls (composed chiefly of circularly disposed smooth muscle) and smaller lumens than their corresponding veins. By using these criteria the student should readily distinguish the vein from the artery in most trabeculae (Figs. 15-11 and 15-13).

**Arteries.** The arteries that travel in from the hilus in the larger trabeculae branch into small branches *that leave the trabeculae* (the smaller trabeculae, therefore, contain only veins) to enter the pulp. To support these, the reticular tissue of the pulp becomes condensed along one side of them, and to some extend around them, to provide them with fairly substantial sheaths. The reticular fibers in these sheaths are disposed so as to hold lymphocytes in their meshes, and as a result the sheaths are heavily infiltrated with lymphocytes (Fig. 15-14). While the supporting sheaths of these arteries, infiltrated with lymphocytes, are not true lymphatic nodules along most of their course, the sheath does become expanded (usually at one side) from time to time to form true lymphatic nodules

Fig. 15-14. Low-power photomicrograph of a section of a human spleen. In this particular section an artery that has left a trabecula and is passing through a red pulp is cut longitudinally. Many lymphocytes, disposed in a fine reticular mesh, are to be seen above the artery. Toward the left-hand side of the picture, the lymphatic tissue accompanying the artery is expanded into a primary nodule. The artery at the site of the primary nodule has given off a branch called the follicular artery, which may be seen in the central part of the nodule.

(Fig. 15-11, *lower left*; Fig. 15-14, *left*), which may contain germinal centers. The white pulp of the spleen, then, is distributed along the arteries that leave the trabeculae.

In each site where the surrounding reticular sheaths of the arteries are expanded into lymphatic nodules, the artery gives off a branch to supply the nodule (Fig. 15-14, *left*). This is termed a follicular artery (in the spleen, lymphatic nodules are often termed lymphatic follicles).

A follicular artery gives off branches to supply the capillary beds of the lymphatic nodules which contain it and then emerges from the follicle into the surrounding red pulp. On entering the red pulp, each follicular artery, according to Solnitzky, divides into from 2 to 6 branches which radiate in different directions from their point of origin. Since these arterial branches are straight, they are called *penicillar arteries* or penicilli. Each of these, according to Solnitzky, divides into 2 or 3 arterioles, most of which soon enter cu-

rious little structures called ellipsoids, whereupon they lose all their arteriolar characteristics (muscular and elastic walls) to become capillaries. Before considering further the structure of ellipsoids or the course of the blood, it is helpful to describe first the structure of the red pulp.

**General Structure of Red Pulp.** The framework of the red pulp consists of a mesh of reticular fibers which are continuous with the collagenic fibers of the trabeculae and the capsule. The reticular mesh of red pulp, though of an open type itself, is permeated by passageways that measure from 12 to 40 microns in width. Since these passageways drain into veins, they are termed the venous sinusoids of the red pulp (Figs. 15-11 and 15-12). The walls of at least some of these are made of long, narrow reticuloendothelial cells that bulge somewhat into the lumen of the sinusoid in the region of their nuclei. The long, narrow cells lining the sinusoids are arranged something like the staves of a bar-

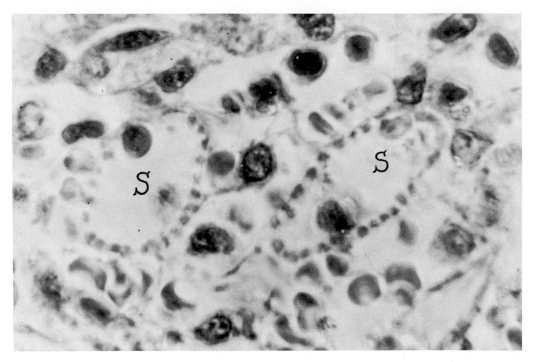

FIG. 15-15. Oil-immersion photomicrograph of a section of distended spleen taken with the phase microscope. In this picture 2 sinusoids are cut in cross section. These are marked S. Their longitudinally disposed stavelike lining cells are cut in cross section and can be seen to be slightly separated from one another.

rel, in particular, a barrel whose staves were fashioned from imperfectly seasoned wood and that has been left empty in the sun, for the sides of the cells lining the sinusoids are separated from each other by longitudinal slits (Fig. 15-15). To carry the analogy still further, it will be recalled that the staves of barrels usually are supported by surrounding iron hoops. The reticuloendothelial staves of the venous sinusoids are somewhat similarly surrounded and supported by hoops of reticular fibers.

In a single section, the red pulp situated between two adjacent sinusoids often resembles a cord (Fig. 15-11, *top, right*); indeed, these areas have been termed *Billroth* or *pulp cords*. However, the student who has zealously practiced 3-dimensional visualization will quickly realize that true cords of pulp do not exist between sinusoids any more than cords exist between the holes made by poking two fingers into dough.

Neither the red pulp between sinusoids nor the sinusoids themselves can be studied to advantage in ordinary sections of spleen.

The reason for this is that the spleen collapses to some extent either before or after death, and this compresses the red pulp and obscures its microscopic structure (Fig. 15-12, *left*). A much better picture of the structure of the red pulp can be obtained if the spleen is redistended to its original size, particularly by injecting fixation into the splenic vein (Fig. 15-12, *right*). Robinson, in his studies, not only has studied distended spleens but has studied thick sections of the red pulp of distended spleens with a binocular microscope arranged to give stereoscopic vision. He describes the pulp between the sinusoids as consisting of a vast, delicate network of starlike reticuloendothelial cells having long, irregular protoplasmic processes running in all directions and uniting one cell with another. The interstices of this cellular network he visualizes as a vast cavernous system of intercellular spaces that are in free communication with the venous sinusoids through the longitudinal slits in the walls of the latter (Fig. 15-15).

In examining the red pulp, particularly

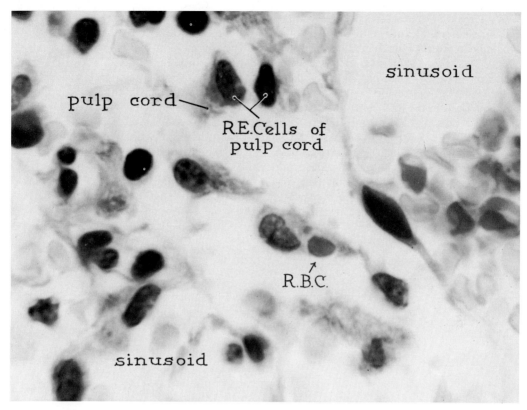

FIG. 15-16. Oil-immersion photomicrograph of a section of distended human spleen removed to alleviate excessive red blood cell destruction. Sinusoids may be seen at the lower left and the upper right; between them is a pulp cord. In this, several reticuloendothelial cells may be seen. One near the center has phagocytosed a red blood corpuscle which is lying in its cytoplasm. The spotty appearance of the cytoplasm of the cell immediately below it is due to granules of pigment formed as a result of the breakdown of hemoglobin in its cytoplasm.

that of a distended spleen, the student will see many types of cells in the interstices of the pulp cords. Red blood cells abound in this situation. If the student is fortunate, he may see reticuloendothelial cells that have phagocytosed worn-out red blood cells (Fig. 15-16). In the cytoplasm of the reticuloendothelial cells (both fixed ones and free macrophages), the hemoglobin of phagocytosed red blood cells is broken down to an iron-containing pigment of a golden-brown color (hemosiderin) and a non-iron-containing pigment variously called hematoidin, bilirubin or bile pigment. The latter pigment is readily soluble and diffuses out of cells as quickly as it is made, but hemosiderin lingers long enough for it to be seen at least sometimes in the cytoplasm of the cells that form it.

**Fine Structure.** Palade has obtained elec-

tron micrographs of phagocytic cells lining a sinusoid in the spleen of the rat (Fig. 15-17). The cells in this illustration do not appear to be of the barrel-stave type, for they fit together closely by means of pseudopodia from adjacent cells being invaginated into the cytoplasm of each other. When a pseudopodium from one cell invaginates the next, it either pushes the cell membrane of the second cell ahead of it or fits into an already existing cleft in the second cell so that the cytoplasm in any pseudopodium is separated from the cytoplasm of the invaginated cell by two cell membranes, one that covers the pseudopodium and the other that lines the cleft. Therefore, invaginated pseudopodia cut in cross section, demonstrate two rings of cell membranes around them (Fig. 15-17, *invag. pseudo.*).

With the EM the cytoplasm of the lining cells of sinusoids reveals granular bodies that probably represent iron-containing pigment (Fig. 15-17, *phago. mat.*). In addition, rough-surfaced flattened vesicles, ribosomes and mitochondria are all evident.

**Other Cells in the Red Pulp.** In addition to red blood cells and fixed and free reticulo-endothelial cells, many lymphocytes may be seen in the pulp. Monocytes may also be present in the pulp (Fig. 15-18). Various numbers of neutrophils and eosinophils may also be seen in the interstices of the pulp cords. Worn-out cells of the granular leukocyte series as well as red blood cells probably are

strained out here to some extent by the reticuloendothelial phagocytes.

**The Formation and the Distribution of Plasma Cells in the Spleen.** As has been noted, the spleen, being situated so that much blood is constantly circulating through it, and being composed of lymphatic tissue, is admirably adapted to responding immunologically to antigens that gain entrance to the bloodstream.

Movat and Fernando have recently studied the changes that occur in the spleens of rabbits when the latter are given an antigen intravenously. They found that the first indication of an immunologic response was the development among lymphocytes of pyronino-

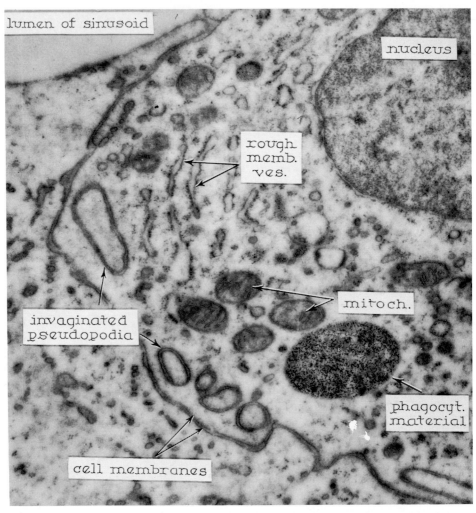

FIG. 15-17. Electron micrograph ($\times$ 42,000) of a section of parts of 2 cells lining a splenic sinusoid in a rat. The labeling has been added. (Palade, G. E.: J. Biophys. & Biochem. Cystol. (Supp.) 2:85)

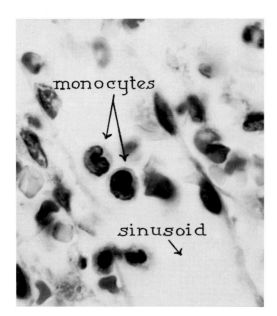

FIG. 15-18. Oil-immersion photomicrograph of a section of distended spleen. A sinusoid may be seen running from the upper left to the lower right portion of the picture. Two monocytes are present in the sinusoid.

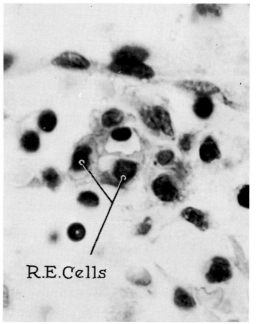

FIG. 15-19. Oil-immersion photomicrograph of a section of distended human spleen. An ellipsoid, cut in cross section, may be seen in the center of the illustration. It consists of an arrangement of reticuloendothelial cells surrounding a capillary. The lumen of the capillary may be seen immediately above the labeled reticuloendothelial cells. A lymphocyte is present in the lumen of the capillary.

philic blast cells which in the EM were characterized by an abundance of free ribosomes in their cytoplasm. Cells of this type appeared between 2 and 4 days and were seen in the lymphocyte sheaths of the arteries and the arterioles that run from trabeculae to primary nodules. Blast cells of this type were also seen at this time in the peripheral parts of primary nodules. By the 6th day both immature and mature plasma cells were seen in these same sites. Moreover, some plasma cells, by this time had spilled over from the white pulp into the red pulp.

Nine days after antigenic stimulation, Movat and Fernando found that the penicillar arteries which radiate from the lymphatic nodules of the white pulp to deliver blood into the red pulp, and which are normally ensheathed with lymphocytes, became ensheathed mostly with plasma cells. Accordingly, it would seem that lymphocytes of the white pulp of the spleen under the influence of antigenic stimulation, become immunoblasts of the same type that appear in the lymphatic follicles of lymph nodes that are stimulated antigenically, and which are char-

acterized by a great abundance of free ribosomes in their cytoplasm. Cells of this type that form in the spleen rapidly migrate toward the red pulp and probably serve as a source of plasmablasts which divide and differentiate to form the plasma cells that are seen in the red pulp, particularly in that adjacent to white pulp.

The reticular fibers of the red pulp can be seen to advantage only in silver or other special types of preparations.

It will be recalled that before we began the foregoing general description of the structure of red pulp we had succeeded in tracing the course of arterial blood through the spleen to the point where it had reached the ellipsoids of the red pulp. Furthermore, in our description of the red pulp, it became apparent that blood delivered into the venous sinusoids would pass by way of the veins of the red pulp to the trabecular veins and hence to the splenic vein. To complete the account of the circulation of blood through the spleen, we have only to trace the course of blood from the ellipsoids of the venous sinusoids. There are differences of opinion about the course that it takes over this short distance. Before discussing the matter, we shall comment very briefly on the structure of ellipsoids.

Ellipsoids are developed to different degrees in different species. Those of man are not very highly developed. So to study the structure and the function of ellipsoids, many investigators have turned to the cat, whose ellipsoids are extremely well developed. Ellipsoids have been suspected of being nervous structures, muscular organs and other things, but the general opinion derived from the more recent studies is that the ellipsoid represents nothing more than a condensation of reticular fibers and reticuloendothelial cells around a capillary (Fig. 15-19). However, in distended cat spleens, there are openings through the sides of the ellipsoids through which blood can escape from the central vessel of the ellipsoid; but in contracted cat spleens, the side openings of the ellipsoids probably are closed. In this sense the ellipsoids of the cat spleen act as arterial sphincters. But their sphincter-like action probably is not due to the cells of the ellipsoids being possessed of contractile powers. It seems more likely that the ellipsoids of the cat open out and shrink down passively along with the whole spleen. In this connection it is of interest that ellipsoids seem to be more highly developed in those species that have much muscle in the capsules and the trabeculae of their spleens; and in these animals it is not unlikely that the ellipsoids cut down the amount of blood entering the spleen when the smooth muscle of the capsule and the trabeculae contract in emergency and certain other conditions (for example, exercise). It is doubtful if the more or less rudimentary ellipsoids in the spleen of man act to any extent even as passive sphincters. What then is their function? The most reasonable explanation is that since they have openings between their reticuloendothelial cells through which blood from the central capillary can escape, they serve as the first filters that arterial blood encounters in the spleen. Robinson has shown that certain foreign particles injected into the bloodstream are first seen in the spleen ad-

herent to the reticuloendothelial cells of the ellipsoids.

Ellipsoids are situated in the pulp tissue (pulp cords) between the venous sinusoids. Although blood can escape into the pulp through the side openings of the ellipsoids, most of the blood that comes to an ellipsoid passes through it in its central capillary, which then opens into the intercellular pulp spaces. Since openings exist between contiguous cells in the pulp, blood delivered into it by the capillary can circulate through it to some extent.

The description of the passage of the blood through the spleen given above constitutes a statement of the *open circulation theory* (Fig. 15-20). This theory is called the open one because it suggests that blood in circulating through the spleen is not confined to a *closed* system of endothelial-lined vessels as it is elsewhere in the body. In a sense, the open theory suggests that from the capillaries of the ellipsoids, hemorrhages occur into the tissue of the pulp cords and that this extravasated blood is transfused back into the vascular system through the openings in the walls of the venous sinusoids (Fig. 15-16).

It is obvious that the filtering function of the spleen would be extremely efficient under conditions of an open circulation. By having red blood cells delivered into the interstices of the pulp where they can move only slowly and in the small spaces of which they come into contact with many reticuloendothelial cells, the worn-out ones can be phagocytosed much more readily than if they were being swept along a vessel, even if it were lined with reticuloendothelial cells. Robinson has shown that the reticuloendothelial cells of the pulp attract and so filter from the circulation particles bearing negative charges.

Many students of the spleen do not agree that the circulation through it is of the open type but think instead that the capillaries from the ellipsoids or other arterial vessels deliver blood directly into the venous sinusoids (Fig. 15-20). Those who subscribe to the closed theory explain the numerous red blood cells present in the pulp cords as being due to their being forced out through the openings between the cells of the walls of the venous sinusoids.

Another opinion is that the circulation can

# CIRCULATION OF BLOOD THROUGH THE SPLEEN

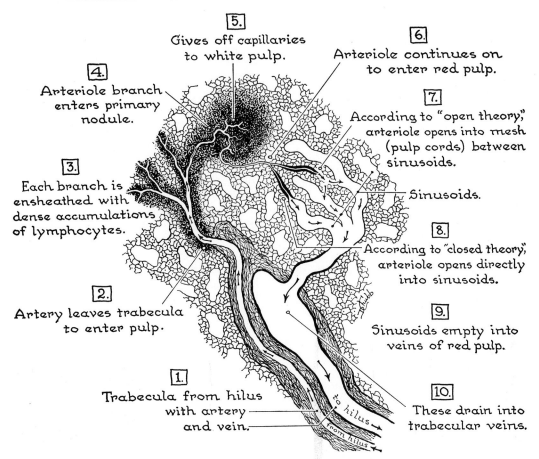

**5.** Gives off capillaries to white pulp.

**6.** Arteriole continues on to enter red pulp.

**4.** Arteriole branch enters primary nodule.

**7.** According to "open theory," arteriole opens into mesh (pulp cords) between sinusoids.

**3.** Each branch is ensheathed with dense accumulations of lymphocytes.

Sinusoids.

**8.** According to "closed theory," arteriole opens directly into sinusoids.

**2.** Artery leaves trabecula to enter pulp.

**9.** Sinusoids empty into veins of red pulp.

**1.** Trabecula from hilus with artery and vein.

to hilus

from hilus

**10.** These drain into trabecular veins.

Fig. 15-20. Diagram to show the course of blood taken through the spleen according to the open and the closed theories of circulation. The legends on the figure should be read in a clockwise fashion.

be either closed or open, depending on circumstances. According to this view, the beginnings of the venous sinusoids which appear as tubular structures in a contracted spleen may, in a distended spleen, exhibit so many openings between the cells of their walls that they cease to be structures and become no more than fairly open passageways through a reticuloendothelial meshwork that abounds with communicating spaces. In other words, some consider that the first parts of the venous sinusoids, when they are distended, are so leaky that they are only spaces in a meshwork, and hence that the circulation under these conditions is open. But when the spleen is contracted, the cells of the walls of the sinusoids come close enough together to

justify the view that they are tubular structures; under these conditions, the circulation is closed.

All the evidence concerning the circulation through the spleen that has been discussed so far has been obtained by means of the study of sections of fixed tissue. In 1936, however, a new approach to the problem was made by Knisely when he utilized the quartz-rod illuminator to study the passageways by which blood circulates between the arteries and the veins in the living animal. Knisely found that the arterial capillaries branch after passing through the region of ellipsoids, and that some of the branches pass directly to the veins. These capillaries (see Fig. 15-21, *capillary shunts*), which are controlled by sphinc-

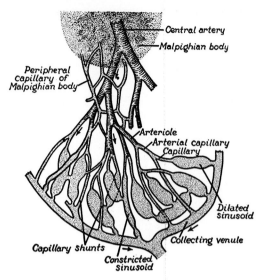

Central artery

Malpighian body

Peripheral
Capillary of
Malpighian body

Arteriole
Arterial capillary
Capillary

Dilated
sinusoid

Collecting venule

Capillary shunts

Constricted
sinusoid

FIG. 15-21. Diagram of splenic circulation, according to Knisely. (Peck, H. M.,
and Hoerr, N. L.: Anat. Rec. *109*:447)

ters, provide a *by-pass* or *shunt* circulation
so that blood can pass through the spleen
without being emptied either into the red
pulp or the sinusoids. Knisely found that the
other set of capillary branches empties into
the sinusoids; in this respect Knisely's findings support the closed circulation theory. But
Knisely found also that there were sphincters
at each end of the sinusoids and that, depending on the contraction or the relaxation of
these sphincters, sinusoids exhibit different
states of form and function which he termed
phases (Fig. 15-21). With both sphincters
open, a sinusoid would be relatively narrow;
in this state it would be said to be in a conducting phase. With the efferent sphincter
contracted and the afferent one open, a sinusoid is said to be in a *filtration-filling* phase
with its walls retaining erythrocytes but allowing plasma to escape into the pulp cords.
When the sinusoid becomes filled with
erythrocytes the afferent sphincter closes, and
the sinusoid enters the *storage phase.* Then,
when both sphincters open, it enters the
*emptying phase,* and the red blood cells that
are packed in it are washed into the circulation.

The study of the circulation of the living
spleen by the quartz-rod illuminator is a difficult technic. In their use of this method, Mac-
Kenzie, Whipple and Wintersteiner were un-

able to confirm many of Knisely's findings.
Accordingly, Peck and Hoerr made a further
study of both the method and the problem.
Their work emphasized the necessity for very
exacting precautions if the method is to yield
information of value, and they found that
when these precautions are taken, the intermediary circulation in the spleen is essentially
as Knisely described it.

The function of the human spleen in storing
blood and delivering stored blood into the circulation under certain circumstances is not as
significant as that of the spleens of certain
other species. The human spleen is somewhat
larger in life than it is after death (when it
has contracted), but this difference is not
nearly so great as that seen in laboratory animals and probably not nearly so great as is
sometimes inferred from studies made on these
other animals. Nevertheless, as Barcroft and
his associates have shown, the human spleen
has a definite function in storing blood and
liberating stored blood under certain circumstances when extra blood would be helpful. It
is not likely that there is enough smooth muscle in the capsule and the trabeculae of the
human spleen to explain its contraction under
these circumstances. The release of blood from
the human spleen is more in the nature of a
passive act that occurs when the smooth
muscle fibers that encircle its arteries and arterioles contract and so restrict the amount of
blood entering the spleen. This permits the
stretched elastic fibers of the trabeculae and
the capsule, aided to some extent by smooth
muscle fibers of the same structures, to contract and so squeeze blood out of the pulp
spaces of the spleen into the venous sinusoids,
and out of them and the trabecular veins into
the circulation.

## THE THYMUS

As was noted at the beginning of this chapter, much of the lymphatic tissue of the body—
that constituting the lymphatic nodules of
loose connective tissue, the lymph nodes and
the spleen—is situated so as to quickly encounter antigens that gain entrance either to
the loose connective tissue or to the circulating
fluids (lymph and blood) of the body. An important function of lymphatic tissue so disposed is to react to antigens by developing

cells that function immunologically against the antigens. In profound contrast to this exposed lymphatic tissue is the large depot of lymphatic tissue of the thymus, for here the emphasis is on protection from, instead of ready exposure to, antigens. The features of the thymus that indicate that it provides an environment where lymphocytes can be produced so that they are relatively protected from antigens are of different sorts:

First, the thymus is relatively deeply located in the body. Secondly, no afferent lymphatics of any consequence lead to it to permit lymph that forms outside its boundaries to drain through it. Accordingly, only antigens that are carried by blood have access to the thymus. However, even antigens in the blood (where their concentration is low in contrast to concentrations that can be reached locally in loose connective tissue or in lymph-draining infected areas) encounter certain obstacles in penetrating into sites of lymphocyte production in the thymus. As will be described, lymphocytes are produced in the interstices of an epithelial cell reticulum in the cortex of the thymus gland. Clark has shown that the epithelial cells possess desmosomes where they abut on each other, and, furthermore, they connect together so as to provide a sort of a barrier between the blood capillaries of the cortex of the thymus and the interstices of the epithelial network where lymphocytes are produced. Clark, by experimental procedures, has shown that this barrier is not complete and that particulate matter can penetrate it. Nevertheless, it would seem to be efficient enough to hinder, even if it does not prohibit, the entrance of antigens into sites of lymphocyte production in this organ.

The fact that sites of lymphocyte production in the thymus are relatively protected from antigens may explain, in part, why the transformation of lymphocytes in the thymus to immunologically functioning cells is most unusual. For example, it seems that lymphocytes do not become transformed into plasma cells in the thymus itself because plasma cells are rarely seen in this organ. Moreover, there is evidence suggesting that lymphocytes produced in the protected environment provided by the thymus are somewhat different with regard to their immunologic responsiveness, even when they are exposed to antigens, than

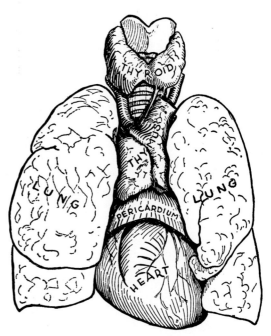

Fig. 15-22. The thymus gland of a child. (Grant, J. C. B.: A Method of Anatomy, ed. 4, Baltimore, Williams & Wilkins)

lymphocytes produced in the exposed lymphatic tissues of the body. For example, if thymic lymphocytes are injected into non-isologous animals they do not, like lymph node and spleen lymphocytes, from the same animal, develop into functioning immunologic cells and so cause runt or wasting disease nearly as effectively as do the lymph node or the splenic lymphocytes. There is thus some reason to think that the lymphocytes produced in the thymus are not quite so far along the road toward attaining immunologic competence of those in the more exposed parts of the body.

What then is the function of the thymus? This question has piqued investigators for decades. Only recently has information become available that has given the leads that were lacking to direct studies that will eventually clarify all the roles served by this organ. Probably no organ of the body is being investigated more actively at the moment than the thymus. After describing its histologic structure we shall describe some of the facts that have been ascertained recently about its function and try to indicate areas where future advances are probable.

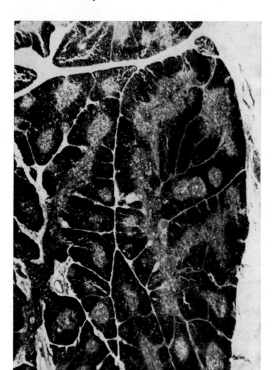 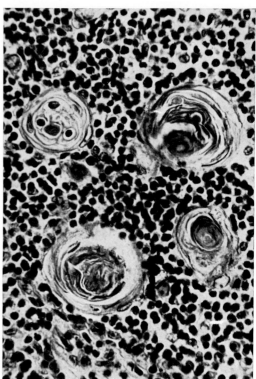

Fig. 15-23. (*Left*) Very low-power photomicrograph of a section of the thymus gland of a child. The septa appear as clear lines. The cortex of the lobules is dark; the medulla is light. Observe that the medulla of one lobule is continuous with that of another. (*Right*) High-power photomicrograph of an area of medulla. Four Hassal's corpuscles are shown.

**Shape and Site.** The thymus gland is a pinkish-gray, broad, flat bilobed mass of tissue. The bulk of the organ lies in the thorax immediately beneath the upper part of the sternum (Fig. 15-22). Its upper part extends up into the neck. Each of the two lobes of the gland resembles a thyme leaf; they are disposed one on each side but are in apposition along the midline.

**Size.** The size of the thymus gland varies greatly in relation to age. It is largest—in relation to the remainder of the body—during fetal life and in the first 2 years of postnatal life. From the 2nd year onward and until the time of puberty, it continues to increase in size but not so rapidly as the remainder of the body. After puberty it begins to involute (*involvere* = to roll up) and as a consequence it slowly becomes smaller as an individual ages.

For many years the size and the weight of a normal thymus gland in childhood and adulthood were underestimated. This was probably because the average figure did not represent the normal. This is to be explained by the fact that serious diseases tend to bring about the premature involution of the gland. Since so many children and adults from whom surveys were made in the past had had serious diseases, the average figure compiled from them was then not representative of the normal. According to modern views, the thymus gland weighs about 10 to 15 Gm. at the time of birth; and at the time of puberty 30 to 40 Gm. From then onward its weight slowly declines, but still retains a substantial size in old individuals.

**Development.** The thymus gland develops as a result of tubes of epithelial cells growing out into mesenchyme from the third pharyngeal pouches of which there are two, one on each side of the body. These epithelial tubes soon become solid cords, and as development proceeds, epithelial cells derived from the pouch on one side meet and join with those from the pouch of the other side and the epithelial arrangement of cordlike structures are pulled down into the thorax and lose their connections with their points of origin. At this stage of development the thymus resembles an endocrine gland because it is composed of cords of epithelial cells. These proliferate and send out side branches which are the forerunners of the cores or (medullas) of lobules. The arrangement of the epithelial cells then begins to change. One thing that happens is that here and there little groups of cells become arranged around a central point, much as football players pile up around and over a loose ball. These little groups of cells are known as Hassal's corpuscles (Fig. 15-23, *right*). Another change that occurs in the cells of the epithelial cords is that they become less densely arranged, tending to spread apart and become arranged into a network.

**The Source of the Lymphocytes of the Thymus Gland.** Mesenchyme surrounds the epithelial outgrowth and dips into it in the clefts between the sites where the epithelium protrudes; at these sites the mesenchyme will form the incomplete septa that later partially separate lobules of thymic tissue. Other changes that occur are very difficult to interpret. Lymphocytes appear in the area where mesenchyme is in contact with networks of epithelial cells; the experimental evidence regarding the source of these lymphocytes is conflicting. One school of thought is to the effect that the lymphocytes are derived from the epithelial cells (see Auerbach). The other school of thought ascribes their origin to mesenchymal cells. Since the thymus gland soon becomes very active in the production of lymphocytes, it is important to know if these lymphocytes originate from epithelium or from mesenchyme. Some experimental work which bears on this problem will now be described.

It has been noted already that the most important effect of radiation is that, in sufficiently large doses, it prevents cells from continuing to divide. For that reason the effects of total-body irradiation are most serious in those parts of the body where there is a relatively rapid turnover of the cell population. Total-body irradiation, for example, results in an almost complete cessation of the formation of blood cells, and since neutrophils in particular have a short life span, there are soon no phagocytic cells of this type to combat

infection. As has been noted, lymphocytes are peculiarly sensitive to irradiation. It is therefore easy to understand that after severe total-body irradiation the lymphocytes of the thymus gland would mostly disappear and that there would be almost no further mitosis occurring in the irradiated gland to repopulate it with lymphocytes.

An animal treated this way can generally be saved if it is immediately injected intravenously with a suspension of bone marrow cells obtained from a (nonirradiated) isologous animal. The injected bone marrow cells repopulate the bone marrow of the host which then resumes production of the various kinds of blood cells ordinarily provided by that tissue. Furthermore, under these circumstances the thymus gland also becomes repopulated with lymphocytes which divide and maintain its normal population. Moreover, it can be shown by using chromosome markers (for example by injecting an irradiated male with bone marrow cells from a female) that the lymphocytes in the repopulated thymus gland of the irradiated animal are derived from the donor and not from the host. This, and similar experiments made by transplanting thymus glands, which regenerate in their hosts, prove that the thymus gland can be repopulated with lymphocytes that are derived from some cell that is present in bone marrow. Further experiments with parabiotic mice (mice surgically joined together so that the blood from each circulates to some extent in the other) have shown that in postnatal life a small proportion of the lymphocytes produced in the thymus of one of the mice are derived from cells that can be shown to have come by way of circulating blood from the other. From all this evidence it seems clear that in postnatal life there are stem cells that circulate and can take up residence in the thymus gland and there form lymphocytes. The most probable source of this cell that can gain entrance to the thymus and produce lymphocytes is the bone marrow. It is difficult to think that both epithelial cells, and circulating, and presumably mesenchymal-derived, cells both develop into thymic lymphocytes. To the author the evidence for the stem cell of the thymus that gives rise to lymphocytes being a free cell derived originally from mesenchyme is stronger than that indicating its being an epithelial cell. In concluding, it may be pointed out that, even though stem cells for lymphopoiesis may exist in the circulation, the healthy thymus may contain enough of them for its ordinary needs.

As the normal development of the thymus gland proceeds in prenatal life lobules can be distinguished as well as a cortex and a medulla; these parts of the gland as they appear in postnatal life will now be described.

**Microscopic Structure.** Each of the two lobes of the thymus is in due course surrounded by a thin capsule of connective tissue. This extends into the substance of each lobe to form septa and to divide the lobes into lobules which are usually from 1 to 2 mm. in width (Fig. 15-23, *left*). The septa, on penetrating into the substance of each lobe, meet and fuse with other septa but not extensively enough to surround the thymic tissue of each lobule completely (although they may appear to do so in a single section); hence, the thymic tissue of each lobule is continuous in the more central part of each lobe with that of other lobules (Fig. 15-23, *left*).

Lymphocytes are not spread evenly throughout the substance of each lobule; instead, they tend to be concentrated toward those borders of each lobule that abut on the capsule or on interlobular septa. The peripheral part of each lobule, heavily infiltrated with lymphocytes, is termed its cortex (Fig. 15-23, *left*), and the more central part of the lobule that does not contain so many lymphocytes is called its medulla (Fig. 15-23, *left*). Lymphocytes are concentrated in the cortices of lobules. Since lobules are not completely surrounded by connective tissue, each lobule has one side that is deficient in cortex, and at this site the medulla of the lobule is continuous with the medullary tissue of other lobules (Fig. 15-23, *left*).

Lymphocytes are so numerous in the cortex that they obscure the network of epithelial reticular cells in whose interstices they lie.

Although lymphocytes are numerous in the medulla, they are not so densely packed as to obscure the cells of the network of reticular cells in which they lie. The nuclei of the cells of this reticulum are large, and although they contain nucleoli, they do not contain very much chromatin and hence stain lightly. The cytoplasm of these cells is pink. That they are arranged in a network is not very clearly shown in sections cut from postnatal glands.

Hassal's corpuscles are numerous in the medulla. The centers of these usually consist of nonliving material: pyknotic and broken-up nuclei, keratin and nondescript hyalin material (Fig. 15-23, *right*). The remainder of each corpuscle consists of a few layers of concentrically arranged epithelial cells; the innermost ones may be dead (Fig. 15-23, *right*). The fact that the reticular cells of the medulla form Hassal's corpuscles suggests that the reticular cells here are epithelial in nature.

Blood vessels supported by connective tissue may be seen in the substance of lobules. They are more numerous and are seen to better advantage in the medulla. According to Metcalf, numerous arteries radiate from the medulla of a lobule into its cortex and end in capillaries that are numerous near the capsule and, in turn, empty into venules that return to the medulla and there join larger vessels.

**Fine Structure.** As has already been mentioned, Clark, from EM studies, found evidence of a continuous epithelium between the smaller blood vessels of the cortex and the intervening tissue in which lymphocytes are produced. Although this epithelial membrane is commonly referred to as an epithelial barrier, Clark has shown that it is to some extent permeable. Nevertheless, it seems reasonable to consider that this barrier permits lymphocytes to be formed in the thymic cortex in an environment which is relatively protected from macromolecules present in the bloodstream as will now be described.

As is shown in Figure 15-24, a capillary in the thymic cortex has a wall which may consist of several endothelial cells joined by junctional complexes; the desmosomes of the latter can be seen in the illustration. The capillaries in the cortex are each surrounded by a connective tissue space (labeled SPACE in Fig. 15-24). Occasional pericytes (PER.) may lie in this space, with processes that partially surround the capillary. Collagenic microfibrils and even finer filamentous material can be seen in the space. This ringlike space is bounded on its exterior by what is normally a continuous sheath of epithelial cells (EP.) which the EM shows are connected together by desmosomes. Lymphocytes formed in the tissue outside these barrierlike epithelial sheaths that surround the spaces (which in

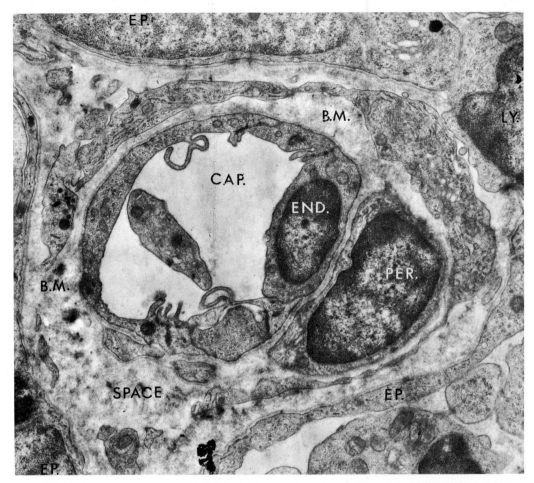

Fig. 15-24. Electron micrograph ($\times$ 12,000) of section of cortex of thymus of mouse. A capillary (CAP.) is cut in cross section. It is surrounded by a connective tissue space (SPACE) which contains a pericyte (PER.) and its processes. Surrounding this space is an epithelial membrane composed of cells (EP.) joined together by desmosomes. At the upper right a lymphocyte (LY.) has been caught in the act of migrating between two epithelial cells of the barrier, presumably to enter the collective tissue space. (Clark, S. L., Jr.: Am. J. Anat. *112*:1, labeling added)

turn surround the capillaries), are sometimes seen penetrating through the epithelial cells of the barrier at sites where the epithelial cells are normally joined together by desmosomes; one such lymphocyte is seen passing between two epithelial cells at the upper right of Figure 15-24. The epithelial cells of barriers are continuous on their outer aspects with a meshwork of epithelial cells that fills the spaces between blood vessels. Lymphocytes are formed in the interstices of the mesh of epithelial cells as will be described in the next section.

It is obvious that any material in blood, to gain entrance to the sites where lymphocytes are produced in the cortex, would have to pass through the endothelium of a capillary, then find its way somehow through the space which surrounds the capillary, and then pass through the epithelial sheathlike barrier. There is, therefore, some reason for thinking that lymphocytes in the thymic cortex are produced in an environment which is relatively protected from macromolecules which might be present in the blood.

**The Formation of Lymphocytes in the Cortex.** Sainte-Marie and Leblond have recently reported on the cytologic features of the cells

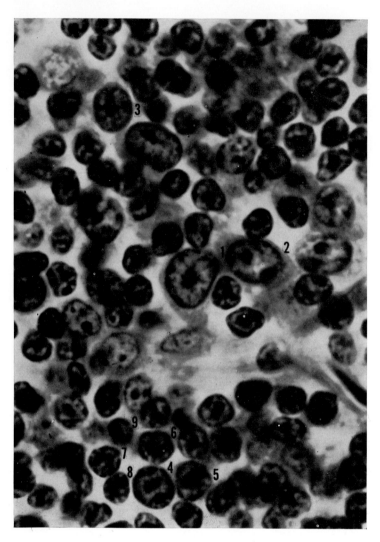

FIG. 15-25. Oil-immersion photomicrograph of a section of cortex of rat thymus. The numbers 1 to 9 are always located to the right of the cell the number indicates. From 1 to 9 the cells are seen to become progressively smaller; the largest are lymphoblasts, the next largest, prolymphocytes, and the smallest, lymphocytes. (From Sainte-Marie, G., and Leblond, C. P.: Blood 23:275)

of the lymphocyte series that are seen in the cortex and the medulla of the thymus gland of rats, and they have also studied the migration of these cells. In the cortex they classify cells of the lymphocyte series into 3 groups depending on the diameters of their nuclei as measured in sections. Cells of the lymphocyte series whose nuclei had a diameter greater than 5.9 microns, were termed large lymphocytes, but according to the terminology used in this book, we would term them lymphoblasts (see Fig. 15-25). The cells whose nuclei have a diameter of less than 4.6 microns were termed lymphocytes (Fig. 15-25) and those with a nuclei with a diameter between 4.6 and 5.9 microns were termed medium-sized lymphocytes but, as was explained in connection with lymphocytes in Chapter 12, we think it less confusing to term them prolymphocytes (see Fig. 15-25) Sainte-Marie and Leblond counted mitotic figures in the 3 types of cells, lymphoblasts, prolymphocytes and lymphocytes, and found that there were 2 to 4 (most probably 4) successive generations of lymphoblasts before they became prolymphocytes. There were then 2 successive generations of prolymphocytes and then, when these became lymphocytes, there were 2 further generations of these. They estimate that each lymphoblast therefore gives rise to 128 (small) lymphocytes.

**Migration of Lymphocytes Formed in the Cortex Into the Medulla.** The medulla was found to contain numerous lymphocytes, but only rarely were prolymphocytes and lymphoblasts observed in this part of the organ. Since mitosis is intense in the cortex, the fact that the cortex does not become overpopulated hinges on lymphocytes leaving the cortex as rapidly as they are formed. Sainte-Marie and Leblond believe that the chief pathway for migration is into the medulla and that there lymphocytes formed originally in the cortex move into perivascular channels which surround the numerous blood vessels of the medulla and then finally into medullary vessels that drain the medulla. In support of this concept they found that there were more lymphocytes in blood draining away from the thymus than in the arterial blood that enters the thymus.

**Relation to Endocrine Glands.** The growth hormone of the pars anterior and the thyroid hormone both stimulate the growth of the thymus gland. Most steroid hormones, on the other hand—if sufficient quantities of them are present in the bloodstream—tend to bring about the involution of the gland. Hence, the appearance of substantial quantities of sex hormone in the circulation at the time of puberty is probably an important factor in causing the thymus gland to begin to involute at this time. Selye believes that the premature involution of the gland observed in children who suffer from serious diseases or other forms of stress is caused by the oversecretion of adrenal cortical steroid hormones that occur as a result of the disease or stress condition. A deficiency of either adrenal cortical hormone or sex hormone in an animal, brought about by removing the endocrine glands responsible for these hormones, is associated with the hypertrophy of the thymus gland. Speaking generally, then, there seems to be an inverse reciprocal relation between the amount of steroid hormones in the circulation and the size of the thymus gland.

### THE FUNCTIONS OF THE THYMUS

A time-tested way for learning something about the function and the importance of an organ is to remove that organ from an experimental animal and see what happens. If there is reason to believe that the organ in question secretes any substance necessary for the body as a whole, another way the function of the organ can be studied is by making extracts of the organ and injecting the extracts into animals, both into those from whom the organ in question has been removed and into normal animals. Until 1961 the thymus had been removed from animals without there being any evidence of its removal exerting a deleterious effect on the animal concerned. Extracts had been made of the thymus gland and injected into animals with no proof that they had much effect on the animal concerned. In 1961, however, both Miller, and Archer and Pierce, reported that removal of the thymus from a *newborn* animal resulted in a serious impairment of its immunologic responses to antigens.

As this discovery was followed up, it became established that animals that were thymectomized at birth had fewer lymphocytes in their blood and lymphatic tissues than normal animals of the same age. It was shown that their ability to reject skin grafts from nonisologous animals was impaired and also that they were unable to produce some of the immunoglobulins that can be produced by normal animals. Furthermore, the members of several strains of mice that were thymectomized at birth were found to develop, in the first few months of life, a condition that resembled the runt or wasting syndrome that has already been described as occurring when immunologically competent cells from a mother or father (of different strains) are injected into an $F_1$ hybrid. Subsequently it has been reported that this latter condition does not occur if mice thymectomized at birth are born and raised in a germ-free environment.

Since it has been generally accepted that the thymus produces lymphocytes, and that its function in producing lymphocytes precedes that of other lymphatic organs in fetal life, it was and is still assumed that lymphocytes produced in the thymus both in prenatal and postnatal life migrate to other lymphatic organs to assist in building up their lymphocyte populations. When it was found that thymectomy performed at birth caused impairment of the immunologic mechanisms of the body, it was naturally first assumed that the defective immunologic mechanism resulting from thymectomy at birth was to be explained by the lymphatic tissue of the body being cut off from the supply of lymphocytes that they would ordinarily and regularly receive from the thymus. It was generally assumed that if the thymus is not removed until a week or two after birth, enough time would have elapsed during the first week or two of life for the thymus to have built up the lymphocyte population of the other lymphatic organs sufficiently for them to carry on independently thereafter.

However, although it still seems to be true that the thymus serves a very important function in feeding lymphocytes to other lymphatic organs, a premature cessation of this function occasioned by its removal at birth did not prove to be the explanation for the impaired immunologic mechanism that results from the removal of the thymus at birth. An important lead indicating some other answer to this problem was the finding that if a thymus is transplanted from another animal (even another newborn animal) into an animal that has been thymectomized at birth, the thymectomized animal with the transplanted thymus recovers most of its immunologic competence. Now it might be thought that this was due to the transplanted thymus immediately producing lymphocytes and feeding them to the other lymphatic organs of the host. But this is not the explanation. First, when a thymus gland is transplanted, the cells in its interior have to live for several days by means of diffusion mechanisms operating in tissue fluid. It takes several days for the capillaries of a host to connect up with the blood vessels of a transplant and to re-establish a circulation in transplanted isologous tissue. Since lymphocytes are sensitive cells, the lymphocytes of a thymic transplant mostly undergo pyknosis before a circulation is established in the transplant, and, as a result, all that lives in the transplant are the hardier epithelial reticular cells and some of the connective tissue cells. Furthermore, it was shown by means of chromosome markers that the lymphocytes which soon became abundant in the lymphatic organs of the host into which a thymus is transplanted develop from host cells and not from the transplanted thymus.

Evidence from transplantation and irradiation experiments thus began to raise the possibility of the reason for the thymus being necessary for animals to become immunologically competent in the first week or so of life being due not to the animals being deprived of lymphocytes made by the thymus but to

some factor that the thymus secreted into blood. To test this hypothesis, bits of thymus tissue were placed in little millipore chambers before they were transplanted into animals that were thymectomized at birth. The pores of the chambers were too small to permit any cells to leave the chambers, but fluid could, of course, enter and leave through the pores of the chambers. Numerous experiments of this kind by Miller and others have shown that thymic tissue in chambers transplanted in newborn thymectomized animals prevent the usual effects of thymectomy. Sections taken from the thymic tissue contained in chambers of this sort that have been transplanted and left in place for some time show that all that remains of the thymic tissue that was placed in the chamber is a mass of cells of the epithelial reticular type. Accordingly, it seems most probable that the epithelial reticular cells of the thymus, through the medium of a soluble product, exert some influence on lymphocytes far away from the thymus, an influence which in the first week or so of life is necessary for lymphocytes in the other lymphatic organs to proliferate, develop and function immunologically in a normal way. This product has not yet been isolated, and the way it acts is not known.

As was mentioned at the beginning of this discussion on thymic function, another way the function of any organ that is believed to elaborate some factor into the circulation can be studied is by making an extract of the organ and injecting this into other animals and see what happens. Experiments of this sort by Metcalf, several years ago, indicated that the thymus produces a lymphocytosis-stimulating factor (L.S.F.). However, L.S.F. has not been shown to be able to replace the functions of the thymus in mice thymectomized at birth and, as yet, no other types of thymus extract have been shown to replace completely thymus function. The nature of the hypothetical humoral factor produced by the thymus in early postnatal life is therefore as yet obscure.

**Summary of Thymic Function.** At the time of writing it would seem that the thymus performs two functions. First, it supplies lymphocytes (or lymphocytic stem cells) which help to populate the other lymphatic tissues of the body even though these have the means to maintain their own populations. Since there seems to be some reason for thinking that thymic lymphocytes are not quite so prepared to develop into functioning immunologic cells as the lymphocytes of the other lymphatic tissues, it might be thought that the thymus provides a more or less continuous but small supply of lymphocytes for the body which are uncommitted immunologically. Hence, thymic lymphocytes may be insurance against the contingency of all the lymphocytes elsewhere becoming committed to react against large amounts of antigen that could appear in the body under conditions of a very severe infection. In other words, the thymus may serve to supply more or less continuously fresh uncommitted lymphocytes to the other lymphatic tissues so that there are always uncommitted lymphocytes available throughout life (but fewer as people age) to react against new antigens.

Secondly, the evidence indicates that thymic epithelium liberates some humoral factor which is necessary early in postnatal life if the lymphatic tissue elsewhere in the body is to become completely developed immunologically. How this as yet hypothetical thymic factor acts is not yet established. In considering possibilities it may be worthwhile to reflect that at the time this factor seems to be essential (roughly the first week of postnatal life) there are two possible phenomena that are more or less interrelated and which the thymic factor could affect. The processes relating to the first phenomena are just ceasing to operate, and those related to the second phenomenon are just beginning to operate.

The phenomenon that is just ceasing is that which up to this time has accounted for all the cells in the body that will in future become, or give rise to, immunologically competent cells, being made immunologically tolerant to all the antigens that have as yet appeared in the body. The ill-understood processes that account for this phenomenon are ceasing to operate at the time of birth. The second phenomenon is observed as the first one ceases. This second phenomenon involves processes which from this time on result in immunologically competent cells recognizing new macromolecules that gain entrance to the body as antigens and by their becoming immunologically functioning cells that act

against these antigens. The new evidence would seem to suggest that thymectomy in the first week of life somehow affects the processes related to the second phenomenon so that the cells of lymphatic tissue do not react as well as they should to new antigens. However, it is difficult to establish whether or not the relative inability of an animal thymectomized at birth to react to antigens properly is due to some perpetuation of the processes whereby tolerance is established to antigens, or whether it is due to some impairment of the processes which make immunologically competent cells develop into functioning cells. For this reason it is possible that full understanding of the action of the hypothetical thymic factor may await further knowledge about why immunologically competent cells in the body develop tolerance to antigens they are exposed to until roughly the time of birth, and then develop the capacity of reacting immunologically against new antigens.

## AUTO-IMMUNITY

Whatever the mechanism is that accounts for immunologic tolerance, the mechanism prevents us from making antibodies against any of the possible antigens that have developed within us until around the time of birth, provided that these possible antigens have been dissolved in, or carried by, the body fluids. However, there are some substances that form in the body that are segregated from the circulation and hence kept from ever coming into contact with reticuloendothelial cells or cells of the lymphocyte or the plasma-cell series. A segregation of a possible antigen occurs for example in the thyroid gland, as will be explained when that organ is considered. If these previously segregated substances gain access in later life to the fluids of the body they may act as antigens and, as a result, the body will make antibodies against one of its own components. Such antibodies are termed *auto-antibodies*. Indeed, it is now believed that there are several mechanisms that can act to cause auto-antibodies to form, even against macromolecules that have not been segregated, and a growing number of hitherto not understood diseases are being considered as possibly being due to this cause. Curiously enough, there are some indications from clinical medicine of an association of some diseases believed to be of an auto-immune type and disorders of the thymus. This finding, together with the fact that the thymus is relatively best developed in the body during prenatal life, when it is essential that tolerance be established to new macromolecules that form in the body, may suggest that the thymus has some as yet ill-understood function in connection with the establishment and the maintenance of immunologic tolerance.

## REFERENCES

### Some General References of the Structure of Lymphatic Tissue

Bloom, W.: Lymphatic tissue: lymphatic organs *in* Downey's Handbook of Hematology, p. 1427, New York, Hoeber, 1938.

Humphrey, J. H., and White, R. C.: Immunology for Students of Medicine, ed. 2, Oxford, Blackwell, 1964.

Krumbhaar, E. B.: Lymphatic tissue *in* Cowdry, E. V. (ed.): Problems of Ageing, p. 149, Baltimore, Williams & Wilkins, 1939.

Movat, H. Z., and Fernando, N. V. P.: The fine structure of lymphoid tissue, Exp. Molec. Path. 3:546, 1964.

———: The fine structure of lymphoid tissue after antigenic stimulation, Exp. Molec. Path., in press, 1965.

Weller, C. V.: The hemolymph nodes *in* Downey's Handbook of Hematology, p. 1759, New York, Hoeber, 1938.

Yoffey, J. M., and Courtice, F. C.: Lymphatics, Lymph and Lymphoid Tissue, Cambridge, Mass., Harvard, 1956.

### Special References on Lymphatic Nodules and Nodes and Plasma Cells and Antibody Production

Andreasen, E., and Christensen, S.: The rate of mitotic activity in the lymphoid organs of the rat, Anat. Rec. 103:401, 1949.

Attardi, G., Cohn, M., Horibata, K., and Lennox, E. S.: Symposium on the biology of cells modified by viruses or antigens. II. On the analysis of antibody synthesis at the cellular level, Bacteriol. Rev. 23:213-223, 1959.

Braunsteiner, H., Fellinger, K., and Pakesch, F.: Demonstration of a cytoplasmic structure in plasma cells, Blood 8:916, 1953.

Braunsteiner, H., and Pakesch, F.: Electron microscopy and the functional significance of a new cellular structure in plasmocytes; a review, Blood 10:650, 1955.

Burnet, M.: The Clonal Selection Theory of Acquired Immunity, Nashville, Vanderbilt Univ. Press, 1959.

Bussard, A. D.: Biosynthesis of antibodies, facts and theories, Ann. Rev. Microbiol. 13:279-296, 1959.

Ciba Foundation Symposium on the Cellular Aspects of Immunity, London, Churchill, 1960.

Conway, E. A.: Cyclic changes in lymphatic nodules, Anat. Rec. 67:487, 1937.

Coons, A. H.: Fluorescent antibody methods *in* Danielli, J. F. (ed.): General Cytochemical Methods, pp. 399-422, New York, Acad. Press, 1958.

———: The cytology of antibody formation, J. Cell. Comp. Physiol. 52: Suppl. 1, 55-67, 1958.

Coons, A. H., Leduc, E. H., and Connolly, J. M.: Leukocytes involved in antibody formation, Ann. N. Y. Acad. Sci. 59:951, 1955.

———: Studies on antibody production: I. A method for the histochemical demonstration of specific antibody and its application to a study of the hyperimmune rabbit, J. Exp. Med. 102: 49, 1955.

Downey, H.: The structure and origin of the lymph sinuses of mammalian lymph nodes and their relations to endothelium and reticulum, Haematologica 3:431, 1922.

Fagraeus, A.: Antibody production in relation to development of plasma cells; *in vivo* and *in vitro* experiments, Acta med. scandinav. 130: Suppl. 204, 3-122, 1948.

Humphrey, J. H., and White, R. C.: Immunology for Students of Medicine, ed. 2, Oxford, Blackwell, 1964.

Jerne, N. K.: The natural-selection theory of antibody formation, Proc. Nat. Acad. Sc. 41:849-857, 1955.

Leduc, E. H., Coons, A. H., and Connolly, J. M.: Studies on antibody production: II. The primary and secondary responses in the popliteal lymph node of the rabbit, J. Exp. Med. 102:61, 1955.

Movat, F. Z., and Fernando, N. V. P.: The fine structure of connective tissue. II. The plasma cell, Exp. Molec. Path. 1:535, 1962.

———: The fine structure of lymphoid tissue after antigenic stimulation, Exp. Molec. Path., in press, 1965.

Nomenclature for human immunoglobulins, Bull. WHO 30:447, 1964.

Nossal, G. J. W.: Genetic control of lymphopoiesis, plasma cell formation, and antibody production, Internat. Rev. Exp. Path. 1:1, 1962.

———: How cells make antibodies, Scient. Am. 211:106, 1964.

Rebuck, J. E. (ed.): The Lymphocyte and Lymphocytic Tissue, New York, Hoeber, 1960.

Sainte-Marie, Guy: Study on plasmocytopoiesis. 1. Description of plasmocytes and of their mitoses in the mediastinal lymph nodes of ten-week-old rats, Am. J. Anat. *114*:207, 1964.

Sainte-Marie, Guy, and Coons, A. H.: Studies on antibody production. X. Mode of formation of plasmocytes in cell transfer experiments, J. Exp. Med. *119*:743, 1964.

Schoenberg, M. D., Mumaw, V. R., Moore, R. D., and Weisberger, A. S.: Cytoplasmic interaction between macrophages and lymphocytic cells in antibody synthesis, Science *143*:964, 1963.

(*See also* References for Chapters 11 and 12.)

### REFERENCES ON THE SPLEEN

Barcroft, J.: Recent knowledge of the spleen, Lancet *1*:319, 1925.

Doggett, T. H.: The capillary system of the dog's spleen, Anat. Rec. *110*:65, 1951.

Foot, N. C.: The reticulum of the human spleen, Anat. Rec. *36*:79, 1927.

Ham, A. W.: The structure of the spleen *in* Blaustein, Ancel (ed.): The Spleen, pp. 1-18, New York, McGraw-Hill, 1963.

Knisely, M. H.: Spleen studies: I. Microscopic observations of the circulatory system of living unstimulated mammalian spleens, Anat. Rec. *65*:23, 1936.

————: Spleen studies: II. Microscopic observations of the circulatory system of living traumatized, and of drying spleens, Anat. Rec. *65*:131, 1936.

Krumbhaar, E. B.: Function of the spleen, Physiol. Rev. *6*:160, 1926.

Kyes, Preston: The spleen *in* Cowdry's Special Cytology, ed. 2, p. 529, New York, Hoeber, 1932.

Lewis, O. J.: The blood vessels of the adult mammalian spleen, J. Anat. *91*:245, 1957.

————: The development of the circulation in the spleen of the foetal rabbit, J. Anat. *90*:282, 1956.

MacKenzie, D. W., Jr., Whipple, A. O., and Wintersteiner, M. P.: Studies on the microscopic anatomy and physiology of living transilluminating mammalian spleens, Am. J. Anat. *68*:397, 1941.

MacNeal, W. J.: The circulation of blood through the spleen pulp, Arch. Path. *7*:215, 1929.

McNee, J. W.: The spleen: its structure, functions and diseases (Lettsomian Lectures), Lancet *1*:951, 1009, 1063, 1931.

Mall, F. P.: On the circulation through the pulp of the dog's spleen, Am. J. Anat. *2*:315, 1903.

Movat, F. Z., and Fernando, N. V. P.: The fine structure of lymphoid tissue after antigenic stimulation, Exp. Molec. Path., in press, 1965.

Peck, H. M., and Hoerr, N. L.: The effect of environmental temperature changes in the circulation of the mouse spleen, Anat. Rec. *109*:479, 1951.

————: The intermediary circulation in the red pulp of the mouse spleen, Anat. Rec. *109*:447, 1951.

Robinson, W. L.: Some points on the mechanism of filtration by the spleen, Am. J. Path. *4*:309, 1928.

————: The vascular mechanism of the spleen, Am. J. Path. *2*:341, 1926.

————: The venous drainage of the cat spleen, Am. J. Path. *6*:19, 1930.

Solnitzky, Othmar: The Schweigger-Seidel sheath (ellipsoid) of the spleen, Anat. Rec. *69*:55, 1937.

Weiss, L.: A study of the structure of splenic sinuses in man and in the albino rat, with the light microscope and the electron microscope, J. Biophys. Biochem. Cytol. *3*:599, 1957.

————: An experimental study of the organization of the reticuloendothelial system in the red pulp of the spleen, J. Anat. *93*:465, 1959.

### GENERAL REFERENCES ON THE THYMUS

Defendi, V., and Metcalf, D. (eds): The thymus *in* A Wistar Institute Symposium Monograph #2, Philadelphia, Wistar Inst. Press, 1964.

Good, R. A., and Gabrielsen, A. E. (eds.): The Thymus in Immunobiology, New York, Hoeber, 1964.

### SPECIAL REFERENCES ON THE THYMUS

Alapper, Clarence: Morphogenesis of the thymus, Am. J. Anat. *78*:139, 1946.

Archer, O. K., and Pierce, J. C.: Role of the thymus in development of the immune response, Fed. Proc. *20*:26, 1961.

Auerbach, R.: Experimental analysis of the origin of cell types in the development of the mouse thymus, Develop. Biol. *3*:336, 1961.

Clark, S. L., Jr.: The thymus in mice of strain 129/J studied with the electron microscope, Am. J. Anat. *112*:1, 1963.

————: The penetration of proteins and colloidal materials into the thymus from the blood stream *in* Defendi, V., and Metcalf, D. (eds.): A Wistar Institute Symposium Monograph #2, p. 9, Philadelphia, Wistar Inst. Press, 1964.

Law, L. W., Trainin, N., Levey, R. H., and Barth, W. F.: Humoral thymic factor in mice: Further evidence, Science *143*:1049, 1964.

Metcalf, D.: The thymic lymphocytosis stimulating factor and its relation to lymphatic leukemia, Ann. N. Y. Acad. Sci. *73*:113, 1958.

Miller, J. F. A. P.: Role of the thymus in immunity, Brit. M. J. *2*:459, 1963.

——: Functions of the thymus *in* Scientific Basis of Medicine, Annual Reviews, p. 218, London, Athlone Press, 1964.

——: The thymus and the development of immunologic responsiveness, Science *144*:1544, 1964.

Rowntree, L. G., Clark, J. H., and Hanson, A. M.: The biologic effects of thymus extract (Hanson), J.A.M.A. *103*:1425, 1934.

——: Biologic effects of thymus extract (Hanson), Arch. Int. Med. *56*:1, 1935.

Sainte-Marie, Guy: Lymphocyte formation in the thymus of the rat, Proceed. Canad. Cancer Conf., vol. 3, p. 337, New York, Acad. Press, 1958.

——: Study on plasmocytopoiesis. 1. Description of plasmocytes and of their mitosis in the mediastinal lymph nodes of ten-week-old rats, Am. J. Anat. *114*:207, 1964.

Sainte-Marie, Guy, and Leblond, C. P.: Tentative pattern for removal of lymphocytes in cortex of the rat thymus, Proc. Soc. Exp. Biol Med. *97*:263, 1958.

——: Origin and fate of cells in the medulla of the rat thymus, Proc. Soc. Exp. Biol. Med. *98*:909, 1958.

——: Cytologic features and cellular migration in the cortex and medulla of thymus in the young adult rat, Blood *23*:275, 1964.

Smith, C.: Studies on the thymus of the mammal: VIII. Intrathymic lymphatic vessels, Anat. Rec. *122*:173, 1955.

Smith, C., and Parkhurst, H. T.: A comparison with the staining of Hassall's corpuscles and the thick skin of the guinea pig, Anat. Rec. *103*:649, 1949.

# 16    Hemopoietic Tissue

## (Continued)

## MYELOID TISSUE

**Functions, Kinds and Distribution.** Myeloid tissue, the second kind of hemopoietic tissue, is the variety that is not only specialized to perform certain phagocytic functions similar to those of lymphatic tissue such as removing worn-out cells and other debris from the circulation, but also to produce the erythrocytes, the granular leukocytes and the platelets required by the body.

Normally, in postnatal life myeloid tissue is confined to the cavities of bones; this is why it is called myeloid tissue (*myelos* = marrow). In the normal, the terms myeloid tissue and bone marrow are often used more or less synonymously.

*Red and Yellow Bone Marrow.* In the adult there are two kinds of bone marrow—red and yellow. Red marrow derives its color from vast numbers of red blood cells in various stages of formation. Red marrow, then, is marrow that is actively producing blood cells. Yellow marrow derives its color from the large quantity of fat it contains. Although yellow marrow has the potentiality to manufacture red blood cells, the fact that it is not red indicates that it is not very actively engaged in doing so, and the fact that it is yellow indicates that it has taken on the more leisurely work of storing fat.

In the fetus the marrow of most bones is red. But during the growing period in postnatal life the marrow of most bones becomes yellow so that, in adult man, red marrow is found only in the diploë of the bones of the vault of the skull, in the ribs and the sternum, in the bodies of the vertebrae and in the cancellous bone of some of the short bones and at the ends of long bones. The marrow in all other sites is yellow and, from the standpoint of producing red blood cells, inactive. However, it must be remembered that yellow marrow has the potentiality to resume the production of red cells. Under conditions in which there is an urgent and prolonged need for increased red blood cell production, some portion of the yellow marrow becomes reconverted to red marrow.

## THE DEVELOPMENT OF MYELOID TISSUE

As we shall see as we study the formation of bone two chapters farther on, the first step in building most of the bones of the body is the construction of a *solid* cartilage model of the bone-to-be; this is done by mesenchymal cells differentiating into cartilage cells. The cartilage model at first is solid; hence there is no room for marrow to form in its interior. But in due course the cartilage in the central part of the model breaks down by means of mechanisms that will be described in the next chapter, and a cavity begins to form within the cartilage model. Simultaneously with the formation of a cavity, blood vessels and mesenchymal cells grow into the cavity, and immediately two things begin to happen.

First, some of the mesenchymal cells that enter the cavity become bone-forming cells and cover up remnants of the cartilage with bone, as will be described in the next two chapters. Here we are more concerned with the second thing that happens which is that some of the cells that grow into the cavity begin to form marrow.

### The Two Main Lines Along Which the Mesenchymal Cells That Form Marrow Differentiate

It has been explained already that hemopoietic tissues have two main functions, that of removing worn-out cells from the circulation and that of adding new cells to the circulation. In order to perform these two functions the mesenchymal cells from which marrow develops set up two main lines of differentiation, as is illustrated in the chart shown on the following page.

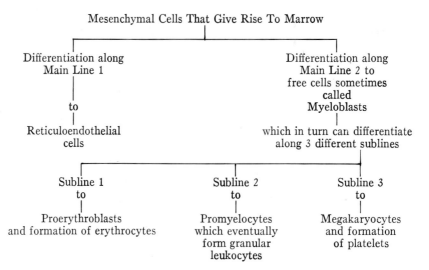

In differentiating along Main Line 1, mesenchymal cells form the cells and the structures responsible for removing worn-out cells from the circulation. In differentiating along Main Line 2, they form free cells that produce the various kinds of blood cells. So, the differentiation of mesenchymal cells along 2 different lines provides cells to perform the 2 different functions of hemopoietic tissue, that of removing cells from, and that of adding cells to, the circulation.

**Fixed Cells and Free Cells.** There is one important distinction that should be emphasized between the cells that develop along the two main lines of differentiation that occur in marrow tissue. At least some of the cells that develop along Main Line 1 produce reticular fibers which form complex networks to support the sinusoids (soon to be described) and also to hold most of the cells that form along Main Line 1 more or less firmly in position. Hence the cells along Main Line 1 are said to be *fixed cells*. Conversely, the cells that form along Main Line 2 are all free cells. Instead of being *attached* to reticular fibers, they lie free in the spaces of the reticular net. Thus the net supports them and holds them more or less in position, without their being attached to the net. That they are free cells accounts for two important features of the cells of Main Line 2: (1) because they are free they become more or less rounded-up, and hence their cytoplasmic borders can be seen to much better advantage than those of many of the cells of Line 1, whose cytoplasm, being

attached to the reticular net, is often drawn out into indistinct thin films, and (2) since the cells of Line 2 are free, they can pass through the meshes of the net and by this means the most differentiated cells of Line 2 eventually escape through openings in the sinusoid walls to enter the bloodstream.

## THE CELLS THAT FORM ALONG LINE 1

In differentiating along Line 1, primitive cells become increasingly specialized for phagocytosis and for lining blood passageways. After they have become thus specialized they are called *reticuloendothelial cells*. The reticuloendothelial cells of hemopoietic tissue are the counterparts of the macrophages that develop in loose connective tissue. However, reticuloendothelial cells, while phagocytic like macrophages, are a little different from them. In addition to lining blood passageways (to be described presently), they have the capacity to make networks of reticular fibers. Both they and the primitive cells are held in these networks. Their ability to make fibers is responsible for the *reticulo* part of their name. As has been mentioned already, they tend to arrange themselves so as to become the walls of the blood passageways that connect the arterial side of the circulation to the venous side in bone marrow. These blood passageways are termed *sinusoids* (Figs. 16-1 and 16-2). Sinusoids occupy the same position in relation to arterial and venous vessels that capillaries

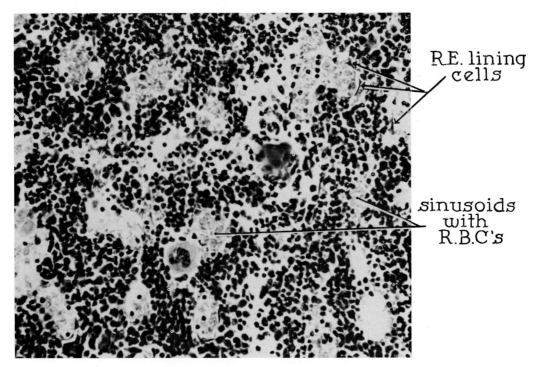

R.E. lining
cells

sinusoids
with
R.B.C's

FIG. 16-1. Low-power photomicrograph of a section of red bone marrow. This section shows numerous sinusoids, most of which contain red blood cells. These are the lighter areas in the photograph. Between them are innumerable cells of the red blood cell and granular leukocyte series. One megakaryocyte is present in the lower middle part of the picture. In a few sites, the thin, flattened reticuloendothelial lining cells of the sinusoids may be seen.

do in most parts of the body. However, they are much wider than capillaries, and their lining cells do not fit together so well. Since all other kinds of blood vessels in the body are lined by endothelial cells (which are not phagocytic), it was thought that these phagocytic lining cells of sinusoids should also have *endothelial* attached to their name, so they were called reticuloendothelial cells.

## THE APPEARANCE OF SINUSOIDS IN SECTIONS

Red marrow is riddled with sinusoids. In the tissue between sinusoids, erythrocytes, granulocytes and platelets all are produced, and the cells that are produced gain entrance to the circulation through the leaky walls of the sinusoids. The lining cells of sinusoids are difficult to distinguish in sections because they are pressed upon by the cells of the surrounding tissue (Fig. 16-1). Furthermore, their walls are so thin that they are easily collapsed, and many are probably partially or completely collapsed in the living state. When a little piece of bone marrow is cut, the blood tends to run out of the sinusoids before it is fixed; subsequently, when the block is fixed, the empty sinusoids may be squeezed and closed and, consequently, difficult to see when the block is sectioned (Fig. 16-10). Sinusoids generally are easier to see in the marrow of a section of a whole bone, for in this they are filled with blood (Fig. 16-1); the reason for this is that if a whole bone is put in fixative, the blood cannot run freely out of the sinusoids. Sinusoids are particularly easy to see in the bone marrow of animals that have been subjected to a near lethal dose of total-body radiation. In the first few days following severe total-body radiation, nearly all the free cells that normally proliferate actively to form blood cells are destroyed and disappear. As a result the sinusoids expand with blood and, since the cells in the tissue between them are mostly destroyed, the sinusoids show up very clearly in sections (Fig. 16-2).

With the light microscope, the reticuloendothelial cells that line sinusoids have ovoid nuclei arranged so that the long axis of each follows the curve of the sinusoid wall (Fig. 16-2). The chromatin granules are fine and numerous, so each nucleus stains evenly and with moderate intensity. The cytoplasm seems to extend off from each pole of the nucleus in a long thin sheet. The sinusoidal walls generally appear to be continuous; the cytoplasm of one lining cell generally can be traced to that of the next.

Pease has described their fine structure. With the EM, the cytoplasm of the reticuloendothelial lining cells is seen to extend along the sinusoid walls in the form of *pseudopodia,* and there are small but distinct gaps between the pseudopodia from adjacent cells at sites where they intermesh. Pease has micrographs showing blood cells entering the sinusoids through the gaps between the cytoplasmic pseudopodia of adjacent cells. The EM appearance of these cells explains why the sinusoid walls can appear to be continuous with the light microscope and yet be permeated with openings, because it could be visualized that in the thicker sections used for light microscopy, imperfectly fitting, but overlapping, pseudopodia of adjacent cells would appear as a continuous thin band of cytoplasm.

With the EM, Pease finds the nucleoli of reticuloendothelial cells to be well developed. The mitochondria are large, the internal membranes of the cytoplasm are only moderately well developed, and the content of ribosomes is low. Phagocytosed material can be demonstrated in their cytoplasm.

*Maintenance of the Cell Population Along Line 1.* Since reticuloendothelial cells are essentially macrophages, and since young macrophages can divide, it would seem that such differentiation as occurs along Line 1 does not materially interfere with the reproductive capacity of the cells that form along this line. Hence, there would seem to be no problem about the less-differentiated cells along this line maintaining the population of reticuloendothelial cells.

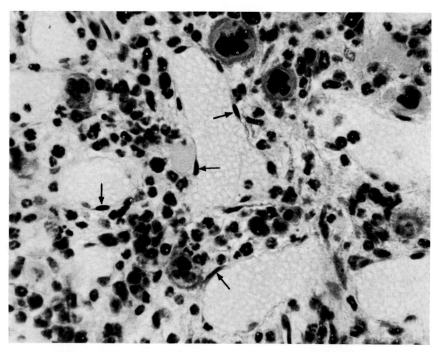

FIG. 16-2. High-power photomicrograph of an H and E section of the bone marrow of a mouse 24 hours after the mouse was given a dose of radiation sufficient to kill most of the mice so treated. Notice that the various cells between sinusoids are undergoing pyknotic changes and that the sinusoids are congested. The arrows point to the nuclei of reticuloendothelial cells that are lining sinusoids.

THE TISSUE BETWEEN THE SINUSOIDS. THE FORMATION OF THE FREE CELLS FOUND ALONG THE SUBLINES OF MAIN LINE 2

The tissue that occupies the space between the sinusoids will be considered now. This is where cell multiplication and differentiation result in the formation of red blood cells, granular leukocytes and platelets.

The tissue between sinusoids is poorly supported. Occasional small arteries or veins are seen in it, and the connective tissue associated with these, as well as the walls of the vessels themselves, provide a basic, though weak, framework for the tissue. Some reticular fibers run from the connective tissue associated with arteries and veins to connect with those reticular fibers that surround the sinusoids. Hence, most of the tissue between sinusoids is supported by no more than a delicate mesh of reticular fibers. The meshes of this network are packed with cells that range all the way from primitive-appearing fixed cells to erythrocytes and granular leukocytes.

## HOW THE PRODUCTION OF FREE CELLS IS MAINTAINED

### PROBLEMS RELATING TO THE NATURE OF THE STEM CELL OF MYELOID TISSUE IN POSTNATAL LIFE

It is generally agreed that both the reticuloendothelial cells and the free cells of myeloid tissue develop from mesenchyme. It has been fairly generally assumed, moreover, that some mesenchymal cells, of the type that in prenatal life give rise to all the cells of myeloid tissue, remain as fixed cells in myeloid tissue throughout postnatal life. These undifferentiated fixed cells have been generally referred to as *primitive reticular cells*, and it has been generally believed that by dividing they maintained a pool of themselves so that some of their members could differentiate into either reticuloendothelial cells or young undifferentiated free cells as was required. Recently, however, evidence has accumulated which suggests that there is a free cell of myeloid tissue which by itself can serve as a stem cell for the maintenance of the population of the various cells concerned in becoming erythrocytes and/or granular leukocytes in myeloid tissue, and this of course throws some doubt

on the need for, or the perpetuation of, primitive reticular cells in myeloid tissue. We shall now comment further on the stem cell of myeloid tissue and the new evidence that indicates that it is a free cell.

### THE NATURE OF STEM CELLS AND WHY ONE IS NEEDED IN MARROW

In Chapter 5 we noted that in general the differentiation of a cell is generally associated with some loss of its reproductive capacity. This is clearly illustrated in myeloid tissue, for the final cells that evolve along the red blood cell route—the erythrocytes—have lost their nuclei and hence are obviously unable to divide. Along the granular leukocyte route, differentiation is likewise associated with a complete loss of reproductive capacity, for fully developed granular leukocytes, even though they still possess nuclei, do not give any indication of being able to multiply.

Therefore, the constant supply of erythrocytes and granular leukocytes for the body must be provided for by cell division occurring in cells that are less differentiated than they are, and by these less differentiated cells constantly differentiating into the mature forms that cannot divide. This of course requires that a pool of less differentiated cells be maintained with some of their members dividing and that there are adequate numbers available for differentiating into the mature cells that cannot reproduce themselves. This would be a simple problem if the immediate precursors of erythrocytes and granular leukocytes had an unlimited reproductive capacity. But the more immediate precursors of erythrocytes and granular leukocytes are themselves differentiated to a considerable degree (although not completely), and hence it can be assumed that their reproductive capacity has suffered somewhat as a consequence of their partial differentiation and therefore that their reproductive capacity is restricted to their being able to undergo *only a limited number of divisions*. Accordingly, since they could not be expected by their own divisions to maintain a pool of cells to differentiate into erythrocytes and leukocytes, we must look beyond them for cells with greater reproductive capacity which differentiate to maintain their numbers; then, when we have found these, we must look farther still to find some cells whose reproductive capacity has not been dimmed to any extent by differentiation and which therefore can serve as stem cells for the family. Recent evidence which will now be described suggests that there is an undifferentiated free cell of myeloid tissue that serves as a stem cell for the formation of cells of both the erythrocyte series and the granular leukocyte series and also for the formation of megakaryocytes. This stem cell gives every evidence of having a capacity for almost unlimited proliferation, and by proliferating it maintains a pool of stem cells from which some cells differentiate into the least differentiated members of the erythrocyte and the granular leukocyte series.

Since the first descendants of the stem cells are the least differentiated members of their respective lines, they still have a very considerable (but nevertheless limited) capacity for proliferation. Therefore, it is by virtue of their own reproductive ability that they do most of the work with regard to maintaining a constant pool of cells of their type. Accordingly, they only require a relatively small supply of stem cells to help them to maintain pools of themselves. Likewise, the cells that they in turn give rise to can still divide a few times and so on. Accordingly, *most mitosis seen in marrow is to be found, not in stem cells, but in the progeny of stem cells.* However without "fresh blood" from stem cells, mitosis would eventually run down and cease in the more differentiated cells in these cell lineages. Practically, this means that stem cells do not have to divide very often to perform their essential work. We shall now consider some of the newer findings which are illustrative of the stem cells of marrow.

In recent years radiation has become a powerful tool for eliciting new information about the formation of cells in hemopoietic tissues. As already noted, an animal that is given a dose of total-body irradiation, that is just in the lethal range, dies chiefly because cell division in its hemopoietic organs is arrested. New plasma cells are not formed to make antibodies, and no new neutrophils are produced to combat the bacteria that soon invade its body. The production of erythrocytes is also stopped, but the erythrocyte count in the blood does not fall as rapidly as the neutrophil count, because erythrocytes are all replaced only every 4 months, while neutrophils have a life span of only a few days. No new megakaryocytes are formed, and hence the platelet count falls and there are not enough platelets to stop the animal from bleeding from and into its tissues.

In due course it was discovered that the life of an animal that had been given what would have been a lethal dose of total-body irradiation could be saved if that animal were given an intravenous injection of marrow cells from a normal donor, preferably isologous, shortly after it was irradiated. Furthermore, by using donor animals that had slightly different chromosomes from those of the irradiated recipient, it was shown that the blood cells that appeared in the circulation of the animal as it recovered were derived from marrow cells that had come from the donor. This showed that some cells from the marrow of the donor animal had repopulated the marrow of the irradiated animal and were now supplying to the irradiated animal adequate supplies of erythrocytes and granular leukocytes. In other words, marrow tissue from the donor was now living and working in the irradiated animal, and since the irradiated animal thus consisted of parts of two animals it was termed a *chimera*. This term was borrowed from classical mythology where a chimera was supposed to be a fire-eating monster with the foreparts of its body those of a lion, the middle parts those of a goat, and the hind parts those of a dragon.

It was not known, however, after it was shown that injection of marrow would save irradiated animals, how the marrow of the host became repopulated. The next step in the story was the demonstration that this was due to the stem cells that were in the marrow that was injected, and not to mitosis continuing in the much more numerous descendants of these stem cells that were in the injected material. The evidence for stem cells of marrow being the important factor in marrow repopulation is described by Till and McCulloch and McCulloch and Till in a series of papers dealing with their findings by developing and using what is now commonly known as the *spleen-colony technic*. It should be explained here that in the mouse, in which the following work was performed, myeloid tissue is common in the spleen, and hence it is not surprising that marrow cells "home out" in the spleen.

In the course of experiments in which ir-radiated mice were injected with suspensions of marrow cells from isologous mice these two investigators found that irradiated animals thus treated and killed 11 days afterward revealed little nodules which projected from the surfaces of their spleens (Fig. 16-3). On histologic examination these nodules proved to be foci of newly forming cells of the erythro-cyte and/or granular leukocyte series (Fig. 16-4). Often the nodules also contained megakaryocytes (Fig. 16-4). The histologic appearance of these nodules that were sprinkled about in splenic tissue suggested to these investigators that each nodule might represent a clone of cells that developed from a single stem cell. To test this hypothesis, Becker, McCulloch and Till treated marrow cells that were to be injected into an irradi-ated animal with just enough irradiation to expect that one chromosome in a few stem cells might be hit, not badly enough to prevent the cell from reproducing, but just enough to cause a slight defect in one chromosome that could serve as a marker for this cell and all its progeny to which it would of course transmit this defect. Suspensions of marrow cells treated as described above were then injected into irradiated hosts. After allowing enough time for colonies to be forming, they then gave the animals colchicine to arrest at the metaphase all dividing cells in the devel-oping colonies. The animals were then killed and the chromosome constitution of the cells of a great many colonies were studied. Most colonies were found to consist of cells with normal chromosomes. However, 4 colonies were found in which the chromosomes were abnormal, and in each of these colonies every mitotic figure that was seen showed the same chromosome abnormality. Furthermore, the abnormality common to all the cells of one colony was different from the abnormality that characterized all the cells of each of the other three colonies. This showed that all the cells of each colony were derived from a sin-gle cell and that this must be a stem cell that can form cells of all the three sublines in Line 2.

The study of the regeneration of any tissue

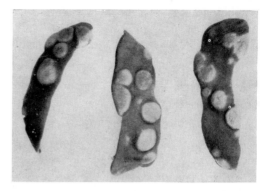

FIG. 16-3. Photograph of 3 mouse spleens with clones of cells derived from mouse marrow. The mice from which these spleens were taken had received 950 rads of x-ray followed by the injection of small numbers of nucleated bone marrow cells. After 10 days the spleens were removed and fixed in Bouin's solution. Each of the nodules visi-ble in the spleens is a colony of proliferating and differentiating cells, each derived from a single hemopoietic stem cell. (Prepara-tion by E. A. McCulloch)

generally indicates clearly the type of cell in that tissue that is responsible for its normal maintenance. In other words, the cells that respond to the presence of a defect in any tissue by dividing and restoring the part to normal are the cells that are normally con-cerned with maintaining that tissue in a nor-mal state of function. This is true, for example, of bone, for the kind of cells that divide to provide the new bone tissue to bring about the repair of a fracture are the same ones that normally provide enough new bone to keep the skeleton in repair. Accordingly, it seems logical to interpret the phenomenon of mye-loid tissue being regenerated by colonies of cells in various stages of differentiation but which all, in each colony, develop from a single stem cell, as indicating that it is by virtue of the proliferative capacity of this same stem cell that myeloid tissue is normally kept functional.

Spleen colonies differ somewhat with re-gard to the extent to which differentiation occurs along the 3 sublines. Most colonies, if they are left long enough, will show represent-atives of all 3 sublines. Younger colonies may show cells forming only along the erythrocyte or the granular leukocyte line. It would seem that the way a colony begins is by one stem cell from the injected marrow taking up a position in the spleen and then beginning to proliferate. Soon some of the cells of the small pool of stem cells that thus form are exposed to influences which induce them to begin to differentiate along one subline. Sooner or later influences induce others to differentiate along another subline. Mitosis continues for a time in these cells that are differentiating along different sublines. Therefore, the character of a given colony probably is influenced by the factors that ordinarily induce the differentiation of stem cells of the marrow to differentiate along one line or another. Evidence for this is as follows. It is known that a humoral (circulating) factor called erythropoietin is concerned in the normal individual with stimulating and thus controlling the formation of erythrocytes. It has been found that if antibody is made to erythropoietin and injected into an animal in which spleen colonies are developing, the colonies that form contain mostly cells of the granular leukocyte series. The relative absence of erythrocytes in the colonies that form is to be explained by the absence of erythropoietin (the normal stimulus for erythrocyte production) due to its having been inactivated by antibody. It would seem, therefore, that the extent to which different colonies in the same or in different animals vary in their content of cells of the 3 sublines, is dependent on factors that are concerned with differentiation and that the stem cells of marrow have the potentiality to form all 3 sublines of cells.

From their quantitative experiments, Mc-Culloch and Till (or Till and McCulloch) estimate that only about 1 out of every 1,000

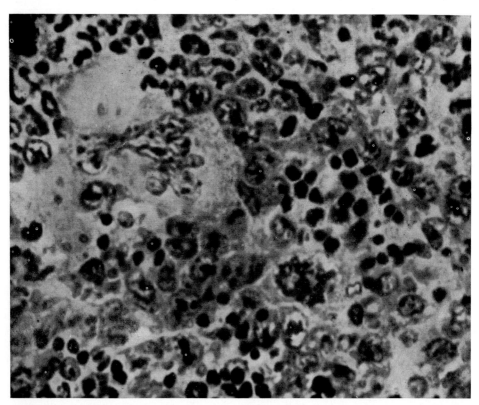

Fig. 16-4. A photomicrograph showing the appearance of a spleen colony. Although the cells shown are derived from a single cell, their appearance differs. The cell slightly left of, and above, center is a megakaryocyte; another just below and to the right of center is in mitosis. The cells with small round dark nuclei are erythroblasts—red cell precursors. Around the megakaryocytes, cells with ring-formed nuclei are visible; such nuclei characterize mouse granulocytes. (Preparation by E. A. McCulloch)

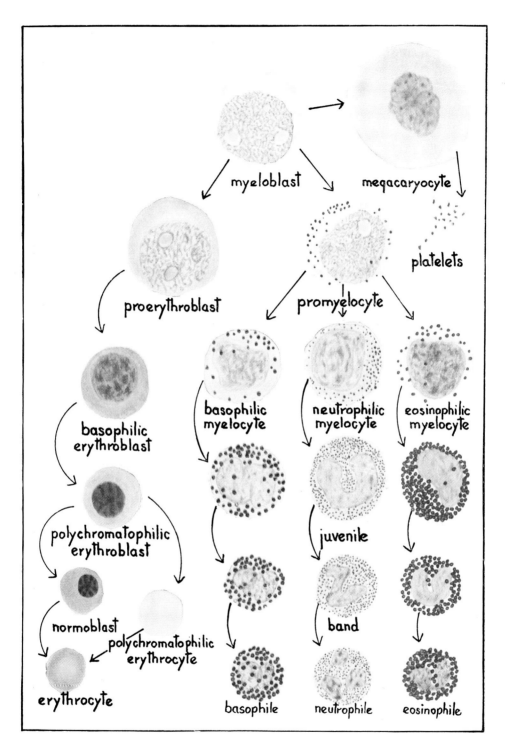

myeloblast

megacaryocyte

platelets

proerythroblast

promyelocyte

basophilic erythroblast

basophilic myelocyte

neutrophilic myelocyte

eosinophilic myelocyte

polychromatophilic erythroblast

juvenile

normoblast

polychromatophilic erythrocyte

band

erythrocyte

basophile

neutrophile

eosinophile

FIG. 16-5. The normal, free cells of marrow as they appear in films stained with a Romanovsky-type stain (Hastings). The promyelocyte and the megakaryocyte should be larger in comparison with other cells.

marrow cells can form a colony. Since these stem cells are so scarce, a problem is created with regard to identifying them morphologically. However, it is established that they must be free cells because it has been shown that the injection of circulating blood cells from a normal animal will result in the formation of some spleen colonies in irradiated animals. Therefore, at least an occasional colony-former must enter the bloodstream and circulate in it. McCulloch and Till hesitate to name the stem cell further than calling it a *colony-forming cell*. However, since their colony-forming cell can form the 3 sublines of cells that characterize marrow, it would seem to the author that functionally it deserves the name of *myeloblast*. The name myeloblast has, of course, been applied in the past to a relatively large free cell of marrow which some believed from indirect evidence to be the stem cell that gives rise to cells of the 3 sublines, as shown in Figure 16-5, while others believed that it gave rise only to the cells of the granular leukocyte series. It has not been established that the cells of marrow that can regenerate marrow and which McCulloch and Till term colony-forming cells have the appearance described for myeloblasts in the past. Provisionally, until further evidence is forthcoming, we shall assume that colony-forming cells—the stem cells of marrow—have the appearance described for myeloblasts. It seems probable, however, that not all cells that have the appearance of myeloblasts can form colonies, because cells having the appearance of myeloblasts are more numerous in marrow than are colony-formers.

*Histologic Technics for Studying Cells of Marrow.* The fact that the practicing physician is interested in detecting free cells of myeloid tissue in blood films stained with blood stains makes it important for the student to learn the appearance of these cells as revealed by blood stains. For this reason, ordinary H and E sections of myeloid tissue are not adequate for learning the appearance of the free cells of marrow because H and E do not color these cells the same way as blood stains. Furthermore, sections are not very satisfactory for this purpose because the mesh of marrow is so packed with cells that individual cells cannot be seen to advantage (Figs. 16-1 and 16-10). Consequently, the appearances of the various cells of marrow usually are learned either from thin films or thin imprints of fresh marrow that are stained with blood stains. Imprints are made by touching fresh marrow lightly to glass slides. Films are made either by smearing the marrow lightly on a slide or by mixing the marrow with blood serum and then spreading the resulting mixture on a glass slide by the same method employed in making a blood film. Imprints or films can be stained rapidly with ordinary blood stains. Students using preparations of this sort to study free cells of marrow should not try to ascertain the nature of every cell that they see, because many cells are altered in some way in the making of this kind of preparation. It is better for students to examine only reasonably perfect cells until typical appearances become familiar to them.

## THE CELLS CONCERNED IN THE FORMATION OF ERYTHROCYTES (SUBLINE 1)

Since erythrocytes arise through many intermediate steps from myeloblasts, we shall consider this cell first. A myeloblast (labeled in Fig. 16-5) is a large cell commonly measuring anywhere from 12 to 20 microns in diameter (Fig. 16-5). Its nucleus is ovoid, and it may show some indentation, but indentation, as a general rule, is not pronounced. With blood stains, its nucleus is red but with a purple tinge to it. The chromatin granules are fine and distributed rather lightly throughout the nucleus with the result that the nucleus as a whole is rather pale. From 2 to 5 nucleoli of a pale-blue color may be seen in the nucleus. The cytoplasm is a light to moderate shade of blue and is scanty to moderate in amount. In some instances it is vacuolated.

The fine structure of this cell has been described by Pease. The EM shows the nuclei to have large nucleolar masses. The mitochondria are large. The Golgi apparatus is well developed, but other intracytoplasmic membranes are only poorly developed. However, ribosomes are numerous, being scattered diffusely through the cytoplasm; this type of arrangement, as has been pointed out already, is common in cells that are synthesizing protein for growth.

Myeloblasts in the meshes of myeloid tissue, in differentiating along the red blood cell route (the first subline), give rise to somewhat smaller cells. These are called *proerythroblasts* (Fig. 16-5) and measure usually from 12 to 15 microns in diameter. The chromatin in their nuclei is somewhat coarser than that in the nucleus of the myeloblast. The staining reaction of the nucleus on the whole is somewhat more basophilic than that of the myeloblast, so the nucleus is somewhat more purple and not quite so red as that of the myeloblast. Two prominent nucleoli are commonly present. The cytoplasm of the proerythroblast is somewhat more basophilic and less in amount than that of the myeloblast. The cytoplasmic basophilia, in the EM, is seen to be due to an abundance of free ribosomes (Fig. 16-6). See also Figure 7-1.

Proerythroblasts give rise to cells known as *erythroblasts*. More specifically, the cell that the proerythroblast gives rise to is called a

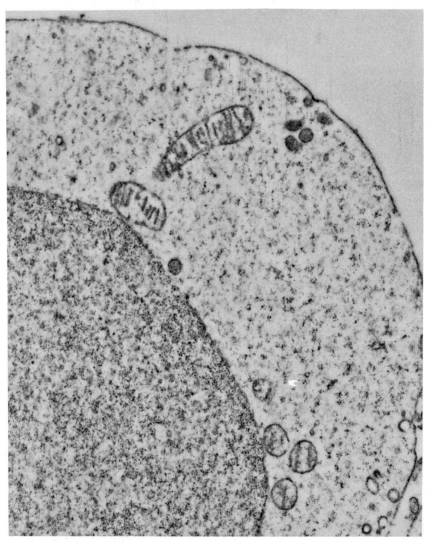

FIG. 16-6. Electron micrograph ($\times$ 32,000) of part of a section of a proerythoblast obtained from human bone marrow. The granular nucleus is at the lower left. The cytoplasm contains a few mitochondria of different sizes. There are only a few membranous vesicles and these tend to be rounded (*lower right*). Ribosomes (in arrangements of polysomes) are spread diffusely through the cytoplasm; these account for diffuse basophilia. Compare with Figure 16-7. (Preparation by A. F. Howatson and E. A. McCulloch)

*basophilic erythroblast* (Fig. 16-5) because of the color of its cytoplasm. The basophilic erythroblast is somewhat smaller than the proerythroblast. The chromatin of its nucleus is more dense and appears in the form of coarse granules which often are clumped. Sometimes the clumped granules are arranged like the spokes of a wheel. The staining reaction of the nucleus is still more basophilic than that of the proerythroblast. Consequently, the red color of the nucleus apparent in the myeloblast is not seen in the nucleus of the basophilic erythroblast. No nucleoli can be seen in its nucleus. The cytoplasm is more basophilic than that of the proerythroblast and ranges from a moderate to a deep blue in color.

Basophilic erythroblasts give rise to cells which are somewhat smaller. These are called *polychromatophilic erythroblasts* (Fig. 16-5). This name has been given to them because their cytoplasm "loves many colors" in the limited sense that it takes up both the acid and the basic components of blood stains. As is demonstrated by the preceding cell (the basophilic erythroblast), the cytoplasm of cells encountered along the red blood cell route is fundamentally basophilic; this is due to free ribosomes (Fig. 16-7). The cause of acidophilia of the cytoplasm, which becomes apparent first in the cytoplasm of the polychromatophilic erythroblast, is hemoglobin, which is being synthesized by, and so comes to be mixed with, the fundamentally basophilic cytoplasm. The net result is that the cytoplasm takes on a muddy-gray or green-violet color. The nucleus of the polychromatic erythroblast is somewhat smaller than that of the basophilic variety, and its chromatin is in the form of coarse granules which commonly are clumped so that the nucleus as a whole is very basophilic. No nucleoli can be seen in it.

Polychromatophilic erythroblasts experience 1 of 2 different fates. Occasionally, under ordinary circumstances (probably less than once in 100 times), and more often when erythroid activity is increased because of a need for more red cells, the nucleus of the polychromatophilic erythroblast becomes pyknotic and is extruded while the cytoplasm is still polychromatophilic. This results in the formation of a polychromatophilic erythro-

cyte, as is shown in Figure 12-4. As has been described already, the polychromatophilic erythrocyte is called a reticulocyte when it is stained by supravital technics; the RNA still present in its cytoplasm shows up under these conditions as if it were in the form of a reticulum.

The other and common fate of polychromatophilic erythroblasts is for them, as they continue to divide, to lose their cytoplasmic RNA so that their cytoplasm loses all its former basophilic properties. When this has happened, the cell is termed a *normoblast* because it is going to give rise to a normocytic erythrocyte. By this time a normoblast has a small spherical dark-staining pyknotic nucleus (Fig. 16-5). Normally, this is lost by extrusion; recently Pease has published electron micrographs of the process. The many extruded nuclei of normoblasts seem to disappear very quickly from marrow. Occasionally, small particles of the nucleus are left behind in erythrocytes; these are called Howell-Jolly bodies. When a nuclear remnant is in the form of a ring it is called a Cabot ring.

**The Fine Structure of Erythroblasts.** Several erythroblasts are seen in the electron micrograph which comprises Figure 16-7. Their most interesting feature is their considerable content of free ribosomes; these in erythroblasts serve two general purposes. First, erythroblasts multiply to some extent and hence a proportion of their free ribosomes, a proportion which decreases as they mature, is concerned with the synthesis of protoplasm required for cell multiplication. Secondly, basophilic erythroblasts become polychromatic erythroblasts because hemoglobin is synthesized in the cytoplasm. Hemoglobin is not synthesized in rough-surfaced vesicles as is protein that is destined for secretion. Instead, hemoglobin is synthesized in association with free ribosomes and thereafter it lies free in the cytoplasm. The free ribosomes that are concerned with the synthesis of hemoglobin are grouped into polyribosomes as was described and illustrated in Chapter 7.

The increasing electron density of the cytoplasm of maturing erythroblasts is to be explained by the hemoglobin that is accumulating in their cytoplasm. Hemoglobin is very electron dense and this accounts for the fact

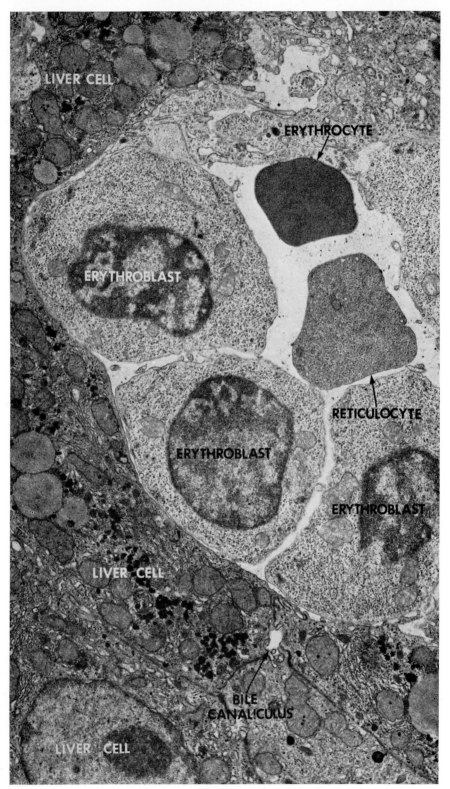

FIGURE 16-7. (*Caption on facing page*)

that the electron density of the next stage along the red blood cell route—the reticulocyte—is electron dense (Fig. 16-7) as are erythrocytes themselves (Fig. 16-7).

In the embryo, the liver is an important source of new red blood cells. Later in fetal life, the spleen takes on the function of producing red blood cells, and only later still does the bone marrow of the fetus become highly specialized for this work and do most of it. At birth, red blood cell production usually is limited to bone marrow, but the distribution of red marrow is more extensive in the bones of the newborn than in the adult.

**The Control of Erythropoiesis.** Under normal conditions the rate of production and liberation of erythrocytes by the marrow evenly matches the rate of their destruction by the reticuloendothelial system, so the normal level of red cells in the circulation is maintained. If the number of red cells in blood is reduced, as a result either of hemorrhage or of their being destroyed at an increased rate, the marrow can increase its production up to 10 times in order to maintain the balance. The method by which regulation is achieved is only partly understood. However, it is certain that anoxia (lack of oxygen) increases red cell production, for people who live at high altitudes, where the air is thin, have unusually high erythrocyte counts. However, it is doubtful if changes in oxygen content of the blood that reaches marrow could provide a regulation as fine as that which must exist. There is now much evidence that anoxia stimulates erythropoiesis in the marrow indirectly by causing an increase in the formation of a substance called *erythropoietin,* which is the agent that directly stimulates red cell production. Convincing evidence of the existence of this factor was provided by an experiment in which parabiotic pairs (a parabiotic pair is

a pair with joined circulations) of rats were placed in chambers so that one of the pair breathed normal air, and the other air with only 8 per cent oxygen. Both animals of each pair developed hyperplasia of their red marrow.

Erythropoietin is probably made in the kidney; however, this may not be its only source.

**Anemia.** An understanding of the factors described above is essential to the systematic investigation of anemia, for in anemia the balance between production and destruction has been disturbed, and the number of cells in the blood becomes reduced. This may result from blood loss or an increased rate of destruction of erythrocytes or from some failure of the marrow to produce erythrocytes. For example, if the marrow is destroyed, or replaced by some other kind of tissue, it will be unable to produce cells, and anemia develops. Or, if red marrow is available, but if a sufficient supply of raw materials for the manufacture of cells is not, the marrow cannot produce enough cells. This happens in *pernicious anemia;* in this condition the marrow does not receive enough vitamin $B_{12}$. Only minute quantities (about 1 gamma or 0.000001 G) of this vitamin are required daily. However, for this to be absorbed from the food, a specific substance, probably a mucopolysaccharide, must be secreted by the stomach. Certain individuals seem to be unable to secrete this latter material and so are unable to absorb sufficient $B_{12}$ from their intestine. The role of $B_{12}$ is that of a coenzyme in the biosynthesis of nucleic acid; it is needed for the formation of DNA and RNA. Under these conditions of a $B_{12}$ deficiency, cell production in the marrow is slowed, and such cells as are produced, in the erythrocyte series, are larger than normal, and the chromatin of their nuclei remains finely granular,

FIG. 16-7. Electron micrograph ($\times$ 6,000) of extramedullary hematopoiesis in the liver of a 5-day-old mouse. Three stages in the maturation of red blood cells can be seen. Erythroblasts (labeled as such) are lying in close apposition to liver cells. Their nuclear chromatin is clumped and their cytoplasm contains large numbers of randomly dispersed free ribosomes. Adjacent to the erythroblasts is a reticulocyte. The nucleus has been extruded from this cell, but at least 1 small mitochondrion can still be seen in the cytoplasm. Ribosomes are present in the cytoplasm but the greater density of the cytoplasm is due to its content of hemoglobin. Adjacent to the reticulocyte is a mature erythrocyte. Its cytoplasm is extremely electron-dense owing to the high content of hemoglobin. Neither ribosomes nor any other organelles can be recognized in the cytoplasm of the mature erythrocyte. (Preparation from K. Arakawa)

even after their cytoplasm accumulates hemoglobin. The cells that develop under these conditions, which are the counterparts of the proerythroblasts seen under normal conditions, are called *megaloblasts,* and, in the absence of $B_{12}$, the whole family of erythrogenic cells that arise from these are larger than normal; the terms early, intermediate and late megaloblasts are used for these cells. When these cells eventually lose their nuclei and appear in the bloodstream, they are larger than normal (Fig. 13-5, *right*), and the anemia is described as a macrocytic anemia.

Curiously enough, the mother cells of the red blood cell series that are present in early embryonic life are similar to the megaloblasts that appear in pernicious anemia. This has led some hematologists to consider the megaloblast as a normal cell. However, it seems best to consider the megaloblast a normal cell only for embryos, for in postnatal life the widespread replacement of proerythroblasts by megaloblasts in the marrow, and the appearance of the latter cells' progeny in the bloodstream, indicates that the marrow is deficient in some material required for the building of normal protoplasm.

When the number of red cells in the blood dwindles in some kinds of anemic states, it is common for the bone marrow to discharge the nucleated, developing forms of blood cells into the circulation. Hence, normoblasts, erythroblasts and even younger forms may be detected in blood films made from patients with at least certain kinds of severe anemias. In pernicious anemia, as has been explained already, the immature nucleated cells of the red blood cell series that appear are larger than usual.

Iron is an ingredient of hemoglobin, hence hemoglobin cannot be made without iron. Under normal conditions, the body is very economical of iron and uses that obtained from old, worn-out red cells in the synthesis of hemoglobin in new ones. But, under certain conditions, the body may suffer from a deficiency of iron, and as a result an iron-deficiency anemia can occur. This is commonly of the hypochromic type (Fig. 13-5, *left*).

### The Formation of Granular Leukocytes (Granulopoiesis) (Subline 2)

The 3 kinds of granular leukocytes that develop in the reticular mesh of red marrow are all descendants of myeloblasts and are produced as a result of differentiation proceeding along what we have termed Subline 2 (see chart). In forming granular leukocytes, the first cell formed along this line of differentiation by the myeloblast is known as a promyelocyte (Fig. 16-5). This cell is very large (even larger than is shown in Fig. 16-5) with a very similar appearance to the myeloblast; indeed, it differs from it only in containing a few azurophilic granules in its cytoplasm. Since the granules that are first formed in cells of the granulocyte series are not specific enough to stain differently, it is impractical to attempt to distinguish 3 types of promyelocytes.

The second step in differentiation along Subline 2 is represented by the formation of myelocytes from promyelocytes. This step involves changes in both the nuclei and the cytoplasm of the cells and a reduction in the size of the cells concerned (Fig. 16-5). The reduction in size is greater than shown in Figure 16-5 because the promyelocyte should be larger. Whereas the nucleus of the promyelocyte is only slightly indented (like that of the myeloblast), the nucleus of the myelocyte exhibits a moderate degree of indentation. Furthermore, the chromatin of the nucleus is more condensed. Hence, the nucleus stains somewhat more darkly than the nucleus of the myeloblast or the promyelocyte. But the nuclei of the cells seen along Subline 2 do not stain nearly so darkly as those seen along Subline 1 (the red blood cell route). The cytoplasm of the myelocyte in which the granules lie is not so basophilic as that of myeloblasts and promyelocytes and is inclined to take on a pale-red color with blood stains. Generally, a cell is not called a myelocyte unless it has at least a dozen granules in its cytoplasm. However, myelocytes may be loaded with granules. Many of the granules seen in myelocytes are large and azurophilic and not specific for the three series of cells. The specific granules at least of neutrophils and eosinophils, however, begin to appear in the cell at this time and are seen to best advantage in the Golgi region (Fig. 16-8). Careful inspection can permit different kinds of myelocytes to be distinguished.

The three kinds of myelocytes form the three kinds of granular leukocytes (Fig. 16-5).

Some authors describe an intermediate metamyelocyte stage. The changes that occur in the nucleus of a neutrophilic myelocyte as it becomes a neutrophilic leukocyte are not precisely the same as those that occur in the nucleus of an eosinophilic myelocyte as it becomes an eosinophilic leukocyte, and these in turn are not precisely the same as those that occur in the nucleus of a basophilic myelocyte as it becomes a basophilic leukocyte. Consequently, the formation of the three kinds of leukocytes from the three kinds of myelocytes will be described separately.

**Formation of Neutrophilic Leukocytes.** A fairly mature neutrophilic myelocyte (neutrophilic metamyelocyte) has an indented nucleus, and its cytoplasm contains a goodly complement of fine, violet granules and a variable quantity of the early formed larger azurophilic granules. Although cells of this type are confined to bone marrow under normal conditions, they may appear in the circulating blood when the body is reacting to

an infection. When detected in blood films, they are called *juvenile neutrophils* (Fig. 12-5). Normally, however, the nucleus of this cell undergoes certain changes before the cell is liberated into the bloodstream. Essentially, this change is brought about by an increasing indentation of the nucleus so that it becomes somewhat darker and assumes the shape of a thin horseshoe. Folding of the horseshoe-shaped nucleus may produce still other appearances. A cell containing such a nucleus is known as a *band* or *filamented* neutrophil (Figs. 12-4 and 12-5). Some neutrophils are released from the bone marrow under normal conditions at this stage of development. But further nuclear changes occur before most neutrophils are released. Essentially, these are due to the long, then horseshoe-shaped nucleus developing constrictions at one or more points. This causes the chromatin to become somewhat more dense; hence it stains more deeply. At the sites of a constriction, the nucleoplasm is reduced to a thin thread,

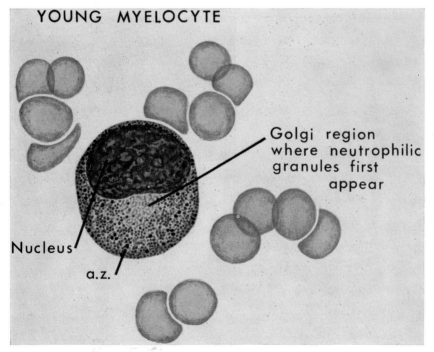

Fig. 16-8. Drawing to show that the first granules that appear in a young myelocyte are of the azurophilic type (a.z.). The specific granules of the neutrophil appear first in the Golgi region and later replace the azurophilic granules (a.z.) that are in the remainder of the cytoplasm. (Illustration from C. P. Leblond)

and sometimes this thread becomes broken. Constrictions result in a nucleus having a multilobed appearance. Cells with such nuclei are commonly termed *segmented neutrophils* (Fig. 12-4). The degree of lobulation (from 1 to 5 or more lobes) generally is regarded as an index of maturation.

**Formation of Eosinophilic Leukocytes.** In forming an eosinophilic leukocyte the slightly indented nucleus of the eosinophilic myelocyte generally develops a deep constriction at the metamyelocyte stage of development. This deepens to divide the nucleus of the eosinophil into two lobes that usually remain joined together only by a strand of nucleoplasm (Fig. 12-4). As the constriction develops, the chromatin of the nucleus becomes somewhat condensed, and as a result the chromatin takes up a little more stain than the nucleus of a myelocyte. But the condensation of chromatin that occurs is not so great as that which occurs in the neutrophil; hence the nuclei of eosinophils are paler than those of neutrophils.

**Formation of Basophilic Leukocytes.** In forming a basophilic leukocyte the nucleus of a mature basophilic myelocyte (metamyelocyte) undergoes less change than occurs in the formation of either a neutrophil or an eosinophil. Irregular constrictions may appear in it to give it an irregular outline. But, in general, it does not become broken up into lobes to the same extent as neutrophils or eosinophils. Since its chromatin does not become condensed, it stains only very lightly. In contrast, its granules stain deeply, and as a result, those that lie in the cytoplasm that is spread over the nucleus tend to obscure it (Fig. 12-4).

**The Fine Structure of Cells Involved in Granulocytopoiesis.** The myeloblast has prominent nucleoli. The mitochondria are large, and the Golgi apparatus is well developed. Although the cytoplasm contains numerous ribosomes, the membranous vesicles of the cytoplasm are not particularly well developed at the myeloblast stage, so most of the ribosomes are spread diffusely through the cytoplasm rather than being attached to membranous vesicles. As the cell becomes first a promyelocyte and then a myelocyte, rough-surfaced membranous vesicles become very much more numerous; this development

seems to be associated with the synthesis of granules. Many of the rough-surfaced vesicles are of about the same size as the granules, and this, of course, gives some suggestion that the material of the specific granules of the cells of the granulocyte series is synthesized inside rough-surfaced vesicles (Fig. 16-9). The Golgi apparatus is well developed at the myelocyte stage (Fig. 16-9); its precise role in the formation or packaging of specific granules has not yet been elucidated. The specific granules of developing neutrophils vary in size and in their affinity for osmium tetroxide and hence in their density. (Fig. 16-9). The specific granules that appear in developing eosinophils, which may contain dense disklike bodies, have already been described in the chapter on blood. Pease has described the granules of basophils as seeming to have a laminated structure, but he notes that these granules are particularly difficult to fix. As has already been described, the granules of neutrophils can exert lysosome activity.

About the time that the cells are developing specific granules in their cytoplasm, the nucleoli disappear from their nuclei. Furthermore, after the granules are formed, both the rough-surfaced membranous vesicles and the mitochondria in the cytoplasm become much fewer in number. Ribosomes scattered throughout the cytoplasm persist.

**Some General Principles Useful for Identifying Different Types of Marrow Cells.** The more primitive stem cells of marrow (blast cells) have large nuclei which are colored a red-purple color with Wright's stain. The chromatin granules in these nuclei are *fine* and *evenly dispersed,* and *several pale blue* nucleoli are generally present. The cytoplasm is a pale to a moderate shade of blue and contains no granules.

Along the erythrocyte line of development the cells become increasingly smaller. The nuclei become smaller and darker with increasingly condensed chromatin, and the nucleoli are lost. The cytoplasm at first becomes more basophilic but later becomes polychromatophilic as hemoglobin forms in it. Eventually it becomes acidophilic as the RNA is lost from it in the final stages of development. Lastly, the nucleus is extruded.

Along the granulocyte line of development the first cell formed is very large. The strik-

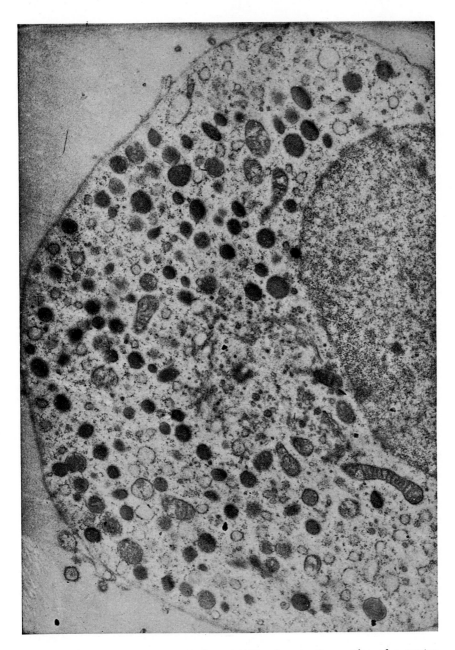

FIG. 16-9. Electron micrograph (× 29,000) of part of a section of a neutrophilic myelocyte obtained from the bone marrow of an individual with pernicious anemia. The finely granular nucleus can be seen on the right. The cytoplasm shows a well-developed Golgi apparatus to the left of the nucleus, a little below the middle of the picture. A moderate number of mitochondria can be seen in the cytoplasm. Moreover, the cytoplasm contains a large number of rounded rough-surfaced membranous vesicles as well as many specific granules of about the same size and shape. Both the vesicles and the granules vary in size. Ribosomes, as well as being distributed around the membranous vesicles, are also spread throughout the cytoplasm. (Preparation by A. F. Howatson and E. A. McCulloch)

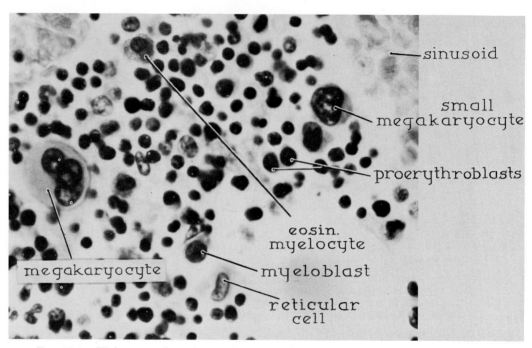

FIG. 16-10. High-power photomicrograph of a section of red bone marrow obtained from an infant. The cells in this specimen are less tightly packed than is usual, and in this photograph a primitive reticular cell, a myeloblast, some megakaryocytes and a myelocyte can be distinguished. The smaller nuclei are those of erythroblasts and normoblasts.

ing feature of development along this line is the appearance of granules in the cytoplasm. The first granules that form are relatively large azurophilic granules and cannot be identified as neutrophilic, eosinophilic or basophilic. The next generation of cells that form are smaller, and the three types of specific granules now begin to appear. As neutrophils and eosinophils mature, that is, when they have become well filled with their specific granules, nucleoli can no longer be seen in their nuclei. But of even greater importance is the fact that as these cells mature their nuclei become increasingly indented and finally lobulated. Hence, a glance at the shape of their nuclei enables one to judge their degree of maturity. Cells of the basophilic series are identified by the fact that they contain large irregular basophilic granules and that these tend to overshadow the nucleus.

## MEGAKARYOCYTES AND THE FORMATION OF PLATELETS (SUBLINE 3)

Myeloblasts differentiate along a third subline to form megakaryocytes (so called be-cause they possess *great* nuclei); these cells give rise to the platelets of the blood.

Both sections and imprints of red marrow are usually employed for the study of mega-karyocytes. The student is advised to become familiar with the appearance of these cells in sections before he tries to identify them in imprints.

In H and E sections of red marrow, studied with the low-power objective, megakaryocytes appear as huge cells scattered throughout the marrow (Fig. 16-10). Under high power each one can be seen to be many times the size of a myeloblast (Fig. 16-10). The nucleus is colored a deep blue with hematoxylin. The nucleus of a megakaryocyte may be ovoid in shape or it may be lobulated in a fashion reminiscent of the nucleus of the segmented neutrophil. Since the nucleus is so large, a megakaryocyte with a lobulated nucleus may, at the first focus at which it is examined, seem to be a multinucleated cell. But careful focusing of the microscope will show that what at first appear to be separate nuclei are in reality connected to one another. Since osteoclasts are sometimes present in marrow, and

are of an order of size comparable to megakaryocytes, this test (focusing) may be used
to help to tell the two cells apart because
osteoclasts (Fig. 18-15) are truly multinucleated cells. The cytoplasm of megakaryocytes seen in H and E sections is pink and of
an even texture. Some cells have large
amounts of it, but others have scarcely any.

In imprints of bone marrow stained with
blood stains, megakaryocytes are not very
sharply outlined. Their nuclei are a deep blue-
purple color, and their cytoplasm is pale blue.
It may be stippled with fine granules that
may be colored anywhere from red to blue
(Fig. 16-11).

It was not until 1906 that evidence was
obtained suggesting that megakaryocytes
manufacture platelets. At that time Wright
devised a special stain (a variation of the
polychrome methylene blue and eosin mixture) and stained thin sections of red marrow,
particularly that of kittens and puppies, with
it. He observed that megakaryocytes not
commonly extended cytoplasmic pseudopodia
into the sinusoids of the marrow and further
that the cytoplasmic pseudopodia stained
identically with platelets in that the red
granules of the pseudopodia resembled the
granular chromatomere of the platelet and
that the substance of the pseudopodia stained
similarly to the hyalomere of the platelet
(Fig. 16-11). Moreover, he pointed out that
only those animals that possess megakaryocytes have platelets. Many observers have
since shown that in certain diseased states
there is a relation between the number of
platelets in the blood and the number of megakaryocytes in the marrow.

Final proof that platelets are detached
portions of megakaryocyte cytoplasm has
come from EM studies. The study of platelets with the EM, as was explained in Chapter
14, revealed that each is surrounded by a
"cell" membrane. Studies of megakaryocyte
cytoplasm, made with the EM, have shown
how each fragment of cytoplasm could become completely surrounded with a "cell"
membrane while the cytoplasm from which
the fragments become detached could remain
covered with a cell membrane, as will now be
explained.

Yamada, in 1955, described how the cytoplasm of megakaryocytes becomes divided

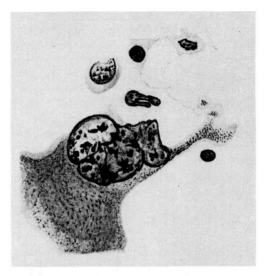

Fig. 16-11. A black-and-white photograph
of one of Wright's colored illustrations of
the appearance of megakaryocytes forming
platelets in a section of the bone marrow
of a kitten, stained with Wright's special
stain. The picture shows a pseudopodium
extending through a thin-walled blood vessel
and liberating 2 platelets. (Wright, J. H.:
J. Morphol. 21:263)

up into small compartments by an extensive
development within the cytoplasm of smooth-
surfaced membranous structures. This is illustrated diagrammatically in Figure 14-7,
and in an electron micrograph in Figure 14-6.
The way platelets form from megakaryocytes
is explained in connection with platelets in
Chapter 14.

As was described in Chapter 14, platelets
have specific granules in them, and these probably are responsible for the staining of the
chromatomere. These specific granules are to
be seen in the cytoplasm in megakaryocytes,
and each developing compartment has a quota
of them (Fig. 14-6).

## OTHER CELLS IN BONE MARROW

**Lymphocytes.** Yoffey's extensive studies
suggest that many lymphocytes are filtered
out of the bloodstream in the bone marrow,
and for this reason lymphocytes are relatively
common members of the marrow cell population. It should be emphasized that lymphocytes are not normally produced in bone marrow but in lymphatic tissue.

As has been noted in our discussion of the thymus gland, marrow cells will not maintain, or injected marrow cells will not restore, the immunity mechanisms of mice that have been thymectomized at birth. Since lymphocytes from lymph nodes and spleen on being injected into thymectomized mice will restore their immunity mechanisms, there must be some fundamental difference between the lymphocytes or lymphocytelike cells that are seen in marrow (where they are numerous) and those of lymphatic tissue. Yet marrow cells will repopulate a thymus gland that has been depleted of lymphocytes. It is not known which cells of marrow perform this function.

**Plasma Cells, Mast Cells and Monocytes.** All these cells are not uncommon in normal marrow. It seems probable that some of the monocytes of marrow come there from other sites in the body, and also that some are produced in bone marrow. As was noted in Chapter 12, the origin of monocytes is somewhat uncertain.

**Fat Cells.** The fat cells of bone marrow doubtless arise from cells that are differentiating along Main Line 1. It seems probable that a cell anywhere along this line could differentiate into one.

## THE STUDY OF BONE MARROW IN CLINICAL MEDICINE

The diagnosis of many diseases is facilitated by studying the cells of the affected person's bone marrow. Red bone marrow is soft to semifluid in consistency; hence, it is possible to aspirate it from certain sites. Commonly, bone marrow is obtained in the clinic by means of a *sternal puncture.* Sometimes it is obtained from an iliac crest. Other sites may be utilized, particularly in children.

Bone marrow so obtained generally is studied by means of making films or imprints of it and staining these with blood stains. As was explained in Chapter 8, the cells of marrow can also be concentrated and sectioned.

The student will find that in most hospital laboratories a particular terminology and a particular chart of the percentage distribution of the different cells in marrow are employed. Therefore, we shall make only a few general comments on the cells that are seen in a preparation of normal marrow, such as the one illustrated in Figure 16-12 *(top).*

Few myeloblasts (labeled 1) are present. Promyelocytes (labeled 2) are more numerous. Myelocytes and metamyelocytes (labeled 3-4) are the most numerous of all cells. Granular leukocytes are fairly numerous, and, as might be expected, neutrophils (labeled 5, 6 and 7) are more numerous than acidophils, and acidophils are more numerous than basophils. Cells of the red blood series (labeled 11-12) are fairly numerous, and the more highly differentiated ones (normoblasts) are much more numerous than the less differentiated ones (proerythroblasts and erythroblasts). A few lymphocytes (labeled 8) and monocytes (labeled 9) may be present, as well as an occasional megakaryocyte (labeled 10).

The way that the bone marrow picture, as seen in films, becomes altered in disease will now be illustrated by two examples.

**Myeloid Leukemia.** Leukemia is a disease characterized by a great overproduction of leukocytes. One main kind is termed myeloid or myelogenous leukemia; in this type, leukocytes from myeloid tissue are overproduced.

Myeloid leukemia occurs in what are described as acute or chronic forms. In the acute and generally rapidly fatal form, the bone marrow becomes very overactive in producing granular leukocytes and pours these into the bloodstream, where their numbers may become increased up to 60 or even more times. The production and the liberation of leukocytes is so rapid that many immature forms appear in the blood (band neutrophils, juvenile neutrophils, metamyelocytes, myelocytes and even myeloblasts). Many of the leukocytes leave the blood to infiltrate tissues; this often crowds the tissues that they infiltrate and causes damage in them. The production of leukocytes in the marrow generally becomes so extensive that cells of the erythrocyte series and megakaryocytes are literally crowded out of the marrow; hence, anemia and thrombocytopenia tend to develop in the later stages of the disease, and the latter defect leads to hemorrhages. An examination of the bone marrow in this condition shows a greatly increased percentage of myeloblasts and a general shift toward increased numbers of immature cells in the

FIGURE 16-12

## BONE MARROW*
(NORMAL: HYPERPLASTIC: APLASTIC)

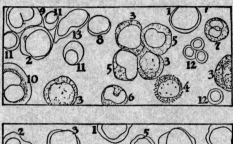

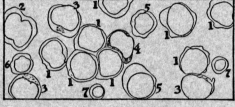

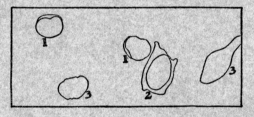

*Top:* Normal Bone Marrow:
1. Myeloblast
2. Premyelocyte
3. Neutrophilic myelocytes
4. Eosinophilic myelocyte
5. Juvenile neutrophils
6. Band neutrophil
7. Segmented neutrophil
8. Lymphocyte
9. Monocyte
10. Megakaryocyte
11. Macroblasts
12. Normoblasts
13. Primitive free cell (?)


* Drawn from serum spread

*Center:* Hyperplastic Bone Marrow with Maturation Arrest at Myeloblastic Level (from Patient with Acute Myeloblastic Leukemia):
1. Myeloblasts
2. Myeloblast in division
3. Premyelocytes
4. Myelocyte
5. Megaloblasts
6. Macroblast
7. Normoblasts

*Bottom:* Aplastic Bone Marrow (from Patient with Aplastic Anemia):
1. Lymphocytes
2. Primitive free cell (?)
3. Degenerating cells

FIGURE 16-17

BONE MARROW*

(NORMAL; HYPERPLASTIC; APLASTIC)

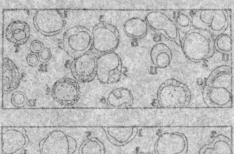

Top: Normal Bone Marrow
1. Myeloblast
2. Premyelocyte
3. Neutrophilic myelocytes
4. Eosinophilic myelocyte
5. Juvenile neutrophils
6. Band neutrophil
7. Segmented neutrophil
8. Lymphocyte
9. Monocyte
10. Megakaryocyte
11. Macroblasts
12. Normoblasts
13. Primitive free cell (?)

* Drawn from serum spread

Center: Hyperplastic Bone Marrow with Maturation Arrest at Myeloblastic Level (from Patient with Acute Myeloblastic Leukemia):
1. Myeloblasts
2. Myeloblast in division
3. Premyelocytes
4. Myelocyte
5. Megaloblasts
6. Macroblast
7. Normoblasts

Bottom: Aplastic Bone Marrow (from Patient with Aplastic Anemia):
1. Lymphocytes
2. Primitive free cell (?)
3. Degenerating cells

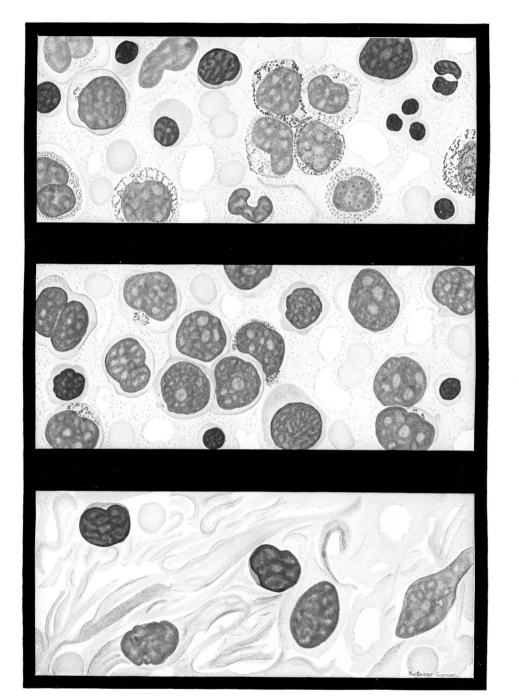

granular leukocyte series (Fig. 16-12, *center*).

**Aplastic Anemia.** The former example is one of an overproductive bone marrow. There are other conditions in which the bone marrow becomes underproductive. For example, there are certain toxic chemicals which, if absorbed by the body in sufficient amounts, literally destroy cell activity in the marrow, and it becomes unable to produce blood cells and platelets in sufficient numbers. In this condition the numbers of erythrocytes, granular leukocytes and platelets in the blood all become reduced. An examination of the bone marrow reveals the reason; films show that it contains only very few cells (Fig. 16-12, *bottom*).

# REFERENCES

## MYELOID TISSUE—GENERAL REFERENCES

Bessis, M.: The blood cells and their formation *in* Brachet, J., and Mirsky, A. E. (eds.): The Cell, vol. 5, p. 163, New York, Acad. Press, 1961.

Downey, H. (ed.): Handbook of Hematology, New York, Hoeber, 1938.

Low, F. N., and Freeman, J. A.: Electron Microscopic Atlas of Normal and Leukemic Human Blood, New York, Blakiston, 1958.

Lucas, A. F.: Atlas of Avian Hematology, Washington, D. C., Department of Agriculture, 1961. (*See also* textbooks on hematology.)

## SPECIAL REFERENCES ON MYELOID TISSUE

Bloom, W., and Bartelmez, G. W.: Hematopoiesis in young human embryos, Am. J. Anat. *67*:21, 1940.

Coleman, D. H., Stevens, A. R., Jr., Dodge, H. T., and Finch, C. A.: Rate of blood regeneration after blood loss, Arch. Int. Med. *92*:341, 1953.

Cunningham, R. S., Sabin, F. R., and Doan, C. A.: The development of leukocytes, lymphocytes and monocytes from a specific stem cell in adult tissues, Contrib. Embryol. *16*:277, 1925.

Doan, C. A.: The circulation of the bone marrow, Contrib. Embryol. *14*:27, 1922.

Downey, H.: The myeloblast—its occurrence under normal and pathological conditions and its relations to lymphocytes and other blood cells, Folia haemat. *35*:65, 145, 1927.

Jacobson, L. O., Plzak, L., Fried, W., and Goldwasser, E.: Plasma factor(s) influencing red cell production, Nature *177*:1240, 1956.

Jones, O. P.: Morphologic hematology, Blood (Special Issue), vol. I, 1947.

———: Morphologic, physiologic, chemical and biologic distinction of megaloblasts, Arch. Path. *35*:752, 1943.

Osgood, E. E., and Seeman, A. J.: The cellular composition of bone marrow as obtained by sternal puncture, Physiol. Rev. *25*:46, 1944.

Piney, A.: The anatomy of bone marrow, Brit. M. J. *2*:792, 1922.

Ponder, E., *et al.*: Some aspects of red cell production and destruction, Ann. N. Y. Acad. Sci., vol. 48, 1947.

## SPECIAL REFERENCES ON THE SPLEEN-COLONY TECHNIC FOR STUDYING THE PROLIFERATIVE CAPACITY AND THE POTENTIALITY OF MARROW CELLS

Becker, A. J., McCulloch, E. A., and Till, J. E.: Cytological demonstration of the clonal nature of spleen colonies derived from transplanted mouse marrow cells, Nature *197*:452-454, 1963.

McCulloch, E. A.: Les clones de cellules hématopoiétiques *in vivo*, Rev. Franç. études clin. biol. *8*:15-19, 1963.

McCulloch, E. A., Siminovitch, L., and Till, J. E.: Spleen-colony formation in anemic mice of genotype $WW^v$, Science *144*:844-846, 1964.

McCulloch, E. A., and Till, J. E.: The sensitivity of cells from normal mouse bone marrow to gamma radiation *in vitro* and *in vivo*, Rad. Res. *16*:822-832, 1962.

Siminovitch, L., Till, J. E., and McCulloch, E. A.: Decline in colony-forming ability of marrow cells subjected to serial transplantation into irradiated mice, J. Cell. Comp. Physiol. *64*:23, 1964.

Till, J. E., and McCulloch, E. A.: A direct measurement of the radiation sensitivity of normal mouse bone marrow cells, Rad. Res. *14*:213-222, 1961.

## SPECIAL REFERENCES ON MEGAKARYOCYTES AND PLATELETS

Campbell, E. W., Small, J., and Dameshek, W.: Metabolic activity of human blood platelets, J. Lab. Clin. Med. *47*:835, 1956.

Garcia, A. M.: Feulgen-DNA values in megakaryocytes, J. Cell Biol. *20*:342, 1964.

Humphrey, J. H.: Origin of blood platelets, Nature *175*:38, 1955.

Johnson, S. A., Monto, R., Rebuck, J., and Horn, R. C. (eds.): Blood Platelets, Boston, Little, 1961.

Kjaerheim, A., and Hovig, T.: The ultrastructure of haemostatic blood platelet plugs in rabbit mesenterium, Thromb. Diath. Haemorrh. *7*:1, 1962.

Pease, D. C.: An electron microscopic study of red bone marrow, J. Hemat. *11*:501, 1956.

————: Marrow cells seen with the electron microscope after ultrathin sectioning, Rev. hémat. *10*:300, 1955.

Thiery, J. P., and Bessis, M.: The formation of platelets by megakaryocytes observed in living cells, C. R. Acad. sc. *242*:290, 1956.

Wislocki, G. B., Bunting, H., and Dempsey, E. W.: Further observations on the chemical cytology of megacaryocytes and other cells of hemopoietic tissue, Anat. Rec. *98*:527, 1947.

Wright, J. H.: The histogenesis of the blood platelets, J. Morphol. *21*:263, 1910.

Yamada, E.: The fine structure of the megakaryocyte in the mouse spleen, Acta anat. *29*:267, 1957.

# 17  The Supporting Connective Tissues: Cartilage and Bone

## CARTILAGE

**Perspective About the Supporting Connective Tissues.** In our study of connective tissue, which is the second of the 4 basic tissues, we first dealt with loose ordinary connective tissue which is more or less of a prototype for all of the various other types seen in the connective tissue family. We then dealt briefly with the second kind of ordinary connective tissue, the dense kind, both the regularly arranged and the irregularly arranged varieties. We have thus been following the order given in the chart, at the beginning of Chapter 8.

We then, in Chapters 15 and 16, considered the first of the special kinds of connective tissue—the hemopoietic tissues. These, of course, perform a negligible connecting function and for this reason the student in learning about them may have forgotten that they belong in the connective tissue family. However, only a little thought is required to see that they belong because they, like all the others, develop from mesenchyme, and it is obvious that their cells are closely related to those in the other connective tissues, particularly to those of loose connective tissue.

We now begin the study of the second and last kind of the special connective tissues, the connective tissues that are specialized to bear weight and hence are termed the *supporting connective tissues*. The two varieties of this kind are *cartilage* and *bone*. Both of these, like dense ordinary connective tissue, have considerable tensile strength because both kinds contain considerable amounts of collagen in their intercellular substance. However, unlike dense ordinary connective tissue, cartilage and bone can both bear weight without bending, and this is due to their both having something extra in their intercellular substance which does not bend readily. What

might be termed the first step taken to achieve a good weight-bearing tissue is illustrated in cartilage and is dependent on its intercellular substance containing, in addition to collagen, a firm rubberlike gelled sulfated mucopolysaccharide which gives cartilage, at least in certain sites, a character not unlike some of our modern plastics. Like some of the modern plastics its surface can take a high polish and hence cartilage surfaces, adequately lubricated, can move against one another with very little friction and wear. For this reason cartilage is superbly adapted to coating the articulating ends of bones in movable joints, for in such a site it can both bear weight and provide a suitable surface on which movement can occur with little friction. (Articular cartilage will be dealt with in detail in Chapter 19.)

What might be termed a much more radical step in the evolution of weight-bearing tissues hinges on the organic intercellular substance becoming impregnated with salts of calcium so that the intercellular substance becomes stonelike in character. The phenomenon is termed calcification. Under normal conditions, all bone that forms in the body becomes calcified—that is, its intercellular substance becomes thoroughly impregnated with calcium salts. Furthermore, under normal conditions most, but not all, of the cartilage that develops in the body becomes calcified. However, cartilage, unlike bone, is not adapted to persisting as a calcified weight-bearing tissue, and hence almost all of the cartilage that develops in the body has only a very temporary life because when it becomes calcified its cells all die and it thereupon breaks down and has to be replaced by the more permanent tissue, bone. If cartilage does not become calcified it can live a long time, and this explains why cartilage persists in a few places in the body throughout life, as

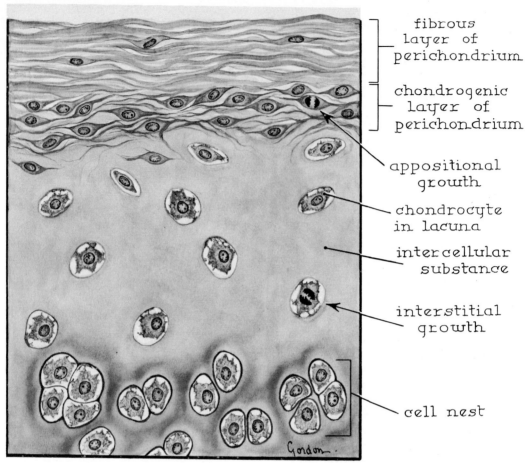

FIG. 17-1. Semidiagrammatic drawing of a section of uncalcified hyaline cartilage covered with perichondrium. It illustrates the processes of both appositional and interstitial growth.

will soon be described, because in these few few places it normally does not become calcified.

There are 3 main types of cartilage:

$$\text{Cartilage}\begin{cases}\text{hyaline}\\\text{elastic}\\\text{fibro}\end{cases}$$

Of the 3 types, hyaline is the most common, so we shall describe it in detail and comment briefly on elastic cartilage and fibrocartilage.

### HYALINE CARTILAGE

The word "hyaline" is derived from the Greek *hyalos*, which means "glass." Hyaline cartilage was so named because it has, in the gross, a pearly white, glassy, translucent appearance. This appearance is due entirely to the special character of its intercellular substance.

As we shall see in the next chapter, most of the hyaline cartilage that develops in the body (and a great deal of it does develop) becomes calcified, dies and is replaced by bone. However, some hyaline cartilage persists in an uncalcified state in a few sites into and throughout adult life. Most notably it persists as articular cartilage to cover the articulating ends of joints; this will be described in connection with joints in Chapter 19. Hyaline cartilage also persists in an uncalcified state to help to support parts of the ear, and it plays a prominent role in providing support in the walls of the upper respiratory passages; in the nose, the larynx, the trachea and the bronchi. The ringlike cartilages of the trachea are commonly studied in the laboratory to illustrate persisting uncalcified hyaline cartilage (Figs. 26-5 and 26-6). Even in these, however, some calcification appears in older people.

**Microscopic Appearance.** Hyaline cartilage consists of cells and intercellular substance.

The *cells* are called *chondrocytes* and reside in little spaces in the intercellular substances called *lacunae* (Fig. 17-1). In some instances, a lacuna contains but a single chondrocyte. In others, pairs or even larger numbers of chondrocytes may be present. When many chondrocytes are present in a single lacuna, it is said to constitute a *cell nest*. Often when several cells are present in a single large lacuna, very fine partitions of intercellular substance may exist between the individual cells so that a large primary lacuna, which is still called a cell nest, is thereby broken up into a number of smaller secondary ones (Fig. 17-1). Typically, chondrocytes have a rounded nucleus with one or more nucleoli. In life, their cytoplasm fills the lacunae in which the cells reside. However, in stained sections the cytoplasm is commonly seen to be shrunken away from the sides of the lacunae because of shrinkage artefact. Glycogen and fat may be demonstrated in the cytoplasm of large chondrocytes. Chondrocytes vary considerably in size and shape. Young chondrocytes, like the lacunae that contain them, instead of being spherical are often flattened (Fig. 17-1). Old or, more precisely, fully differentiated cartilage cells tend to be large and rounded (Fig. 17-1). Size, then, is an important indication of the degree to which any given chondrocyte has differentiated. Small, more or less flattened, chondrocytes are to be regarded as not nearly so well differentiated as the large hypertrophied rounded ones.

The *intercellular substance* of hyaline cartilage is a firm gel. Although it appears to be homogeneous both in the gross and in most ordinary kinds of microscopic preparations, it contains considerable quantities of both formed and amorphous kinds of intercellular substance. The formed kind is represented by collagenic fibrils and fibers, and a considerable quantity of these are present. However, they are immersed in a relatively large quantity of amorphous intercellular substance.

Most of this is one of the sulfated mucopolysaccharides described in Chapter 2 and is known as *chondroitin sulfuric acid*. This probably is bound to a protein, and the complex between the mucopolysaccharide and the protein is either mixed with, or chemically united to, the collagen which is also present. The intercellular substance of cartilage may be mildly PAS positive. Since chondroitin sulfuric acid is not PAS positive, there is probably some other as yet imperfectly understood carbohydrate component present. The amorphous intercellular substance of cartilage is of approximately the same refractive index as the collagen fibrils and fibers which lie in it; hence, the collagen fibers cannot be seen at all distinctly unless the amorphous intercellular substance is dissolved away. The collagen in the intercellular substance is, however, obvious in the electron microscope (Fig. 19-9). The lining of each lacuna seems to consist of an intercellular substance of a somewhat different consistency from that present throughout most of the substance of cartilage (Fig. 17-1). If cartilage is stained with toluidine blue, strong metachromasia is evidenced by the thin layer of intercellular substances that lines each lacuna. This suggests that it is largely chondroitin sulfuric acid because this substance stains metachromatically with toluidine blue. Frequently, this lining layer of the lacuna is referred to as the *capsule* of the cartilage cell. For the fine structure of hyaline cartilage see Chapter 19.

**Perichondrium.** Except at articular surfaces, where cartilaginous surfaces are exposed to one another or to other connective tissues in the joint, each piece, or structure, of cartilage in the body is completely surrounded by a connective tissue membrane called its *perichondrium* = "about cartilage" (Fig. 17-1). The outer part of this membrane is composed of densely arranged collagenic connective tissue. In young growing cartilage the inner layer of the perichondrium shows some cartilaginous characteristics; indeed, it is often difficult to decide exactly where the inner border of the perichondrium stops and the cartilage begins. In other words, the inner surface of the perichondrium of young growing cartilage usually exhibits a gradual transition from ordinary connective tissue into

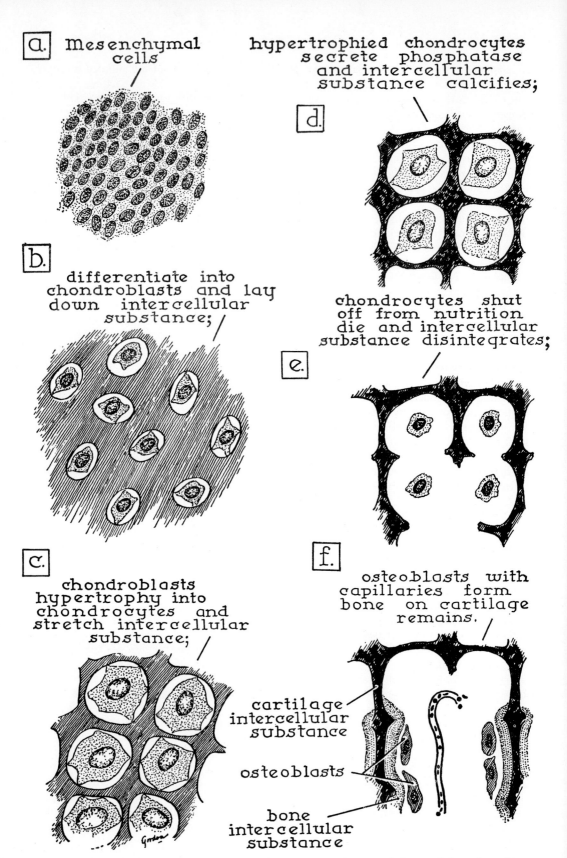

a. Mesenchymal cells

b. differentiate into chondroblasts and lay down intercellular substance;

c. chondroblasts hypertrophy into chondrocytes and stretch intercellular substance;

d. hypertrophied chondrocytes secrete phosphatase and intercellular substance calcifies;

e. chondrocytes shut off from nutrition die and intercellular substance disintegrates;

f. osteoblasts with capillaries form bone on cartilage remains.

cartilage intercellular substance

osteoblasts

bone intercellular substance

FIG. 17-2. Diagrams to show the development, the life history and the usual fate of cartilage in the body.

cartilage. This is because the cells in the *inner* part of the membrane have the potentiality of becoming chondroblasts and, as we shall see, their continued growth and differentiation into chondrocytes can cause a piece of cartilage to become larger. The inner layer of the perichondrium tends to be less prominent after cartilage is full grown, and in later life, where cartilage persists in the body, the perichondrium is often reduced to only the outer fibrous layer.

## THE DEVELOPMENT OF CARTILAGE

Cartilage, like the other connective tissues, develops from mesenchyme. In an area of mesenchyme where cartilage is to develop the mesenchymal cells lie in an amorphous type of intercellular substance which contains few formed elements. To form cartilage, the mesenchymal cells first come closer together and lose the processes which, up to this time, have extended off from their cytoplasm. Soon, then, the area in which cartilage is to form becomes composed of rounded mesenchymal cells which are packed closely together (Fig. 17-2). The next change to be observed is that these cells gradually become separated from one another again. This is due to their beginning to form the intercellular substance of cartilage which, as it is laid down in increasing amounts between the cells, gradually pushes them apart (Fig. 17-2). Since the mesenchymal cells have now differentiated and lie in lacunae in intercellular substance, they are called *chondrocytes* (cartilage cells).

The mesenchyme surrounding the area in which cartilage develops remains closely applied to the forming cartilage and becomes its perichondrium. In the outer part of this mesenchyme, the mesenchymal cells tend to differentiate into fibroblasts and to form collagenic fibers. In the inner part of the perichondrium, that is, the part applied closely to the cartilage tissue, the mesenchymal cells of the perichondrium do not differentiate into fibroblasts but remain in a relatively undifferentiated state, retaining their capacity to form chondroblasts and chondrocytes. When they exercise this capacity, there is, of course, a gradual transition between perichondrium and cartilage in the inner part of the perichondrium.

## THE GROWTH OF CARTILAGE

**Interstitial Growth.** Young cartilage can grow in 2 different ways: (1) by interstitial growth and (2) by appositional growth.

Since *interstitium* means a small hole in the substance of a tissue, the word *interstitial* refers to the cells in the lacunae in the substance of the cartilage. These cells (the chondrocytes), unless they have become greatly hypertrophied and very mature, retain their ability to divide; hence, more chondrocytes can form within the substance of cartilage. The new cells that are formed by this growth mechanism can give rise to new and more intercellular substance. The formation of new cells with their subsequent formation of intercellular substance within the substance of cartilage causes the cartilage to expand from within (Fig. 17-1). A piece of cartilage growing by the mechanism of interstitial growth increases in size in much the same way as dough "rises" when bread is made. For this type of growth to occur in cartilage, it is obvious that the intercellular substance must be sufficiently malleable to allow the cartilage to expand from within when internal cells divide and make new intercellular substance. It is obvious that cartilage in which the amount of intercellular substance is not yet great permits interstitial growth to occur much more readily than cartilage which has become older and in which the intercellular substance has become great in amount and of a stiffer consistency. Interstitial growth, then, is limited to moderately young cartilage.

**Appositional Growth.** The second mechanism by which any piece of cartilage can increase in size is known as *appositional growth*. As the name implies, this means a mechanism whereby new layers of cartilage are apposed to one of its surfaces. Appositional growth depends on activity in the inner part of the perichondrium. In this there is first a division of the deeper cells of the perichondrium which increases their numbers. Some of the cells so formed then differentiate into chondroblasts and then into chondrocytes, and, as they do so, they surround themselves with intercellular substance. By this mechanism a new layer of cartilage is laid down under the perichondrium on the surface of the cartilage model. Furthermore, since the deeper cells of the perichondrium divide before differentiation

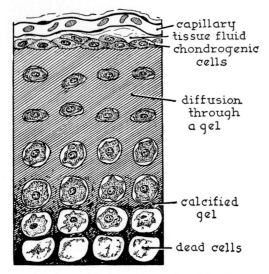

capillary
tissue fluid
chondrogenic
cells

diffusion
through
a gel

calcified
gel

dead cells

Fig. 17-3. Diagram of a section of hyaline cartilage. A capillary which forms tissue fluid is shown outside the limits of the cartilage. For the cells of the cartilage to be nourished, substances, dissolved in tissue fluid, must diffuse through the gelled intercellular substances of the cartilage to deeply buried cells. If the intercellular substance becomes calcified, as is indicated in the lower part of the diagram (black), diffusion cannot occur and the cells die. (Ham, A. W.: J. Bone Joint Surg. *34-A*: 701)

occurs, their numbers are not depleted by the process, and so there are plenty more should additional growth by this mechanism be necessary. (Fig. 17-1 illustrates the appositional growth of cartilage.)

## THE NUTRITION OF CARTILAGE

Cartilage is a nonvascular tissue: although blood vessels sometimes pass through it, it contains no capillaries within its substance to provide it with nourishment. The invasion of cartilage by capillaries generally is associated with its calcification and death. Blood vessels, without associated calcification, are seen occasionally in cartilage in some sites (e.g., epiphysial plates), but they lie in special protected canals and only pass through the cartilage on their way to a destination elsewhere. Therefore, the capillaries that supply cartilage with nourishment are outside the peri-

chondrium of cartilaginous structures (Fig. 17-3). Consequently, chondrocytes are nourished by means of substances diffusing through the gelled intercellular substance that surrounds them (Fig. 17-3). The tissue fluid of cartilage is the bound water—the dispersion medium—of the gelled intercellular substance.

**The Calcification of Cartilage.** As a general rule, the organic intercellular substance surrounding large well-developed and fully matured chondrocytes becomes impregnated with calcium salts (Fig. 17-2, d). At first thought, it might seem that if the intercellular substance of cartilage were impregnated with mineral salts to make it stonelike in character, it could bear much more weight than it could in an uncalcified state. But in the preceding paragraph it was pointed out that chondrocytes depend on receiving substances essential for their welfare by diffusion through the bound water of the gelled intercellular substance surrounding them. When this intercellular substance becomes calcified, that is, thoroughly impregnated with a mineral deposit, it no longer permits the ready diffusion of gases or ions. The result of this is that the chondrocytes in their lacunae are shut off from their normal source of nutrition, so they die (Fig. 17-3, e). This might seem to be of no consequence, since it might be assumed that the strong calcified intercellular substance would remain. But living cells seem to be necessary for the permanence of calcified intercellular substance in the body, for, when the chondrocytes die, the calcified intercellular substance tends to dissolve away (Fig. 17-3). Hence, the fate of calcified cartilage is almost always that of death and resorption, and this is followed by its replacement by bone. In the following chapter it will be explained how bone can become calcified without its cells being shut off from nutrition and why for this reason it constitutes a much more permanent type of calcified tissue than calcified cartilage.

The student might well wonder what useful purpose is served by such cartilage whose fate is to become calcified, die, and be replaced by bone. As will be explained in detail in the next chapter, the hyaline cartilage out of which most of the skeleton is first constructed serves two essential purposes. First, before it becomes calcified it can grow interstitially; this is something that bone cannot do, and indeed, if it were not for the interstitial growth of cartilage in the developing skeleton, most bones could not grow in length. Secondly, after it becomes calcified, it serves as a temporary model and framework on which bone can be formed in the right places and in the most economical fashion, as will also be explained in detail in the next chapter.

Before concluding our preliminary discussion of hyaline cartilage we should comment briefly on the mechanisms concerned in its calcification. These mechanisms also will receive further consideration in the next chapter.

## Some Mechanisms Involved in the Calcification of Cartilage

First, the intercellular substance of cartilage normally becomes calcified only in sites where the chondrocytes become large and mature—such cells are commonly said to be hypertrophied cartilage cells. Under normal conditions the intercellular substance that surrounds young chondrocytes does not become calcified (see Fig. 17-3).

Secondly, although the composition of the salt that precipitates into cartilage is probably a complex salt of the nature of a hydroxyapatite, $CA_3(PO_4)_2$ enters largely into its composition, so that in discussing calcification, we can reason to some extent about factors that could be concerned with bringing about a precipitation of $CA_3(PO_4)_2$ from body fluids.

Thirdly, there are enough *dissociated* calcium and phosphate ions in blood and tissue fluid to approach the concentration necessary for a precipitate of calcium phosphate to form. Experimentally it is easy to increase the amount of calcium in the blood to the point where a precipitate does form and in undesirable sites such as the walls of blood vessels and in the kidneys; this can be done by giving an animal a very large dose of vitamin D, or parathyroid hormone (which hormone normally controls the level of calcium in the blood) or even by maintaining animals on a diet that has a very high content of calcium salts.

Fourthly, various salts dissolved in body fluids act as buffers in that the composition of these salts changes in the presence of extra acid or alkali, and this prevents the extra acid or alkali from materially changing the pH of the body fluid. The calcium salts in the blood are not abundant enough to exert much effect in buffering the blood, but nevertheless their form could be changed by the same factors that change the form of the salts that are effective buffers. For example, it could be expected that extra acid could change calcium phosphate into a calcium acid phosphate. The latter salt is much more soluble than calcium phosphate. Hence precipitation of calcium salts is aided by an alkaline environment and impeded by an acid environment. Any local factor which encourages alkalinity therefore favors precipitation of calcium salts into the intercellular substance of cartilage, whereas any local factor that encouraged acidity would tend to reverse the process by creating the formation of a salt more difficult to precipitate.

Fifthly, the calcification of the intercellular substance of cartilage is associated in some fashion with the production of the enzyme alkaline phosphatase by the hypertrophied cartilage cells. Around 1930, Robison became interested in whether compounds of sugar and phosphate (phosphoric esters and sugar phosphates) played any role in calcification. One interesting thing about these compounds of sugar and phosphate is that although they are soluble they are not ionized; hence, they can be present in an almost saturated solution of calcium phosphate without their causing precipitation of calcium phosphate. Robison and his associates discovered that hypertrophied cartilage cells and the cells that produce the intercellular substance of bone both manufacture an enzyme termed *alkaline phosphatase* and that this enzyme hydrolyzes sugar phosphates and frees $PO_4$ ions from them. Accordingly, a theory arose to the effect that the calcification of mature cartilage and forming bone was dependent on the cells of these tissues producing alkaline phosphatase that acted on sugar phosphates locally to free extra $PO_4$ ions from them. Since the tissue fluid of the part already would be almost saturated with calcium phosphate, the extra $PO_4$ ions from the sugar phosphates would cause a precipitation of calcium phosphate in the organic intercellular substance adjacent to the cells that make alkaline phosphatase.

One difficulty with this theory was that there did not seem to be any explanation for there being a substantial amount of sugar phosphate in calcifying cartilage or bone. However, it has been shown that hypertrophied cartilage cells contain glycogen and that they make another enzyme, phosphorylase, which conceivably could act to convert glycogen to a sugar phosphate which could serve as a substrate for alkaline phosphatase. Gutman and his associates have shown that interference with phosphorylase activity blocks the calcification mechanism in vitro. Although the matter is too complex to be dealt with in any detail in a book of this kind, there does seem to be evidence to the effect that phosphorylase and glycogen are involved in providing a substrate for alkaline phosphatase in the very site in cartilage where extra $PO_4$ ions could institute calcification.

As was described in Chapter 4, there is an excellent histochemical test for phosphatases (see Fig. 18-32).

Finally, the organic intercellular substance of cartilage seems to have a physical affinity for calcium salts if such salts are in concentrations at or around the precipitation point. Well showed many years ago that even dead cartilage that was transplanted in the body tended to become calcified. From the study of calcifying cartilage made by Robinson and Cameron with the EM, it would seem that calcium is deposited in the amorphous organic component of the intercellular substance of cartilage. The percentage of amorphous organic material in cartilage is much greater than it is in bone and for this reason it seems that cartilage can take up more mineral than bone. Robinson and Cameron found that the deposition of mineral crystals begins in the organic intercellular substance, not immediately beside hypertrophied chondrocytes, but some little distance from them. There is evidence indicating that in bone the deposition of crystals begins along, or even perhaps in, collagenic microfibrils and in a definite relation to their periodicity. In cartilage, however, calcification seems to begin in the amorphous material without collagenic fibrils or microfibrils having to serve as "nuclei" on which crystals just deposit.

To sum up: There must be some local mechanism operating in the tissue fluid that bathes the intercellular substance that surrounds hypertrophied cartilage cells that either increases the number of calcium or phosphate ions in that site or acts toward lowering the pH so that less soluble salts of calcium are formed in that local area. The intercellular substance of cartilage seems to have a spongelike affinity for calcium precipitates should any be forming, and since the numbers of calcium and phosphate ions in body fluids approach the concentration necessary for precipitations, the local factors that would be necessary to institute precipitation in cartilage would not have to bring about very substantial changes in order to institute the calcification of the intercellular substance. Since calcification occurs around the hypertrophied cartilage cells that are known to produce alkaline phosphatase, this enzyme would seem to be concerned somehow in the calcification process, but its role is probably not so entirely simple as was first visualized.

**Radioautography.** The deposition of various elements into the intercellular substance of cartilage can be investigated to advantage by means of radioautographs and by the use of different radioactive compounds. Belanger has made extensive use of radioactive sulfur which enters into the composition of the sulfated mucopolysaccharides of cartilage intercellular substance; this permits the formation of the amorphous intercellular substance to be followed. The calcification of the organic intercellular substance can be visualized in radioautographs by giving animals radioactive calcium, strontium or phosphorus. Leblond and his group have shown that radioactive carbon labels organic intercellular substance as it forms.

**Elastic Cartilage.** Although hyaline cartilage is elastic to some degree, it is not as elastic as cartilage that is made with considerable numbers of elastic fibers in its intercellular substance. In some sites, for example, in the external ear and in the epiglottis, it is desirable that there should be a stiff tissue present, yet one that is very elastic. In these sites elastic cartilage is found. In many respects it is similar to hyaline cartilage, but its intercellular substance, in addition to collagen fibers and chondroitin sulfate, contains elastic fibers that are scattered throughout it (Fig. 17-4).

elastic fibers
in intercellular subst.

FIG. 17-4. Low-power photomicrograph of a section cut through the external ear. Elastic fibers may be seen as dark, fine lines in the intercellular substance.

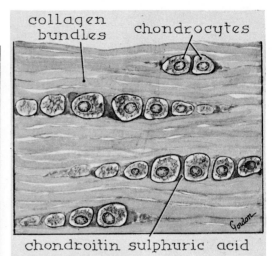

collagen bundles    chondrocytes

chondroitin sulphuric acid

FIG. 17-5. High-power drawing of an H and E section of fibrocartilage that was taken from a tendon close to its point of insertion.

Hyaline cartilage and fibrocartilage will both be considered further in connection with joints.

### GENERAL CONSIDERATIONS ABOUT THE TRANSPLANTATION OF CARTILAGE

Autogenous transplants of cartilage commonly are obtained from the cartilages of the ribs or the nose. The cells of free autogenous transplants of cartilage seldom divide, but they may remain alive for at least many years, and, as a result, the transplant may persist for long periods of time. Since cartilage does not require capillaries within its substance, cartilage transplants do not have to be vascularized for their cells to live. Furthermore, cartilage cells probably do not require any oxygen but live anaerobically by glycolysis; this probably makes it easier for them to be nourished by diffusion phenomena, which could continue to operate after free transplantation.

The fact that cartilage cells live by diffusion, which occurs through the intercellular substance, probably accounts for the fact that the cells of homogenous transplants also may survive for a comparatively long time. It is probable that the intercellular substance prevents antibodies that might form in re-

**Fibrocartilage.** Because hyaline cartilage contains collagen, its intercellular substance possesses a certain degree of tensile strength. However, in some sites in the body, it is desirable to have a tissue which has the general stiffness of cartilage but which, in addition, has great tensile strength, as, for example, in a tendon insertion. In these sites a type of cartilage called *fibrocartilage* commonly is employed. This is much like hyaline cartilage except that there is an excessive amount of collagen in its intercellular substance. Moreover, the collagen fibers tend to be disposed in a plane parallel with the pull made on the structure (Fig. 17-5). The chondrocytes tend to be disposed in rows between the strong collagenic bundles (Fig. 17-5).

The intercellular substance that is between the cells that are arranged in the rows, and between them and the fiber bundles, is more basophilic than the intercellular substance in the fiber bundles and hence is probably predominately chondroitin sulfuric acid (Fig. 17-5).

sponse to the transplant from reaching the cells deep within a transplant. In any event, the cells of homogenous transplants of cartilage survive much better than those of homogenous transplants of other types of tissue, and the same is true, to some extent, of heterogenous transplants.

Cartilage treated in any way to kill its cells represents, on transplantation, nothing more than a transplant of intercellular substance. Such transplants do not seem to persist as well as autogenous transplants with living cells; the latter would seem to be the transplants of choice.

The repair of cartilage is considered in Chapter 19.

## REFERENCES

### CARTILAGE REFERENCES OTHER THAN THOSE ON CALCIFICATION

Amprino, R.: Uptake of $S^{35}$ in the differentiation and growth of cartilage and bone *in* Wolstenholme, G. E. W., and O'Connor, C. M. (eds.): Ciba Foundation Symposium on Bone Structure and Metabolism, p. 89, London, Churchill, 1956.

Bélanger, L. F.: Autoradiographic studies of the formation of the organic matrix of cartilage, bone and the tissues of teeth *in* Wolstenholme, G. E. W., and O'Connor, C. M. (eds.): Ciba Foundation Symposium on Bone Structure and Metabolism, p. 75, London, Churchill, 1956.

Benninghoff, A.: Form und Bau der Gelenkknorpel in ihren Beziehungen zur Funktion, Z. Zellforsch. *2*:783, 1925.

Fell, H. B.: Skeletal development in tissue culture *in* Bourne, G. H. (ed.): The Biochemistry and Physiology of Bone, p. 401, New York, Acad. Press, 1956.

Laskin, D. M., Sarnat, B. G., and Bain, J. A.: Respiration and anaerobic glycolysis of transplanted cartilage, Proc. Soc. Exp. Biol. Med. *79*:474, 1952.

Leblond, C. P., and Greulich, R. C.: Autoradiographic studies of bone formation and growth *in* Bourne, G. H. (ed.): The Biochemistry and Physiology of Bone, p. 325, New York, Acad. Press, 1956.

Martin, A. V. W.: Fine structure of cartilage matrix *in* Randall, J. T., and Jackson, S. F. (eds.): Nature and Structure of Collagen, p. 129, New York, Acad. Press, 1953.

Montagna, W.: Glycogen and lipids in human cartilage with some cytological observations on the cartilage of the dog, cat, and rabbit, Anat. Rec. *103*:77, 1949.

Peer, L. A.: Transplantation of Tissues, vol. 1, Baltimore, Williams & Wilkins, 1955.

Pritchard, J. J.: A cytological and histochemical study of bone and cartilage formation in the rat, J. Anat. *86*:259, 1952.

Robinson, R. A., and Cameron, D. A.: Electron microscopy of cartilage and bone matrix at the distal epiphyseal line of the femur in the newborn infant. J. Biophys. Biochem. Cytol. (Suppl.) *2*:253, 1956.

Scott, B. L., and Pease, D. C.: Electron microscopy of the epiphyseal apparatus, Anat. Rec. *126*:465, 1956.

Sylvén, B.: The ground substance of connective tissue and cartilage *in* Bourne, G. H. (ed.): The Biochemistry and Physiology of Bone, p. 53, New York, Acad. Press, 1956.

### CALCIFICATION OF CARTILAGE

Bélanger, L. F.: The entry of $CA^{45}$ into the skin and other soft tissues of the rat: An autoradiographic and spodographic study, J. Histochem. Cytochem. *5*:65, 1957.

Bourne, G. H.: Phosphatase and bone *in* The Biochemistry and Physiology of Bone, p. 251, New York, Acad. Press, 1956.

Dixon, T. F., and Perkins, H. R.: The chemistry of calcification *in* Bourne, G. H. (ed.): The Biochemistry and Physiology of Bone, p. 287, New York, Acad. Press, 1956.

Durning, W. C.: Submicroscopic structure of frozen-dried epiphyseal plate and adjacent spongiosa of the rat, J. Ultrastr. Res. *2*:245, 1958.

Gutman, A. B., and Yu, T. F.: Concept of the role of enzymes in endochondral calcification *in* Reifenstein, E. C., Jr. (ed.): Tr. of the Second Conference on Metabolic Interrelations, p. 167, New York, Macy, 1950.

———: A further consideration of the effects of beryllium salts on *in vitro* calcification of cartilage *in* Reifenstein, E. C., Jr. (ed.): Tr. of the Third Conference on Metabolic Interrelations, p. 90, New York, Macy, 1951.

———: Further studies of the relation between glycogenolysis and calcification in cartilage *in* Reifenstein, E. C., Jr. (ed.): Tr. of the First Conference on Metabolic Interrelations, p. 11, New York, Macy, 1949.

Hass, G. M.: Pathological calcification *in* Bourne, G. H. (ed.): The Biochemistry and Physiology of Bone, p. 767, New York, Acad. Press, 1956.

Rathbun, J. C.: Hypophosphatasia, a new developmental anomaly, Am. J. Dis. Child. *75*:822, 1948.

Robison, R.: The Significance of Phosphoric Esters in Metabolism, New York, New York Univ. Press, 1932.

Sheldon, H., and Robinson, R. A.: Studies on cartilage: electron microscope observations on normal rabbit ear cartilage, J. Biophys. Biochem. Cytol. *4*:401, 1958.

Wells, H. G.: Chemical Pathology, ed. 5, Philadelphia, Saunders, 1925.

(*See also* references for Chapters 18 and 19).

# 18   Bone

## THE DIFFERENCES BETWEEN CALCIFIED CARTILAGE AND BONE

In the preceding chapter it was explained that when the intercellular substance of cartilage becomes impregnated with calcium salts the intercellular substance can no longer serve as an efficient medium through which substances dissolved in tissue fluid can diffuse to reach and nourish cartilage cells (Fig. 17-3, e). Accordingly, the calcification of the intercellular substance of cartilage results in the death of its cells. Without a content of living cells, calcified cartilage tends to dissolve away (Fig. 17-3, e and f). Hence calcified cartilage cannot serve as a permanent type of a calcified supporting tissue.

Bone, though similar to cartilage in that its cells live in lacunae in an intercelluar substance, differs from cartilage in certain respects which will now be considered. Perhaps the most important way in which it differs is that its intercellular substance can become thoroughly impregnated with calcium salts without its constituent cells that live in lacunae being shut off from nutrition. Bone therefore can persist as a living tissue even though its intercellular substance is calcified; this, of course, is something that cartilage cannot do, and so it represents a fundamental difference between the two supporting tissues. The basis for this first difference between bone and cartilage will be described first, and then other differences will be described.

**1. Bone Has a Canalicular Mechanism.** First, the intercellular substance of bone, unlike that of cartilage, is permeated by a system of tiny canals called *canaliculi* (Figs. 18-1 and 18-2). These extend from one lacuna to another and to bony surfaces where capillaries are situated. These tiny canal-like passageways that permeate the solidly calcified intercellular substance contain the cytoplasmic processes of the cells whose main cell bodies are contained in lacunae. The processes of adjacent bone cells connect with one another in the canaliculi, and for this reason transport mechanisms concerned in providing metabolites required by cells can operate via these connecting cytoplasmic processes between bone surfaces where capillaries are situated and the bodies of bone cells that are otherwise buried in calcified intercellular substance some little distance away from the capillaries. Furthermore, such space in canaliculi as is not filled with cytoplasmic processes would become filled with tissue fluid which could permit diffusion of nutriment from surfaces to cells. Canaliculi are therefore the lifelines that reach out from entombed bone cells to sources of nutrition. Without canaliculi the cells within bone would all die from starvation or asphyxia.

**How Canaliculi Are Formed.** The cells that synthesize and secrete the organic intercellular substance of bone are called *osteoblasts*. After osteoblasts have surrounded themselves with intercellular substance and settled down to a sedentary life they are called *osteocytes*. Osteoblasts, as is shown in Figure 18-1, always have long cytoplasmic arms that extend off from their main cell bodies in various directions. When the osteoblasts secrete organic intercellular substance, the cytoplasmic processes serve as molds for the tiny canals— the canaliculi—that subsequently permeate through the organic intercellular substance after it "sets" and becomes calcified. Since the cytoplasmic process of adjacent osteoblasts connect with one another, the canaliculi connect with one another. Since osteoblasts always end their work of forming bone at some surface where there are capillaries that are forming tissue fluid, the last formed canaliculi open on that surface. The cytoplasmic processes in these latter canaliculi are exposed to tissue fluid and hence to a source of nutrition, and from this source nutritive substances can be conducted to more deeply buried osteocytes.

Unfortunately, canaliculi cannot be seen in

Fig. 18-1. Diagrams to show how bone forms. As shown in the top picture, special cells called osteoblasts must be present before bone is made. The osteoblasts always have cytoplasmic arms that connect with one another. The osteoblasts secrete the organic intercellular substance of bone both around their cell bodies and around the cytoplasmic arms that extend from the cell bodies. During the time when the intercellular substance is being secreted, the cytoplasmic arms serve as molds for tiny passageways called canaliculi; these passageways remain to provide communication between adjacent osteoblasts and the surface on which the bone is forming. When the osteoblasts are completely surrounded by the intercellular substance they have secreted, they are termed osteocytes. The organic intercellular substance then becomes impregnated with calcium salts and so rendered stonelike. However, the osteocytes entombed in the stonelike intercellular substance are not cut off from oxygen and nutrition, because the canaliculi provide a means whereby materials can be transported between surfaces and the cells buried in the calcified intercellular substance provided that the distance over which transport has to be effected is not very great.

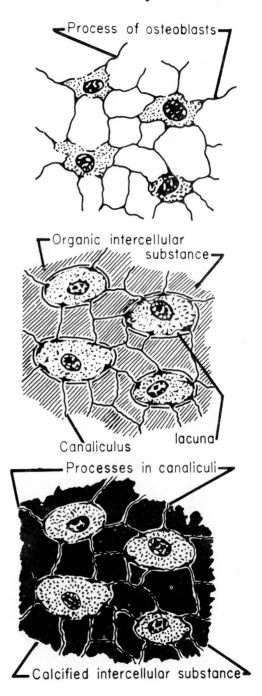

H and E sections. However, certain basic dyes that stain cartilage brilliantly sometimes stain canaliculi selectively; this suggests that they are lined with a sulfated mucopolysaccharide (Fig. 18-2).

2. **Bone Is Vascular.** As might be expected, the canalicular mechanism is not a very efficient one, and it cannot maintain the life of cells over very great distances. This means that no bone cell can survive if it is more than a fraction of a millimeter from a capillary. This necessitates that bone be exceedingly well supplied with capillaries. Even what appears to the naked eye to be dense solid bone will be found, on microscopic examination, to be built on such a plan that no bone cell is more than a fraction of a millimeter from a capillary (Figs. 18-41 and 18-55). The second fundamental difference between cartilage and bone is, then, that bone, in contrast to cartilage, is a vascular tissue—its substance is relatively richly supplied with capillaries.

3. **Bone Can Grow Only by the Apposi-** tional Mechanism; This Requires a Stem Cell Mechanism. Under normal conditions, the formation of the organic intercellular substance of bone is followed almost immediately by some degree of its calcification. This feature of bone is another point of difference

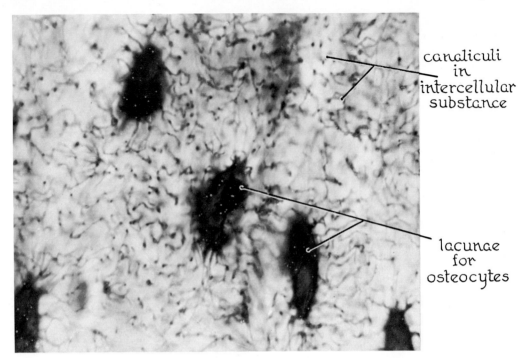

canaliculi in intercellular substance

lacunae for osteocytes

Fig. 18-2. High-power photomicrograph of a section cut from the rib of a rabbit and stained with Giemsa's stain. The canaliculi that pass between the different lacunae may be seen in this type of preparation. (Ham, A. W.: *In* Cowdry's Special Cytology, vol. 2, ed. 2, New York, Hoeber)

between it and cartilage. Cartilage, it will be recalled, can exist in the body in an uncalcified state, and in an uncalcified state its intercellular substance is sufficiently malleable to permit interstitial growth to occur. Bone, however, because its intercellular substance begins to calcify almost as soon as it forms, is not malleable enough to expand from within. Furthermore, osteocytes are so differentiated that they probably have lost all capacity to reproduce themselves. So, for all practical purposes, any given piece of *bone can increase in size only because new bone is added to one of its surfaces.*

**The Stem Cells of the Bone Cell Family.** Since bone does not grow by the interstitial mechanism but only because new bone is added to pre-existing surfaces, it follows that there must be a "pool" of stem cells maintained on bone surfaces to provide cells that can differentiate into osteoblasts and then into osteocytes. Experiments with labeled thymidine have shown that neither mature osteocytes nor well-developed osteoblasts du-

plicate their DNA; these cells therefore do not divide. It would seem, therefore, that the differentiation of the stem cells, even into osteoblasts, involves an almost complete loss of reproductive capacity on the part of the differentiating cell. So we must next inquire into the nature of the stem cells which by their division can maintain a constant pool of cells on bone surfaces, even though members of the pool differentiate into osteoblasts and so cause new bone to be added to the surface.

The cells that normally cover and line all normal bone surfaces and serve as the stem cells for bone are generally termed *osteogenic cells.* The formation of new bone on any surface is brought about by these cells dividing so as to increase their numbers, as is shown in Figure 18-3A and B. The innermost cells formed as a result of the mitoses can then differentiate into osteoblasts which secrete intercellular substances about themselves to become osteocytes as is shown in Figure 18-3C. By this means a new layer of bone is added to a surface without the number of stem cells that cover the surface being depleted in numbers (Fig. 18-3C).

As we shall see presently, the stem cells—the osteogenic cells—that cover and line bone surfaces have the potentiality to differentiate along two other pathways in addition to that which leads to bone formation. The pathway along which osteogenic cells differentiate depends on environmental influences. Studies made by the author on the repair of fractures indicate that when osteogenic cells differentiate in the presence of capillaries they differentiate into osteoblasts. However, if they proliferate and differentiate in a nonvascular environment, where it could be assumed the oxygen content would be low, they differentiate into chrondroblasts and form cartilage. We shall see, also, that under still different conditions the stem cells of bone can fuse together to become multinucleated cells known as osteoclasts which are associated, not with building bone on, but with resorbing bone from, surfaces.

## SPECIAL TYPES OF PREPARATIONS ARE REQUIRED FOR A ROUNDED-OUT STUDY OF BONE

Since bone is calcified it is difficult to slice it into thin sections without first removing the mineral from its intercellular substance. Hence, as a prelude to embedding blocks of bone tissue in paraffin it is usual to immerse the block of bone tissue in a decalcifying agent which removes the mineral from it. Afterward the decalcifying agent and the dissolved mineral can be washed away and the tissue can then be dehydrated, cleared, embedded in paraffin and cut into thin sections and stained in the same way that blocks of other tissues are cut and stained. The decalcification of blocks of bone tissue can be accomplished by immersing the blocks in solutions of any of several different acids; commonly a 15 per cent solution of formic acid is now used for this purpose. Bone can also be decalcified by chelating agents, and commonly E.D.T.A. (eythlene diamine tetraacetic acid) at a pH 7.2 is used for this purpose.

Bone that has been decalcified by any of the methods described above contains all of

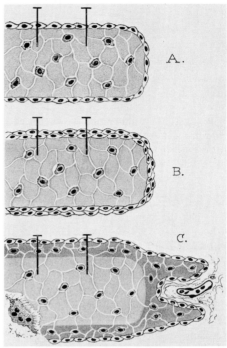

FIG. 18-3. Diagrams showing that bone cannot grow by the interstitial mechanism, but only by appositional growth which requires new layers of bone being deposited on surfaces. (A) This shows that a trabecula of bone is covered on all surfaces with a layer of osteogenic cells (or osteoblasts). (B) This shows that the surface cells can proliferate so as to increase their numbers. (C) This shows that the innermost layer of surface cells can form a new layer of bone by secreting organic intercellular substance about them, and that the surface still remains covered by a continuous layer of osteogenic cells except at sites of resorption where osteoclasts are present. One is shown at the lower left corner. At the right end, the diagram illustrates how new bone can be laid down on surfaces, extending the length of a trabecula to surround a capillary, so that the cells of the newly formed bone will have a source of nutrition. (Ham, A. W.: J. Bone Joint Surg. *34-A*:701)

the cells that were present in and on it and it also still contains the organic intercellular substance that its cells had secreted around themselves. Only the mineral that was contained in the organic intercellular substance has been dissolved away. Hence a decalcified

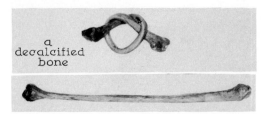

FIG. 18-4. This illustration shows that although a decalcified bone closely resembles a calcified bone, it may be tied into knots, as is illustrated in the upper picture.

bone (and it is possible to decalcify a whole bone), has the same form as a normal calcified bone (Fig. 18-4 *bottom*). The great difference between a decalcified bone and a calcified bone is not in their gross appearance but in the fact that the decalcified bone cannot bear weight; indeed, it bends readily and can be tied into a knot as is shown in Figure 18-4.

Sections of decalcified bones permit the study of the cells of bone and the organic intercellular substance of bone, but they provide no direct information about the mineral content of bone, for example, where it is first deposited, or whether some parts of a bone contain more than others. To study the mineral content of bone it is necessary to use sections of bone that are prepared without the bone being decalcified. There are two ways of preparing such sections.

The first and older way is to cut sections of calcified bone as thinly as possible with a fine saw and then grind them down to greater thinness on a stone. Such sections are termed *ground bone sections*. Since they must be prepared from dried bone, the cells in such a preparation are shrivelled, and hence ground bone sections are of no use for studying the cells of bone. Since the mineral is still present in ground bone sections the intercellular substance remains rigid and hence the canaliculi remain open and stand out as dark lines and can be seen much as they appear in Figure 18-41. Furthermore, the lacunae which contain the osteocytes can also be seen as dark ovoid cavities (Fig. 18-41), as can certain canals that run through bone and which will be described later. The arrangement of lamellae (layers) of bone around the canals can also be seen in such sections.

Though they are much more difficult to prepare, it is now possible, by using special embedding media and special kinds of microtomes adapted for heavy work, to cut sections of bone that has not been decalcified. The advent of this technic has permitted many kinds of studies to be made that were not previously possible. For example, it is possible to feed animals radioactive isotopes of calcium or phosphorus and see where mineral is first deposited in a growing bone (see Fig. 18-35). It is also possible to expose undecalcified sections to soft x-rays and study the pictures thus obtained under the microscope to see how dense the mineral is in different parts of a bone (see Fig. 18-43) as will be described somewhat later in this chapter.

## THE DEVELOPMENT OF BONE

### SOME GENERAL CONSIDERATIONS

The process by which bone is formed in the body is termed *osteogenesis* or *ossification*. It is very important to understand that osteogenesis or ossification is not the same thing as calcification. Ossification or osteogenesis are words that refer to the formation of all the components of bone, not just its mineral content.

For osteogenesis to occur in any part of the body it is necessary for special cells of mesenchymal origin, called *osteoblasts,* to make their appearance in that part of the body, for only osteoblasts can secrete, or otherwise form, the special organic intercellular substance of bone.

As has been mentioned already, the cell bodies of osteoblasts have many fine cytoplasmic processes extending out from their cell bodies, and these processes join with those of adjacent osteoblasts. When osteoblasts produce organic intercellular substances they generally surround both their cell bodies and their processes with it (Fig. 18-1, B). Thereafter the cell bodies come to lie in little spaces in the organic intercellular substance called lacunae; after this has happened the cells are termed *osteocytes*. The processes of the cells lie in tiny passageways in the intercellular substance called canaliculi (Fig. 18-1, B and C).

The light microscope appearance of osteo-

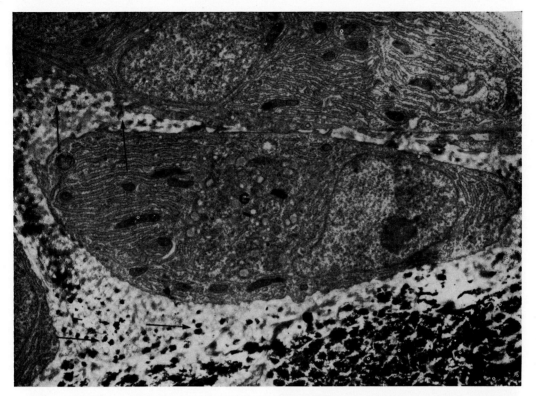

Fig. 18-5. Electron micrograph ($\times$ 7,600) of undecalcified bone showing an osteoblast which extends across the middle of the picture, and part of another above it. In the lower one a nucleus can be seen near its right end, a Golgi apparatus (G) in its central region, and many flattened rough-surfaced vesicles of endoplasmic reticulum at its left end. The vertical arrows point to cytoplasmic processes that extend off from the cell body and which are cut in cross and oblique section. The horizontal arrows point to mineral deposits that are just forming. At the lower right the mineral is more dense. In the intercellular substance just below the nucleus some collagenic microfibrils with cross banding can be seen. (Preparation by B. Boothroyd and N. M. Hancox)

blasts in a stained section of decalcified bone is illustrated in Figure 7-11. Brief reference to that illustration will show that they generally have eccentrically placed nuclei and a large amount of basophilic cytoplasm which surrounds an extensive pale negative Golgi area. It could be assumed from this appearance that they are secretory cells and that their cytoplasmic basophilia would prove to be due, in the EM, to very numerous rough-surfaced vesicles of endoplasmic reticulum, and that the large negative Golgi region would reveal in the EM an extensive arrangement of the various vesicles of the Golgi apparatus.

Figure 18-5 shows two osteoblasts as they appear in the EM in a section of *undecalcified* bone. These osteoblasts are synthesizing

organic intercellular substance and as it is formed it is becoming calcified. The calcium salts that are being deposited are electron dense and hence appear as black material that is seen best at the bottom of the illustration. The osteoblast that extends across the middle of the fields shows extensive and closely packed flattened rough-surfaced vesicles of endoplasmic reticulum at its left end. The nucleus of the cell is toward its right end. Halfway between the two, in the middle part of the cell, is a large and well-developed Golgi apparatus; this is labeled G.

It could not be expected that the cytoplasmic processes that extend off from osteoblasts could be followed for any distance in a single thin section. In the thin sections used

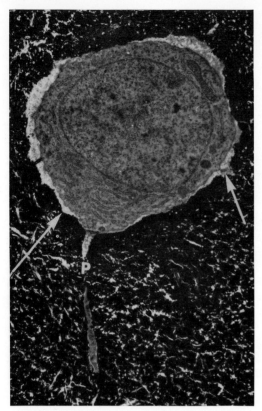

FIG. 18-6. Electron micrograph (× 7,500) of undecalcified section of bone, showing an osteocyte in its lacuna which is surrounded by heavily calcified intercellular substance. The osteocyte has less cytoplasm than an osteoblast and fewer rough-surfaced vesicles. The arrows point to sites where cytoplasmic processes probably extend off from the main cell body but disappear from the substance of the section. However, one process is cut in longitudinal section for some little distance; this is labeled P. (Preparation by B. Boothroyd and N. M. Hancox)

for electron microscopy they are almost always seen in cross or oblique section. The two vertical arrows at the left side of the picture point to groups of cytoplasmic processes that are *between* the cell bodies of the two osteoblasts; these processes, of course, are cut in cross and oblique section. Very occasionally a process may be sectioned longitudinally for a short distance along its length; one such process from an osteocyte is shown in Figure 18-6.

The organic intercellular substance of bone is a secretory product of osteoblasts. It has two main components, collagen and mucopolysaccharides. Tropocollagen molecules are probably synthesized in the rough-surfaced vesicles of endoplasmic reticulum and secreted in the same way that they are synthesized and secreted by fibroblasts; this was described in Chapter 11. The periodicity of the microfibrils of collagen that are polymerized just outside osteoblasts can be seen with the EM to be the same as that seen in collagen that is formed in loose connective tissue by fibroblasts (the explanation for the periodicity of newly formed microfibrils was given in Chapter 10). Close inspection of Figure 18-5 shows some newly polymerized microfibrils of collagen just below the cytoplasm that is beneath the nucleus. The second secretory product of the osteoblast that helps constitute the organic intercellular substance of bone differs from that secreted by fibroblasts in ordinary connective tissue. This special secretory product of osteoblasts is an assortment of mucopolysaccharides, most of which are probably of the sulfated types. It seems probable that the well-developed Golgi apparatus of the osteoblast (see in Fig. 18-5) is concerned in the synthesis of the carbohydrate component of these. The mucopolysaccharide content of the organic intercellular substance of bone acts as a cement substance in which collagenic fibrils are embedded. Perhaps it also cements microfibrils together to form fibrils.

In the process of calcification, which under normal conditions begins almost as soon as the organic intercellular substance is formed, tiny crystals of mineral begin to be deposited in the organic intercellular substance. Small islands of newly deposited crystals are indicated by horizontal arrows in Figure 18-5. It might be thought that crystal formation would demand the same set of circumstances as are required to bring about precipitation, that is, that the solubility product of the ions that enter into the formation of bone salt be exceeded in the tissue fluid that bathes the newly formed matrix. As was mentioned in connection with the calcification of cartilage in the preceeding chapter, one theory that received more support in past than in recent years is that alkaline phosphatase secreted by the osteoblasts does act to bring about an increased concentration of $PO_4$ ions in this area. However, all aspects of the phenomenon of calcification are not as yet thoroughly understood. There is evidence that indicates that the solubility product of the ions concerned in bone salt may be influenced to begin crystal formation without a supersaturated solution of them being attained. It is thought that because of some physical attribute of collagen that is dependent on its periodicity, collagen may serve as a nucleus to initiate crystal formation. Evidence for this concept is that reconstituted collagen has been shown to initiate crystal formation in suitable solution containing calcium and phosphate ions. Once crystal formation begins, the process spreads (Fig. 18-5, *lower right*), and it would seem that for the most part bone salt first appears as rodlike crystals 50 Å wide or perhaps narrower in the cement substance of bone, but in close association with the collagenic microfibrils. Moreover, there is some evidence that suggests that crystals may form to some extent within the substance of collagen itself.

It seems probable that the composition of the crystals that first form in bone may become altered because of different ions in them being exchanged for those in tissue fluid (and hence in blood) for at least a short period of time. The most recently deposited mineral in bone is probably more labile than mineral that has been in bone for any length of time. As we shall see later, mineral that has been in bone a long time is generally in bone that has been covered by new layers of bone and so is generally relatively distant from capillaries. Close association with blood in capillaries would be necessary if ion transfer was to occur readily. It is the mineral in bone intercellular substance that has just been formed that is close to capillaries and accessible to exchange.

The ions in bone salt are mainly Ca, $PO_4$ OH and $CO_3$. Small amounts of sodium, magnesium and iron are also present in bone mineral. Citrate ions are also present. The crystalline structure of bone mineral is thought to be that of a hydroxyapatite.

When an osteoblast has surrounded all its processes and its cell body with organic intercellular substance it no longer requires the extensive cytoplasmic machinery for synthesizing and secreting protein and mucopolysac-

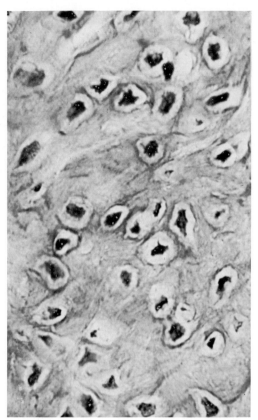

Fig. 18-7. High-power photomicrograph of an H and E section of decalcified immature bone.

charide that it previously required; hence, when its work is done, and the osteoblast has become an osteocyte, its cytoplasm becomes reduced in amount (Fig. 18-6). However, osteocytes retain some rough-surfaced vesicles of endoplasmic reticulum (Fig. 18-6). The calcification of its surrounding organic intercellular substance, that began when the cell was an osteoblast, under normal conditions continues as the cell becomes an osteocyte, until it is solidly impregnated with mineral as is shown in Figure 18-6. The section from which this illustration was made represents a fortunate cut because it shows what is rarely seen, a portion of one cytoplasmic process of osteocyte cut in longitudinal section and extending off from the cell body for a short distance in a canaliculus; this is labeled P.

The structure of calcified matrix is very much like that of reinforced concrete. The collagenic fibrils in calcified matrix are com-

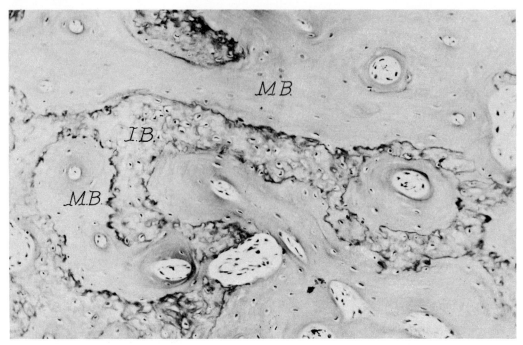

FIG. 18-8. Low-power photomicrograph of an H and E section of decalcified bone, showing areas of immature bone (I.B.) that have been surrounded or otherwise encroached upon by mature bone (M.B.) that formed later.

parable to the rods of iron in reinforced concrete, and the calcium salts are comparable to the concrete itself.

It might be thought that the proportion of collagen to cement substance always would be constant in bone, but this is not so. Baker, Pritchard and Weinmann and Sicher all have placed great and deserved emphasis on the fact that there are two kinds of bone, as will now be described, which have different relative contents of cells, collagen and mucopolysaccharide.

### IMMATURE BONE

The first bone that develops in embryonic development or in the repair of bone fractures, as well as the bone that generally forms in certain types of bone tumors, is termed *immature bone*. It has proportionately more cells and more collagen and less cement substance and mineral than the mature bone that forms later and makes up most of the adult skeleton. Immature bone is also termed *woven bone* or *coarsely bundled bone* because of its large content and arrangement of col-

lagenic fibers. This type of bone is commonly very cellular (Fig. 18-7), and the lacunae in which the osteocytes reside are not as flattened as they are in mature bone (Fig. 18-8). The intercellular substance is characterized by relatively thick bundles of collagenic fibrils which are not disposed in any regular arrangement but in an irregular and often interlacing fashion. The content of cement substance in the intercellular substance is proportionally less than in mature bone; hence, immature bone probably takes up less mineral than mature bone, so it is neither as strong nor as opaque to x-rays as mature bone.

The matrix of immature bone stains very unevenly, but it often demonstrates a patchy basophilia; hence, areas of immature bone that have become surrounded by mature bone may be spotted easily on low-power examination (Fig. 18-7).

Almost all the immature bone that forms during embryonic life is later replaced with mature bone, which will be described next. Pritchard, who gives an excellent and comprehensive account of types of bone, states that some immature bone persists in tooth sockets, near cranial sutures, in the osseous labyrinth and near tendon and ligament attachments, but that in these sites it usually is mixed with mature bone.

## MATURE BONE

The formation and the growth of mature or lamellated bone is characterized by new layers being added to bony surfaces in an orderly way (Fig. 18-3). Each layer, according to Weinmann and Sicher, is from 4 to 12 $\mu$ thick. The osteoblasts responsible for producing the successive layers of lamellated bone become incorporated as osteocytes within the layers or between the layers of bone matrix that they form. In general, the direction of the fibrils in any given layer is usually at an angle to that of the fibrils in immediately adjacent layers. Sometimes the direction of the fibrils in one layer is at right angles to the direction of those in the next. Since the direction of the fibrils in immediately adjacent layers is not the same, adjacent layers may appear to be optically different.

Mature bone is to be distinguished from immature bone because it stains evenly and lightly (Fig. 18-8), by the regularity of its lamellae, by the fact that the direction of fibrils in immediately adjacent lamellae is different, by its relatively greater content of cement substance and mineral and by its fewer cells, which are more regularly arranged and in flatter lacunae than they are in immature bone (Fig. 18-8).

## WHAT IS MEANT BY THE TERMS INTRAMEMBRANOUS, ENDOCHONDRAL AND HETEROTOPIC OSSIFICATION

In the embryo, osteoblasts become differentiated from mesenchymal cells in two general environments. In the first, and this is seen to advantage in connection with the development of the flat bones of the skull, they appear in what are called *membranous areas*. This term is justified by the fact that certain of the mesenchymal cells in these areas already have differentiated into fibroblasts which have formed some collagenic fibers to give the areas a membranous character. However, for ossification to begin, it is necessary for some of the mesenchymal cells to differentiate into osteoblasts, which thereupon secrete or otherwise form the characteristic organic intercellular substance of bone. Since the general environment in which this occurs is sometimes membranous, in that some collagenic fibers may be present, the process is spoken of as *intramembranous ossification*. Moreover, bones that form in these areas sometimes are referred to as *membrane bones*. This is an unfortunate term because it suggests false inferences—for example, that membrane turns into bone, or that the bone formed in these areas has a special membranous character.

Most ossification that begins in the body, however, does not begin in membranous areas but in cartilaginous areas. The process by which bone is formed in a cartilaginous environment is termed *endochondral ossification*.

**Endochondral Ossification.** In sites to be occupied later by most of the bones of the skeleton, cartilage models of the bones-to-be are formed first (the details will be given later). Subsequently, and gradually, the cartilage models are replaced by bone which forms as a result of ossification occurring along the sides and in the interior of the cartilage models. Ossification occurring in a cartilaginous environment is described as endochondral, and the bones that result from it are often referred to as *cartilage bones*. This latter term (like the term "membrane bones") is unfortunate because it conveys the impression that cartilage changes into bone. Actually, in endochondral ossification cartilage does not change into bone. Instead, osteoblasts developed from mesenchyme appear in the vicinity of the cartilage models, and as the models become calcified, bit by bit, the dead cartilage is replaced by new bone formed as a result of the activities of the osteoblasts that surround and invade the cartilage models.

**Heterotopic Ossification.** Under pathologic conditions, in postnatal life, bone sometimes forms in tissues other than those comprising the skeleton. Little pieces of bone may develop in the scars of wounds, in the tonsils, in the kidney or in other sites. Such bone forms as the result of what is called *heteroplasia* (*heteros* = other; *plasis* = forming),

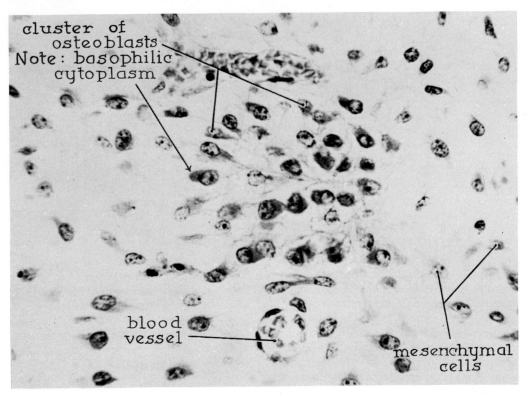

cluster of
    osteoblasts
Note: basophilic
    cytoplasm

blood
vessel

mesenchymal
    cells

Fig. 18-9. A cluster of osteoblasts differentiating from mesenchyme in the developing skull of a pig embryo.

and is spoken of as *heteroplastic* or *heterotopic (topos* = place).

Since the literature dealing with bone is not always clear about this matter, it is perhaps important to emphasize that the terms intramembranous, endochondral and heterotopic, when applied to ossification, refer only to the environments in which the process occurs and not to the kind of bone that forms. It is to be emphasized that other adult tissues, for example, cartilage or muscle, never undergo mysterious transformations into bone. In every instance where bone forms, special bone-buildings cells, the osteoblasts, must first make their appearance—these cells alone are capable of manufacturing the special organic intercellular substance of bone. Such bone as develops in any site is a result of their progressive activity; it is not the result of a tissue transformation. So there are no such entities as "membrane bone," "cartilage bone" or "heterotopic bone." The only two kinds of bone formed under normal conditions are immature and mature bone. Commonly, in embryonic development the first bone to form in any site is of the immature type, but as growth of bone continues, mature bone forms and replaces the immature. Intramembranous and endochondral ossification will now be considered in detail.

## INTRAMEMBRANOUS OSSIFICATION

This process is illustrated beautifully by the formation of the bones that come later to comprise the vault of the skull. Sections show that the areas in which these bones develop are occupied first by mesenchyme. Some fibers appear in this to give it a *membranous* character. Intramembranous ossification begins when a cluster of mesenchymal cells differentiate into osteoblasts; these are plump cells with abundant and very basophilic cytoplasm (Figs. 18-5, 18-9 and 18-10). Their borders may show a prickly outline (Fig. 7-11); the prickles are the roots of cytoplasmic processes which generally cannot be seen in H and E sections. The nuclei of osteo-

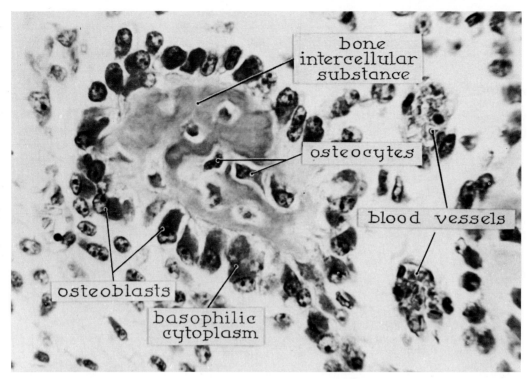

FIG. 18-10. High-power photomicrograph of a section cut through a newly formed spicule of bone in the developing skull of a pig embryo. Observe that some of the osteoblasts have differentiated into osteocytes and have surrounded themselves with intercellular substance so that they have come to reside in lacunae. Note that osteoblasts are arranged around the periphery of the spicule, where they are engaged in increasing its extent.

blasts often are disposed eccentrically. In good preparations, a pale area, the negative image of the Golgi net, often can be seen beside the nucleus (Fig. 7-11). The fine structure of osteoblasts has already been described (Fig. 18-5).

The sites where clusters of osteoblasts first appear are spoken of as centers of ossification. There are usually two centers for each of the bones of the vault of the skull.

After the osteoblasts appear, it is not very long before some of them secrete or otherwise form the characteristic organic intercellular substance of bone. If they completely surround themselves with this, so that they come to lie in the lacunae, they are said to have become osteocytes (Fig. 18-10). However, not all the cells of the osteoblast-osteocyte family that arise from mesenchyme differentiate immediately into functioning secretory osteoblasts. Instead, the youngest, least dif-

ferentiated ones, which we term osteogenic cells, proliferate to supply new osteoblasts in the region. Both kinds of cells remain fairly closely applied to the margin of the bone already formed, with some of them continuing to proliferate and others differentiating and then secreting intercellular substance about themselves to become osteocytes. Osteoblastic activity on the periphery of the first-formed bone is greater at some points than at others. At the sites where osteogenic cells proliferate and differentiate more rapidly, spiderlike processes of new bone, radiating out from the first bone formed, soon are developed. These are called spicules. Figure 18-10 is a cross section of one. Figure 18-3 shows how one forms.

Well-developed spicules that radiate out from the ossification center are termed *trabeculae* (*trabs* = a beam). This term is apt because individual trabeculae (beams) of bone

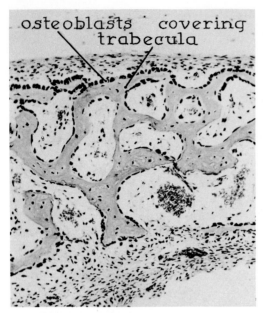

FIG. 18-11. Low-power photomicrograph of a section cut from the skull of a pig embryo somewhat more developed than that in Figure 18-10. This picture illustrates trabeculated (cancellous) bone, with the trabeculae arranged so as to enclose spaces. Observe the osteoblasts, with their dark-staining cytoplasm, arranged along the surface of the trabeculae.

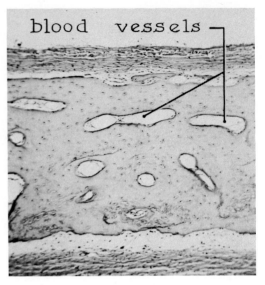

FIG. 18-12. Low-power photomicrograph of a section cut through the skull of a child. The trabeculated bone shown in Figure 18-11 has become filled in to constitute a plate of compact bone, as is shown here. The former spaces in the trabeculated area are reduced to canals which transmit the blood vessels.

commonly are joined together in much the same way that beams of wood are joined together to form a scaffolding (Fig. 18-11). Bone that consists of a scaffolding of trabeculae joined together is called *cancellous* (*cancellus* = a grating) bone.

Osteoblasts and osteogenic cells cover both the sides and the free ends of the individual trabeculae in a cancellous network (Fig. 18-11). If the covering young cells continue to proliferate, with some of their members differentiating into osteocytes, new bone is added both to the free ends and to the sides of the trabeculae of the network. The new bone added to the free ends of the trabeculae increases their length and so accounts for the spread of osteogenesis from the center of ossification. The new bone that is added to the sides of the trabeculae usually is deposited in the form of fairly even *lamellae* (*lamella* = a plate)

**How Cancellous Bone Can Become Compact Bone.** Although the initial bone that is formed in intramembranous ossification is of the immature type (Fig. 18-10), the subsequent bone that forms is of the mature type. By the time networks of cancellous bone have formed, like the one illustrated in Figure 18-11, the type of bone that is being formed is predominantly of the mature variety. If new lamellae are added to the sides of trabeculae in a cancellous network, the spaces between the trabeculae are correspondingly narrowed, exactly in the same way that a tunnel becomes narrowed if workers inside the tunnel continue to apply further layers of stone or reinforced concrete to its walls. Accordingly, the continued deposition of fresh bone lamellae on trabeculae that enclose spaces soon changes the character of the bone in that it changes from a structure consisting of large spaces with little bone (Fig. 18-11) to one of narrow spaces with much bone (Fig. 18-12). *When bone substance (instead of spaces) becomes the predominant feature of the tissue, it is said to be compact or dense bone.* It is obvious from the foregoing that the continued deposition of lamellae on the trabeculae of cancellous bone gradually converts cancellous (trabeculated) bone into dense or compact bone.

**The Relation of the Structure of Bone Tissue to Its Blood Supply.** It has already been said that the canalicular mechanism is relatively inefficient, and that the distance over which it permits diffusion or other transport mechanisms to operate effectively is no more than a fraction of a millimeter. Such measurements as have been made by the author in the bones of dogs suggest that one fifth of a millimeter is about the greatest distance over which it can maintain the life of osteocytes. But this is unusual, for the great majority of osteocytes, in both cancellous and compact bone, are at most no more than one tenth of a millimeter from a capillary. The fact that the canalicular mechanism cannot operate effectively over greater distances explains much that otherwise might seem meaningless with regard to the microscopic structure of both cancellous and compact bone, as will now be described.

THE NOURISHMENT OF THE CELLS OF CANCELLOUS (TRABECULATED) BONE. The trabeculae of cancellous bone are bathed in tissue fluid which is derived from the capillaries of the spaces between the trabeculae. Within each trabecula, canaliculi extend out from each lacuna and anastomose with canaliculi from all adjacent lacunae (Fig. 18-3). Moreover, canaliculi from the more superficial lacunae extend to the exterior of the trabecula and so permit tissue fluid or substances dissolved in tissue fluid to enter the anastomosing canalicular system of the trabecula. Consequently, food substances, to reach the bone cells in the middle of a trabecula that is one fifth of a millimeter in thickness, must pass along the canalicular system for one tenth of a millimeter. In the experience of the author, trabeculae of more than one fifth of a millimeter in thickness generally have blood vessels disposed in canals near their middles to provide the more deeply disposed bone cells with nourishment. Accordingly, the thickness of solid trabeculae is limited. If too many layers are deposited on the surface of one, the osteocytes that are disposed deeply within it are too far from capillaries to survive. Hence, the trabeculae of cancellous bone generally do not become more

than about one fifth of a millimeter in thickness without their having blood vessels present in canals in their substance.

THE ARRANGEMENTS IN COMPACT BONE THAT PROVIDE OSTEOCYTES WITH NOURISHMENT. As has been explained already, the development of the bones of the skull is associated first with the formation of trabeculae (Fig. 18-10) and next with the trabeculae anastomosing with one another so that they enclosed spaces (Fig. 18-11). Each space, of course, contains a blood vessel (Fig. 18-11). The trabeculae that become arranged into networks are at first thin (Fig. 18-11) in intramembranous ossification. Hence, several layers of new bone can be added to the trabeculae— and this, of course, correspondingly diminishes the sizes of the spaces between trabeculae— without the osteocytes in the original trabeculae having to receive nourishment via canaliculi over a distance greater than one tenth of a millimeter from the central blood vessel of the space to be nourished by the canalicular mechanism (Fig. 18-12). Even when the spaces in the cancellous bone are nearly filled in with bone, the osteocytes in the original trabeculae are no more than about one tenth of a millimeter away from the central blood vessel of the space, which space by this time has become greatly narrowed. Hence, the procedures by which cancellous bone is converted to compact bone are such that they generally permit all the osteocytes of both the original trabeculae and the new layers that have almost completely filled in the space to be close enough to the blood vessel of the central canal to exist by means of the canalicular mechanism. So, when cancellous bone is converted to compact bone, the blood vessels between trabeculae become the central vessels of canals that are ringed by layers of bone, and the central vessel supplies nutriment via canaliculi to both the old and the new bone.

**Growth of Bones of the Skull.** At birth the ossification process has not advanced sufficiently to make the bones of the skull complete. However, it has advanced far enough so that over most of their periphery the individual bones approach one another so closely that they are separated from one another only by narrow seams of relatively undifferentiated connective tissue. An arrangement whereby adjacent bones are joined by connective tissue

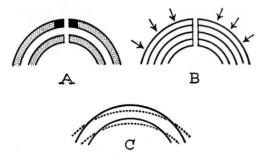

FIG. 18-13. (A) Diagram to show how appositional growth in sutures could enlarge the vault of the cranium. The new bone is black. (B) Diagram to show how appositional growth on the convex surfaces of the bones could enlarge the cranium without new bone being deposited in the sutures. It is to be understood that resorption would occur from the concave surfaces as new bone is laid down on convex surfaces. (C) Diagram to show how apposition at some sites and resorption from others could change the curvature of a skull bone.

is termed a *suture* (Fig. 19-1). However, at points where more than 2 bones meet, the sutures are wide, and such areas are termed *fontanelles*. There are 6 of these membranous areas in the skull of the newborn infant. The most prominent one, the anterior or frontal fontanelle, is situated at the point where the 2 parietal bones and the bone advancing from the 2 centers of ossification of the frontal bone meet. Its inspection, in an infant, can give valuable information as to whether ossification is proceeding normally.

The vault of the skull enlarges in postnatal life by appositional growth. However, there are somewhat different views as to whether the appositional growth that is primarily responsible occurs in the sutures (Fig. 18-13) or on the convex surfaces of the bones that comprise the vault. As Figure 18-13 illustrates, appositional growth on the convex surfaces alone could account for the individual bones becoming larger (resorption on their inner surfaces would keep them from getting much thicker) without bone actually being deposited *in* the sutures. Weinmann and Sicher favor sutural growth and say that in some sutures more bone is added to one bone

than the other. Brash, however, favors the second view.

As the cranium enlarges, the curvature of its bones must decrease. This requires that the bones of the skull be remodeled continuously as they grow, and this involves the deposition of bone on some surfaces and resorption of bone from others. Figure 18-13 shows how deposition and resorption, at different sites, could change the curvature of a skull bone. We shall shortly consider the resorptive process.

## BONE GROWTH AND BONE RESORPTION

It has been explained already that any bone can become increased in size only by having new layers of bone added to one or more of its surfaces. Bone growth is a surface phenomenon. Likewise, the resorption of bone is a surface phenomenon. Hence, we may postulate that all alterations in the shapes of bones that occur through their development and growth (their remodeling) are the result of bone being added to surfaces and resorbed from surfaces.

The statement made above deserves serious consideration. It means that the *skeleton of a fetus becomes the skeleton of an adult only through the operation of processes that are concerned with forming bone on surfaces of the pre-existing skeletal surfaces*. What is even more impressive is that *the deposition of bone on pre-existing surfaces must be accomplished in a way so that no cell in the newly formed bone will be more than a fraction of a millimeter away from a blood capillary*. If it is thoroughly understood that bone can be applied only to surfaces and that newly formed bone must always be provided with capillaries to nourish the cells of the new bone, the ways that bones grow and are remodeled throughout life seems logical and easy to understand. Without this thought in mind, the study of the growth and the remodeling of bone is needlessly difficult and unsatisfactory.

Under normal conditions, the two processes of formation and resorption of bone are nicely balanced; for example, as new bone is added to the outside of a shaft of a long bone

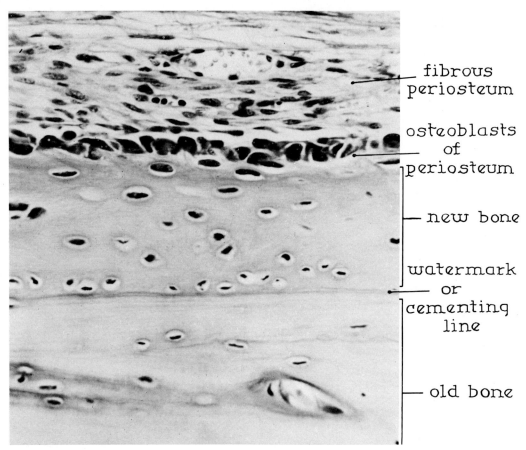

fibrous periosteum

osteoblasts of periosteum

new bone

watermark or cementing line

old bone

FIG. 18-14. High-power photomicrograph of an *active* periosteum near the site of fracture. Observe the difference between the cell types in the fibrous and the osteogenic layers. Notice the intense basophilia of the cytoplasm of the osteoblasts that abut on the bone (RNA), and the difference between the appearance of newly formed bone and the pre-existing bone. Observe how osteoblasts are being surrounded by intercellular substance to become osteocytes.

during the growing period, to make the shaft increasingly wider, bone must be resorbed simultaneously from the inside of the shaft to make the lumen (marrow cavity) increasingly wider. If the two processes of growth and resorption get out of balance with one another, bones become abnormal. For example, there is a disease of man called *osteopetrosis,* or *marble bone disease,* which is characterized by the resorptive processes falling behind the growth processes; as a consequence, the shafts of bones become thicker than usual and marrow cavities are not widened and variously expanded as they should be. It is of interest that there are cer-

tain strains of mice and rats in which this, or a very similar condition, is hereditary, and these experimental animals demonstrate very effectively the problems that arise if bone resorption does not occur at a normal rate. To give another example, there is disease of man called *generalized osteitis fibrosa* which is characterized by a greatly increased rate of bone resorption occurring in many parts of the skeleton. This condition generally is caused by one or more of the parathyroid glands secreting much more hormone than is normal, as will be described later. Here it is enough to point out that it represents a condition where the balance between bone build-

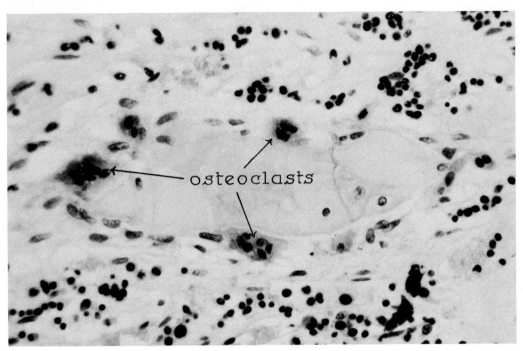

Fig. 18-15. High-power photomicrograph of a section cut through a trabecula of bone in the marrow cavity of a long bone of a dog. The trabecula occupies the middle of the picture. It is covered with osteogenic cells except in 4 sites where osteoclasts are present. The dark-staining nuclei in the periphery of the picture are those of cells concerned in producing red blood cells and granular leukocytes. (Ham, A. W.: *In* Cowdry's Special Cytology, vol. 2, ed. 2, New York, Hoeber)

ing and bone resorption is upset by resorption being accelerated.

## THE DIFFERENT APPEARANCES PRESENTED BY BONE SURFACES ON WHICH BONE DEPOSITION OR BONE RESORPTION IS OCCURRING

**Surfaces Where Bone Deposition Is Occurring.** Figure 18-14 is a photomicrograph of a section of a rabbit's rib taken close to the site of a recent fracture. Repair of the fracture is in progress, and as part of this process new layers of bone are being laid down by osteoblasts on the pre-existing shaft of bone that was close to the break in the bone. The line between the pre-existing bone and the new bone is obvious: this line is labeled a *watermark* or *cementing line,* and such lines are commonly seen when new layers of bone are deposited on pre-existing bone. The surface of the new bone is covered with a layer of large cells which have dark blue cytoplasm;

these are osteoblasts and are actively engaged in forming new bone intercellular substance and thus becoming young osteocytes. Almost every transition can be seen between these osteoblasts and young osteocytes—the latter are seen just below them and are either completely or partly surrounded by the new bone intercellular substance that they have formed. To sum up, a surface where new bone is being deposited on pre-existing bone generally shows a watermark between the new and the old bone. Secondly, the surface of the new bone is covered by a row of osteoblasts, each of which is a discrete cell. On close inspection each osteoblast would be seen to have abundant basophilic cytoplasm (due to their possessing an abundance of rough-surfaced vesicles in their cytoplasm which are concerned with the synthesis of protein destined for secretion) and a well-developed (negative) Golgi region (which is related to the secreting of the intercellular substance they are synthesizing). Thirdly,

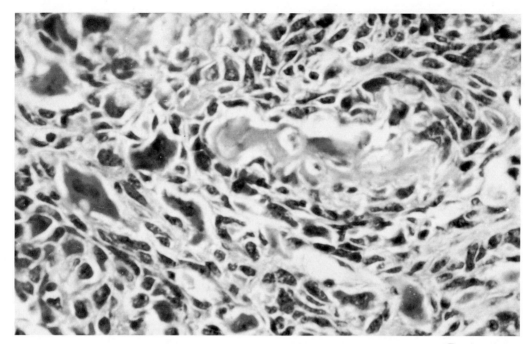

FIG. 18-16. Photomicrograph of section of osteogenic sarcoma of a mouse. A small spicule of immature bone can be seen near the center; this is surrounded by tumor cells which are of 3 main types—osteogenic cells, osteoblasts and osteoclasts. The osteoclasts are the larger dark cells seen particularly at the left.

transitional forms between osteoblasts and young osteocytes are seen in the most recently formed new bone, just below the layer of osteoblasts.

**Surfaces Where Resorption Is Occurring.** We shall next turn to a consideration of bone surfaces where resorption is occurring. The surfaces of the single trabecula illustrated in Figure 18-15 illustrate such surfaces. Perhaps the first thing to point out is that the surfaces of this trabecula are not covered with osteoblasts which are obviously engaged in laying down bone. Instead, the cells that surround this trabecula are of two types. First, there are some cells (quiescent osteogenic cells) that have elongated nuclei and seem to more or less ensheath the trabecula except at certain sites where they more or less merge into multinucleated cells that are labeled *osteoclasts*. At the left end of the trabecula a large osteoclast is seen abutting on what appears to be a bone surface undergoing erosion. That osteoclasts erode bone is also suggested by the fact that they commonly occupy little rounded pits on the surface of

the bone on which they abut; these little pits which they seem to have eroded are termed Howship's lacunae. The osteoclast illustrated in Figure 18-19 occupies one.

There are therefore very good histologic guides to indicate whether bone apposition or bone resorption is occurring on any bone surface that is examined under the microscope. Sometimes the two appearances may be seen at different sites along the same surface, for it is common for bone to be added at one place and taken away from another place that may be close to the site where it is being added.

**Resting Surfaces.** Finally, there are some bone surfaces where neither formation nor resorption are in progress; these might be termed resting surfaces. Such surfaces are covered or lined by elongated cells that have ovoid nuclei and cytoplasm that extends off from the ends of their nuclei to meet the cytoplasm of the cell beside it. In resting bone these cells do not seem to be active; for example, their cytoplasm is not deeply basophilic but only becomes so (indicating the begin-

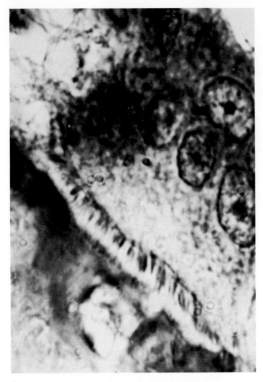

Fig. 18-17. Oil-immersion photomicrograph of an osteoclast, showing a well-developed striated border. The bone is lower left, the osteoclast is above. (Preparation by W. Wilson)

ning of protein synthesis) when they are called upon to form more bone. However, these cells, that normally cover or line resting bone surfaces can divide; indeed, they have a vast capacity for proliferation, as is shown diagramatically in Figure 18-3. After they are called into activity and divide, some of their members can differentiate into osteoblasts.

**The Stem Cells of Bone.** As has been mentioned already, the more or less flattened cells *that normally cover and line all surfaces of resting bone* are the *stem* cells of the bone (and cartilage) cell family. They are commonly called *osteogenic cells*. When a bone is broken, as will be described in detail later, these cells divide, and some of the cells that result from their proliferation then differentiate into osteoblasts and form bone. Others differentiate into cartilage cells for reasons to be described later. Still others may differen-

tiate into osteoclasts. Malignant tumors called osteogenic sarcomas occasionally develop in bone; these arise from these stem cells, and sections of these tumors show the malignant cells variously attempting to differentiate into osteoblasts and osteoclasts (Fig. 18-16). Immature bone and also cartilage is sometimes formed in these tumors.

Bone Surfaces Reflect Influences Brought To Bear on the Covering and Living Stem Cells. To understand the various appearances presented by bone surfaces we can begin with the fact that surfaces of resting bone are always covered or lined by stem cells, called osteogenic cells, which under resting conditions do no more than divide often enough to keep the covering or the lining of the bone intact. However, under a stimulus for growth, these cells can multiply and some of their members then differentiate into osteoblasts which in turn differentiate into osteocytes as is shown diagrammatically in Figure 18-3 and in a photomicrograph in Figure 18-14. Under certain conditions (absence of a capillary blood supply) these cells instead of differentiating into osteoblasts may differentiate into chondroblasts (as will become obvious when we study endochondral ossification and the repair of fractures). Under another kind of stimulus, however, these lining cells act in a very different manner. Instead of multiplying they clump together and fuse to form multinucleated masses that are termed *osteoclasts* (Fig. 18-15). When this happens the bone surface is no longer completely covered or lined with osteogenic cells. It is probably *partly because the bone surface is no longer protected by osteogenic cells, and partly because the fused cells that become osteoclasts exert some temporary specific resorptive activity, that bone erosion occurs in sites where the normal covering or lining of bone gives way to osteoclasts.*

We shall now consider some of the features of osteoclasts.

## OSTEOCLASTS

Osteoclasts, seen in the usual section of bone where resorption is occurring, may seem to have anywhere from one to many dozen nuclei (Fig. 18-15); most show about half a dozen. However, it must be remembered that osteoclasts are large cells; hence, what appears as an osteoclast in a section is only a slice cut through one, and that if an osteoclast were cut into serial sections it would be found to contain many more nuclei than would be apparent in any single slice cut through it.

The nuclei in any osteoclast are usually similar to one another, but those of different osteoclasts may be different. In what are interpreted as young osteoclasts the nuclei are ovoid. The nuclear membranes are smooth, the chromatin granules are fine and evenly distributed, and each nucleus contains 1 to 2 nucleoli (Fig. 18-17). In older osteoclasts the nuclear membranes are wrinkled, and the nuclei are more darkly stained; indeed, they may be pyknotic.

The cytoplasm of very young osteoclasts may be slightly basophilic, but the typical osteoclast has acidophilic cytoplasm. The acidophilia becomes pronounced as the cell ages. The cytoplasm of many osteoclasts has a frothy appearance (Fig. 18-17).

Shrinkage artefact must be a factor in producing the appearance that most osteoclasts have, because pronounced shrinkage spaces commonly are seen on one side or the other of them. Shrinkage is sometimes responsible for osteoclasts being widely separated from bony surfaces that they abutted on during life.

**Differences Between Osteoclasts and Megakaryocytes.** Since megakaryocytes are large cells in marrow and so may be seen close to a bone surface they are sometimes confused with osteoclasts. The following points may help the student to distinguish between the two cell types.

Their position is different. Megakaryocytes commonly are disposed throughout the substance of bone marrow, while osteoclasts commonly are disposed along bone surfaces. Sometimes, however, osteoclasts may be removed some little distance from bone. These may be distinguished from megakaryocytes by their nuclei and their cytoplasm, as follows: At first glance megakaryocytes seem to be multinucleated. However, it will be found, by focusing the microscope up and down, that the structures that appear as individual nuclei are in reality the lobes of a single continuous nucleus; this particular type of nucleus is characteristic of the megakaryocyte.

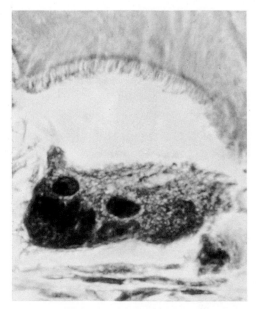

FIG. 18-18. Photomicrograph ($\times$ 1,250) of an osteoclast which has shrunken away from the bone. The striated border is present on the bone surface instead of on the osteoclast.

Furthermore, the cytoplasm of megakaryocytes is generally basophilic.

**The Striated or Brush Borders of Osteoclasts.** There is another feature of osteoclasts which, although exhibited by only some of them, is regarded as being both important and specific; this is that they have, on the surface which they expose to bone, a *striated or brush* border. With the light microscope this appears to be constituted of hairlike processes that extend out from the cell and reach toward the bone (Fig. 18-17). Moreover, it has been generally assumed that this border is instrumental in facilitating the osteoclast's ability to resorb bone (Fig. 18-17). It has even been suggested from time to time through the years that the brush or striated border represented an instrument that acted in some fashion to help to erode bone, for example, that the hairlike processes acted like cilia.

In considering the striated border that can be seen with the light microscope, it should be pointed out that striated borders are not demonstrable, at least in the author's experience, in all osteoclasts, and they appear to better advantage in some species than others. In the author's experience, moreover, striated

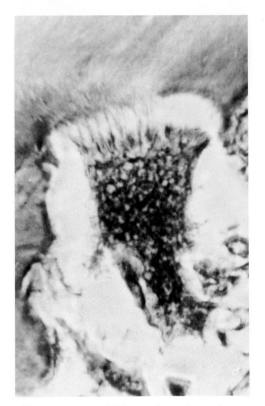

Fig. 18-19. Oil-immersion photomicrograph, taken with the phase microscope, of an osteoclast. This shows that the striations of its striated border continue into the intercellular substance of the bone as collagenic fibers and fibrils.

borders are clearest on bone surfaces where the collagenic fibrils of the bone intercellular substance approach the bone surface more or less at right angles, and they are not seen clearly where the collagenic fibrils of the bone run more or less parallel with the surface. Furthermore, the author became doubtful about attributing striated borders to osteoclasts, even in sites where they could be seen clearly, because the striated borders were sometimes seen on the bone surface from which the osteoclast had become detached during fixation, as in Figure 18-18, and only sometimes on the osteoclasts that had shrunken away from the surface as in Figure 18-17. The evidence therefore seemed to be inconclusive as to whether the striated border was a striated border of the bone surface

or a striated border of the osteoclast. On studying, with the phase microscope, striated borders that were attached both to the bone and to the adjacent osteoclast, it appeared that there were fibrils that accounted for striation in the border that could be followed into the bone substance (Fig. 18-19). As a result of these various observations the author concluded that the striated border that can sometimes be seen with the light microscope and which had been described as part of the osteoclast, was in reality an appearance caused by the collagenic fibrils of the bone substance being freed of the cement substance and mineral that existed between them at resorbing surfaces so that the collagenic fibrils projected for a short distance as a fringe. Then, when material was fixed and decalcified, the fringed border of the bone sometimes adhered to the osteoclast and shrank away with it, while on other occasions it remained adherent to the bone (compare Figs. 18-17 and 18-18).

It might be thought, when it became possible to study osteoclasts with the EM, that the question of the striated border would be quickly settled. What the EM has shown is that osteoclasts in various species have a ruffled border that is apposed to bone surfaces. The ruffled border described by Hancox and Boothroyd in the osteoclasts of briefly cultured chick embryo bones consists of innumerable villouslike processes of various shapes and sizes (Fig. 18-20). The villouslike projections in a ruffled border, in the author's opinion, are not regular enough (as are microvilli in the intestine) to account for a striated appearance with the light microscope. In this connection it must be remembered that in sections of the thickness used for light microscopy the irregular villouslike projections of the ruffled border of the osteoclast would be variously superimposed on one another in a most irregular way. Superimposed irregular villouslike projections would not seem to provide a basis for the regular and sizeable striations seen with the light microscope, as for example those shown in Figure 18-17.

Recently, Hancox and Boothroyd have observed in the EM, microfibrils of collagen lying between the villouslike processes of the ruffled borders of osteoclasts. This important

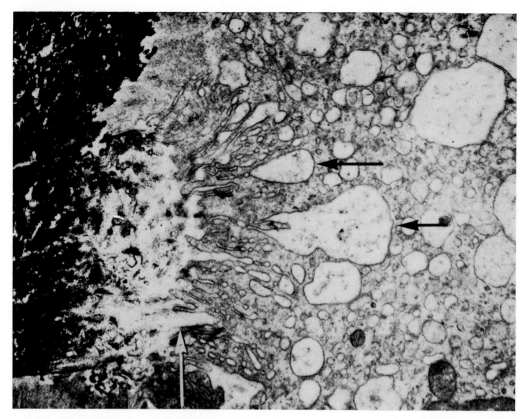

Fig. 18-20. Electron micrograph ($\times$ 20,000) of section of a bone surface undergoing resorption. Calcified bone appears black at the left. The main part of the picture is occupied by the cytoplasm of an osteoclast. Extending from the top to the bottom, in the middle of the picture, is the ruffled border of the osteoclast; this consists of complex folds and projections which abut on the bone at the left. Between the ruffled border of the osteoclast and the heavily calcified bone is an area where the calcium content is much less, which suggests that the osteoclast is dissolving or otherwise removing mineral from this area. Black granules of mineral can be seen in some of the large vesicles which are indicated by horizontal arrows and which probably form because of the bottom of crypts being pinched off. In the original print a collagenic microfibril showing typical periodicity could be seen at the site indicated by the vertical arrow. (Preparation by B. Boothroyd and N. M. Hancox)

finding suggests that bone salt and mucopolysaccharide of bone are removed ahead of the collagen at a resorptive surface. This finding suggests a possible basis for collagenic microfibrils and fibrils projecting in a fringelike fashion from a resorbing bone surface so as to give it, when the direction of the fibrils is more or less at right angles to the surface, the striated appearance seen with the light microscope.

**The Fine Structure of Osteoclasts.** A ruffled border, already mentioned, is shown in Figure 18-20; it consists of branching villouslike projections of cytoplasm that have clefts between them. The processes are most irregular in shape, size and direction. Clefts penetrate deep into the cytoplasm between the bases of the villouslike projections. The deepest parts of some clefts probably become pinched off to form cytoplasmic vesicles; these are indicated by horizontal arrows in Figure 18-20. Dark electron-dense granular material, representing mineral removed from the bone (that is on the left), can be seen in the clefts and in the cytoplasmic vesicles that have probably formed from the deepest parts of clefts. The cytoplasm has a poor representation of most organelles in and around the ruffled border. Although dense bodies, which are the bodies considered to represent lysosomes in other cell types, are not seen in osteoclasts, according to Hancox and Boothroyd, these workers find numerous small vesicles in osteoclast cytoplasm. There are indications, particularly from light microscopy, that acid phosphatase and other enzymes are present in the cytoplasm of osteoclasts, and it would seem logical that hydrolytic enzymes would be contained in vesicular structures, and that such vesicles need not be dense. It seems very probable that much more information about lysosomes in osteoclasts will be forthcoming in the near future.

**Mode of Action of Osteoclasts.** The EM studies on osteoclasts indicate that the villouslike processes of the ruffled border abut on naked bone surfaces and that mineral comes away, passing into the clefts in the ruffled border and even reaching vesicles that bud off from the deepest parts of the clefts. There are various theories about the mechanisms that could be involved in releasing mineral from the naked bone surface. Actually, any metabolically active cytoplasm that abuts on a naked bone surface, unless it is the cytoplasm of the special cells that normally protect bone surfaces, might be expected to dissolve mineral; this happens, for example, when tumor cells of many sorts invade bone. The cytoplasmic processes of osteoclasts may lower the pH so that tiny bits of bone salt becomes etched away, or they may be concerned somehow in a chelating phenomenon, or they may act in some fashion not yet imagined. As has already been suggested, the problem of mineral dissolving from an unprotected bone surface may not depend so much on very special factors being required to bring about it; it may be instead that bone surfaces *must be protected by special cells* if mineral is not to dissolve away under a variety of circumstances.

**Factors Influencing the Differentiation of the Covering and Lining Cells of Bone into Osteoclasts.** The hormone of the parathyroid gland, when it is administered to animals in excessive amounts, or when it is produced in excessive amounts in a person by a parathyroid tumor, has a profound effect in causing the covering and lining cells of bone to differentiate into osteoclasts. Certain sites, which ordinarily demonstrate active bone formation with many osteoblasts, can be changed under the influence of parathyroid hormone in 48 hours to sites that abound in osteoclasts and show a great loss of bone substance (Fig. 28-22). It seems probable that under normal conditions the parathyroid hormone is one factor which helps to regulate bone resorption in the body, to keep it more or less in harmony with bone formation. However, under conditions of excessive amounts of the hormone, the balance between formation and resorption of bone is disrupted because of the excessive resorption induced by the hormone, and the skeleton thus suffers.

**The Origin of Osteoclasts.** In the opinion of the author, the common source of the osteoclasts of bone are the stem cells that cover and line bone surfaces and which we have termed osteogenic cells. In order to form an osteoclast, the stem cells that are present in some site along a bone surface simply fuse together. Mitotic figures are not seen in osteoclasts; their multinucleated state is therefore always caused by pre-existing cells fusing with one another. Any other cells in the environment where the fusion occurs may be incorporated into osteoclasts as the fusion occurs; it is not unusual to see osteocytes, osteoblasts or even other cells incorporated into osteoclasts.

The concept of the osteoclasts that normally form in bone developing from the osteogenic (stem) cells that cover and line all resting bone surfaces is supported not only by the abundant presence of transition forms between covering and lining cells and osteoclasts in sites where resorption is beginning, but also by the fact that osteogenic sarcomas, which are malignant tumors of bone, and which presumably arise from the stem cells of bone, reveal in such differentiation as is seen in these tumors, the potentialities of the cell that give rise to these tumors. In such tumors differentiation along 3 different lines may be observed into: (1) immature bone, (2) cartilage and (3) osteoclasts (see Fig.

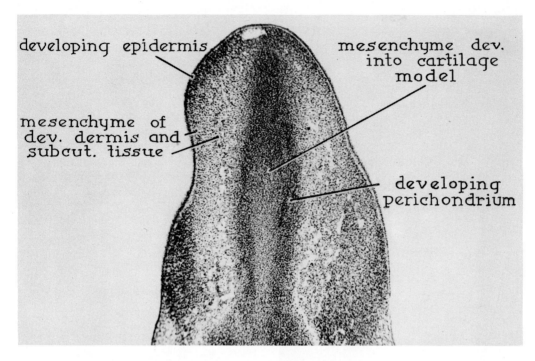

developing epidermis

mesenchyme dev.
into cartilage
model

mesenchyme of
dev. dermis and
subcut. tissue

developing
perichondrium

Fig. 18-21. Low-power photomicrograph of a longitudinal section cut through the developing toe of an embryonic rabbit. In the central part of the developing toe the mesenchyme is becoming condensed and is beginning to differentiate into the cartilage model of the terminal phalanx.

18-16). However, whereas the osteogenic cells that cover and line bone surfaces can be held responsible for the osteoclasts that form in bone tissue, it is possible for osteoclasts to develop from another cell type, as will now be described.

If bone chips, treated so as to kill all the cells that they contain, are transplanted into some tissue other than bone, such as muscle, typical osteoclasts soon form about the chips and seemingly assist in their resorption. Since there are no living stem cells associated with the transplanted *dead* bone, the osteoclasts that develop around dead bone that has been transplanted to muscle must develop from some other cell type; most probably from macrophages which gather around the bone and fuse together in the same way that they gather around and fuse beside any other foreign body. In the opinion of the author, osteoclasts that form in bone from osteogenic cells or from macrophages in association with dead transplanted bone are the same; they are both, in effect, foreign body giant cells. That

these fused cells should under changed circumstances break up again into healthy individual cells, which could for example build bone, as is sometimes suggested in the literature, would seem to us to be most improbable. Osteoclasts, in our opinion, are end products.

## THE FURTHER GROWTH OF THE SKULL

Remodeling procedures, dependent both on the addition and the removal of bone from surfaces, are responsible for the decrease in the curvature of the bones of the vault of the skull as this enlarges in postnatal life. The bones that are remodeled in this fashion are, for some time after birth, composed of only a single plate of bone which, however, contains some spaces filled with mesenchyme and thin-walled veins (Fig. 18-12). As the growth of the skull continues, the remodeling process gradually converts these single plates of bone, over most of the skull, into double plates of compact bone, with cancellous bone and a considerable amount of marrow between them.

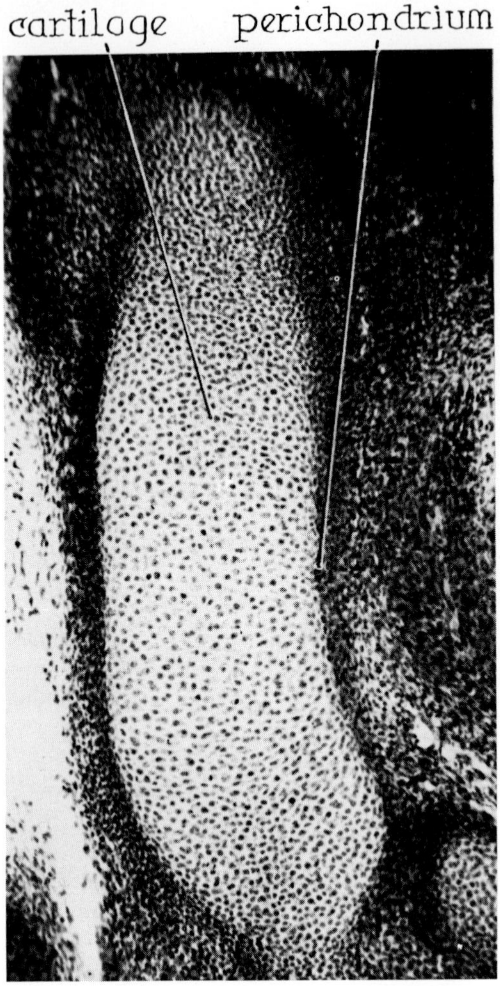

cartilage    perichondrium                    hypertrophied
                                               chondrocytes

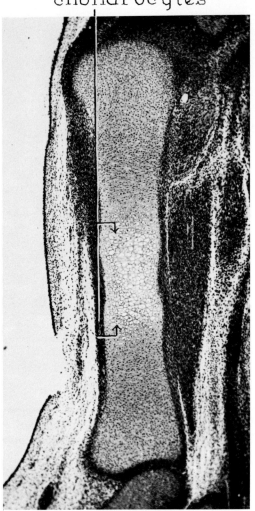

FIG. 18-22. Low-power photomicrograph of a longitudinal section of a developing leg (rabbit). In the middle of this picture a cartilage model is differentiating from the mesenchyme. In its more central part, the cartilage is fairly well developed. The mesenchyme along the side of the cartilage model forms a sheath for it; this is called the perichondrium.

FIG. 18-23. Low-power photomicrograph of a longitudinal section of a developing leg (rabbit). This shows a cartilage model in a somewhat more advanced stage than that shown in Figure 18-22. The form of the bone-to-be is well outlined. Furthermore, the cartilage cells in the central part of the model have become hypertrophied and are about to secrete phosphatase.

The layer of cancellous bone and marrow between the 2 plates of compact bone is termed the diploë, and it comes to contain many large, thin-walled veins called the diploic veins. The double-plate arrangement over most of the skull is attained in childhood (around the age of 8). Later on, in adult life, the bones meeting at the various sutures become fused, and it becomes possible for diploic veins to pass from one bone to another.

## ENDOCHONDRAL OSSIFICATION

Most of the skeleton forms as a result of endochondral ossification. The process can be followed to advantage in observing the histologic changes that occur in the limb buds of an embryo as they form and grow.

In the various sites where bones are to form, the mesenchyme of a limb bud begins to differentiate into cartilage (Fig. 18-21). The result is that cartilage models of the bones-to-be make their appearance (Fig. 18-22). The mesenchyme immediately adjacent to the sides of each cartilage model becomes arranged into a surrounding membrane for the model; this is called its *perichondrium* (Fig. 18-22). This has 2 ill-defined layers. The cells in the outer part of this membrane differentiate into fibroblasts, and these form collagen. The outer part of the perichondrial membrane thus becomes a connective tissue sheath. The mesenchymal cells in its inner part (between its fibrous layer and the cartilage of the model) do not differentiate to any great extent. Instead, they remain relatively undifferentiated and so possess almost all the potentiality of the mesenchymal cells from which they are derived. They constitute the inner or chondrogenic layer of the perichondrium (see Fig. 17-1).

**The Growth of the Model.** Cartilage models increase in length by the mechanism of interstitial growth. This entails division and hypertrophy of chondrocytes in the substance of the cartilage. Moreover, the models grow in width. Although interstitial growth may be a factor in this, it is likely that most growth in width is accomplished by the appositional mechanism; that is, new layers of cartilage are added to the surface of the sides of the model by the proliferation and the differentiation of the cells of the chondrogenic layer of the perichondrium.

The interstitial growth responsible for the increase in length of any model tends to occur near its end rather than in its midsection. Hence, as growth continues, the chondrocytes left in the midsection of the model have time to mature. As they become larger, the intercellular substance about them becomes somewhat thinned out (Fig. 18-23), and when they have become sufficiently hypertrophied to manufacture phosphatase, the intercellular substance becomes calcified (Fig. 18-24). This shuts the hypertrophied chondrocytes off from their source of nutrition, so they die. With the death of the cells, the intercellular substance, particularly in the central part of the midsection of the model, begins to break up and some of it dissolves away to leave cavities

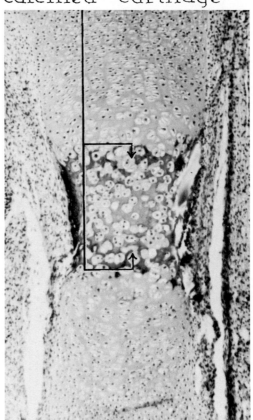

calcified cartilage

FIG. 18-24. Low-power photomicrograph of a longitudinal section of a developing phalanx (human). At this stage of development, the cartilage cells in the central part of the model have become hypertrophied and have secreted phosphatase. This has resulted in the calcification of the organic intercellular substance of the cartilage in this part of the model. The calcified cartilage appears in sections as somewhat darker than the uncalcified, which constitutes the remainder of the model.

within the substance of the model (Fig. 18-26).

During the period in which the changes described above are taking place in the midsection of a cartilage model, the progressive development of the vascular system of the embryo is responsible for the perichondrium of the model being invaded by capillaries. Before their appearance, the relatively undifferentiated cells of the inner (chondrogenic) layer of the perichondrium, by proliferation and dif-

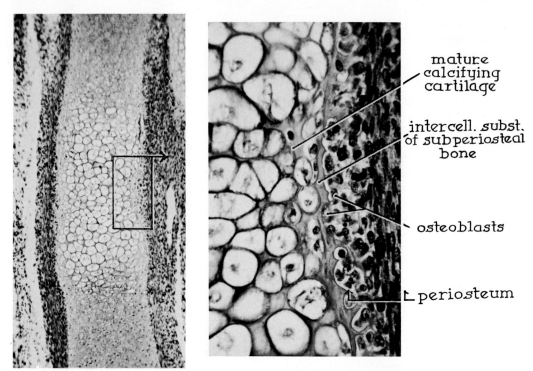

mature
calcifying
cartilage

intercell. subst.
of subperiosteal
bone

osteoblasts

periosteum

FIG. 18-25. At the left is a low-power photomicrograph of a longitudinal section of the developing leg of a rabbit. The cartilage cells in the central part of the model are seen to be hypertrophied and are presumably secreting phosphatase, which is bringing about the calcification of the intercellular substance about them. Furthermore, as may be seen in the picture at the right, which is a high-power photomicrograph of the area indicated by a rectangle in the picture on the left, the osteogenic cells of the perichondrium have differentiated into osetoblasts and have laid down a thin layer of bone intercellular substance (subperiosteal bone) on the side of the model.

ferentiation into chondroblasts and cartilage cells, have been adding new layers of cartilage to the sides of the model (appositional growth). However, the appearance of capillaries in the perichondrium is associated with a changing differentiation pattern on the part of the relatively undifferentiated cells of its inner layer. For, instead of continuing to differentiate into chondroblasts and chondrocytes, they, in the presence of capillaries, begin to differentiate into osteoblasts and osteocytes, with the result that a thin layer or shell of bone is soon laid down around the model (Fig. 18-25). Since the perichondrium thereafter covers bone tissue, its name is changed from perichondrium to *periosteum*.

It should be kept in mind that the differentiation of the cells of the inner layer of the perichondrium into osteoblasts at this period of development does not represent a change in

the nature of these cells so much as it does a change in their environment brought about by the invading capillaries. Indeed, the cells of the inner layer of the periosteum retain their ability to differentiate into chondroblasts and form cartilage even into adult life. This is easily demonstrated in the repair of broken bones, for, when bones are fractured, the cells of the inner layer of the periosteum situated close to the break proliferate vigorously and, in sites where capillaries are unable to keep up with their rapid growth, differentiate into chondroblasts and so form cartilage (Fig. 18-48). However, in other sites, where capillaries are able to keep up with their growth, they differentiate into osteoblasts and so form bone.

These relatively undifferentiated cells of mesenchymal origin that are first encountered mixed with chondroblasts in the inner layer

FIG. 18-26. Low-power photomicrograph of a longitudinal section cut through a developing human phalanx. At this stage of development the calcified cartilage in the central part of the model has broken down and this has resulted in the formation of spaces in this area. Subperiosteal bone has formed along the sides of the model; this stains more darkly than the cartilage which it covers. Furthermore, osteogenic cells and blood vessels from the periosteum have grown into the spaces in the breaking-down cartilage, and the osteogenic cells in this area are beginning to differentiate into osteoblasts and lay down bone on what is left of the old calcified cartilage matrix.

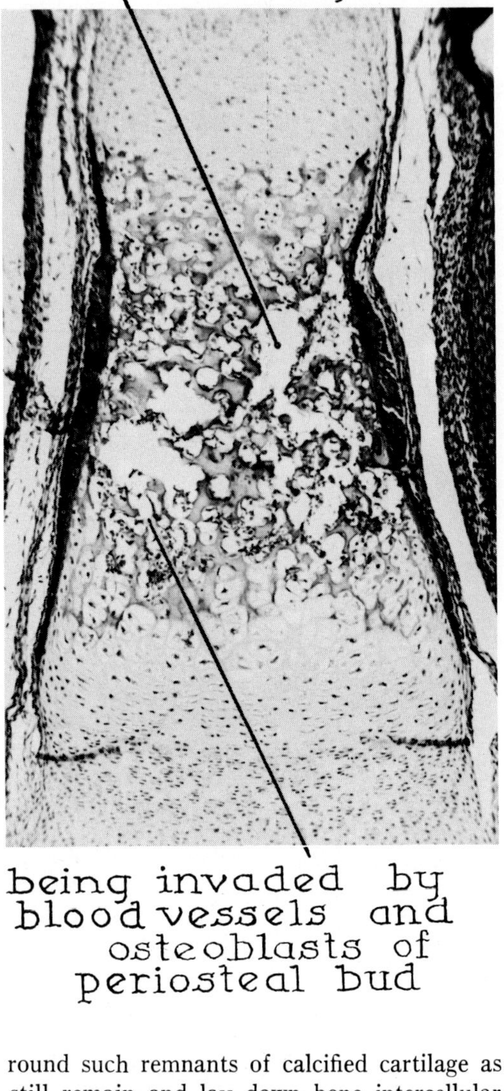

spaces in breaking-down calcified cartilage

being invaded by blood vessels and osteoblasts of periosteal bud

of the periosteum usually are termed *osteogenic* cells. We shall use this term with the understanding that the term osteogenic cell refers to a cell somewhat less differentiated than the chondroblast or the osteoblast and which differentiates into either, depending on the environment in which it differentiates. As has been noted already, these cells which we term osteogenic cells are the stem cells of the bone and cartilage family. Osteogenic cells cover and line all resting bone surfaces and can form osteoblasts, chondroblasts or osteoclasts depending on circumstances.

At this stage of development, then, the calcified cartilage in the midsection of the model is beginning to break down, and the shaft of the model has gained a surrounding shell of bone which has been laid down by the recently vascularized perichondrium which is now termed the periosteum. The inner layer of the periosteum at this time consists of osteogenic cells, and osteoblasts which have formed from them. It also contains capillaries. As the calcified cartilage in the midsection of the model begins to disintegrate, osteogenic cells and osteoblasts, together with capillaries, begin to move from the inner layer of the periosteum into the breaking-down midsection of the cartilage model (Fig. 18-26). The invading osteogenic cells, osteoblasts and capillaries constitute what is called the *periosteal bud*.

When the osteogenic cells, the osteoblasts and the capillaries of the periosteal bud reach the interior of the midsection of the cartilage model, they are said to constitute a center of ossification. In this area the osteoblasts gather round such remnants of calcified cartilage as still remain and lay down bone intercellular substance on them (Fig. 18-26). The calcified cartilaginous intercellular substance that still remains at this time is, in this part of the model, in the form of an irregular network riddled with spaces; so, since the first bone that is formed in this area is deposited on the remnants of the cartilaginous network, the first formed bone in this area is cancellous in type, with its individual trabeculae having cores of calcified cartilage. In a good H and E section, this makes a very pretty picture because the cores of cartilage intercellular sub-

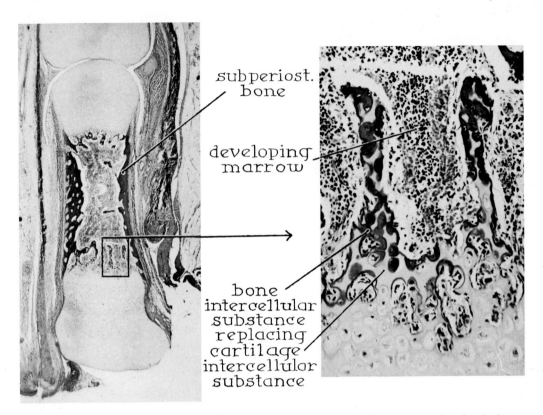

subperiost.
bone

developing
marrow

bone
intercellular
substance
replacing
cartilage
intercellular
substance

FIG. 18-27. (*Left*) A low-power photomicrograph of a longitudinal section of a developing human phalanx. This shows a stage somewhat more advanced than that illustrated in Figure 18-26. The amount of subperiosteal bone is increased, and the cartilage of the entire central part of the model has disappeared. Marrow now occupies the central part of the model. Bone formation is advancing toward each end. (*Right*) The photograph shows the characteristic picture of bone being deposited on cartilage remnants. The bone intercellular substance is dark, that of the cartilage is light in this particular illustration.

stance are blue, while the bone covering them is pink or red. The osteoblasts applied to the surface of the trabeculae are blue. Trabeculae of bone with cores of cartilage are illustrated on the right side of Figure 18-30.

Up to this time the only cartilage in the model that has matured, become calcified and died, is that part which was situated in its midsection and whose remnants by this time are covered with bone. The cartilage at each end of the model continues to grow by means of the interstitial growth mechanism. The continued growth at the ends of a cartilage model tends to increase the total amount of cartilage in the model and would do so if it were not for the fact that those cartilage cells next to the bone that has formed from the ossification center continue to mature. They become large and hypertrophied, manufacture phosphatase,

and the intercellular substance about them becomes calcified. This brings about their death. When this occurs, the calcified cartilage intercellular substance breaks up into cavities, and these are rapidly invaded by capillaries, osteogenic cells and osteoblasts that are migrating up and down the model from the center of ossification. Soon there is a marrow cavity in the model (Fig. 18-27). The osteogenic cells and the osteoblasts that invade the calcifying cartilage toward each end of the model quickly line up along those remnants of cartilage intercellular substance that still persist and lay down bone on them to form trabeculae similar to those in the ossification center itself (Fig. 18-27, *right*). By this mechanism the process of ossification gradually extends into each of the growing ends of the cartilage models (Figs. 18-27 and 18-28).

cartilaginous
epiphysis

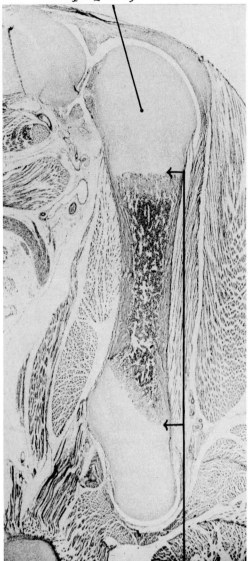

bony
diaphysis

FIG. 18-28. A very low-power photomicrograph of a longitudinal section of the developing thigh of a rabbit. At this stage the cartilage of the model is replaced by bone except at its ends. The bone that has formed from the periosteum and periosteal bud constitutes the diaphysis. The cartilage left at each end constitutes the epiphyses.

developing ossification
center in epiphysis
epiphyseal disk

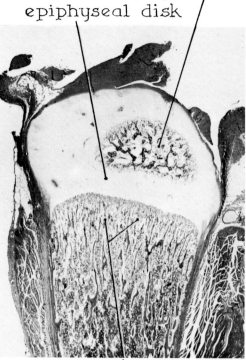

trabeculae on diaphyseal
side of epiphyseal disk

FIG. 18-29. Low-power photomicrograph of a longitudinal section of the upper part of the tibia of a kitten. This shows the stage of development shortly after the appearance of a center of ossification in an epiphysis. The cartilage that remains between the bone that forms from the epiphysial center of ossification and that from the diaphyseal center constitutes an epiphysial disk.

While bone formation is extending from the ossification center toward each end of a cartilage model, the periosteum continues to add further bone to the sides of the model. As the periphery of the model thus becomes stronger, the cancellous bone in its central part is no longer necessary for support, so it tends to dissolve away and leave a cavity that is called the marrow cavity (Figs. 18-27, *left,* and 18-28). This soon becomes filled with the various cells that are concerned in making erythrocytes, granular leukocytes and platelets. However, during the postnatal growing period,

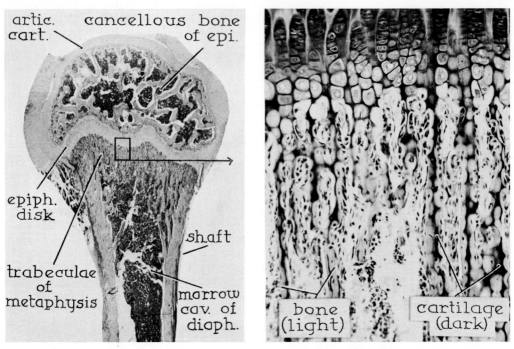

FIG. 18-30. At the left is a low-power photomicrograph of a longitudinal section cut through the end of a long bone of a growing rat. At this stage of development osteogenesis has spread out from the epiphysial center of ossification so that only the articular cartilage above and the epiphysial disk below remain cartilaginous. On the diaphysial side of the epiphysial plate are the metaphysial trabeculae, which, as may be seen from the high-power picture on the right, consist of cartilage cores on which bone has been deposited. The cartilage cores of the trabeculae formerly were partitions between columns of cartilage cells in the epiphysial disk.

the marrow cavity never extends quite all the way to the cartilaginous ends of a model but instead is always separated from each cartilaginous end by a region of cancellous bone (Fig. 18-29) in which trabeculae are disposed longitudinally.

An ossification center that arises in the midsection of a cartilage model, as has been described, is spoken of as a *diaphysial center* of ossification since it gives rise to the shaft or diaphysis of the bone concerned. However, the development of many bones of the body is complicated by the development of further centers of ossification in their cartilage models. In the long bones these further centers of ossification appear in the growing cartilaginous ends of the models and are termed *epiphysial centers* of ossification (Fig. 18-29). These are responsible for forming the bone that comes to exist in the epiphyses or ends of the bones.

The development of an epiphysial center of

ossification is heralded by the maturation of the cartilage cells situated in and near the central part of the cartilaginous end of a model. As the chondrocytes enlarge and make phosphatase, the intercellular substance about them becomes thinned out and calcified and they die. The intercellular substance about them then breaks up to form cavities which soon are invaded by capillaries, osteogenic cells and osteoblasts (Fig. 18-29). The latter lay down bone on the remnants of the cartilage intercellular substance. Meanwhile, the living chondrocytes immediately surrounding this area have begun to mature and die; hence the process of ossification is able to spread out from the center in all directions. However, ossification stops short of replacing all the cartilage in the end of a model. Enough is left at each articulating end of a model to constitute an articular cartilage (Fig. 18-30, artic. cart.). Furthermore, a transverse disk or plate

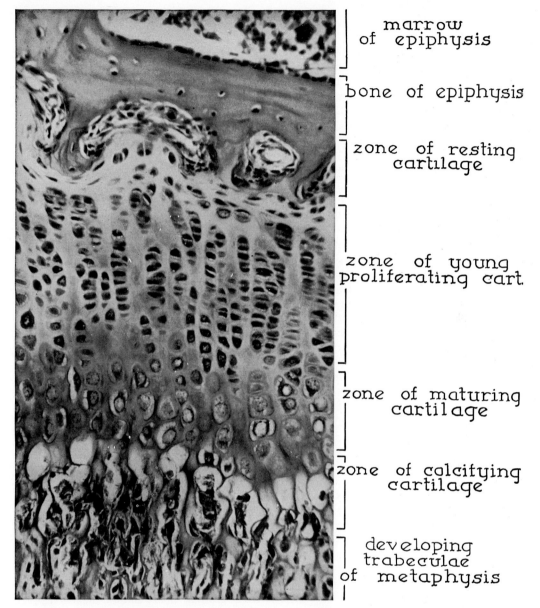

marrow
of epiphysis

bone of epiphysis

zone of resting
cartilage

zone of young
proliferating cart.

zone of maturing
cartilage

zone of calcifying
cartilage

developing
trabeculae
of metaphysis

FIG. 18-31. High-power photomicrograph of a longitudinal section cut through the upper end of the tibia of a guinea pig. This picture illustrates the different zones of cells in the epiphysial plate.

of cartilage is left between the bone derived from the epiphysial center of ossification and that from the diaphysial center. This transverse disk or plate of cartilage that separates epiphysial bone from diaphysial bone is termed the *epiphysial disk or plate* (Figs. 18-29 and 18-30), and it persists until the postnatal longitudinal growth of bones is completed; only then is it replaced by bone.

The route by which capillaries and osteogenic cells gain entrance to the central part of an epiphysis probably is indicated later by the course of the larger blood vessels that supply that epiphysis. The blood supply of epiphyses will be described later in connection with the blood supply of bones.

**Further Growth of the Model.** The further longitudinal growth of a model of a long bone in which epiphysial centers of ossification have appeared is accounted for by the continuance of the interstitial growth of cartilage cells in the epiphysial disk. Since epiphysial disks separate bony epiphyses from bony diaphyses, interstitial growth in them (Fig. 18-34) constantly tends to move the bone of the epiphyses away from the bone of the diaphysis. The result is that the total length of the model becomes increased. However, the thickness of the epiphysial disks does not become increased because of the interstitial growth that occurs in them. This is because another process that tends to reduce the thickness of the disk is at work simultaneously, namely, the continuing maturation, death and replacement of cartilage on the diaphysial side of the disk. Hence, in an epiphysial disk there is a persistent race between 2 processes: (1) interstitial growth, which tends to thicken it, and (2) calcification, death and replacement of cartilage at its diaphysial surface, which tends to thin it.

An epiphysial disk and that part of the diaphysis adjacent to it constitute what is termed a *growing zone* of a long bone. (The term "zone" is used in this connection in the same way that it is commonly used, for example, in zoning by-laws, to indicate a region, not necessarily an encircling band or region, which is its more precise meaning.) In a child, this zone is the site of tremendous cellular activity. Many different processes (the interstitial growth, maturation, calcification, death and disintegration of cartilage, and the formation, calcification and destruction of bone) are at work in this area simultaneously. Any interference with any one of these different processes, while the others continue, is quickly reflected by an alteration in the normal histologic picture of the part.

Since different abnormal states (for example, dietary deficiencies and endocrine gland imbalances) affect different processes at work in this region and so produce different kinds of alteration in the histologic picture in the part, we shall consider the growing zone of long bones in some detail.

If a longitudinal section of a growing bone is placed under the microscope and examined so as to allow the eye to sweep across the thickness of the epiphysial disk from its epiphysial to its diaphysial aspect (Fig. 18-31), the cartilage of the disk will be seen to present 4 successively different appearances. Accordingly, the epiphysial disk is divided into 4 different parts. From the epiphysis to the diaphysis these regions, commonly called zones, are: (1) the zone of resting cartilage, (2) the zone of proliferating young cartilage, (3) the zone of maturing cartilage and (4) the zone of calcified cartilage. These 4 zones are not distinctly separated from one another but more or less merge into one another. Their special characteristics and functions will now be described.

1. The layer of resting cartilage is that layer situated immediately adjacent to the bone and the marrow spaces of the epiphysis. Chondrocytes of moderate size are scattered irregularly throughout its intercellular substance. The part of the cartilage of this zone that actually touches the bone or marrow spaces of the epiphysis sometimes has a perichondrial-like appearance.

This zone of cartilage does not participate in the growth of the epiphysial plate. It serves, first, to anchor the plate to the bone of the epiphysis, and, secondly, as will be described later under "the blood supply of bone," capillaries present in it (Fig. 18-31) provide nourishment for the growth of the disk.

2. The second zone is composed of young proliferating cartilage cells. These are commonly thin and many of them are wedge-shaped. The cells in this zone are more or less piled on top of one another like stacks of coins so that they form columns whose axes are parallel with that of the bone (Fig. 18-31). In a growing bone, mitotic figures can be found among these cells. The plane in which mitosis occurs exhibits considerable variability. It seems likely that the column arrangement is maintained because the bundles of collagenic fibrils in the partitions of intercellular substance between the columns run longitudinally. The function of this zone is cell proliferation. This is the site where a sufficient number of new cells must be produced to replace those that hypertrophy and die at the diaphysial surface of the disk, as will be described.

3. The third zone or layer contains cartilage

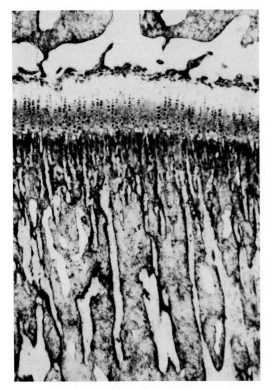

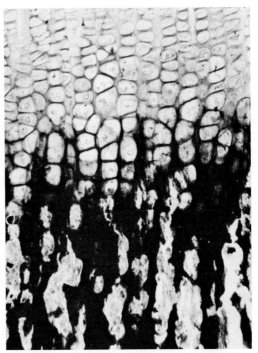

FIG. 18-33. Low-power photomicrograph of a longitudinal section of the end of the tibia of a young rat. This section was cut without the bone's being decalcified and has been stained by von Kossa's method, by which the phosphate of the calcium phosphate reacts with a silver salt to become blackened. The blackened material seen in the illustration represents the calcified cartilage of the epiphysial plate and the calcified bone underlying it.

FIG. 18-32. Photomicrograph of a section of the growing done of a tibia of a normal rat. The section was prepared so that the darkened areas are due to the presence of alkaline phosphatase. Notice that there is a dark band of phosphatase activity in the region of the hypertrophied cartilage cells in the plate and another in the region of the osteoblasts that are invading the diaphysial side of the plate. Notice that the zone of calcified cartilage is relatively free from phosphatase (it contains few living cells). (Morse, A., and Greep, R. O.: Anat. Rec. *111*:193)

cells that are in various stages of maturation. These, too, are arranged in columns. Those nearest the zone of proliferating cartilage are the least mature, and those nearest the diaphysis are the oldest and most mature (Fig. 18-31).

The cells in this zone were originally in the proliferating zone but were left behind as their neighbors on their epiphysial side continued to proliferate and so drew away from them. The cells left behind in this zone gradually mature. In this process they become larger

and accumulate glycogen in their cytoplasm. In becoming larger they take up more space and hence expand the epiphysial disk longitudinally. The epiphysial plate then is expanded in the long axis of the bone by the proliferation of cells in the second zone and by the maturation of cells in the third zone. Moreover, the cells of this zone produce phosphatase, as may be demonstrated in sections by histochemical methods (Fig. 18-32). The phosphatase may assist in bringing about the calcification of the intercellular substance that surrounds the hypertrophied cells so that the latter die and disappear. When this happens the third zone has turned into the fourth zone which will now be described.

4. The fourth zone is very thin, being only

one or a few cartilage cells thick. This zone abuts directly on the bone of the diaphysis. Most of the cells in this zone are dead because the intercellular substance about them became calcified and hence they died (Fig. 18-31). If sections of undecalcified bone are stained with silver salts, the phosphate of the recently deposited calcium phosphate in the cartilaginous intercellular substance in this zone reacts with the silver to form black silver phosphate (Fig. 18-33). This clearly marks the zone of calcifying cartilage.

Osteogenesis is very active at the diaphysial side of the epiphysial disk and results in bone being formed in very intimate contact with

the cartilage of the disk (Figs. 18-30 and 18-34). It is important to understand exactly where this bone is formed. A glance at the zones of maturing and calcified cartilage of a disk will show that the partitions of cartilaginous intercellular substance between the columns of cartilage cells vary somewhat in thickness but that in general they are thicker than the partitions between the individual cells in any single column. Hence, as the cartilage cells in the zone of calcification die and the intercellular substance about them begins to disintegrate, the partitions between the cells in any given column and the thinner partitions between adjacent columns are the first to melt

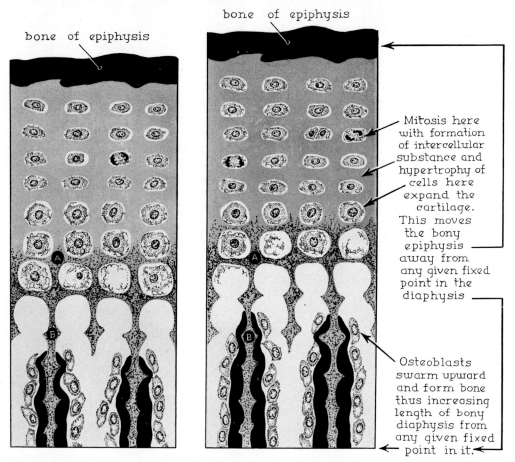

bone of epiphysis

bone of epiphysis

Mitosis here with formation of intercellular substance and hypertrophy of cells here expand the cartilage. This moves the bony epiphysis away from any given fixed point in the diaphysis

Osteoblasts swarm upward and form bone thus increasing length of bony diaphysis from any given fixed point in it.

FIG. 18-34. Diagrams of 2 longitudinal sections cut through the same epiphysial plate and part of the diaphysis of growing long bone. The diagram on the right illustrates the changes that occur in what is represented in the left over a short space of time. Cartilage is gray, calcified cartilage is stippled and bone is black. The sites labeled A and B are fixed points and remain at the same level in both diagrams. Note, however, that the "bone of epiphysis" has moved upward in the diagram on the right and that the level of calcified cartilage and bone is also higher in the diagram on the right. (Ham, A. W.: J. Bone Joint Surg. *34-A*:701)

away. Only the stouter partitions between columns remain, and these are immediately utilized as sites for bone deposition (Figs. 18-34 and 18-36). Osteoblasts from the diaphysis invade the breaking-down cartilage and line up along the sides of these stouter partitions and quickly deposit bone on their surfaces. This results on the diaphysial side of the epiphysial disk (the metaphysis) in the formation of longitudinally disposed bony trabeculae with cartilaginous cores, the cartilage of which is continuous with the cartilaginous intercellular substance of the disk (partitions between columns), and by this means the newly formed bony trabeculae are united firmly with the cartilaginous disk. By this arrangement the metaphysis of a bone is joined firmly to the epiphysial disk (Figs. 18-34 and 18-36).

The part of the metaphysis in direct contact with the epiphyseal disk in a growing bone is a site of active osteogenesis. This is the region wherein new bone is added to the ends of the diaphysis by means of osteoblasts that develop from proliferating osteogenic cells, advancing into the breaking-down cartilage in the zone of calcification of the epiphysial disk and there laying down bone on the stouter cartilaginous partitions to extend the length of the bony trabeculae. They make phosphatase also; this may assist in bringing about the calcification of the organic intercellular substance that they form (see Fig. 18-32 for the intense band of phosphatase activity in this zone; the osteoblasts are responsible for this). The growth mechanism described above is the only mechanism by which the diaphysis can become lengthened. Bone cannot grow by interstitial growth. It can grow only by appositional growth, and the new bone that is "apposed" and accounts for the growth in length of the diaphysis *is added to the tips of the prolongations of bone that extend into the cartilage*; this increases the penetration of the cartilage and makes the metaphysis longer (Fig. 18-34).

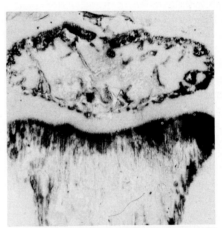

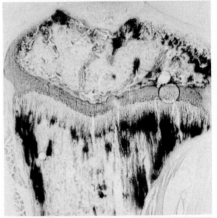

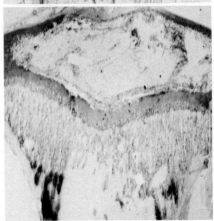

FIG. 18-35 (*Top*) Coated radioautograph of a safranin-stained section of the end of a tibia of a 50-Gm. rat sacrificed 5 minutes after injection of radiophosphorus. (*Middle*) Similar preparation from rat sacrificed 2 days after the injection. (*Bottom*) Semilar preparation from rat sacrificed 8 days after the injection. (All 3 preparations from Leblond, C. P., Wilkinson, G. W., Bélanger, L. F., and Robichon, J.: Am. J. Anat. *86*:289)

Since the (epiphysial) ends of the bony trabeculae in this zone are constantly being added
to by the deposition of bone in the zone of
calcification of the cartilaginous disk, it might
be thought that the zone of trabeculated bone
in the metaphysis would become increasingly
elongated. Instead, however, except at its periphery, this zone of trabeculated bone does
not become elongated during the growing
period (see Fig. 18-36). This can only mean,
then, that as rapidly as bone is added to the
(epiphysial) ends of the metaphysial trabeculae in the zone of calcification, bone is resorbed from their free (diaphysial) ends that
project toward the marrow cavity of the diaphysis. Osteoclasts commonly are seen here;
often they are wrapped around the free ends
of the trabeculae.

That the trabeculae that are present under
the more central part of an epiphysial disk
of a growing animal at any given time are
not the same ones that are present several
days later is illustrated beautifully by means
of radioautography. Leblond, Wilkinson,
Bélanger and Robichon, by means of administering radiophosphorus, have shown that although there is some exchange between circulating phosphate and the phosphate in bones,
there is a substantial precipitation of administered radiophosphorus into bone that is
forming and calcifying at the time the radiophosphorus is administered. This precipitated
radiophosphorus is sufficiently stable to permit the fate of the bone into which it precipitates to be followed thereafter by means of
radioautographs. As a glance at Figure 18-35,
*top*, will show, radiophosphorus, 5 minutes
after it is injected into a young growing rat,
is deposited in the new bony trabeculae that
are forming and calcifying on the diaphysial
side of epiphysial disks. This, for the practical
purposes with which we are concerned, removes the radiophosphorus from the circulation. However, the bone continues to grow in
length, and so new bone is added continuously
to the (epiphysial) ends of the trabeculae—
the ends that extend into the epiphysial disk—
and this new bone is not labeled by radiophosphorus because now there is not enough in
the circulation to mark it. A considerable band
of new unlabeled bone is already present 2
days after the administration of the radiophosphorus (Fig. 18-35, *middle*). Meanwhile,

the labeled bone of the trabeculae has been
dissolving from the free (diaphysial) ends of
the trabeculae, so that the average total length
of labeled bone in the trabeculae is shorter
than it was 2 days previously. After 8 days,
all the labeled bone has been eroded from the
trabeculae under the central part of the disk
(Fig. 18-35, *bottom*); hence, the trabeculae
that are present at this time (8 days after the
radiophosphorus was administered) are composed of bone that has formed and calcified
during the 8 days; therefore, they are not the
same trabeculae that were present 8 days before. However, it is to be noted that Figure
18-35, *bottom*, shows the persistence of some
of the labeled bone under, and some distance
away from the *peripheral* portion of the epiphysial disk; the significance of this will be
discussed soon.

Under the *periphery* of the epiphysial disk,
the fate of the metaphysial trabeculae is different from that described for the trabeculae
under its more central part. However, an explanation of what happens to these involves a
discussion of how a long bone *as a whole*
changes during the growing period, so we shall
discuss this matter first.

## THE GROWTH OF A LONG BONE AS A WHOLE

Although there are a few exceptions to the
rule, it can be stated as a generalization that
the growth in length of bones that develop in
cartilage is fundamentally dependent on the
ability of the cartilage that persists in them
and on their ends to grow by the interstitial
mechanism, as follows:

The growth in length of short bones, which
have no epiphysial disks, depends on such interstitial growth as occurs in their articular
cartilages (Fig. 18-27).

In long bones that have epiphysial disks,
the interstitial growth of the articular cartilages provides only for the growth in size of
the epiphyses and not for the growth of the
diaphysis. Articular cartilage may provide for
growth in width of the epiphysis as well as for
its growth in length (Fig. 18-36).

In long bones that have epiphysial disks,
the interstitial growth of the cartilage in the
disks does not assist in the growth of the
epiphysis after the bony epiphyses are reason-

ably well developed. After an epiphysis is well developed, the cartilage of an epiphysial disk is no longer replaced with bone on its epiphysial side but only on its diaphysial side (Fig. 18-31). Hence, the interstitial growth of cartilage in epiphysial disks accounts only for the growth in length of diaphyses during all

but the early stages of the growing period (Fig. 18-36).

With these facts established we can now consider some further points about the growth of a long bone as a whole.

The diaphyses of many long bones funnel outwardly as they approach their epiphyses;

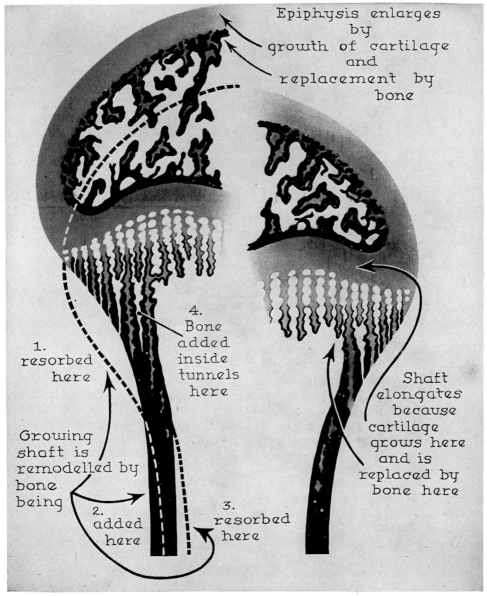

FIG. 18-36. Diagram showing surfaces on which bone is deposited and resorbed to account for the remodeling that takes place at the ends of growing long bones that have flared extremities. (Ham, A. W.: J. Bone Joint Surg. *34-A*:701)

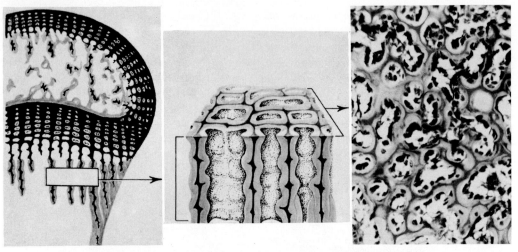

FIG. 18-37. The diagram at the left illustrates the appearance seen in a longitudinal section of the end of a growing long bone. The trabeculae appear stalactitelike in such a preparation. However, if they could be seen in 3 dimensions, as illustrated in the drawing in the middle, it would be seen that, close to the plate, the structures that appear as trabeculae in a longitudinal section are slices that have been cut through walls that surround spaces; they are slices cut through the walls of tunnels. The photomicrograph at the right represents what is seen in a cross section cut through the metaphysis of a growing long bone of a rabbit, close to the epiphysial disk. In it the trabeculae of bone have cartilaginous cores and they surround spaces. These spaces under the periphery of the disk become filled in to form haversian systems, and such compact bone as is present in the flared extremities of bone is built by spaces such as these becoming filled in.

hence, many bones are of a much greater diameter in their metaphysial regions (the metaphysis is the part of the shaft responsible for growth in length: the epiphysial disk and the trabeculae on its diaphysial side) than in their midsections (Fig. 18-36). As may be seen by comparing the left and the right sides of Figure 18-36, the site, along the longitudinal axis of a bone, that is occupied by the flared metaphysial portion of the diaphysis will, as the bone continues to elongate, be occupied later by the tubular and considerably narrower portion of the shaft. This means that as growth in length continues, the diameter of the portion of the shaft that is flared at any given time subsequently must become decreased. This requires that bone be resorbed continuously from the exterior of the flared portion (and osteoclasts are numerous here) and built up continuously on its inner aspect so that it can become a narrower shaft. We shall now consider how bone is built up on the inner aspect of the flared portion so that bone can be resorbed safely from its outer aspect.

It is easy to get the impression from longitudinal sections of growing bone that the trabeculae of the metaphysis are like stalactites, hanging down from the diaphysial side of the plate. However, if cross sections are cut of the metaphyses of larger mammals, close to the plate, it will be found that only the free ends of the trabeculae are stalactitelike. Closer to the plate the structures that in longitudinal sections appear as stalactitelike trabeculae are revealed in cross sections to be connected together to constitute a network that is honeycombed with spaces (Fig. 18-37). Why the newly formed bony trabeculae (which have cartilaginous cores) appear to be isolated from one another in longitudinal sections and should appear, when they are seen in cross section, to comprise a cancellous network will now be explained.

To explain why the newly formed bone should exist in a honeycomblike cancellous network in this area it is necessary to refer again to the way in which the calcified cartilage in the epiphysial plate disintegrates.

In the zone of maturing cartilage the cartilage cells are arranged in longitudinal rows that are separated from one another by partitions of intercellular substance. If this area is visualized in 3 dimensions, it will be obvious that the rows of cells are contained in longitudinal tunnels and that the partitions of intercellular substance between the rows of cells are the walls of these longitudinally disposed tunnels. As the cartilage cells in a tunnel mature and die at its diaphysial end, the thinner partitions between tunnels tend to dissolve, and by this means tunnels only one cartilage-cell wide fuse with others of the same size to become relatively large tunnels (Fig. 18-34), which are invaded from the diaphysis by osteogenic cells, osteoblasts and capillaries. The osteoblasts line up along the sides of the tunnels and deposit bone on the tunnel surfaces (Fig. 18-34). Hence, in a longitudinal section, the wall between 2 adjacent tunnels will appear as a trabecula with a cartilage core that is covered on each side by a layer of bone (Fig. 18-37). In other words, the bone seen covering the cartilaginous cores of the trabeculae in longitudinal sections is the bone that in cross section is seen to line the tunnels in cartilage (Fig. 18-37). The osteoblasts that cover the trabeculae of longitudinal sections similarly are the osteoblasts that line the insides of the tunnels that are seen in cross sections. And the capillaries and the osteogenic tissue that fill the spaces between the trabeculae of longitudinal sections are the contents of the tunnels seen in cross section.

On the diaphysial side of the more central part of the epiphysial disk only a single layer of bone is commonly deposited inside the cartilaginous tunnels. Hence, the trabeculae seen in a longitudinal section of this area are narrow. However, at the periphery of the disk successive layers of bone are deposited inside the tunnels. This narrows their lumens and imparts a lamellar appearance to their thickened walls. The successive layers of bone deposited inside the tunnels are the result of appositional growth. The osteogenic cells in the tunnel proliferate by mitosis to increase their numbers. Simultaneously some of them differentiate into osteoblasts and then into osteocytes and in doing so surround themselves with intercellular substance. This results in a layer or lamella of bone being deposited inside

the tunnel. The osteogenic cells that remain to line the tunnel then repeat the full procedure, so a second layer of bone is deposited. Finally, after several layers have been deposited, the tunnel is reduced to a narrow canal, which contains a blood vessel, some osteoblasts or osteogenic cells and perhaps a lymphatic. This arrangement of a canal with concentric layers of bone surrounding it is called a *haversian system* or an *osteon*, (Fig. 18-41). Haversian systems, in a sense, are units of structure of compact bone. Each has a blood vessel in its canal, and this provides tissue fluid to nourish the osteocytes in the surrounding lamellae. Haversian systems are limited with regard to the number of lamellae they can contain by the distance over which the canalicular mechanism can nourish osteocytes. This, of course, is not very great; hence, commonly a haversian canal is surrounded by less than half a dozen concentric lamellae (Fig. 18-41).

*A haversian system (osteon) can develop only by means of a tunnel being filled in from its inside with concentric layers of bone.* A haversian system, then, is in the nature of a bony tube with thick walls and a very narrow lumen. However, if tubes are bundled together side by side, crevices are left between them. Compact bone, though made of longitudinally disposed haversian systems, does not exhibit such crevices. With what are they filled?

Since the first compact bone that forms under the periphery of a disk is the result of a cartilaginous tunnel being filled in with bone, the crevices between the haversian systems that form in this manner are filled with cartilage. Hence, in the shaft of a very young growing bone, irregular bits of cartilage commonly will be seen (Fig. 18-36). It should be kept in mind by any student who wishes to understand bone growth well, that each of these bits of cartilage seen incorporated into the shaft of bone and situated between haversian systems was once part of a partition between rows of cartilage cells in the epiphysial plate and somewhat later was the cartilaginous core of a metaphysial trabecula under the periphery of the plate. In the shafts of older bones the crevices between adjacent haversian systems are filled with what are termed interstitial lamellae (Fig. 18-41); the origin of these will be described later.

periosteal    surface

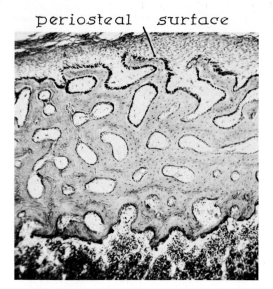

Fig. 18-38. Low-power photomicrograph of a cross section of the radius of a growing puppy. It is to be noted that the periosteal surface is not smooth but consists of longitudinally disposed ridges and grooves. The ridges are covered by osteoblasts and the grooves are lined by them. Developing haversian systems can be seen throughout the substance of the shaft.

## HOW SHAFTS OF BONES GROW IN WIDTH

A long bone does not grow in length alone; it also grows in width. This is accomplished by new layers of bone being added to the outside of the shaft while at the same time bone is dissolved away from the inside of the shaft. The result of these two processes proceeding simultaneously is that, although the shaft as a whole becomes wider, its walls do not become unduly thick, and the width of the marrow cavity gradually increases.

The shaft of a bone grows in width by the appositional mechanism (Fig. 18-3). New bone is laid down under the periosteum by the osteogenic layer of that membrane. However, if a cross section through the shaft of a young bone that is growing in width is examined, it will be seen that much of the new bone that is being added under the periosteum is in the form of haversian systems. It has been explained that haversian systems always are formed as a result of tunnels (not necessarily

cartilaginous ones) being filled in from the inside. How, then, can bony tunnels, to be subsequently filled in from the inside, be formed under the periosteum of a young growing bone?

A brief study of the periphery of a cross section of an actively growing shaft of a young animal will reveal how this occurs. The surface of such a shaft is not smooth; instead, it demonstrates a series of longitudinal ridges with grooves between them (Fig. 18-38). The osteogenic cells and the osteoblasts of the periosteum cover the tops of ridges and extend down to the bottoms of the grooves between them. The periosteum here also contains blood vessels (Fig. 18-39, 1). Longitudinal tunnels form from this arrangement as follows: the osteogenic cells of the periosteum covering the ridges proliferate, and some differentiate into osteoblasts which lay down bone so as to gradually extend the ridges over toward one another (Fig. 18-39, 2) till they meet (Fig. 18-39, 3). This converts the groove that formerly existed between 2 ridges into a tunnel. Since the groove was lined with periosteum containing osteogenic cells, osteoblasts and blood vessels, the tunnel now contains a lining of osteoblasts with a blood vessel somewhere in its lumen. As is shown in Figure 18-39 (4, 5 and 6), the continued proliferation of the osteogenic cells lining the tunnel with their subsequent differentiation into osteoblasts and osteocytes, results in the tunnel being converted into a haversian system. It is in this manner that new haversian systems are added beneath the periosteum to the periphery of a young actively growing shaft.

As the growth in width of a bone slows down, the surface of the shaft becomes smoother. Appositional growth occurring under the periosteum, then, tends to add smooth, even layers to the surface of the shaft (Fig. 18-40). These are called *circumferential lamellae* because they tend to surround the whole shaft. It is obvious that, if several circumferential lamellae were laid down under the periosteum, the osteocytes farthest away from the periosteum (in the deepest lamellae) soon would be unable to receive enough nourishment by the canalicular mechanism for their survival. Hence, lamellar bone of this type does not tend to persist if it becomes thick. Sooner or later it is replaced by haversian systems. The

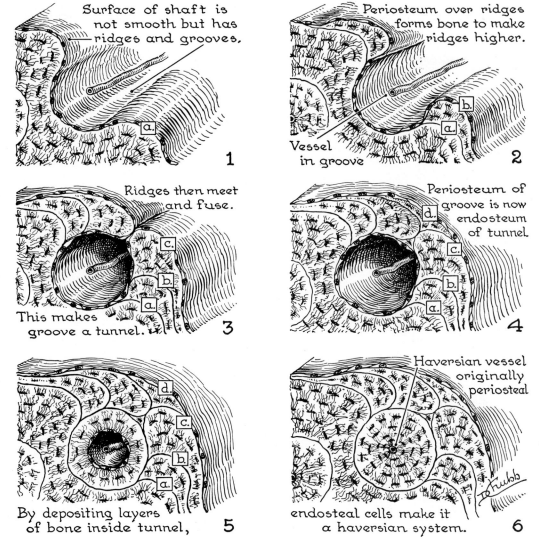

FIG. 18-39. Three-dimensional diagrams showing how the longitudinally disposed grooves on the exterior of a growing shaft become roofed over to form tunnels and how these become filled in to form haversian systems which thereupon are added to the exterior of the shaft. These diagrams also show how the blood supply of a shaft of a long bone comes to be derived, when it is fully grown, to a great extent from the periosteum by means of vessels having been buried in its substance.

replacement is brought about by means of longitudinal troughs being eroded on the surface of the shaft. Osteoclasts may be seen in these (Fig. 18-40). When a longitudinal trough becomes sufficiently deep, the osteogenic cells and the osteoblasts of the periosteum roof over the trough and so convert it into a tunnel (Fig. 18-40), which thereupon is filled up from its interior by osteogenic cells and osteoblasts laying down successive lamellae of bone. By this means, bone consisting originally of circumferential lamellae can be repaced by bone consisting of haversian systems. In this instance, the crevices between the haversian systems would be the remains of the former circumferential lamellae.

Osteoclasts

Osteogenic cells

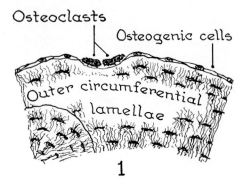

Outer circumferential lamellae

**1**

Longitudinal groove

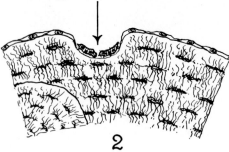

**2**

Groove becomes deepened.

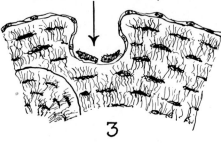

**3**

Periosteum with periosteal vessel descends into groove.

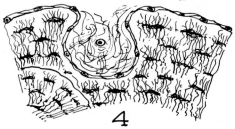

**4**

Periosteum forms bone to make groove a tunnel.

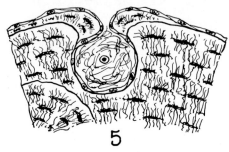

**5**

Tunnel is filled in to become haversian system.

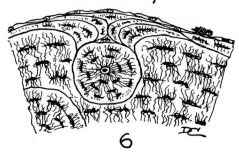

**6**

FIG. 18-40. Diagrams of cross sections of the shaft of a bone showing how haversian systems are laid down under the periosteum in older bones to replace outer circumferential lamellae.

**The Incorporation of Periosteal-derived Blood Vessels into Growing Shafts of Bone —The Nature of Volkmann's Canals.** As the two processes of bone deposition and bone resorption, on the outside and the inside of a shaft respectively, continue through the growth period, it comes to pass that the bone of the original shaft is all resorbed and that the shaft comes to be composed entirely of bone that has been deposited under the periosteum during the growing period. Since each haversian system that forms under the periosteum is built around a periosteal vessel (Fig. 18-39), the blood supply of the shaft, as growth in width continues, would seem to be derived more and more from the periosteum. It will be recalled that haversian systems are added to the outer surfaces of a bone by means of troughs containing periosteal vessels being roofed over. However, the roof that forms over each trough is not quite complete. A hole is left in it at the site at which the periosteal vessel descends into the trough. As the successive haversian systems are added to the

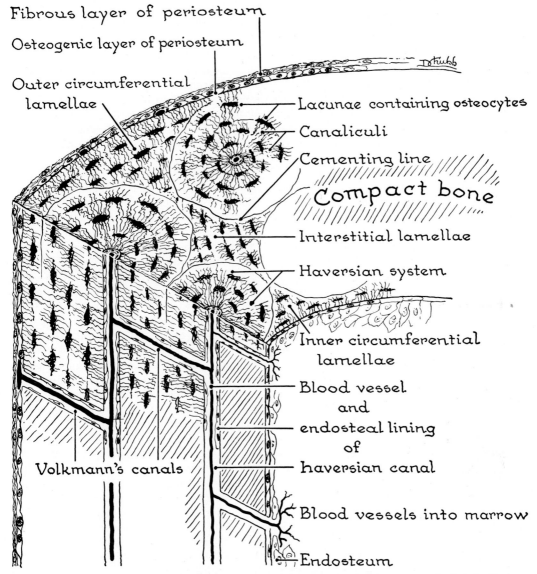

Fibrous layer of periosteum

Osteogenic layer of periosteum

Outer circumferential
    lamellae

Lacunae containing osteocytes

Canaliculi

Cementing line

Compact bone

Interstitial lamellae

Haversian system

Inner circumferential
    lamellae

Blood vessel
    and
endosteal lining
    of
haversian canal

Volkmann's canals

Blood vessels into marrow

Endosteum

Fig. 18-41. A 3-dimensional diagram showing the appearance of both a cross and a longitudinal section of the various components that enter into the structure of the cortex of the shaft of a long bone. It should be kept in mind, of course, that there would be many more haversian systems in the cortex than are shown here. The diagram shows the different kinds of lamellae that are present and the relation between the blood vessels of the periosteum, Volkmann's canals, haversian canals and the marrow cavity.

surface, the first-formed ones become more deeply buried, and so what were originally only holes in the roofs of troughs become elongated to constitute canals which run at right angles to the haversian systems between them and the periosteum. These canals that convey periosteal vessels into the haversian canals are called "Volkmann's canals" (Fig. 18-41). Because of the way they are formed, they are not surrounded by concentric lamellae like haversian canals.

From the foregoing account of how a bone

grows in width, it would seem that most of the blood vessels of the cortex of the diaphysis of a fully grown bone would be derived from the periosteum. However, the circulation is more complicated than it seems, as will be described presently.

As a bone attains its full width, it is usual for the osteoblasts covering its outer, and lining its inner, surfaces to smooth these by adding a few more or less final circumferential lamellae. These are called the "outer" and the "inner" circumferential lamellae respectively (Fig. 18-41). In a sense, they are like the finishing coats that a plasterer applies to the walls of a room as he completes his work. Between the outer and the inner circumferential lamellae, the shaft of a bone consists of haversian systems (Fig. 18-41). The crevices between these (interstitial lamellae) are filled either with the remaining parts of old outer circumferential lamellae or old haversian systems (Fig. 18-41). There would be, of course, infinitely more haversian systems in the wall of a shaft than is shown in the simplified diagram that is Figure 18-41.

### THE REMODELING OF COMPACT BONE THAT OCCURS THROUGHOUT LIFE

The remodeling of compact bone does not cease when full growth is attained. The compact bone of the shafts of the bones of adults continues to change throughout life. It could not be expected that the life span of haversian systems would be unlimited, because the canalicular mechanism on which the nutrition of osteocytes is dependent constitutes at best a frail sort of life line, and it is not surprising that it sometimes fails to function and so causes the local death of osteocytes, and that this leads to the need for the dead bone to be replaced with living bone.

The integrity of bone structure may also be affected because of a second function that

bone performs, that of serving as a calcium reservoir for the body. In this connection it should be pointed out that mechanisms operate to maintain the calcium content of the blood at a very constant level. If calcium is not forthcoming from the diet when it is needed to maintain a proper level of calcium in the blood it is taken from bone, and the process by which calcium is taken from bone probably involves the stimulation of bone resorption.

It is not known to what extent mineral may be extracted from bone to maintain the calcium level of the blood without bone substance being destroyed in the process. It is possible that some of the mineral from the most recently formed lamellae of haversian system (the lamellae closest to the central capillary or capillaries in the canal) may be to some extent accessible and be taken back into the bloodstream without the organic intercellular substance in which the mineral lies necessarily being eroded to free this mineral. There are reasons for thinking that mineral in this site is more labile than that in the deeper lamellae of haversian systems. Nevertheless, any substantial withdrawal of mineral from the skeleton, or perhaps any withdrawal of mineral from the skeleton, which is required to maintain the level of the blood calcium is associated with osteoclastic activity and bone destruction.

There are therefore at least two possible reasons for parts of pre-existing haversian systems being eroded: (1) either the cells of a part of the system have died or (2) the factors that demand that the level of the calcium in the blood be maintained stimulate osteoclastic activity in haversian canals.

It follows that if parts of old haversian systems are more or less constantly dying and being resorbed, the structure of the compact bone would become less and less dense unless

FIG. 18-42. Photomicrographs of cross sections of compact bone showing a haversian system nearing completion above and a resorption tunnel forming below. Notice in the top illustration that the canal is lined with osteoblasts and its surface is smooth and even and that the last deposited organic intercellular substance does not stain as darkly as that deposited previously. Note in the lower picture that the inner surface of the tunnel has an etched appearance and that there are large dark-staining osteoclasts distributed around it. Note that the tunnel has eroded into several different haversian systems. (Photomicrographs from C. P. Leblond)

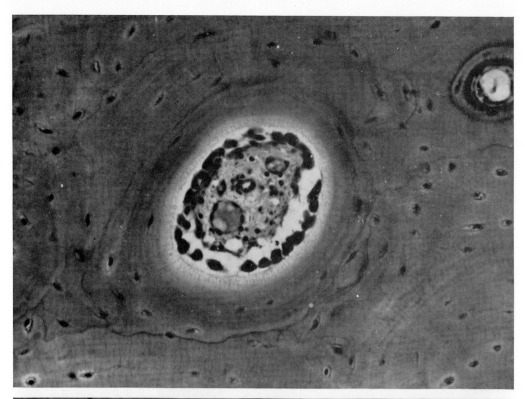

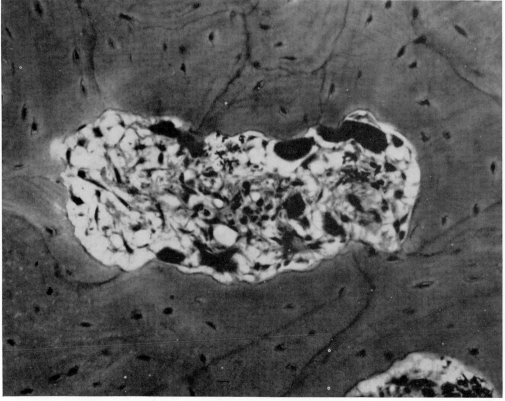

Fig. 18-42. (*Caption on facing page*)

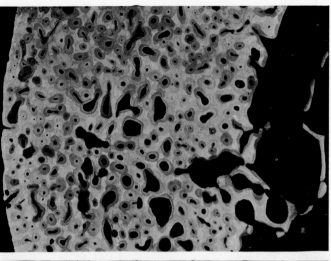

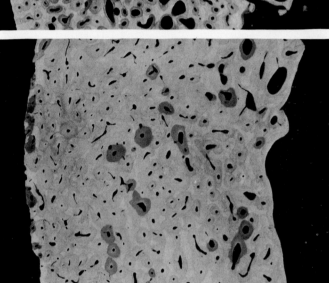

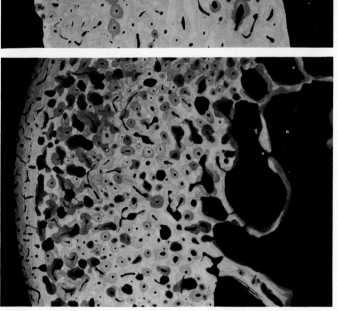

FIG. 18-43. Microradiographs of undecalcified sections from the midshaft of the femur of people of different ages. (*Left*) This section was from a 7-year-old, and it indicates the relatively rapid turnover of bone normal for this age in that it shows many resorption tunnels and many newly formed haversian systems (the bone of which shows darker than that of the older and hence more heavily calcified systems which, being denser, are whiter in the illustration). (*Middle*) This section was from a 25-year-old person. There is little indication here of the turnover of systems, for there are almost no resorption tunnels and most of the systems are well calcified and of the same density. (*Right*) This section was from an 85-year-old person. It shows two features characteristic of bone of people this age in that (1) there are many resorption tunnels, which indicate an increased rate of resorption, and (2) the new layers of bone which are beginning to fill in some of the tunnels are poorly calcified (darker than well-calcified bone), and hence bones of the old have a higher content of bone of low density than the bone of young adults. (Microradiographs by Jennifer Jowsey)

the breaking-down haversian systems were just as constantly replaced with new ones. In order to maintain the integrity of compact bone the two processes must be in balance. In growing bones, bone formation far exceeds bone resorption. When growth is over, the two processes come more or less into balance with the structure of compact bone remaining more or less constant because new systems are built at about the same rate as old ones are dissolved away. As people become older, however, the process of resorption seems to become accelerated, and for this reason the bones of the old are less dense than those of people of middle life. In the development of the disease graphically termed *osteoporosis* the two processes are far out of balance. Bone resorption takes precedence over bone formation, and the density of compact bone is thereby greatly decreased.

The two processes of (1) old haversian systems being resorbed and (2) new ones being formed can be studied in cross sections of decalcified compact bone and also by means of microradiographs. First we shall consider the two type of histologic pictures seen in cross sections of decalcified bone which are associated with the formation of new systems and the resorption of old ones respectively.

**The Respective Appearances of Forming Systems and Resorption Tunnels.** A forming haversian system is illustrated in the top picture in Figure 18-42. The canal is rounded in shape. Secondly, the edges of its lumen are smooth, and the lumen is lined by a row of osteoblasts which appear as individual dark cells in this illustration. Thirdly, the innermost layer of intercellular substance (on which the osteoblasts abut) stains lightly; this is the most recently deposited intercellular substance and is as yet only partially calcified. Fourthly, just outside this ring of newly formed intercellular substance, a previously formed lamella can be seen; this follows the contours of the canal. In contrast to the appearance presented by the newly forming haversian system, the developing resorption tunnel illustrated in the lower picture in Figure 18-42 shows many points of difference. First, the edge of the lumen is not smooth, but instead has an eroded, etched-out appearance. Secondly, the space is not lined by osteoblasts; instead, several large dark *osteoclasts* can be seen dis-

tributed around the edges of the lumen of the resorption cavity. Thirdly, the intercellular substance that immediately borders the lumen of the resorption tunnel is not lightly stained and different from that farther away from the tunnel; instead it is precisely the same as that farther away (hence it is not of recent formation as in a developing system). Fourthly, the tunnel is not ringed by lamellae that are parallel with the contour of the tunnel; instead the tunnel is seen to be surrounded by parts of several old haversian systems.

**Microradiography.** Determining the extent to which different lamellae in a given haversian system are calcified and different, and the extent to which different haversian systems in the same section of bone are calcified has been made possible by the development of the technic of microradiography. Undecalcified sections must of course be employed, and they should be of a constant and known thickness. Sections so prepared are placed over and in direct contact with a film or plate covered with fine-grain emulsion. The preparation is then exposed (section side up) to very soft x-rays from a special source. The soft x-rays penetrate the section in relation to the amount of calcium present in its different parts. The developed film or plate constitutes a microradiograph of the section and shows the extent to which its different parts are calcified. The microradiograph can be compared with the actual section under the microscope. By this means histologic appearances can be correlated with the sites of different densities indicated in the microradiograph. Three microradiographs of cross sections of cortical bone from people of different ages and kindly supplied by Jennifer Jowsey are seen in Figure 18-43. The interpretation is explained in the legend which should be read carefully.

## HOW CERTAIN NUTRITIONAL AND METABOLIC FACTORS CAN AFFECT GROWING BONES AND THE STRUCTURE OF BONES IN THE ADULT

First, the metaphysial region of a growing bone is the site of great *anabolic* activity. Both the multiplication and the growth of cartilage cells and the multiplication of osteogenic cells and their differentiation into large osteoblasts requires a great deal of protein synthesis. Moreover, the synthesis of collagen by chondroblasts and osteoblasts also requires a great deal of protein synthesis. The formation of the mucopolysaccharide content of the intercellular substance of both cartilage and bone also requires synthetic activity. With all this anabolic activity taking place it is obvious that any nutritional deficiencies or metabolic alterations that affect protein, or even carbohydrate, synthesis might quickly be reflected in some alteration of the growth pattern in this region.

Secondly, the metaphysial region of a growing bone is a site where calcium salts are being deposited into organic intercellular substance at a very rapid rate. The normal growth of bone in the metaphysial region depends on calcification occurring normally just as it depends on protein synthesis occurring normally. In the normal the two processes, (1) the synthesis of organic materials and (2) the calcification of organic intercellular substance, are synchronized. If, however, synthesis occurs without proper calcification following in its wake, an altered histologic picture is soon seen in the metaphysial region.

It is important for the student to realize that the normal growth of bone depends on *two different processes* that generally operate in harmony with one another. The factors that affect the anabolic synthetic processes are not the same factors that affect the calcification process and vice versa. So if a disturbance of the normal growth pattern is seen in the metaphysis of a growing bone, perhaps the first question to ask is which process is primarily affected, the synthesis of the organic components of bone or the calcification of the organic intercellular substance.

To illustrate that interference with each of these processes is reflected in a different kind of histologic picture in the metaphysis, we shall briefly describe one example of an interference with (1) the synthesis of the organic components of bone and (2) the calcification of the organic intercellular substance of bone.

1. **Scurvy.** Perhaps what is the most dramatic interference with the synthesis of organic materials in the metaphysis of a growing bone is seen in the disease called scurvy. This disease affects adults as well as children. It was once the greatest threat to the life and welfare of sailors who were on long voyages (where it was noted that the disease often appeared after they ran out of potatoes). The possibility of an outbreak of scurvy always hung heavily over the heads of those who engaged in polar exploration and, indeed, in the early days of the settlement of the northern part of this continent scurvy became so widespread and serious in the long winters that it is a wonder that anyone stayed here unless they had to.

In the 18th century it became fairly well established that scurvy did not develop in children and adults whose diets contained a supply of fresh fruits and vegetables, and by the end of the century it became compulsory for all ships of the British navy to carry supplies of lime juice to prevent the disease from occurring on long voyages. However, it took much longer to establish that scurvy was a disease caused by a *lack* of an essential food factor, vitamin C, that is present in fresh fruits and vegetables. It is interesting to study the development of knowledge about scurvy because it illustrates how preconceived ideas can keep one from seeing a truth that would otherwise be obvious. The preconceived idea held at the time when it was found that fresh fruits and vegetables would prevent scurvy was that disease must be caused by a *positive agent* of some sort, and therefore it was assumed that fresh fruits and vegetables somehow prevented this unknown positive agent from exerting its evil effects. It was not until this present century that it became clear that diseases could be caused by a *lack of something*, for example the essential food factors that we now term vitamins. It is saddening to read accounts of Scott's expedition to the South Pole, shortly after the turn of this century, and read that when scurvy broke out they did their best to evolve some way of telling which tins of meat contained the "taint" that was believed to be responsible for scurvy and so avoid using these tins of meat, when, as we now know, it was a lack of an essential ingredient in their diet that was causing the trouble and not a positive factor.

Although a vitamin C deficiency affects the metabolism of types of various cells in the body, its effects are particularly noticeable in the metaphysis of a growing bone where a lack of vitamin C prevents the proper multiplication of both chondroblasts and osteogenic

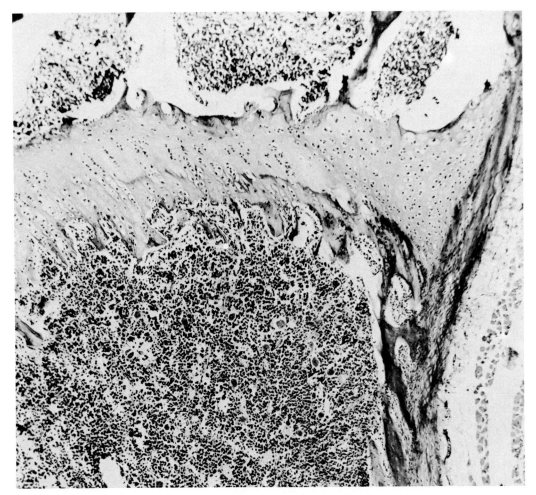

Fig. 18-44. A low-power photomicrograph of a longitudinal section of the upper end of the tibia of a guinea pig that for some weeks had been fed a diet containing an inadequate amount of vitamin C. Under conditions of prolonged vitamin C deficiency, bone building almost ceases on the diaphysial side of the disk, and, as a result, the epiphysial plate is not supported by a proper number of trabeculae. Furthermore, bone building almost ceases in the shaft, and, as a result, it becomes fragile and breaks easily. (Ham, A. W., and Elliott, H. C.: Am. J. Path. *14:323*)

cells and in particular prevents them from synthesizing and elaborating organic intercellular substance. The net result is that on a diet inadequate, but not completely deficient, in vitamin C the metaphysis of, for example, the upper end of the tibia of a guinea pig (guinea pigs, like man, are sensitive to dietary deficiencies of vitamin C; many animals can make their own), shows very little anabolic activity (Fig. 18-44). Growth in the epiphysial plate is slowed, and almost no new bone for-

mation occurs on the diaphysial side of the epiphysial plate (Fig. 18-44). The almost complete cessation of the formation of bone results in the shaft of the bone being very thin (Fig. 18-44). As a consequence, both the epiphysial plate lacking support by bony trabeculae beneath it, and the shaft, are easily fractured.

The process of calcification, however, is *not* interfered with by scurvy. Such organic intercellular substance that forms becomes heavily calcified. Scurvy, therefore, represents a condition in which the defect lies in anabolic activities that are concerned with the multiplication of cells and their synthesis of organic intercellular substances. There are other metabolic defects which act in a different way to interfere with normal growth and the formation of organic intercellular substances; for example, we shall see, when we consider the endocrine glands, that the synthesis of protein can be affected by several of the hormones.

2. **Rickets.** The mechanism of calcification has been described as being dependent on a concentration of calcium and phosphate ions being achieved in the vicinity of calcifying bone or cartilage that approaches or perhaps exceeds their solubility product. It has been shown that in general this condition is not attained in a growing infant if the product obtained by multiplying the number of milligrams of calcium per 100 ml. of serum by the number of milligrams of phosphorus per 100 ml. of blood is less than 40. It is to be noted that a reduced level of calcium *or* phosphorus in the blood does not necessarily interfere with calcification; it is the concentration of the product of the two ions that determines whether precipitation will continue in the sites of calcification.

In a baby the growing skeleton normally absorbs large amounts of calcium phosphate. For the CaP product of the blood to be maintained above 40 consequently necessitates that the infant's diet contain an adequate amount of calcium and phosphorus. Further, for these minerals to be absorbed into the bloodstream, the infant also requires an adequate supply of vitamin D.

If an infant's diet is deficient in these essentials, the CaP product of the blood may fall below 40, with the result that a condition known as *rickets* develops. Rickets is associated with characteristic changes in the growing zones of long bones. The earliest one to be seen is that although growth continues and organic intercellular substances continue to be synthesized, the calcification of cartilage almost ceases in the epiphysial disks. If the intercellular substance about the cells in this zone fails to become impregnated with mineral, the cells of this zone are not shut off from nutrition. Hence, they do not die but continue to live. The result is that, since growth continues in the growing zone of the disks, the epiphysial disks become thicker than normal (Fig. 18-45). Inasmuch as calcification is not entirely arrested but occurs in a few sites on the diaphysial sides of the disk, the thickening of the disks tends to be irregular (Fig. 18-45). In the meantime, osteoblasts continue to lay down the organic intercellular substance of bone in the metaphysis, but this also does not become calcified because of the low CaP product. Instead, it exists in an uncalcified state until the diet is remedied. New bone, during the time it remains uncalcified, is termed *osteoid tissue* (Fig. 18-45). Furthermore, it would seem as if the osteoblasts of the periosteum in the region of metaphysis realized that calcification was not proceeding normally, for they increase their activities and lay down large amounts of osteoid tissue in the metaphysial region under the periosteum. This makes the metaphysial regions knobby. The knobs so produced at the growing ends of the ribs are responsible in a rachitic child's chest for what is termed the "rachitic rosary."

It is to be kept in mind that the changes that occur in the growing zones of bone in rickets are the result of growth continuing while calcification fails. For this reason, a disturbed mineral metabolism will cause more severe rickets in a child who is actively growing than in one who is not. The poorly calcified intercellular substance of bone, seen in rickets, bends with weight bearing. Hence, rachitic children may be bowlegged.

CHANGES IN THE BONE OF ADULTS

Nutritional and metabolic defects show up in the metaphyses of growing bones much more quickly than they do in the bones of adults. However, as has been described, there is a turnover of both cancellous and compact bone throughout life. As has already been described, parts of old haversian systems die, resorption tunnels develop, and new haversian systems form in the tunnels. As people become older, it seems that the rate of resorption becomes greater and as a result the compact bone of skeleton becomes more porous than it is in middle life (Fig. 18-43). Not uncommonly, particularly in women who have passed the menopause, the resorptive processes exceed the building processes to a point beyond what can be considered normal, and bone

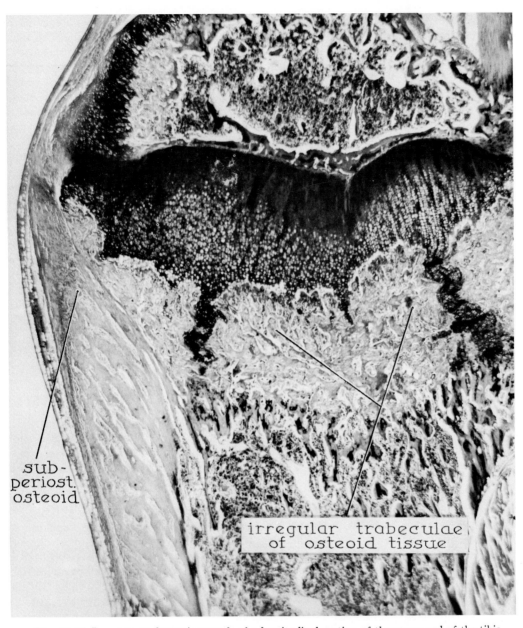

sub-
periost.
osteoid

irregular trabeculae
of osteoid tissue

FIG. 18-45. Low-power photomicrograph of a longitudinal section of the upper end of the tibia of a young rat that had been fed a Steenbock diet with calcium carbonate added to produce a blood-calcium level of 10 mg. and a blood-phosphorus level of 2 mg. per 100 ml. Since the product of calcium and phosphorus was only 20, proper calcification did not ensue on the diaphysial side of the epiphysial plate. This has resulted in the cartilage cells living much longer than they should, and as a result the epiphysial disk has become thicker than normal and in some sites very thick. Furthermore, such trabeculae as have formed on the diaphysial side of the disk are irregular and poorly calcified (osteoid tissue). Osteoid tissue also may be seen to have formed under the periosteum at the left side of the picture. This is an example of severe low-phosphorus rickets.

becomes unduly porous and fragile; this condition is termed osteoporosis. The cause of this condition is not entirely clear, and at the moment osteoporosis is the subject of much research.

## WOLFF'S LAW

Bone responds to increased function or altered function with structural changes. That the internal architecture and the external form of a bone are related to its function and change with altered function was observed many years ago by Wolff, whose particular postulate regarding this general principle, which is somewhat too detailed to be quoted here, is often spoken of as "Wolff's law." Sir Arthur Keith has fittingly likened osteoblasts to architects. Certainly the arrangement of trabeculae in the upper end of the femur is a magnificent demonstration of engineering principles put into practice.

**Atrophy of Disuse.** Just as increased function leads to bone formation, a lack of use leads to the atrophy of bone. The condition is termed the *atrophy of disuse* and is observed in bones that are immobilized for considerable periods of time for one reason or another. Without the stimulus of use, bone formation slows and hence an immobilized bone becomes more porous than is normal.

## PERIOSTEUM AND ENDOSTEUM

Those students who have occasion to read the older literature on bone will find that there have been many arguments as to whether or not periosteum is osteogenic or merely a fibrous limiting membrane. The probable reason for much confusion in this field is that many surgeons through the years have regarded the fibrous membrane that they could strip from bones as the complete periosteum of those bones. Histologists regard the periosteum as having 2 layers: an outer fibrous layer and an inner osteogenic or osteoblastic layer (Figs. 18-41 and 18-46). If "periosteum" is stripped from bone, the inner osteogenic layer is prone to adhere to the bone. Hence, the layer that is stripped, which some surgeons have called the (whole) periosteum, is only the outer fibrous layer of what the histologists term periosteum. This argument, which confused matters for a long time, seems now, however, to be fairly well resolved, for there is now

much more complete agreement to the effect that the periosteum has 2 layers. The inner layer becomes less noticeable with age.

The endosteum is the cellular membrane that lines the marrow cavities of bone and all haversian canals of bone (Fig. 18-41). It develops from the periosteal bud and is composed of osteogenic cells that can become active osteoblasts when required.

*The cells of the inner layer of the periosteum and of the endosteum form a continuous covering for all bony surfaces that are not undergoing resorption.* The osteogenic cells that make up the membrane that covers and lines bone surfaces are stem cells with considerable potentiality. These cells are direct descendants of the cells of the inner layer of the perichondrium of bones that develop in cartilage, so it should not be surprising that these cells, when they multiply to repair fractures, can produce cartilage as well as bone. And, as noted previously, under conditions that induce resorption, the osteogenic cells can fuse to form osteoclasts.

## THE REPAIR OF FRACTURES

The healing of broken bones is a matter of concern to every practicing doctor. Consequently, the process by which fractures heal receives considerable attention in medical schools. A student ordinarily receives instruction and is interrogated about this matter in every year of his medical course. The time when it is easiest to grasp the fundamentals of the process is when the facts of the development and the growth of bone are still fresh in the mind. For this reason, the repair of fractures will be considered briefly at this time.

In the usual fracture a single bone is broken into 2 parts, each of which is termed a *fragment*. Further, in the usual fracture the periosteum is torn and the fragments are displaced so that their ends are not in perfect apposition to one another. Because of this, it is usually necessary for fractures to be reduced; that is, the fragments are led back, usually by manipulation but sometimes by an open operation, so that their broken ends are in apposition to one another and the line of the bone is restored.

The student may think, and indeed he should be entitled to think, that by this time the repair of fractures would have been stud-

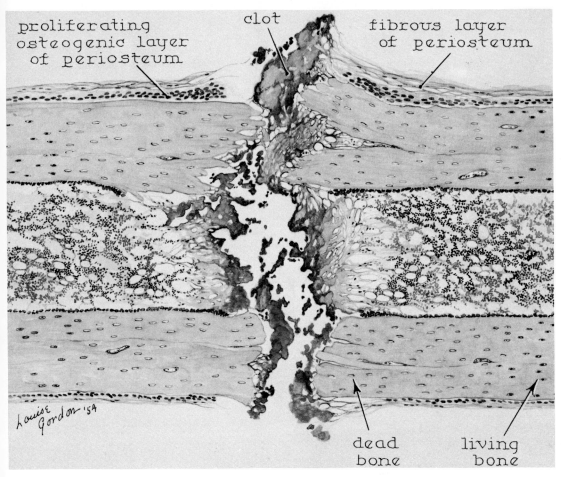

proliferating osteogenic layer of periosteum

clot

fibrous layer of periosteum

Louise Gordon '54

dead bone

living bone

Fig. 18-46. A drawing of a longitudinal H and E section of a rabbit's rib in which a fracture had been healing for 48 hours. The territory encompassed by the drawing was that which could be seen with a very low-power objective, but the detail has been depicted at higher magnification to obviate the necessity of making several drawings at different magnifications. (Ham, A. W., and Harris, W. R.: *In* Bourne's Biochemistry and Physiology of Bone, New York, Acad. Press)

ied enough for the accounts of the process given in modern books dealing with surgery, pathology, histology and even bone itself to be very much alike. Unfortunately, they are not, and the best way to resolve any confusion resulting from reading different accounts of the process is to study a set of sections cut from fractures that have healed for different lengths of time. Such a set can be prepared easily from the ribs of rabbits.

## THE REPAIR OF A SIMPLE FRACTURE

### EFFECTS OF THE INJURY

In a simple fracture there is both direct and indirect injury to tissue. The trauma itself causes direct injury; it breaks the bone and tears the soft tissues associated with the bone. As a result of the trauma, all the blood vessels crossing the fracture line are torn. The first result of this is that blood pours from their torn ends into the fracture area. This blood soon coagulates to form a clot in and about the site of the fracture (Fig. 18-46, *clot*). The next and second type of injury caused by a fracture is indirect; it depends on the fact that when the ends of the torn blood vessels are sealed off by hemostatic mechanisms (see Chap. 14), circulation stops in all these vessels back to sites where they anastomose with still functioning vessels. Cessation of circulation in these vessels—an indirect cause of tissue damage—leads to considerable death of tissue as follows.

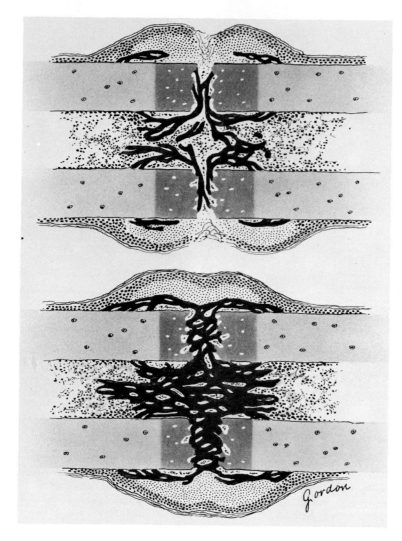

FIG. 18-47. Drawings to show the periosteal collars that form, approach each other and fuse in the repair of a fracture. The drawings also show the formation of internal callus and how the trabeculae become cemented to the original fragments. Living bone of the original fragments is light gray, dead portions of the original fragments are dark gray, and new bone in the external and the internal callus is black. In the external callus, cartilage is stippled lightly, and proliferating osteogenic cells are stippled darkly.

It has been explained already that the life of the osteocytes in any haversian system is precarious, being dependent on canaliculi transmitting nutriment to osteocytes from the central vessel or vessels of the system. The blood vessels run more or less longitudinally in bone. When the bone is broken, these vessels in haversian systems are all torn at the fracture line, and circulation in them stops back to sites where they anastomose with other haversian vessels. Since anastomoses between vessels of adjacent haversian systems are probably not overly abundant, this means that circulation ceases in haversian vessels for some distance each side of the fracture line. This results in the death of the osteocytes for a considerable distance from each side of the fracture line (Fig. 18-46). Hence, when a fracture occurs, bone dies, not only at the fracture line from the direct effects of trauma, but also for a considerable distance from each side of the fracture line because of the interruption of circulation in the haversian vessels that cross the fracture line.

The same factors that cause the death of bone are also responsible for the death both of periosteal tissue and some marrow tissue on each side of the fracture line. However, since both these tissues have a better blood supply than the bone itself, the periosteal tissue and the marrow tissue do not die for as great a distance from each side of the fracture line as does the bone (Fig. 18-46).

Dead bone is generally recognized because

dead osteocytes undergo lysis; hence, in most dead bone the lacunae appear to be empty (Figs. 18-46, 18-47 and 18-48). However, the osteocytes, before dissolving, sometimes become pyknotic (dark and rounded). After 48 hours, the irregular line of demarcation between the dead bone (with empty lacunae), that extends from both sides of the fracture line, and living bone (the lacunae of which contain normal osteocytes), farther away from the fracture line, generally can be recognized, as in Figures 18-46, 18-47 and 18-49. The distance from a fracture line over which bone dies as a result of its blood supply being interrupted differs depending on the site of the fracture in the bone and the particular bone that is fractured.

### EARLY STAGES OF REPAIR

**The Term Callus.** A fracture is repaired by a growth of the new tissue that develops in and around the site of the fracture; this new tissue, which soon or late forms a bridge between the fragments so that they are united

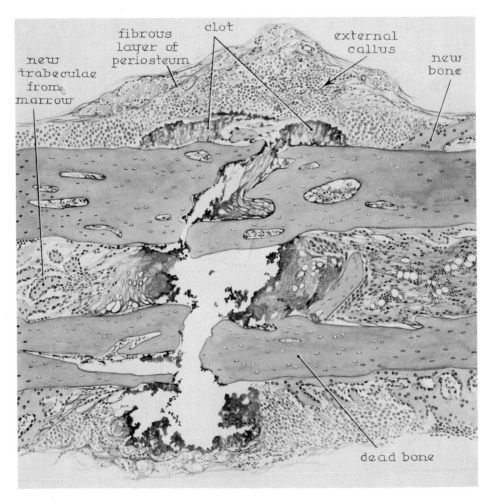

Fig. 18-48. A drawing of a longitudinal H and E section of a rabbit's rib in which a fracture had been healing for 1 week. The territory encompassed by the drawing was that which could be seen with a very low-power objective, but the detail has been filled in at higher magnification to obviate the necessity of making several drawings at different magnifications. (Ham, A. W., and Harris, W. R.: *In* Bourne's Biochemistry and Physiology of Bone, New York, Acad. Press)

(Figs. 18-47, 18-48 and 18-49), is termed a *callus*. A great amount of literature dealing with bone repair is unnecessarily complicated by authors attempting to distinguish different stages of callus development by different names such as provisional callus, temporary callus, bridging callus and permanent callus. These terms suggest that different calluses exist at different times, each being replaced by another. Actually, what happens is that only one callus develops and, like any bony structure, is remodeled as it grows. However, there is one classification that is helpful in describing callus formation; that is to speak of the callus that forms *around* the opposing ends of the bone fragments as the *external callus* and that which forms *between* the 2

ends of the bone fragments and between the 2 marrow cavities as the *internal callus* (Fig. 18-49).

**The Origin of Callus.** Many accounts of fracture healing describe the first important step in the repair process as depending on the invasion of the blood clot by a growth of new young capillaries and fibroblasts (granulation tissue). This alleged phenomenon often is described also as bringing about the formation of a temporary or transient callus. Many authors, having described the formation of a temporary callus, do not seem to know what to do with it and become vague about its subsequent fate, whether it is replaced by, or turns into, permanent callus. Furthermore, so far as the external callus is concerned,

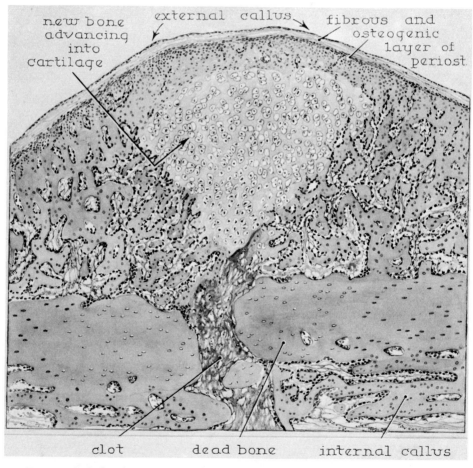

Fig. 18-49. A drawing of part of a longitudinal H and E section of a rabbit's rib in which a fracture had been healing for 2 weeks. (Ham, A. W., and Harris, W. R.: *In* Bourne's Biochemistry and Physiology of Bone, New York, Acad. Press)

invasion and replacement of the blood clot is *not* an early or important step in the healing of the fracture; in fact, the blood clot remains more or less intact for days and seems only to be in the road of the repair process (Figs. 18-46, 18-48 and 18-49). So far as the internal callus is concerned, such blood clot as exists between the 2 marrow cavities is soon invaded by osteogenic cells from the endosteum and from marrow cells of great potentiality; both of these types of cells form new bone trabeculae, so there is nothing temporary about the callus tissue they build (Fig. 18-47, *bottom*).

How does a fracture become repaired? Forty-eight hours after a fracture, or even sooner, the cells that will be responsible for the repair are actively dividing by mitosis and increasing rapidly in numbers. These cells are: (1) the osteogenic cells of the deep layer of the periosteum (Figs. 18-46 and 18-48) and (2) the cells of the endosteum of the marrow cavity and the undifferentiated (reticular) cells of bone marrow (Figs. 18-46 and 18-47). After 48 hours the cells of the deep layer of the periosteum of both fragments close to, but not directly adjacent to, the line of fracture have proliferated so extensively that they form a layer several cells thick (Fig. 18-46). As a result of this growth, the fibrous layer of the periosteum, which remains relatively inactive, is lifted away from the bone at this site (Fig. 18-46). The cells of the endosteum that line the marrow cavity, or cover any trabeculae in the marrow cavity that are close to the line of fracture, also proliferate, and this causes the endosteal layer, which is normally only 1 cell thick, to become composed of 2 or more layers. Moreover, the endosteal cells grow toward the fracture line with their numbers being augmented by undifferentiated cells from the marrow. During the first week after the fracture, these cells have begun to form some new trabeculae of bone in the marrow cavity close to the line of fracture (Fig. 18-48). These trabeculae may be cemented, at one end, to one fragment or the other (Fig. 18-47, *top*).

Over the next few days, the proliferation of osteogenic cells continues in both periosteal and endosteal regions, but those cells in the deep layer of the periosteum show the greater activity. They proliferate so rapidly that

they soon form a distinct collar around each fragment close to the line of the fracture (Fig. 18-47, *top*). In addition to proliferating, these cells now begin to manifest signs of differentiation. To understand how they differentiate it is necessary to recall that the deep layer of the periosteum normally contains some capillaries. When the osteogenic cells begin to proliferate after a fracture the capillaries among them also proliferate, but they do not seem to grow as quickly as the osteogenic cells. As a result, the osteogenic cells that are more deeply disposed in the collars (those closest to the bone) differentiate in the presence of a blood supply; consequently, they become osteoblasts and form bony trabeculae in this region (Fig. 18-48). The new trabeculae that develop are cemented firmly to the bone matrix of the fragment, even though the bone of the fragment may be dead (Fig. 18-48). Those osteogenic cells in the more superficial parts of a collar (those farther away from the bone) seem to grow so quickly that the capillaries from the periosteum cannot keep up with them. When these osteogenic cells differentiate they must do so in a nonvascular environment, so they tend to differentiate into chondroblasts and chondrocytes and, as a result, cartilage develops in the outer parts of the collars (Figs. 18-47 and 18-48).

Two comments should be made about the significance of cartilage in the external callus. (1) Its development here should not be unexpected, because the osteogenic cells that cover bone surfaces, which proliferate to repair a fracture, are direct descendants of the cells of the perichondrium of embryonic bones where they, of course once formed cartilage. (2) The amount of cartilage that forms in a callus is probably dependent on how quickly the callus tissue grows; if it grows very rapidly, capillaries probably cannot keep up with it, so its outer parts become nonvascular and cartilaginous. However, if callus tissue develops more slowly, new capillaries can keep pace with the osteogenic cells, so the osteogenic cells in such a callus differentiate in a vascular environment and so form bone. There also may be other factors that influence the amount of cartilage that forms, for example, species and movement.

When the collars resulting from the growth

and the differentiation of the osteogenic cells of the deep layer of the periosteum are well developed, they generally exhibit 3 layers that merge into one another (Figs. 18-47 and 18-48). The layer closest to the fragment consists of bony trabeculae that are cemented to the bone; the next and intermediate layer consists of cartilage which merges imperceptibly into the outer parts of the bony trabeculae on one side and into the third and outer layer of the callus on the other. The third and outer layer consists of proliferating osteogenic cells.

The collars continue to grow chiefly because of the proliferation of osteogenic cells in their outer layer and to a lesser extent because of the interstitial growth of cartilage in their middle layers. Such growth as occurs in the collars makes them thicker and makes them bulge toward each other. Sooner or later the collars from the 2 fragments meet and fuse (Figs. 18-47 and 18-48); when this occurs union of the fragments has been achieved. Union is also achieved in the marrow cavity by developing trabeculae there forming a bridge (Fig. 18-47). Soon the histologic picture of the healing fracture comes to resemble that illustrated in Figure 18-49.

**The Fate of the Cartilage.** The cartilage that develops in a callus normally has a temporary existence only; like that which develops in embryonic bones, it is eventually replaced with bone. Those cartilage cells that are closest to the newly formed bone mature and the intercellular substance around them becomes calcified and this causes their death. The region in which this occurs is seen as a V-shaped line in a longitudinal section of a fracture at this stage of healing (Fig. 18-49). As the cartilage becomes progressively calcified it is replaced progressively with bone; this makes the angle of the V become increasingly acute. Finally the cartilage is all replaced with bone; this is of the cancellous type. It is to be observed that the trabeculae of this cancellous bone that replace the calcified cartilage have cores of cartilage as do those that replace calcified cartilage on the diaphysial side of an epiphysial plate.

**The Remodeling of the Callus.** To understand the remodeling process it is important to realize that those trabeculae of bone that form close to the original fragments are firmly cemented to the fragments. Since they also connect with one another, the 2 fragments are firmly bridged by a cancellous network (Fig. 18-47, *bottom*). Moreover, it is important to realize that osteoblasts in building new trabeculae can lay down their matrix on dead portions of the fragments (as well as on living portions of them), so that by this means new trabeculae of bone become firmly cemented here and there to dead bone. However, between these trabeculae there are spaces, and the matrix of the dead bone is dissolved away in these spaces. By this mechanism the matrix of the dead bone is slowly etched away (except where new trabeculae fasten onto it). Next, osteoblasts grow into the spaces that have been deepened into the matrix of the dead bone by this process and lay down new living bone in them. By this means the matrix of the dead bone eventually is almost all replaced with new living bone.

At this stage the callus constitutes a fusiform mass of cancellous bone around the 2 fragments from which most of the dead bone has been resorbed. We have already described how cancellous bone can be converted into compact bone, and this phenomenon occurs in the cancellous bone that is directly between the 2 fragments and around their immediate periphery. This makes the bone very strong in this site, and, as a consequence, the trabeculae in the periphery of the callus are no longer necessary to provide strength, so they are gradually resorbed. Eventually, the original line of the bone may be so well restored by this process that the site of the fracture can no longer be felt as a bony thickening.

It should be remembered that these various steps in the remodeling procedure merge into one another and proceed simultaneously to some extent.

**The Healing of Fractures in Which Only One Fragment Remains Alive.** As will be explained in the section on the blood supply of bones, a fracture near an epiphysis sometimes may destroy the blood supply to that epiphysis. A common example of this phenomenon is seen in many fractures of the neck of the femur in older people. In treating this type of fracture, the head of the femur, which is often left without any blood supply, is commonly attached to the neck, which has a blood supply, with some kind of metallic pin. In such a fracture all the callus tissue, which is generated to repair the fracture, must come from the living neck. There is a good amount of cancellous bone in this area, and osteogenic cells from the trabeculae, together with blood vessels from the spaces between the trabeculae, grow slowly into the dead cancellous bone and dead marrow of the head. Here the osteogenic cells become osteoblasts and form new trabeculae that become firmly cemented to the dead trabeculae of the head. This process brings about union between the dead head and the living neck. Gradually, osteogenesis extends farther and farther into the head, and under the best conditions the dead trabeculae of the head are almost all replaced with new living bone. The dead marrow likewise is replaced with living marrow. Curiously enough, the articular cartilage covering the head (even though the head is completely detached from its blood supply) may live through the whole process because it obtains its nourishment from the synovial fluid and not from the blood supply of the head that was destroyed.

**Do Fibroblasts Form Bony Callus?** Some of the ways in which different accounts of fracture healing differ from one another have already been described. Another and most important way in which they differ is related to the extent to which they attribute the formation of bony or cartilaginous callus to the activities of fibroblasts.

In our account we have stressed what we believe is the extremely important role of the osteogenic cells that normally cover and line surfaces. The view has been taken that these cells represent a special family of cells that develop from mesenchyme, and the members of this family inherit an innate capacity to form tissues of the bone and cartilage types in the repair process. However, some investigators do not seem to think that these cells are any different from fibroblasts because of their inheritance but that they only seem different because of their environment, and if fibroblasts were in the same environment (against bone) they would be as competent at forming bone.

The student may be interested in what gave origin to the idea that environment is all-important. This idea seems to have arisen

because pathologists occasionally found that little areas of bone had developed in sites where there were normally no osteogenic cells but in which there was a pathologic deposit of calcium salts such as in the scar of an old abdominal wound, a diseased tonsil or a calcified and sclerotic artery. Here, some reasoned, bone developed from fibroblasts growing up against the calcified material; this provided an environmental stimulus that made the fibroblasts turn into osteoblasts. Then Huggins made the very interesting discovery that transplanting the mucosa of the urinary bladder of a dog to its abdominal wall would cause bone to form in the wall; this seemed to be a true example of experimentally induced bone formation. Since then many experimenters have tried many means to obtain extracts or materials, calcified and otherwise, that on injection into different soft tissues would induce bone formation.

There is no question about the fact that bone sometimes develops in sites far removed from the skeleton. However, this does not prove that fibroblasts are as competent at forming bone as the cells that cover and line bone surfaces. Indeed, such examples of heteroplastic bone formation as occur are to be explained more readily, we think, by the presence of occasional undifferentiated mesenchymal cells in these tissues that are led to differentiate along the osteogenic-osteoblastic line than by assuming that any fibroblasts can form bone under the right stimulus.

We shall discuss this matter somewhat further when we consider bone transplantation. Here, however, we should like to point out that many investigators have shown that if they strip the covering and lining cells from bone, fractures almost never become repaired properly. Furthermore, even if the periosteum is not disturbed, if there is a sufficiently large gap between the fragments of a fracture, so that the collars of osteogenic cells from the fragments take too long a time to meet and fuse, fibroblasts from nearby tissues may grow through the gap between the fragments and fill it in, not with bone, but with ordinary dense connective tissue; this gives rise to a fibrous union which, of course, does not provide a proper repair. So, despite the fact that bone sometimes forms in ordinary connective tissue, we think it is unjustifiable to reason from this fact that fibroblasts can repair bone as effectively as the covering and lining cells of bone. Furthermore, we think that in our present state of knowledge it would be calamitous for an orthopedic surgeon to put his trust in fibroblasts and induction phenomena for bone repair instead of in the heredity of the covering and lining cells of bone.

## THE TRANSPLANTATION OF BONE

Bone transplants often are used when fractured bones fail to heal by the ordinary method. They are also used when substantial parts of a bone are destroyed by accident or disease. They are useful in permitting certain reconstructions of the face to be made by plastic surgeons. They are sometimes employed to bring about bony union between 2 bones separated by a joint which has become diseased. Indeed, the transplantation of bone has become a common surgical operation.

The fate of a piece of compact bone that is transplanted in the body is a matter about which there has been considerable dispute. In the earlier days of bone grafting, it was believed by many who utilized the procedure that transplanted compact bone continues to live in its new site. More recently, however, it has become fairly generally realized that most of the osteocytes of a piece of compact bone that is transplanted die, and that sooner or later the dead transplanted bone is replaced by new bone.

When a graft of compact bone is cut, it is, of course, severed from its blood supply. When it is fitted into its new position, its osteocytes, if they are to live, must obtain all their oxygen and nourishment through canaliculi. Hence, the only osteocytes that survive after a piece of compact bone is transplanted are those that are close enough to functioning capillaries to permit the canalicular mechanism to function. This means that at best only a few surface osteocytes survive in transplanted bone.

However, the osteogenic cells of the periosteum and such endosteal cells as are present on a transplant, being situated at surfaces, are more likely to be sufficiently well bathed in tissue fluid to survive than the osteocytes within the transplant. Indeed, some of the covering and lining cells of compact bone do survive and grow if they are in a suitable

environment, and they contribute toward osteogenesis, which, however, comes mostly from the bones into which the transplant is inserted (Fig. 18-50).

If most of the osteocytes of a transplanted piece of bone die, it might be thought that a bone transplant would be of little use. However, bone transplants are of the greatest use even if most of their constituent cells do die. Bone transplants are placed so that each of their ends extends well into living bone tissue of the 2 fragments they bridge. Cells from the osteogenic layer of the periosteum, the endosteum and the marrow of the host bone proliferate and push out toward the transplant, forming new trabeculae of bone (Fig. 18-50), and, in some instances, cartilage. After a time, the bony trabeculae, increasing in length and breadth by new bone being deposited on their surfaces, reach the transplant and unite with it (Fig. 18-50). It is to be understood that new bone deposited on dead bone becomes firmly cemented to it, as the new bone that is deposited on the calcified cartilage on the diaphysial side of the epiphysial plate becomes firmly cemented to the cartilage. This step in the history of a compact bone transplant is illustrated in Figure 18-50 and shows that new trabeculae from the host have firmly united with the dead bone of the transplant. It is also obvious in this illustration that the osteogenic cells and the osteoblasts from which these new trabeculae arose came from some little distance behind the dead edge of the graft bed.

After the transplant is united to its host it must be resorbed slowly and replaced with new bone. Resorption occurs in 2 general sites: (1) on the outer surfaces of the transplant in between areas where trabeculae of new bone have become cemented to it, and (2) on the inner surfaces of haversian canals (Fig. 18-50, bottom).

It is to be understood that functioning blood vessels are as necessary for the resorption of bone as for the deposition and the maintenance of the life of bone. Accordingly, little resorption can occur from the inner surfaces of the haversian canals of a transplant until there are functioning blood vessels in these haversian canals. Commonly it takes many weeks for new blood vessels to grow into the haversian canals of a compact bone graft.

# HISTORY OF A COMPACT BONE GRAFT

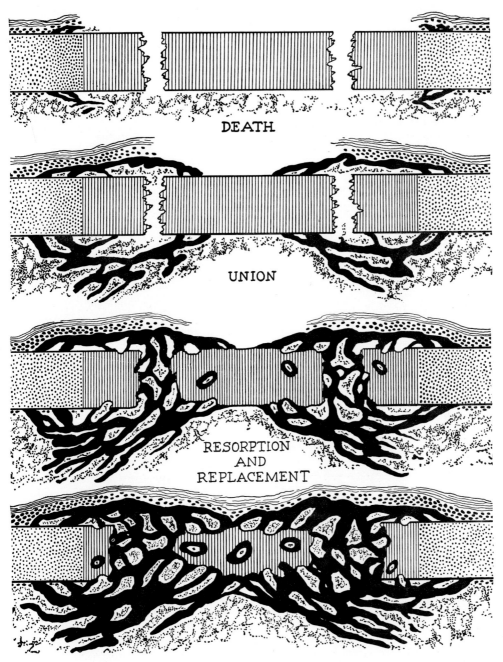

DEATH

UNION

RESORPTION
AND
REPLACEMENT

Fig. 18-50. Diagrams to show the steps in the history of a block of cortex of a bone which is cut free from its blood supply and placed back into the defect its removal caused. The periosteal surface is above and the marrow surface is below in each of the 4 pictures. Pre-existing bone still alive is shown in medium stipple, dead bone is lined and new bone is black. (Ham, A. W.: J. Bone Joint Surg. *34-A*:701)

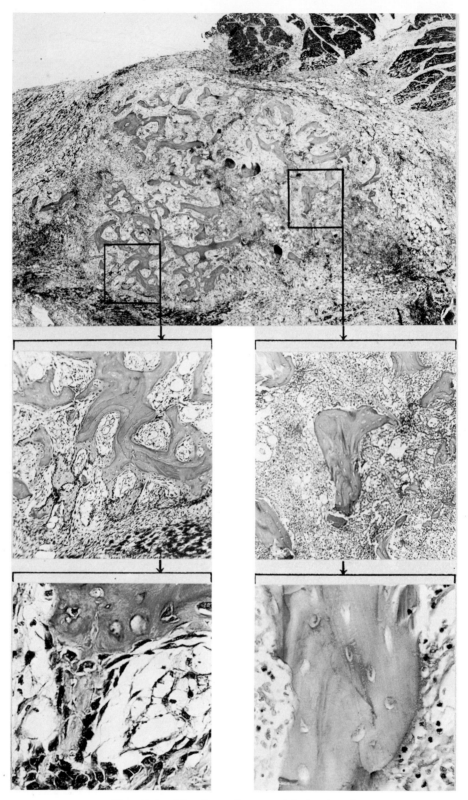

Fig. 18-51. (*Caption at bottom of facing page.*)

The growth of new blood vessels into the haversian canals of the transplant is associated with both the resorption of dead bone from the canals, which widens them (Fig. 18-50), and also with the deposition of new bone on the sides of the canals, which narrows them again (Fig. 18-50). The same 2 processes operate simultaneously on the exterior of the transplant and also at the dead edges of the graft bed, so before long the transplant and the edge of the bed both become a conglomerate of living and dead bone (Fig. 18-50, *bottom*). Eventually, nearly all, if not all, of the dead bone is resorbed with new bone being substituted for it, but this takes considerable time because the dead bone always must be resorbed from a *free* surface and the new bone deposited on a *free* surface. This has been termed the "creeping replacement" of a transplant.

As the dead bone of a compact bone transplant is irregularly eroded at different sites around its outer surface, and as its haversian canals become opened up by resorptive processes occurring within them, it tends to resemble cancellous bone as much as it does compact bone. But the deposition of new bone on all these surfaces eventually takes precedence over resorptive phenomena, so it once more begins to resemble compact bone, thus providing another illustration of the fact that the filling in of spaces surrounded by trabeculae converts cancellous bone to compact bone.

## TRANSPLANTS OF CANCELLOUS BONE

It might be thought that the bone cells in a transplanted cancellous trabecula would have a much better chance of surviving transplantation than the bone cells in a block of compact bone. No bone cell in a small cancellous trabecula is very far away from a free surface, and, when a trabecula is transplanted, the free surface conceivably could be bathed in tissue fluid. But the canalicular mechanism is evidently so inefficient that even though a cancellous trabecula is transplanted into an area close to functioning capillaries, nearly all the bone cells of the trabecula die. Gordon and the author, in an extensive experiment, followed the day-to-day appearance of autogenous cancellous fragments transplanted into both bone defects and muscle and have concluded that, for all practical purposes, the cells in transplanted cancellous fragments fail to survive transplantation (Fig. 18-51) and hence that the ultimate fate of the substance of the transplanted bone is resorption.

Although the osteocytes of cancellous fragments survive transplantation little better than the cells of compact bone, the possibilities with regard to the survival and the growth of the covering and the lining cells of cancellous fragments is much greater than those of compact bone. The first reason for this is that cancellous trabeculae are completely covered with osteogenic cells and osteoblasts, and since the trabeculae themselves are small, there is a relatively high proportion of surface cells to bone cells in cancellous bone. This is in contrast with compact bone (and in particular with chips from adult compact bone) wherein the proportion of surface cells to bone cells is very low. Accordingly, vast numbers of surface cells are available when cancellous trabeculae are transplanted, and since the surface cells cover all aspects of the trabecu-

Fig. 18-51. The upper picture is a very low-power photomicrograph of a site in a dog's muscle where cancellous fragments obtained from the crest of the ilium had been planted 7 days before. The 2 lower left pictures are higher-power views of an area where the transplanted fragments were situated close to capillaries in living tissue and hence bathed in reasonably fresh tissue fluid. Under these conditions, although the osteocytes of the transplanted fragments have died and left empty lacunae, as may be seen in the left middle picture, the covering and lining osteogenic cells and osteoblasts have survived and have grown toward the capillaries in the living tissue. Osteoblasts with their basophilic cytoplasm may be seen in the lower left picture. The 2 lower right pictures are higher-power representations of fragments transplanted to a site in the muscle where they were far removed from living capillaries and hence from a fresh supply of tissue fluid. Under these conditions both the osteocytes within the fragments and the covering and lining cells of the fragments all have died. (Gordon, S., and Ham, A. W.: The Gallie Addresses, Toronto, Univ. Toronto Press)

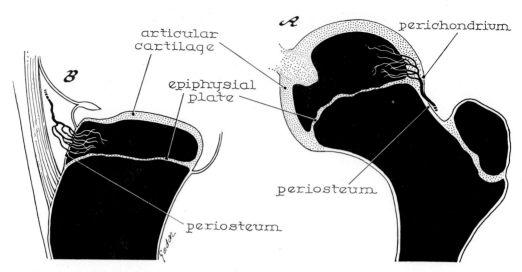

Fig. 18-52. Diagram to demonstrate that when an epiphysis is entirely covered by articular cartilage (*A*) (*right side*), its blood vessels must enter it by traversing the perichondrium at the periphery of the epiphysial plate. This makes them vulnerable to rupture after epiphysial displacement. By contrast, when an epiphysis is only partly covered by articular cartilage (*B*) (*left side*), its blood vessels enter it in such a way that separation could occur without serious damage to them. (Dale, G. G., and Harris, W. R.: J. Bone Joint Surg. *40-B*:116)

lae, they face in every direction and so are able to take advantage of such nutritive tissue fluid as may exist in the site to which they are transplanted (Fig. 18-51, *left*).

It is to be understood, of course, that even without any of the surface cells of cancellous fragments surviving transplantation, cancellous fragments serve a very useful purpose in bone defects. This is because they stimulate the osteogenic cells, the osteoblasts and the undifferentiated marrow cells of the host bone to grow into their midst and lay down bone on many of their surfaces. By this means the dead transplanted fragments become incorporated into a new network of cancellous bone that connects them with the bone of the host. However, the dead fragments do not persist indefinitely in such a network, but are resorbed.

In addition to stimulating and conducting osteogenesis, cancellous fragments can perform another function under very suitable circumstances—that of setting up new centers of osteogenesis. They can do this if they are transplanted into living tissue where there is a sufficiently good capillary bed to provide their surface cells with adequate tissue fluid.

In order to prove that their surface cells can survive transplantation and give rise to new bone, the common experiment performed is to transplant them into muscle where there are no other cells of a bony origin to confuse the issue. Gordon and the author have done this several times and have found repeatedly that when a mass of cancellous chips is placed in a muscle, the surface cells of the fragments that are around the periphery of the mass of fragments, close to functioning capillaries in the muscle, live and give rise to new bone which tends to grow toward the capillaries of the muscle (Fig. 18-51, *left*).

It could be argued that cancellous or compact bone chips have still another function—that of inducing bone formation by metaplasia from fibroblasts. The author and Gordon have investigated this matter by studying the fate of thrice-fast-frozen-and-thawed autogenous cancellous fragments transplanted into muscle. In contrast with untreated fragments, about which some new bone formed in each animal, no new bone was found to develop in association with any of the thrice-frozen-and-thawed fragments. Since the repeated fast-freezing of a tissue probably destroys its cells by physical means and does not alter its chemical constituents nearly as much as other procedures which destroy cells, our experiment shows, we think, that the bone that forms around cancellous fragments transplanted into muscle originates from the covering cells of the chips and not from fibroblasts by metaplasia. This experiment, like many others, suggests that those who seek osteogenesis should, in our present state of knowledge, continue to put their trust in the cells that cover and line bone surfaces and their close relatives in the bone marrow rather than on cells such as fibroblasts that are specialized for other functions.

## THE BLOOD SUPPLY OF A LONG BONE AND ITS VARIOUS PARTS

First we shall consider the blood supply of a long bone that is growing in length because of growth activity in the epiphysial plate. We shall first consider the blood supply of the epiphysis and the epiphysial plate, and then the blood supply of the diaphysis.

**Blood Supply of Epiphyses.** Dale and Harris point out that in growing bones there are two kinds of epiphyses in the sense that in one kind the articular cartilage is continuous with that of the epiphysial plate as is shown in the picture on the right in Figure 18-52, and in the other kind the articular cartilage is not continuous with the epiphysial plate, as is shown in the left picture in Figure 18-52. In the first kind the blood vessels that supply the epiphysis have to travel through the site where the cartilage of the epiphysial plate is continuous with articular cartilage in order to reach the marrow cavity of the epiphysis (right side in Figure 18-52). In the second kind of arrangement, shown on the left in Figure 18-52, the blood vessels that enter the epiphysis do not have to pass through articular or epiphysial plate cartilage to enter the epiphysis; instead they pierce the perichondrial-like tissue that covers one side of the epiphysis. These two types of epiphysis behave differently if a separation occurs across the epiphysial plate, as will now be described.

Epiphysial separations sometimes occur in children. If some shearing or other force oper-

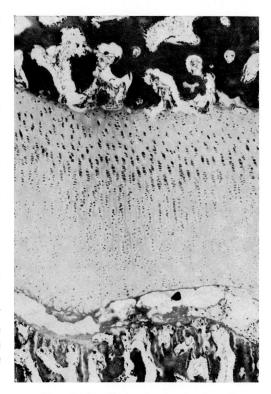

Fig. 18-53. Photomicrograph of section or radial epiphysial plate of a rabbit 10 days after the epiphysis with the epiphysial plate was separated from the diaphysis. Note that the line of separation occurs across the zone of hypertrophied cells. During the 10 days that followed the separation, the plate has grown greatly in thickness which shows that its source of nutrition was provided from the epiphysis by the vessels illustrated in Figure 18-54. (Dale, G. G., and Harris, W. R.: J. Bone Joint Surg. *40-B*:118)

ates to cause an epiphysial separation, the separation, as has been shown by both Haas and Harris, generally occurs in the zone of hypertrophied cartilage cells of the plate as is shown in Figure 18-53, for this is the weakest part of the plate. If this happens in an epiphysis of the type illustrated on the right side of Figure 18-52, the blood vessels that are conducted through the cartilage at the edge of the plate are likely to be ruptured. On the other hand, if a separation occurs in the type illustrated at the left of Figure 18-52, the epiphysis still retains its blood supply.

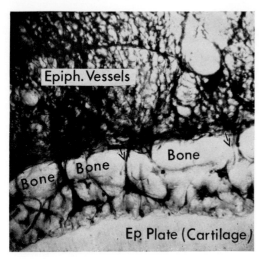

Epiph. Vessels

Bone    Bone    Bone    Bone

Ep. Plate (Cartilage)

FIG. 18-54. Photomicrograph of longitudinal section that passes through epiphysial plate and part of an epiphysis of a growing long bone of a rabbit. The arteries supplying the epiphysis were injected with an opaque material and the illustration shows that arterial vessels from the epiphysis penetrate the bone that lies between the marrow of the epiphysis and the epiphysial plate of cartilage to supply nutriment to the epiphysial border of the epiphysial plate. These vessels can support the life and growth of the plate if it is separated from the diaphysis. (Salter, R. M., and Harris, W. R.: J. Bone Joint Surg. *45-A*:587)

Harris and Hobson showed that the upper femoral epiphysis is of the type illustrated on the right of Figure 18-52, and that separation of an epiphysis of this type, by experimental means, leads to the death of the detached fragment. Dale and Harris, however, have shown that the epiphysis of the type illustrated at the left of Figure 18-52 may be detached without death of the fragment occurring. (Fig. 18-53). Furthermore, the experimental detachment of this type of epiphysis gave valuable information regarding the source from which the proliferating cells of an epiphysial plate receive their nourishment, as will next be described.

**The Nutrition of the Epiphysial Plate.** Since the diaphysial side of an epiphysial plate abounds in capillary loops which are disposed between the forming trabeculae of

bone in that region, and which penetrate into the zone of calcifying cartilage of the plate, it might be assumed that these capillaries of metaphysial origin provided the nourishment necessary for the cell division that occurs toward the epiphysial side of the plate and for the synthesis of such intercellular substance that occurs in association with the chondrocytes in a growing plate. However, as has been stressed by the author, the calcification of the intercellular substance of cartilage makes it much less able to serve as a medium for diffusion, and hence nourishment might have difficulty in penetrating from diaphysial capillaries through the zone of calcified cartilage to reach the zone of proliferating cells. Moreover, inspection of Figure 18-31 will show that there are on the diaphysial side of the layer of epiphysial bone that abuts on the epiphysial plate, in the zone labeled *resting cartilage,* canals that contain capillaries. These have been studied by injection methods by Salter and Harris, one of whose preparations is seen in Figure 18-54; this shows branches from epiphysial vessels penetrating the bone of the epiphysis to supply the zone of "resting" cartilage cells of the plate. That nourishment from these capillaries diffuses through the remainder of the plate to nourish the cells of its various living layers was shown by Dale and Harris; for they found that if the blood supply of the epiphysis remained intact, epiphysial plates could be separated from the metaphysis (and hence from metaphysial blood vessels) and yet the separated plates would continue to grow in thickness (Fig. 18-53). These experiments and others show clearly that the cartilage of the epiphysial plate obtains the nutriment it requires for growth from its epiphysial side and probably principally from the small vessels seen in the canals, immediately on the diaphysial side of the bone of the epiphysis illustrated in Figures 18-31 and 18-54. Some nourishment may also diffuse in from the periphery of the plate.

## THE BLOOD SUPPLY OF THE METAPHYSIS OF A GROWING BONE

1. *The Nutrient Artery or Arteries.* It will be recalled that a diaphysial center of ossification is set up in a cartilage model of a

developing bone by a periosteal bud or buds that invade the cartilage. The blood vessels of the periosteal bud or buds become larger, as development proceeds, to become eventually the nutrient artery and vein of the diaphysis. The diaphysis of some bones, for example, the femur, normally has several nutrient arteries, while the diaphysis of others, for example, the tibia, has only one.

2. *The Metaphysial and the Epiphysial Vessels.* The segment of a long bone occupied by an epiphysial disk and by the adjacent newly forming trabeculae on the diaphysial side of the disk is called a *metaphysis*. In many bones, as is illustrated in Figure 18-36, the shaft, as it passes from the diaphysis into a metaphysis, widens to become more or less funnel-shaped. Since the trabeculae of the metaphysis are parallel with the longitudinal axis of the bone, they form acute angles with the side of the funnel (Fig. 18-36). Likewise, the longitudinally disposed spaces between the trabeculae also form angles with the sides of the funnel, so they provide ready communication between the interior and the exterior of the bone (Fig. 18-36). Therefore, at this site, blood vessels from the exterior of the bone could easily enter the interior of the bone, and it seems probable that the many small vessels that enter the shaft in this region, that constitute the metaphysial vessels, use this route of entry.

3. *The Periosteal Vessels.* It has been explained already that, because of the way that bone grows in width, periosteal vessels become successively buried in the cortex of the diaphysis as central vessels of haversian systems, and they retain their connection with the periosteum or more superficial haversian vessels through Volkmann's canals (Figs. 18-39, 18-40 and 18-41).

**Changes That Occur When Growth Is Over.** After growth in length is over, the cartilage of epiphysial disks is resorbed and replaced by bony trabeculae. The spaces between the latter permit ready communication between the interior of the epiphysis and the metaphysis. Under these conditions, anastomoses between the epiphysial and the metaphysial vessels occur (this has been investigated by Trueta and Harrison in the head of the femur in man), and the complex of epiphysial and metaphysial vessels that enter and leave the bone in this region then generally are referred to as the *metaphysial-epiphysial* vessels.

**Results of Experiments Indicating Respective Roles of the 3 Sets of Vessels in Adult Animals.** Johnson's studies revealed that the nutrient artery will maintain the life of the marrow and the inner two thirds of the cortex of the diaphysis. Moreover, he showed that there are excellent anastomoses between the branches of the nutrient artery and the metaphysial vessels, and that the metaphysial-epiphysial complex of vessels maintain the life of the marrow and the inner half of the bone of the cortex (there are some results that conflict with this latter finding). The periosteal vessels alone maintain the life of only the outer half of the cortex of the bone. De Hass and Macnab point out that a nutrient vein is generally smaller than its companion artery, and this, as well as certain of their experimental results, suggests that there is normally some flow of the blood that reaches the marrow from the nutrient artery out through the cortical veins to the periosteum. More recently, Brookes and Harrison have reported that the normal flow of blood in the cortex is from the medullary arteries out through the cortex to the capillaries of the deep periosteal layer and from there into veins. However, if there is a lack of blood flow in the medullary arteries, the flow through the cortex can be reversed, with blood from the periosteal vessels flowing through the vessels of the cortex to the medullary cavity. This reversal of blood flow, which occurs when the medullary circulation is impaired, has been demonstrated in ischemic bones in man and experimentally in bones of rabbits by Brookes.

**The Blood Vessels of Haversian Systems (Osteons) of Compact Bone.** The arrangement of haversian systems in compact bone is very complex and probably becomes increasingly complex as new ones are substituted for old ones in the slow remodeling of compact bone that takes place during life. Jonathan Cohen and William H. Harris have made a 3-dimensional study of haversian systems and their anastomoses in compact bone, and their report should be read for details about their sizes and the courses they pursue.

As has been described previously, the osteocytes in the lamellae of any haversian system receive their nutriment through anastomosing canaliculi which finally extend to the central canal of the system. Since the distance over which nutriment can be transported along canaliculi is limited, it is obvious that haversian systems cannot be of a very great diameter without the osteocytes in their outer lamellae suffering from a lack of nourishment. In the author's experience, haversian systems are commonly about one fifth of a millimeter in diameter so that no osteocyte is farther away than around one tenth of a millimeter from the vessel or vessels that are present in haversian canals. In completed haversian systems there may be only a single vessel, as is shown on the left in Figure 18-55, or two vessels, as shown on the right in Figure 18-55.

The vessel in the left is of the order of a large capillary, while those on the left are a pre-capillary arteriole and a beginning venule, respectively.

The author knows of no precise information regarding the number of anastomoses between the vessels of adjacent haversian systems. Since many systems have only a single vessel, it follows that any interruption to the flow in a single vessel would be reflected in effects extending from the site of interruption to a site where that vessel anastomosed with one that was functioning. Accordingly, any blockage or break in a haversian vessel can result in the death of the cells of the system over a considerable length of the system. This is shown clearly in fractures, for osteocytes of many haversian systems that course

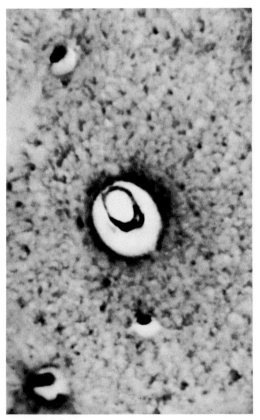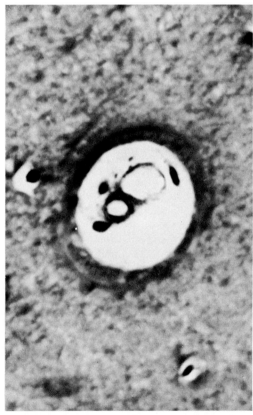

FIG. 18-55. Photomicrographs (× 800) of blood vessels in haversian canals as they appear in cross sections of the radius of a dog. (Left) The canal in the center contains a single vessel which is a large capillary. (Right) The canal in the center contains 2 vessels, a very small arteriole and a very small venule. The stippled appearance of the bone intercellular substance is due to the presence of canaliculi that are cut in cross section and obliquely. A few bone cells in lacunae may be seen. (Ham, A. W.: J. Bone Joint Surg. 34-A:701)

through the site of the fracture die for some distance to either side of the break (Figs. 18-47 and 18-48).

## REFERENCES

### COMPREHENSIVE GENERAL REFERENCES ON BONE

Bourne, G. H.: The Biochemistry and Physiology of Bone, New York, Acad. Press, 1956.

Weinmann, J. P., and Sicher, H.: Bone and Bones: Fundamentals of Bone Biology, ed. 2, St. Louis, Mosby, 1955.

### OTHER GENERAL REFERENCES ON BONE

Greep, R. O., et al.: Recent advances in the study of the structure, composition and growth of mineralized tissues, Ann. N. Y. Acad. Sci. 60: 543, 1955.

Ham, A. W.: Some histophysiological problems peculiar to calcified tissue, J. Bone Joint Surg. 34-A:701, 1952.

Jackson, S. F.: Connective tissue cells in Brachet, J., and Mirsky, A. E. (eds.): The Cell, vol. 6, p. 387, New York, Acad. Press, 1964.

McLean, F. C., and Urist, M. R.: Bone: An Introduction to the Physiology of Skeletal Tissue, Chicago, Univ. Chicago Press, 1956.

Stein, Irvin, Stein, R. O., and Beller, M. L.: Living Bone in Health and Disease, Philadelphia, Lippincott, 1955.

Wolstenholme, G. E. W., and O'Connor, C. M.: Ciba Foundation Symposium on Bone Structure and Metabolism, London, Churchill, 1956.

### SPECIAL REFERENCES ON SPECIAL TECHNICS, EXCEPT ELECTRON MICROSCOPY, USED FOR THE STUDY OF BONE

Amprino, Rodolfo: Uptake of S$^{35}$ in the differentiation and growth of cartilage and bone in Bone Structure and Metabolism, London, Churchill, 1956.

Armstrong, W. D.: Radiotracer studies of hard tissues, Ann. N. Y. Acad. Sci. 60:670, 1955.

Axelrod, D. J.: An improved method for cutting undecalcified bone sections and its application to radio-autography, Anat. Rec. 98:19, 1947.

Bélanger, L. F.: Autoradiographic studies of the formation of the organic matrix of cartilage bone and the tissues of teeth in Bone Structure and Metabolism, London, Churchill, 1956.

————: Autoradiographic visualization in vitro exchange in teeth, bones, and other tissues, under various conditions, J. Dent. Res. 32:3, 1953.

Bélanger, L. F., and Leblond, C. P.: Method for locating radioactive elements in tissue by covering histological sections with photographic emulsion, Endocrinology 39:8, 1946.

Bevelander, G., and Johnson, P. L.: A histochemical study of membrane bone, Anat. Rec. 108: 1, 1951.

Bohatirchuk, F.: Medico-biologic research by microradiography: Theory and technique in Clark, G. L. (ed.): The Encyclopedia Microscopy, p. 591, New York, Reinhold, 1961.

Comar, C. L., Lotz, W. E., and Boyd, G. A.: Autoradiographic studies of calcium, phosphorus and strontium distribution in the bones of the growing pig, Am. J. Anat. 90:113, 1952.

Davies, D. V., and Young, L.: The distribution of radioactive sulphur (S$^{35}$) in the fibrous tissues, cartilages and bones of the rat following its administration in the form of inorganic sulphate, J. Anat. 88:174, 1954.

Davies, H. G., and Engstrom, A.: Interferometric and x-ray absorption studies of bone tissue, Exp. Cell Res. 7:243, 1954.

Dempster, W .T., and Liddicoat, R. T.: Compact bone as a nonisotropic material, Am. J. Anat. 91:331, 1952.

Fell, Honor B.: Skeletal development in tissue culture in The Biochemistry and Physiology of Bone, New York, Acad. Press. 1956.

Gomori, G.: The distribution of phosphatase in normal organs and tissues. J. Cell. Comp. Physiol. 17:71, 1941.

Leblond, C. P., Wilkinson, G. W., Bélanger, L. F., and Robichon, J.: See under references on Growth, etc.

Morse, A., and Greep, R. O.: Effect of abnormal metabolic states upon the histochemical distribution of alkaline phosphatase in the tibia of the albino rat, Anat. Rec. 111:193, 1951.

Pritchard, J. J.: A cytological and histochemical study of bone and cartilage formation in the rat, J. Anat. 86:259, 1952.

Sissons, H. A., Jowsey, J., and Stewart, L.: Quantitative microradiography of bone tissue, Proc. 2nd International Symposium on X-ray Microscopy and X-ray Microanalysis, Stockholm, 1959.

Sognnaes, R. F.: Microstructure and histochemical characteristics of the mineralized tissues, Ann. N. Y. Acad. Sci. 60:545, 1955.

Trautz, O. R.: X-ray diffraction of biological and synthetic apatites, Ann. N. Y. Acad. Sci. 60:696, 1955.

### SPECIAL REFERENCES ON THE DEVELOPMENT OF BONE

Ascenzi, A., and Benedetti, L.: An electron microscope study of the foetal membranous ossification, Acta anat. Basel 37:370, 1962.

Bassett, A. L.: Current concepts of bone formation, J. Bone Joint Surg. 44-A:1217, 1962.

Bertelson, A.: Experimental investigation into post-foetal osteogenesis, Acta orthop. scand. *15*:139, 1944.

Bevelander, G., and Johnson, P. L.: An histochemical study of the development of membrane bone, Anat. Rec. *108*:1, 1950.

Fell, H. B.: Skeletal development in tissue culture *in* The Biochemistry and Physiology of Bone, New York, Acad. Press, 1956.

Felts, W. J. L.: The prenatal development of the human femur, Am. J. Anat. *94*:1, 1954.

Gardner, Ernest: Osteogenesis in the human embryo and fetus *in* The Biochemistry and Physiology of Bone, New York, Acad. Press, 1956.

Ham, A. W., and Gordon, S. D.: The origin of bone that forms in association with cancellous chips transplanted into muscle, Brit. J. Plast. Surg. *5*:154, 1952.

Huggins, C. B.: The formation of bone under the influence of epithelium of the urinary tract, Arch. Surg. *22*:377, 1931.

Jackson, S. F.: The structure of developing bone in the embryonic fowl, Proc. Roy. Soc. London, s.B. *146*:270, 1957.

Johnson, F. R., and McMinn, R. M. H.: Transitional epithelium and osteogenesis, J. Anat. *90*:106, 1956.

Lacroix, P.: L'os et les méchanismes de la formation, J. physiol. Paris *43*:385, 1951.

————: Recent investigations on the growth of bone, Nature *156*:576, 1945.

Levander, Gustav: Tissue induction, Nature *155*:148, 1945.

Pritchard, J. J.: The osteoblast *in* The Biochemistry and Physiology of Bone, New York, Acad. Press, 1956.

Strangeways, T. S. P., and Fell, H. B.: Experimental studies on the differentiation of embryonic tissues growing *in vivo* and *in vitro*, Proc. Roy. Soc. London *99*:340, 1926.

Urist, M. R., and McLean, F. C.: Osteogenic potency and new bone formation by induction in transplants to the anterior chamber of the eye, J. Bone Joint Surg. *34-A*:443, 1952.

SPECIAL REFERENCES ON THE GROWTH
OF BONE

Bhaskar, S. N.: Growth pattern of the rat mandible from 13 days insemination age to 30 days after birth, Am. J. Anat. *92*:1, 1953.

Brash, J. C.: Some problems in the growth and developmental mechanics of bone. Edinburgh M.J. *41*:305, 365, 1934.

Frandsen, A. M., Nelson, M. M., Sulon, E., Becks, H., and Evans, H. M.: The effects of various levels of dietary protein on skeletal growth and endochondral ossification in young rats, Anat. Rec. *119*:247, 1954.

Gans, B. J., and Sarnat, B. G.: Sutural facial growth of the Macaca rhesus monkey: a gross and serial roentgenographic study by means of metallic implants, Am. J. Orthodont. *37*:927, 1951.

Giblin, N., and Alley, A.: Studies in skull growth: Coronal suture fixation, Anat. Rec. *88*:143, 1944.

Haines, R. W.: Cartilage canals, J. Anat. *68*:45, 1933.

Ham, A W.: Some histophysiological problems peculiar to calcified tissues, J. Bone Joint Surg. *34-A*:701, 1952.

————: The variability of the planes of cell division in the cartilage columns of the growing epiphyseal plate, Anat. Rec. *51*:125, 1931.

Harris, H. A.: Bone Growth in Health and Disease, London, Oxford, 1933.

Lacroix, P.: The Organization of Bones, translated from the amended French edition by Stewart Gilder, New York, Blakiston Division of McGraw-Hill, 1951.

————: The histological remodelling of the adult bone: an autoradiographic study *in* Bone Structure and Metabolism, London, Churchill, 1956.

Leblond, C. P., and Greulich, Richard C.: Autoradiographic studies of bone formation and growth *in* The Biochemistry and Physiology of Bone, New York, Acad. Press, 1956.

Leblond, C. P., Wilkinson, G. W., Bélanger, L. F., and Robichon, J.: Radio-autographic visualization of bone formation in the rat, Am. J. Anat. *86*:289, 1950.

Moss, M. L.: Growth of the calvaria in the rat; the determination of osseous morphology, Am. J. Anat. *94*:333, 1954.

Murray, P. D. F.: Bones, A Study of the Development and Structure of the Vertebrate Skeleton, London, Cambridge, 1936.

Scott, B. L., and Pease, D. C.: Electron microscopy of the epiphyseal apparatus, Anat. Rec. *126*:465, 1956.

Sisson, H. A.: Experimental determination of rate of longitudinal bone growth, J. Anat. *87*:228, 1953.

————: The growth of bone *in* The Biochemistry and Physiology of Bone, New York, Acad. Press, 1956.

SPECIAL REFERENCES ON THE CHEMICAL
COMPONENTS AND THE STRUCTURE OF
BONE INCLUDING FINE STRUCTURE

Baker, S. L.: Introduction of the pathology of bone *in* X-ray Diagnosis, ed. 2, Philadelphia, Saunders, 1952.

Cameron, D. A.: The fine structure of osteoblasts in the metaphysis of the tibia of the young rat, J. Biophys. Biochem. Cytol. *9*:583, 1961.

Carlstrom, D., and Engstrom, A.: Ultrastructure and distribution of mineral salts in bone tissue *in* The Biochemistry and Physiology of Bone, New York, Acad. Press, 1956.

Dudley, H. R., and Spiro, David: The fine structure of bone, J. Biophys. Biochem. Cytol. *11*:627, 1961.

Eastoe, J. E.: The organic matrix of bone *in* The Biochemistry and Physiology of Bone, New York, Acad. Press, 1956.

Enstrom, Arne: Structure of bone from the anatomical to the molecular level *in* Bone Structure and Metabolism, London, Churchill, 1956.

Hancox, N. M., and Boothroyd, B.: Ultrastructure of bone formation and resorption *in* Clark, J. M. (ed.): Modern Trends in Orthopaedics, vol. 4, Science of Fractures, p. 26, London, Butterworth, 1963.

Jackson, S. F.: The fine structure of developing bone in the embryonic fowl, Proc. Roy. Soc., London, s.B *146*:270, 1957.

Meyer, Karl: The mucopolysaccharides of bone *in* Bone Structure and Metabolism, London, Churchill, 1956.

Neuman, W. F., and Neuman, M. W.: The nature of the mineral phase of bone, Chem. Rev. *52*:1, 1953.

Pritchard, J. J.: General anatomy and histology of bone *in* The Biochemistry and Physiology of Bone, New York, Acad. Press, 1956.

Robinson, R. A.: Electron microscopy of the primary spongiosa of the metaphysis at the distal end of the femur in the newborn infant, J. Bone Joint Surg. *40-A*:687, 1958.

Robinson, R. A., and Cameron, D. A.: Electron microscopy of cartilage and bone matrix at the distal epiphyseal line of the femur in the newborn infant, J. Biophys. Biochem. Cytol. (Supp.) *2*:253, 1956.

Robinson, R. A., and Watson, M. L.: Collagen-crystal relationships in bone as seen in the electron microscope, Anat. Rec. *114*:383, 1952.

———: Crystal-collagen relationships in bone as observed in the electron microscope: III. Crystal and collagen morphology as a function of age, Ann. N. Y. Acad. Sci. *60*:596, 1955.

Robson, R.: Bone phosphatase, Ergebn. Enzymforsch. *1*:280, 1932.

———: The possible significance of hexosephosphoric esters in ossification, Biochem. J. *17*:286, 1923.

Ruth, E. B.: Bone studies: I. Fibrillar structure of adult human bone, Am. J. Anat. *80*:35, 1947.

———: Bone studies: II. An experimental study of the haversian type vascular channels, Am. J. Anat. *93*:429, 1953.

———: Gross demonstration of the vascular channels in bone, Anat. Rec. *98*:59, 1947.

Sheldon, H.: Electron microscope observations on rickets, Bull. Johns Hopkins Hosp. *105*:52, 1959.

Stack, M. V.: The chemical nature of the organic matrix of bone, dentin and enamel, Ann. N. Y. Acad. Sci. *60*:585, 1955.

Watson, M. L., and Robinson, R. A.: Collagen-crystal relationships in bone: II. Electron microscope study of basic calcium phosphate crystals, Am. J. Anat. *93*:25, 1953.

GENERAL REFERENCE ON RESORPTION

Sognnaes, R. F. (ed.): Mechanisms of Hard Tissue Destruction, Washington, D. C., Am. Assoc. Adv. Sci., 1963.

SPECIAL REFERENCES ON THE RESORPTION OF BONE AND ON OSTEOCLASTS

Arey, L.: Phagocytosis by osteoclasts, Anat. Rec. *13*:269, 1917.

Arnold, J. S., and Jee, W. S. S.: Bone growth and osteoclastic activity as indicated by radioautographic distribution of plutonium, Am. J. Anat. *101*:367, 1957.

Barnicott, N. A.: The local action of the parathyroid and other tissues on bone in intracerebral grafts, J. Anat. *82*:233, 1948.

Bhaskar, S. N., Mohammed, C. I., and Weinmann, J. P.: A morphological and histochemical study of osteoclasts, J. Bone Joint Surg. *38-A*:1335, 1956.

Chang, Hwei-Ya: Grafts of parathyroid and other tissues to bone, Anat. Rec. *111*:23, 1951.

Cooley, L. M., and Goss, R. J.: The effects of transplantation and x-irradiation on the repair of fractured bones, Am. J. Anat. *102*:167, 1957.

Dodds, G. S.: Osteoclasts and cartilage removal in endochondrial ossification of certain mammals, Am. J. Anat. *50*:97, 1932.

Greep, R. O.: A hereditary absence of the incisor teeth, J. Hered. *32*:397, 1941.

Ham, A. W., and Gordon, S. D.: Nature of the so-called striated border of osteoclasts, Anat. Rec. *112*:147, 1952.

Hancox, N. M.: The osteoclast, Biol. Rev. *24*:448, 1949.

———: The osteoclast *in* The Biochemistry and Physiology of Bone, New York, Acad. Press, 1956.

Hancox, N. M., and Boothroyd, B.: Structure-function relationships in the osteoclast *in* Sognnaes, R. F. (ed.): Mechanisms of Hard Tissue Destruction, p. 497, Washington, D. C., Am. Assoc. Adv. Sci. 1963.

Kroon, D. B.: The bone-destroying function of the osteoclasts (Koelliker's "brush border"), Acta anat. *21*:1, 1954.

McLean, F. C., and Bloom, W.: Calcification and

ossification; mobilization of bone salt by para-thyroid extract, Arch. Path. *32*:315, 1941.

Scott, B. L.: Electron microscopy of the epi-physeal apparatus, Anat. Rec. *124*:470, 1956.

Scott, B. L., and Pease, D. C.: Electron micros-copy of the epiphyseal apparatus, Anat. Rec. *126*:465, 1956.

Weinmann, J. P., and Sicher, H.: The gray-lethal mouse and the "incisor absent" rat *in* Bone and Bones, ed. 2, p. 163, St. Louis, Mosby, 1955.

Young, R. W.: Histophysical studies on bone cells and bone resorption *in* Sognnaes (*see* General Reference).

COMPACT BONE: REMODELLING OF COMPACT BONE; BONE TURNOVER; EFFECTS OF METABOLIC ALTERATIONS ON GROWING BONE AND ADULT BONE

*General Reference on Turnover in Bone*

Frost, H. (ed.): Bone Biodynamics, Boston, Little, 1964.

*Special References*

Albright, F., Bloomberg, E., and Smith, P. H.: Post-menopausal osteoporosis, Tr. Ass. Am. Physicians *55*:298, 1940.

Asling, C. W., and Evans, H. M.: Anterior pitui-tary regulation of skeletal development *in* The Biochemistry and Physiology of Bone, New York, Acad. Press, 1956.

Bailie, J. M., and Irving, J. T.: Changes in the metaphysis of the long bones during the de-velopment of rickets, Brit. J. Exp. Path. *29*: 539, 1948.

Barnicot, N. A., and Datta, S. P.: Vitamin A and bone *in* The Biochemistry and Physiology of Bone, New York, Acad. Press. 1956.

Bourne, Geoffrey H.: Vitamin C and bone *in* The Biochemistry and Physiology of Bone, New York, Acad. Press, 1956.

Campo, R. D., and Dziewiatkowski, D. D.: Turn-over of the organic matrix of cartilage and bone as visualized by autoradiography, J. Cell Biol. *18*:19, 1963.

Cohen, Jonathan, and Harris, W. H.: The three-dimensional anatomy of haversian systems, J. Bone Joint Surg. *49-A*:419, 1958.

Dodds, G. S., and Cameron, H. C.: Studies on experimental rickets in rats, Am. J. Path. *14*: 273, 1939; *15*:723, 1939; *19*:169, 1943; Am. J. Anat. *55*:135, 1934.

Fitch, L. W. N.: Osteodystrophic diseases of sheep in New Zealand: I. Rickets in hoggets; with a note on the aetiology and definition of the dis-ease, Australian Veter. J. *19*:2, 1943.

Follis, R. H., Jr.: Diseases, particularly of bone, associated with derangements of calcium and phosphorus metabolism *in* Fifth Conf. on Me-tabolic Interrelations, New York, Macy, 1954.

Hall, Kathleen: Changes in the bone and cartilage of the symphysis pubis of the mouse during pregnancy and after parturition, as revealed by metachromatic staining and the periodic acid-Schiff technique, J. Endocrinol. *11*:210, 1954.

Ham, A. W., and Elliott, H. C.: The bone and cartilage lesions of protracted moderate scurvy, Am. J. Path. *14*:323, 1938.

Harris, L. J.: Vitamin D and bone *in* The Bio-chemistry and Physiology of Bone, New York, Acad. Press, 1956.

Hess, A. F.: Collected Writings, Springfield, Ill., Thomas, 1936.

————: Rickets, Including Osteomalacia and Tetany, Philadelphia, Lea & Febiger, 1929.

Howard, J. E.: Present knowledge of parathyroid function, with especial emphasis upon its limita-tions *in* Bone Structure and Metabolism, pp. 206-221, London, Churchill, 1956.

Jowsey, Jennifer: The microradiography of bone resorption *in* Sognnaes, R. F. (ed.): Mecha-nisms of Hard Tissue Destruction, p. 447, Washington, D. C., Am. Assoc. Adv. Sci., 1963.

McLean, F. C.: The parathyroid glands and bone *in* The Biochemistry and Physiology of Bone, New York, Acad. Press, 1956.

McLean, F. C., and Roland, R. E.: Internal re-modelling of compact bone *in* Sognnaes, R. F. (ed.): Mechanisms of Hard Tissue Destruction, p. 371, Washington, D. C., Am. Assoc. Adv. Sci., 1963.

Munson, P. L.: Studies on the role of the para-thyroids in calcium and phosphorus metabolism, Ann. N. Y. Acad. Sci. *60*:776, 1955.

Murray, P. D. F., and Kodicek, E.: Bones, muscles and vitamin C: I. The effect of a par-tial deficiency of vitamin C on the repair of bone and muscle in guinea pigs, J. Anat. *83*: 158, 1949.

————: Bones, muscles and vitamin C: II. Par-tial deficiencies of vitamin C and mid-dia-physeal thickenings of the tibia and fibula in guinea pigs, J. Anat. *83*:205, 1949.

————: Bones, muscles and vitamin C: III. Repair of the effects of total deprivation of vitamin C at the proximal ends of the tibia and fibula in guinea pigs, J. Anat. *83*:285, 1949.

Silberberg, Martin, and Silberberg, Ruth: Steroid hormones and bone *in* The Biochemistry and Physiology of Bone, New York, Acad. Press, 1956.

Wilkins, Lawson: Hormonal influences on skeletal growth, Ann. N. Y. Acad. Sci. *60*:763, 1955.

Wolbach, S. B., and Bessey, O. A.: Tissue changes in vitamin deficiency, Physiol. Rev. *22*:233, 1942.

(*See also* references on parathyroid glands.)

## SPECIAL REFERENCES ON THE REPAIR AND TRANSPLANTATION OF BONE

Bassett, A. L.: Current concepts of bone formation, J. Bone Joint Surg. *44-A*:1217, 1962.

Gallie, W. E., and Robertson, D. E.: The repair of bone, Brit. J. Surg. *7*:211, 1920.

Gordon, S., and Ham, A. W.: The fate of transplanted cancellous bone *in* The Gallie Addresses, p. 296, Univ. Toronto Press, 1950.

Haas, S. L.: The importance of the periosteum and the endosteum in the repair of transplanted bone, Arch. Surg. *8*:535, 1924.

Ham, A. W.: An histological study of the early phases of bone repair, J. Bone Joint Surg. *12*: 827, 1930.

Ham, A. W., and Gordon, S. D.: *See reference under* Special References on the Development of Bone.

Ham, A. W., and Harris, W. R.: Repair and transplantation of bone *in* The Biochemistry and Physiology of Bone, New York, Acad. Press, 1956.

Ham, A. W., Tisdall, F. F., and Drake, T. G. H.: Experimental noncalcification of callus simulating non-union, J. Bone Joint Surg. *20*:345, 1938.

Keith, A.: Menders of the Maimed, Philadelphia, Lippincott, 1952.

Pritchard, J. J.: Repair of fractures of the parietal bone in rats, J. Anat. *80*:55, 1946.

Pritchard, J. J., and Ruzicka, A. J.: Comparison of fracture repair in the frog, lizard and rat, J. Anat. *84*:236, 1950.

Simpson, M. E., van Dyke, D. C., Asling, C. W., and Evans, H. M.: Regeneration of the calvarium in young normal and growth hormone-treated hypophysectomized rats, Anat. Rec. *115*:615, 1953.

Urist, M. R., and Johnson, R. W.: Calcification and ossification: IV. The healing of fractures in man under clinical conditions, J. Bone Joint Surg. *25*:375, 1943.

Urist, M. R., and McLean, F. C.: Calcification and ossification: I. Calcification in the callus in healing fractures in normal rats, J. Bone Joint Surg. *23*:1, 1941.

————: Calcification and ossification: II. Control of calcification in the fracture callus in rachitic rats, J. Bone Joint Surg. *23*:283, 1941.

————: Calcification and ossification: III. The role of local transfer of bone salt in the calcification of fracture callus, J. Bone Joint Surg. *24*:47, 1942.

Wilkinson, G. W., and Leblond, C. P.: The deposition of radiophosphorus in fractured bones in rats, Surg., Gynec. Obstet. *97*:143, 1953.

## SPECIAL REFERENCES ON THE BLOOD SUPPLY OF BONES

Brookes, M.: Femoral growth after occlusion of the principal nutrient canal in day-old rabbits, J. Bone Joint Surg. *39*:563, 1957.

————: Sequelae of experimental parietal ischemia in long bones of the rabbit, J. Anat. *94*: 552, 1960.

Brookes, M., and Harrison, R. G.: The vascularization of the rabbit femur and tibiofibular, J. Anat. *91*:61, 1957.

Dale, G. G., and Harris, W. R.: Prognosis of epiphyseal separation, J. Bone Joint Surg. *40-B*: 116, 1958.

Ham, A. W.: Some histophysiological problems peculiar to calcified tissues, J. Bone Joint Surg. *34-A*:701, 1952.

Harris, W. R., and Bobechko, W. P.: The radiographic density of avascular bone, J. Bone Joint Surg. *42-B*:626, 1960.

Johnson, R. W.: A physiological study of the blood supply of the diaphysis, J. Bone Joint Surg. *9*:153, 1927.

Salter, R. B., and Harris, W. R.: Injuries involving the epiphyseal plate, J. Bone Joint Surg. *45-A*:587, 1963.

Trueta, J., and Harrison, M. H. M.: The normal vascular anatomy of the femoral head in adult man, J. Bone Joint Surg. *35*:442, 1953.

# 19 Joints

## INTRODUCTION

Diseases of joints constitute the greatest single cause of disability in the civilized world. The microscopic study of the different parts of the various types of joints is therefore a matter of great importance, not only for permitting one to understand how they function, but also in providing a proper basis for understanding the nature of the various types of pathologic lesions to which they are subject.

**Definition and Function.** The words *articulation* (*articulare* = to connect) and *joint* (*jungere* = to join) are used synonymously with reference to those structural arrangements that exist to connect two or more bones together at their site of meeting. It is by means of joints that the individual bones of the body are connected together to form a skeleton. Although many joints permit movement between the two or more bones that they connect, the permitting of movement is not essential for a connecting structure to be termed a joint; indeed some joints become as solid as the bones they connect. Another function of joints, which will be described later, is that they make it possible for the structures they connect to grow in extent.

**Classification.** Joints may be classified in several ways: according to how they develop (on an embryologic basis), according to their structure (on a morphologic basis) or according to the kind of movement they permit (on a physiologic basis). We shall classify them on a morphologic basis, and, accordingly, there are 5 kinds:

1. Syndesmoses
2. Synchondroses
3. Synostoses
4. Symphyses
5. Synovial

The above terms are not so difficult to understand and remember as at first might be thought. It is easy to associate the prefix *syn* with joints because it means *together*. The term *desmosis* refers to a *band* or a *bond*, but in connection with joints the term has become restricted to imply bands or bonds of dense connective tissue. Syndesmoses, then, are joints wherein bones, at their site of meeting, are held together by bands of dense fibrous tissue. It is important to understand that in a syndesmosis the bands of dense connective tissue extend from one *bare* bony surface to another; if the bones that are connected with dense fibrous tissue are capped with cartilage, another term, as we shall see, is employed to describe them. *Synchondroses,* as might be supposed, are joints wherein two bones are connected with cartilage. Likewise, since *osteon* means *bone, synostoses* are joints wherein two bones are cemented together with bone. A synostosis, in effect, makes two bones into one, but synostoses are thought of as joints because they connect bones that developed separately and remained individual through the growing period, during which time they were connected by some other tissue (cartilage or fibrous tissue). The term *symphysis* means literally a *growing together*; actually the term is used with reference to joints wherein bones that are capped with cartilage at the joint site are held together (through the medium of their cartilage caps) by dense fibrous tissue or fibrocartilage. In one sense, then, a symphysis is a type of syndesmosis, but it is easier to think of it as a different type of joint, the difference lying in the fact that the dense fibrous tissue of the joint, in a syndesmosis, is inserted into bone tissue, and in a symphysis, into the cartilage that caps the bones of the joint at their site of meeting. The term *synovial* is derived from *syn* and *ovum*. Ovum, as used here, refers to the egg of the domesticated bird, and in particular, to the "white" of the egg, which is a glairy fluid. Synovial joints, then, are joints wherein a glairy fluid is present (in a closed cavity, called a synovial cavity) between the ends of the bones that participate in the joint. The glairy fluid, as we shall see, is of the nature of a lubricant to allow the

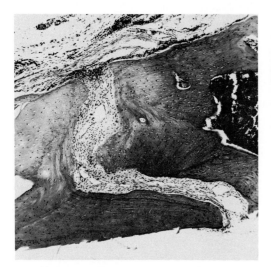

FIG. 19-1. Low-power photomicrograph of a section cut through the parietotemporal joint of an adult rat. This is an example of a suture and a syndesmosis.

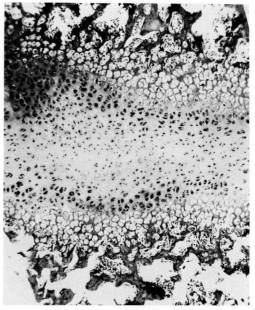

FIG. 19-2. Low-power photomicrograph of a section cut through the basisphenoid joint of an adult rat. Notice that the cartilage is being replaced by bone on both its sides.

smooth surfaces of the cartilage-capped bones that meet in the joint to slide freely on one another. Synovial joints, then, represent a specialized type of joint for free movement. Synovial joints, moreover, are sometimes termed *diarthroses* (*di*-apart, *arthron*-joint) because the two bones entering into one are, in a sense, kept *apart* by the synovial cavity. Furthermore, any of the first 4 types given in our classification can be termed a *synarthrosis* because in this type 2 bones are not kept apart, but *together,* by the joint.

The particular features of the various types of joints will now be described.

## SYNDESMOSES

The sutures of the skull are good examples of this type of joint. The way in which membrane bones develop, grow and give rise to sutures has already been described (Chap. 18). Individual membrane bones, it will be recalled, develop from separate centers of ossification and thereafter grow in extent because new bone is continuously added to their edges by means of the appositional growth mechanism. As a result of this, the young connective tissue situated between the edges of 2 adjacent bones becomes reduced eventually to a narrow band (Fig. 19-1). This

narrow band of connective tissue joins the edges of the 2 bones together; hence, a suture is a syndesmosis. Osteogenic cells between the 2 bones in the suture can still proliferate and differentiate into bone cells. Because of the latter phenomenon layers of new bone can be added to the edges of the bones in the suture, and this permits the 2 bones that meet at the suture to grow in extent. Therefore, a syndesmosis provides a site wherein membrane bones can increase in extent by means of the appositional growth mechanism. When growth is over, the connective tissue in a suture may be replaced by bone; thus the syndesmosis becomes converted into a synostosis. When this occurs, the 2 bones that meet at the joint can no longer grow in extent.

Suture lines are commonly irregular; the edges of the bones concerned may be serrated or they may interlock by means of toothlike processes. When a suture is cut in cross section, the suture line is usually seen to be oblique (Fig. 19-1). Not uncommonly an isolated ossicle, called a Wormian bone, may be seen in the connective tissue of a suture; such a bone forms as a result of the detachment of

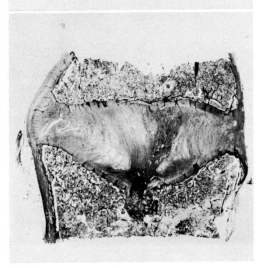

a little group of osteoblasts or a little spicule from the edge of one of the bones that meet in the suture.

## SYNCHONDROSES

Epiphysial disks, which were described at great length when the development and growth of long bones were considered, are good examples of synchondroses because they consist of hyaline cartilage and connect bony epiphyses with bony diaphyses. It is to be understood that in most epiphysial plates any substantial growth of bone occurs only on the diaphysial side of the plate. But such new bone as forms in the epiphysis, as it grows larger, is due mostly to osteogenesis advancing into the articular cartilage and replacing it as it grows; the articular cartilage serves, as it were, as the "epiphysial disk" for the growth of the epiphysis. However, the synchondrosis between the basioccipital and the basisphenoid bones is unlike an epiphysial plate in this respect, for it provides for the growth of both of the bones that meet at this joint; in sections, then, it appears as a "double-sided" epiphysial disk (Fig. 19-2).

## SYNOSTOSES

When growth is over, most syndesmoses and synchondroses become synostoses. This is emphatic evidence to the effect that the chief

FIG. 19-3. (*Top*) Very low-power photomicrograph of a horizontal section cut through an intervertebral disk. The circularly disposed fibers in the annulus fibrosus may be seen in the periphery of the picture. The central dark area is the nucleus pulposus. (*Middle*) Very low-power photomicrograph of a vertical section cut through the bodies of 2 vertebrae and the disk between them. The fibers of the annulus fibrosus may be seen near the edges of the disk; the paler material in the more central part of the disk is the nucleus pulposus. (*Bottom*) Very low-power photomicrograph of a vertical section cut through 2 vertebrae and the disk between them. The nucleus pulposus has ruptured into the substance of the body of the vertebra below. (Dr. William Donohue)

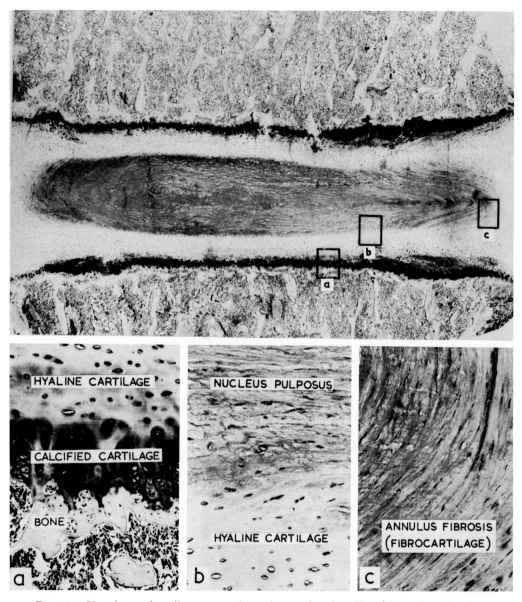

Fig. 19-4. Very low and medium power photomicrographs of an H and E section of an intervertebral disk of a young child. The areas marked a, b and c in the upper picture are shown in higher magnifications in the lower pictures.

function of the first two described types of joint is to permit growth rather than movement. It is of interest that operative procedures (including the use of bone transplants) are often employed to convert symphyses and synovial joints into synostoses when pathologic conditions arise which make movement undesirable.

## SYMPHYSES

In a symphysis, the ends of the bones meeting in the joint are each capped with hyaline cartilage, and in turn the cartilage caps are joined by strong fibrous tissue which blends with the hyaline cartilages through a transitional zone of fibrocartilage. This arrangement provides great strength with a limited amount of movement.

In the *symphysis pubis* the tissue between the cartilage caps of the bones concerned consists almost entirely of fibrocartilage. A tiny slitlike space exists in the fibrocartilage, and in women during pregnancy this becomes larger, thus allowing for greater movement between the pubic bones during the passage of the fetus through the birth canal. In some lower animals the pubic bones actually become separated during pregnancy. Hall and her associates have studied the process in pregnant mice and have investigated the effects of hormones on the process (see references).

The *intervertebral joint* or, as it is often called, the *intervertebral disk* is a specialized type of symphysis. In each of these joints the flat bony surfaces of the bodies of the vertebrae concerned are capped with a layer of hyaline cartilage; the cartilage of one is joined to that of the other by fibrocartilage and dense fibrous tissue that is disposed so as to form a ring around the periphery of the joint (Figs. 19-3 and 19-4). This ring, called the annulus fibrosus, surrounds a central space that is filled with a pulpy semifluid material; this central space, so-filled, is termed the nucleus pulposus (Figs. 19-3 and 19-4). The nucleus pulposus is believed to represent a remnant of the notochord. It contains cells (at least in the young) and intercellular substance, and under normal conditions it is under pressure; this, since the annulus fibrosus is slightly elastic, makes the spine more resilient than it would be otherwise. In the aged, the nucleus pulposus loses some of its water content and so becomes smaller. This change is partly responsible for the spine becoming shorter and less resilient in old age.

In recent years it has become recognized that the nucleus pulposus may herniate through the annulus fibrosus into the spinal canal, where it may press on the roots of the spinal nerves. These herniations or extrusions of the nucleus pulposus commonly occur between the 4th and the 5th lumbar vertebrae or between the 5th lumbar and the 1st sacral vertebrae. Pressure on the roots of the 5th lumbar or the 1st sacral nerve as a result of this condition is a common cause of a painful condition known as sciatica. Extrusions of the nucleus pulposus through the annulus fibrosus

may also occur in the cervical region, where the extrusion may compress the entire spinal cord or the roots of the nerves of the brachial plexus. Sometimes the nucleus pulposus herniates through the hyaline cartilage covering the body of a vertebra into the cancellous bone of its substance; this causes a characteristic lesion called a Schmorl's nodule (Fig. 19-3, *bottom*).

## SYNOVIAL JOINTS

**Development.** It has been explained already that the central mesenchyme in the limb buds of embryos gradually differentiates into cartilage in such a way that cartilage models of the bones-to-be are formed (Figs. 18-22 and 18-23). It has also been explained that the mesenchyme immediately surrounding the shaft of a cartilage model becomes arranged into an indistinctly 2-layered membrane, the perichondrium, that the outer layer of this membrane assumes a fibrous nature, and that the inner remains cellular and chondrogenic so that by the appositional growth mechanism it can add further layers of cartilage to the sides of the shaft, thus causing the shaft to grow in width. We shall now consider the series of events that transpire in regions where the ends of cartilage models approach one another and where synovial joints develop.

The mesenchyme between the ends of two developing models becomes condensed; this ill-defined area of condensed mesenchyme between the two ill-defined ends of the developing cartilage models of the bones-to-be is called the *articular disk of mesenchyme* or the primitive joint plate (Fig. 19-5). And, in a fashion similar to that in which the perichondrium forms around the shafts of the cartilage models, the mesenchyme that surrounds the whole area in which the two ends of the cartilage models are developing also becomes condensed to form the counterpart of the perichondrium in this region (Fig. 19-5). This latter condensation of mesenchyme around the joint area is the forerunner of what is called the *capsule* of the joint. This fits like a sleeve over the end of each of the cartilage models that enters into the joint and extends along the sides of their ends for a sufficient distance to become continuous with the perichondrium that covers and is adherent to the sides of their shafts.

As development proceeds, the jellylike amorphous intercellular substance and tissue fluid disposed between the mesenchymal cells of the articular disk begin to increase, and as a result, the cells in the disk become widely separated from one another in at least certain areas in the disk. The continuance of this process soon leads to the appearance of fluid-filled clefts in the substance of the disk; these gradually fuse with one another so that soon or late a continuous cavity, the *synovial cavity*, comes to occupy the site formerly occupied by the bulk of the disk. This permits the ends of the two cartilage models to come into contact and articulate with each other.

The process which accounts for the formation of a synovial cavity is not confined to the area between the two ends of the models; the same process operates to cause the cavity to extend along the sides of the ends of the two models for some distance. The condensed mesenchyme which surrounds the joint area and which is the counterpart of the perichondrium of the shafts of the models, thereby become separated from the sides of the ends of the models. However, the developing joint capsule becomes continuous with the tightly attached perichondrium (or periosteum as the case may be) that covers the shaft of the models some little distance back from the end of each model.

As development continues, differentiation occurs in the forming joint capsule. The mesenchyme comprising its outer and thicker layer tends to differentiate into dense fibrous tissue, while that of its inner layer becomes more or less specialized to constitute its synovial layer, or, as it is often called, the *synovial membrane* of the joint. Its finer structure will be described presently.

To summarize: Since the synovial cavity is nothing more than a large cleft that forms in the substance of mesenchyme, it can scarcely be expected to have a continuous cellular lining of mesothelium like that possessed by the great body cavities. Moreover, its contents (synovial fluid) should be expected to be what might be termed diluted intercellular substance, and, indeed, a good way to regard synovial fluid is to think of it as ground substance (hyaluronic acid) diluted with tissue fluid. Because of the way the joint capsule

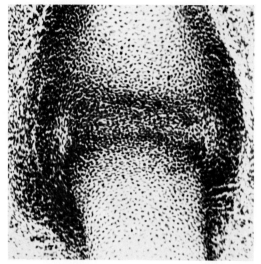

FIG. 19-5. Low-power photomicrograph of a longitudinal section cut through the developing interphalangeal joint in a 20-mm. human embryo. The developing cartilaginous ends of the 2 bones-to-be are pale. The dark-staining material that extends across the middle of the picture is the condensed mesenchyme that makes up the articular disk. The dark-staining stripes that run up and down each side of the ends of the developing cartilage models represent the condensed mesenchyme that is destined to form the capsule of the joint. The little clear areas seen in the dark-staining, otherwise condensed, mesenchyme of the disk represent the beginnings of the synovial cavity.

forms, the latter structure could be expected to have many of the properties of perichondrium and periosteum.

**General Structure.** The appearance of a longitudinal section of a synovial joint—the knee joint of man—is illustrated in Figure 19-6. This figure shows the various structures that are involved in a complex synovial joint and their relations to one another. This figure should be consulted frequently as the microscopic structure of various components of a synovial joint are considered in the following section.

**Articular Cartilage.** This is a typical example of hyaline cartilage. It has no blood vessels, nerves or lymphatics. The cells in it are arranged in 3 ill-defined layers (Fig.

19-7): (1) a superficial layer in which the cells are flattened and small and are disposed with their long axes running parallel with the articular surface; (2) an intermediate layer in which the cells are somewhat larger and more nearly round and often are disposed in columns that run at right angles to the surface; (3) a deep layer that is composed of large cells. In the deepest part of this layer the intercellular substance is calcified and stains more deeply even in decalcified H and E sections than does the intercellular substance that surrounds the cells in the outer part of this layer. During the period of growth this layer is more or less constantly being replaced by bone, while the cartilage cells in the more (but not the most) superficial layers proliferate by mitosis and grow away from the advancing bone.

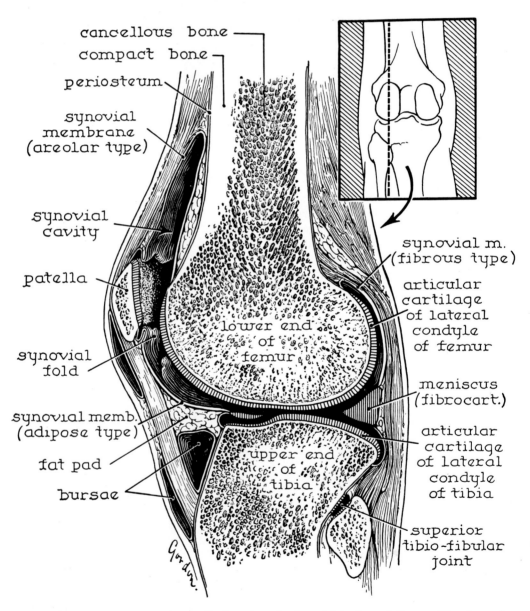

Fig. 19-6. A drawing of a longitudinal section of a knee joint of an adult man. The plane of the section that is illustrated in the main drawing is indicated in the insert (*upper right*).

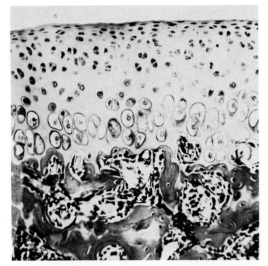

FIG. 19-7. Low-power photomicrograph of a longitudinal section cut through the upper end of the tibia of a guinea pig. This picture illustrates the appearance of normal articular cartilage.

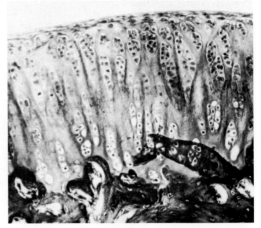

FIG. 19-8. Low-power photomicrograph (taken with the phase microscope) of a section cut through the upper end of the tibia of an aged rat. The direction of the collagenic fibers in the articular cartilage may be seen.

The intercellular substance of articular cartilage consists of collagenic fibers embedded in a sulfated amorphous type of intercellular substance (chondroitin sulfuric acid). In sections cut from the articular cartilages of young animals the fibers are effectively masked by the amorphous intercellular substance. But in older animals, the fibers are demonstrated more readily and can be seen (Fig. 19-8) to form coarse bundles that, deep in the cartilage, run at right angles to the surface between the rows of cells. As the fibers approach the surface, however, they become separated into smaller bundles which eventually spread out in a fountainlike fashion to run parallel with the surface (Fig. 19-8). This creates a densely tangled network of fibers immediately under the surface; this network probably is suited to bear the constantly altered stresses to which a joint surface is subjected.

THE FINE STRUCTURE OF ARTICULAR CARTILAGE. The EM appearance of both the cells and the intercellular substance of articular cartilage varies in relation to the age of the cartilage and the particular position the specimen occupied in the articular cartilage, whether for example the specimen was taken from a site close to the articular surface or close to the underlying bone. Silberberg and

Silberberg and their co-workers have studied this matter in some detail. Here, we shall deal only with general features. During the phase of growth the chondrocytes of the articular cartilage are synthesizing and secreting both the protein and the mucopolysaccharide components of the intercellular substance. As might be expected, chondrocytes in this phase of activity manifest well-developed rough-surfaced vesicles of endoplasmic reticulum in their cytoplasm as well as a well-developed Golgi apparatus (Fig. 19-9). The borders of chondrocytes are very ragged; this appearance is caused by their cytoplasm extending off for short distances into the intercellular substance in the form of processes which are much like microvilli but which are generally termed cytoplasmic footlets. The intercellular substance, which is best seen in the lower right part of Figure 19-9, consists of interlacing fibrillar material which is collagen and an amorphous material which appears structureless in the EM and which is of the order of a sulfated mucopolysaccharide.

As chondrocytes become older, the organelles associated with protein synthesis and secretion, the rough-surfaced vesicles and the Golgi apparatus, become less prominent, and glycogen and lipid material accumulates in the cytoplasm. Silberberg and Silberberg think

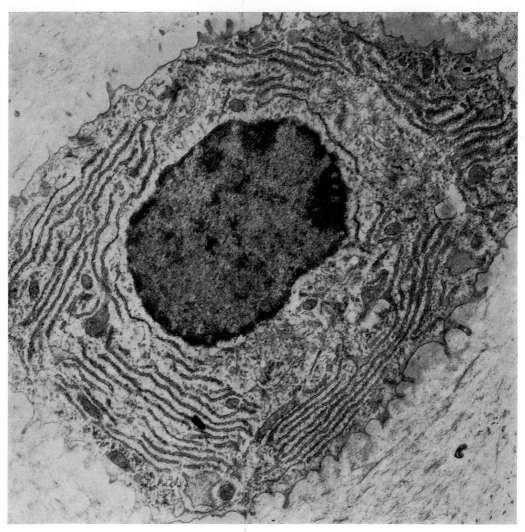

FIG. 19-9. Electron micrograph ($\times$ 19,500) of chondrocyte of articular cartilage. Note well-developed rough-surfaced vesicles, Golgi material, cytoplasmic footlets and fibrillar material lying in an amorphous intercellular substance. (Preparation by Ruth and Martin Silberberg)

that chondrocytes that die in the substance of the cartilage and hence are not immediately replaced by bone are replaced by fibrillar scars.

NOURISHMENT AND METABOLISM OF ARTICULAR CARTILAGE. Since articular cartilage is nonvascular, nourishment must diffuse into its cells from outside its substance. The calcification of its intercellular substance in its deeper layers probably shuts off nutriment from the capillaries of the cancellous bone that underlies it; it is said, however, that there are cer-tain sites where some nourishment may percolate through to it by this route. Around its periphery articular cartilage probably obtains some nourishment from the vessels of the synovial membrane in a manner to be described presently. But the greater part of the articular cartilage obtains its nourishment from the synovial fluid. It has been demonstrated repeatedly that fragments of cartilage, detached by injury or disease and floating freely in the synovial fluid, not only can survive, but also in many instances can grow and increase greatly in size. Furthermore, in experimentally produced fractures of the necks of the femurs of dogs, in which the heads are separated completely from all blood supply and then pinned in place, the articular cartilages of the heads, over the succeeding months, as seen in sections, seem generally to survive. When good results are obtained in such fractures the dead bone and marrow of the head is all replaced, as has been described in connection with the healing of a fracture, and new bone develops to support the living articular cartilage which has survived through the whole procedure. Since a head has no blood supply until it is revascularized, and since the region directly beneath the articular cartilage is the last part of the head to be revascularized, it seems evident that the synovial fluid is capable of supporting the life of the chondrocytes of articular cartilage. This suggests that synovial fluid, under normal circumstances, provides the chief source of nourishment for most of the cells of articular cartilage.

Chondrocytes probably have a low metabolic rate. There is evidence indicating that their metabolism is of the anaerobic type, for their oxygen consumption is almost negligible (Bywaters). Moreover, their oxygen consumption diminishes with advancing age (Rosenthal).

GROWTH, MAINTENANCE AND REPAIR OF ARTICULAR CARTILAGE. As has been noted before, the articular cartilage provides for the growth of the bony epiphysis in the same way that an epiphysial disk provides for the growth in length of a bony diaphysis; indeed, in short bones in which there are no epiphysial disks, the articular cartilages serve as the sites wherein the bones as a whole grow in length. During the growing period, mitotic figures are to be observed among the chondrocytes of articular cartilage, not in the most superficial layer of flat cells (which might otherwise be assumed to be the youngest cells in the cartilage), but somewhat deeper, in about the third or fourth layer of cells below the surface. Deep to this layer the chondrocytes of articular cartilage are more mature, and still deeper, next to the bone, they are hypertrophied, and the intercellular substance surrounding them is calcified. During the period of active growth this zone of calcified cartilage is continuously being replaced by bone, which forms from

osteogenic cells and osteoblasts, which invade this layer of cartilage from the bone below.

However, when the epiphysis has grown to its full size these 2 processes—the growth of the cartilage and its replacement by bone—appear to cease. It is the author's experience that mitotic figures can no longer be found in the articular cartilage after growth is over. Elliott, when a graduate student with the author, could not find mitotic figures in the articular cartilages of adult animals even if they were specially exercised.

From the foregoing it seems dubious if there is enough maintenance growth in articular cartilage to compensate for much wear, so it is generally assumed that under normal conditions articular cartilage wears only slightly and gradually. Rosenthal and his associates have shown that the number of cells in articular cartilage decreases in relation to the amount of intercellular substance throughout life; this may mean that some wear and tear is compensated for by such cells as persist continuing to produce more intercellular substance.

The foregoing suggests that once that growth is over the regenerative capacity of the cells of articular cartilage would not be great, and this suggestion is borne out by the experimental evidence. Superficial wounds, made anywhere except around the edges of articular cartilage or close to any other attachment of synovial membrane, apparently remain quiescent and unhealed for long periods of time; the chondrocytes of the articular cartilage appear to be too highly differentiated to give rise to new tissue which would heal the defect. However, if the wounds are deep and extend to and through the bone of the epiphysis which supports the articular cartilage, healing occurs. Such wounds, however, represent the healing of the fractured bone below the articular cartilage rather than the healing of articular cartilage itself, for osteogenic cells, osteoblasts and capillaries grow up into the wound from the bone below. This results in the filling of the defect in the cartilage with what amounts to a callus; this, of course, may contain calcified cartilage and bone as well as uncalcified cartilage, and these other types of tissue are not suitable for an articular surface. Hence, although fractures through the articular cartilage into its supporting bone below

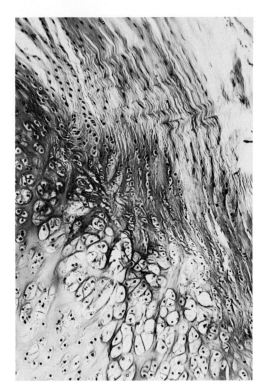 

FIG. 19-10. (*Left*) Low-power photomicrograph of a section cut through the site of the insertion of the patellar tendon of an adult rat. (*Right*) Low-power photomicrograph of a section cut through the site of the insertion of the anterior cruciate ligament of an adult rat. Observe the bundles of collagenic fibers buried in bone (Sharpey's fibers).

will heal, the end result commonly leads to the development of an arthritic condition in the joint at a later date.

If wounds are made in articular cartilage at sites close to the attachment of the synovial membrane, the cells of the latter, being relatively undifferentiated, respond by producing fibrocartilage, and this leads to healing. This is further evidence to the effect that the synovial membrane (the lining of the joint capsule) is in many respects similar to the osteogenic layer of the perichondrium or periosteum.

**Joint Capsule.** As noted before, this consists of 2 layers: an outer fibrous layer which commonly is called the fibrous capsule of the joint and an inner layer which commonly is called the synovial membrane of the joint (Fig. 19-6).

The fibrous capsule of a joint is continuous with the fibrous layer of the periosteum of the bones that meet at the joint (Fig. 19-6). It

is composed of sheets of collagenic fibers that run from the periosteum of one bone to that of the other. It is relatively inelastic and hence makes a contribution to the stability of the joint. Occasionally, gaps are present in fibrous capsules; if so, the synovial membrane rests on muscles or such other structures as surround the joint. The ligaments of a joint represent cordlike thickenings of the capsule. These may be incorporated in the capsule or may be separated from it by bursae that are formed by outpouchings of the synovial lining (Fig. 19-6, *bursae*). Near their attachments the structure of ligaments undergoes a transition into fibrocartilage (Fig. 19-10). The collagenic fibers become associated with increased amounts of amorphous intercellular substance, and the fibroblasts become encapsulated and resemble chondrocytes (Fig. 19-10). The collagenic fibers extend into the substance of the bone to which they are attached as typical Sharpey's fibers (Fig. 19-10, *right*). It is to be

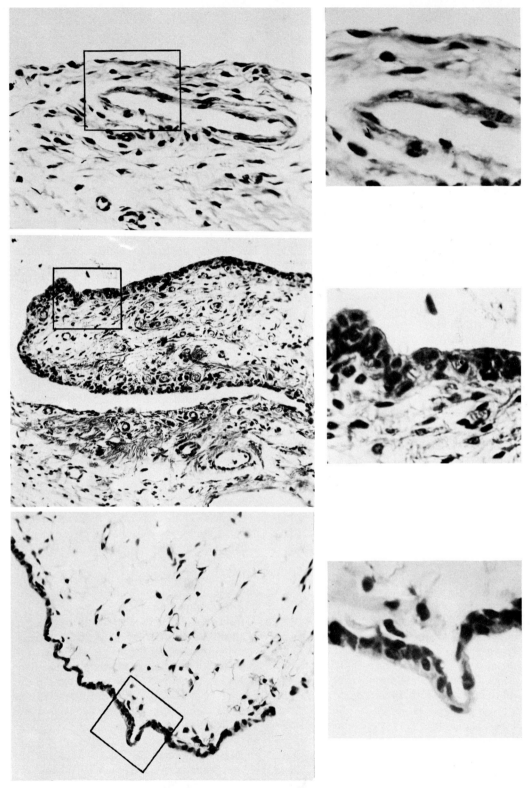

FIG. 19-11. (*Top*) Low- and high-power photomicrographs of a section of synovial membrane of the fibrous type. (*Middle*) Low- and high-power photomicrographs of a section of synovial membrane of the areolar type. (*Bottom*) Low and high-power photomicrographs of a section of a synovial membrane of the adipose type. All of the sections are of rat tissue.

remembered that bundles of collagenic fibers can become buried in bone as Sharpey's fibers to serve as an anchorage for tendons, muscles or the periodontal membrane only when the fibers are formed before or as bone intercellular substance is deposited around them and onto the surface of the bone (appositional growth mechanism) by the osteoblasts which lie between the fiber bundles close to the bone. In this sense, a tendon serves as the periosteum of a bone at the site of its insertion (see Sharpey's fibers, Fig. 19-10, *right*).

The synovial membrane, the inner layer of the joint capsule, lines the joint everywhere except over the articular cartilages (Fig. 19-6). The inner surface of the synovial membrane is usually smooth and glistening and it may be thrown into numerous processes; some of these are termed *villi*. It is abundantly supplied with blood vessels, nerves and lymphatics, as will be described presently.

The cells in this membrane are called synovial cells. They are of a relatively undifferentiated type and tend to be concentrated along the inner border of the membrane; indeed, in some instances, they may be so concentrated as to give the appearance of forming a continuous cellular membrane. However, the careful microscopic study of such a membrane will show that the cells disposed along its inner surface lie *in among* rather than *on* the collagenic fibers which also participate in forming the inner lining of the membrane.

The inner lining of the joint capsule, which contains the synovial cells, may lie directly on the fibrous capsule of the joint or may be separated from the fibrous capsule by a layer of areolar tissue or a layer of adipose tissue (Fig. 19-6). Accordingly, Key distinguishes 3 morphologic types of synovial membrane: (1) fibrous, (2) areolar and (3) adipose. These are illustrated in Figures 19-6 and 19-11 and will now be described.

The fibrous type is found over ligaments and tendons and in other areas where the synovial lining is subjected to pressure (Fig. 19-6). The surface cells are characteristically widely separated from one another (Fig. 19-11, *top*), and although they are slightly larger and more numerous than the fibroblasts that are farther removed from the surface, it is often difficult to distinguish them from ordinary fibroblasts in sections. Since intercellular

substance, rather than cells, comprises most of the lining of this type of synovial membrane, this type of membrane provides strong evidence in favor of the concept that synovial cavities are of the nature of connective tissue spaces.

The areolar type of synovial membrane is found where the membrane is required to move freely over the fibrous capsule of the joint, as, for example, in the suprapatellar pouch of the knee joint (Fig. 19-6). The surface cells are grouped fairly closely together in this type of lining (Fig. 19-11, *middle*), usually in 3 or 4 rows, and are embedded in a layer of collagenic fibers which blend smoothly into those of the areolar tissue. Usually many elastic fibers are present in this type of lining; these usually are arranged in a lamina and this probably serves to keep synovial projections from being nipped between the articular cartilages (Davies).

The adipose type of synovial lining covers the intra-articular fat pads (Fig. 19-6) and most closely resembles a true cellular lining membrane in appearance. The surface cells are usually formed into a single layer which appears to rest on the adipose tissue (Fig. 19-11, *bottom*). However, careful inspection will reveal that the surface cells are more or less embedded in a thin layer of collagenic fibers, as are the surface cells in the other two types of lining membrane.

Synovial cells vary quite a bit in appearance, as might be expected if they represented a mesenchymal-derived family of cells the members of which were in different stages of differentiation. Recently Asboe-Hansen has observed that there are numerous mast cells in synovial membranes.

**Transition Zone.** At the site of attachment of the synovial membrane to the periphery of the articular cartilage, the synovial cells undergo a transition into chondrocytes. This region is known as the *transition zone*. In this site a fold or fringe of synovial tissue may be seen to overlie the articular cartilage for a short distance. This fold, which is cut in cross section in a longitudinal section of a joint, appears wedge-shaped (Fig. 19-12). The tip of the wedge is relatively noncellular and the base is cellular. The areolar tissue that underlies the base of the wedge undergoes an abrupt change into fibrous tissue as it nears the articular cartilage, and this tissue, in turn, merges with the articular cartilage.

Since the synovial cells are relatively undifferentiated, synovial tissues are capable of rapid and complete repair. It is helpful to know this fact because synovial tissues must be removed in certain types of operations on joints. Key found that following the removal of a portion of the synovial lining from the knee joints of rabbits, there was a rapid deposition of fibrin in the wounded area and that this quickly became organized by young connective tissue cells which grew in from the fibrous capsule. These soon differentiated into synovial cells, so that within 60 days the newly formed synovial lining could not be distinguished from that of undamaged adjacent areas.

**Intra-articular Menisci.** These structures (Fig. 19-6) develop from portions of the articular disk of mesenchyme (Fig. 19-5) which once occupied the space between the developing articular cartilages of the joint concerned. In these, the mesenchyme tends to differentiate into fibrocartilage. They may have a free inner border, as they have in the knee joint, or they may traverse the joint, dividing it into 2 separate synovial cavities, as in the sternoclavicular joint.

The menisci of the knee joint may be torn as the result of an injury, and it is common practice to excise an affected meniscus. Following the removal of a meniscus, a new one sometimes forms, growing in from the fibrous capsule of the joint. The new structure that forms in this fashion is an almost complete duplicate of the former meniscus but it consists of dense fibrous tissue rather than of fibrocartilage. New menisci that form in this fashion may themselves become injured and require removal; indeed, it was because of this that it was found that intra-articular menisci can regenerate (Smillie).

**Blood Vessels and Lymphatics.** Synovial joints have a relatively rich blood supply. The branches of arteries that approach a joint commonly supply 3 structures, one goes to the epiphyses, a second to the joint capsule and a third to the synovial membrane. In these sites they supply capillary beds. There are arteriovenous anastomoses in joints; the significance of these has not yet been determined.

The synovial membrane has a very rich sup-

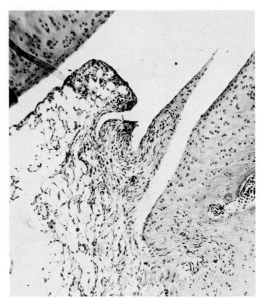

Fig. 19-12. Low-power photomicrograph of a section cut through the border of the patella of a rat. The synovial fold is wedge-shaped in this section.

ply of capillaries and in many sites these approach the inner surface of the membrane very closely. As a result blood may escape into the synovial fluid from a relatively minor injury to the joint.

Blood vessels are arranged in a circular network at the periphery of the articular cartilage in the transition zone; this arrangement constitutes the circulus articuli vasculosus of Hunter.

Gardner's paper should be consulted for details regarding the blood supply of joints.

The lymphatic plexus lies somewhat more deeply from the synovial surface than the blood capillaries. The lymphatic capillaries begin as blind tubes; these are often enlarged at their blind ends. After piercing the elastic lamina of the synovial lining they converge into larger vessels which pass in the general direction of the flexor aspect of the joint. Here they anastomose freely with the periosteal lymphatics and then empty into the main lymphatic vessels of the limb (Davies).

**Nerve Supply.** The student will find it easier to understand the following section if he returns to it after reading the section on nervous tissue. Hilton's law, first enunciated by John

Hilton* in 1863, continues to be the fundamental statement about the nerve supply of joints: "The same trunks of nerves whose branches supply the muscles moving a joint also furnish a distribution of nerves to the skin over the insertions of the same muscles, and . . . the interior of the joint receives its nerves from the same source." Articular cartilage contains no nerve endings. The capsular structures contain different types of endings, as will now be described.

Joints are supplied with both myelinated and nonmyelinated fibers.

The larger myelinated fibers that reach joints are those of afferent neurons. These terminate for the most part in the joint capsule. The nerve endings on these fibers, according to Gardner, are mostly of the Ruffini type, and these, in this site, are sensitive to changes in pressure and probably other types of stimuli concerned in providing a proprioceptive function. The endings are aggregated chiefly in sites in the capsule that are most likely to be compressed by joint movements.

Small myelinated fibers pass to the joint capsule and to the ligaments of the joint where they end in free endings. These fibers are concerned with the sense of pain. There are very few of these free endings in the connective tissue of the synovial membranes, hence it would not seem to be very sensitive to pain. That the synovial membrane is not very sensitive to pain has been confirmed at operations in which joints have been opened under local anesthesia. The free endings in the capsule and ligaments of joints seem to be stimulated most easily by stretching or twisting these structures. Small myelinated fibers also form free endings in the adventitia of blood vessels; these are probably vasosensory and at least some probably are concerned with the sense of pain. Endings of this type in the adventitia of blood vessels are probably the only kind of free afferent endings in synovial membranes.

Nonmyelinated sympathetic fibers, which, of course, are efferent, end in the smooth muscle of the blood vessels of joints to regulate flow through them.

Fibers reach larger joints from many spinal

---

*Hilton, J.: Rest and Pain, ed. 5, London, Bell.

nerves, and any given nerve may supply more than one joint. Joint pain is generally poorly localized.

Gardner has made extensive studies on the nerve supply of joints, and his papers should be read to obtain detailed information on this subject.

**Synovial Fluid.** Since the synovial cavity develops as a connective tissue space, it should contain a ground substance and be perfused with tissue fluid. This concept of the cavity and its contents has been supported by the investigations of Bauer and his colleagues, who showed that synovial fluid was an ultrafiltrate or dialysate of blood (as is tissue fluid) plus mucin. Meyer identified the mucin of synovial fluid as hyaluronic acid. In synovial fluid, in contrast to the aqueous humor, hyaluronic acid is highly polymerized; this accounts for the viscous quality of synovial fluid and doubtless adds to its lubricating qualities.

The various projections of the synovial membrane that extend into the synovial cavity and the closeness of the capillaries to the surface of the cavity make it easy to understand how tissue fluid readily could gain access to the cavity. The presence of hyaluronic acid in synovial fluid is to be explained by the fact that synovial cells produce it, and that which is produced constitutes the ground substance of the synovial membrane and also gains entrance to the synovial fluid.

The cell content of synovial fluid appears to vary considerably from joint to joint and from species to species. Key points out that it tends to become increased after death. Counts of from 80 to several thousand cells per cubic millimeter have been found by different investigators. Key found a typical differential count to yield 58 per cent monocytes, 15 per cent macrophages, 14 per cent ill-defined types of phagocytes, 1 per cent primitive cells, 3 per cent synovial cells and 5 per cent of other types of blood leukocytes.

The passage of substances into and out of the synovial fluid depends upon their size. Crystalloids diffuse readily in both directions. This is of importance in the treatment of joint diseases, for soluble drugs given an individual can quickly enter the synovial fluid. Gases also diffuse readily in both directions. Hence, in caisson disease (the bends), nitrogen bubbles frequently appear in joint cavities. This disease occurs when divers or other people working under high atmospheric pressure return too quickly to normal atmospheric pressure. The sudden decompression of the individual as a whole causes a too sudden release of gases dissolved in the bloodstream and other fluids, just as carbon dioxide bubbles from soda water when the cap is removed from a bottle.

Proteins, with their large colloidal molecules, leave synovial fluid by way of lymphatics. Particulate matter must be removed from synovial fluid by phagocytosis. Although synovial cells have some phagocytic powers, most of the phagocytosis of particulate matter introduced into synovial fluid is brought about by macrophages. The removal of particulate matter from joints is a slow process, and phagocytes containing hemosiderin may be seen in the synovial tissues of joints months after blood has escaped into the synovial fluid.

Age Changes. A condition called *osteoarthritis* tends to develop in joints as individuals age. This condition is so common that its development to some degree is considered, by some investigators, to be a normal consequence of the aging process. Should the condition develop prematurely or in a severe form, it is, of course, considered to be pathologic. It consists essentially of a curious combination of degenerative and proliferative phenomena.

The degenerative changes that occur are seen to best advantage in the more central parts of articular cartilages (rather than at the periphery of articular cartilages). The cement substance of the cartilage (chondroitin sulfuric acid) appears to be involved and to change in character. As a result, the collagenic fibers and even the fibrils of the intercellular substance of the cartilage become unmasked and visible in sections (Fig. 19-13, *right*). As the condition progresses, the collagenic fibers become freely exposed on the articular surface; this gives the surface an appearance like the "pile" of a carpet, and the condition is termed fibrillation of the cartilage (Fig. 19-13, *right*).

The proliferative changes occur around the edges of the articular cartilage, particularly in the transition zone and at the sites of attachment of tendons and ligaments. Cartilage proliferates in these regions and is replaced by bone in such a fashion that bony spurs,

Fig. 19-13. (*Left*) Low-power photomicrograph of a section of the upper end of the tibia of a guinea pig. This is the normal appearance. (*Right*) Low-power photomicrograph of a section of the head of a first metatarsal bone removed at operation; note the fibrillation of the articular cartilage.

termed *osteophytes*, grow so as to form lips around the joint. It may be that these outgrowths represent Nature's attempt to restrain movement in the joint.

This combination of degenerative and proliferative changes, although it occurs commonly in the aged, may occur in younger individuals, particularly if the direction of a stress borne by a joint has been altered by some kind of an injury. Hence the condition appears to be the consequence of joints having to perform too much, or the wrong kind of, work.

Effects of Compression on Articular Cartilage. Salter, having observed that degenerative changes were sometimes associated with joints that had been immobilized in forced positions, has made an experimental study with Field and shown that artificially induced compression on joint cartilages will lead to their degeneration. Moreover, they have shown experimentally that if joints are immobilized in forced positions degeneration will occur. Degenerative changes may appear as soon as 6 days after the compression has been applied. They think that the effects of compression interfere with the nutrition of the cells of the articular cartilage which, as has been explained, is probably dependent on diffusion through the synovial fluid and then through the intercellular substances of the cartilage. It would seem logical to assume that the maintenance of a joint in one position with a compression of the cartilage would interfere with this mechanism of nutrition which, it might be thought, would ordinarily be facilitated by movement, which would result in surfaces being more or less continuously coated with fresh synovial fluid.

## REFERENCES

### References for Joints
### General References

Davies, D. V.: The anatomy and physiology of joints *in* Copeman's Textbook of the Rheumatic Diseases, ed. 2, p. 40, Edinburgh, Livingstone, 1955.

### Special References on Joints

Adkins, E. W. O., and Davies, D. V.: Absorption from the joint cavity, Quart. J. Exp. Physiol. 30:147, 1940.

Bauer, W., Ropes, M. W., and Waine, H.: The physiology of articular structures, Physiol. Rev. 20:272, 1940.

Bennett, G. A., Waine, H., and Bauer, W.: Changes in the Knee Joint at Various Ages, New York, Commonwealth Fund, 1942.

Benninghoff, A.: Form und Bau der Gelenkknorpel in ihren Beziehungen zur Funktion (II), Z. Zellforsch. mikr. Anat. 2:783, 1925.

Bradford, F. K., and Spurling, R. G.: The Intervertebral Disc, Springfield, Ill., Thomas, 1941.

Bywaters, E. G. L.: The metabolism of joint tissues, J. Path. Bact. 44:247, 1937.

Clark, W. E. LeGros: The Tissues of the Body, ed. 2, Oxford, Clarendon, 1945.

Crelin, E. S., and Southwick, W. O.: Changes induced by sustained pressure in the knee joint articular cartilage of adult rabbits, Anat. Rec. 149:113, 1964.

Davies, D. V.: Anatomy and physiology of diarthrodial joints, Ann. Rheumat. Dis. 5:29, 1945.

Elliott, H. C.: Studies on articular cartilages. I. Growth mechanisms, Am. J. Anat. 58:127, 1936.

Gardner, E.: The anatomy of the joints, Instruct. Lect. Am. Acad. Orthop. Surg. vol. 9, Ann Arbor, Edwards, 1952.

———: Blood and nerve supply of joints, Stanford M. Bull. 11:203, 1953.

———: The innervation of the elbow joint, Anat. Rec. 102:161, 1948.

———: The innervation of the hip joint, Anat. Rec. 101:353, 1948.

———: The innervation of the knee joint, Anat. Rec. 101:109, 1948.

———: The innervation of the shoulder joint, Anat. Rec. 102:1, 1948.

———: The nerve supply of diarthrodial joints, Stanford M. Bull. 6:367, 1948.

———: Physiology of movable joints, Physiol. Rev. 30:127, 1950.

Gardner, E., and Gray, D. J.: Prenatal development of the human hip joint, Am. J. Anat. 87:163, 1950.

Grant, J. C. B.: Interarticular synovial folds, Brit. J. Surg. 18:636, 1931.

Haines, R. W.: The development of joints, J. Anat. 81:33, 1947.

Hall, Kathleen: The effect of hysterectomy on the action of oestrone on the symphysis pubis of ovariectomized mice, J. Endocrinol. 7:299, 1951.

———: The effect of oestrone and progesterone on the histologic structure of the symphysis pubis of the castrated female mouse, J. Endocrinol. 7:54, 1950.

Hall, Kathleen, and Newton, W. H.: The action of "Relaxin" in the mouse, Lancet 1:54, 1946.

———: The effect of oestrone and relaxin on the x-ray appearance of the pelvis of the mouse, J. Physiol. 106:18, 1947.

———: The normal course of separation of the pubes in pregnant mice, J. Physiol. 104:346, 1946.

Key, J. A.: The reformation of synovial membrane in the knees of rabbits after synovectomy, J. Bone Joint Surg. (N.S.) 7:793, 1925.

———: The synovial membrane of joints and bursae *in* Cowdry's Special Cytology, ed. 2, p. 1053, New York, Hoeber, 1932.

Lanier, R. R.: The effects of exercise on the knee-joints of inbred mice, Anat. Rec. 94:311, 1946.

Lever, J. D., and Ford, E. H. R.: Histological, histochemical and electron microscopic observations on synovial membrane, Anat. Rec. 132:525, 1958.

McDermott, L. J.: Development of the human knee joint, Arch. Surg. 46:705, 1943.

Meyer, K., Smyth, E. M., and Dawson, M. H.: The nature of the mucopolysaccharide of synovial fluid, Science 88:129, 1938.

Paulson, S., Sylvén, B., Hirsch, C., and Snellman, O.: Biophysical and physiological investigations on cartilage and other mesenchymal tissues. III. The diffusion rate of various substances in normal bovine nucleus pulposus, Biochem. biophys. acta *7*:207, 1951.

Ropes, M. W., and Bauer, W.: Synovial Fluid Changes in Joint Disease, Cambridge, Mass., Commonwealth Fund, Harvard Univ. Press, 1953.

Rosenthal, O., Bowie, M. A., and Wagoner, G.: Studies in the metabolism of articular cartilage. I. Respiration and glycolysis of cartilage in relation to its age, J. Cell. Comp. Physiol. *17*:221, 1941.

Ruth, E. B.: Metamorphosis of the pubic symphysis. I. The white rat (Mus norvegicus albinus), Anat. Rec. *64*:1, 1935.

————: Metamorphosis of the pubic symphysis. III. Histological changes in the symphysis of the pregnant guinea pig, Anat. Rec. *67*:409, 1937.

————: A note on the fibrillar structure of hyaline cartilage, Anat. Rec. *96*:93, 1946.

Salter, R. B., and Field, P.: The effects of continuous compression on living articular cartilage, J. Bone Joint Surg. *42-A*:31, 1960.

Silberberg, M., Silberberg, R., and Hasler, M.: Ultrastructure of articular cartilage of mice treated with somatotrophin, J. Bone Joint Surg. *46-A*:766, 1964.

Silberberg, R., Silberberg, M., and Feir, D.: Life cycle of articular cartilage cells: An electron microscope study of the hip joint of the mouse, Am. J. Anat. *114*:17, 1964.

Sigurdson, L. A.: The structure and function of articular synovial membranes, J. Bone Joint Surg. *12*:603, 1930.

Smillie, I. S.: Injuries of the Knee Joint, Edinburgh, Livingstone, 1946.

Sylvén, B., Paulson, S., Hirsch, C., and Snellman, O.: Biophysical and physiological investigations on cartilage and other mesenchymal tissues. II. The ultrastructure of bovine and human nuclei pulposi, J. Bone Joint Surg. *33-A*:333, 1951.

Walmsley, R., and Bruce, J.: The early stages of replacement of the semilunar cartilages of the knee joint in rabbits after operative excision, J. Anat. *72*:260, 1938.

Whillis, J.: The development of synovial joints, J. Anat. *74*:277, 1940.

# 20    Muscular Tissue

Each of the 4 primary tissues represents a structural specialization for the performance of special functions. With a few exceptions (for example, the supporting function of connective tissue, performed by intercellular substance) the special functions performed by the different tissues are due to a specialized development of one or more of the general properties of protoplasm. Among these is the property of contractility. It is this property of protoplasm that is brought to a high state of development in muscular tissue. Another fundamental property of protoplasm, conductivity, is also well developed in muscular tissue, although not so highly as in nervous tissue.

Muscle *cells* are the contractile elements in muscular tissue. However, they are not commonly called cells but *fibers*. To a student who has just studied connective tissue and so becomes familiar with the nonliving fibers of intercullular substance, the designation of muscle cells as fibers may be confusing. It should be emphasized that muscle fibers and the fibers of intercellular substance are of fundamentally different natures; they are similar only in that they have threadlike forms. The shape of cells is often obviously adapted to their function (for example, the shape of the erythrocyte). It takes only a few seconds of reflection to realize that the shortening produced in any one diameter by a rounded cell's contracting would be very limited. If, however, contraction occurs in the cytoplasm of a cell that is drawn out into a long threadlike structure (a fiber), it can effect a substantial reduction in the length of the cell. Muscle cells, being in the form of fibers, are therefore designed so that their cytoplasmic contractions may be effective.

The kinetic energy and the heat that are obtained on the contraction of muscle are obtained from the potential chemical energy of food substances brought to the muscle cells by the bloodstream. It follows, then, that any muscle exercised for any length of time requires an extremely good blood supply so that it may be furnished with a constant supply of fuel and oxygen. An extensive blood supply is also needed to dissipate the heat that is produced simultaneously with the kinetic energy and to take away the waste products of metabolism. As is usual, the blood vessels are carried in connective tissues; hence, connective tissue penetrates and extends throughout muscular tissue. Connective tissue is also needed in muscular tissue to form a harness, so that the pull exerted by muscle fibers may be applied usefully, and also to convey the nerves that supply the muscle fibers. Muscular tissue, then, is not composed entirely of muscle fibers; it is a mixture of muscle fibers and connective tissue.

Muscular tissue is often said to constitute the engines of the body. To pursue the analogy: anyone familiar with power boats knows that it is not customary to install the same type of engine in a fast runabout as is required in a work boat. For the former, a relatively light type of engine capable of "turning up" a vast number of revolutions per minute might be chosen. Although such an engine might be built fairly sturdily, it could scarcely be expected to stand up if it were run at full capacity hour after hour and day after day without frequent opportunities for rehabilitation. But, if an engine is to be called upon to deliver full power day after day and hour after hour, such as may be needed for a work boat, a heavier engine that turns more slowly is usually chosen, one that, in general, is designed to go on day after day with no trouble. The same kind of problem exists in connection with "powering" the different parts of the human body. For some actions, the equivalent of the high-speed light engine is required—for example, the actions of the muscles of a baseball pitcher who pitches only for a short time every few days. For other actions, such as moving the contents of the intestine along hour after hour, something more in the nature of the work-boat engine is required. So, for this reason, the human body contains different kinds of muscular tissue. These will now be discussed.

## CLASSIFICATION OF MUSCLE

Each of the different kinds of muscle in the body has several names. This is partly because muscle is classified on two different bases; a morphologic one and a functional one. First, if muscle fibers, under the microscope, exhibit a regular series of stripes or striations that cross the fibers at right angles, the muscle is said to be *striated* or *striped* muscle. If, however, muscle fibers exhibit no cross stripes or striations but only the longitudinal ones that all muscle fibers exhibit, they are said to be *smooth, nonstriated* or *nonstriped* muscle fibers. This classification of all muscle into striated and smooth is therefore made on a morphologic basis. However, muscle is also classified as to whether or not its action is controlled by the will, that is, on a functional basis. If any muscle can be controlled voluntarily, it is said to be *voluntary* muscle; however, if its actions are outside the control of the will, it is said to be *involuntary*. It so happens that most of the striated muscle of the body is under the control of the will, and almost all, if not all, of the smooth muscle is outside the control of the will. So it is usual to use the terms "striated" almost synonymously with voluntary, and "smooth" with involuntary. However, there is one important exception to this general rule. The muscle of the heart is striated, but it is not under the control of the will. Therefore, it is usually given a separate category and called *cardiac* muscle.

Striated or voluntary muscle is so often attached to one or more points on the skeleton that it is also called skeleton muscle.

A useful classification of muscle is as follows:

    Smooth involuntary
    Striated voluntary (skeletal)
    Striated involuntary (cardiac)

To complete the analogy about engines—the striated (voluntary) muscle of the body is comparable with the flexible, high-speed engines capable of developing great power per unit of weight, which should not be expected to run at full capacity all the time but only for moderate periods with intervals for rehabilitation. The smooth muscle of the body is more like the slow-speed, heavy-duty engine used in a work boat; it goes on day after day at much the same pace. Cardiac muscle has the virtues of smooth muscle in that it works on steadily day after day with no absolute rest, yet, it, like the high-speed engine, is flexible and capable of responding to temporarily increased needs by working faster for limited periods of time without being damaged.

These 3 types of muscle will be considered in detail.

## SMOOTH MUSCLE

**Origin.** Most smooth muscle develops from mesenchyme. This is accomplished by the differentiation of mesenchymal cells into smooth muscle fibers. The cytoplasm of each mesenchymal cell participating in this process becomes drawn out to form a long, tapering smooth muscle fiber. The nucleus of each also becomes elongated. In a few sites in the body in relation to glands (e.g., salivary, sweat, lacrimal), cells are found which have the appearance of smooth muscle cells but are developed from ectoderm. Such cells are called *myo-epithelial* cells.

**Growth and Regeneration.** The given amount of smooth muscle in certain parts of the body may increase in mass during postnatal life, even in adult life. Some of these increases are physiologic; for example, that which occurs in the wall of the uterus during pregnancy. Others are pathologic, such as the increase in the amount of smooth muscle that occurs in the arterioles of people suffering from hypertension. Therefore, it is of interest to inquire how a given mass of smooth muscle can increase in amount in adult life. There are 3 possibilities to be considered. (1) Under the stress of function, individual smooth muscle cells may become increased in size (hypertrophy). (2) Smooth muscle fibers are not very highly differentiated, so they can divide by mitosis. (3) Because they arise from mesenchymal cells, and because residual un-

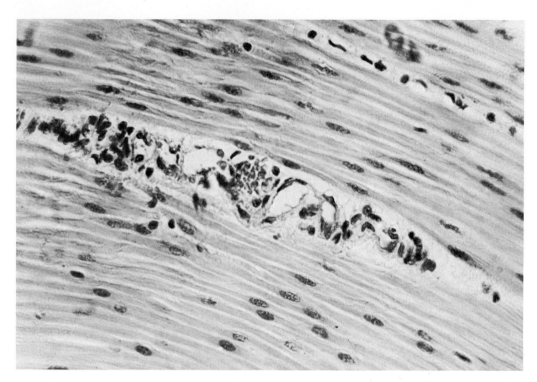

FIG. 20-1. Medium-power photomicrograph of a portion of a section of the small intestine of a dog. The smooth muscle fibers in the wall of the intestine are cut longitudinally. In the middle part of the photograph the fibers are separated by some areolar tissue containing blood vessels and nerves. The remainder of the fibers are separated from one another only by slight amounts of intercellular substance, which shows up in the photograph as light lines.

differentiated mesenchymal cells probably persist as such in many parts of the body, it is by no means impossible that new smooth muscle fibers may arise as a result of the differentiation of residual undifferentiated mesenchymal cells, even in adult life.

**Microscopic Structure.** Smooth muscle fibers have an elongated, tapered form (Fig. 20-1). Their size varies considerably according to their location. The smallest are those that encircle very small blood vessels (Fig. 22-6, *right*); these may be only about 20 $\mu$ in length. The largest are those that are encountered in the wall of the pregnant uterus; here they may be 0.5 mm. in length. However, the usual smooth muscle fiber is probably around 0.2 mm. long and at its widest part is somewhat wider than an erythrocyte.

The *cytoplasm* of smooth muscle cells (fibers) consists of 2 chief elements: myofilaments and sarcoplasm. Bundles of myofilaments may be large enough to appear as a

threadlike structure less than 1 $\mu$ in width and which are longitudinally disposed in the fiber; when these are seen they are termed myofibrils. They lie in the other and more fluid constituent of muscle cytoplasm, the *sarcoplasm*. The myofibrils cannot be seen in every section. If they are not evident, the cytoplasm with the light microscope appears to be homogeneous. The myofilaments can be seen only with the EM.

The cytoplasm of muscle cells is characteristically pink or red in H and E sections. Sometimes empty spaces may be seen in it. These represent deposits of glycogen which have dissolved away in preparing the section. The significance of glycogen in muscle cells will become apparent when physiology is studied.

The *nucleus* of a smooth muscle fiber lies in its widest part (Figs. 20-1 and 20-2), but, instead of being in the middle of the cell, it is situated somewhat eccentrically; this is seen

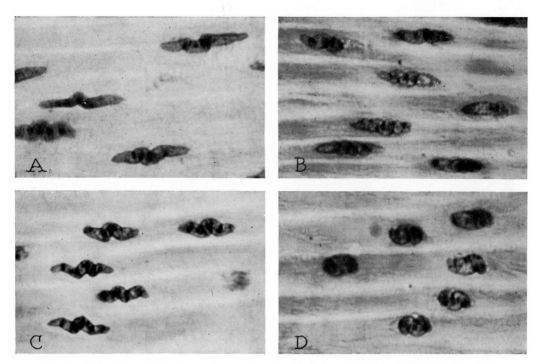

FIG. 20-2. High-powered photomicrographs of smooth muscle of the intestine, showing how the elongated nuclei of the fibers are thrown into folds (pleats) when the fibers, on contraction, become shorter and thicker. In D they are folded so tightly that they appear, on superficial examination, to be ovoid.

to best advantage in cross sections (Fig. 20-3). The nucleus tends to have a cylindrical form with either pointed or blunt, rounded ends (Fig. 20-1). It contains fine chromatin granules; hence, it does not stain very intensely. It may contain several nucleoli. Often the nuclei of smooth muscle cells seen in longitudinal sections seem pleated along their longitudinal axes. The rodlike nuclei become passively pleated to fit into shorter spaces as the cytoplasm contracts; hence, the degree to which their nuclei are folded (Fig. 20-2) gives an indication of the extent to which fibers are contracted.

As smooth muscle fibers and connective tissue cells both arise from mesenchymal cells, it is not surprising that smooth muscle and connective tissue are intimately associated in the body. Smooth muscle cells occasionally exist as single fibers surrounded by connective tissue but as a general rule smooth muscle fibers are arranged together in bundles or sheets (Fig. 20-1). In these, a little reticular intercellular substance usually lies between the

fibers that comprise the bundle or sheet (Fig. 20-1). It seems likely that this is made by the smooth muscle fibers—another indication of their close relationship to connective tissue cells. Bundles or sheets of fibers are surrounded by connective tissue, often of a fairly elastic type (Fig. 20-3); however, the intercellular substance of this is made by the fibroblasts it contains. This connective tissue conveys capillaries and nerve fibers to the group of muscle fibers it surrounds (Fig. 20-1, center).

**Fine Structure.** The myofibrils of the smooth muscle cell contain longitudinally disposed myofilaments. These may be arranged side by side to form loose bundles termed myofibrils. Between myofibrils there are clefts for the nucleus, the mitochondria and other cytoplasmic components, for example, glycogen. The nucleus often contain 1 or 2 nucleoli.

Since smooth muscle fibers are commonly packed together in sheets which form one of the wrappings in the walls of various kinds of tubes in the body, for example, in the walls of

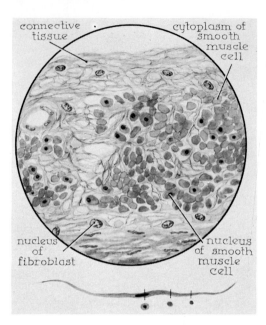

FIG. 20-3. Drawing (high-power) of a group of smooth muscle cells cut in cross section. Since smooth muscle fibers are elongated, cross sections cut through them seldom pass through their nuclei. Hence, most of the smooth muscle fibers seen in this illustration do not reveal nuclei. Those that are present are either centrally or eccentrically disposed. The single fiber illustrated in the lower part of the picture shows how cross sections through different parts of a fiber appear.

arteries and the intestine, and since adjacent smooth muscle fibers in these sites contract more or less in unison to narrow the lumen of the tube in whose wall they are disposed, it is obvious that there must be some arrangement that permits adjacent fibers to all contract simultaneously. There are two ways this could be accomplished: (1) by means of a separate nerve fiber passing to each muscle cell and by impulses for contraction passing via these different fibers simultaneously to all the fibers in a given area so that they would all contract simultaneously, or (2) by a nerve impulse arriving at one muscle cell in a given area being conducted rapidly from this cell to others in the same area so that they all contract more or less simultaneously. Recent studies indicate that both types of arrangement exist; Bozler refers to these as the multiunit and the vis-

ceral types of arrangement, respectively. In the multiunit type of arrangement, which is found for example in the smooth muscle coat of the vas deferens, the smooth muscle fibers are completely separate from one another and there is a nerve ending comparable to a motor end plate (which will be described in connection with striated muscle) on each smooth muscle fiber. The simultaneous contraction of adjacent cells in this type of arrangement would depend on nerve impulses arriving simultaneously at all the cells of the area. In the second type of arrangement, which is found in the intestine and termed the visceral type, the impulse for contraction, on arriving at the muscle fiber, is transmitted from it to others rapidly enough for adjacent fibers to contract together. We might then ask what sort of mechanism exists in these fibers to permit the impulse for contraction to be conducted rapidly from one smooth muscle cell to another.

One explanation held by many authors through the years was that there was cytoplasmic continuity between smooth muscle fibers of the visceral type so that a wave of excitation could flow just as readily from cell to cell as it could from one part of a cell to another. And indeed some observations with the light microscope seemed to confirm this view. When the EM became available it became apparent that the kind of cytoplasmic continuity that existed between adjacent fibers was probably not due to gaps in the cell membranes of adjacent cells, but instead due to fusions of the cell membranes of adjacent fibers. In the intestine it has been estimated that about 5 per cent of the surface of a smooth muscle fiber is in very intimate contact with other fibers. At these sites of contact, illustrated in a low-power electron micrograph in Figure 20-4, the outer layers of the cell membranes of the adjacent cells are seen, in a micrograph of great magnification, to be fused (Fig. 20-5), just as they are in the zonula occludens of the junctional complex described in Chapter 8. There is, in effect, cytoplasmic continuity between adjacent cells in the visceral type of arrangement even though there are probably no gaps in the cell membrane through which semifluid cytoplasm reaches from one cell to another as was formerly visualized.

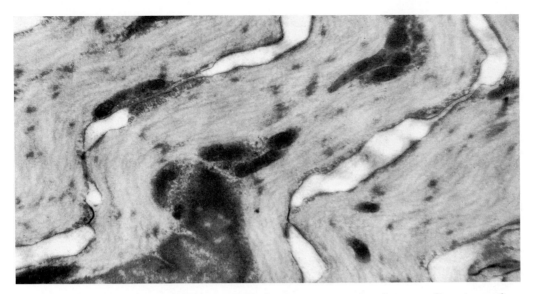

FIG. 20-4. Electron micrograph (× 40,000) showing contact regions between adjacent smooth muscle cells in the rat intestine. For higher magnification of contact regions see Figure 20-5. (Oosaki, T., and Ishii, S.: J. Ultrastruct. Res. *10*:567)

**Function and Distribution.** Although smooth muscle is used in certain sites for performing active contractions as, for example, in the wall of the intestine, where active contractions of smooth muscle force the intestinal content along its way, it is also used for maintaining a state of sustained contraction called *tonus*. In its employment for maintaining tonus, smooth muscle usually is disposed so as to encircle the lumen of a tube. In this situation the state of tonus of the encircling muscle regulates the diameter of the tube. The size of arterioles depends to a great extent on the tonus of the encircling smooth muscle fibers in their walls (Fig. 22-6), and this, it will be learned, is of great importance in regulating blood pressure. Not uncommonly (for example, in the intestine) smooth muscle is employed to serve both purposes: to maintain tonus constantly and to contract actively and inconstantly.

As various organs and structures are de-

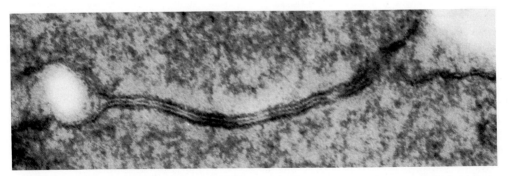

FIG. 20-5. Electron micrograph (× 500,000) of contact region between two adjacent smooth muscle cells. The outer layers of the contiguous cell membranes are fused to form what appears as a single dark line that runs along the middle of the contact region. The arrangement is similar to that seen in the *zonula occludens* of junctional complexes in epithelial cells illustrated and described in Chapter 8. (Oosaki, T., and Ishii, S.: J. Ultrastruct. Res. *10*:567)

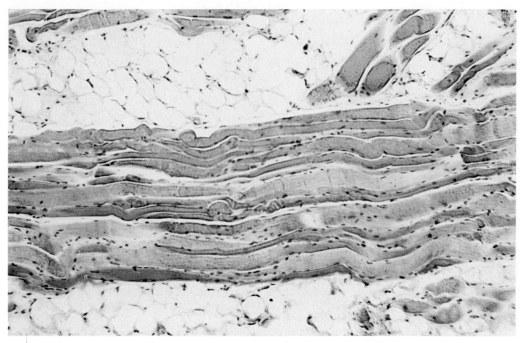

Fig. 20-6. A very low-power photomicrograph of a portion of a section of human tongue. A bundle of striated muscle fibers may be seen horizontally disposed in the middle of the picture. Fat tissue is present on both sides of the bundle. A few obliquely cut fibers are present in the upper right-hand corner. The striated muscle fibers in the bundle may be seen to be multinucleated.

scribed, the distribution of smooth muscle in the body will become apparent. For the present it is enough to state that its chief role is to supply the viscera where either movement or the maintenance of tonus is needed.

**Some Points About the Recognition of Smooth Muscle.** In tissues in which smooth muscle and connective tissue are intimately mixed, it is sometimes difficult to tell them apart. The cytoplasm of the smooth muscle fibers (cells) may be confused with the collagen fibers of the connective tissue, and the nuclei of smooth muscle cells with the nuclei of fibroblasts or other connective tissue cells.

The cytoplasm of smooth muscle fibers generally stains somewhat more pink or reddish than collagen in H and E sections; it has a more "meaty" appearance. If cut longitudinally, the nuclei of smooth muscle fibers are longer and less ovoid (Fig. 20-1) than the nuclei of young fibroblasts (Fig. 11-3). The nuclei of old fibroblasts, particularly in tendons, are often fairly long (Fig. 11-20), but if so, they tend to be thinner than the nuclei

of smooth muscle fibers. Furthermore, the nuclei of smooth muscle fibers (if seen in longitudinal section) often exhibit a regularly wrinkled (snakefence) appearance (Fig. 20-2).

Sometimes special staining is necessary to decide whether a given area of tissue is smooth muscle or collagen. Mallory's and Van Gieson's stains, which color collagen blue and red, respectively, are commonly used for this purpose.

## STRIATED, SKELETAL OR VOLUNTARY MUSCLE

This constitutes what the layman calls the "muscles" with which man performs voluntary actions. It is capable of rapid powerful contraction (example, throwing a baseball) and also of maintaining prolonged states of partially sustained contraction—tonus (example, holding the head erect).

Like smooth muscle, the striated variety is made up of muscle fibers supported by con-

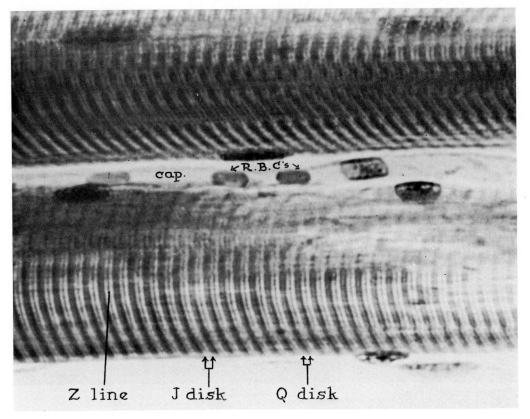

FIG. 20-7. Very high-power photomicrograph of a longitudinal section of two striated muscle fibers (human) with a capillary between them.

nective tissue. However, the fibers are much larger than those of smooth muscle, measuring from 1 to 40 mm. in length and from 10 to 40 $\mu$ in width. A single nucleus is not sufficient for such an extensive mass of cytoplasm; hence, striated muscle fibers are multinucleated cells (Fig. 20-6). The nuclei are of an elongated, ovoid shape, and in the striated muscles of man (but not in those of some animals), most of them are situated in the peripheral cytoplasm of the cylindrically shaped fibers (Figs. 20-7 and 20-20). The peripheral distribution of the nuclei constitutes an important criterion by which the student may distinguish striated from smooth and cardiac muscle, for in the latter two the nuclei have a more central position in the fiber (compare Fig. 20-3 with 20-20 and 20-24). The peripheral distribution of striated muscle fiber nuclei is seen to better advantage in cross sections than in longitudinal sections,

because a peripheral nucleus at the very top or bottom of a round fiber, on being viewed from above in a longitudinal section, will seem to be in its middle.

Each striated fiber is enclosed by a thin, apparently structureless membrane called the *sarcolemma*, much as a sausage is covered with a skin. The sarcolemma is formed by, and hence is a part of, the muscle fiber instead of being a product of, and hence a part of, the connective tissue that surrounds the fiber. The sarcolemma cannot be seen in ordinary sections, not only because it is very thin and stains poorly, but also because it remains tightly adherent to the sides of the fiber.

The most striking way that striated muscle differs from smooth muscle cells, however, is that the fibers of striated muscle exhibit *cross striations* along their course—this is why they are termed striated muscle fibers (Fig. 20-7).

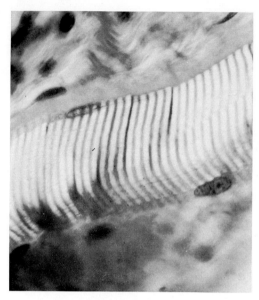

FIG. 20-8. High-power photomicrograph of a longitudinal section of a striated muscle fiber taken with crossed polaroid filters. The A bands are light, and the I bands are dark. (Preparation by P. M. Hartroft)

It should not be expected that every longitudinally cut striated muscle fiber seen in a section will clearly exhibit cross striations. For technical and other reasons they may not. But a search of different fields in a section, or of other sections, should reveal some fibers that show cross striations clearly. The cross striations of longitudinally sectioned fibers may appear as straight lines, but if the upper surface of a fiber is seen in a section, and that fiber does not lie exactly in a longitudinal plane, its cross striations will appear as crescents (Fig. 20-7), as will the individual coins in a pile of coins if the side of the pile is looked at obliquely.

When fibers showing good striations are found and studied, the first impression one obtains is that the cross-striated appearance is due to the cytoplasm of the fiber consisting of alternating thin disks or bands (these two terms are used interchangeably) of light and dark material (Fig. 20-7). With polarized light the disks that seem darker with the ordinary light microscope are anisotropic (birefringent) (Fig. 20-8) while those that are lighter are isotropic (Fig. 20-8). Accordingly, the darker disks are called A bands (A

for anisotropic) or Q bands (Q for the German *Querscheibe*, which means transverse disk). The light transverse disks are called I bands (I for isotropic) or J bands.

In good preparations each I band can be seen to be bisected by a thin dark disk or line; this is called the Z line or disk, (Z for the German *Zwischenscheibe*, which means intermediate disk) (Fig. 20-7).

In the usual preparation of striated muscle, seen in the light microscope (Fig. 20-7) or even under polarized light (Fig. 20-8), the cross striations seem to be continuous from one side of a fiber to the other. But they are not. With excellent resolution a striated muscle fiber is seen to consist of longitudinally disposed myofibrils which are slightly separated from one another (examine Fig. 20-9). The substance between myofibrils is termed sarcoplasm; it shows no cross striations but does contain certain organelles of the cytoplasm, for example, mitochondria and smooth-surfaced endoplasmic reticulum, as will be described presently. Since cross striations are features of the *myofibrils,* they do not extend from one side of a fiber to the other. Why then do they seem, in the light microscope, to extend across whole fibers?

The chief reasons for cross striations in the usual preparation seen with the light microscope *seeming* to extend from one side of a fiber to the other is that the myofibrils are close together but, what is more important, their cross striations *are usually (but not always) in register with one another.* As is shown in the diagram (Fig. 20-9) the A band of one myofibril is beside the A bands of the myofibrils that are beside it; likewise the I bands and the Z disks are always beside their counterparts in adjacent myofibrils. Without excellent resolution, the A bands, the I bands and the Z disks therefore all *seem* to extend in continuous stripes from one side of a fiber to the other.

The portion of one myofibril between two Z disks is termed a *sarcomere* (Fig. 20-9). As we shall see presently, the sarcomere is the unit of contraction.

### THE FINE STRUCTURE OF STRIATED MUSCLE FIBERS

**Introduction.** The foregoing has explained that a striated muscle fiber is a long cell with

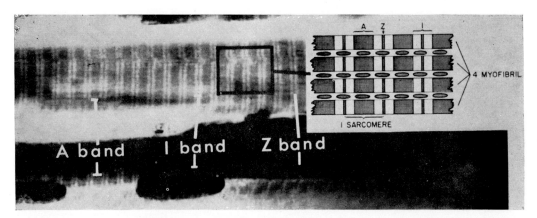

Fig. 20-9. Photomicrograph of longitudinal section of two striated muscle fibers. The drawing at the right is designed to show that the appearance of striations being continuous across fibers is due to the segments (bands) of adjacent myofibrils being in register with one another. The individual myofibrils are slightly separated from one another by sarcoplasm that contains mitochondria (oval structures in the inset). A sarcomere is the portion of one myofibril between two Z bands.

occasional nuclei distributed along its edges. The cytoplasm of the fiber is made up of two main components: (1) longitudinally disposed myofibrils and (2) sarcoplasm. (Actually the myofibrils are organelles of the cytoplasm and hence part of the sarcoplasm, but in muscle it is customary to use the term sarcoplasm for the substance in which myofibrils are immersed.) The sarcoplasm contains mitochondria and endoplasmic reticulum including tubular extensions from the sarcolemma that encloses the fiber.

The myofibrils are the components of the fiber that contract, and the sarcomere is the contractile unit of the myofibril. The components of the sarcoplasm serve other functions. The mitochondria disposed between myofibrils (Figs. 20-9 and 20-13) are concerned with providing energy needed for the work of the fiber. Particles of glycogen, which material is a source of fuel, may be seen as inclusions in the sarcoplasm (Fig. 20-13, gg). The sarcoplasm also contains membranous vesicular structures which are the representatives in striated muscle fibers of the endoplasmic reticulum seen in other kinds of cells. The predominant kind is of the smooth-surfaced variety. Finally, the striated muscle fiber is enclosed by a sarcolemma. A nerve fiber extends to each muscle fiber and at the site where it makes contact with the sarcolemma there is an arrangement known as a motor end plate. When a nerve impulse reaches a motor end plate a wave of depolarization sweeps over the sarcolemma, and all the sarcomeres within the fiber contract. There must therefore be some means for the wave of depolarization to be conducted to all the sarcomeres of all the myofibrils within the fiber. This means is provided by vast numbers of *centrotubules*; these are tubular prolongations derived from, and continuous with, the sarcolemma. From the sarcolemma they pass into the fiber at right angles to its surface, branch, and surround each myofibril. In frog muscle (which is the best known), the centrotubules surround the myofibril at the level of its Z disks. The location of the centrotubules may be different in mammals. By means of the centrotubules every sarcomere is in contact with the sarcolemma and a means is provided for waves of depolarization to reach every sarcomere in the fiber.

We shall now describe the fine structure of these various components of a fiber in more detail. We shall first describe the fine structure of myofibrils and the changes they undergo when they contract. Afterward we shall consider the sarcoplasm and in particular the endoplasmic reticulum and the inward tubular extensions of the sarcolemma which form a conducting system within the fiber.

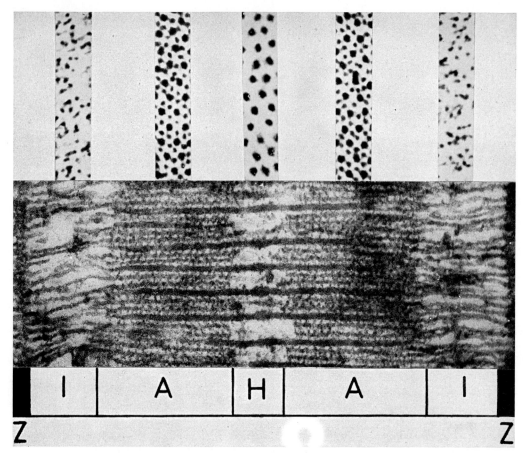

FIG. 20-10. Electron micrographs (× 150,000) of cross (above) and longitudinal (below) sections of relaxed striated muscle, taken from the rabbit psoas muscle. The thick (myosin) and the thin (actin) myofilaments are easily distinguished. Note that neither extends the full length of the sarcomere. Cross sections of the various bands are illustrated above. The cross bridges between the myosin and the actin filaments can be seen in the longitudinal sections. (Electron micrographs by Dr. H. E. Huxley)

### THE CYTOPLASMIC ORGANELLES OF STRIATED MUSCLE FIBERS

#### (1) The Fine Structure of Myofibrils

Light microscopy showed clearly that muscle fibers are composed of myofibrils embedded in sarcoplasm. Furthermore, light microscopy suggested the existence of more delicate fibrils within the myofibril for, in 1888, Kolliker described myofibrils as containing still finer filaments within them. That the myofibrils were indeed made up of *myofilaments* was confirmed when it became possible to study sections of striated muscle with the EM. The earlier studies with the EM, al-though they disclosed myofilaments in the myofibrils, did not resolve them sufficiently well to make it obvious that in a relaxed fiber (1) the filaments do not extend from one end of a sarcomere to the other, and (2) there are two different types of myofilaments. Both of these latter facts have been established in recent years by Huxley and by Huxley and Hanson.

Proof that the sarcomere contains two types of filaments, and that neither type extends throughout the whole length of the sarcomere, came only from high-resolution studies of both cross and longitudinal sections of myofibrils. From these studies it became apparent that the relative lack of density of I bands and H bands, noticed with the light microscope and the earlier studies with the EM, was due to their each containing only one kind of myofilament, and that the greater density of the A band was due to its containing both kinds of filaments, which interdigitated with each other (Figs. 20-10, 20-11 and 20-12).

The two types of filaments differ in diameter, length, position and composition. The most convenient way to designate them is by their different diameters, so we shall term them the *fine* and the *coarse* filaments.

The fine ones in the rabbit psoas muscle, according to Huxley, are 50 Å in diameter and $2 \mu$ in length. One end of each fine filament is attached to a Z disk. From the Z disks the fine filaments extend toward the middle of each adjacent sarcomere (Figs. 20-10, 20-11 and 20-12) where they terminate in free ends

before reaching the middle. The gap between the free ends of the fine filaments accounts for the H bands (Figs 20-10 and 20-11).

The coarse filaments, according to Huxley, are 100 Å in diameter and $1.5 \mu$ in length. In relaxed muscle they are disposed longitudinally in the middle part of the sarcomere extending toward but not reaching each end of the sarcomere (Figs. 20-10, 20-11 and 20-12). In the middle of each sarcomere *only* coarse filaments are present, and this accounts for the H band (Figs. 20-10, 20-11 and 20-12). However, proceeding from the H band toward both ends of the sarcomere, they interdigitate with the fine filaments which are extending from the Z disks toward, but not reaching, the middle. Since the coarse filaments do not reach the Z disks, there is a region on each side of each Z disk which has only fine filaments; this accounts for the I band and its relatively

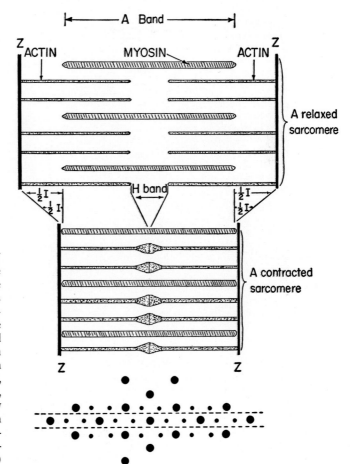

FIG. 20-11. Diagram of part of one sarcomere of striated muscle to show how, in contraction, the thick and the thin myofilaments slide along each other with resulting shortening of the sarcomere and disappearance of the H and the I bands. The small diagram (below) illustrates a cross section through the A band. As indicated, a very thin longitudinal section, cut in the proper plane, will show two fine myofilaments between each pair of coarse ones. (Diagrams based on the sliding-filament hypothesis of H. E. Huxley)

light density. The site where the coarse and the fine filaments interdigitate is the A disk, and the greater density of the myofibril in this site is, of course, due to its possessing both types of filaments; this is why the A band is dark when seen with the light microscope.

The Z disk is a narrow band of dense material.

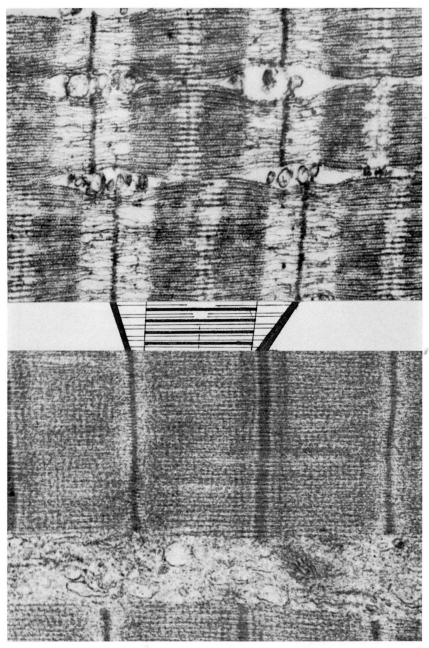

Fig. 20-12. Electron micrographs (× 60,000) of longitudinal sections of relaxed (above) and a contracted (below) rabbit psoas muscle, illustrating the shortening of a sarcomere. Note the differences between the two micrographs as a result of the sliding that has occurred between thick and thin myofilaments. See also Figure 20-11. (Assembled from illustrations by Huxley, H. E.: J. Biophys. Biochem. Cytol. 3:631)

Cross sections cut through the I band of a relaxed fiber will reveal only the fine filaments (Fig. 20-10), and cross sections through the H band will reveal only the coarse filaments (Fig. 20-10). Of course, cross sections through the A band will reveal both coarse and fine filaments (Fig. 20-10).

Where the filaments interdigitate in the relaxed vertebrate muscle (the A band), the fine filaments are seen in a cross section to be arranged so as to form hexagons with a coarse filament in the center of each hexagon. The coarse filaments are arranged so as to form triangles, each of which has a fine filament in its center (Figs. 20-10 and 20-11, *bottom diagram*). The bottom diagram in Figure 20-11 shows how a longitudinal section of a myofibril can be cut so as to show two fine filaments between each coarse one. It also shows how sections cut in a different plane would be very difficult to interpret and why the study of cross sections is so essential to revealing the true arrangements of the filaments.

Huxley has described also an intricate system of cross bridges between the coarse and the fine filaments. These project from the coarse filament at fairly regular intervals along their course and are arranged in a spiral. These bridges connect each thick filament at intervals to each of its three adjacent thin filaments in human muscle. They can be seen in Figure 20-10.

**The Mechanism of Contraction.** From the studies of Huxley it has become apparent that the contraction of a sarcomere (and hence of a muscle fiber) does not entail any significant shortening of either the coarse or the fine filaments. Contraction of the sarcomere is due to the fine filaments (which extend from each end of the sarcomere toward but, in a relaxed muscle, not reaching its middle) sliding farther and farther into the interstices between the coarse filaments (with which they interdigitate), pulling the Z disks to which they are attached with them, until at full contraction the free ends of the fine filaments meet each other in the middle of the sarcomere where they may even bulge against one another. Of course, this pulls the Z disks closer together and so shortens the sarcomere (Figs. 20-11 and 20-12).

Since the relative lack of density of the H zone in a relaxed myofibril is due to its containing only coarse filaments, it is obvious that in a contracted myofibril, in which the fine filaments slide into this area to meet one another, this area will then have both types of filaments and so will be as dense as the former A band. Likewise, the sliding of the fine filaments into the coarse ones pulls the Z bands so close to the free ends of the coarse filaments that the relative lack of density of the I bands disappears, for it too, as the fibril contracts, comes to contain both kinds of filaments.

From the foregoing it would seem that contraction is due to the fine and the coarse filaments suddenly coming to possess an increased attraction for each other, an attraction that is of a kind that results in one kind of filament sliding along the other so that the maximum attachment between their respective surface areas can be obtained. To inquire into the nature of the attraction that forms between the two types of filaments at contraction and the loss of the attraction that occurs on relaxation requires that the chemistry and the biochemistry of muscle be discussed briefly.

Three proteins have been isolated from muscle—myosin, actin and tropomyosin. Both chemical studies and interference microscopy have shown that the coarse filaments are composed of myosin. Furthermore, if myofibrils are treated so as to extract actin, the I bands of relaxed muscle are removed, which indicates that the fine filaments are composed of actin. It seems probable that the fine filaments also contain the tropomyosin of muscle.

Next, it has been shown that muscles derive their energy from the breakdown of adenosine triphosphate (ATP) to adenosine diphosphate (ADP). This reaction *releases* large amounts of energy. Conversely, the resynthesis of ATP from ADP *requires* energy. This energy for the latter step is supplied by the breakdown of carbohydrates. Thus, the energy released in the breakdown of carbohydrates is stored in the form of ATP, which is, therefore, spoken of as a high-energy compound.

It has been known for a long time that actin would combine with myosin to form actomyosin, and some years ago it was shown that if artificially prepared threads of precipitated actomyosin were placed in a solution containing ATP they would contract. This finding seemed to suggest that energy donated

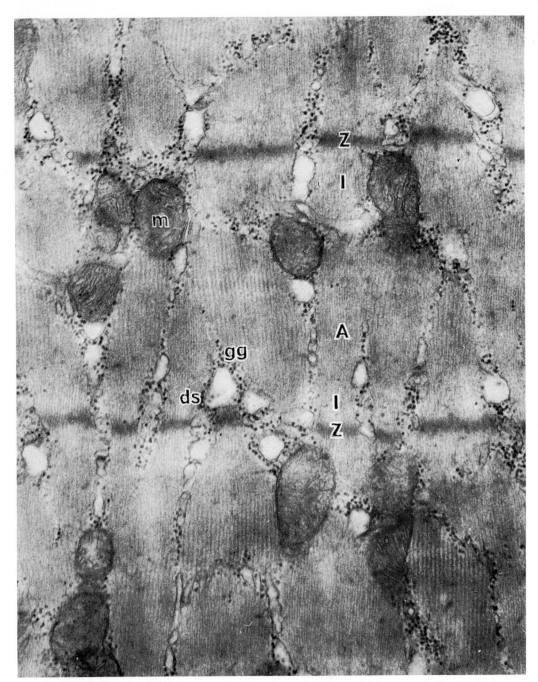

FIG. 20-13. Electron micrograph of section of rat tongue muscle showing mitochondria (m) and sarcoplasmic reticulum (ds) surrounded by particles of glycogen (gg). The letters Z, I and A refer to the corresponding bands of myofibrils. (Preparation by A. Coimbra)

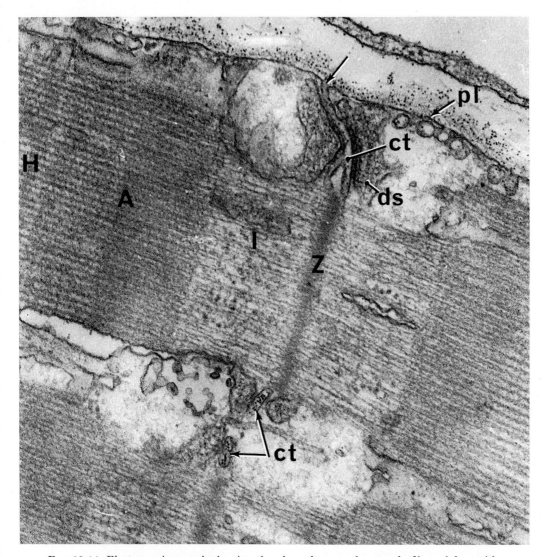

Fig. 20-14. Electron micrograph showing the plasmalemma of a muscle fiber of frog with an underlying myofibril. Particulate material (Ferritin in a Ringer solution) has been placed in contact with the sarcolemma (*plasmalemma* = pl) and may be seen as fine black particles. The arrow shows the opening of a centrotubule (ct) at the surface of the plasmalemma. The centrotubule is shown dividing into two branches that will go on each side of the myofibril. Two cross sections (arrows) of centrotubules are also seen between the two myofibrils. The presence of particulate material in their lumens demonstrates the migration of this material into the centrotubule. (Preparation by R. I. Birks)

by ATP could be utilized by actin and myosin that were already combined with one another and that it somehow led to a contraction of the combined proteins. More recently it has been shown that the action of ATP is not a direct one that induces a shortening of actin and myosin that are already combined, but instead its presence leads to their dissociation, and this is what occurs when ATP is added to a solution of actomyosin—the actin and the myosin become dissociated. In the muscle fiber the action of ATP in dissociating the actin and the myosin filaments permits the muscle fiber to relax. Whenever the ATP is converted to ADP the actin and the myosin recombine, and this results in contraction. Therefore, the ATP has two actions: (1) its presence prevents actin and myosin from combining, and (2) the energy it gives off in being converted to ADP provides the energy for contraction. Hence, the energy for contraction in a relaxed muscle is stored in its ATP much in the same way that energy is stored in the spring of a cocked air rifle. When the trigger is pulled the potential energy of the spring is released. Similarly, when an impulse for con-

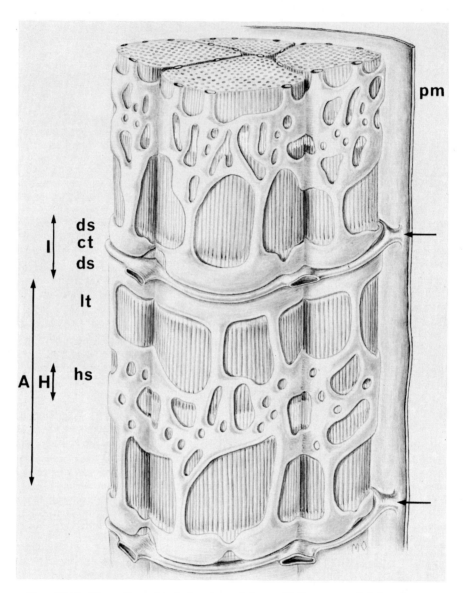

FIG. 20-15. Three-dimensional drawing of 3 myofibrils surrounded by the sarcoplasmic reticulum. The reticulum is composed of the centrotubule (ct) which circles the myofibril over the Z disk and opens at the surface of the plasmalemma (arrow). The second part of the sarcoplasmic reticulum is more complex, consisting of (1) distended sacs (ds) on either side of the centrotubule, (2) longitudinal tubules (lt), and (3) the flat H-zone sacs (hs); the 3 structures are interconnected. (Preparation provided by C. P. Leblond)

traction arrives at the muscle, ATP is broken down to ADP. This reaction is catalyzed by myosin, and the reaction provides the energy required for the myosin and actin filaments combining along their lengths.

Huxley has observed that when a muscle contracts, the extent of the sliding of the actin filaments along the myosin filaments is much greater than the distance between any two lateral projections on the myosin filaments, by which they are anchored to the actin filaments. Therefore, it is reasonable to suppose that during contraction, these lateral projections alternately disconnect and reconnect the myosin to new sites along the actin filament.

### (2) The Other Organelles of the Cytoplasm of Striated Muscle Fibers

Having considered myofibrils we shall now consider the other organelles of muscle fibers. Although there are small Golgi complexes and a few ribosomes in the region of the nuclei that are scattered along the periphery of striated muscle fibers, the most important organelles seen with the EM are the mitochondria and smooth-surfaced endoplasmic reticulum which in striated muscle fibers is termed the *sarcoplasmic reticulum*.

The numerous mitochondria are disposed between the myofibrils (Fig. 20-13) in sarcoplasm which also contains some particles of glycogen (g.g.).

The sarcoplasmic reticulum consists of two kinds of membranous structures which, as we shall see, come into contact with one another. These, and the arrangements in which they exist in striated muscle fibers, will now be described.

The first kind consists of what are termed centrotubules. These are very numerous. Each begins (top arrow in Fig. 20-14) as a funnel-like invagination of the sarcolemma at sites along a fiber where Z disks are in register (Fig. 20-14). The centrotubule enters the substance of a fiber more or less at right angles to it. Each tubule branches and rebranches so as to surround every myofibril at that site along the fiber, which in frog muscle is at Z disk, as is shown in the 3-dimensional drawing that comprises Figure 20-15. However, it seems in some species the tubules surround sarcomeres at the sites of other disks.

The lumen of tubular system, that extends in from the sacrolemma, is open to the outside of the fiber (Fig. 20-14). Ferritin, which is a finely granular but dense material that shows up as black dots in the EM can, under experimental conditions, be shown to pass from outside a fiber into the funnel-like opening of a branching system of centrotubules and from there pass deep into fiber by way of the lumen of centrotubules (Fig. 20-14). The lumen of each branching system of centrotubules is therefore continuous with the outside of a fiber. The system of centrotubules that enters into the fiber at every site where, in frog muscle, Z disks are in register, is in effect a continuation of the sarcolemma.

The sarcolemma is a membrane with remarkable electrical properties. It acts to maintain a higher concentration of sodium and chloride ions outside than inside the fiber, and a higher concentration of potassium ions inside than outside the fiber; the net result of this ion balance is a potential difference of about 10 millivolts between the inside and the outside of a resting muscle fiber. When a nerve impulse arrives at a motor nerve ending in a fiber (these will be described presently), the potential difference is wiped out. This depolarization progresses rapidly along the sarcolemma. As a result, the fiber contracts. Until recently it was a mystery as to how the impulse for contraction could be conducted into the interior of the fiber quickly enough for all its parts to contract more or less simultaneously. It seemed impossible that ions could diffuse into the fiber from its surface quickly enough to accomplish this end. Now that the system of centrotubules has been shown to exist it is thought that the impulse for contraction is conducted into the fiber via the systems of centrotubules that project into the fibers at each Z disk. Since they are invaginations of the sarcolemma, they could act similarly to the sarcolemma and so permit a wave of depolarization to sweep into the fiber and reach every sarcomere. Indeed, Huxley and co-workers found that, provided a centrotubule was present, a highly localized subthreshold depolarization of the muscle surface (produced by a 5-$\mu$ electrode) induced a contraction of individual sarcomeres. When the dose was increased, the contraction spread transversally across the fiber, that is, via the centrotubules, but never longitudinally along myofibrils. However, the second kind of membranous vesicles, which are found between adjacent sarcomeres, and which will now be described, may be concerned in conducting a wave of depolarization from one end to the other of each sarcomere (but not from one sarcomere to the two adjoining ones) as will be described presently.

The second portion of the sarcoplasmic reticulum consists of membranous structures of 3 different shapes and sizes: The first are of the order of distended vesicles (400-1,000 Å thick) which, beside the centrotubules, surround each sarcomere over each of its I bands, so that there is one at each end of each sarcomere (as in Fig. 20-15). They often contain granular material. These distended vesicles are in contact with one myofibril on one face and with other adjacent myofibrils on their other face (Fig. 20-15). These vesicles connect with the second kind of membranous structures which are longitudinal tubules (300-600 Å in diameter) which lie over the A band (as in Fig. 20-15). These tubules which form a sort of network pass from each end toward the middle of the sarcomere where they open into an irregular branching system of tubules that surrounds the myofibril at the level of the H band; the latter tubules accordingly are said to constitute the H-band sac (h.s. in Fig. 20-15); this is rather flat, being only 250 to 300 Å thick (Fig. 20-15).

**Relations Between the Two Arrangements of Sarcoplasmic Reticulum: The Centrotubules and the Vesicles and Tubules That Lie Between Sarcomeres.** Near the plasma membrane, the wall of a centrotubule is smooth (Fig. 20-14), but, when it comes into contact with the distended membranous vesicles (as in Fig. 20-15) of the sarcoplasmic reticulum, the common wall has a beaded appearance which, according to Birks, might be due to the presence of a number of tiny passages connecting the lumens of the two structures. Huxley on the other hand considers that centrotubules make up a completely closed system. If tiny passages exist to connect the centrotubules and the distended vesicles that are over the I band (ds in Fig. 20-15), waves of depolarization could be conducted from the centrotubules to, and over, the distended vesicles (ds in Fig. 20-15). There is granular material

in the latter. There is evidence that this granular material binds calcium ions or at least that the distended sacs do so, because, by differential centrifugation, a calcium-binding fraction is obtained which the EM shows to be composed of large vesicles with the same diameter as the distended sacs. Presumably then, on stimulation the distended sacs would release calcium, which would diffuse among the myofilaments, thereby activating the myosin-bound adenosine triphosphatase. This enzyme in turn would split ATP to provide the energy for the inward sliding of actin filaments as previously described. Activity, the hypothesis suggests, would be terminated when ATP splitting is arrested. Perhaps, as the actin filaments approach the A band, the H-band sacs of the reticulum, by virtue of their calcium-pumping action, would induce the liberated calcium ions to be reaccumulated into the reticulum and rejoin the granular material.

It may be added that the sarcoplasmic reticulum is associated with particulate glycogen (differing from the rosettelike glycogen of liver, to be described later). This glycogen stands out in the cytoplasm next to the sarcoplasmic reticulum (Fig. 20-13). It is thought that this glycogen provides a ready source of calories.

**Cohnheim's Fields.** With the light microscope the myofibrils of some striated muscle fibers seen in cross section are seen to be arranged more or less into bundles within the fiber. Sarcoplasm, of course, extends between each and every myofibril within each bundle, but there is more between bundles than between the myofibrils within a bundle. The thicker partitions of sarcoplasm between bundles more or less divide the fiber up into fields (each of which is a bundle of myofibrils), and these are sometimes termed *Cohnheim's fields.*

## DEVELOPMENT AND GROWTH OF STRIATED MUSCLE FIBERS

The first sign of development of a striated muscle is the appearance of myoblasts; these are spindle-shaped cells, each with a single nucleus, and they undergo repeated mitoses at a rapid rate. Eventually some of the myoblasts stop dividing and fuse into elongated

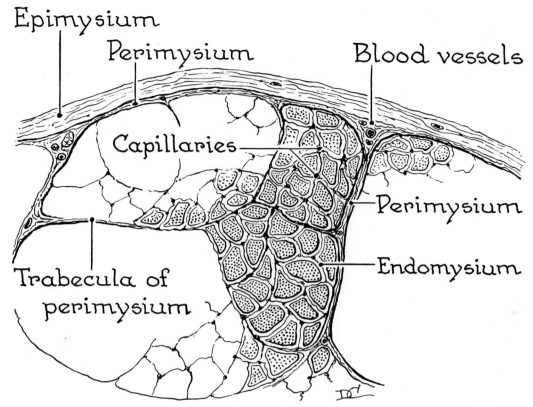

Epimysium

Perimysium

Blood vessels

Capillaries

Perimysium

Endomysium

Trabecula of perimysium

Fig. 20-16. Diagram of a cross section of a muscle. This shows the connective tissue epimysium that surrounds the muscle. The partitions of perimysium that divide the muscle into bundles and the delicate connective tissue endomysium that extends between the individual fibers in the bundles and carries the capillaries may also be seen.

structures known as myotubes. Addition of myoblasts to the myotubes continues; this eventually results in long, narrow tubules containing large numbers of nuclei. In the myotubes, striated areas appear which become more and more numerous, and eventually each myotube becomes a muscle fiber.

It is accepted that the nuclei of myoblasts undergo mitosis, but those of myotubes do not. Similarly, during muscle regeneration, myoblasts appear, which divide, whereas the nuclei in muscle fibers show no mitoses. These findings were recently confirmed by Bintliff and Walker using thymidine-$H^3$. Nevertheless, in young animals, during muscle growth, Mac-Connachie *et al.* found the number of muscle nuclei to increase and they saw mitotic figures. The discrepancy may be explained by the finding by Mauro in frogs and by Birks in

young guinea pigs that mononucleate cells—which they call muscle satellite cells—may be seen with the electron microscope to lie between the sarcolemma and the PAS-positive layer outlining it. These cells would seem to be myoblasts persisting in growing animals and would be responsible for the mitotic figures observed in their muscles. Perhaps the presence or absence of such cells explains why some muscles may and others may not regenerate!

It is generally believed that the growth of muscles that occurs in postnatal life is due to the individual fibers of muscles becoming larger and not more numerous. It is also believed that the hypertrophy of muscles that can result from much exercise is due to the fibers becoming larger and not to their becoming increased in numbers.

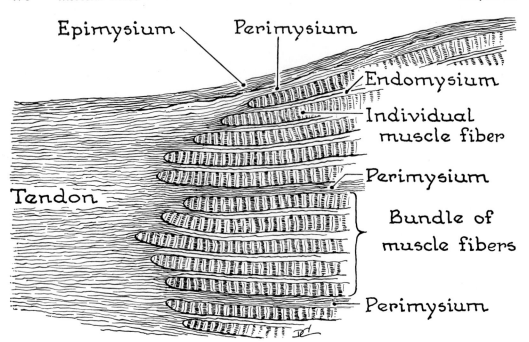

Fig. 20-17. Diagram of a longitudinal section of a muscle, showing how muscles terminate in tendons. The connective tissue of the epimysium, the perimysium and the endomysium is continuous with the connective tissue of the tendon. The sarcolemma covering each muscle fiber also is adherent to the connective tissue of the tendon.

## HOW STRIATED MUSCLES ARE HARNESSED

As noted previously, muscle *tissue* does not consist of muscle cells alone; it has a connective tissue component. This, as we shall see, serves several purposes. Further, different muscles contain different amounts of connective tissue. This fact has application for the cook as well as for the doctor. Since the collagen of connective tissue is much tougher than muscle fibers (which are protoplasm and hence tender), the toughness of any cut of meat depends largely on how great a component of connective tissue the particular muscle from which it was taken contains. For example, the psoas major muscle (filet mignon) contains little.

Any given muscle may contain connective tissue, not only in its wrappings, but also in internal partitions of several different orders. First, the whole muscle is usually wrapped with a fairly substantial connective tissue sheath. This is termed the *epimysium* (upon the muscle) (Fig. 20-16). Second, if a whole muscle is cut in cross section and the cut sur-

face viewed with the naked eye or under very low magnification, it will be seen that more or less longitudinally disposed partitions of connective tissue extend from the epimysium into the muscle to divide it into bundles (fasciculi). These bundles are of several different orders; for example, the whole muscle may be divided into a few big bundles, but with each of these being subdivided, by similar but thinner partitions of connective tissue, into smaller bundles, and so on. The connective tissue that divides a muscle into bundles of different orders constitutes its *perimysium*, so called because this tissue surrounds bundles of fibers (Fig. 20-16). Third, very delicate connective tissue extends from the perimysium surrounding each *bundle* of fibers into the interior of each bundle so as to penetrate between all its fibers. This constitutes the *endomysium* of the muscle and is not to be confused with the sarcolemma sheaths of the fibers, which are parts of the muscle fibers. The endomysium is seen to advantage in cross sections of muscle (Figs. 20-16 and 20-20). Here it appears as a delicate net carrying capillaries, in the interstices of which single sarcolemma-surrounded muscle fibers may be seen.

The connective tissue elements of a muscle, its epimysium, perimysium and endomysium, are all continuous with the connective tissue structures to which the muscle is attached and on which it exerts pull on contraction (Fig. 20-17). Such a structure may be tendon, aponeurosis, periosteum, dermis of skin, a raphe, or almost any other kind of dense connective tissue structure found in the body. The connective tissue elements of muscle, by being continuous with the connective tissue structures on which muscle pulls, have a function something like a harness. But this is not the only way muscles are attached to the connective tissue structures on which they pull. The sarcolemma covering of each rounded end of each muscle fiber that approaches a tendon or the periosteum or any other connective tissue structure to which a muscle is attached blends firmly with it. Hence, the ends of the muscle fibers themselves, as well as the connective tissue elements of a muscle, are firmly attached to the connective tissue structures on which they pull. Several observers have thought that the myofibrils of the muscle fibers actually continue directly through the ends of the muscle fibers proper to merge insensibly with the collagen fibers of the tendon. However, this extreme view is not usually accepted. When observed with the phase microscope, the muscular fibers seem to end fairly abruptly (Fig. 20-18).

In the opinion of the author not enough attention is paid to certain physical factors which would operate to make it impossible for muscle fibers to pull themselves out of a tendon insertion. Muscle fibers that extend into a tendinous insertion (Figs. 20-17 and 20-18) would be comparable with fingers extending into a wet rubber glove, with no possibility of the fingers of the glove being peeled off so as to let air or fluid enter and substitute for the finger that was being withdrawn. In other words, for a muscle fiber to pull out of a tendon insertion would require the creation of a vacuum.

## BLOOD VESSELS AND LYMPHATICS

As noted previously, striated muscle has a very rich blood supply. Arteries are carried from the epimysium by the perimysium into

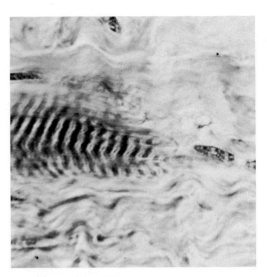

Fig. 20-18. Oil-immersion photomicrograph (taken with the phase microscope) of the termination of a striated muscle fiber in a tendon.

the substance of the muscle (Fig. 20-16). The arteries branch into arterioles and give off capillaries which are carried by the delicate endomysium. Most of the capillaries run parallel with the muscle fibers (Fig. 20-19), but side branches from them often run at right angles to the fibers. The capillary beds of striated muscle can be studied to advantage in cross sections where individual capillaries appear as delicate rings either empty or containing a red blood cell or a leukocyte (Fig. 20-20). A crescentic nucleus may be seen at one side of them; these are the nuclei of the endothelial cells comprising their walls (Fig. 20-20).

Although several capillaries usually abut on each muscle fiber, most of the exterior of each fiber is not in direct contact with capillaries. It has been assumed that a thin film of tissue fluid exists between the sarcolemma of the muscle fiber and the connective tissue endomysium that carries the capillaries and that this permits an interchange of dissolved substances between all points on the periphery of the fiber and the capillaries of the endomysium. However, it has been suggested recently that there may be a film of amorphous intercellular substance (a mucopolysaccharide) between the sarcolemma of the fiber and the endomysium. A gelled amorphous intercellular

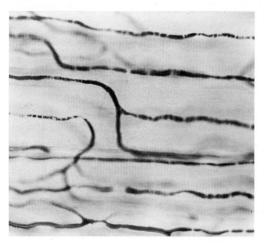

Fig. 20-19. Medium-power photomicrograph of a longitudinal section of striated muscle, the blood vessels of which were injected with India ink. The illustration shows how capillaries run between and parallel with the fibers in the endomysium. Compare with Figure 20-20. Some cross connections are also shown. (Preparation by W. S. Hartroft)

substance in this situation might facilitate diffusion.

It should be noted that the capillaries in striated muscle are much more numerous than they are in smooth muscle, where relatively few capillaries between adjacent fibers may be seen (Fig. 20-1). The nutrition of smooth muscle depends to a considerable extent on the diffusion of substances through the fibers and the intercellular substance between them to and from capillaries in the tongues of connective tissue which penetrate the muscle (Fig. 20-1, center).

The lymphatics of striated muscle are confined almost entirely to its thicker connective tissue components, the perimysium and the epimysium. In this way it differs from cardiac muscle, which has lymphatics as well as capillaries in its endomysium.

## THE EFFERENT INNERVATION OF STRIATED MUSCLE

Nerves are conducted into muscles by the connective tissue components of muscle. The number of muscle fibers supplied by a single motor nerve fiber varies greatly. In one of

the extrinsic muscles of the eye, in which the greatest delicacy of movement is required, there is a separate nerve fiber for every muscle fiber. The other extreme is represented by muscles which are not required to perform delicate movements and in which one nerve fiber may branch and supply over 100 muscle fibers. A nerve fiber, together with all the muscle fibers it supplies, is described as a *motor unit*. If a single nerve fiber supplies many muscle fibers in a muscle, the latter do not, as might at first be expected, constitute a localized group of fibers; instead, the muscle fibers innervated by a single nerve fiber may have a considerable distribution throughout a muscle. This is important because a single muscle fiber, under the influence of a nervous stimulation, always contracts to its maximum capacity; this is spoken of as the *all or none law*. Accordingly, the ability of a muscle *as a whole* to contract with different degrees of intensity is dependent, not on the ability of individual muscle fibers to contract with different degrees of intensity—for they cannot—but on the fact that different *numbers* of the fibers in the muscle can be stimulated to contract under different conditions. Hence, if a weak contraction is required, only a small proportion of the fibers in the muscle are stimulated to contract. Under these conditions it is desirable for those that do contract to be representative of the muscle as a whole so that the contraction is general rather than local. And, since many fibers are supplied by a single nerve fiber, and since in minor contractions only a small proportion of the nerve fibers are stimulated, it is desirable that each fiber supply a group of fibers that extend fairly well throughout the length of the muscle—which they do—rather than a localized group.

Single nerve fibers from the terminal branches of peripheral nerves lead to striated muscle fibers. As a nerve fiber approaches a muscle fiber, its myelin sheath is lost. The endoneurium surrounding the nerve fiber appears to become continuous with the endomysium surrounding the muscle fiber. The axon, with its neurolemma, contacts the muscle fiber at a site along the muscle fiber where the sarcoplasm of the fiber forms a little mound-like protuberance. The sarcoplasm in this mound *under* the nerve ending is called the *sole* plasm, and its has more mitochondria and more nu-

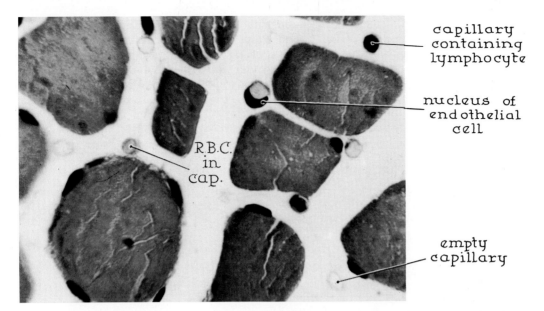

capillary
containing
lymphocyte

nucleus of
endothelial
cell

R.B.C.
in
cap.

empty
capillary

FIG. 20-20. Oil-immersion photomicrograph of a cross section of striated muscle, showing the various appearances presented by capillaries in cross section. In some instances the line of section passes through a capillary at a site where a nucleus of an endothelial cell is present; if so, the nucleus appears as a blue crescent, as may be seen above. If a capillary is cut at a site where no nucleus is present, it appears as a thin cytoplasmic ring. Either red blood cells or leukocytes may be present in capillaries at the sites where they are sectioned.

clei than sarcoplasm in general. For many years it was commonly believed that the nerve fiber, before it branched into terminal arborizations, penetrated the sarcolemma and entered the substance of the sole plasm where it ended in many little treelike networks (arbortrees, Fig. 20-21). The whole complex is called a motor end-plate. Some observers in more recent years, from studies made with the light microscope, have doubted that the nerve fiber actually penetrated the sarcolemma of the muscle fiber. For example, Gutmann and Young, from studying the reinnervation of muscle fibers, concluded that nerve fibers ending in muscle were always separated from the sarcoplasm by a membrane. By means of vital staining Couteaux identified heavily stained membranous areas beneath nerve endings on muscle fibers and considered these to be a continuation of the sarcolemma. Studies with the EM have confirmed that the nerve fiber that reaches a muscle is always separated from it by a membrane, as will now be described.

A muscle fiber, at a site where a nerve fiber approaches it to end in a motor end-plate, has a tiny trough or groove on its surface, which

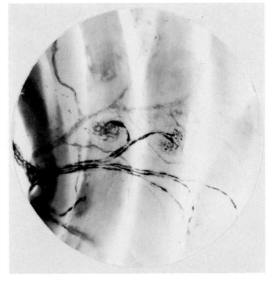

FIG. 20-21. High-power photomicrograph of a teased preparation of striated muscle fibers. The 2 that cross the middle of the field from top to bottom show motor end-plates on their upper surfaces. The end-plates and the nerve fibers that lead to them have been rendered dark by an impregnation technic.

dips into the relatively abundant sarcoplasm which at this site is termed *sole plasm* (labeled in Fig. 20-22). The sarcolemma that covers the muscle fiber follows the contour of the groove by dipping into it to provide a lining for the groove. In Figure 20-22 the groove dips into the muscle from the left and the sarcolemma lining the bottom of the groove is seen extending from the top of the illustration down through its middle (at a slight angle) to

its bottom. The sarcolemma that lines the groove is thickened, taking on more or less the character of a basement membrane, and it projects irregularly into the sarcoplasm of the muscle fiber (on the right in Fig. 20-22) in the form of folds or ridges (labeled ridges of thick sarc. memb. in Fig. 20-22); these greatly increase the amount of surface area of the sarcolemma at this site. The ridges or folds are commonly termed *junctional folds*. The nerve

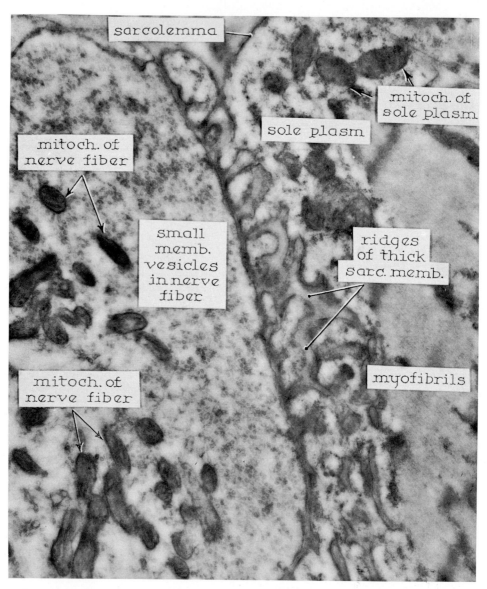

FIG. 20-22. Electron micrograph ($\times$ 34,000) of a section of a rat's diaphragm, showing part of a neuromuscular junction (motor end-plate). See text for description of the various components. (Preparation by G. Palade, labeling added)

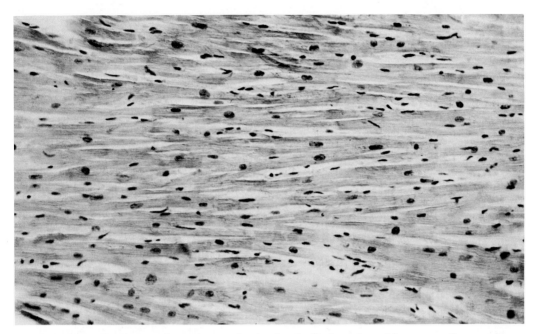

FIG. 20-23. Low-power photomicrograph of a longitudinal section of human cardiac muscle. Observe that the muscle fibers branch and anastomose and that the interstices so created are filled with light-staining connective tissue. This carries the blood and lymph capillaries and the nerves.

fiber (on the left in Fig. 20-22) that ends in the trough loses both its myelin sheath and its sheath of Schwann covering before it ends in the trough and so it lies naked against the sarcolemma covered only with its axolemma. The axoplasm of the axon in the trough contains many mitochondria and many small vesicles (called synaptic vesicles) which are believed to contain acetylcholine. It is believed that the arrival of a nervous impulse at the motor end-plate results in the release of acetylcholine from the synaptic vesicles and that this institutes contraction of the muscle fiber. Acetylcholine is thus considered as the *chemical mediator of the nervous impulse in the motor end-plates of striated muscle*. The chemical mediation of nervous impulses will be discussed further in the next chapter and also in connection with the adrenal gland.

## CARDIAC MUSCLE

Until recently it was believed that cardiac muscle differed fundamentally from both smooth and striated muscle in that its fibers were not divided up into individual cells but instead were all joined together in such a way that they formed a huge protoplasmic network or syncytium (Fig. 20-23). In general, each muscle fiber in this network tends to be disposed in the same plane as its neighbors, and as a result the interstices of the network are slitlike, with the long axes of the slits being parallel with those of the fibers. The interstices contain the endomysium of cardiac muscle. This is of the nature of loose connective tissue and is abundantly supplied with capillaries which are thereby brought into close contact with the muscle fibers of the network. Moreover, the endomysium of cardiac muscle is provided with lymphatic capillaries as well as blood capillaries, and it also carries nerve fibers.

The nuclei of cardiac muscle fibers tend to be disposed in the middle parts of the fibers (Fig. 20-24). They are usually ovoid in shape, but their ends, instead of being rounded, sometimes may be more or less squared (Fig. 20-23). They are pale.

The cytoplasm of cardiac muscle fibers contains myofibrils and sarcoplasm and shows cross striations similar to those described for

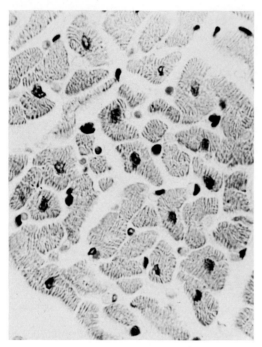

Fig. 20-24. Medium-power photomicrograph of a cross section of human cardiac muscle. The connective tissue endomysium separating the individual fibers is too delicate and stains too faintly to be seen. Observe that the nuclei are present in the central parts of the fibers. The cytoplasm does not appear homogeneous because of the myofibrils in it. Note that the myofibrils are ribbonlike rather than cylindrical.

striated muscle. The cross striations of cardiac muscle, although due to A and I disks, and Z lines similar to those of striated muscle, are not usually so distinct as those of striated muscle. In addition, cardiac muscle fibers are crossed every now and again by unique dark-stained bands called *intercalated disks* (intercalated means inserted). These disks which are more or less *inserted* between some sarcomeres are seen, with the light microscope, to be less than a sarcomere in thickness and to be present at the sites of Z bands (Fig. 20-25). Sometimes intercalated disks cross fibers in straight lines, but sometimes they cross fibers in a stepwise fashion (Fig. 20-25); this is due to the intercalated disks of different myofibrils of the fiber not being in register. There has been much speculation about their nature and function through the years. It was

not until they were examined in thin sections with the EM that their true nature was definitely established. With the EM they were seen to be cell membranes of the cardiac muscle cells. Until this was discovered it was generally assumed that cardiac muscle represented a syncytium; that there were no cell boundaries that extended across the fibers that branched and anastomosed. However, the EM has shown that this assumption was erroneous, and that the sarcolemma of cardiac muscle fibers crosses fibers to separate them into segments which are individual cells, bounded along their sides and at each end with a cell membrane.

**Fine Structure.** In most respects the fine structure of cardiac muscle is similar to that of striated skeletal muscle. The fibers of cardiac muscle are made up of myofibrils between which is sarcoplasm. The filaments of the myofibrils and the cross striations are similar to those of striated skeletal muscle. Furthermore, it seems very probable that the smooth-surfaced endoplasmic reticulum in cardiac muscle cells is at least very similar to that which has been described for striated skeletal muscle in that there is a transverse tubular system that is continuous with the sarcolemma of fibers and which passes into fibers to surround myofibrils at Z disks (but perhaps other sites in other species), and other components of the reticulum that are distributed along myofibrils between the sites where the centrotubules cross and surround myofibrils.

There are, however, some differences between the fine structure of cardiac muscle and striated voluntary muscle which will now be described.

First, mitochondria are particularly abundant in the sarcoplasm between the myofibrils of cardiac muscle; this of course might be expected because the energy requirements of cardiac muscle can at times be great.

Secondly, as has already been described, the fibers of cardiac muscle, although they appear under low power with the light microscope to be arranged in the form of a syncytium, are actually divided up into individual cells which are joined end-to-end by intercalated disks. There are several interesting features about intercalated disks which will now be described.

First, intercalated disks always cross myo-

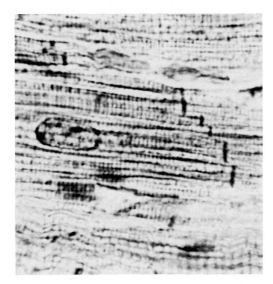

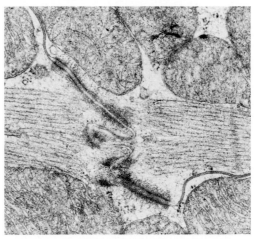

Fig. 20-26. Electron micrograph showing the fine structure of intercalated disks. Notice that as a disk crosses a myofibril it pursues an irregular course; this provides for a large surface area over which the two adjacent sarcomeres can be firmly joined. Next, as the disk crosses the myofibril, the arrangement seen is that seen in desmosomes, but if an intercalated disk, after crossing a myofibril, makes a right-angle turn and runs parallel with the myofibril, before it crosses another myofibril, it shows an arrangement like that seen in a zonula occludens, in which the apposed outer layers of the two contiguous cell membranes are fused so a 3-line structure is seen. See Fig. 20-26 B, page 506. (Preparation by F. S. Sjöstrand)

Fig. 20-25. High-power photomicrograph of a longitudinal section of cardiac muscle (dog) stained by Mallory's phosphotungstic hematoxylin method. This brings out the intercalated disks, which appear as dark lines crossing the fibers, sometimes in a steplike fashion.

fibrils at Z disks. However, they do not always cross fibers by means of Z disks that are in register across the fiber; indeed, they often cross a few myofibrils at Z disks that are in register and then make a right-angle turn and run parallel with and between myofibrils for the distance of one sarcomere, and then make another right-angle turn, and cross a few more myofibrils at Z disks that are themselves in register but not with the ones crossed previously. The fact that intercalated disks pass across fibers by means of replacing Z disks that are not all in register with one another accounts for the fact that intercalated disks often present a steplike arrangement when seen with the light microscope as is shown in Figure 20-25.

Secondly, intercalated disks are sites where adjacent cardiac muscle cells are very firmly connected to one another. Since each cardiac muscle cell is completely covered with its own cell membrane this means that the cell membranes of individual cardiac muscle cells that meet at intercalated disks must be firmly joined to one another. There are two factors involved in how this is done. First, although the line along which the ends of cardiac muscle

cells come into close contact in an intercalated disk can be seen in the light microscope to be irregular because of its steplike nature, as has already been described, it is seen in the EM to be more irregular still because, as it crosses myofibrils it follows projections that extend from one cell to fit closely into depressions on the other (Fig. 20-26). By this means the area of contact between the ends of individual cells is greatly increased. Secondly, electron-dense fibrillar material is scattered along the cytoplasmic sides of cell membranes as they follow their devious course across fibers; this electron-dense material is similar to that seen in desmosomes. Hence, in effect the junction between the ends of fibers (the intercalated disk) is more or less of the nature of a continuous desmosome. However, where the cell membranes of an intercalated disk run parallel with, and between, myofibrils, to jump from one set of Z disks that are in register to the next Z disk along the fiber, the type of junction between the cell membranes, as they run parallel with myofibrils, is probably more intimate, with some fusion of their outer layers being involved as shown in Figure 20-26.

**Pigment.** Beginning at the age of 10, granules of golden-yellow pigment tend to accumulate in the sarcoplasm at each end of the nuclei of cardiac muscle fibers. It seems probable that these granules represent a type of "wear and tear" pigment described in Chapters 7 and 25. This pigment becomes very prominent in a condition termed "brown atrophy of the heart."

**Growth.** Many disease conditions require that the heart do more work. These lead to the heart becoming heavier and larger. Such a heart is said to be hypertrophied. There has been some question as to whether the increase in the amount of cardiac muscle in hypertrophy is brought about by an increase in the number or the size of its fibers. The studies of Karsner, Shapiro and Todd indicate that it is due to an increase in the size of the fibers and not in their number.

### THE IMPULSE-CONDUCTING SYSTEM OF CARDIAC MUSCLE

This matter is considered in Chapter 22, which deals with the Circulatory System.

### HOW TO DISTINGUISH BETWEEN SECTIONS OF THE 3 KINDS OF MUSCLE

In identifying sections of muscle on practical examination the student will find it helpful to examine the unknown section with particular reference to certain points:

1. The width of the fibers (smooth are narrowest; striated, widest; and cardiac, between).

2. The position of the nuclei in the fibers (in the periphery of striated, toward the middle of smooth and cardiac).

3. Whether the fibers branch and anastomose (cardiac).

4. Whether the fibers exhibit cross striations (striated, cardiac).

5. Whether intercalated disks are present (cardiac).

However, the use of these commonly listed criteria is not so simple as to render practice and experience unimportant. In ascertaining whether the nuclei of the fibers are in the middle or the peripheral parts of the fibers, the student must take care not to confuse the nuclei of the connective tissue endomysium with the nuclei of the muscle fibers themselves. Further, as has been explained, in longitudinal section, a peripheral nucleus of a striated muscle fiber may *seem* to be in the middle of the fiber. The position of the nuclei can be determined to better advantage if an area of the section can be found in which the muscle fibers are cut in cross section instead of longitudinally. However, with regard to point 3, the student should find a place on the section where the fibers are cut in longitudinal section. With regard to the fourth point, it should be recalled that cross striations are not always seen easily, and in particular they are often difficult to find quickly in sections of cardiac muscle. They can be seen to better advantage if the light is cut down by lowering the condenser or by partly closing the diaphragm. Likewise, intercalated disks do not always show up well in sections, and they too can be seen to better advantage if the light is cut down. Furthermore, it should be remembered that positive evidence is better than negative evidence. For example, a student who sees nuclei disposed in the middle parts of fibers that clearly branch and anastomose and yet cannot see cross striations or intercalated disks, should place his trust in his positive evidence and diagnose cardiac muscle rather than smooth.

### REFERENCES

#### GENERAL REFERENCE ON MUSCLE

Bourne, G. H. (ed.): The Structure and Function of Muscle, vols. 1 and 2, New York, Acad. Press, 1960.

#### MUSCLE—SPECIAL REFERENCES

Basmajian, J. V.: Control and training of individual motor units, Science *141*:440, 1963.

Beams, H. W., Evans, T. C., Janney, C. T., and Baker, W. W.: Electron microscope studies of the structure of cardiac muscle, Anat. Rec. *105*:59, 1949.

Bennett, H. S.: An electron microscope study of sectioned breast muscle of the domestic fowl, Am. J. Anat. *93*:61, 1953.

———: The microscopical investigation of biological materials with polarized light *in* McClung's Handbook of Microscopical Technique, ed. 3, pp. 591-677, Hoeber, New York, 1950.

———: The sarcoplasmic reticulum of striped muscle, J. Biophys. Biochem. Cytol. *2*:171 (Supp.), 1956.

Bintliff, S., and Walker, B. E.: Radioautographic study of skeletal muscle regeneration, Am. J. Anat. *106*:233-239, 1960.

Caesar, R., Edwards, G. A., and Ruska, H.: Architecture and nerve supply of mammalian smooth muscle tissue, J. Biophys. Biochem. Cytol. *3*:867, 1957.

Clark, W. E. Le Gros: An experimental study of the regeneration of mammalian striped muscle, J. Anat. *80*:24, 1946.

Dempsey, E. B., Wislocki, G. B., and Singer, M.: Some observations on the chemical cytology of striated muscle, Anat. Rec. *96*:221, 1946.

Edwards, G. A., Ruska, H., Santos, P. de S., and Vallejo-Freire, A.: Comparative cytophysiology of striated muscle with special reference to the role of the endoplasmic reticulum, J. Biophys. Biochem. Cytol. *2*:143 (Supp.), 1956.

Enesco, M., and Puddy, Della: Increase in the number of nuclei and weight in skeletal muscle of rats of various ages, Am. J. Anat. *114*:235, 1964.

Fawcett, D. H.: The sarcoplasmic reticulum of skeletal and cardiac muscle, Circulation *24*:336, 1960.

Fawcett, D. W., and Revel, J. P.: The sarcoplasmic reticulum of fast-acting fish muscle, J. Biophys. Biochem. Cytol. (Suppl.) *10*:89, 1961.

George, J. C., and Jyoti, D.: Histological features of the breast and leg muscles of bird and bat and their physiological and evolutionary significance, J. Animal Morphol. Physiol. *2*:1, 1955.

Goldstein, D. J.: Some histochemical observations of human striated muscle, Anat. Rec. *134*:217, 1959.

Goss, C. M.: The attachment of skeletal muscle fibers, Am. J. Anat. *74*:259, 1944.

Hanson, J., and Huxley, H. E.: The structural basis of contraction in striated muscle, Symposia Soc. Exper. Biol., no. 9, 228-264, 1955.

———: Structural basis of the cross-striations in muscle, Nature *172*:530, 1953.

Hodge, A. J.: The fine structure of striated muscle: A comparison of insect flight muscle with vertebrate and invertebrate skeletal muscle, J. Biophys. Biochem. Cytol. *2*:131 (Supp.), 1956.

Huxley, H. E.: The double array of filaments in cross-striated muscle, J. Biophys. Biochem. Cytol. *3*:631, 1957.

———: The contraction of muscle, Scient. Amer. *199*:66, 1958.

Huxley, A. F., and Taylor, R. E.: Function of Krause's membrane, Nature *176*:1068, 1955.

———: Muscular contraction. Endeavour *15*:177, 1956.

Jones, W. M., and Barer, R.: Electron microscopy of the sarcolemma, Nature *161*:1012, 1948.

Kisch, B.: Studies in comparative electron microscopy of the heart: II. Guinea pig and rat, Exp. Med. Surg. *12*:335, 1955.

Knappeis, G. G., and Carlsen, F.: The ultrastructure of the Z disc in skeletal muscle, J. Cell Biol. *13*:323, 1962.

Long, M. E.: The development of the muscle-tendon attachment in the rat, Am. J. Anat. *81*:159, 1947.

MacConnachie, H. F., Enesco, M., and Leblond, C. P.: The mode of increase in the number of skeletal muscle nuclei in the postnatal rat, Am. J. Anat. *114*:245-253, 1964.

Mark, J. S.: An electron microscope study of uterine smooth muscle, Anat. Rec. *125*:473, 1956.

Mauro, A.: Satellite cell of skeletal cell fibres, J. Biophys. Biochem. Cytol. *9*:493-494, 1961.

Muir, A. R.: An electron microscope study of the embryology of the intercalated disc in the heart of the rabbit, J. Biophys. Biochem. Cytol. *3*:193, 1957.

Nelson, D. A., and Benson, E. S.: On the structural continuities of the transverse tubular system of rabbit and human myocardial cells, J. Cell Biol. *16*:297, 1963.

Oosaki, Takeo, and Ishii, Saburo: The junctional structure of smooth muscle cells, J. Ultrastr. Res. *10*:567, 1964.

Peachey, L. D., and Porter, K. R.: Intercellular impulse conduction in muscle cells, Science *129*:721, 1959.

Pease, D. C., and Baker, R. F.: The fine structure of mammalian skeletal muscle, Am. J. Anat. *84*:175, 1949.

Perry, S. V.: Relation between chemical and contractile function and structure of the skeletal muscle cell, Physiol. Rev. *36*:1, 1956.

Porter, K. R.: The myo-tendon junction in larval forms of *Amblystoma punctatum*, Anat. Rec. *118*:342, 1954.

———: The sarcoplasmic reticulum in muscle cells of amblystoma larvae, J. Biophys. Biochem. Cytol. *2*:163 (Supp.), 1956.

Porter, K. R., and Bonneville, M. A.: An Introduction to the Fine Structure of Cells and Tissues, ed. 2, Lea & Febiger, 1964.

Robertson, J. D.: Some features of the ultrastructure of reptilian skeletal muscles, J. Biophys. Biochem. Cytol. *2*:369, 1956.

Sjöstrand, F. S., and Andersson, E.: Electron microscopy of the intercalated discs of cardiac muscle tissue, Experientia 10:369-370, 1954.

———: The ultrastructure of the skeletal muscle myofilaments at various states of shortening, J. Ultrastr. Res. 1:74, 1957.

Sjöstrand, E. S., Andersson-Cedergren, E., and Dewey, M. M.: The ultrastructure of the intercalated discs of frog, mouse, and guinea pig cardiac muscle, J. Ultrastr. Res. 1:271, 1958.

Smith, D. S.: Reticular organizations within the striated muscle cell, J. Biophys. Biochem. Cytol. (Supp.) vol. 61, 1961.

Speidel, C. C.: The fundamental transverse arrangement of cross striae in myofibrils of striated muscle, Anat. Rec. 100:91, 1948.

Spiro, D.: The filamentous fine structure of striated muscle at different stages of shortening, Exp. Cell Res. 10:562, 1956.

———: The ultrastructure of striated muscle at various sarcomere lengths, J. Biophys. Biochem. Cytol. 2:157 (Supp.), 1956.

———: The ultrastructure of heart muscle, Trans. N. Y. Acad. Sci. Ser. II, 24:879, 1962.

Szent-Gyorgyi, A.: Chemistry of Muscular Contraction, ed. 2, New York, Acad. Press, 1951.

———: A study on muscle in Nature of Life, New York, Acad. Press, 1948.

Thaemert, J. C.: Intercellular bridges as protoplasmic anastomoses between smooth muscle cells, J. Biophys. Biochem. Cytol. 6:67, 1959.

Tower, S.: Atrophy and degeneration in skeletal muscle, Am. J. Anat. 56:1, 1935.

van Breemen, V. L.: Intercalated discs in heart muscle studied with the electron microscope, Anat. Rec. 117:49, 1953.

———: Myofibril development observed with the electron microscope, Anat. Rec. 113:179, 1952.

Weinstein, H. J.: An electron microscope study of cardiac muscle, Exp. Cell Res. 7:130, 1954.

SPECIAL REFERENCES ON MOTOR NERVE ENDINGS IN MUSCLE

Andersson-Cedergren, E.: Ultrastructure of motor end plate and sarcoplasmic components of mouse skeletal muscle fiber as revealed by three-dimensional reconstructions from serial sections, J. Ultrastr. Res. Suppl. 1, 1959.

Barrnett, R. J.: The fine structural localization of acetylcholinesterase at the myoneural junction, J. Cell Biol. 12:247, 1962.

Beams, H. W., and Evans, T. C.: Electron micrographs of motor end-plates, Proc. Soc. Exp. Biol. Med. 82:344-346, 1953.

Couteaux, R.: Contribution a l'étude de la synapse myoneurale, Rev. Canad. Biol. 6:563, 1947.

Gutmann, E., and Young, J. Z.: The reinnervation of muscle after various periods of atrophy, J. Anat. 78:15, 1944.

De Harven, E., and Coers, C.: Electron microscopy of the human neuromuscular junction, J. Biophys. Biochem. Cytol. 6:7, 1959.

Palade, G. E.: Electron microscope observations on interneuronal and neuromuscular synapses, Anat. Rec. 118:335, 1954.

Reger, J. F.: Electron microscopy of the motor end-plate in intercostal muscle of the rat, Anat. Rec. 118:334, 1954.

———: Electron microscopy of the motor end-plate in rat intercostal muscle, Anat. Rec. 122:1, 1955.

Richardson, K. C.: The fine structure of autonomic nerve endings in smooth muscle of the rat vas deferens, J. Anat. 96:427, 1962.

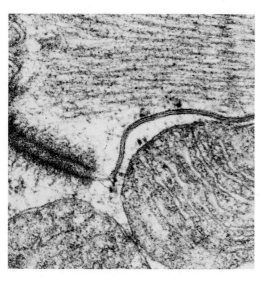

FIG. 20-26 B. A higher-power view of the 3-line structure referred to in Figure 20-26.

# 21 Nervous Tissue and the Nervous System

## PRELIMINARY CONSIDERATIONS

### PROPERTIES OF NERVOUS TISSUE

Epithelial tissue, the first tissue we studied, was found to be structurally specialized to permit the superior expression of two of the basic properties of protoplasm: *absorption* and *secretion*. Nervous tissue, the fourth and last basic tissue we study, will be found to be structurally specialized for the superior—if not the exquisite—expression of two other basic properties of protoplasm, *irritability* and *conductivity*.

**Irritability and Conductivity.** Irritability is the basic property of protoplasm that enables a cell to respond to a stimulus. It should be emphasized that irritability is not a response, but that a cell must be irritable if it is to respond. For example, epithelial cells, on being stimulated, can *respond* by *secreting*, muscle cells by *contracting* and nerve cells by *conducting* waves of excitation over their whole extents. In order to respond to a stimulus, in any one of these three ways, a cell must first be irritable.

Some people are more irritable than others and become angry in response to stimuli that do not disturb their more placid companions. Similarly, some kinds of cells are more irritable than others; they are stimulated more easily to respond. It is in the cells of nervous tissue that irritability is most highly developed. Not only are nerve cells in general very sensitive to stimuli, but some kinds are specialized to respond to very special kinds of stimuli, for example, certain nerve cells in the eye respond to the stimulus of light.

The response elicited in nerve cells—no matter what kind of stimulus is responsible for it—*is always the same*; the cell conducts a wave of excitation (called a nervous impulse) over its whole extent. Since the cytoplasm of nerve cells commonly is drawn out into long threadlike extensions, called *nerve fibers,* which are sometimes several feet long, nerve cells are specialized *to conduct* nervous impulses over long distances. They are also specialized to transmit the impulses very rapidly; in nerve fibers impulses travel at speeds up to 100 meters per second.

### ROLES OF NERVOUS TISSUE IN THE BODY ECONOMY

With the foregoing paragraphs in mind, it is easy to understand the *basic* function of nervous tissue in the body. It is: (1) to serve as a tissue that is receptive to various types of stimuli that arise or are present either outside or inside the body and (2) on being stimulated, to conduct rapidly, and sometimes over great distances, nervous impulses to *muscle* and *gland* cells. Nervous impulses conducted to muscle cells make them contract; those conducted to gland cells make them secrete. Therefore, nervous impulses are the usual stimuli that evoke responses in muscle and gland cells.

Superimposed on this basic role of nervous tissue are others of a more complex nature. Environment provides so many stimuli that an individual literally would be in a chronic state of convulsion if all stimuli were immediately translated into responses. Therefore, there must be within nervous tissue some mechanism for more or less sorting out the nervous impulses that are set up by stimuli and for permitting only certain of these impulses to reach muscle and gland cells. There must also be a mechanism for permitting delayed responses to stimuli, for memory, for the initiation of voluntary activities, for consciousness and for the appreciation of different sensations—in short, for all those phenomena classed as higher nervous functions.

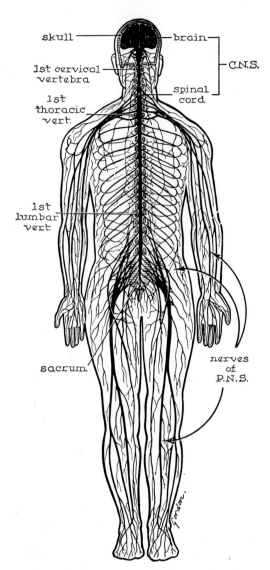

skull

brain

C.N.S.

1st cervical vertebra

spinal cord

1st thoracic vert.

1st lumbar vert.

sacrum

nerves of P.N.S.

FIG. 21-1. Drawing to illustrate the position of the various parts of the nervous system in the body. Part of the brain is not shown so that the sites of certain cranial nerves could be indicated.

the *nervous system*. However, nervous tissue is not equally apportioned to all parts of the body. In particular, there is a great depot of it which fills the skull as the *brain* and continues down the canal of the backbone as the *spinal cord* (Fig. 21-1). This great concentration of nervous tissue in the midline of the body—the brain and the spinal cord—constitutes what is known as the *central nervous system,* which hereafter we shall refer to as the C.N.S. The remainder of the nervous tissue of the body constitutes the other division of the system; this is known as the *peripheral nervous system,* which hereafter we shall refer to as the P.N.S. This part consists of cordlike nerves that extend out through foramina in the skull and the vertebral column, from the brain and the spinal cord, as cranial and spinal nerves, to reach almost all parts of the body (Fig. 21-1).

The higher functions of nervous tissue, of course, are dependent on the C.N.S. However, the basic function of nervous tissue is more dependent on the P.N.S. because it is responsible for conducting nervous impulses from sites of stimulation to the C.N.S. and then back again to muscles and glands. Nervous impulses always take this roundabout course. Those that arise, for example in the skin, are carried by the nerves of the P.N.S. into the C.N.S., where they are, so to speak, sorted out and evaluated. Only then are they sent out to muscles and glands again by way of the nerves of the P.N.S. The reason for their taking this seemingly roundabout route between sites of stimulation and muscles and glands is easily understood if a few of the factors that operated in the evolution of nervous systems are first reviewed; hence, we shall deal briefly with this matter next.

## AN ACCOUNT (IN WHICH IMPORTANT NEW TERMS ARE INTRODUCED) OF SOME STEPS IN THE EVOLUTION OF NERVOUS TISSUE

Anyone whose activities are distributed over many fields of endeavor can scarcely expect to become expert in all; and so it is with cells. Since the protoplasm of a unicellular organism, such as an amoeba, must be competent with regard to all the properties of proto-

### THE WAY NERVOUS TISSUE IS DISTRIBUTED IN THE BODY TO PERFORM ITS BASIC AND HIGHER FUNCTIONS

Nervous tissue extends into almost every part of the body. Yet every portion of nervous tissue in a body is connected to other portions, so that it is all welded together to form a great anatomic and functional unit termed

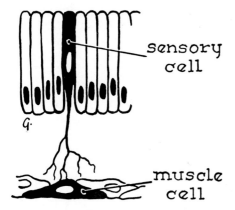

FIG. 21-2. Diagram of a simple type of receptor-effector system such as is seen in the tentacles of sea anemones. (Redrawn from Parker, G. H.: The Elementary Nervous System, Philadelphia, Lippincott)

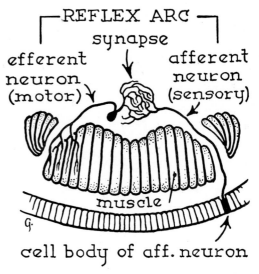

FIG. 21-3. Diagram of an afferent and efferent neuron arranged to constitute a reflex arc in the earthworm. (Redrawn from Parker, G. H.: The Elementary Nervous System, Philadelphia, Lippincott)

plasm, it could scarcely be expected to exhibit irritability, conductivity or contractility to a high degree; indeed, an amoeba is a sluggish creature.

The advent of the multicellular organism made it practicable for cells to become specialized. Muscle cells—specialized for contractility—probably appeared in the animal kingdom before nerve cells, because certain of the sponges, though vegetablelike in their general immobility, possess contractile cells around their pores. These are in direct contact with sea water, and, should it contain a noxious substance, the muscle cells are directly stimulated to contract and close the pores.

As multicellular organisms became more complex, muscle cells came to be more deeply located, hence not in direct contact with the external environment of the organism. This arrangement required that some sufficiently irritable cells of the organisms be exposed to surface stimulation and arranged so that they could conduct waves of excitation to the deeply situated muscle cells. One of the first arrangements of this sort to evolve is found in the tentacles of the sea anemone (Fig. 21-2). In this illustration one of the ectodermal cells (the black one) has differentiated into a *nerve cell* (labeled *sensory cell*), and although its cell body, which contains the nucleus of the cell, remains at the surface, its cytoplasm has extended in the form of a long threadlike process, called a *nerve fiber,* to a deeply dis-

posed muscle cell. A combination of a nerve cell and a muscle cell such as this constitutes a simple *neuromuscular mechanism.* In such an arrangement the nerve cell bears much the same relationship to the muscle cell as does a detonator to an explosive shell.

**Neurons.** The term "neuron" refers to a complete and single nerve cell, including its cell body, which contains the nucleus, and one or more cytoplasmic extensions, called *processes;* some of these may be thick at first, but they all become thinned down to nerve fibers eventually. As neurons evolved further, they came to have two kinds of processes. The first kind are called *dendrons (dendron =* tree) or, more commonly, *dendrites,* because they branch like trees (Fig. 21-6). These carry nervous impulses toward the cell body. Most neurons have several dendrites. The second kind of process of a neuron is always single, and since it tends to be straight and long it is called an *axon (axon =* axis) (Fig. 21-6). The axon carries nervous impulses away from the cell body. The further evolution of nervous tissue hinged on the development of nervous pathways consisting of two or more neurons. In these pathways the processes of one neuron come into contact with

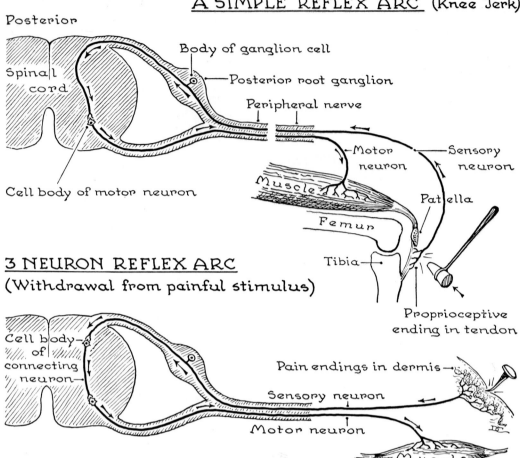

# A SIMPLE REFLEX ARC (Knee Jerk)

# 3 NEURON REFLEX ARC
## (Withdrawal from painful stimulus)

FIG. 21-4. Diagrams illustrating reflex arcs involving 2 and 3 neurons, respectively. Notice that the cell body of the afferent (sensory) neuron is situated in the posterior root ganglion outside the central nervous system.

either the cell body or a process of another. These points of contact with one another are termed *synapses*.

Synapses. The word synapse was derived from a Greek word which means *to clasp*, and as the tissues of two individuals who clasp hands are in contact, but not in continuity, so the cytoplasm of a neuron at a synapse is in contact but is not continuous with that of another neuron. Synapses vary in form. In one common type, neurons come into contact with others solely through their fibers. In this arrangement the end of a fiber of one neuron approaches the end of a fiber of another neuron, and the ends of the respective fibers, at their point of contact, break out into filamentous little fingers which literally clasp each other (Fig. 21-3). In another common type, fibers from other neurons come into contact with the cell body of a given neuron; here the synaptic terminals of the fibers on the cell body are more like little feet than hands (Fig. 21-21); indeed, this type of terminal is called an *end-bulb* or *foot*. From histologic studies with the light microscope it was very difficult to establish whether synapses were points of contact or continuity between neurons. The EM has shown clearly that these are merely points of contact, as will be described later. There is other evidence showing that synapses represent only points of contact; for example, (1) there is a slight delay as a nervous impulse passes over a synapse; (2) a synapse, unlike a nerve fiber, will transmit a nervous impulse in only one direction—it is said to be *dynamically polarized*; (3) synapses become fatigued more easily than nerve fibers; (4) they are more susceptible than nerve fibers to the action of certain drugs; (5) if the cell body of any given neuron is destroyed, all its fibers degenerate, but the degeneration that spreads throughout the entire affected neuron stops at all its synapses.

**The Reflex Arc—Afferent and Efferent Neurons.** Arrangements of two or more neurons generally are required if a stimulus, received anywhere by an animal, is to evoke a response in a muscle or a gland. A simple example of a working arrangement of two neurons is to be seen in each segment of an earthworm (Fig. 21-3).

The first neuron, which has its cell body at the surface, sends a nerve fiber into the substance of the segment where the fiber terminates in synaptic connection with the fiber of a second neuron. The first neuron, because it carries a nervous impulse toward the more central part of the earthworm, is said to be an *afferent* (*affere* = to carry to) neuron. The second neuron in turn carries the impulse away from the deeper part of the organism to the muscle and is said to be an *efferent* (*effere* = to carry away) neuron (Fig. 21-3). The two neurons together constitute the very simplest form of a *reflex arc*. This term (derived from *reflectere* = to bend back, and from *arcus* = a bow or a curved line) aptly describes the arrangement, because the nervous impulse brought into the organism by means of the afferent neuron is *reflected* outwardly again by means of the efferent neuron.

**Most Actions of Man Involve Reflex Arcs.** The reader will soon be testing the reflexes of patients to learn if various parts of their nervous system are functioning properly. A common and important reflex tested is the knee jerk. This is done by having a patient cross his knees and relax; then the upper knee is given a sharp tap just below the patella, as is shown in Figure 21-4. The proper functioning of this reflex is indicated by the leg kicking forward smartly (but not too far) in response to the stimulus. Only two neurons are involved in

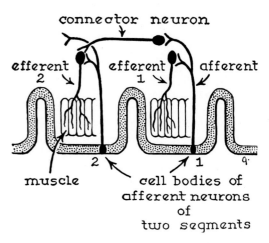

FIG. 21-5. Diagram of a portion of a theoretical segmented organism, showing how connector neurons permit correlation between segments.

this reflex. The cell body of the afferent neuron is contained in what is termed a posterior root ganglion (these structures will be described presently). From it, nerve fibers extend (1) in a peripheral nerve, to the ligament of the patella, and (2) into the spinal cord; in the cord the latter fiber synapses with the cell body of an efferent neuron, which sends a fiber, by means of a peripheral nerve, to the muscle fibers of the quadriceps femoris, as is shown in Figure 21-4. A slightly more complex reflex arc is shown in the second diagram in this illustration. However, most reflex arcs in the body are necessarily more complex than these, for reasons which will be explained in the following section.

Notice, as is shown in Figure 21-4, that both afferent and efferent fibers travel in the same peripheral nerve.

**Segmented Animals and Connector Neurons.** As evolution proceeded, larger animals appeared in the world. In becoming larger most animals became elongated. The mechanism for elongation generally depends on basic units of structure, called segments, becoming duplicated and reduplicated in the longitudinal axis of an animal. In lowly segmented organisms, such as the earthworm, the boundaries between segments are easily seen, and each segment retains a considerable amount of autonomy. Of particular interest to us is the fact that each segment contains an afferent and an efferent neuron and an individual unit of muscle to which the efferent neuron leads; hence, reflex activity is possible within each segment.

However, the evolution of the elongated segmented organism required the evolution of a new type of neuron, one that could provide nervous connections between segments and so permit the activities of the various segments to be regulated in the interests of the animal as a whole. Hence, segmented organisms have, in addition to afferent and efferent neurons, *intersegmental connector neurons*. In the diagram of a theoretical segmented animal (Fig. 21-5) it may be seen that these intersegmental connector neurons permit a stimulus received in one segment to cause a response in another. Intersegmental connector neurons *broaden the base of reflex arcs from one segment to many segments.*

In understanding the nerve supply of any part of the body it is of the greatest importance to remember that man is a segmented organism (Fig. 21-1). The spinal cord, as we shall see, contains intersegmental connector neurons; it is, in a sense, the outcome of the need for large numbers of connector neurons in an organism with many segments. Each of the spinal nerves that pass out from the spinal cord, one from each side, through the foramen between individual vertebrae, represents in man the afferent and the efferent neurons that are in the individual segments of the earthworm; the nerves that extend through each foramen contain many afferent and efferent neurons. Moreover, the afferent fibers in these nerves will be found to extend only to sites in the skin and other tissues that develop from that same segment. Likewise, the efferent fibers in each spinal nerve will be found to pass only to muscle fibers that develop from that same segment. During development, the muscle fibers that develop from any given segment only sometimes remain independent of those from other segments as, for example, occurs in the intercostal muscles; more commonly they meet with muscle fibers from other segments to become parts of larger muscles that traverse many segments. Nevertheless, the fibers that develop from any segment retain their efferent innervation from that segment; hence, large muscles may have innervation from several segments.

The spinal nerves of man are named according to the vertebra (cervical, thoracic, lumbar and sacral) above or below (in the cervical regions above, in others below) which they pass to emerge into the body (Fig. 21-1). Since the arm develops from the 5th, 6th, 7th and 8th cervical and the 1st thoracic segments, the nerve supply of the arm is obtained from the spinal nerves that leave the vertebral column in this region (Fig. 21-1). The legs develop from the 2nd, 3rd, 4th and 5th lumbar and the 1st, 2nd and 3rd sacral segments; hence, they are innervated by spinal nerves that emerge from the spinal cord below each of these vertebrae, as may be seen in Figure 21-1.

**Positions Assumed by the Cell Bodies of Afferent, Efferent and Connector Neurons.** The study of animals representing different stages in the evolution of nervous tissue shows that the operation of the *tendency for the centralization of nervous tissue* gradually influenced the form and the position of nervous tissue in the body. The operation of this factor has led to as much nervous tissue as possible having a protected central position in the organism. How the operation of this tendency affected the position assumed in higher animals of afferent, efferent and connector neurons will now be described. For convenience we shall first describe its effects on connector neurons.

**Connector Neurons.** These neurons, as has been explained already, evolved so that the afferent and the efferent neurons of individual segments could be linked with those of others (Fig. 21-5). As evolution proceeded there came to be more and more of these connector neurons, with some running for only short distances and others for long distances. As more and more appeared they tended to become bundled together in the longitudinal axis of animals in a more or less central position to become the chief components of the *spinal cord*. In the head region the spinal cord is expanded, as it were, into the brain; this expansion, as will be explained presently, was due not only to a still greater increased number of connector neurons being required in this region but also to other factors. From the foregoing it is obvious that all connector neurons are contained in the C.N.S. However, in addition to these, the C.N.S. contains parts of both the afferent and the efferent neurons of each segment. The remaining parts of the afferent and the efferent neurons—and these, of course, are outside the C.N.S.—constitute the P.N.S. To explain which parts of the segmental afferent and efferent neurons are contained in the P.N.S. requires that we discuss the changes in position that took place in the cell bodies of these neurons as evolution continued.

**Afferent Neurons.** The first sensory cells to evolve had their cell bodies at the surface of the organism (Fig. 21-2), and the cell bodies remained there in a few lower animals, for example, the earthworm, that have neurons, synapses and reflex arcs (Fig. 21-3). But the surface of an animal is not a suitable place for the cell bodies of afferent neurons, for in this position they are too easily injured and destroyed. The destruction of the *body* of a nerve cell is a very serious matter, because nerve cells seem to be too highly specialized to be able to undergo division; hence, if one is destroyed another cannot divide to provide a replacement for it. Although nerve cells cannot divide, they, in the P.N.S. (but not in the C.N.S.), can regenerate new fibers under suitable circumstances. Accordingly, in higher animals the expedient was adopted of having the cell bodies of the afferent neurons of the segments migrate inwardly so as to be out of harm's way, with the important provision, however, of their retaining connection with the surface by means of a fiber (Fig. 21-6). This is a much better arrangement than the original because fibers, injured at the surface, can be regenerated from the cell body, and by this means sensory function can be restored after surface injuries.

In some lower animals the cell bodies of afferent neurons migrated only a short distance inwardly (Fig. 21-6, *middle*), but in the higher animals they seem to have come as close to the C.N.S. as they could without actually getting into the C.N.S. In this position the cell bodies of afferent neurons are housed in little nodules of nervous tissue called *ganglia* (a ganglion is a lump) (Fig. 21-4). The particular ganglia that house the cell bodies of those afferent neurons that enter the spinal cord from each segment of the body are termed *spinal ganglia* or *dorsal* or *posterior root ganglia*. There are two of them for each segment, and they are situated one on each side, close to the spinal cord, toward its pos-

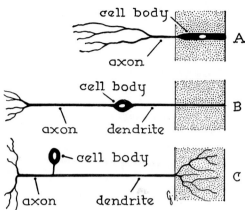

Fig. 21-6. Diagrams showing how the position of the cell body of afferent neurons changed as evolution proceeded. A is a sensory cell in a coelenterate, B is one in a mollusk and C is one from a vertebrate. (Redrawn from Parker, G. H.: The Elementary Nervous System, Philadelphia, Lippincott)

terior surface. (It is important at this time to examine Figs. 21-4 and 21-39, to see where these ganglia are situated.)

As has been noted already, some afferent neurons enter the brain by way of certain cranial nerves. The cell bodies of these afferent neurons also are situated in ganglia that are close to, but not actually inside, the brain. These are termed cranial ganglia. The term *cerebrospinal* ganglia refers to both groups. All the cell bodies of the afferent neurons that enter the C.N.S. from the body segments are housed in spinal or cranial ganglia.

The first afferent neurons to evolve were unipolar cells, having only one process which was an axon which passed inwardly from the surface (Fig. 21-2). When the cell body left the surface to migrate inwardly, the afferent neurons became bipolar cells, having a dendrite that passed out to the surface and brought impulses into the cell body and an axon which passed inwardly to conduct the impulse away from the cell body (Fig. 21-6). When the cell body migrated still farther inwardly and took up a position in a spinal or a cranial ganglion, it remained fundamentally a bipolar cell, with a dendrite leading into it and an axon leaving it, but the parts of the two processes close to the cell body seem to have swung around like the hands of a clock until they came together, as the hands of the clock do every hour, and then fused. As a result the bipolar cells become unipolar (Fig. 21-4). The single process of each, however, is short and soon branches into two, one of which extends to a sensory ending and the other into the spinal cord (Fig. 21-4). Functionally, the peripheral branch is a dendrite, and the second an axon, but since both processes have the histologic structure of axons, the peripheral processes of afferent neurons, although functionally dendrites, are commonly termed axons.

The axonal processes that enter the spinal cord from afferent neurons do so via the posterior roots of the cord (Fig. 21-4). On entering the cord they may synapse directly with efferent neurons, as is shown in Figure 21-4, or with connector neurons, or they may pass for short distances down the cord or for longer distances up the cord, before synapsing with efferent neurons of other segments or with connector neurons.

**Efferent Neurons.** The cell bodies of all efferent neurons, with the exception of certain of those of the autonomic nervous system, which will be described later, are all confined to the C.N.S. (Fig. 21-4).

**Connector Neurons.** The cell bodies of all connector neurons are, of course, confined to the C.N.S.

**Neurobiotaxis.** This term refers to a force that has operated through the period of evolution of nervous tissue and has acted to cause the cell bodies of efferent and connector neurons to move as close as possible to their chief sources of stimulation. Accordingly, the dendrites of efferent and connector neurons tend to be short and their axons long. This is not true of afferent neurons because in these the tendency for centralization is more potent than neurobiotaxis.

**To sum up:** The cell bodies of all afferent neurons are in spinal or cerebral ganglia outside the C.N.S. The cell bodies of all connector neurons, and all efferent neurons, except certain of those of the autonomic nervous system, are in the C.N.S.

**Further Uses for the Terms "Afferent" and "Efferent."** So far, these two terms have been used to indicate whether neurons carry impulses into or away from the C.N.S. The student should be warned that these terms are used in neuro-anatomy for a further purpose; connector neurons in the C.N.S. that bring impulses to some nerve station are said to be afferent with regard to that station, and those that carry impulses away from it are said to be efferent with regard to that station.

**The Basis for Sensation.** Perhaps the most extraordinary development in the evolution of nervous tissue was the advent of consciousness and the ability to experience different kinds of sensation. Man has many senses: touch, pressure, heat, cold, pain, sight, hearing, taste, position and movement. These sensations are experienced in the brain. However, the stimuli that give rise to these sensations do not reach the brain; only nervous impulses reach the brain. How can nervous impulses from different afferent neurons give rise to different sensations and make some of them, such as cold, seem as if they were being experienced in one's toes or fingers?

The passage of a nervous impulse along a nerve fiber has much in common with the passage of an electric current along a wire. Any amateur electrician could wire up a battery and an induction coil so that he can give himself a shock when he closes a switch. Furthermore, switches can be obtained or made which could be said to be specialized with regard to different kinds of stimuli. For example, a telegraph key (Fig. 21-7, *top*) completes a circuit if it is touched or pressed; it is either a touch or pressure receptor, depending on how tightly its spring is adjusted. Contrivances can also be built which would complete a circuit if they were heated or cooled (Fig. 21-7). Indeed, it is possible to build or obtain electrical contrivances that will set up an electrical impulse in, and so complete, a circuit when they are exposed to any of the different kinds of stimuli that can stimulate the afferent neurons of man (Fig. 21-7).

Much the same kind of arrangement exists in the nervous system of man to enable him to discern various kinds of sensation. Instead of possessing instruments such as those illustrated in Figure 21-7, which set up electrical currents in different wires, man has sense organs and nerve endings which will be described in Chapter 31; they are selectively stimulated by different kinds of stimuli such as heat, light and sound, and are connected by chains of neurons to different parts of the brain. For example, the neuron chains that lead from the light-sensitive receptors in the eye pass to a special part of the brain. If this special part is stimulated electrically during an operation on the brain the patient experiences the sensation of light. Or, if it were possible to connect the neuron chains from the sound receptors to this part of the brain, the individual, on being subjected to what anyone else would say was a noise, would interpret it as light. Therefore, the basis for the understanding of different kinds of sensation depends on there being several different kinds of afferent receptors in the body, with each kind highly sensitive with regard to some particular kind of stimulus, and on these different kinds being "wired," so to speak, by means of afferent pathways, to different parts of the brain which, on receiving nervous impulses, give rise to different kinds of sensation.

**Inherited and Conditioned Reflex Responses.** It is a common analogy to liken the brain to a giant switchboard. Afferent pathways from all parts of the body lead to it, and efferent pathways lead from it to all parts of the body. Although connections exist between afferent and efferent neurons in the spinal cord, most afferent impulses that are set up in the body pass to the brain by means of afferent pathways before they activate efferent systems. Hence, it is in the brain—the giant switchboard—that circuits are set up between afferent and efferent systems. The number of different circuits available between afferent and efferent systems in this organ is enormous, and the same ones are not used to the same extent in all individuals. A sight that makes one woman laugh may make another cry. Why, in the first woman, should afferent impulses be directed over a circuit to efferent pathways that control the muscles employed in laughing, and in the second woman, to efferent pathways controlling the secretion of tears? In other words, what makes people behave differently to what would seem to be the same stimulus?

One fundamental factor in determining behavior is the fact that all higher animals are born with certain instinctive reflex responses. A puppy makes swimming motions as soon as he falls into the water. He inherits, in his brain, a preferential circuit between the affer-

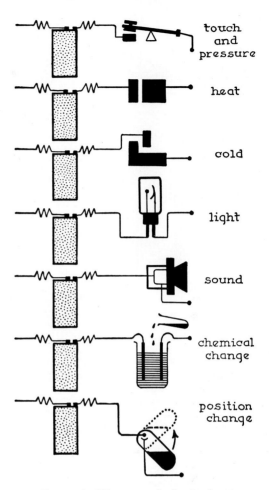

Fig. 21-7. Diagrams of pieces of apparatus which could be employed to complete an electrical circuit when subjected to the different kinds of stimuli listed on the right side.

ent pathways that are activated by the stimulus of immersion and the efferent pathways that control the muscles of the legs. Another inherited reflex response possessed by puppies is that they will salivate if food is placed in their mouths.

By showing how further reflex responses could be superimposed on inherited instinctive ones, Pavlov, the famous Russian physiologist, showed that the only stimulus that would evoke salivation in a newborn puppy was the actual presence of food in its mouth. The afferent pathway activated in this instance would be a pathway leading from receptors in the mouth itself. In its brain, the puppy

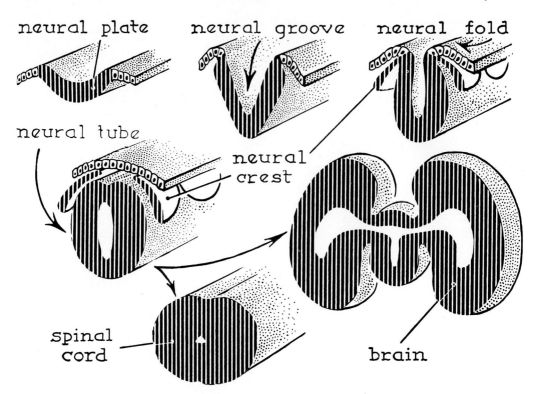

FIG. 21-8. Diagrams showing how the neural plate forms from ectoderm and how it becomes the neural groove and then the neural tube. The diagrams also show that the neural tube, in different sites, turns into the spinal cord and the brain respectively.

had inherited a preferred connection, as it were, between this afferent pathway and the efferent pathway that controls the salivary glands. Then Pavlov showed that the puppy, after being fed a few times, would salivate as soon as he smelled the food that was put before him. Obviously, this would require the use of a different afferent pathway from the first one employed—one from the nose rather than from the mouth. So there must be some connection in the brain between afferent pathways from the nose and the afferent pathways from the mouth. The neurons by which such connections are made are termed *association neurons*. These permit the puppy to associate the taste of food with the smell of food, and once this association is built up the proper stimulus applied to the nose brings about the same reflex response as does food in the mouth. This new reflex response, which involves a different afferent pathway, and association neurons, Pavlov termed a *conditioned response*. He showed that the possibilities in

conditioned responses are very considerable. A pup, for example, soon learns to salivate at the sight of food and can even be trained to salivate at the ringing of a bell, if a bell is rung every time it is fed. Then, by further conditioning procedures which need not be described here, the conditioned response to the ringing of the bell can be inhibited. Therefore, conditioning procedures are not only effective in broadening the base of our possible responses; they can also be used to broaden the base of our inhibitions. All in all, we are exposed to so many different associations in our lives that it is not strange that all stimuli are not the same to all men and that what may attract one may repel another.

## DEVELOPMENT OF THE CENTRAL NERVOUS SYSTEM

**Formation of Neural Tube and Neural Crests.** Soon after the 3 germ layers—ectoderm, mesoderm and endoderm—are distinguishable in the embryo, the ectoderm along the midline of the back, beginning in the mid-dorsal region, and then extending both forward and backward, becomes stratified to form a thickened band called the *neural plate* (Fig. 21-8). Almost as soon as it is formed, the neural plate becomes depressed along its midline to form the *neural groove* (Fig. 21-8) and elevated along its two edges to form two *neural folds* (Fig. 21-8). Near the crest of each fold, below the line along which the thickened ectoderm of the plate becomes continuous with the ordinary ectoderm of the back, some thickened ectoderm bulges laterally; these bulges, one on each side, constitute what are termed *neural crests*. Next, the edges of the two neural folds come together; this entails three fusions: (1) the edges of the thickened ectoderm of the neural groove fuse to convert the groove into a *neural tube* (Fig. 21-8); (2) the two neural crests fuse, but only temporarily, because they soon become separated again to appear as shown in Figure 21-8; and (3) as the tops of the two neural folds come together, the edges of the ordinary ectoderm, which extends up the lateral aspect of each fold to its top, meet and fuse with one another (Fig. 21-8). As this occurs the neural crests and the neural tube become detached from the ordinary ectoderm and sink into the mesoderm along the midline of the embryo, the back of which is covered thereafter with a continuous layer of ordinary ectoderm.

The cells of the neural tube and crests constitute the *neuro-ectoderm*. We shall now consider its further history and learn how the neuro-ectodermal cells of the neural tube develop into the C.N.S. and then, a few pages further on, how those of the neural crests give rise to most of the P.N.S.

## MORPHOGENESIS OF THE SPINAL CORD

In order to form the spinal cord the walls of the neural tube thicken. The cellular proliferation that accounts for most of the thickening occurs in its lateral walls. The dorsal and the ventral walls of the tube are relatively passive, and they become known as the *roof plate* and the *floor plate*, respectively, of the tube. All sectors of the lateral walls do not thicken equally; actually, each lateral wall

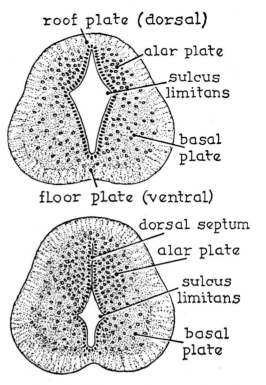

Fig. 21-9. Diagrams of cross sections of neural tube developing into spinal cord.

reveals two lines of thickening: one dorsal and the other ventral. The lumen extends out into the depression formed on each side between these two lines of thickening; this depression on each side is termed a *sulcus limitans* (Fig. 21-9). The two dorsal thickenings, seen in a cross section of a developing cord, resemble a pair of wings (Fig. 21-9, *top*) and are referred to as the *alar (ala = wing) plates* of the developing cord. The two ventral thickenings of the lateral walls form the *basal plates* of the developing cord. The unequal growth rate of the different parts of the wall of the tube makes the lumen diamond-shaped for a time (Fig. 21-9, *top*). Later, however, the edges of the part of the lumen that extends toward the roof plate fuse, and, as a result of this, a *dorsal septum* (Fig. 21-9, *bottom*) is formed. Eventually, the lumen of the neural tube is relatively very small and becomes known as the *central canal* of the cord; this can be seen in Figure 21-8 (*lower left*), and in Figure 21-14.

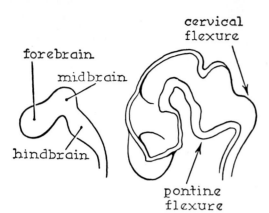

FIG. 21-10. Diagrams showing the early changes that occur as the neural tube in the head region begins to develop into a brain.

## MORPHOGENESIS OF THE BRAIN

It seems almost incredible to anyone who examines a brain for the first time that an organ of such a complex appearance (Fig. 21-11) could have developed from something as simple as a neural tube. Probably two mechanisms are involved: (1) the dissimilar growth rates in different parts of the wall of the tube, and (2) an increasing state of compression in the long axis of the neural tube at its anterior end.

The first change seen as the anterior end of the tube begins to form a brain is that it develops three swellings separated by two constrictions (Fig. 21-10). The swellings are called *vesicles* and are named the forebrain, the midbrain and the hindbrain, respectively (Fig. 21-10). Almost coincidentally a hairpin bend called the *cephalic flexure* occurs ventrally between the midbrain and the forebrain; this becomes so pronounced that the forebrain almost touches the hindbrain (Fig. 21-10). Following this, another kind, which is called the *pontine flexure*, occurs; this results in the hindbrain's bending acutely in a direction opposite (dorsal) to the cephalic flexure. Therefore, the primitive brain is "N"-shaped (Fig. 21-10).

We shall now describe some of the further changes that occur as the anterior part of the neural tube develops into a brain. We shall begin with the portion of the tube that becomes the hindbrain and work forward. If the student remembers that the brain develops from a tube, and that the various structures, which we shall now name and describe, represent *thickenings* or *bulgings* of the wall of the tube, it should be easily possible, from the following description, to obtain a general idea of the position and the nature of some of the more important parts of the brain that are illustrated in Figure 21-11. In order to keep oriented the student should understand that the lumen of the tube, which becomes the ventricles of the brain, is shown in dark stipple in Figure 21-11.

**The Hindbrain.** As already described, this is divided into two parts by the *pontine flexure*. If a rubber tube is bent or kinked upon itself, the region of the kink is no longer tubular but broad and flattened, and the lumen is distorted to a transverse slit. Thus, when the neural tube is bent at the pontine flexure, the lateral walls diverge, and the form described for the rubber tube is assumed. However, the thin roof plate stretches more than the floor of the tube, so it becomes a thin cover over the shallow, widened cavity of the neural tube with the alar and the basal plates forming the floor of the tube, which accordingly becomes *very thick* in the hindbrain (Fig. 21-11). The hindpart of the flexed tube is called the *medulla oblongata* (Fig. 21-11) because of its oblong-shaped cavity and is distinguishable from the cord, with which it is continuous, by its greater width, thicker floor and thinner roof.

The forepart of the hindbrain at first resembles the hindpart, but further development alters its appearance. As in the medulla oblongata, the alar and the basal plates form the floor for the lumen of the tube. The floor here becomes very thick and resembles a bridge and so is called the *pons* (*pons* = bridge) (Fig. 21-11). However, apart from this, the alar portions undergo rapid development and form two large lateral swellings on its forepart; these eventually meet and fuse medially and dorsally to constitute a large mass, the *cerebellum* (Fig. 21-11), which forms the roof over the lumen at this site. These two lateral swellings which fuse medially are termed the *cerebellar hemispheres* (Fig. 21-11). As noted, the alar and the basal plates at the flexure form the *pons*, which is to include a great bundle of fibers which *appear to*

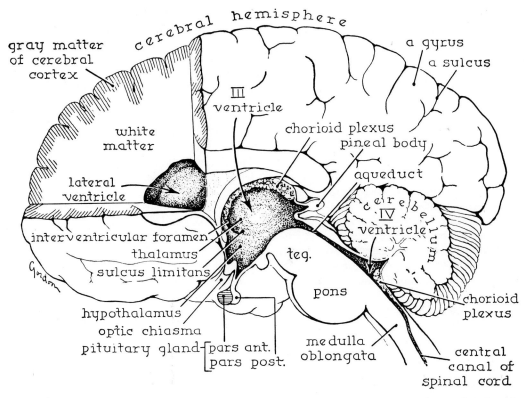

gray matter of cerebral cortex

cerebral hemisphere

a gyrus

a sulcus

white matter

III ventricle

chorioid plexus

pineal body

aqueduct

lateral ventricle

cerebellum

IV ventricle

interventricular foramen

thalamus

teg.

sulcus limitans

Gordon

hypothalamus

optic chiasma

pituitary gland — pars ant. / pars post.

pons

medulla oblongata

chorioid plexus

central canal of spinal cord

FIG. 21-11. A median sagittal section of the brain of man. A portion of the frontal lobe has been cut out (*upper left*) so as to disclose the lateral ventricle. What was originally the lumen of the neural tube is shown in dark stipple. In reading the text the student should begin at the right lower corner and follow the central canal of the cord into the various ventricles of the brain and visualize how the main parts of the brain have developed from the parts of the wall of the neural tube that originally surrounded the divisions of its lumen that later became ventricles.

*bridge* one cerebellar hemisphere to the other, around the ventral surface of this part of the hindbrain.

The lumen of the neural tube persists in the hindbrain as a flattened cavity called the *fourth ventricle* (Fig. 21-11). The thin roof plate, which covers it behind the cerebellum, is called the *posterior medullary vellum* (*vellum* = veil).

**The Midbrain.** Of the 3 divisions of the primitive brain, the midbrain alone retains a frank tubular structure, for the growth rate of the different parts of the wall of the tube is more equal here than elsewhere. During development its vesicular character is lost by the thickening of the alar and the basal plates, particularly the latter, which reduces the lumen to a small ductlike passage in the dor-

sal part of the midbrain. This passage, called the *aqueduct* (Fig. 21-11), connects the cavities of the forebrain and the hindbrain.

The medulla, the pons and the midbrain contain many important groups of cell bodies of neurons. These areas of frank gray matter are termed *nuclei*. Fiber tracts of white matter containing either ascending or descending fibers may synapse in these regions or pass through them uninterruptedly.

**The Forebrain.** The cephalic flexure that develops between midbrain and forebrain does not produce the rubber-tube effect that occurs in the instance of the pontine flexure. Here the neural tube is *relatively* constricted and conforms more readily to bending, without its lumen becoming flattened.

The forebrain undergoes so many changes,

particularly in its forepart, that it is helpful to regard it as consisting of two portions. The hindpart of the forebrain gives rise to thickenings of the wall of the tube called the *thalamus*, the *hypothalamus* and the *subthalamus*, and the forepart to two huge thickened bulges, the *cerebral hemispheres* (Fig. 21-11).

In the hindpart of the forebrain the growth rate is less than the forepart. The alar and the basal parts retain their positions with the alar portion becoming the thalamus and the basal plate the hypothalamus and the subthalamus. The thalamus is concerned primarily with relaying afferent (particularly sensory) impulses from the lower levels of the brain and the cord to the higher centers of the cerebral hemispheres. The hypothalamus is concerned essentially with the automatic innervations of smooth muscles and glands; this matter will be described when the autonomic nervous system is considered.

The cavity of this part of the brain becomes a vertical slit and is known as the *third ventricle* (Fig. 21-11).

In the forepart of the forebrain, whereas the basal plates remain small, becoming the forepart of the hypothalamus, the alar plates undergo enormous development and form two huge evaginations called the *cerebral hemispheres* (Fig. 21-11). The cavities of these become the *lateral ventricles* (Fig. 21-11), which connect with the third ventricle through interventricular foramine (Fig. 21-11). In man the surface of the brain becomes greatly corrugated. The deeper grooves are termed *fissures*, and the shallower ones *sulci*. The latter separate *gyri* (Fig. 21-11).

## HISTOGENESIS OF THE SPINAL CORD

Having considered briefly the changes that occur in the form of the neural tube as it develops into a spinal cord and a brain, we are now prepared to study the microscopic changes that occur in the walls of the tube which are responsible for the gross changes. In particular, we shall learn how the cells of the tube give rise to gray matter and to white matter, the differences between these two types of matter and why they come to be distributed differently in the spinal cord and the brain.

Before describing the details of histogenesis

it may be helpful to point out that the cells of the wall of the neural tube in forming the spinal cord and the brain differentiate only along two main pathways to form either (1) *neurons* or (2) *neuroglia (glia = glue) cells* (Fig. 21-13). Neuroglia is a general term for the cells that provide internal support for the tissues of the C.N.S., and the few varieties of these will be named and described presently.

**The Layers of the Walls of the Neural Tube.** The thin wall of the newly formed neural tube becomes thicker because of the continued proliferation of the cells that abut on its lumen. Therefore, these cells are termed *germinal cells* (Fig. 21-12) and they constitute what at first is called the *inner* or *germinal layer* of the tube (Fig. 21-12). The cells to which they give rise are pushed in to the *middle layer* of the wall of the tube where they become much longer than they are wide and radially arranged (Fig. 21-12). Moreover, many of these cells attain more cytoplasm at their outer than at their inner ends, and, as a consequence, a third and *outer layer* appears in the wall of the tube which is composed of the outer cytoplasmic ends of cells whose nuclei are the prominent feature of the middle layer (Fig. 21-12). The cytoplasm in this outer layer takes on a reticulated spongy appearance (Fig. 21-12) and this provides a basis for naming some of the cells of the tube *spongioblasts*.

## DIFFERENTIATION OF THE INNER LAYER AND THE FORMATION OF THE EPENDYMA

As development proceeds, the germinal cells which comprise the inner layer of the wall of the tube develop long cytoplasmic processes that extend out to the periphery of the tube (Fig. 21-12) (*bottom*—silver stain). Their cell bodies, instead of being rounded as formerly, take on the appearance of columnar epithelial cells, and for a period these have cilia on their inner borders (Fig. 21-12). When they assume the appearance of columnar epithelial cells with long processes that extend out into the wall of the tube, they are known as *ependymal spongioblasts* instead of germinal cells. It is not clear why this name was chosen, because ependyma refers to an *outer garment*, whereas these cells actually form the lining of the tube. As development proceeds further, the epen-

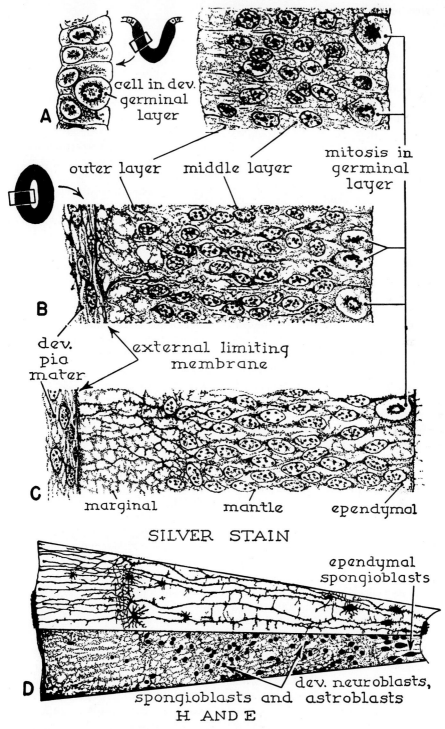

A cell in dev. germinal layer

outer layer    middle layer    mitosis in germinal layer

A

B

dev. pia mater

external limiting membrane

C

marginal    mantle    ependymal

SILVER STAIN

ependymal spongioblasts

D

dev. neuroblasts, spongioblasts and astroblasts

H AND E

FIG. 21-12. (A, *left*) Section of a developing neural tube (just before closure) of a rabbit embryo. (A, *right*) Section of a developing neural tube of a pig embryo of 5 mm. (B) Section of a developing neural tube of a pig embryo of 7 mm. (C) Section of a developing neural tube of a pig embryo of 10 mm. (D) Section of a developing spinal cord of a pig embryo 55 mm. long. The upper part of this illustration shows the way the tissue appears when a silver technic is employed, and the lower part shows the way the same structure appears with H and E. (Modified from Haresty, Irving: Am. J. Anat. *3:229*)

dymal spongioblasts become increasingly differentiated into ordinary ependymal cells. These form an epithelial lining for the central canal of the cord and the ventricles of the brain. Mature ependymal cells vary from columnar to flattened cuboidal types (Fig. 21-29). In some sites they are somewhat rounded.

## DIFFERENTIATION IN THE MIDDLE LAYER AND THE FORMATION OF GRAY MATTER

As previously noted, cells produced as a result of mitosis in the germinal layer are pushed into the middle layer of the tube. Here, for a time, they all have a similar appearance, but as development proceeds they begin to differentiate along two main pathways. Most of them become neuroblasts and eventually nerve cells (Fig. 21-13, *left*). However, a minority become free spongioblasts (Fig. 21-13, *right*). These, as shown in Figure 21-13, differentiate along two sublines to form either astroblasts, which in turn form cells with so many radiating processes that they are star-shaped, and hence called *astrocytes* (*astron* = star), or *oligodendroglia*, which are small cells with few processes or branches (*oligos* = few; *dendron* = tree).

In giving rise to neuroblasts, the neuroectodermal cells of the middle layer develop larger nuclei than they do in giving rise to free spongioblasts. The middle layer soon comes to consist of neuroblasts and spongioblasts, which can be distinguished from each other by their nuclei. The neuroblasts become neurons, and the spongioblasts become astrocytes and oligodendroglia cells. This combination of neurons and supporting cells constitutes *gray matter*. Hence, the middle layer of the tube becomes the gray matter of the spinal cord. It does not form an even and continuous layer in the wall of the tube but becomes arranged in the form of a structure which roughly resembles an "H" when it is seen in cross section (Fig. 21-14). From its appearance in a single cross section, this H-shaped mass of gray matter is said to have two dorsal or posterior *horns* and two ventral or anterior horns (Fig. 21-14). Actually, the continuous horns are columns that extend up and down the cord. In some parts of the cord there is a lateral horn or column on each side as well (Figs. 21-30 and 21-31).

## DIFFERENTIATION IN THE OUTER LAYER AND THE FORMATION OF WHITE MATTER

The axons that sprout from the neuroblasts of the developing posterior horns of gray matter and the axons that enter the dorsolateral aspect of the cord from the neuroblasts of the developing spinal ganglia pass into the outer layer of the developing cord, and in this layer they extend, mostly up, but some down, for considerable distances. Meanwhile, some of the neuroblasts that develop in the lower part of the brain also send axons down the outer layer of the developing cord. Furthermore, although most axons from anterior horn cells pass out of the cord as efferent fibers, a few pass down and up the cord to contribute also to the white matter. Therefore, the outer layer of the cord comes to contain vast numbers of axons which pass up and down the cord to comprise the afferent and the efferent pathways between different levels of the cord and the brain. However, the afferent and the efferent fibers are segregated from one another in different sectors of the cord. The fibers are subdivided further; for example, the fibers that carry impulses that give rise to the sensation of pain are bundled together on each side of the cord.

The outer layer of the part of the neural tube destined to become the spinal cord is invaded, not only by axons, but also by some free spongioblasts (from the developing middle layer) which differentiate into *fibrous astrocytes* and *oligodendroglia*. These two types of neuroglia cells fit into the crevices between the axons and send their processes out among them (Fig. 21-14). The oligodendroglia are sometimes arranged in rows between adjacent axons (Fig. 21-26).

**Myelinization.** As most copper telephone wires are covered with a coat of rubber insulation, so most axons in the outer layer of the developing cord become covered with white glistening fatty material called *myelin*. As myelinization occurs, the whole outer layer of the developing spinal cord becomes white; it is then said to be *white matter*. Therefore, white matter consists of myelinated fibers supported by fibrous astrocytes and oligodendroglia cells. White matter does not contain the cell bodies of neurons but only their fibers.

Myelin is a nonliving fatty material. It con-

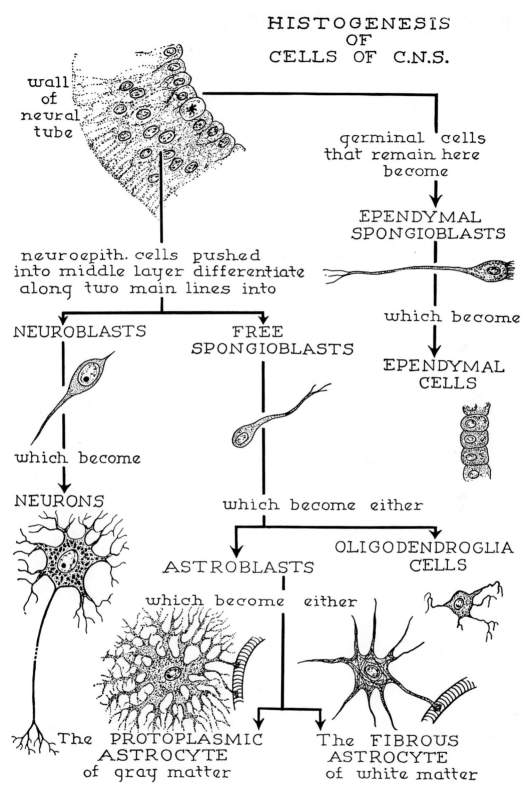

# HISTOGENESIS
## OF
## CELLS OF C.N.S.

wall of neural tube

germinal cells that remain here become

EPENDYMAL SPONGIOBLASTS

neuroepith. cells pushed into middle layer differentiate along two main lines into

which become

NEUROBLASTS

FREE SPONGIOBLASTS

EPENDYMAL CELLS

which become

NEURONS

which become either

OLIGODENDROGLIA CELLS

ASTROBLASTS

which become either

The PROTOPLASMIC ASTROCYTE of gray matter

The FIBROUS ASTROCYTE of white matter

FIG. 21-13. Diagrams showing the main lines along which the neuro-ectodermal cells of the neural tube differentiate.

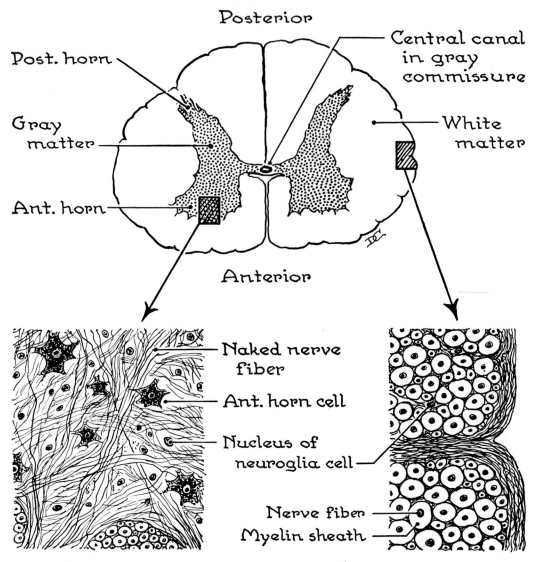

FIG. 21-14. (*Top*) Diagram of a cross section of the spinal cord (low-power), showing the distribution of gray and white matter in it. (*Bottom*) Two diagrams (high-power), showing the contents of the gray and the white matter, respectively.

tains cholesterol, cerebroside and phospholipids, the most important phospholipid being sphingomyelin. Much of the lipid material is present in the form of lipid-protein complexes. Myelinization usually begins near the cell body and advances along the axon toward its termination. Myelinization begins early in the 4th month and is not completed at birth; some fiber tracts become myelinated afterward. The total amount of myelin in the C.N.S. increases from birth to maturity; individual fibers become more heavily myelinated during the growth period. Myelin is not necessary for fibers to conduct nervous impulses but seems to be necessary for fibers to conduct nervous impulses sufficiently well to permit muscles to make delicate and precise movements.

Myelin is soluble in fat solvents; hence, when ordinary paraffin sections of the spinal cord are prepared, most of the myelin of the white matter dissolves away in the dehydrating and clearing agents. When such sections are stained, the sites where myelin was present appear as empty spaces (Fig. 21-14, *right*). However, there are special fixatives, most notably *osmic acid*, which fix myelin so that it does not dissolve away as paraffin sections are prepared. Osmic acid, in itself, colors myelin black, so that if a cross section of spinal cord, fixed in osmic acid, is examined under very low power, the white matter of the cord appears black (Fig. 21-15). If the white matter is examined under higher power the blackened myelin will be seen to be arranged in little rings around each nerve fiber (Fig. 21-15, *top*).

EM investigations of the formation and structure of myelin are described in connection with the P.N.S.

## HISTOGENESIS OF NERVOUS TISSUE OF BRAIN

As has been explained already, different parts of the walls of the neural tube that forms the brain grow unequally so that the brain assumes a complex shape. Nevertheless, although there are certain points of difference that need not be described here, the histogenesis of the gray and the white matter of the brain is similar to that which occurs in the spinal cord. Gray matter forms from the cells of the middle layer of the tube, and white matter forms in the outer layer of the neural tube. Hence, in the medulla, the pons, the midbrain and in parts of the forebrain, gray matter develops in positions that are roughly comparable with those in which it develops in the spinal cord, and it becomes covered by the white matter that develops in the outer layer of the tube as it does in the cord. But in certain parts of the developing brain, neuroblasts from the middle layer of the neutral tube migrate out through the outer layer of developing white matter to take up a position on the outside of the tube. Because of this phenomenon the cerebral and the cerebellar hemispheres come to possess a thin covering or *cortex* of gray matter (Fig. 21-11). Hence, in these two parts of the brain, gray matter exists not only deep to the white matter but superficial to it as well.

*It should now be clear why the surface of the spinal cord is white and why the surface*

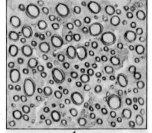

myelinated fibers embedded in neuroglial web

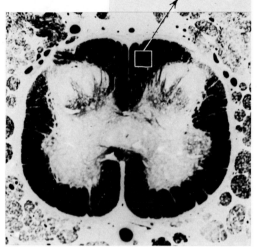

Fig. 21-15. (*Bottom*) Low-power photomicrograph of a cross section of spinal cord (sacral region) fixed in osmic acid. The white matter appears black. (*Top*) High-power drawing of a small area of white matter showing that the black material seen in the low-power illustration is the myelin of the sheaths of the nerve fibers. Observe that the fibers are of different calibers.

*of the cerebral hemispheres is gray. It should be understood that white matter is white because of myelin and that it contains the bodies of no nerve cells but only neuroglia cells. All the bodies of the nerve cells of the C.N.S. are in gray matter. Furthermore, the reason for the tissue of the C.N.S. being so soft and jellylike should now be apparent; it is because its supporting tissue is not ordinary connective tissue with tough intercellular substances such as collagen and elastin but only delicate ectodermal-derived cellular nerve glue—the neuroglia.*

Having considered the histogenesis of the nervous tissue of the C.N.S., we shall now describe in some detail the histologic appear-

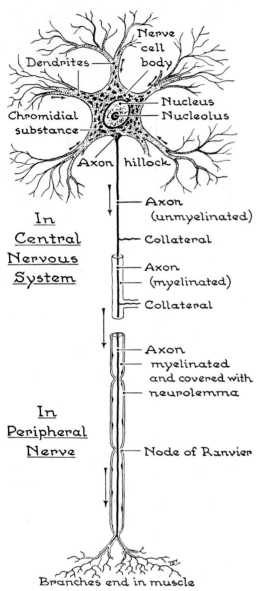

FIG. 21-16. Diagram of a multipolar neuron.

ance of the different kinds of cells of which it is composed and then discuss briefly their arrangements in some of its representative parts.

## THE CELLS OF THE NERVOUS TISSUE OF THE C.N.S.

### NEURONS

Most neurons of the C.N.S. are said to be multipolar because they possess 3 or more processes. Multipolarity is gained by neurons

having 2 or more dendrites; they never have more than one axon. However, axons may branch, as will be described, so one neuron can send impulses to many others.

**Cell Bodies.** The *cell body* is that part of the neuron that contains the nucleus; for this reason it is sometimes called the *perikaryon* (*peri* = around; *karyon* = nut or nucleus). The cell bodies of neurons vary from being small to large. The larger ones are among the largest cells in the body. The cell bodies of different kinds of neurons vary in shape; they may be round, oval, flattened ovoid or pyramidal.

**Nuclei.** The nucleus commonly has a central position, but in at least one type of neuron it is eccentrically disposed. Nuclei are generally large and spherical (Figs. 21-16 and 21-17). In small neurons the nucleus, though actually smaller, is larger in relation to the size of the cell body than it is in larger neurons. The nuclear membrane usually stains well with hematoxylin; nevertheless, it does not stand out sharply against the cytoplasm because this also stains well. The nucleus consists chiefly of pale-staining nuclear sap which causes it to resemble a vesicle (*vesica* = bladder); hence, the nuclei of neurons are sometimes said to be *vesicular* in type (Fig. 21-17). The chromatin granules are fine and dispersed (Fig. 21-16). One large nucleolus is commonly present, but there may be more. Since the nucleolus stands out so clearly against the pale nucleoplasm (Fig. 21-17), and since the nuclear membrane does not stand out sharply against the cytoplasm, the beginner is prone to confuse the nucleolus with the nucleus and the nucleoplasm with cytoplasm. The sex chromatin of neurons, illustrated in Figure 21-17, is described in Chapter 6.

**Centrosomes** can be demonstrated by special technics in the proliferating neuroblasts of embryonic tissue but only occasionally in the cell bodies of mature neurons. Since centrosomes are concerned in cell division their general absence in neurons may be of some significance with regard to the inability of neurons to divide.

**Neurofibrils.** With the light microscope and certain technics it is possible to demonstrate what seem to be fibrils in the cytoplasm of nerve cell bodies and also in nerve fibers. With the EM, what are termed *neurofilaments* are demonstrable in the cytoplasm (Fig. 21-45).

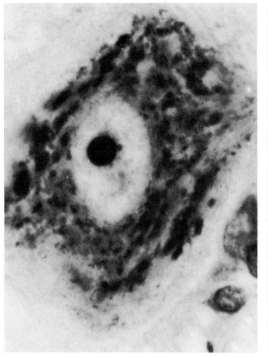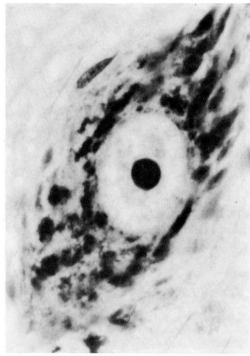

FIG. 21-17. Oil-immersion photomicrographs of anterior horn cells in sections of the spinal cord of the cat stained with cresyl violet. (*Left*) Picture taken from the cord of a female cat. (*Right*) From the cord of a male cat. Both pictures show chromidial substance to advantage. (Barr, M. L., Bertram, L. F., and Lindsay, H. A.: Anat. Rec. *107*:283)

The latter, of course, are much too fine to be seen with the light microscope. What is seen with the light microscope may be due to these filaments becoming aggregated.

**Nissl Bodies (Clumps of Chromidial Substances).** Chromidial substance is a very prominent feature of the cytoplasm of nerve cells. Its distribution and appearance differ to some extent in different kinds of nerve cells, but, in general, in fixed material, stained with basic dyes, it appears in the form of irregular clumps, which may be small enough to be granules, in the sites in the cytoplasm which are probably the interstices of the network of bundles of neurofibrils (Figs. 21-16 and 21-17).

In honor of Franz Nissl, who studied this material intensively in the last century, the clumps of chromidial substance in the cytoplasm of nerve cells are often termed Nissl bodies. The studies instituted by Nissl have been continued; indeed, chromidial substance is perhaps the most studied feature of neurons. If the axon of a neuron is severed, what is

known as an axon reaction occurs: the chromidial substance of the cell body tends to melt away temporarily (chromatolysis), and the nucleus moves to one side (Fig. 21-18).

**Fine Structure of Nissl Bodies.** Nissl bodies (clumps of chromidial substance) seen with the EM consist of aggregations of rough-surfaced flattened membranous vesicles with numerous ribosomes scattered between the adjacent flattened vesicles of which they are composed. Nissl bodies, as such, are not surrounded by any kind of limiting membrane but each consists of an aggregation of flattened rough-surfaced membranous vesicles. The arrangement of the flattened vesicles in Nissl bodies differs in different kinds of nerve cells. In large motor neurons the Nissl bodies are large, and the flattened vesicles in each are arranged more or less parallel with one another (Fig. 21-19). In other types of nerve cells the arrangement of the flattened vesicles is not so regular, and in some kinds of nerve cells the rough-surfaced vesicles are disposed in an irregular fashion in the cytoplasm. Palay

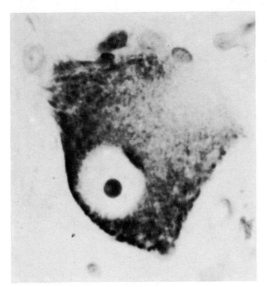

Fig. 21-18. High-power photomicrograph of a nerve cell, showing severe chromatolysis during axon reaction. The axon hillock of this cell is at the upper right, and the chromatolysis is typically most severe between the nucleus and the axon hillock. The nucleus has taken up an eccentric position, and a good "nuclear cap" is shown. (Barr, M. L., and Hamilton, J. D.: J. Comp. Neurol. *89*:93)

and Palade should be read for the details.

Free ribosomes are even more abundant than membrane-attached ribosomes in Nissl bodies. As was explained in Chapter 7, free ribosomes are concerned in the synthesis of protein required by the cell, for example, to replenish that which is metabolized. An important clue as to why the bodies of nerve cells should be equipped for the synthesis of much new protein for cell replenishment was provided by Weiss and Hiscoe in 1948 who evolved the axonal flow theory. This theory postulates that new protein is more or less continuously being synthesized in the bodies of nerve cells and that it flows down to the end of the axon where it is presumably metabolized. It was shown that protein accumulated at sites where nerve fibers were constricted and that a high concentration of enzymes appeared in the proximal stump of a sectioned nerve. Further evidence for the axonal-flow hypothesis has been provided recently by radioautographic studies made by

Droz and Leblond. They gave animals labeled amino acids and then followed the course of the labeled protein synthesized in nerve cells by preparing radioautographs of nervous tissue at different times afterward. They found that within minutes after the labeled amino acid was given that label appeared over the nucleus and the adjacent cytoplasm in nerve cell bodies. Shortly afterward the label was seen in axon hillocks and somewhat later still in the axons. They found that the labeled protein migrated down the axon at a rate of around 1.5 mm. per day.

**Mitochondria.** The mitochondria show no unusual features and are disposed in the cytoplasm between Nissl bodies.

**Golgi Apparatus.** It was in the cell bodies of neurons that Golgi first demonstrated the network that bears his name. The location of the Golgi net varies in different kinds of nerve cells; not uncommonly it can be seen to surround the nucleus, lying closer to it than the cell surface, as is illustrated in Figure 21-20.

According to both Cajal and Penfield, the Golgi net breaks up after the axon of a cell is severed.

The EM shows that in addition to the rough-surfaced membranous vesicles, the cytoplasm of nerve cells contains many groups of smooth-surfaced flattened vesicles closely arranged in parallel array. These are the flattened vesicles of the Golgi apparatus, and aggregations of these are disposed in what seems to be a haphazard fashion in the cytoplasm. Small smooth-surfaced spherical vesicles are commonly associated with these.

**Pigments.** Two kinds of pigments may appear in nerve cells. The first, a golden *lipochrome* pigment (Fig. 7-28), appears during postnatal life, first in ganglion cells and later in cells of the C.N.S. Its amount increases with age. Its significance is not known. *Melanin* occurs in nerve cells in a few parts of the C.N.S., perhaps most notably in what is termed the *substantia nigra* (*niger* = black) —a landmark in the midbrain—that will be seen by the student when the brain is dissected. The significance of the presence of melanin in the bodies of some nerve cells of the C.N.S. is not known.

**Dendrites** extend from the various surfaces of multipolar neurons like branches from the trunk of a tree (Fig. 21-16). The dendrites

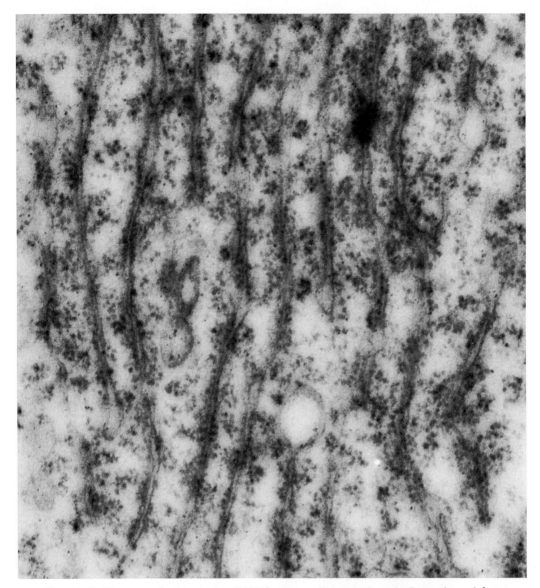

FIG. 21-19. Electron micrograph ($\times$ 85,000) of a section cut through the nucleus abducens of a rat. The field illustrated here is that of a Nissl body in a motor neuron. The illustration shows ribosomes to advantage; they are arranged along the flattened membranous vesicles (which appear in the illustration as double lines) and between adjacent flattened vesicles. The seemingly empty ovoid area below the center of the picture is the expanded end of a vesicle. (Palay, S., and Palade, G.: J. Biophysic. & Biochem. Cytol. *1*:69)

themselves branch; hence, several different orders of branches that become smaller with branching are common. In their stouter parts, close to the cell body, the cytoplasm of dendrites contains both chromidial substance and mitochondria. Neurofibrils probably extend into their finest branches. In special prepara-

tions impregnated with silver, little buds called *gemmules* (*gemmula* = a little bud), which take the form of little knobs or spines, can be seen to project from dendrites along their sides. Since dendrites branch so extensively, it is obvious that through them a nerve cell body can make contact with, and so receive impulses from, large numbers of other neurons.

**Axons.** In contrast with dendrites, only one axon extends from the cell body of even a multipolar neuron. It arises from a special part of the periphery of the cell body termed the *axon hillock* (Fig. 21-16). This area contains no chromidial substance, perhaps because neurofibrils converge through this area to enter the axon. Axons carry impulses away

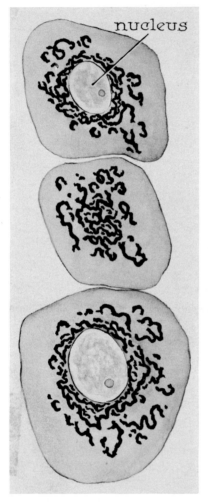

FIG. 21-20. Drawing of a section of a dorsal root ganglion of a mouse (high-power). The material was fixed in a ferric chloride-osmic acid mixture. This treatment results in the blackening of the Golgi network. The section missed the nucleus in the middle cell. (Preparation by S. H. Bensley)

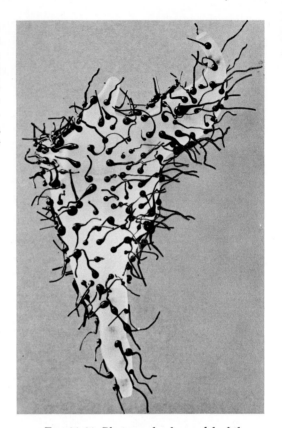

FIG. 21-21. Photograph of a model of the body of a nerve cell in the dorsal horn of the cat's spinal cord. The model as a whole was made by fitting together individual models made from serial sections and it shows the enormous number of nerve fibers that terminate as end-bulbs (end-feet) on the body of the nerve cell to effect synaptic relations with it. (Haggar, R. A., and Barr, M. L.: J. Comp. Neurol. *93*:17)

from the cell body. They vary from being part of a millimeter to several feet in length. The axons of different neurons vary in diameter from less than a micron to several microns. Each is of a constant diameter throughout its length. The larger ones conduct impulses more rapidly than the smaller ones. Axons may give off branches; these are termed *collaterals* (Fig. 21-16) because they come off the axon at right angles (laterally).

The axons that pass up and down the white matter of the cord, in the different afferent and efferent pathways, and those that extend through the white matter of the brain are

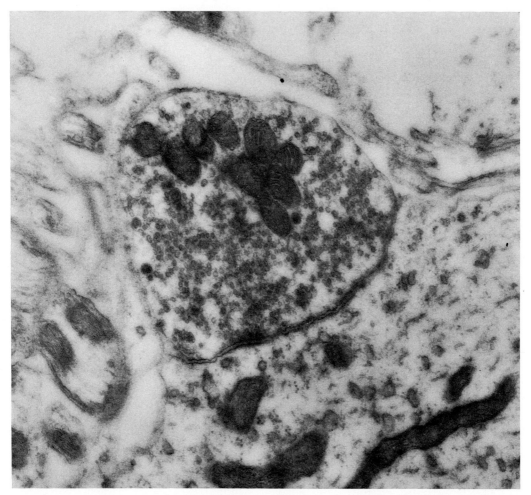

FIG. 21-22. Electron micrograph (× 57,000) of a section of the facial colliculus of a rat. The large central body seen in the picture is an end-foot which abuts on the surface of a neuron, the cytoplasm of which fills the right lower part of the picture. At the point of contact a dark double line is seen; one of the lines is the cell membrane of the end-foot and the other the cell membrane of the cell body of a neuron. The space between the 2 cell membranes is about 200 Å wide. Notice that the end-foot contains many mitochondria and very numerous neurovesicles. (Preparation by S. Palay)

myelinated. However, outside of their myelin sheaths they have no covering except that provided by the processes of fibrous astrocytes and oligodendroglia (Fig. 21-14). Unlike the axons of peripheral nerves, they are not covered with neurolemma sheaths, which will be described when peripheral nerves are considered. This fact is mentioned here because their lack of neurolemma sheaths is an important reason for axons of the C.N.S. not regenerating after they are severed or otherwise destroyed.

The way in which a nerve fiber becomes myelinated is complex and will be described in detail in connection with the nerve fibers of peripheral nerves. Here it is enough to say that the myelinated nerve fibers of the central nervous system become myelinated by a similar mechanism. In peripheral nerves each fiber that is to become myelinated is surrounded by a sheath cell. Each sheath cell sends out a flat cytoplasmic extension that becomes so thin it consists of no more, or little more, than 2 cell membranes. The thin flat wrapping material that is obtained this way becomes wound around the fiber so as to ensheath it in many layers, and this forms the layered material that is myelin. In the central nervous system the neuroglia cells perform the function that is performed by sheath cells in the peripheral nervous system; cell membranes derived from neuroglia cells become the myelin that surrounds nerve fibers of the central nervous system.

**Types and Structure of Synapses in the C.N.S.** Synapses were defined and some of their general characteristics were described early in this chapter. Their structure will now be considered in more detail.

The common type of synapse in the C.N.S. is one in which an axon from one neuron terminates on a dendrite or a cell body of another. In this type of termination, the axon, as it makes contact with the second neuron, becomes swollen into a little bulb that abuts on the cell body or the dendrite of the second neuron. The little swollen terminations of axons are called *end-bulbs, end-feet* or *boutons*. The reconstruction made by Haggar and Barr (Fig. 21-21) of the cell body of a neuron shows dramatically the vast number of axons that can come into synaptic association with another neuron in the C.N.S. by means of this type of termination.

The fine structure of synapses of this type has been investigated extensively by Palay, one of whose illustrations is Figure 21-22. With the EM, three very important features about end-feet are clearly apparent. First, there is an aggregation of mitochondria in them (Fig. 21-22). Some of these have longitudinally disposed cristae. The abundance of mitochondria in this site is probably related to the enzymatic activity and the ion transport concerned with the electrical phenomena that occur. Secondly, the cytoplasm of the end-foot contains innumerable tiny spherical vesicles from about 200 to 650 Å in diameter (Fig. 21-22). These *neurovesicles*, which are also seen in motor end-plates (Fig. 20-23), are filled with a material that is denser than the cytoplasm outside them. These neurovesicals that are so densely aggregated at this site are probably concerned in the production and the liberation of the chemical agent involved in the transmission of nervous impulses across

synapses; these chemical agents will be discussed at the end of this chapter. Thirdly, the EM shows clearly that the membrane of the presynaptic neuron (that of the end-foot) and the membrane covering the body or dendrite of the cell body of the neuron on which the end-foot lies, are both continuous and separate entities. They are seen in Figure 21-22 as dark lines separated from each other by a light space about 200 Å wide.

## NEUROGLIA

A proper understanding of the function of neuroglia cells in providing internal support for the nervous tissue of the C.N.S. awaited the development of special histologic technics. Ordinary stains such as H and E give no intimation that these cells possess innumerable processes that permeate the substance of the nervous tissue of the C.N.S. and so bind it together and to the blood vessels that course through it. With ordinary stains only the nuclei of the neuroglia cells can be seen to advantage. However, the nuclei of neuroglia cells, as seen in ordinary sections, are of different sorts, suggesting that there are different kinds of neuroglia cells, and this concept is confirmed when the cells are studied by the special technics that will be described presently; they demonstrate their cytoplasmic outlines to better advantage than H and E.

In the past it has been customary to classify the neuroglia cells in postnatal nervous tissue into 3 groups: astrocytes, oligodendroglia and microglia. Recently, Smart and Leblond have utilized thymidine labeled with tritium to trace cell relationships in these cells in the brain of the mouse, and their studies suggest that there are 4 categories of cells in postnatal life, instead of 3, with the fourth type consisting of cells with small dark or medium-dark nuclei. Cells of this fourth type are probably the counterparts in postnatal life of the spongioblasts that give rise to astrocytes and oligodendroglia in fetal life.

**Turnover of Cells in the Neuroglia Series.** In their study of the mouse brain in postnatal life, Smart and Leblond showed that after a mouse was given labeled thymidine the label appears first in cells which have small dark or medium dark nuclei (Fig. 21-23). These cells are of the spongioblast type, and since

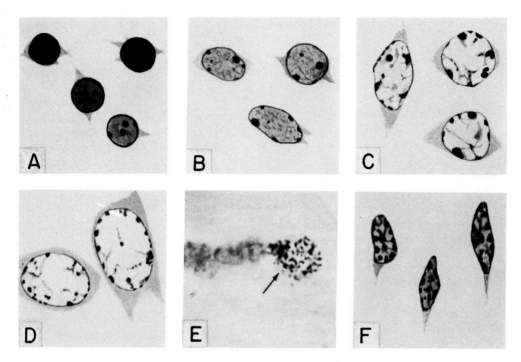

Fig. 21-23. All except E are drawings of cells seen in 3 micron sections of mouse brain stained with H and E. The drawings are at a magnification of 2,500. (A) Cells with dark round nuclei; these are probably spongioblasts. (B) Cells of the same general type with medium-dark nuclei. These are probably somewhat more differentiated than those seen in A. (C) Oligodendroglia. (D) Astrocytes. (E) Photomicrograph (× 1,300) of a radioautograph of a section of brain 7 days after labeled thymidine was injected into the animal. The astrocyte indicated by the arrow is heavily labeled. (F) Microglia. (Smart, I., and Leblond, C. P.: J. Comp. Neurol. *116*:349)

they are the ones that take up the labeled thymidine they must be the ones in which DNA is being duplicated in preparation for division. Label does not appear in astrocytes or oligodendroglia until later and at a time when label is no longer available; this indicates that these latter cells do not take up label in preparation for division (for none is then available) but, instead, label appears in them because previously labeled spongioblasts have differentiated, in due course, into oligodendroglia or into astrocytes. Since labeled oligodendroglia are seen before labeled astrocytes make their appearance, it seems probable that oligodendroglia may sometimes differentiate into astrocytes.

Smart and Leblond consider from their findings that there must be a turnover of cells in the neuroglia series throughout life, even though this is relatively slow. It would seem

that astrocytes grow old and die and that new ones are formed from oligodendroglia and spongioblasts. Oligodendroglia, which become astrocytes or die as oligodendroglia, are replaced by spongioblasts differentiating into oligodendroglia.

Since Smart and Leblond, by using labeled thymidine, were able to show that spongioblast type cells took up label, which would mean that their DNA was being duplicated, it could be assumed that these cells would divide. These investigators next used colchicine to see if they could not detect examples of these cells in the metaphase of mitosis. Their search in this respect was disappointing, for they could not find enough examples of cells of this type arrested in the metaphase of mitosis to account for the number of cell divisions that their studies with labeled thymidine indicated must take place. They lean to the

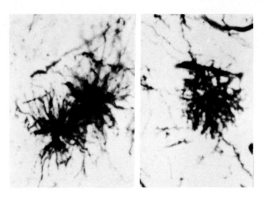

FIG. 21-24. Medium-power photomicrographs of 2 protoplasmic astrocytes in a Golgi preparation of the cerebral cortex of a dog. The heavy black line obliquely crossing the top of the picture on the right is a blood vessel, and the feet of the processes of the astrocyte are attached to it.

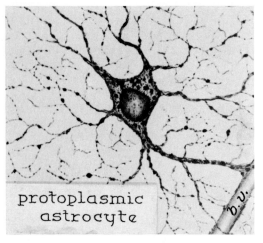

FIG. 21-25. A protoplasmic astrocyte. (Penfield, W.: Neuroglia and microglia; the interstitial tissue of the central nervous system *in* Cowdry's Special Cytology, ed. 2, New York, Hoeber)

view that the process of cell division in cells of the spongioblast type must be less obvious in some way than it is in the usual cell division. Indeed, if mitotic figures were as easy to detect in this type of cell as they are in most types they doubtless would have been observed before, and the concept of there being a turnover of cells of the neuroglia series would have come into existence long ago.

**The Characteristics of the Nuclei of the Neuroglia Cells.** *Astrocytes* have the largest nuclei. Generally, these are ovoid or round, and pale. The chromatin granules are fine, and sparse except at the nuclear membrane where many may adhere (Fig. 21-23 D). Nucleoli can be demonstrated in the nuclei of astrocytes, but they are generally not obvious in the ordinary preparation. An astrocyte labeled with thymidine as seen in a radioautograph is shown in Figure 21-23 E.

**Oligodendroglia.** The nuclei of these are the most common ones seen. Typically, an oligodendroglia nucleus is round or oval and somewhat smaller than the nucleus of an astrocyte. In routine sections the nucleus is dark-staining because its chromatin is closely packed. In very thin sections more detail can be seen in the nucleus, and in such sections coarse and fine granules can be seen to adhere to the nuclear membrane (Fig. 21-23 C). Here again nucleoli can be demonstrated but they are not prominent by any means in the usual section.

**Spongioblast-type Cells.** The nuclei of these tend to be round, and they are of a smaller diameter than either the nuclei of astrocytes or oligodendroglia (Fig. 21-23 A and B). The chromatin is more closely packed than that of either astrocytes or oligodendroglia so that these nuclei generally are very dark staining. The medium dark ones are shown in Figure 21-23 B.

**Microglia.** These cells, although classed as one type of neuroglia cell, develop from mesenchyme and not from spongioblasts. Their nuclei are elongated and narrow (Fig. 21-23 F). The chromatin granules are spread more evenly through the nucleus than they are in oligodendroglia and astrocytes, where they tend to be associated with the nuclear membrane. A tail of cytoplasm from each end of the nucleus can commonly be seen in H and E sections.

**Evolution of Silver-impregnation Methods.** If tissues are soaked in a weak solution of silver nitrate, the silver nitrate combines with some tissue ingredients more than with others. If tissues so treated are exposed to light, the silver is reduced and blackened; hence, the tissue ingredients with which it particularly combined are disclosed to advantage. However, silver nitrate by itself was not a sufficiently good agent to permit the nature of nervous tissue of the C.N.S. to be elucidated.

But, in 1872, a discovery was made which greatly enhanced the scope of its application.

At this time, an Italian anatomist, Camillo Golgi, was forced by economic circumstances to terminate temporarily this association with a proper laboratory and take a position as chief resident physician and surgeon in a hospital for incurable patients. Such was his zeal for anatomic research that he attempted to set up a histologic laboratory in the kitchen of his house where he could work at night. He had little more than a microscope and a few simple instruments, and with these he made the discovery that revolutionized the study of nervous tissue.

Golgi had fixed some tissue of the C.N.S. in a solution of potassium bichromate and had left the tissue in this solution for a long time. He then soaked the tissue in silver nitrate, and a miracle occurred. Silver bichromate was deposited on only some of the cells in the tissue but not on most of them. Accordingly, the ones that were impregnated stood out against a clear background as if they had been mounted in a clear plastic for demonstration purposes. Curiously enough, this method does not impregnate parts of cells as erratically as it does cells in general; those cells that do become impregnated are generally well impregnated over their whole extent.

At first Golgi's discovery was not received enthusiastically by histologists in other countries. His method was considered freakish and unreliable. However, at that time, there was a young man in Spain who was destined to become the greatest neurohistologist of all time. Santiago Ramon y Cajal saw the great possibilities of Golgi's method, made improvements in it and, with his pupils, devised still further metallic impregnation methods. By means of these he systematically investigated the histology of nervous tissue. He was instrumental, among many other things, in providing histologic evidence for the individuality of neurons. Cajal published nearly 300 papers and many books on neurohistology, and much of what we know today about neurohistology can be traced to him. His great contributions to this field were acknowledged in 1906 by his being awarded, jointly with Golgi, the Nobel prize in Physiology and Medicine. Medical students will find inspiration and enjoyment in reading his *Recollections of My Life*. (This has been translated into English by E. Horne Craigie.)

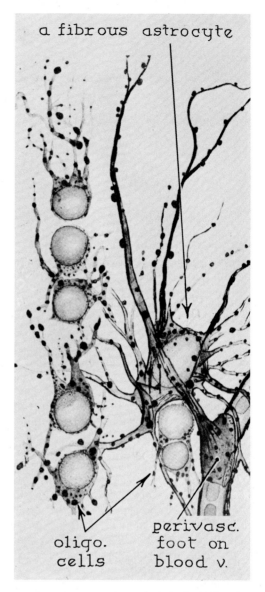

Fig. 21-26. White matter of the brain of a rabbit stained by Del Rio-Hortega's method for gliosomes. It shows a row of oligodendroglia cells on the left and a fibrous astrocyte on the right. (Modified from Penfield, W.: Brain 47:430)

The improvement and the use of silver and gold impregnation methods by Cajal and Del Rio-Hortega, who was one of his pupils, permitted neuroglia cells to be classified properly and their form and function clarified. Their nuclei, which appear to advantage with ordinary technics, have already been illustrated in Figure 21-23. Their morphology as shown by

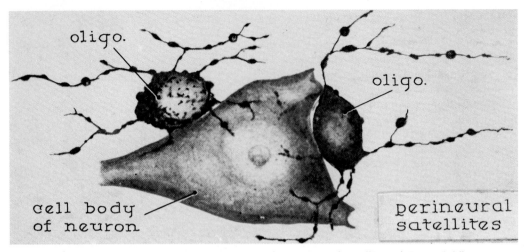

Fig. 21-27. The cell body of a neuron and 2 perineural satellites. (W. Penfield)

metallic impregnation methods will now be described.

*Protoplasmic astrocytes,* with few exceptions, are confined to gray matter. They have wavy branching cytoplasmic processes that extend out from all aspects of their cell bodies so that they resemble bushy shrubs (Figs. 21-24 and 21-25). Their processes often terminate on one or more small blood vessels in little structures called *perivascular feet* (Figs. 21-24 and 21-25). Since their processes extend through the nerve fibers of gray matter and are anchored to blood vessels, they not only hold the substance of gray matter together but also anchor it to the blood vessels that extend through it. Little granules, called *gliosomes* (Fig. 21-25), which may be the counterparts in astrocytes of the mitochondria of other cells, may be demonstrated in the cytoplasm of astrocytes.

*Fibrous astrocytes,* with few exceptions, are confined to white matter where their cell bodies are disposed between myelinated fibers and their processes run along and between myelinated fibers, binding them together and to blood vessels. Their processes are longer and straighter and do not branch so extensively as those of the protoplasmic variety (Fig. 21-26). Moreover, their processes, unlike those of protoplasmic astrocytes, contain fibers. Some have thought that at least the ends of these fibers were extracytoplasmic, but now it is generally believed that the fibers are completely covered with cytoplasm. In favor of the latter view is the fact that gliosomes, which are composed of cytoplasmic constituents, can be demonstrated at and near the end of the processes, even in the perivascular feet which clasp small blood vessels (Fig. 21-26).

*Oligodendroglia* exist in both gray and white matter. They were given their name by Del Rio-Hortega because, as has been explained before, they have fewer processes than astrocytes. They are also much smaller. Their processes contain no fibers and do not end in perivascular feet. Consequently, they do not function nearly so efficiently as astrocytes in holding nervous tissue together.

In the gray matter, they are commonly seen close to the cell bodies of neurons; here they are termed *perineural* satellites (Fig. 21-27). Their rounded-to-oval, fairly dark-staining nuclei (but not their cytoplasmic processes) can be recognized easily in H and E sections in this position (Fig. 21-34).

In the white matter, oligodendroglia are commonly distributed in rows between myelinated fibers (Fig. 21-26). Here their processes form very incomplete sheaths for myelinated fibers and assist the fibrous astrocytes in holding the white matter together.

They also are arranged close to blood vessels as *perivascular satellites,* both in gray and white matter.

*Microglia.* As noted before, the nuclei of neuroglia cells appear to advantage in thin sections stained with ordinary stains such as H and E (Fig. 21-23 F). In this type of

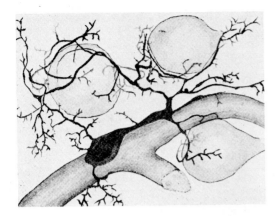

Fig. 21-28. Microglia perivascular satellite from cerebral cortex. (Modified from Penfield, W.: Brain *47*:430)

preparation, the nuclei of astrocytes and oligodendroglia cells are seen to have a regular outline. However, scattered among them are nuclei of about the same size as those of oligodendroglia cells, but they have irregular outlines. These are the nuclei of the cells that comprise what is termed the *microglia* or the *mesoglia* (Fig. 21-23 F). The nature of these cells long remained a mystery; it was not until 1920 that Del Rio-Hortega devised a metallic impregnation method that revealed their cell bodies and their processes clearly and showed that they neither formed fibers nor had perivascular feet.

Microglia cells are more common in gray than in white matter. In gray matter they are distributed as perineural satellites; of course, they are not so numerous in this position as oligodendroglia cells. They are also arranged on blood vessels as perivascular satellites (Fig. 21-28). In white matter they are distributed, but more sparingly than oligodendroglia cells, between myelinated fibers.

Del Rio-Hortega showed that microglia did not appear in the C.N.S. until blood vessels had begun to grow into it. As will be described presently, the brain and the cord become enveloped in a mesenchymal-derived sheath, the pia mater, and extensions from this sheath accompany blood vessels as they leave it to penetrate the brain. Microglia cells first appear as ameboid cells beneath the pia in certain regions and also in association with some of the blood vessels that pass into the substance of the C.N.S. The developing microglia cells

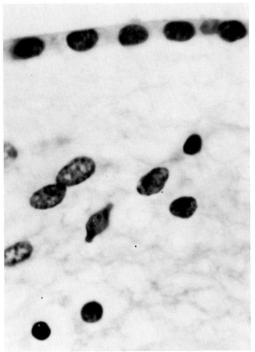

Fig. 21-29. High-power photomicrograph of an H and E section of brain, showing the ependyma lining the lateral ventricle.

are ameboid and migrate through the substance of the C.N.S. to take up various positions in it. From the evidence at hand it seems justifiable to consider that the microglia, in contrast with the other types of neuroglia, are mesenchymal-derived, probably from the developing pia mater. From their behavior after brain injuries, in that they change their form and become large phagocytes, known as *compound granular corpuscles*, it seems probable that they are the counterparts of the macrophages of other parts of the body and that they are, therefore, members of the reticuloendothelial system.

*Ependyma.* The cells that line the lumen of the neural tube perform three more-or-less consecutive functions. At first their function is proliferative; they are the germinal cells that give rise to most of the cells that come to occupy the middle (mantle) layer of the wall of the tube and become neuroblasts and free spongioblasts. Their second function is supportive. As the wall of the neural tube thickens, the lining cells send out long proc-

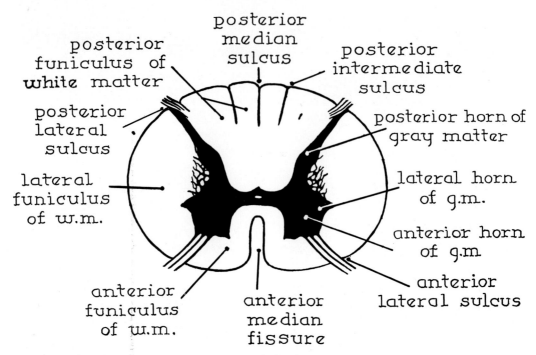

FIG. 21-30. Cross section of the spinal cord. (Redrawn from Villiger, E.: Brain and Spinal Cord, Philadelphia, Lippincott)

esses that, for a time at least, reach the exterior of the tube and help to form the external limiting membrane that surrounds the tube (Fig. 21-12). At this time inner borders of the lining cells may be ciliated (Fig. 21-12), and they are called *ependymal spongioblasts*. Still later they gradually relinquish their supporting role and function chiefly in forming a continuous epithelial lining, known as the ependyma, for the ventricles of the brain (Fig. 21-29). They also persist in the central canal of the spinal cord. In certain sites in the ventricles the ependyma is pushed inwardly by vascular tufts. These arrangements are called choroid plexuses, as will be explained presently. This matter is mentioned here only because the ependyma that comes to cover the capillaries of the choroid plexuses comes to be known as *choroid plexus epithelium* rather than as ependyma. Ependymal cells are classified as one type of neuroglial cells.

## MICROSCOPIC STRUCTURE OF THE SPINAL CORD

**General Considerations.** The spinal cord is a cylindrical column but it is flattened notice-

ably in front, and less noticeably behind, so that a cross section of it is ovoid (Fig. 21-30).

The anterior horns of gray matter are broader and shorter than the posterior horns and do not approach the surface of the cord as closely as do the posterior horns (Fig. 21-30). In the thoracic and the first two or three lumbar segments of the cord a lateral horn of gray matter is also to be seen on each side of the cord (Figs. 21-30 and 21-31). The gray matter that forms the cross bar of the H is said to constitute a *commissure* (*commissure* = a joining together); that which lies in front of the central canal constitutes the *anterior commissure* of gray matter and that which lies behind the canal, the *posterior commissure* of gray matter. Immediately around the central canal there is a network of neuroglia cells that constitute what is termed the *central gelatinous substance*.

The white matter is divided up into funiculi (little cords) by longitudinal sulci (furrows) and a fissure. The posterior median sulcus (Fig. 21-30) overlies the dorsal median septum, the formation of which is illustrated in Figure 21-9. To each side of the posterior median sulcus on the posterior surface of the

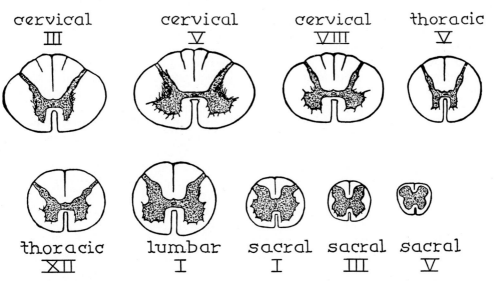

cervical III    cervical V    cervical VIII    thoracic V

thoracic XII    lumbar I    sacral I    sacral III    sacral V

FIG. 21-31. Cross sections of the spinal cord at different levels. (Villiger, E.: Brain and Spinal Cord, Philadelphia, Lippincott)

cord are two shallow sulci, termed separately the *posterior intermediate sulcus* and the *posterior lateral sulcus*. Between the posterior median sulcus and the posterior lateral sulcus on each side lies a *posterior funiculus* of white matter (Fig. 21-30). Between the posterior lateral sulcus and the anterior lateral sulcus lies, on each side, a *lateral funiculus* of white matter, and between the two lateral sulci and the anterior median fissure lie the two *anterior funiculi* of white matter (Fig. 21-30).

**Segmentation of the Cord.** As has been noted already, man is a segmented organism, and each segment is represented by an individual vertebra. The afferent neurons that extend into the cord from any given body segment pass through the intervertebral foramen belonging to that segment and into the vertebral canal, where they extend to and enter the posterior horn of gray matter of the segment of the spinal cord that belongs to that body segment (Fig. 21-39). Likewise, the efferent fibers that extend out from anterior horns of gray matter of that same segment of the cord pass through the same intervertebral foramen to reach and innervate the muscles that belong to that particular body segment (Fig. 21-39). However, it so happens that during development the vertebral column elongates to a much greater extent than the spinal cord that is contained in its canal. This has two impor-

tant effects. First, since the cord must remain connected to the brain, the lower end of the cord in the adult does not reach nearly to the lower end of the vertebral canal but only to the level of the 1st or the 2nd lumbar vertebra. Secondly, the various segments of the cord, which originally are in line with the body segments to which their afferent and efferent fibers are connected, gradually assume higher levels than their respective body segments; hence, the afferent and the efferent fibers that pass out from each segment of the cord to reach their respective body segments must pass down along the sides of the cord to reach their intervertebral canals. This condition, of course, becomes increasingly prominent as the caudal end of the cord is approached and accounts for the fact that although the caudal division of the vertebral canal does not contain any spinal cord, it does contain afferent and efferent fibers that are extending down from the lower segments of the cord to reach their proper intervertebral foramina.

**Appearance at Different Levels.** An expert can tell from the microscopic appearance of any given cross section of the spinal cord the approximate segmental level from which it was obtained. If a student learns a few general facts he, too, can demonstrate a certain amount of skill at making identifications.

The first fact to remember is that the

amount of white matter in the cord thickens as the cord passes from lower to higher levels for the same reason that telephone cables from outlying districts become thicker as they approach a metropolis. The white matter consists chiefly of axons that are passing between the brain and the various levels of the cord. It is obvious then that in the sacral region—an outlying district, as it were—the white matter has to accommodate only those axons which are passing between the sacral portion of the cord and the brain, while in the cervical region—where the cable is nearing the metropolis—the white matter has to·accommodate the axons that are passing between the brain and the cervical, the thoracic, the lumbar and the sacral levels, which, of course, requires that there be much more white matter here than in the sacral region. (See Fig. 21-31 and compare the appearance of cervical and sacral cross sections.)

Next, to continue our analogy, let us imagine that the cable from the outlying district, before reaching the metropolis, passes through two small cities. It is only to be expected that there would be substations in these cities with a corresponding local expansion of the wiring facilities. So it is with the cord; the two divisions of it which are concerned with the innervation of the arms and the legs —the counterparts of the two cities—are the cervical and the lumbar regions respectively, and the cord in both these sites is expanded into fusiform enlargements. Hence, cross sections of the cervical and the lumbar regions of the cord show its size to be greater in these sites than in others (Fig. 21-31). The enlargement in the cervical region has been shown by Donaldson and Davis to be due to both the gray matter and the white matter being increased, while the enlargement in the lumbar region is due entirely to an increase in the amount of gray matter in this site.

Another point that aids in identifying the site from which any given section of cord is taken is the fact that the lateral horns of gray matter are obvious only in the thoracic and the first two lumbar segments. There are, of course, other distinguishing features of cross sections of cord at different levels, but their explanation would require a more detailed description of the histology of the cord than is required here.

**Some Features of the Gray Matter.** The gray matter of the cord consists of the cell bodies of neurons, unmyelinated fibers, some myelinated fibers, protoplasmic astrocytes, oligodendroglia cells and some small blood vessels with a little connective tissue that accompanies them, including some microglia cells. The pale-blue background seen in an H and E section, and against which the cell bodies of neurons and the nuclei of neuroglia cells stand out, is a complex network of nerve fibers and the processes of neuroglia cells (Fig. 21-14).

The cell bodies of neurons are not distributed evenly in the gray matter of the cord but in aggregates, some of which are termed *nuclei*. These extend for varying distances up and down the cord in the gray matter. It is not necessary to describe here the positions occupied by these or the types of cell bodies seen in different ones. Only a few general remarks will be made about the types of cells in the different horns of gray matter.

The cell bodies in the anterior horn (Fig. 21-17) are the largest seen in the cord, and those of the posterior horn the smallest. Those of the lateral horns are of an intermediate size. The most notable cells in the anterior horns are those which are called *root cells*, which give rise to the axons that constitute the efferent fibers that extend out to the muscles of each segment. These neurons constitute the "final common path" by which all neural activity which is to result in muscular action converges. They are generally referred to by the term *anterior horn cells*. They are large and multipolar with abundant chromidial substance in their cytoplasm (Fig. 21-17). These are the cells that are most likely to be affected by the virus that causes anterior poliomyelitis (infantile paralysis), and if they are destroyed the muscles which they normally innervate become paralyzed. There are other types of cells in the anterior horns as well; some have very short processes that terminate in the gray matter; others, called *column* or *tract cells*, send axons to other parts and levels of the cord.

The cells of the lateral columns give rise to axons which extend out to ganglia of the autonomic nervous system, as will be described later in connection with that system.

The neurons, the cell bodies of which are disposed in the posterior horns, are of the intrasegmental and the intersegmental types. Afferent fibers coming in from the body segments on entering the cord, as well as ascending and descending in white matter, enter the posterior horns of gray matter and make synaptic connections with them. By means of their axons they relay impulses received from the afferent neurons to various parts of the C.N.S.

**Some Features of the White Matter.** The general microscopic structure of the white matter of the cord has been described already. Before leaving this subject, however, it is pertinent to mention that the axons that pass up and down the cord and are related to different functions are not mixed together haphazardly but are segregated in a remarkable way. The axons of the efferent pathways are segregated in special sectors of the cord, as are the axons of the afferent pathways. Moreover, within these divisions there is further segregation; for example, the axons of neurons concerned in conveying impulses relating to touch and pressure sensation from all levels of the cord are bundled together in a special sector of the cord on each side, and those carrying impulses relating to pain are likewise isolated. Indeed, the segregation is so remarkable that if a nick is made in the white matter at some point around the circumference of the cord, the loss of muscle functions and/or sensory functions resulting from it can be accurately predicted. Armed with full knowledge on this matter, the physician, from studying the particular kinds and sites of sensory and motor disturbance that follow an injury to, or disease of, the cord, can predict the particular site at which the cord is damaged; should an operation be required, he can indicate the site at which the cord should be exposed.

## MICROSCOPIC STRUCTURE OF SOME PARTS OF THE BRAIN

**The Gray Matter That Is Enclosed by White Matter.** As has been noted already, the gray matter of the brain develops from the middle (mantle) layer of the neural tube, as it does in the spinal cord. As occurs in the spinal cord, much of it comes to be surrounded in some fashion by white matter. The great exceptions to this rule are, of course, the cerebral and the cerebellar cortices; and, as has been explained already, these are due to cells of the middle layer growing out through the outer layer of the developing neural tube in these sites to take up a position on the periphery of the tube. Except for the cortices, the gray matter that forms in the hindbrain, the midbrain and the forebrain is more or less buried in white matter, and it is comparable with the gray matter of the cord, though it is arranged somewhat differently. For example, it is not divided into posterior and anterior horns but rather is present as masses of various shapes and sizes which, however, are related either to sensory or motor functions, as are the horns of the cord. Moreover, it is generally not as pure as it is in the spinal cord; in many sites it is more or less obviously broken up by myelinated fibers; but it, like the gray matter of the spinal cord, consists essentially of the cell bodies of neurons, neuroglia cells, naked nerve fibers and in some instances, as has been mentioned above, myelinated fibers as well. In some sites there is so much white matter mixed with the gray that the mixture is called *reticular substance.*

Some of these masses of gray matter that are surrounded by white matter in the brain serve a similar function in relation to the cranial nerves that the posterior and the anterior horns of gray matter in the cord serve in relation to the spinal nerves. Consequently, afferent fibers in cranial nerves may terminate in association with neurons in sensory masses of gray matter; likewise, axons from motor masses of gray matter may extend out in cranial nerves that have efferent components. But the functions of these masses of gray matter in the brain are generally more complex than serving as the cranial counterparts of the anterior and the posterior horns of gray matter of the cord. In indicating some of their further functions it may be helpful to return to our analogy.

In likening the C.N.S. to a telephone system it is important to understand that there is one way in which its organization is different. In a telephone system the same wire can be used both for the reception and the sending of messages; in the nervous system two fibers, or more commonly, two chains of fibers, are generally necessary to serve these two functions, one of which is afferent and the other efferent.

The cerebral cortex, as we shall see, is the giant switchboard wherein are innumerable

LAYERS   OF   CEREBRAL   CORTEX

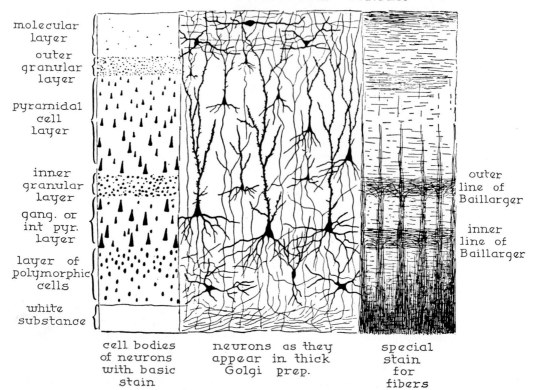

molecular
layer

outer
granular
layer

pyramidal
cell
layer

inner
granular
layer

gang. or
int pyr.
layer

layer of
polymorphic
cells

white
substance

outer
line of
Baillarger

inner
line of
Baillarger

cell bodies
of neurons
with basic
stain

neurons as they
appear in thick
Golgi prep.

special
stain
for
fibers

FIG. 21-32. Schematic representation of the structure of the cerebral cortex. (Modified from Villiger, E.: Brain and Spinal Cord, Philadelphia, Lippincott)

circuits by which afferent impulses can be redispatched on efferent pathways. We have already learned that inherited reflex patterns and conditioning are important factors in determining which of the innumerable circuits are used most extensively. We have also suggested that the white matter of the cord represents a trunk line that reaches out through the district served by the system. The gray matter at each level of the cord represents, as it were, a village exchange office, situated along the trunk line, with wires for both incoming and outgoing calls passing out into the particular body segment served by that local office. It has already been mentioned that two enlargements of the cord, the cervical and the lumbar, represent expansions of such local office facilities as are necessary for servicing the counterparts of two cities, the arms and the legs. As the trunk line—the white matter of the cord—passes toward the brain it becomes thicker because it must contain additional wires (fibers)

from each community office along its way. If we traced any of the afferent fibers of the cord into the substance of the brain we should find that they would enter one of the masses of gray matter that are enclosed by white matter and there make synaptic connection with further neurons. This has the effect of enabling connections to be made with several further neurons and so widens the pathways over which the afferent impulse may possibly spread thereafter.

*To sum up:* The gray matter that is surrounded by white matter in the brain serves, like that of the cord, as local exchanges for territories serviced by cranial nerves, for providing connections with other substations and, finally, in providing relay stations which, like the repeater stations on a long-distance telephone line, redispatch signals that are received from one direction along the next set of wires that lead to the next station. The last station, to which and from which messages are dispatched, is, of course, the cortical switchboard.

**The Gray Matter That Covers White Matter.** It will be recalled that the wall of the neural tube in the front part of both the hindbrain and the forebrain undergoes massive development to form the cerebellar and the cerebral hemispheres, respectively. Moreover, it will be recalled that as these are being formed, some of the cells of the middle (mantle) layer of the tube migrate through the outer (marginal) layer of the wall of the tube and take up a position and form gray matter on the surface of the developing hemispheres. It has already been mentioned that the gray matter covering the cerebral hemispheres provides the circuits by which innumerable connections are made between the afferent pathways which extend to it and the efferent pathways that lead away from it. It has also been explained that the stimulation of different parts of the cerebral cortex by different afferent pathways accounts for the interpretation of different kinds of sensation and its localization. We shall now consider very briefly the microscopic structure of the cerebral cortex.

The cerebral cortex is a layer of gray matter that varies from around 1.5 to 4 mm. in thickness and covers the white matter of the cerebral hemispheres (Figs. 21-11 and 21-32). The extensively convoluted surface of the hemispheres of man (Fig. 21-11) permits the gray matter to be much more extensive than it would be if the surfaces of the hemispheres were smooth, as they are in some animals. Sections cut through the cerebral cortex from different parts of the hemispheres show the same general plan of microscopic structure but also that the general plan is sufficiently modified in different cortical areas to imply that these different areas of the cortex perform somewhat different functions. The cortex, speaking generally, exhibits 6 layers (Fig. 21-32). The extent to which each of these 6 layers is developed differs in various areas, and since different areas have been shown to be related to somewhat different functions, some generalizations can be drawn about the relation of the cells of the various layers to particular functions. However, this matter is one for consideration in neuro-anatomy textbooks; here we shall describe only some of the characteristics of the 6 layers.

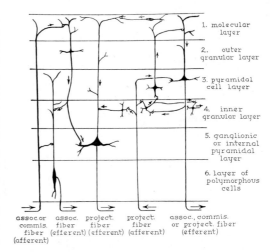

1. molecular layer
2. outer granular layer
3. pyramidal cell layer
4. inner granular layer
5. ganglionic or internal pyramidal layer
6. layer of polymorphous cells

assoc. or commis. fiber (afferent) | assoc. fiber (afferent) | project. fiber (efferent) | project. fiber (afferent) | assoc., commis. or project. fiber (efferent)

FIG. 21-33. Diagram showing some of the connections that are effected in the cortex between the fibers that lead to it and those that lead away from it.

The outermost is called the *molecular layer* (Fig. 21-32). It contains relatively few cells and consists chiefly of fibers of underlying cells which run in many directions but generally parallel with the surface (Fig. 21-32, *right*). The second layer is called the *outer granular layer* because it contains many small nerve cells which give this layer a granular appearance when it is examined under low power (Fig. 21-32). The third layer is called the *pyramidal cell layer* because of its content of the pyramidal-shaped cell bodies of neurons (Fig. 21-32). The fourth layer is termed the *inner granular layer* because it is "granulated" with small nerve cells (Fig. 21-32). The fifth layer is termed the *ganglionic* or *internal pyramidal layer*. The latter name describes its most prominent feature which is its content of pyramidal cell bodies. In one part of the cortex called the *motor area*, the pyramidal cells of this layer are huge; they are called *Betz cells*. The sixth and final layer is named the *layer of polymorphous cells* because the cells of this layer have many shapes. Of course, neuroglia cells are disposed in all 6 layers; the naming of the layers is based on their nerve cell and fiber content rather than on their neuroglia content.

Before commenting on some of the ways in which the neurons of the different layers of the cortex are connected, we shall describe the white matter which lies below the cortex. This

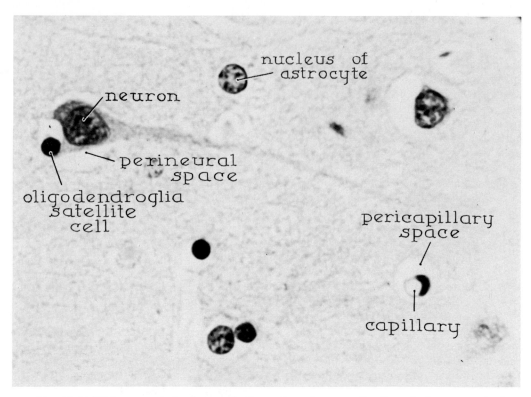

FIG. 21-34. High-power photomicrograph of a section of gray matter from the human cerebral cortex. The almost structureless-appearing background constituting most of the photograph can be studied to advantage only by means of special technics. It is probable that the perineural and the pericapillary spaces are the result of artefact.

consists of interlacing bundles of myelinated fibers which pass in almost all directions. Some of these fibers connect one part of the cortex to another part on the same side and, accordingly, are termed *association fibers*. Some connect cortical areas of one side with those of cortical areas of the other side and hence are known as *commissural fibers*. Still others, and these may be either afferent or efferent, connect the cortex with subcortical centers (areas of gray matter surrounded by white matter) and are termed *projection fibers*. The meaning of this term is clear with regard to afferent fibers because impulses dealing with, say a certain sensation, can be visualized as being projected from subcortical centers to certain parts of the cortex. Why the efferent fibers that lead away from the cortex to subcortical stations should be called projection fibers is not so clear.

Figure 21-33 shows some of the connections that exist in the cerebral cortex between the cells of its different layers and between them and the afferent association, commissural and projection fibers that lead into it (left and fourth from left). It also shows how the cell bodies of different layers in the cortex give rise to intracortical and extracortical association fibers and to commissural fibers (third from left) which pass to subcortical centers of gray matter. It has been estimated that there are close to 10,000 million neurons in the cerebral cortex, and since one neuron may effect synaptic connection with several others the possibilities with regard to the number of pathways that are available here are indeed overwhelming.

**H and E Appearance of Gray Matter.** It is to be understood that the most common type of histologic preparation—a thin section stained with H and E—reveals only a few features of cerebral cortex to advantage. Nevertheless, since such sections are used routinely, particularly for the detection of pathologic conditions, the student must be able to interpret them intelligently. Brief comment will now be made on what may be seen in one at moderately high magnification.

As may be seen in Figure 21-34, most of such a section consists of a pale-blue, almost structureless-appearing background. This is the so-called *neuropil* and it consists of a felt-work (*pilos* = felt) of naked nerve fibers and the processes of neuroglia cells. Since these are distributed in all planes, they are, for the most part, cut in cross section or obliquely in a thin section; therefore, they appear as ill-defined dots that stain very lightly. In the aggregate these give the neuropil, as it is seen in a thin H and E section, a stippled appearance. It is obvious that in order to trace the direction of the fibers in the different layers of the cortex it would be necessary to use thick sections stained by methods which impregnate the fibers and show them as dark lines, as in Figure 21-32, *right*.

Nuclei, as might be expected, show up well in thin sections of cortex stained with H and E. Those of large neurons are recognized easily, and generally those of the 3 types of neuroglia can be distinguished also (Fig. 21-34). The student should see examples of the dark round nuclei of oligodendroglia cells close beside the cell bodies of neurons (Fig. 21-34, *left*) where the oligodendroglia cells are acting as perineural satellites. The cytoplasm of astrocytes is scarcely apparent in H and E sections, and no intimations are given of the processes of these cells that are revealed by special technics. However, the nuclei of astrocytes can be recognized by their size (Fig. 21-34), by the lack of cytoplasm around them (Fig. 21-34) and perhaps also by the fact that their nucleoli are very poorly developed as compared with neurons. Other things that may be seen in an H and E section are perineural and pericapillary spaces (Fig. 21-34). It was generally believed in the past that these spaces were real and that they were filled with cerebrospinal fluid. The recent work of Woollam and Millen suggests that they are merely artefact spaces that do not exist in life and so do not contain cerebrospinal fluid.

*Cerebellum.* This (Fig. 21-11) consists of two *hemispheres* and a wormlike midportion, the *vermis*. Transverse fissures divide it into lobes. Each lobe consists of numerous transverse folds called *folia*.

Like the cerebrum, the cerebellum has a thin cortex of gray matter that overlies white

FIG. 21-35. Low-power photomicrograph of an H and E section of the cerebellum.

matter. It also has a central mass of gray matter that is surrounded by white matter. However, the cerebellar cortex has only 3 layers (Fig. 21-35): (1) an outer molecular layer of few cells and many nonmedullated fibers, (2) an intermediate single layer of large flask-shaped cells, called *Purkinje cells*, and (3) an inner granular or nuclear layer that consists of the bodies of small nerve cells.

The Purkinje cells give rise to a few main dendrites (Fig. 21-35) which branch in a fan-like fashion through the molecular layer to the

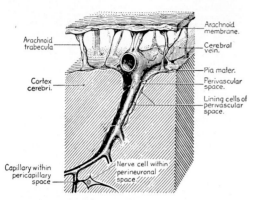

FIG. 21-36. Schematic diagram to show the relations of the pia mater, the arachnoid, the blood vessels and the brain. (Weed, L. H.: Am. J. Anat. *31*:202)

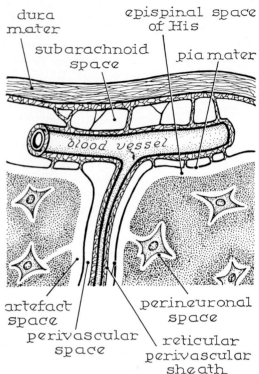

FIG. 21-37. Diagram to illustrate the relations of the perivascular space. Note that the epispinal space of His is not a true space but is due to artefact. (Redrawn from Woollam, D. H. M., and Millen, J. W.: J. Anat. *89*:193)

surface. The axons of the Purkinje cells arise from the opposite end of the cell to the dendrites and extend through the granular layer to enter the white matter of the folia and eventually reach the central mass of gray matter. Along their course the axons may give off collaterals that connect with other Purkinje cells.

The cells of the granular layer are small. Each has from 3 to 6 short dendrites that end in the granular layer and a long axon that ascends into the molecular layer where it divides and its branches run parallel with the surface. Therefore, the axons of these cells run at right angles through the dendritic arborizations of the Purkinje cells. Some larger cells also may be observed in the granular layer.

The stellate cells of the molecular layer are both superficial and deep; the latter are termed *basket cells*. The axons of these envelop Purkinje cells, whereas their dendrites ramify throughout the molecular layer.

Afferent cerebellar fibers of 2 types, mossy and climbing fibers, are seen in the cerebellum. The latter twine about the branches of the Purkinje cells. Mossy fibers synapse with dendrites of cells in the granular layer; climbing fibers twine about the dendrites of Purkinje cells like a vine climbing through the branches of a tree.

The cerebellum is related to the maintenance of equilibrium and to the coordination and the strength of muscular movements. Its connection with substations along afferent and efferent pathways in the brain is too complex a matter to discuss here.

## THE MENINGES

The brain and the spinal cord are protected (1) by a bony encasement (the cranium and the vertebral column and (2) by 3 connective tissue wrappings called the *meninges* (*meninx* = membrane) (Figs. 21-38 and 21-39). The innermost of these is applied directly to the surface of the brain and the cord and is called the *pia mater* (Figs. 21-36 to 21-39). The second and middle one is called the *arachnoid* (Figs. 21-36, 21-38 and 21-39), and the third and outermost one is called the *dura mater* (Figs. 21-38 and 21-39). In some sites this is adherent to the periosteum of the surrounding bone. The structure of these 3 membranes will now be considered in turn.

**Pia Mater.** As its name implies (*pia* = tender; *mater* = mother), this membrane that is applied directly to the surface of the brain is delicate. It consists of interlacing bundles of collagenic fibers but has some fine elastic networks in it as well. It is covered with a continuous membrane of flattened squamous cells which are morphologically similar to those of the mesothelial membranes of the great body cavities. The substance of the membrane contains a few fibroblasts and macrophages and many blood vessels; these blood vessels are distributed by the pia mater over the surface of the brain (Fig. 21-37). From the pia mater these blood vessels penetrate into the substance of the brain. The pia mater dips into the brain substance with them to both line the spaces that conduct the vessels and to cover the vessels that are in the spaces. Between the piarachnoid that lines the spaces and that which covers the vessels there is a true *perivascular space*. This is found only in connection with the larger vessels; it does not extend as far as the capillaries, as was believed formerly. This true perivascular space communicates with the subarachnoid space and contains cerebrospinal fluid. Figure 21-36 depicts the older view which postulated that perivascular spaces communicate with little spaces in which the cell bodies of neurons lie, which are called *perineuronal spaces*. The investigations of Woollam and Millen have shown that the perineuronal space is an artefact, and, in addition, a space that is often seen between the pia and the brain substance (Fig. 21-37, *epispinal space of His*) is also an artefact. It is this latter artefact space that often seems to communicate with the artefact-induced perineuronal spaces (Fig. 21-37).

**The Arachnoid.** The middle membrane of the meninges is called the arachnoid because it is separated from—and at the same time joined to—the pia by a cobwebby (*arachnoid = cobweb*) network of trabeculae (Figs. 21-36, 21-37 and 21-38). The term arachnoid includes both the tissue that forms a continuous roof over the pia and the network of pillars which extend from the pia to the roof.

The pia and the arachnoid, because they are joined together, are sometimes described as a single membrane, the *piarachnoid*.

Both the membrane that is supported by the trabeculae and the trabeculae themselves are composed chiefly of delicate collagenic fibers together with some elastic fibers. Both the outer and inner surfaces of the membranous roof, and the trabeculae, are covered with a continuous lining of thin, flat lining

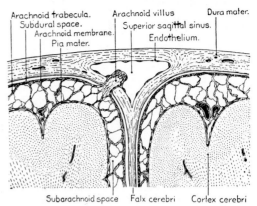

FIG. 21-38. Schematic diagram to illustrate the meninges, the sagittal sinus and the arachnoid villus. The potential subdural space is shown of greater size than is normal. The subarachnoid space over the convolutions also is increased so as to illustrate the character of the subarachnoid mesh. (Weed, L. H.: Am. J. Anat. *31*:203)

cells that are similar to those that cover the pia. The space between the membranous roof of the arachnoid and the pia mater, that is, the space through which the delicate arachnoid trabeculae extend, is filled with cerebrospinal fluid.

The surface of the brain is extraordinarily convoluted (Fig. 21-11). Whereas the pia extends down into the sulci and the fissures to cover the surface of the brain intimately, the membranous part of the arachnoid, except in the instance of some of the larger fissures, does not. Hence, over grooves there is more accommodation for cerebrospinal fluid than there is in other sites (Fig. 21-38, *not in the middle, but left and right*). Indeed, there are some sites where the brain surface is a considerable distance from the covering arachnoid, and, in these, there is accommodation for considerable amounts of cerebrospinal fluid. The precise location and nature of these will be learned in neuro-anatomy; they are termed *cisternae*.

**Dura Mater.** As its name implies (*dura = hard*, *mater = mother*), this outermost membrane is of a tough consistency and consists chiefly of dense, connective tissue (Fig. 21-38). The collagenic fibers tend to run longitudinally in the spinal dura but somewhat irregularly in the cranial dura. Elastic fibers

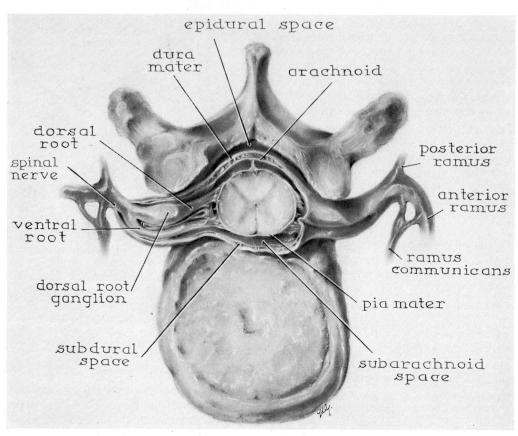

Fig. 21-39. Semidiagrammatic drawing of a cross section of the vertebral column at the level of an intervertebral foramen. It shows the relations of the meninges to the spinal cord and the way the central nervous system is connected to the peripheral nervous system.

are mixed with the collagenic to some extent. There are certain differences between the dura of the vertebral canal and that of the cranium. In the vertebral canal the dura consists of a relatively free dense connective tissue sheath. The potential space between its inner surface and the outer surface of the arachnoid is called the *subdural space* (Fig. 21-39) and it normally contains a slight amount of fluid which is *not* cerebrospinal fluid. The outer surface of the spinal dura abuts on the *epidural space* (Fig. 21-39), which is filled with loose areolar tissue containing a certain amount of fat and many veins. The internal periosteum of the vertebrae, which lines the vertebral canal, forms the outer limit of the epidural space.

In the vertebral canal, the dura, as has been pointed out, is separated from the periosteum lining the vertebral canal. In the cranium no such separation occurs, for in this region the membrane, which in the vertebral canal is called the dura, is fused with the internal periosteum of the bones of the cranium. This accounts for the cranial dura having 2 layers, its inner being the counterpart of what has been termed *dura* in the vertebral canal, and its outer, the internal periosteum of the bones of the cranium. Since these 2 layers adhere to one another, the dura of the cranium is adherent to the bones of the skull. Furthermore, since its outer layer serves as the inner periosteum of the bones, its outer layer must contain many blood vessels. The inner layer is much less vascular than the outer layer. Although the outer and the inner layers of the cranial dura are continuous with one another over most of the brain, they are separated in a few specific sites. In these sites the inner layer of the dura extends deeply into fissures in the brain to form large partitions (Fig.

21-38, *middle*). Along the line from which the partition extends into the fissure a cavity may exist between the 2 layers of the dura. This is roughly triangular on cross section (Fig. 21-38) and is bordered on its base by the outer layer of the dura and on the other 2 sides by the inner layer, which sweeps from .both sides of the fissure into it to form a partition there (Fig. 21-38). These spaces between the layers of the dura which are disposed along the lines from which partitions originate are lined by endothelium and they constitute the *sinuses of the dura mater* (Fig. 21-38).

## FORMATION, CIRCULATION AND ABSORPTION OF CEREBROSPINAL FLUID

The nervous tissue of the C.N.S. is soft and susceptible to injury. Accordingly, the brain and the cord are contained in bony cavities and are protected against shock by a fluid-filled cushion which encompasses them on all sides. This cushion is the piarachnoid, and all the interstices of its cobwebby structure are filled with a modified tissue fluid called *cerebrospinal fluid* (Figs. 21-36, 21-38 and 21-39). The fluid-filled piarachnoid completely surrounds the brain and the cord and functions as a hydraulic shock absorber for them as they are subjected to the bumps and the jars of everyday life. The fluid-filled membrane has another function as well; it helps to transmit and so disseminate over a wide area the impact of a localized blow on the skull which, if it were concentrated in a small area, might cause serious local damage to the underlying brain. The ventricles of the brain, which form a continuous passageway (Fig. 21-11), also are filled with cerebrospinal fluid. The fluid inside the brain is in communication with that outside the brain through the medium of 3 openings in the roof of the 4th ventricle. Normally, fluid flows through these openings from the interior of the brain to the exterior.

As will be described later, some cerebrospinal fluid is formed on the exterior of the brain, but most of it is formed in the ventricles by means of structures called *choroid plexuses*; as the thoughtful student will already suspect, they have a structure and a function somewhat similar to that of the glomeruli of the kidney. They are specialized structures for

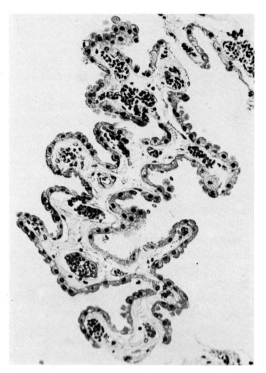

Fig. 21-40. High-power photomicrograph of a portion of a section cut from a human choroid plexus. (Section from Professor E. A. Linell)

the production of tissue fluid. However, the tissue fluid produced by the capillaries in them has to pass through a layer of cuboidal choroid plexus epithelium before it enters the cavity of a ventricle, and in passing through this epithelial membrane it is probably modified to some extent by the secretory activities of the epithelial cells. Accordingly, cerebrospinal fluid is spoken of as a modified tissue fluid.

**Development of Choroid Plexuses.** It has been noted already that the part of the wall of the neural tube that becomes the roof of the 3rd and the 4th ventricles becomes very thin; indeed, it comes to consist of no more than the single layer of cuboidal cells that comprise the ependyma plus the vascular piarachnoid which covers it. In these sites the piarachnoid, pushing the ependyma ahead of it, projects into the ventricles to form tufted structures called *choroid plexuses* (Fig. 21-11). A similar phenomenon occurs in the medial wall of the cerebral hemispheres along the line of attachment of the hemispheres to the hindpart (thalamus) of the forebrain; this accounts for the development of the choroid plexuses of the lateral ventricles. Thus, there are 4 choroid plexuses formed: one in the 4th, one in the 3rd and one in each of the lateral ventricles of the brain.

The choroid plexuses consist essentially of blood vessels, connective tissue remnants of the piarachnoid and a covering consisting of a single layer of cuboidal epithelium. As already noted, the tissue fluid produced by the capillaries is modified by the epithelium through which it passes to enter into the ventricles and become known as cerebrospinal fluid.

**Microscopic Structure of Choroid Plexuses.** The vascular arrangement of the plexuses is designed to expose as much of the capillary bed to epithelium as possible (Fig. 21-40). Thus the projections of the choroid plexuses are leaflike; these are said to be pedunculated if they resemble the leaves of a tree, or sessile or elongated if they resemble the leaves of a book. Secondary leaflike elevations may extend from the surface of primary leaves. A small artery or arteriole entering the attachment of a leaf usually extends to its free edge where it bifurcates, and thereafter its branches run an irregularly spiral or straight course along the edge in each direction. A capillary plexus extends from this into the body of the leaf where venules form and empty into a small vein that leaves the same way that the artery entered. The capillaries, becoming tortuous, produce elevations in the epithelium called *villi*, as may be seen in Figure 21-40, which is a section cut through a leaf and from which villi, containing large capillaries, project on either side.

As noted before, the epithelium that covers the leaves and the villi of the choroid plexuses develops from the inner layer of the wall of the neural tube and hence is the counterpart of, if not actual, ependyma. It is of the cuboidal type and is termed choroid plexus epithelium (Fig. 21-40). It rests on delicate connective tissue derived from the little piarachnoid that is pushed in ahead of the blood vessels.

With the EM, the free surfaces of the epithelial cells of the choroid plexus are seen to be studded with microvilli, the free ends of which are often somewhat bulbous (Fig. 21-41, villous outfoldings). Furthermore, at sites where the basal borders of the cells turn toward the free surfaces to become the sides of the cell, the cell membrane of both the base of the cell and the sides of the cell extends into the cystoplasm to form many complex infoldings (Fig. 21-41, infoldings of cell membrane). It is assumed that the complex infoldings on the basal surface and sides of the cell and the outfoldings of the free surfaces of the cells are both designed to increase the surface area through which fluid can be taken up, transported and delivered from the cells.

The choroid plexuses of the lateral ventricles, as have been described by Hudson and Smith, go through many changes during development which modify their vascular pattern considerably. They point out that the degenerative changes that may be seen in these plexuses relatively early in life, before degenerative changes are general elsewhere, occur at the site of confluence of the large veins of the plexuses; this suggests that these changes have a vascular origin. The degenerative changes are manifested by calcium deposits (termed *concentric bodies*), which may be scattered or concentrated in masses and/or by cysts. Rarely, the latter may become large enough to almost fill a portion of a lateral ventricle.

Since the cerebrospinal fluid is liberated into the ventricles it is apparent that if the outflow through the roof of the 4th ventricle were blocked, the cerebrospinal fluid would accumulate in the ventricles and cause them to expand and so stretch the brain from within. Such a condition can occur as a result of disease or deformity and is called *internal hydrocephalus*.

The cerebrospinal fluid produced in the lateral ventricles must circulate through the interventricular foramina and, with that produced in the 3rd ventricle, pass through the cerebral aqueduct of the midbrain to the 4th ventricle and out through its roof into the subarachnoid space. Most of the cerebrospinal fluid in the piarachnoid spaces surrounding the brain and the cord is formed inside the brain. But not all of it is formed there. It will be recalled that vessels penetrate into the brain substance from its surface and that these vessels lie in channels which are filled with tissue fluid which diffuses through their walls (Fig. 21-36). A certain amount of the tissue

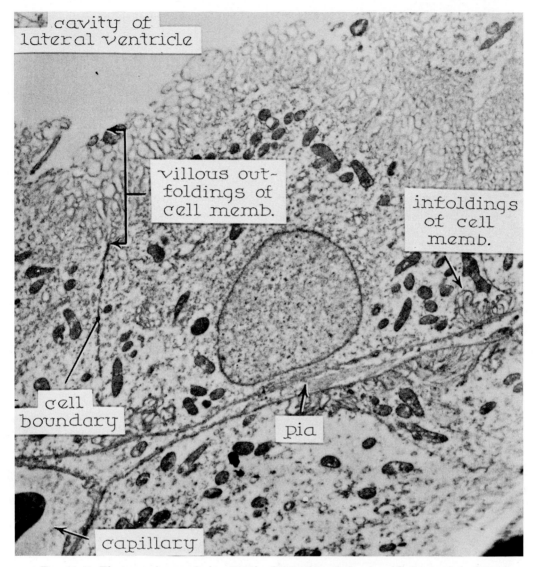

cavity of lateral ventricle

villous out-
foldings of
cell memb.

infoldings
of cell
memb.

cell
boundary

pia

capillary

Fig. 21-41. Electron micrograph ($\times$ 7,000) of a section of the choroid plexus of the lateral ventricle of a rat. The free surface of the epithelial cell is greatly increased by numerous polypoid projections which extend into the cerebrospinal fluid. The basal surface of the cell is also increased by complicated infoldings. (Preparation by R. C. Buck)

fluid formed in these sites makes its way back via these channels to the piarachnoid spaces on the surface of the brain to mix with, and become part of, the cerebrospinal fluid.

Since cerebrospinal fluid is formed more or less continuously, of course it must be absorbed continuously or a great increase in intracranial pressure would result. There must be some means whereby cerebrospinal fluid can be absorbed as fast as it is produced. This is accomplished chiefly by little structures known as arachnoid villi, which are buttonlike projections of the arachnoid into certain of the venous sinuses of the dura mater (Fig. 21-38). The more or less hollow cores of these arachnoid villi are filled with cerebrospinal fluid, which is separated from the blood in the sinus only by the cellular caps of the villi (Fig. 21-38). Cerebrospinal fluid diffuses through these to enter the venous blood of the sinus.

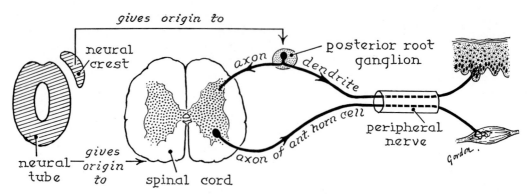

FIG. 21-42. Diagram illustrating the origin of the P.N.S. The neural crest gives rise to posterior root ganglion cells. Processes from these grow both outwardly and inwardly; hence, the neural crests give rise to the afferent components of the P.N.S. The efferent components of the P.N.S. develop from the neural tube by means of axons from anterior horn cells growing out from the developing spinal cord.

The whole arrangement for the formation and the absorption of tissue fluid reminds one of the mechanisms by which tissue fluid is formed and absorbed in most parts of the body (Chap. 10). Presumably, the hydrostatic pressure in the capillaries of the choroid plexuses is fairly high (for capillaries); this could be inferred from the congested state that many of them exhibit. Tissue fluid, then, would be produced readily in choroid plexuses. On the other hand, the hydrostatic pressure in the venous sinus, into which the arachnoid villi project, is low, and in this site it might be expected that the greater osmotic pressure of the blood, imparted to it by its colloid content, would draw cerebrospinal fluid (which is normally of a low protein or colloid content) back into blood through the cells of the arachnoid villi. However, this arrangement differs from that ordinarily concerned in the absorption of tissue fluid because lymphatics are not provided in the central nervous system to draw off excess fluid. Some cerebrospinal fluid may be drained away in other ways than by the arachnoid villi, but these other mechanisms are not so important and will not be considered here.

Cerebrospinal fluid is clear and limpid. Like tissue fluid, it contains inorganic salts but very little protein. In its normal state it contains only a very few cells, and these are mostly lymphocytes. Its examination in suspected injuries or diseases of the central nervous system is of the greatest help in diagnosis. For example, finding blood in the cerebrospinal fluid may provide confirmation of a skull fracture involving a rupture of vessels from which blood has escaped. Or an increase in the number of cells in the cerebrospinal fluid may be of assistance in diagnosing certain inflammatory diseases of the nervous system or the meninges. Even the pressure under which the cerebrospinal fluid exists is often a great help in distinguishing between different types of pathologic conditions of the brain or the cord. However, a complete study of the cerebrospinal fluid is not usually made in histology but is reserved for the later and clinical years of the medical course.

## THE PERIPHERAL NERVOUS SYSTEM

The P.N.S. consists of:

1. **Nerves.** These are branching cordlike structures that extend out from the brain as cranial nerves and from the cord as spinal nerves to reach almost every part of the body. These nerves, or *nerve trunks* as they are sometimes called, are like telephone cables that house many wires; each contains many wirelike nerve fibers—both afferent and efferent—which are distributed by means of the continued branching of the nerves to almost all parts of the body.

2. **Ganglia.** These little nodules contain the cell bodies of neurons. There are two general kinds of ganglia in the P.N.S. One kind contains the cell bodies of afferent, the other,

of efferent neurons. The first kind is the cerebrospinal ganglia which has been described already (Fig. 2-14). These contain the cell bodies of the afferent neurons of the body segments. The second kind is the ganglia of the autonomic nervous system (soon to be described) which contain the cell bodies of efferent neurons.

**3. Nerve Endings and Organs of Special Sense.** A description of these is given in a separate chapter at the end of this book because these structures can be studied to better advantage after the organs and the structures in which many of them are distributed have been described.

The foregoing outline of the components of the P.N.S. provides a basis for completing our classification of nervous tissue as follows:

Nervous Tissue

The tissue of the C.N.S. ⎰—Gray matter
                        ⎱—White matter

The tissue of the P.N.S. ⎡—Nerves
                         ⎢—Ganglia
                         ⎣—Nerve endings

## THE DEVELOPMENT OF THE P.N.S.

The P.N.S. contains both afferent and efferent components, and these are developed from somewhat different sources. The development of the afferent components will be considered first.

The neural plate gives rise to two neural crests as well as to the neural tube. The neural crests are at first continuous strands of neuro-ectoderm that lie on the dorsolateral aspect of each side of the developing spinal cord (Fig. 21-18). Soon, however, each neural crest breaks up into a chain of nodules, and these are the forerunners of the posterior (dorsal) root ganglia of the spinal cord and their cranial counterparts (Fig. 21-42). Each segment of the cord has two: one on each side in a posterolateral position (Fig. 21-39).

The neuro-ectodermal cells of the developing posterior root ganglia differentiate along two main lines, as they do in the neural tube. Along one line of differentiation they form neuroblasts. These are at first bipolar cells, but as they differentiate into neurons their two processes, like the hands of a clock, move around their circumference toward each other

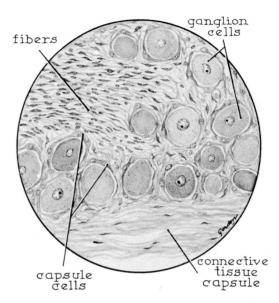

Fig. 21-43. Drawing of a portion of a section cut from a human spinal ganglion (high-power).

until they meet and fuse; by this maneuver the bipolar neurons become unipolar neurons. However, their single process branches, with one branch, the axon, growing centrally along the line indicated with an arrow in Figure 21-42 to the dorsal root of the spinal cord; the other process, which is functionally a dendrite, grows peripherally and becomes enclosed with other fibers in a nerve trunk through which it extends to reach the tissue in which it is to provide a sensory ending (Fig. 21-42). The peripheral processes of these cells, while they are functionally dendrites in that they conduct impulses toward the cell bodies of the ganglion cells, have the histologic characteristics of axons. Accordingly, they are generally termed *axons*, but it is understood that physiologically they are dendrites.

The neuro-ectodermal cells of the developing spinal ganglia differentiate along a second pathway to form supporting cells. In differentiating along the second line they do not form true neuroglia, as they do in the neural tube, but certain other cells that are the counterparts of the neuroglia of the C.N.S. These cells are of 2 main types: *capsule* cells, which form capsules around the cell bodies of the ganglion cells (Fig. 21-43), and *neurolemma*

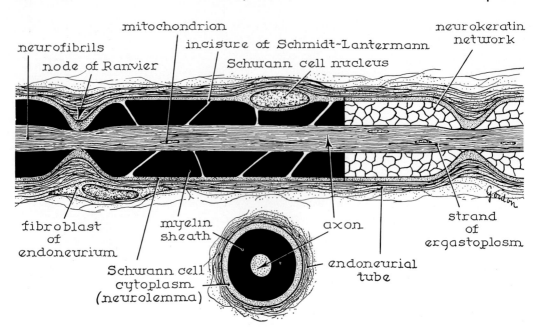

FIG. 21-44. Semidiagrammatic drawing of a longitudinal and cross section of a single myelinated nerve fiber and its endoneurial sheath. The left side of the upper drawing reveals what would be seen after fixation in osmium tetroxide, while the right side of the drawing represents what is seen after the fatty component of myelin has been dissolved away, as occurs with ordinary technics.

or *sheath of Schwann cells* (Fig. 21-44), which form sheaths for the nerve fibers that extend from the ganglion cells, as will be described presently.

The efferent components of the P.N.S. arise from the middle layer of the neural tube (Fig. 21-42). Neuroblasts that develop in what is to become the anterior and lateral horns of gray matter sprout axons that extend out from the anterolateral surface of the spinal cord. These escape the confines of the C.N.S. by passing out through their proper intervertebral foramina (Fig. 21-39), and from there into nerve trunks along the line indicated by arrows in Figure 21-42 by which they are distributed to the structures that they innervate.

When we deal with the autonomic nervous system—and this part of the P.N.S. will be defined and described presently—we shall find that it consists of efferent neurons, and that the cell bodies of some of these are in the brain and the cord, but the cell bodies of many others are scattered in autonomic (not posterior root) ganglia in various parts of the body. Therefore, the cell bodies that are in these ganglia represent the cell bodies of effer-

ent neurons that are outside the confines of the C.N.S. They develop from neuro-ectodermal cells of the neural tube but they leave the tube and migrate outwardly early in development.

## MICROSCOPIC STRUCTURE OF SPINAL GANGLIA

The bodies of the nerve cells of spinal ganglia usually are rounded. Many of them are large (Fig. 21-55) but some are small. Their nuclei, like those of the large multipolar neurons of the C.N.S., are large and pale and contain prominent nucleoli (Fig. 21-43). Their cytoplasm contains neurofibrils and chromidial substance; the latter is characteristically more dispersed than in anterior horn cells (Fig. 21-55). Accumulations of yellow-brown pigment may be present in the cytoplasm (Fig. 7-28). The significance of this is not known; perhaps it is a normal manifestation of aging. The rounded cell bodies of ganglion cells do not lie in direct contact with the connective tissue that surrounds them but are separated from it by a single layer of special flattened cells called *capsule* cells or amphicytes (Fig. 21-43). These cells are also termed *satellite* cells. They are derived from neuro-ectoderm and, although they are not classified as neuroglia cells, they bear a somewhat similar relation to the bodies of nerve cells of ganglia that neuroglial satellite cells bear to the cell bodies of neurons in the C.N.S.

The single process of each ganglion cell extends from its cell body, sometimes pursuing a devious course in the immediate vicinity of the cell body, to approach the main stream of fibers in the dorsal root. Somewhere between the cell body and the main stream of fibers the process divides into two branches. One of these branches passes into the spinal nerve to pass out to a receptor ending (Fig. 21-42). The other passes inwardly via the dorsal root to reach the posterior column of gray matter on that side of the cord (Fig. 21-42). Structurally, both processes have the appearance of axons and most of them are myelinated. As noted before, the branch that extends to the receptor functions as a dendrite. The connective tissue in which the ganglion cells and their processes lie is the counterpart of the connective tissue sheaths of nerves; it will be described shortly.

## MICROSCOPIC STRUCTURE OF PERIPHERAL NERVES

In the routine study of sections in a histology course, students often fail to identify peripheral nerves when they see them cut in cross, oblique and longitudinal sections. Somewhere, in almost every section taken from the body, a nerve sectioned in some plane or other is present. The student should become skilled in identifying them and should learn their structure well.

A peripheral nerve, encountered in gross dissection, has a cordlike structure. It is of a much firmer consistency than the nervous tissue of the C.N.S. because it contains collagen. Indeed, ordinary connective tissue, and not neuroglia, is the supporting tissue for peripheral nerves.

**Histologic Structure of Nerve Fibers of Peripheral Nerves.** All of the nerve fibers of the P.N.S. are covered with a thin delicate protoplasmic sheath termed the *neurolemma* (also spelled neurilemma) or *sheath of Schwann* (Figs. 21-44, 21-47 and 21-48). The

cells that comprise this sheath are derived from neuro-ectodermal cells that grow out along with the nerve fibers as they push out from the neural crests or the neural tube. In some nerve fibers the sheath of myelin between the nerve fiber and the neurolemma is of a substantial thickness (Figs. 21-44 and 21-47); hence, such fibers are termed *myelinated fibers*. Other fibers, and these tend to be smaller, are covered with only a trace of myelin; these are termed *nonmyelinated fibers*, and anywhere up to a dozen or more of these are enclosed by the cytoplasm of the same sheath of Schwann cell (Fig. 21-48).

The myelin of myelinated fibers is not continuous; it is interrupted periodically by constrictions (also called nodes) of Ranvier (Fig. 21-44).

The neurolemmal sheaths of the nerve fibers dip down in these constrictions but do not completely cover the nerve fibers. In these situations, as has been shown by Robertson, the nerve fiber is partially uncovered. There is one neurolemma cell between each two constrictions. Constrictions of Ranvier are present also in the C.N.S. as well as in peripheral nerves. In the C.N.S., the satellite cells, which have a similar morphologic relation to myelinated fibers as do Schwann cells in the P.N.S., dip down in the constrictions to partially cover the nerve fibers.

In peripheral nerves fixed with osmic acid, the myelin between constrictions of Ranvier is broken up by little incisures or clefts that extend down into it from the surface; these are termed the *clefts of Schmidt-Lantermann*, and the segments between them are termed *Schmidt-Lantermann segments* (Fig. 21-44, *left*). The clefts have been studied recently by histochemical methods by Shanklin and Azzam whose results suggest that the middles of the clefts are rich in carbohydrate while to each side of their middles (the layers that abut on the myelin) the material in the incisure is rich in phospholipids. Their work therefore suggests that the incisures are not merely artefact types of clefts but are occupied by stainable material. Moreover, these workers point out that the clefts in the fibers of a nerve are generally oriented in the same direction but that the clefts in some fibers of a nerve may be oriented in a direction different from that of the majority.

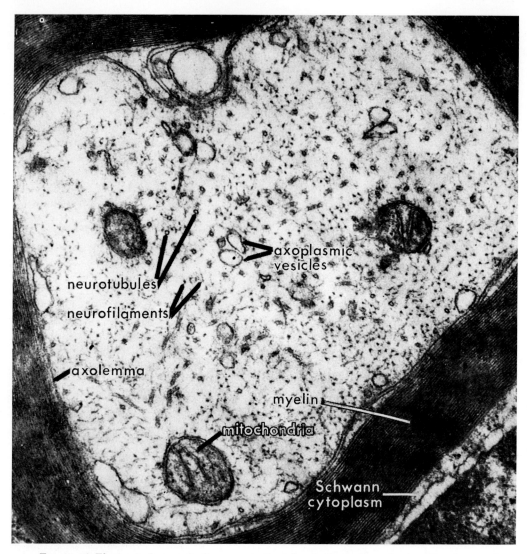

Fig. 21-45. Electron micrograph of a cross section of a single myelinated nerve fiber (an axon) showing mitochondria, axoplasmic vesicles, neurofilaments and neurotubules, all of which are labeled. (Preparation by B. Droz)

Recently, Pinner, Davison and Campbell have demonstrated the presence of an alkaline phosphatase both in the clefts of Schmidt-Lantermann and at the nodes of Ranvier of myelinated nerves fibers.

**The Fine Structure of Axons.** A cross section of a myelinated fiber is shown in Figure 21-45. It reveals the following organelles: (1) Mitochondria; these are arranged generally with their longer diameters parallel with the axon. Three can be seen in the cross section illus-

trated in Figure 21-45. (2) Axoplasmic vesicles; these are the representatives in the nerve fibers of smooth-surfaced endoplasmic reticulum. Several are labeled in Figure 21-45. (3) Neurofilaments; these are very delicate filaments that run longitudinally in the axon. They appear as small dots in a cross section seen in the EM (Fig. 21-45). These are probably seen best in longitudinal sections at nodes of Ranvier where they are more crowded together. (4) Neurotubules; these have been

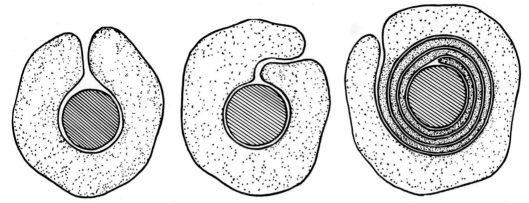

Fig. 21-46 A. Diagram illustrating the earlier stages of the formation of a myelin sheath according to the jelly-roll hypothesis. (Diagrams based on those of Geren, B. B., and Schmitt, F. O.: Symposium on the Fine Structure of Cells, p. 251, Groningen, Holland, Noordhoff, and diagrams supplied by Schmitt in a personal communication)

demonstrated only recently; they too are very delicate, being only slightly larger than neurofilaments. Most of them seem to run longitudinally and so appear in cross section in Figure 21-45, but some run in other directions and hence are cut at various angles in this illustration. The axon is surrounded by a cell membrane; this is termed the axolemma, and it abuts directly on the myelin sheath. Few or no ribosomes or rough-surfaced vesicles of endoplasmic reticulum are to be seen in axons. Elements of the Golgi apparatus are likewise not seen. The absence of the cytoplasmic com-

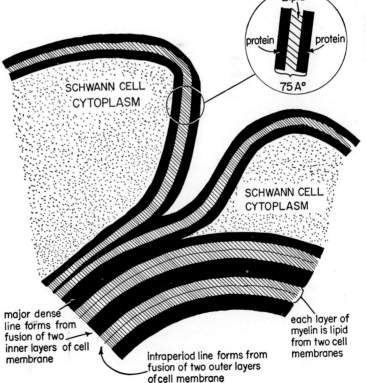

Fig. 21-46 B. Diagram illustrating the fine structure of cell membranes and how cell membranes of Schwann cells become myelin sheaths, and which parts of the cell membranes become the dense major and the intraperiod lines of the myelin sheaths. (Diagram based on descriptions and illustrations of J. D. Robertson)

ponents that are concerned in protein synthesis and secretion in axons is perhaps to be expected because it has been shown that protein synthesis is active in the cell bodies of neurons and that the protein formed in the cell bodies travels down the axon at a fairly regular rate. Replenishment of the axon is therefore performed by the cell body.

**The Formation and the Fine Structure of Myelin Sheaths.** A relatively early but exceedingly informative study of this matter with the EM was made by Uzman (née Geren) and Schmitt, and from this study they suggested what is now generally termed the jelly-roll hypothesis for explaining the formation of myelin sheaths. According to this hypothesis, which is now generally accepted, a Schwann cell embraces, and so far as possible encircles, an axon (Fig. 21-46 A, *left*). The axon then lies in a long trough in the Schwann cell. The Schwann cell then begins to rotate around the axon (Fig. 21-46 A, *center and right*). It should be noted here that the cell membrane of the Schwann cell is represented in this diagram (Fig. 21-46 A) as a single line. When the Schwann cell begins to wind around the axon, the cell membrane lining one side of the groove in which the axon lies comes into contact with the cell membrane that lines the other side of the groove (Fig. 21-46 A, *left and center*). These two membranes that come and stay together are seen, as the cell continues to wind around the axon, as a series of rings made of double lines (Fig. 21-46 A, *right*). Between adjacent double rings there is at first cytoplasm (stippled in Fig. 21-46 A). As the winding continues the cytoplasm is squeezed out, or lost in some other way. Accordingly, the myelin sheath evolves from 2-layered rings of cell membrane. To understand how a sheath made up of these rings of membrane becomes myelin, we no longer have to consider cytoplasm, for this is all squeezed out or lost; all that we have to consider is how a structure consisting of concentric rings, with each ring consisting of 2 cell membranes, takes on the appearance of myelin.

Under high resolution a fully formed myelin sheath reveals concentric dark rings that are each around 25 Å thick, separated from each other by rings of a lighter material about 100 Å thick (Fig. 21-47, *bottom*). The dark repeating lines are termed the *major dense lines*,

and these, and the lighter material separating them, can be seen in the bottom picture in Figure 21-47. However, with special fixation, and excellent resolution, a thinner dark line can be seen in the middle of each of the lighter layers; these fine lines that are halfway between the major dense lines are termed *intraperiod lines* (Fig. 21-47, *bottom*). We shall now consider how this appearance can evolve from concentric layers of cell membranes.

In Figure 21-46 A, a cell membrane is illustrated as a single line, and this is the way it appears in most electron micrographs. To establish how cell membranes evolve into myelin, with its major dense lines and intraperiod lines, however, it was necessary to make studies with special fixatives and extremely high resolution as has been done by Robertson. Under the appropriate conditions a cell membrane appears as 2 dark lines with a light space between them (Figs. 7-4 and 21-46 B, *upper right*), the whole membrane being about 75 Å thick. Evidence suggests that the middle layer of the cell membrane (the light layer) contains lipid while the 2 dark layers which bound the membrane on each of its sides, contain protein. To follow the formation of myelin further, we must think from now on of each of the 2 cell membranes that come together, as the Schwann cell rotates, as *each* being a double line with light material which is probably lipid between each double line; they are represented this way in Figure 21-46 B.

As is shown in Figure 21-46 B, as the Schwann cell continues to encircle the nerve fiber, the outer layers of the 2 cell membranes come together and fuse (Fig. 21-46 B). The dark line so-formed becomes compressed to form the fine intraperiod line (Fig. 21-46 B). Next, as cytoplasm is squeezed away, the inner layers of the cell membranes that previously bordered this cytoplasm come together and fuse, and this forms the major dense line (Fig. 21-46 B). Therefore, the myelin that fills the space between two major dense lines is derived chiefly from the lipid that existed in the middle of one major dense line to the middle of the next, which is roughly the thickness of 2 cell membranes. Why the fusion of 2 outer layers of 2 cell membranes should result in only a thin dark (intraperiod) line and the fusion of 2 inner layers of cell membrane in a heavy major dense line is not entirely

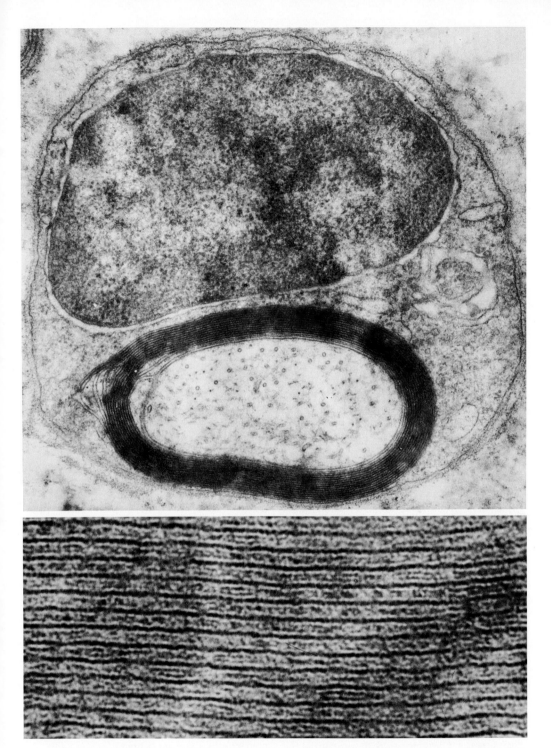

FIG. 21-47. Electron micrographs (*top* × 70,000, *bottom* × 360,000) of cross sections of sciatic nerve of rat. (*Top*) This is a cross section of a single myelinated nerve fiber surrounded by a sheath of Schwann. The upper part is occupied by the nucleus of a sheath of Schwann cells. Below the nucleus, lying in the cytoplasm of the Schwann cell, is a myelin sheath surrounding a nerve fiber. Details of a fiber are shown at higher magnification in Figure 21-45. (*Bottom*) This shows the major dense lines of the myelin sheath. Between the major dense lines, the intraperiod lines (the formation of which is illustrated in Fig. 21-46 B) can be seen; these are often double. (Preparation by Martha Nagai and A. F. Howatson)

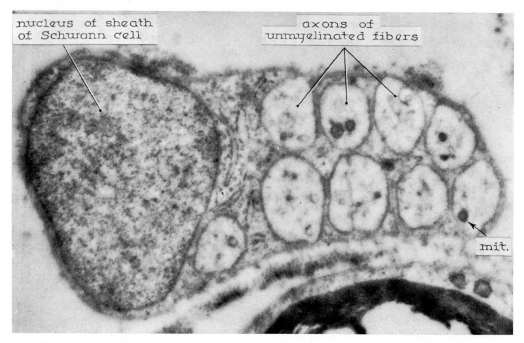

FIG. 21-48. Electron micrograph (× 32,250) of a cross section of a rat's sciatic nerve, showing 9 nonmyelinated fibers running in the cytoplasm of the same sheath of Schwann cell. This is the usual arrangement. Nonmyelinated fibers do not each have their own sheath of Schwann as do the myelinated fibers; instead, several share a sheath of Schwann in common.

clear. Both lines can be seen in Figure 21-47, *bottom picture*.

The fine structure of nonmyelinated fibers is illustrated in Figure 21-48; this shows that several such fibers lie in the cytoplasm of a single Schwann cell.

**Microscopic Structure of Peripheral Nerves.**
If a peripheral nerve is cut in cross section (Figs. 21-49 and 21-51), it will be seen to be more or less surrounded by a sheath of connective tissue. This wrapping, which is generally composed of loose connective tissue and extends around the whole nerve, is known as its epineurium (*epi* = upon). Inside this outer wrapping several bundles of nerve fibers may be seen, and each of these is also wrapped in a special dense and relatively strong sheath of connective tissue. These wrappings of bundles of nerve fibers are said to constitute the perineurium (*peri* = around) of the nerve (Figs. 21-49 and 21-51). Inside these bundles are the nerve fibers. These, each surrounded with its myelin sheath and neurolemma (Fig. 21-47), are each surrounded by tubes, the walls of which are composed of networks of

delicate fibrils that are associated with some sticky amorphous intercellular substances. These tubes are termed *endoneurial* tubes (Fig. 21-44), and they are very important in nerve regeneration. The endoneurial tubes, each containing a nerve fiber, are packed in a delicate connective tissue medium that extends throughout the interior of each nerve bundle. This connective tissue in which the ensheathed nerve fibers lie is known as endoneurium (*endo* = inside) (Fig. 21-49).

Large nerves consist of several fascicles of fibers. Each fascicle is surrounded with a dense sheath of perineurium (Fig. 21-49). Sunderland has shown that there is much communication between fascicles and that nerve fibers pass from one to another. Consequently, the relative size of the fascicles in a nerve changes continually along its course.

If small sections of a nerve are destroyed by trauma it is desirable to join the two stumps so that the fascicles in one are correctly apposed to those of the other. The fact that the size of fascicles changes so much along the course of a nerve makes this de-

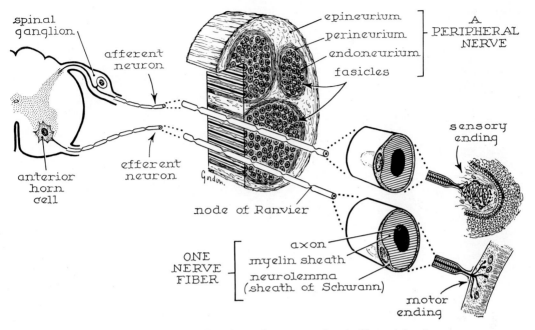

spinal ganglion

afferent neuron

epineurium
perineurium
endoneurium
fascicles

A PERIPHERAL NERVE

anterior horn cell

efferent neuron

Gordon.

sensory ending

node of Ranvier

ONE NERVE FIBER

axon
myelin sheath
neurolemma
(sheath of Schwann)

motor ending

F ɪ ɢ. 21-49. Diagram showing the various parts of a sizable peripheral nerve.

sirable end almost impossible to attain, because if a portion of a nerve is destroyed the fascicles in the two stumps will not match each other.

In order to join the two stumps of a nerve, a portion of which has been, for example, shot away, recourse may be taken to stretching the two parts of the nerve that are to be joined. Nerves can be stretched to some extent without damage to them (see Sunderland). This is probably due at least in part to the fact that nerve fibers do not pursue a straight course along a nerve but instead a zigzag course (Fig. 21-50). Stretching a nerve (up to a point) merely straightens out the fibers and does not stretch them. The strong perineurial sheaths provide a limiting factor in stretching a nerve (for details on these points see Sunderland).

Small nerves are composed of only a single fascicle; this is surrounded by a perineurial sheath (Fig. 21-50). A large nerve has several (Fig. 21-51).

The number of nerve fibers within a fascicle varies greatly, as does the diameter of the nerve fibers in the fascicle. Sunderland, Lavarack and Ray found, for example, that the lateral cutaneous nerve on the right side of one subject consisted of only one fascicle and

that it contained 3,160 fibers. The same nerve on the left side consisted of 7 fascicles that contained a total of 10,178 fibers. They measured the diameters of the fibers in one fascicle that contained 1,242 fibers and found that around 60 per cent of these were less than $8 \mu$ wide, 15 per cent were between 8 and $15 \mu$ wide, 23 per cent were between 16 and $23 \mu$ wide and 0.5 per cent were wider than $23 \mu$.

Lavarack, Sunderland and Ray have counted the number of fibers in nerves at different levels and have found more fibers in the distal parts of some nerves than at more proximal levels. The increased numbers of fibers is attributed to the branching of fibers within nerves.

**The Blood Supply of Nerves.** This matter has been investigated at length by Sunderland, whose papers should be read for details. It so happens in surgical procedures that nerves must sometimes be freed of their attachments for certain distances, and it is important to know whether or not this will interfere sufficiently with their blood supply to cause serious damage within them. Fortunately, nerves are supplied by a profusion of vessels that anastomose freely. The vessels are of several orders. There are longitudinally disposed

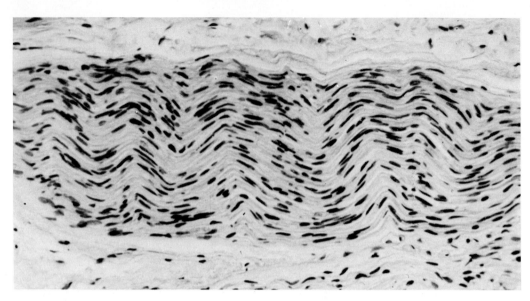

Fig. 21-50. High-power photomicrograph of a longitudinal section of a small peripheral nerve, showing the snake-fence appearance which is typical in longitudinal sections of nerves unless they are prevented from contracting.

epineurial interfascicular, perineurial and intrafascicular arteries and arterioles. The endoneurium contains a capillary network. Nutrient arteries from vessels outside the nerve, and from longitudinally disposed vessels accompanying the nerve, penetrate the nerve frequently along its course to communicate with the neural vessels. The number of anastomoses between all these vessels is so great that nerves can be freed for considerable distances from their surrounding attachments; Sunderland states that in his experiments nerves sometimes were stripped from surrounding attachments for distances up to 15 cm., and yet when the nerve was cut at the distal end of the freed section, the nerve bled. Sunderland stresses the importance of preserving the superficial vessels that run along nerves when the nerves are being freed from adjacent structures, for these superficial ves-

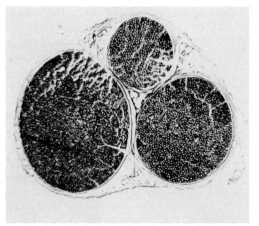

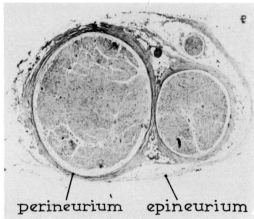

perineurium    epineurium

Fig. 21-51. (*Left*) A low-power photomicrograph of a cross section of the sciatic nerve of a dog; this was cut from material fixed in osmic acid. (*Right*) A photomicrograph, at the same magnification, of a cross section cut from material fixed in Zenker-formol solution and stained with H and E.

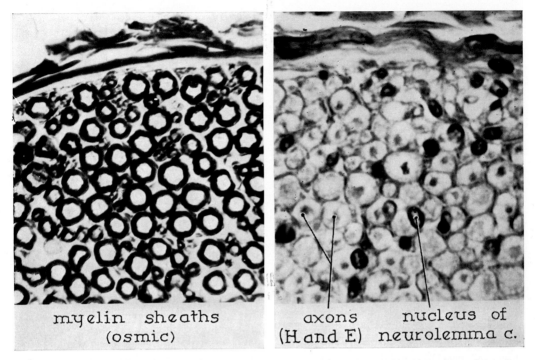

myelin  sheaths          axons        nucleus of
(osmic)              (H and E)  neurolemma c.

FIG. 21-52. (*Left*) High-power photomicrograph of a portion of a cross section of a peripheral nerve fixed in osmic acid. (*Right*) A similar preparation of a nerve fixed in formalin and stained with H and E.

sels are important links in the system that provides such efficient anastomoses.

There are certain differences between the cross section appearance of nerves prepared differently. In preparing an ordinary paraffin section to be stained with H and E, the myelin surrounding the individual nerve fibers, unless it is treated with special mordants, will, because of its fatty nature, dissolve away in the dehydrating and clearing agents. This allows the nerve fiber to slip to one side of the tubular space that is left by the myelin dissolving away. Hence, ordinary H and E cross sections of nerves show the sites previously occupied by the myelin sheaths as little rounded spaces, mostly empty except for the nerve fiber, and this may be situated toward one side rather than in the center of the space (Fig. 21-52, *right*). At the exterior of the space, or bulging somewhat into it, the faint-staining neurolemma may be seen. The nuclei seen in the substance of a nerve bundle in an H and E preparation are those of the neurolemma or sheath of Schwann cells and those of the fibro-

blasts and macrophages of the endoneurium together with the nuclei of the cells of the blood vessels which lie in the endoneurium. However, in an osmic acid preparation the myelin surrounding the nerve fibers is not dissolved away but is preserved and blackened. Hence, the myelin sheaths of nerve fibers appear as blackened rings in this type of preparation (Fig. 21-52, *left*). However, the other elements of the nerve do not show up very well in the usual osmic acid preparation. Osmic acid preparations show very clearly that the fibers in a nerve are of different sizes.

In routine H and E preparations, nerves cut obliquely, or in planes approaching the longitudinal, have an appearance which is often substantially different from that which might be expected from their cross-section appearance. Instead of seeing rings, where myelin has dissolved away, one sees streaks. Moreover, the streaky appearance of obliquely and longitudinally sectioned nerves is accentuated by the long, thin, flat nuclei seen between the fibers; those are the nuclei of the neurolemma cells and the cells of the endoneurium

(Fig. 21-50). The streaks do not run directly longitudinally but in a wavy snake-fence manner along it (Fig. 21-50).

Most peripheral nerves are of the mixed variety; they contain both afferent and efferent fibers. The endings of the afferent fibers are described in Chapter 31. All efferent fibers end either in or about muscle or gland cells. The ones that end in smooth muscle and glands are described later in this chapter in connection with the autonomic nervous system. The endings of efferent fibers in voluntary muscle were described in Chapter 20.

## NERVE INJURIES AND THE DEGENERATION AND THE REGENERATION OF PERIPHERAL NERVES

Nerve injuries are of different orders of severity. Sunderland has made a useful classification that will be followed in part here.

**First-Degree Injuries.** Such injuries have been suffered by most of us. This type of injury is generally caused by pressure being applied to a nerve for a limited time; this probably acts by squeezing the blood vessels in the nerve to cause local anoxia of the axons sufficient to interfere with their function. However, it may be that pressure affects axons adversely in some more direct fashion. Sensory fibers are affected more readily by pressure than motor fibers, and different kinds of sensory fibers vary in their susceptibility. After the pressure is released, recovery of function of the affected fibers may occur in a matter of minutes, hours or weeks, depending on the severity of the injury. If recovery does not occur in a *few weeks* the injury must be regarded as more severe than a first-degree type, as will now be described.

**Second-Degree Injuries.** This kind is generally caused by prolonged and/or severe pressure being exerted on some part of the nerve. Nerves sometimes are injured purposefully in this fashion to bring about the temporary paralysis of some muscle or muscles whose actions are interfering with the rest and the recovery of some part of the body (for example, the nerves to one side of the diaphragm sometimes are crushed to put the lung on that side to rest).

The severe pressure required to bring about second-degree injuries to nerves causes the *death of the axons* of the nerve at the site where the pressure is applied. In this respect, the second-degree type of injury is fundamentally different from the first-degree type. When even a small segment of an axon dies the part of the axon distal to the injury also dies because it is separated from the cell body on which it depends for its existence. Accordingly, nerve function in a second-degree type of injury can be restored only by all parts of axons distal to the injury being regenerated. In a first-degree type of injury the axon is not destroyed; it is merely incapacitated temporarily and subsequently recovers its full health.

It has been mentioned already that the bodies of nerve cells continuously produce axoplasm. However, the crushing of an axon has repercussions in the cell body of that axon. It causes an axon reaction in that cell body; this involves a solution of the Nissl bodies (chromatolysis, Fig. 21-18), changes in the site of the nucleus and the sex chromatin and other effects. When the cell body recovers from the axon reaction it begins again to synthesize new axoplasm. This results in new axoplasm pushing into and through the site where the axon was crushed. To discuss its further fate we must consider certain other changes that result from the injury.

When the axons distal to the site of injury die, the myelin sheaths surrounding them also degenerate. The degeneration of the axon and its myelin sheath were first described by Waller, so the process often is termed wallerian degeneration. The degenerating myelin can be stained selectively, so it is possible to distinguish fibers that have been cut from those that have not been cut; this method is used experimentally to trace the course of certain nerve tracts in the C.N.S. The degenerating axon and myelin in the distal stumps of cut peripheral nerves attract macrophages from the endoneurium, and these phagocytose the degenerating material. It is believed that Schwann cells also become phagocytic and help rid the area of debris.

A second-degree type of injury, although it causes serious temporary repercussions in the axons, the myelin and the sheaths of Schwann cells distal to the injury, *does not interrupt the continuity of the endoneurial tubes at the site of injury.* Accordingly, when the cell bodies supplying the axons in the nerve recover and begin to send axoplasm into and through the site of the injury, the new axoplasm from each neuron pushes into the same endoneurial tube that formerly was occupied by the axon from that same neuron. Axoplasm generally extends down the endoneurial tubes at a rate of about 2 to 3 mm. per day, but the rate is said to become slower as the new axoplasm approaches the terminations of the fibers. The new axoplasm becomes myelinated and covered with a sheath of Schwann similarly to the way it does in third-degree injuries, as will now be described.

**Third-, Fourth- and Fifth-Degree Injuries.** In third-degree injuries the endoneurial tubes do not retain continuity at the site of injury but fascicles do. In fourth-degree injuries the fascicles as well as tubes become disorganized, and in fifth-degree injuries the nerve trunk is severed. The last type of injury will now be considered in detail. If a peripheral nerve is cut, the muscular action in, and the reception of sensation from, the part of the body it supplies need not be lost forever. If the two cut ends of the nerve are brought together and fastened in place by sutures through their connective tissue wrappings, or held together by some other means, function, after a considerable period of time, may be restored to the part affected. How this is effected will now be considered. In discussing this matter we shall refer to the portion of the nerve between the spinal cord and the site of the cut as the proximal part or stump and the part between the cut and the termination of the nerve as the distal part or stump.

In the part of the nerve distal to the cut, the nerve fibers of afferent and efferent neurons are, of course, severed from their cell bodies, so they die and become necrotic. The disintegration of the axons takes only a short time, and in a few days only a little debris is left in the space that the living axon formerly occupied (Fig. 21-53). The myelin sheaths of these axons that are severed from their cell bodies also decompose (Fig. 21-53). The myelin breaks down rather more slowly than the material of the axon, but soon it becomes reduced to droplets (Fig. 21-53). The cells of the sheaths of Schwann proliferate and form cords that lie in the endoneurial tubes (Fig. 21-53). Macrophages from endoneurium phago-

cytose and digest the droplets of broken-down myelin and the remnants of the dead axons. After they phagocytose this debris, they move away. The fibroblasts of the endoneurium and the perineurium, particularly those close to the place where the nerve is cut, proliferate, but unless the site of the cut has become infected, they do not usually proliferate as rapidly as the cells of the sheath of Schwann, which at this site bulge from the cut ends of the endoneurial tubes of the distal stump, and also, but not so rapidly, from the endoneurial tubes of the proximal stump. The slitlike spaces between the proliferating sheath of Schwann cells offer a means for nerve fibers to grow across the gap into the distal stump (Fig. 21-53).

While all these changes are taking place in the portion of the nerve distal to the cut, changes also take place near the cut in that portion of the nerve which is still connected to the central nervous system. Near the cut the axons at first degenerate. As has been mentioned already, the sheath of Schwann cells proliferate and grow out into the gap and meet those from the distal stump. Thus, continuity is established across the cut by sheath of Schwann cells, and, as noted before, these cells have longitudinally disposed slits between them. The axons from the proximal portion of the severed nerve now start to push forward a little each day, and after a few days they reach the space where union has occurred between the two outgrowths of sheath of Schwann cells. The axons on growing into this mazelike arrangement often branch into many branches (Fig. 21-53), and the various branches push their way through such slits and spaces as are available, and before long many may manage to traverse the region of the cut and from then on grow along the tiny passageways that exist in the syncytium provided by the sheath of Schwann cells into the open ends of the endoneurial tubes of the distal stump: these, while they have become smaller, are still open. Under good conditions, the fibers grow down these tubes at a rate that has been variously estimated at from 1 to 4 mm. a day (Fig. 21-53 B). As they near the termination of the nerve they grow somewhat more slowly.

It is to be observed that no matter how carefully severed nerves are sutured together,

# DEGENERATION AND REGENERATION OF A SEVERED NERVE

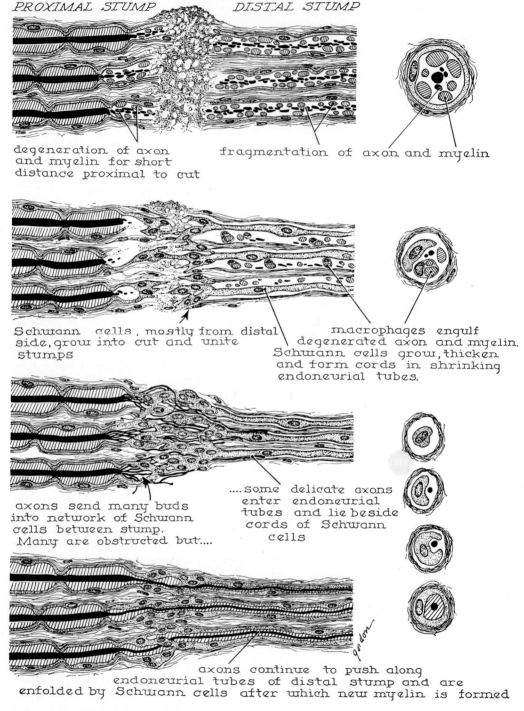

PROXIMAL STUMP                    DISTAL STUMP

degeneration of axon
and myelin for short
distance proximal to cut

fragmentation of axon and myelin

Schwann cells, mostly from distal
side, grow into cut and unite
stumps

macrophages engulf
degenerated axon and myelin.
Schwann cells grow, thicken
and form cords in shrinking
endoneurial tubes.

axons send many buds
into network of Schwann
cells between stump.
Many are obstructed but....

....some delicate axons
enter endoneurial
tubes and lie beside
cords of Schwann
cells

axons continue to push along
endoneurial tubes of distal stump and are
enfolded by Schwann cells after which new myelin is formed

FIG. 21-53. Diagram showing the changes that occur in a nerve when it is severed and regenerates.

it could scarcely be expected that the majority of axons that grow down it would ever find their proper paths. For example, a motor axon might invade an endoneurial tube that led it to an afferent ending, or an axon which formerly connected with a nerve ending designed to be stimulated by heat might, after repair, end up in a touch ending. It seems almost incredible, under the circumstances, that efficient motor function and reasonably good sensation should ever return to a part of the body after the nerve supplying it has been severed. Nevertheless, good results often are obtained by the suturing of cut nerves. Perhaps one thing that helps is that the axons, on reaching the sheath of Schwann syncytium that forms at the site of the cut, branch into many branches. Hence, more axons actually may try to grow down the severed nerve than were present in the first place. Sometimes several enter one endoneurial tube; perhaps only the one that should be there survives.

In an endoneurial tube the new axon lies against a cord of Schwann cells (Fig. 21-53). The latter gradually enfold the axon, probably much as occurs in normal development (Fig. 21-53). New myelin then forms, probably as it does during development, and the cordlike Schwann cells once more assume their mature appearance.

It is obvious from the foregoing that the pathway across the cut and through which the axons can grow down into the severed portion of the nerve is provided by the sheath of Schwann cells which grow rapidly into the area of the cut from both the distal and the proximal portions of the severed nerve. However, should the cut become infected, with inflammation supervening, more fibroblasts from the endoneurium and the perineurium proliferate than is usual, with the result that a relatively impenetrable fibrous scar tends to form at the site of the cut. If this is extensive, it may comprise a complete obstruction. Scar tissue, then, is to be avoided if good regeneration is to be obtained.

**Nerve Transplantation.** In certain types of injuries—for example, gunshot wounds—a whole section of a nerve may be destroyed. Under these conditions, the two cut ends cannot be approximated, hence recourse may be taken to what is called *nerve grafting*. In this procedure a piece of some superficial nerve

that is not essential is removed, and this is placed and sutured so as to fill the gap. On transplantation, the sheath of Schwann cells in a nerve graft appear to survive and proliferate. Hence, in this respect the graft acts very much like the distal fragment. However, even though its sheath of Schwann cells proliferate at both of its cut ends, to join with the distal and the proximal fragments of the injured nerve, respectively, it is obvious that the use of a graft necessitates axons finding their way through two mazes rather than one. It is understandable, then, that the results from nerve grafting are not nearly so satisfactory as those that are obtained by joining the two cut ends of a nerve directly.

## THE AUTONOMIC NERVOUS SYSTEM

To recapitulate: nervous tissue is structurally specialized to be excited selectively by different kinds of stimuli, originating both within and without the body, and to conduct nervous impulses rapidly to (1) the gland cells of epithelial tissue and (2) the muscle cells of muscular tissue.

It is to be observed further that only some of these responses are under the direct control of the conscious mind—those that occur in striated muscle. The control of all cardiac and smooth muscle, and all glandular secretion, is outside the direct influence of the conscious mind. However, these activities are controlled by reflex phenomena. Some of the afferent impulses concerned in these reflexes make their way into consciousness; for example, stimulation of the nerve endings in the taste buds of the mouth gives rise to the sensation of taste as well as initiating the response of salivation. But other afferent impulses (for example, those arising from the stimulation of nerve endings in the viscera) do not ordinarily appear even dimly in consciousness. Hence, we say that the function of smooth and cardiac muscle and glands is automatically controlled in the body because (1) many of the afferent impulses concerned in it give rise to no sensation in consciousness and (2) even though they do, the efferent control of the function of smooth and cardiac muscle and glands is not a function of consciousness.

The *efferent* neurons concerned in the innervation of the smooth and cardiac muscle and

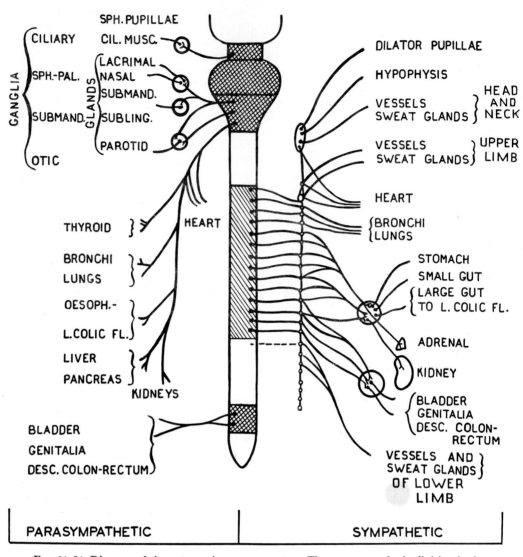

Fig. 21-54. Diagram of the autonomic nervous system. The parasympathetic division is shown on the left, and the sympathetic division on the right. (Slightly modified from Grant, J. C. B.: A Method of Anatomy, ed. 4, Baltimore, Williams & Wilkins)

the glands of the body constitute the *autonomic nervous system*. It is to be kept in mind that this is not a segregated anatomic division of the nervous system because many of the neurons of which it is comprised are intermingled with neurons, both in peripheral nerves and in the central nervous system, that are concerned with consciously controlled activity. The term autonomic nervous system, then, is generally said to refer to a *functional* division of the nervous system rather than an anatomic one. It is not always easy to keep this distinction in mind because there are certain parts of the system that are anatomically distinct.

As explained before, although the activity in this system is reflex and therefore requires afferent neurons to pick up the stimuli which set its nervous impulses in motion, these afferent neurons are not considered to be part of the system. Hence, the term autonomic nervous system is limited only to efferent neurons—the efferent supply of the smooth and cardiac muscle and the glands of the body.

post. root gang.          two sympathetic ganglia

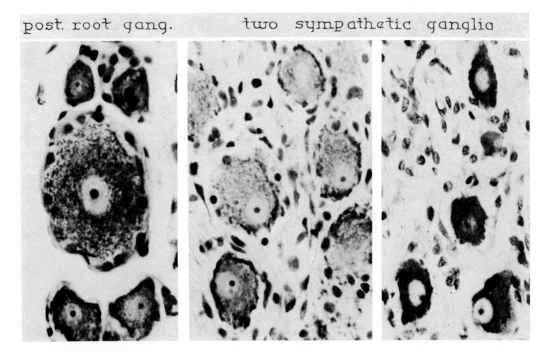

FIG. 21-55. High-power photomicrographs of ganglion cells as they appear in sections stained with cresyl blue. Observe the larger size of the dorsal root ganglion cell on the left and the eccentric distribution of the nuclei in some of the sympathetic ganglion cells.

Next, cardiac muscle and most of the smooth muscle and glands of the body are doubly innervated by this system. This is accomplished by there being two divisions of the autonomic nervous system, with each division sending efferent neurons to most bits of muscle or gland that it innervates (Fig. 21-54) so that each has a double supply. Further, the efferent impulses arriving at muscle or gland by neurons of the two divisions tend to cause different physiologic effects. For example, the impulses arriving by way of the neurons of one division may lead to the contraction of a certain bit of smooth muscle, while those arriving at the same muscle by way of the neurons of the other division cause it to relax. The two divisions of the autonomic system are thus, at least to a considerable extent, functionally antagonistic to each other, with the responses in the muscle and the glands controlled by the system being more or less the result of a balance struck between the activities of the two divisions of the system.

The two divisions of the autonomic nervous systems are termed the *sympathetic* and the *parasympathetic* division, respectively, and as noted before, with certain exceptions, each division sends efferent fibers to each structure innervated by the autonomic system. Both divisions of the system arise in the C.N.S. but from different parts of it (Fig. 21-54). Hence, the neurons by which muscle and glands are innervated by the two systems travel along different routes. Moreover, in each system two efferent neurons are always required to join the C.N.S. with each gland or muscle innervated (Fig. 21-54). The cell body of the first neuron in each efferent chain in each system is situated in the C.N.S.; the cell body of the second in a ganglion. We shall now consider briefly the microscopic structure of the ganglia of the autonomic nervous system and then consider the two systems in more detail.

**Autonomic Ganglia.** The ganglia of the autonomic nervous system are generally similar to cerebrospinal ganglia in that both have connective tissue framework and contain ganglion nerve cells. However, there are certain differences. Whereas the nerve cells of cerebrospinal ganglia are unipolar, those of autonomic ganglia are multipolar, and since they give off

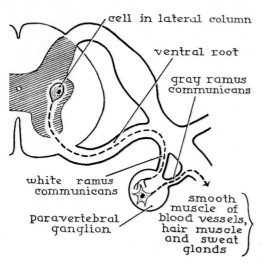

FIG. 21-56. Diagram showing one course taken by preganglionic and postganglionic fibers of the sympathetic division of the autonomic nervous system.

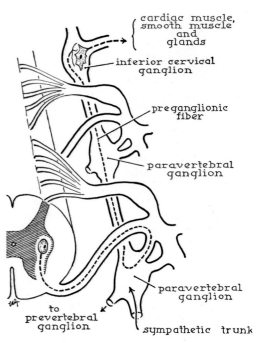

FIG. 21-57. Diagram showing a second course taken by preganglionic and post-ganglionic fibers of the sympathetic division of the autonomic nervous system.

many dendrites they have somewhat more irregular contours than those of cerebrospinal ganglia cells (Fig. 21-55). In general, the nerve cells of autonomic ganglia are smaller than those of cerebrospinal ganglia and not all of them are surrounded by capsules. Moreover, the nuclei are disposed eccentrically more often than those of cerebrospinal ganglia cells (Fig. 21-55). The terminal ganglia of the para-sympathetic system may be very small (Fig. 24-39); indeed, sometimes a single ganglion cell may be encountered.

**The Sympathetic Division.** In the thoracic, and upper part of the lumbar, portion of the spinal cord, a lateral, as well as an anterior and a posterior, column of gray matter is present (Fig. 21-31). The nerve cell bodies in these lateral columns of gray matter differ somewhat from those in the ventral columns; they are smaller, have fewer Nissl bodies and peripherally rather than centrally disposed nuclei. These cell bodies give rise to thin, lightly myelinated axons which leave the cord by way of the ventral roots to reach the spinal nerves (Figs. 21-56, 21-57 and 21-58) along which they extend to enter the ventral branches of these nerves. The axons extend along these ventral branches of the spinal nerves for only a short distance whereupon they leave them by way of little nerve trunks

(Fig. 21-56) called *white rami communicantes* (*ramus* = branch; *communicans* = communicating, and white because the axons are myelinated). Before considering the course of these axons further, it is necessary first to describe the ganglia of the sympathetic division of the autonomic nervous system. According to their position these are called *para-vertebral* or *prevertebral* ganglia.

The paravertebral ganglia are disposed in the form of chains, one on each side of the vertebral column, and are said to constitute two sympathetic *trunks* (Fig. 21-57). In the cervical region there are 3 ganglia in each; the superior, the middle and the inferior cervical ganglia, respectively. The middle cervical ganglia are not always present. In the thoracic region 10 or 11 ganglia are distributed along each side of the vertebral column (Fig. 21-54, *right*). In some instances, the first thoracic ganglion is fused with the inferior cervical; if so, the fused mass is termed the stellate ganglion. In the lumbar region 4 ganglia are present on each side, and in the sacral region 4 also are present on each side of the vertebral column. Nerve fibers extend between the ganglia in each chain. Since the position and the connections of these ganglia will be presented in detail in other courses, the student should not attempt to obtain anything but a general knowledge of them at this time (see Fig. 21-54, *right*).

The prevertebral ganglia constitute a group of ganglia that lie in front of the vertebral column and in closer association with the viscera than the paravertebral ganglia. There are 3 of them—the celiac ganglion, the superior mesenteric and the inferior mesenteric. An extension of the last may be present in the pelvis. These, too, will be learned about in detail in other courses, so the names need not be memorized here.

The axons from the bodies of nerve cells in the lateral column of the spinal cord, which we have traced to the white rami communicantes, end either in the paravertebral (Figs. 21-56 and 21-57) or the prevertebral (Fig. 21-58) ganglia. Therefore, they are all called preganglionic fibers. They reach one or the other of these ganglia by 3 different courses.

1. Some of them terminate in the paravertebral ganglion to which the white ramus from the adjacent spinal nerve extends (Fig. 21-56). In the paravertebral ganglion, the axon comes into synaptic relationship with the second neuron of the efferent chain, whose cell body is situated in the ganglion. This cell body of the second neuron of the chain sends out an axon, which is not myelinated and hence is gray in color, into a little nerve trunk (some may go directly) called the *gray ramus communicans* (Fig. 21-56), which conducts it back to the spinal nerve (Fig. 21-56), along which it travels to reach gland or muscle. Since this axon proceeds from a ganglion to nerve or muscle, it is called a *postganglionic* fiber.

2. Some of the axons from the bodies of nerve cells in the lateral column of gray matter in the spinal cord, on reaching adjacent paravertebral ganglia by way of the white rami, pass up or down along the sympathetic trunk to terminate in a paravertebral ganglion at some other level. Some, for example, travel up to the superior cervical ganglia (at which level, it is to be noted, no preganglionic fibers emerge from the cord) where they come into synaptic relationship with the second neurons of the efferent chains, whose cell bodies are

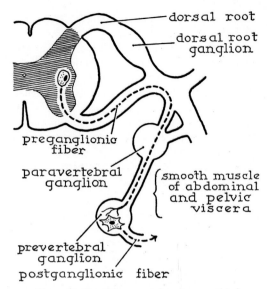

FIG. 21-58. Diagram showing a third course taken by preganglionic and postganglionic fibers of the sympathetic division of the autonomic nervous system.

situated in the ganglia (Fig. 21-57). The cell bodies of the second neurons send postganglionic fibers out to muscle and glands (Fig. 21-57, *top*).

3. Some axons from the bodies of nerve cells in the lateral column of gray matter of the spinal cord, after reaching the paravertebral ganglia by way of white rami communicantes, pass through the paravertebral ganglia concerned to proceed more or less directly to one of the prevertebral ganglia, where they come into synaptic relationship with the second neuron of the efferent chain, the cell body of which is situated in that particular prevertebral ganglion (Fig. 21-58). The cell body of the second neuron sends an axon, a postganglionic fiber, out to muscle or gland (the innervation of the medulla of the adrenal gland is different from the ordinary arrangement and will be described when this gland is considered later in this book).

The number of postganglionic fibers that emerge from a sympathetic ganglion is considerably greater than the number of preganglionic fibers that enter it. Preganglionic fibers, then, in ganglia must enter into synaptic relation with many different neurons whose cell bodies are situated in that ganglion. This arrangement allows ganglia to serve as instruments for broadening the stream of nervous impulses that enter them.

**The Parasympathetic Division.** Nerve fibers belonging to the parasympathetic division of the system also innervate most of the glands and muscles innervated by the sympathetic division, and, as noted before, the two systems are to some extent antagonistic to each other. Between each structure innervated by the parasympathetic division and the C.N.S., from which the parasympathetic division arises, a chain of two efferent neurons is always to be found.

The parasympathetic division has its origin from two widely separated parts of the C.N.S. The bodies of the nerve cells that give rise to one group of its preganglionic fibers are situated in nuclei of gray matter in the medulla and the midbrain, and the preganglionic fibers arising from these cell bodies make their way out of the C.N.S. by way of the 3rd, 7th, 9th and 10th cranial nerves (Fig. 21-54, *left*). The cell bodies from which the remainder of its preganglionic fibers arise are found in the lateral column of the sacral portion of the spinal cord, and they make their way out of the C.N.S. by way of the 2nd, 3rd and 4th sacral spinal nerves, which they soon leave by way of the visceral rami of these nerves (Fig. 21-54, *bottom, left*).

Since the preganglionic fibers of the parasympathetic division of the autonomic system emerge by way of cranial and sacral nerves from the C.N.S., the parasympathetic division is also termed the craniosacral division of the autonomic system (in contrast with the thoracolumbar division).

The preganglionic fibers of the parasympathetic division are, in general, longer than those in the sympathetic division, and with certain exceptions, they proceed all the way to the muscle or the gland with whose innervation they are concerned. When they approach the gland or the muscle, they generally end in small ganglia that are closely associated, particularly in the viscera, with the gland or the muscle innervated. These are sometimes called *terminal ganglia,* and in them the preganglionic fibers come into synaptic relation with the second neurons, whose cell bodies are situated in the terminal ganglia and send axons, the postganglionic fibers, to the nerve endings in muscle or gland. The postganglionic axons are, then, generally short.

However, in the head region the ganglia of the parasympathetic division of the system are not within, or on the surface of, the gland or the muscle innervated, and in these instances the postganglionic fibers are correspondingly longer (Fig. 21-54, *top, left*).

### Nerve Endings in the Autonomic Nervous System

The endings of the postganglionic fibers of the sympathetic and the parasympathetic systems in smooth or cardiac muscle or glands cannot be seen in H and E sections, although the terminal ganglia of the parasympathetic system show to advantage (Fig. 24-39). For the demonstration of the nerve endings of the fibers of the autonomic system in muscle or glands special technics are necessary. Silver impregnation methods or the treatment of fresh tissue by methylene blue are commonly employed to reveal them. Even with these special technics it is difficult to establish definitely how and where the fibers end. It is relatively easy to see that they form networks between muscle or gland cells. But it is not easy with the light microscope to determine whether the terminal fibers actually possess free endings and whether these, when the technics reveal them, end outside or inside muscle or gland cells. Recent work with the EM has disclosed nerve endings on smooth muscle cells somewhat similar to the motor end plates on striated muscle fibers (see Fig. 20-23).

### Chemical Factors Involved in the Mediation of the Nervous Impulse

A nervous impulse arriving at nerve endings in either muscle fibers or gland cells evokes a response. The mechanisms involved will be considered only briefly since this matter is dealt with in detail by the physiologist.

As will be explained later, the cells of the inner portions of the adrenal glands manufacture two hormones called *epinephrine* and *norepinephrine,* respectively. An injection of only a very small amount of either hormone into a person or an experimental animal produces a great many effects. In general, these are almost identical with those that are obtained when the sympathetic division of the autonomic nervous system of that individual is stimulated.

In 1904, Elliott observed that injecting epinephrine into an animal would induce a response in gland or smooth muscle even though the sympathetic nerves supplying that particular gland or muscle had been severed. This was enough to make him wonder if the stimulation of a sympathetic nerve does not normally produce an effect in the muscle or the gland because the nerve endings in the muscle or the gland, on being stimulated by the arrival of a nervous impulse, locally produce epinephrine, which thereupon evokes a response. Cannon, in particular, made many later investigations on this matter, and Elliott's suspicions were found to be justified. It is now known that the substance formed at the endings of sympathetic nerves when the nerves were stimulated was not epinephrine but norepinephrine.

Beginning about 1914, evidence accumulated, largely through the work of Dale, that a substance responsible for bringing about a response in gland or muscle forms at the endings of the nerves of the parasympathetic system when these nerves are stimulated. This substance formed at the nerve endings of parasympathetic nerves is called *acetylcholine.*

Responses in the muscle and the glands innervated by the autonomic nervous system, then, are evoked by the production of norepinephrine or acetylcholine. These are the *chemical mediators* of the nervous impulse.

As studies in this field continued, it became apparent that some sympathetic endings make acetylcholine (for example, those ending in the sweat glands of the skin). Furthermore, it was found that the endings of preganglionic fibers of the sympathetic system make acetylcholine at the sites of their synaptic relation with postganglionic neurons in sympathetic ganglia, and that the formation of acetylcholine at these synapses by the preganglionic nerve endings is responsible for the postganglionic fibers becoming stimulated. Dale has suggested that sympathetic nerve fibers be classified as either *adrenergic* or *cholinergic* according to whether their nerve endings produce adrenal hormone or acetylcholine.

As studies continued in this field, it became established that chemical mediators of the nervous impulse were not confined to the autonomic nervous system, but that acetylcholine was released at motor end-plates in striated muscle (Fig. 20-23). Chemical mediators are also produced in synapses in the C.N.S. (Fig. 21-22). As matters now stand there is much

theorizing about different aspects of the matter, but the following working hypothesis seems to have been established on good grounds.

When a nervous impulse reaches an end-plate it causes a release of acetylcholine which previously was stored and inactive. From EM studies it seems very probable that the acetylcholine is stored in neurovesicles (Fig. 20-23) which are very abundant in this region. The active acetylcholine causes a change in the permeability of the membranes that separate the termination of the axon from the sole plasm of the muscle cell, and this permits potassium ions to pass from the muscle and the sodium ions into the muscle. The change in permeability of the membrane is accompanied by a change in electrical potential along the sarcolemma, and this, as was suggested in the previous chapter, may reach all interior parts of the fiber via the centrotubules (Fig. 20-15). The free acetylcholine that sets all the above machinery into motion is inactivated by the enzyme acetylcholinesterase in a matter of milliseconds, and the whole apparatus is then ready to respond to the arrival of another nervous impulse which probably causes the release and the activation of acetylcholine from certain others of the almost innumerable neurovesicles.

Much of the same sequence of events seems to occur at synapses in the C.N.S. The arrival of a nervous impulse at an end-foot probably liberates some chemical mediator from the neurovesicles in the end-foot (Fig. 21-22). This acts to change the permeability of the membranes separating the end-foot from the cell body on which it lies, and it is also associated with a change in the electrical potential of the membranes. As a result of these actions, a nervous impulse is set up in the neuron on which the end-foot abuts.

## REFERENCES

General References on Nervous Tissue

Ariens Kappers, C. U., Huber, G. C., and Crosby, E. C.: The Comparative Anatomy of the Nervous System of Vertebrates, Including Man, vols. 1 and 2, New York, Macmillan, 1936.
Hyden, H.: The neuron *in* Brachet, J., and Mirsky, A. E. (eds.): The Cell; Biochemistry, Physiology, Morphology, p. 213, New York, Acad. Press, 1960.

Penfield, W.: Cytology and Cellular Pathology of the Nervous System, vols. 1, 2 and 3, New York, Hoeber, 1932.

Symposium: The submicroscopic organization and function of nerve cells, Exp. Cell Res. (Suppl.) 5:644, 1958.

(*See also* textbooks on neuro-anatomy, neurophysiology and neurology.)

### Special References on the Central Nervous System

Altschul, Rudolf: Lipofuscin distribution in the basal ganglia, J. Comp. Neurol. 78:45, 1943.

Barr, M. L.: Axon reaction in motor neurons and its effect upon the end-bulbs of Held-Auerbach, Anat. Rec. 77:367, 1940.

————: The morphology of neuroglial nuclei in the cat, according to sex, Exp. Cell Res. 2: 288, 1951.

Barr, M. L., and Bertram, E. G.: The behaviour of nuclear structures during depletion and restoration of Nissl material in motor neurons, J. Anat. 85:171, 1951.

Barr, M. L., Bertram, L. F., and Lindsay, H. A.: The morphology of the nerve cell nucleus, according to sex, Anat. Rec. 107:283, 1950.

Barr, M. L., and Hamilton, J. D.: A quantitative study of certain morphological changes in motor neurons during axon reaction, J. Comp. Neurol. 89:93, 1948.

Bodian, D.: Further notes on the vertebrate synapse, J. Comp. Neurol. 73:323, 1940.

————: A note on the nodes of Ranvier in the central nervous system, J. Comp. Neurol. 94: 475, 1951.

————: The structure of the vertebrate synapse, J. Comp. Neurol. 68:117, 1937.

————: The generalized vertebrate neuron, Science 137:323, 1962.

Bunge, R. P., Bunge, M. B., and Ris, H.: Ultrastructural study of remyelination in an experimental lesion in adult cat spinal cord, J. Biophys. Biochem. Cytol. 10:67, 1961.

Cameron, G.: Secretory activity on the chorioid plexus in tissue culture, Anat. Rec. 117:115, 1953.

Costero, I., and Pomerat, C. M.: Cultivation of neurons from the adult human cerebral and cerebellar cortex, Am. J. Anat. 89:405, 1951.

Donaldson, H. H., and Davis, D. J.: A description of charts showing the areas of the cross sections of the human spinal cord at the level of each spinal nerve, J. Comp. Neurol. 8:19, 1903.

Elliott, H. C.: Studies on the motor cells of the spinal cord, Am. J. Anat. 70:95, 1942.

Golgi, C.: Sur la structure des cellules nerveuses (1), Arch. ital. biol. 30:60, 1898.

Gray, E. G.: Axo-somatic and axo-dendritic synapses of the cerebral cortex: an electron microscope study, J. Anat. 93:420, 1959.

Haggar, R. A., and Barr, M. L.: Quantitative data on the size of synaptic end-bulbs in the cat's spinal cord; with a note on the preparation of cell models, J. Comp. Neurol. 93:17, 1950.

Haguenau, F., and Bernhard, W.: Aspect de la substance de Nissl au microscope électronique, Exp. Cell Res. 4:496, 1953.

Hartman, J. F.: Electron microscopy of motor nerve cells following section of axones, Anat. Rec. 118:19, 1954.

————: An electron optical study of sections of central nervous system, J. Comp. Neurol. 99: 201, 1953.

Herrera, J. M.: Estudios sobre el problema de la genesis microglial: 1. La capacidad reaccional de la microglia en el encefalo post-mortem, Arch. méd. paname. 2:3, 1953.

Hess, A., and Young, J. Z.: Nodes of Ranvier in the central nervous system, J. Physiol. 108: 52P, 1949.

Hudson, A. J., and Smith, C. G.: The vascular pattern of the choroid plexus of the lateral ventricle, Anat. Rec. 112:43, 1952.

Hyden, H.: The neuron and its glia—a biochemical and functional unit, Endeavour 21:144, 1962.

Luse, S. A.: Electron microscopic observations of the central nervous system, J. Biophys. Biochem. Cytol. 2:531, 1956.

————: Formation of myelin in the central nervous system of mice and rats as studied with the electron microscope, J. Biophys. Biochem. Cytol. 2:777, 1956.

————: Fixation and embedding of mammalian brain and spinal cord for electron microscopy, J. Ultrastr. Res. 4:108, 1960.

————: The ultrastructure of normal and abnormal oligodendroglia, Anat. Rec. 138:461, 1960.

————: Electron microscopic observations of the central nervous system *in* Roberts, E. (ed.): Inhibitions of the Nervous System and Gamma-Aminobutyric Acid, p. 29, New York, Pergamon Press, 1960.

McCulloch, W. S.: The functional organization of the cerebral cortex, Physiol. Rev. 24:390, 1944.

Maxwell, D. S., and Pease, D. C.: Electron microscopy of the choroid plexus, Anat. Rec. 124:331, 1956.

Morrison, G. E., Jr., and Gibson, W. C.: The staining of synaptic terminals within the central nervous system by Rio-Hortega's double impregnation silver method, Science 117:1, 1953.

Ortiz-Picon, J. M.: The neuroglia of the sensory ganglia, Anat. Rec. *121*:513, 1955.

Palade, G. E., and Palay, S. L.: Electron microscope observations of interneuronal and neuromuscular synapses, Anat. Rec. *118*:335, 1954.

Palay, S. L.: Structure and function in the neuron *in* Korey, S. R., and Nurnberger, J. I. (eds.): Trends in Neurochemistry and Allied Fields, vol. 1, New York, Hoeber, 1955.

————: Synapses in the central nervous system, J. Biophys. Biochem. Cytol. (Suppl.) *2*:193, 1956.

Palay, S. L., and Palade, G. E.: The fine structure of neurons, J. Biophys. Biochem. Cytol. *1*:69, 1955.

Pease, D. C., and Baker, R. F.: Electron microscopy of nervous tissue, Anat. Rec. *110*:505, 1951.

Pease, D. C., and Schultz, R. L.: Electron microscopy of rat cranial meninges, Am. J. Anat. *102*:301, 1958.

Schultz, R. L., Maynard, E. A., and Pease, D. C.: Electron microscopy of neurons and neuroglia of cerebral cortex and corpus callosum, Am. J. Anat. *100*:369, 1957.

Smart, I., and Leblond, C. P.: Evidence for division and transformations of neuroglia cells in the mouse brain, as derived from radioautography after injection of thymidine-H[3], J. Comp. Neurol. *116*:349, 1961.

Van Breemen, V. L.: The structure of neuroglial cells as observed with the electron microscope, Anat. Rec. *118*:438, 1954.

Weed, L. H.: The cerebrospinal fluid, Physiol. Rev. *2*:171, 1922.

————: Certain anatomical and physiological aspects of the meninges and cerebrospinal fluid, Brain *58*:383, 1935.

————: Meninges and cerebrospinal fluid, J. Anat. *72*:181, 1938.

Wislocki, G. B.: The cytology of the cerebrospinal pathway *in* Cowdry's Special Cytology, ed. 2, p. 1485, New York, Hoeber, 1932.

Woollam, D. H. M., and Millen, J. W.: The perivascular spaces of the mammalian central nervous system and their relation to the perineuronal and subarachnoid spaces, J. Anat. *89*: 193, 1955.

SPECIAL REFERENCES ON THE PERIPHERAL
NERVOUS SYSTEM

Causey, G., and Hoffman, H.: The relation between the Schwann cell and the axon in peripheral nerves, J. Anat. *90*:1, 1956.

Droz, B., and Leblond, C. P.: Axonal migration of proteins in the central nervous system and peripheral nerves as shown by radioautography, J. Comp. Neurol. *121*:325, 1963.

Fernand, V. S. V., and Young, J. Z.: The sizes of the nerve fibres of muscle nerves, Proc. Roy. Soc., London, B *139*:38, 1951.

Fernandez-Morán, H.: Observations on the structure of submicroscopic nerve fibers, Exp. Cell Res. *4*:480, 1953.

Fernandez-Morán, H., and Finean, J. B.: Electron microscope and low-angle x-ray defraction studies of the nerve myelin sheath, J. Biophys. Biochem. Cytol. *3*:725, 1957.

Finean, J. B., Sjöstrand, F. S., and Steinmann, E.: Submicroscopic organization of some layered lipoprotein structures (nerve myelin, retinal rods and chloroplasts), Exp. Cell Res. *5*:557, 1953.

Geren, B. B., and Raskind, J.: Development of the fine structure of the myelin sheath in sciatic nerves of chick embryos, Proc. Nat. Acad. Sc. *39*:880, 1953.

————: The formation from the Schwann cell surface of myelin in the peripheral nerves of chick embryos, Exp. Cell Res. *7*:558, 1954.

————: Structural studies of the formation of the myelin sheath in peripheral nerve fibers *in* Cellular Mechanisms in Differentiation and Growth, Princeton, N. J., Princeton Univ. Press, 1956.

Geren, B. B., and Schmitt, F. O.: Electron microscope studies of the Schwann cell and its constituents with particular reference to their relation to the axon *in* Fine Structure of Cells, p. 251, Groningen, Holland, Noordhoff, 1955.

————: The structure of the nerve sheath in relation to lipid and lipid-protein layers, J. Appl. Physics, *24*:1421, 1953.

————: The structure of the Schwann cell and its relation to the axon in certain invertebrate nerve fibers, Proc. Nat. Acad. Sc. *40*:863, 1954.

Hess, A.: The fine structure of young and old spinal ganglia, Anat. Rec. *123*:399, 1955.

Hess, A., and Lansing, A. I.: The fine structure of peripheral nerve fibers, Anat. Rec. *117*:175, 1953.

Lavarack, J. O., Sunderland, S., and Ray, L. J.: The branching of nerve fibers in human cutaneous nerves, J. Comb. Neurol. *94*:293, 1949.

Peterson, E. R., and Murray, M. R.: Myelin sheath formation in cultures of avian spinal ganglia, Am. J. Anat. *96*:319, 1955.

Pinner, B., Davison, J. F., and Campbell, J. B.: Alkaline phosphatase in peripheral nerves, Science *145*:936, 1964.

Robertson, J. D.: The unit membrane of cells and mechanism of myelin formation *in* Ultrastructure and Metabolism of the Nervous System, p. 94, Proc. Assoc. for Research in Nervous and Mental Disease, Baltimore, Williams & Wilkins, 1962.

———: The Molecular Biology of Cell Membranes *in* Nachmansohn, D. (ed.): Molecular Biology, New York, Acad. Press, 1960.

Shanklin, W. M., and Azzam, N. A.: Histological and histochemical studies on the incisures of Schmidt-Lanterman, J. Comp. Neurol. *123*:5, 1964.

Simpson, F. O., and Oertelis, J. J.: The fine structure of sheep myocardial cells; sarcolemmal invaginations and the transverse tubular system, J. Cell Biol. *12*:91, 1962.

Speidel, C. C.: Adjustments of nerve endings, Harvey Lect. *18*:625, 1942.

Usman, B. G., and Nogueira-Graf, G.: Electron microscope studies of the formation of nodes of Ranvier in mouse sciatic nerves, J. Biophys. Biochem. Cytol. *3*:589, 1957.

SPECIAL REFERENCES ON NERVE
REGENERATION

Aitken, J. T.: Growth of nerve implants in voluntary muscle, J. Anat. *84*:38, 1950.

Aitken, J. T., Sharman, M., and Young, J. Z.: Maturation of regenerating nerve fibers with various peripheral connexions, J. Anat. *81*:1, 1947.

Bacsich, P., and Wyburn, G. M.: The effect of interference with the blood supply on the regeneration of peripheral nerves, J. Anat. *79*:74, 1945.

Bensley, S. H.: Cytological studies of the reaction of myelinated nerve fibers to section of the nerve, Anat. Rec. *90*:1, 1944.

Bueker, D., and Meyers, E.: The maturity of peripheral nerves at the time of injury as a factor in nerve regeneration, Anat. Rec. *109*:723, 1951.

Clark, E. R., and Clark, E. L.: Microscopic studies on regeneration of medullated nerves in living mammal, Am. J. Anat. *81*:233, 1947.

Guth, L.: Regeneration in the mammalian peripheral nervous system, Physiol. Rev. *36*:441, 1956.

Gutmann, E., and Guttmann, L.: Factors affecting recovery of sensory function after nerve lesions, J. Neurol. Psychiat. *5*:117, 1942.

Gutmann, E., Guttmann, L., Medawar, P. B., and Young, J. Z.: The rate of regeneration of nerve, J. Exp. Biol. *19*:14, 1942.

Gutmann, E., and Sanders, F. K.: Functional recovery following nerve grafts and other types of nerve bridge, Brain *65*:373, 1942.

———: Recovery of fibre numbers and diameters in the regeneration of peripheral nerves, J. Physiol. *101*:489, 1943.

Highet, W. B., and Sanders, F. K.: The effects of stretching nerves after suture, Brit. J. Surg. *30*:355, 1943.

Holmes, W., and Young, J. Z.: Nerve regeneration after immediate and delayed suture, J. Anat. *77*:63, 1942.

Ramon y Cajal, S.: Degeneration and Regeneration of the Nervous System, London, Oxford, 1928.

Sanders, F. K.: The repair of large gaps in the peripheral nerves, Brain *65*:281, 1942.

Sanders, F. K., and Young, J. Z.: The degeneration and re-innervation of grafted nerves, J. Anat. *76*:143, 1941.

Seddon, H. J.: Three types of nerve injury, Brain *66*:237, 1943.

———: War injuries of peripheral nerves, Brit. J. Surg. (War Surg., Supp. No. 2), p. 325, 1948.

Seddon, H. J., Medawar, P. B., and Smith, H.: Rate of regeneration of peripheral nerves in man, J. Physiol. *102*:191, 1943.

Sunderland, S.: The capacity of regenerating axons to bridge long gaps in nerves, J. Comp. Neurol. *99*:481, 1953.

———: Capacity of reinnervated muscles to function efficiently after prolonged denervation, Arch. Neurol. Psychiat. *64*:755, 1950.

———: A classification of peripheral nerve injuries producing loss of function, Brain *74*:491, 1951.

———: Factors influencing the course of regeneration and the quality of the recovery after nerve suture, Brain *75*:19, 1952.

———: Rate of regeneration in human peripheral nerves, Arch. Neurol. Psychiat. *58*:251, 1947.

———: Regeneration phenomena in human peripheral nerves *in* Weiss, P. (ed.): Genetic Neurology, p. 105, Chicago, Univ. Chicago Press, 1950.

Windle, W. F.: Regeneration of axons in the vertebrate central nervous system, Physiol. Rev. *36*:427, 1956.

Young, J. Z.: The effect of delay on the success of nerve suture, Proc. Roy. Soc. Med. *37*:551, 1944.

———: Effects of use and disuse on nerve and muscle, Lancet *2*:109, 1946.

———: Factors influencing the regeneration of nerves, Advances Surg. *1*:165, 1949.

———: The functional repair of nervous tissue, Physiol. Rev. *22*:318, 1942.

———: Histology of peripheral nerve injuries *in* Cope, Z. (ed.): Medical History of the Second World War: Surgery, p. 534, London, Her Majesty's Stat. Off., 1953.

———: Structure, degeneration and repair of nerve fibers, Nature *156*:132, 1945.

Young, J. Z., Holmes, W., and Sanders, F. K.: Nerve regeneration—importance of the peripheral stump and the value of nerve grafts, Lancet 2:128, 1940.

## SPECIAL REFERENCES ON THE BLOOD SUPPLY OF NERVES

Adams, W. E.: The blood supply of nerves, J. Anat. 76:323, 1942.

Sunderland, S.: Blood supply of the nerves of the upper limb in man, Arch. Neurol. Psychiat. 53:91, 1945.

————: Blood supply of peripheral nerves, Arch. Neurol. Psychiat. 54:280, 1945.

————: Blood supply of the sciatic nerve and its popliteal divisions in man, Arch. Neurol. Psychiat. 54:283, 1945.

## GENERAL REFERENCES ON THE AUTONOMIC NERVOUS SYSTEM

Cannon, W. B.: Bodily Changes in Pain, Hunger, Fear and Rage, New York, Appleton, 1920.

————: The Wisdom of the Body, ed. 2, New York, Norton, 1939.

Cannon, Walter B., and Rosenblueth, Arturo: Autonomic Neuro-Effector Systems, New York, Macmillan, 1937.

Kuntz, Albert: The Autonomic Nervous System, ed. 4, Philadelphia, Lea & Febiger, 1953.

Pavlov, I. P.: Conditioned Reflexes, London, Oxford, 1927.

White, J. C.: The Autonomic Nervous System, ed. 3, New York, Macmillan, 1952.

## SPECIAL REFERENCES ON THE AUTONOMIC NERVOUS SYSTEM

Boeke, J.: Some observations on the structure and the innervation of smooth muscle fibers, J. Comp. Neurol. 56:27, 1932.

————: The sympathetic endformation, its synaptology, the interstitial cells, the periterminal network, and its bearing on the neurone theory; discussion and critique, Acta anat. 8:18, 1949.

Dale, H. H.: The transmission of nervous effects by acetylcholine, Harvey Lect. 32:229, 1936-1937.

Elfvin, L. G.: Electron microscopic investigation of the plasma membrane and myelin sheath of autonomic nerve fibers in the cat. J. Ultrastr. Res. 5:388, 1961.

————: The ultrastructure of the nodes of Ranvier in cat sympathetic nerve fibers. J. Ultrastr. Res. 5:374, 1961.

Hard, W. L., Peterson, A. C., and Fox, M. D.: Histochemical and quantitative studies on choline esterase distribution in cervical sympathetic ganglia, J. Neuropath. & Exper. Neurol. 10:48, 1951.

Rosenblueth, A.: The transmission of sympathetic nerve impulses, Physiol. Rev. 17:514, 1937.

# PART FOUR

# The Histology of the Systems

# 22    The Circulatory System

When many different parts of the body collaborate with one another to carry out some specific function they are said to constitute a system. For example, the various tubes and hollow structures concerned in circulating the blood throughout the body are said to constitute the circulatory system. In the following chapters we shall deal briefly with the functions of those systems that lie within the scope of general histology and consider how the histologic structure of their different parts is related to the function of these parts and to the function of the system as a whole.

Certain parts of some systems are called *organs* (*organum* = instrument). However, not all the parts of each system are thus honored. Although there is no fixed rule about the matter, the term organ usually is reserved for the more impressive parts of a system in which some important function is segregated.

In discussing the microscopic structure of organs the terms stroma and parenchyma are commonly employed. *Stroma* (*stroma* = a mattress) refers to the supporting tissue in an organ and *parenchyma* (*parencheo* = I pour in, as into a mold) to the cells of the organ that perform the specific function of the organ. Many organs are glands; in these, epithelium constitutes the parenchyma, and connective tissue, the stroma.

**General Function.** In Chapter 10 it was explained that most of the cells of the body live in tissue fluid from which they obtain oxygen and food and into which they excrete their waste products. If there were no mechanism for constantly changing or freshening the tissue fluid of the body it would soon become depleted of food and oxygen and saturated with waste products. In most sites in the body the tissue fluid is kept fresh, not so much because it is changed rapidly, but because the substances dissolved in it always tend to come into equilibrium with those dissolved in the blood contained in the capillaries. The blood in the capillaries in any given part of the body supplied by the systemic circulation is

always fresh because it is changed continuously. In these capillaries, blood that has recently passed through the lungs, where it has become charged with oxygen and rid of carbon dioxide, is continuously substituted for that which has lost oxygen to, and gained carbon dioxide from, the tissue fluid of the part. Moreover, in making the rounds of the circulatory system, a certain amount of blood is diverted through the kidneys, where waste products other than carbon dioxide are eliminated; this keeps the concentration of these waste products in the blood of the circulatory system as a whole at a low level. Likewise, part of the blood of the body passes through the intestine, where food can be absorbed. This food, because the blood circulates, is supplied to the tissue fluid of all parts of the body to replace that used by the cells it bathes. The chief function of the circulatory system, then, is to maintain the quantity and the quality of the tissue fluid in all parts of the body.

## SOME MECHANICAL PROBLEMS INHERENT IN A CIRCULATORY SYSTEM

**Heart and Arteries.** The continuous circulation of a fluid in a closed circuit of tubes requires that a pump be inserted somewhere in the circuit. Indeed, since the circulatory system of the human body consists of two circuits, the pulmonary and the systemic, joined together in series, two pumps are required, one for each. The heart is a double pump; its right side circulates blood through the pulmonary circulation, and its left side through the systemic circulation. Although each of these pumps is different from the ordinary pump that the student has studied in his course in physics, such as is illustrated in Figure 22-1, each acts like the one-cylinder pump in the illustration because it delivers fluid in spurts and under considerable pressure. The tubes into which blood is delivered

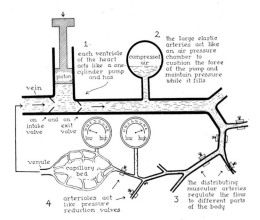

FIG. 22-1. Diagram illustrating the mechanical functions that must be performed by the different parts of the circulatory system. Begin at the upper left and proceed clockwise.

from the heart are called *arteries,* and their walls must be strong in order to withstand the pressure that is generated in the heart and transmitted into them. Arteries deliver blood from the heart to the capillary beds of the body. Several problems arise in this connection. It is desirable for blood to flow evenly through capillary beds and not in spurts. This is a problem similar to that of a householder who has a one-cylinder pump connected to a well and wishes water delivered from his kitchen tap evenly instead of in spurts. He can achieve his wish by placing an air chamber on the pipe leading from the pump, as is shown in Figure 22-1, 2. This cushions the force of the pumping stroke, and, in addition, the air in the chamber, compressed by the pumping stroke, maintains the pressure in the circuit as a whole during the filling stroke of the pump. The same effect is accomplished in the human body by having the arteries that lead directly from the heart constructed chiefly of elastic tissue. These are termed *elastic* arteries. Blood delivered into them by the contracting heart both widens and lengthens them and thereby stretches the elastic tissue of their walls. Then, after the heart has finished contracting, its exhaust valves close, and the stretched walls of the elastic arteries passively contract to maintain pressure within the system for the short interval that elapses before the heart fills and contracts again.

**Systolic and Diastolic Blood Pressure.** The pressure within the arterial system, generated during the contraction of the heart, is called the *systolic* (*systole* = a contracting) blood pressure, and it is slightly more than half as much again as the pressure which is maintained by the stretched elastic tissue of the arterial walls between the contractions of the heart; the latter is called the *diastolic* (*diastole* = dilatation) pressure.

It should be emphasized that the function of maintaining the pressure within the arterial system during diastole is performed chiefly by the largest arteries of the body; hence, these are the only ones that have walls consisting chiefly of elastin. The branches that arise from the largest arteries to deliver blood to the different parts of the body have a function different from that of the elastic arteries, and for this reason they have walls of a different character. Since different parts of the body, under different conditions of activity, require different amounts of blood, the arteries that supply them must be capable of having the size of their lumens regulated so that different amounts of blood can be delivered at different times. For example, the muscles in the right arm of a right-handed tennis player require more blood during a match than those of his left arm. For the size of these *distributing* arteries to be regulated by nervous control requires that their walls be made mostly of circularly disposed smooth muscle fibers (which are living and can respond to nervous stimuli) rather than of elastin (which is nonliving and can only contract passively), and, for this reason, distributing arteries are also called *muscular* arteries. The distributing arteries, then, variously regulate the flow of blood to different parts of the body according to the needs of these parts. In this way, they function like the valves on the pipes illustrated in Figure 22-1, 3.

Still other mechanical problems inherent in a circulatory system must be considered. A substantial pressure must be maintained within the system, otherwise blood would not be delivered in sufficient quantities to the various capillary beds of the body, particularly those of the brain, the supplying of which requires overcoming the force of gravity. However, the maintenance of a relatively high pressure within the arterial system must be accomplished in such a way that blood is delivered into capillary beds under greatly reduced pressure because the walls of capillaries must necessarily be thin (and therefore weak) to permit ready diffusion through them. A high pressure within the arterial system, and the delivery of blood into capillary beds under relatively low pressure, could be accomplished in a mechanical model by inserting pressure reduction valves between the ends of arteries and the capillary beds, as is shown in Figure 22-1, 4. The same effect is achieved in the human body by *arterioles*. These, as their name implies, are very small arteries, but they are of a special construction, having relatively narrow lumens and thick muscular walls. Since blood is of a certain viscosity, their narrow lumens offer considerable resistance to its flow, and this permits relatively high pressures to be built up behind them. The degree of pressure within the arterial system as a whole is regulated mainly by the degree of tonus of the smooth muscle cells in the walls of arterioles. If this becomes increased, hypertension (high blood pressure) results.

**Capillaries.** The formation and the absorption of tissue fluid by capillaries is considered at length in Chapter 10.

**Veins.** Capillaries empty into small veins (venules) which join with others to form larger veins, and so on. The blood from all the veins in the systemic circulation eventually drains into either the superior or the inferior vena cava and so into the right heart.

Blood enters venules from capillaries under a very low pressure. Indeed, the pressure in veins is so low that they do not require very thick walls. But, since the blood in them is under very low pressure, it travels relatively slowly. For this reason, veins require lumens much larger than those of arteries. Hence, in cross section, a vein always has a thinner wall and a larger lumen than its arterial counterpart (Fig. 22-7).

The pressure in veins draining dependent parts of the body overcomes the force of gravity only with difficulty. To assist, most of these veins are provided with valves to prevent backflow. Valves also have other functions, which will be discussed presently. Since there is no need for veins to cushion the contraction of the ventricle, there are no venous counter-parts of elastic arteries. And, since there is no need for a strong mechanism for narrowing their lumens against the force of arterial pressure, as is necessary in distributing arteries, there is no need for much smooth muscle in their walls. Collagen, then, is used more extensively in the walls of veins than in arteries.

Having considered some of the mechanical problems inherent in a circulatory system, we shall discuss the histologic features of its different parts in some detail.

## THE MICROSCOPIC STRUCTURE OF ARTERIES

**Introduction.** The student should be particularly interested in arteries, for, in all probability, more of his future patients will die from arterial disease than from any other single cause. Arterial disease is the great enemy of those who pass middle life. The tissues of the body begin to deteriorate shortly after a man has reached the age of 40. Of all the tissues of the body, those that make up the walls of arteries commonly deteriorate the soonest.

**The Problem of Nourishing Cells in the Walls of Arteries.** Why should the tissues of the walls of arteries be the first to be so affected? There is some reason for this. The walls of arteries live, as it were, under constant tension; only death relieves them from having to withstand continually the pressure within the arterial system. This may assist in causing their relatively early deterioration. But it is probably not so important a factor as the fact that the arterial wall, stretched by pressure from within the artery, presents unique problems with regard to its nutrition.

The usual arrangement in the body for permitting any considerable mass of tissue to be supplied abundantly with oxygen and nourishment is to have it permeated with capillaries. Ordinarily, capillaries are supplied with blood under relatively low pressure. If low-pressure capillary beds were present in the walls of arteries, it could be expected that they would be collapsed because the pressure transmitted into the wall of the artery from its lumen would be much greater than that in the capillaries. In any event, low-pressure capillaries are not present in the walls of arteries except in their outer layers; here they can remain

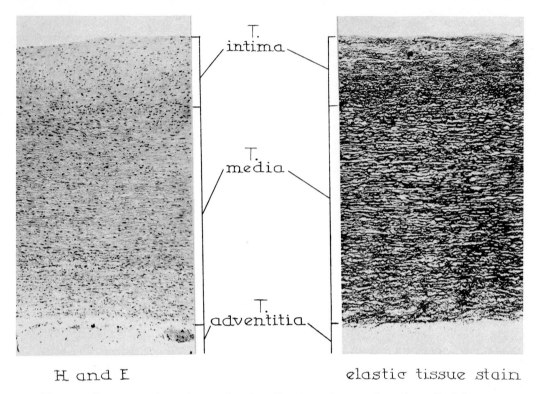

T. intima

T. media

T. adventitia

H and E                                                    elastic tissue stain

FIG. 22-2. Low-power photomicrographs of 2 adjacent sections cut from the wall of the aorta; the elastic fibers and the laminae are stained specifically in the section on the right.

open because the force of the pressure of the blood in the lumen of the artery is taken up by the inner and the middle layers of the artery walls. Lacking capillaries, cells in the inner and the greater part of the middle layers of the walls of arteries must be nourished by diffusion from (1) blood in the lumen and (2) blood in the capillaries in the outer part of the wall. Therefore, the situation in the inner layers of the wall is not unlike that which exists in hyalin cartilage where diffusion must occur over relatively long distances. It will be recalled that precipitation of materials in the gelled intercellular substance of cartilage can interfere with the nutrition of its cells. It could be visualized that the deposition or accumulation of substances in artery walls likewise could interfere with the diffusion mechanism on which they are dependent and hence with the health of such cells as live in those layers of the wall.

The pressure within lymphatic capillaries is even less than that within blood capillaries; hence, patent lymphatic capillaries could not

be expected to be present in those layers of the walls of arteries that bear the brunt of arterial pressure. It will be recalled that lymphatic capillaries, in addition to draining off that part of the tissue fluid that is not returned to blood capillaries, are responsible for keeping the tissue fluid free from the colloids that normally escape from blood capillaries to some extent in healthy, and more abundantly in damaged, tissue. It could be anticipated, then, that the tissue of arterial walls might not be able to rid itself of such colloidal materials as might gain entrance to, or be set free in, it as readily as the tissues in most parts of the body.

From the foregoing it might be expected that degeneration and necrosis might occur more readily in the tissues of arterial walls than in most sites in the body and, further, that arterial walls might be more likely to become the sites of accumulations of colloidal material of various sorts than the tissues of those parts of the body that have lymphatic capillaries to drain colloids away. Indeed, de-

generation of, and accumulations in, the walls
of arteries are two prominent features of what
is termed *arteriosclerosis*, the general term employed to designate the condition in which
arterial walls are variously deteriorated.

**Coats of the Walls of Arteries.** The walls
of arteries generally are described as consisting
of 3 coats or layers. The innermost is termed
the *tunica intima;* the middle one, the *tunica
media,* and the outermost one the *tunica adventitia.* The tunica media is the thickest of
the 3. The structure of these 3 coats in elastic
and distributing arteries and in arterioles will
now be considered.

ELASTIC ARTERIES. The aorta and the innominate, the subclavian, the common carotid
and the pulmonary arteries are grouped in this
class. Since the aorta is the usual representative of the type studied by students, we shall
consider the histologic structure of its wall in
some detail.

*Tunica Intima.* The intima constitutes about
one sixth of the thickness of the wall (Fig.
22-2). It is lined by a pavement of endothelial
cells. The cytoplasm of these cannot be seen
to advantage in sections, but their nuclei are
apparent (Fig. 22-2, *left*). The endothelium
rests on the "subendothelial layer" of the intima. This constitutes one fourth to one fifth
of its total thickness and consists of fairly
delicate elastic fibers that are disposed longitudinally and are immersed, along with some
collagenic fibers, in amorphous intercellular
substances (Fig. 22-2, *right*). The nuclei of a
few cells may be seen in this layer (Fig. 22-2,
*left*). They are mostly the pale-staining nuclei
of fibroblasts, but the nuclei of macrophages
also may be seen. The remainder of the intima
is termed its *deep* or *external layer.* It consists
of somewhat coarser elastic fibers embedded
with collagenic fibers in an amorphous intercellular substance (Fig. 22-2, *right*). It has
more cells than the subendothelial layer.
Where it abuts on the tunica media its elastic
fibers are condensed to form a thick, fenestrated plate of elastic tissue (*fenestra* = window), called the *internal elastic lamina.* This
is similar to the elastic laminae of the media
and will be described presently.

*Tunica Media.* This coat constitutes the
bulk of the wall and consists chiefly of concentrically arranged fenestrated laminae of
elastic tissue similar to the internal elastic

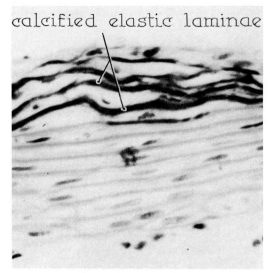

FIG. 22-3. High-power photomicrograph
of a section of the wall of the aorta of a
rat. The 4 inner elastic laminae are calcified as a consequence, they stain a deep
blue with hematoxylin. Calcification of the
elastic laminae of arteries is an indication
of one kind of arteriosclerosis.

lamina of the intima. They appear as dark
lines in Figure 22-2, *right,* and as lighter ones
in Figure 22-2, *left.* The number of these varies
with age. There are around 40 in the newborn
and up to 70 in the adult. The laminae become
thicker in adulthood than they are in childhood. Although they contain no mineral (Fig.
4-4), in the young aorta they show a disposition to become calcified in certain types of
arteriosclerosis (Fig. 22-3). Collagenic fibers,
delicate elastic fibers and amorphous intercellular substance, probably of the sulfated mucopolysaccharide type, together with fibroblasts and smooth muscle fibers, fill the spaces
between adjacent laminae. That the fibroblasts
found here make more amorphous intercellular
substance than those of ordinary connective
tissue suggests that they have some of the
properties of chondrocytes. This suggestion
is supported by the fact that, under certain
pathologic conditions, they sometimes form
cartilage, or even bone, in these sites. The
outermost lamina of the tunica media is termed
the *external elastic lamina.*

*Tunica Adventitia.* This is thin in elastic
arteries. It consists of irregularly arranged

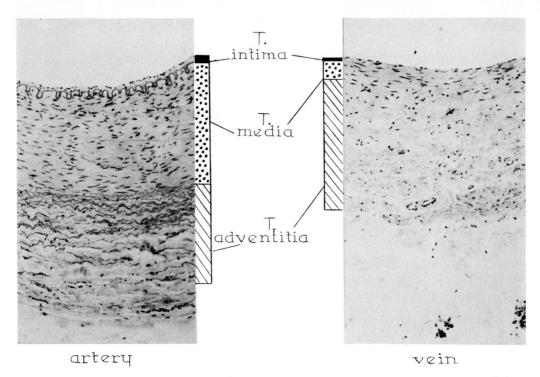

artery

vein

FIG. 22-4. (*Left*) A medium-power photomicrograph of a cross section of the wall of a distributing artery. (*Right*) A photomicrograph, taken at the same magnification, of a cross section of the wall of one of its two companion veins. Note the great disparity between the thickness of the media of the artery and the vein.

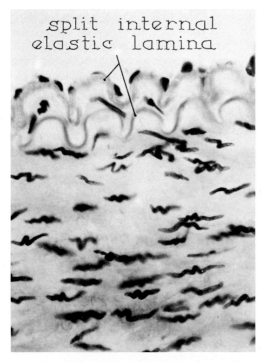

FIG. 22-5. High-power photomicrograph of a cross section of the wall of a distributing artery, showing a split internal elastic lamina.

connective tissue which contains both collagenic and elastic fibers. Small blood vessels are present in it, and in suitable sections these may be followed into the outer parts of the tunica media. They are called the *vasa vasorum* (vessels of the vessels). They tend to become affected in the later stages of syphilis; hence, in this disease, parts of the adventitia and the tunica media may be denied a proper blood supply and so undergo necrosis.

DISTRIBUTING ARTERIES. Most arteries are of this type.

*Tunica Intima.* This is relatively thin. Its most prominent feature is a well-developed internal elastic lamina (Fig. 22-4, *left*). This consists of a single thick layer of elastic fibers (in the larger distributing arteries it forms a fenestrated plate) in youth, but it often splits into 2 layers in late adulthood (Fig. 22-5). It presents a wavy appearance in sections (Fig. 22-4, *left*), but it is not wavy in life, when it is stretched by the pressure within the vessel. Between the internal elastic lamina and the endothelium there is a very delicate layer of connective tissue.

*Tunica Media.* This is a fairly thick coat and consists chiefly of circularly disposed

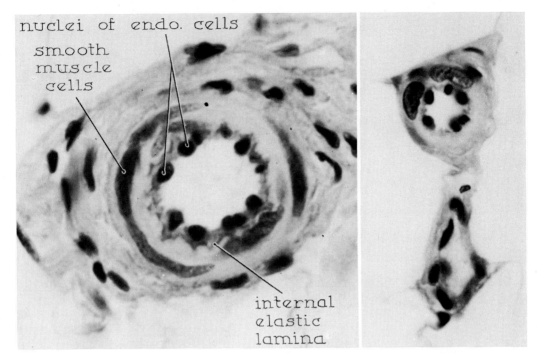

FIG. 22-6. (*Left*) A high-power photomicrograph of a cross section of an arteriole of moderate size. (*Upper right*) A photomicrograph of a cross section of a small arteriole. Its companion venule shows below.

smooth muscle fibers held together to form a cohesive whole by reticular, collagenic and delicate elastic fibers (Figs. 22-4, *left*, and 22-7, *left*). The proportion of intercellular substance in relation to smooth muscle varies with the size of the vessel; hence, the media of a small vessel is mostly smooth muscle.

*Tunica Adventitia.* The thickness of this layer varies in distributing arteries but usually it is from one half to two thirds the thickness of the media (Fig. 22-4, *left*). It consists chiefly of elastic fibers but it also contains collagenic ones. The elastic fibers of the adventitia are condensed to form a noticeable external elastic lamina that is applied to, and continuous with, the outer border of the media. Vasa vasorum are present in the adventitia, particularly in the larger arteries.

**Arterioles.** Arteries with an over-all diameter of 100 μ or less generally are called *arterioles*, but some authors class considerably larger vessels as arterioles also. Cowdry has pointed out that the over-all diameter is not as important a criterion in determining whether any given vessel is an arteriole as is the thickness of the wall of the vessel in relation to its

lumen. Kernohan, Anderson and Keith measured this relationship in a large number of arterioles in muscle tissue obtained both from normal people and from those suffering from hypertension (high blood pressure). They found that in the arterioles of normal people the ratio of the thickness of the wall of the vessel to the diameter of its lumen was 1:2, with variations from 1:1.7 to 1:2.7. They found that in hypertension the arterioles had thicker walls in relation to their lumens.

The walls of the larger arterioles have 3 coats (Fig. 22-6, *left*). The intima consists of endothelium applied directly, or with a trace of intervening connective tissue, to an internal elastic lamina. The media consists of circularly arranged smooth muscle fibers. In the larger arterioles some intimation of an external elastic lamina is present (Fig. 22-6, *left*). The adventitia may be as thick as the media, and it consists of a mixture of collagenic and elastic fibers.

As arterioles branch and become smaller, their walls become thinner, and their lumens smaller. The internal elastic lamina becomes very thin in the smaller arterioles (Fig. 22-6,

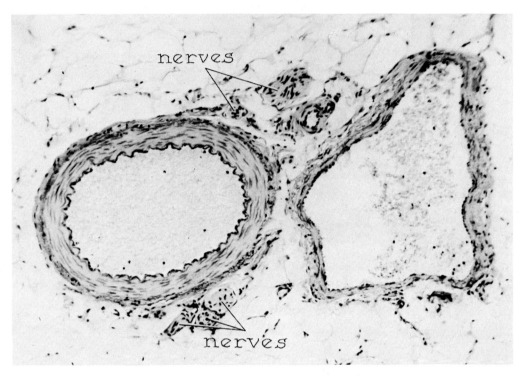

FIG. 22-7. Medium-power photomicrograph of a cross section of a distributing artery and its companion vein. Small nerves, cut in cross section, may be seen closely associated with the adventitia. Notice that the vein has a thinner wall and a larger lumen than the artery.

*right*), and in the smallest it is absent. The smooth muscle cells of the media of a small arteriole are correspondingly small; if they were of usual length they would overlap each other in encircling the lumen (compare those on the left and the right sides of Fig. 22-6). In the smallest arterioles one or two smooth muscle cells constitute the media that is seen in a cross section (Fig. 22-6, *right*). The adventitia of small arterioles consists chiefly of collagenic fibers, and in the very small ones it is greatly reduced in amount.

A very small arteriole, with a lumen not much larger than a red blood cell and a wall consisting of only a layer of smooth muscle surrounded by a little connective tissue, is termed a *precapillary arteriole*.

## NERVOUS CONTROL OF ARTERIES AND ARTERIAL PRESSURE

There are two problems to consider here: (1) the mechanism that regulates the flow of blood to different parts of the body according to their needs and (2) the control of the pressure within the system as a whole. We shall now discuss briefly these rather complex and somewhat interrelated problems in the order mentioned.

**1. Regulation of Flow to Different Parts According to Different Needs.** If cross sections of distributing arteries or arterioles are examined, bundles of, or even single, nerve fibers, cut either in cross section or obliquely, are seen in the adventitia (Fig. 22-7). Both nonmyelinated efferent fibers and myelinated afferent fibers are present in these. The efferent fibers in the nerves of most arteries are mostly sympathetic. Some, but probably not all, arteries have parasympathetic innervation as well. The nonmyelinated fibers end in association with the smooth muscle cells of the media. The myelinated afferent fibers end in special sensory endings in the adventitia. The student will not be able to see the endings of these fibers unless special preparations are used.

VASOCONSTRICTOR NERVES. Most sympathetic fibers act to increase the tone of the smooth muscle of the arteries concerned and hence are vasoconstrictor in type. However, some sympathetic fibers are of the vasodilator type. Some years ago it was believed that the sympathetic fibers of the smaller arteries and arterioles reached their destination by traveling along the main distributing arteries and then along their branches. Accordingly, surgical attempts were made to relieve those unfortunate individuals who suffer from painful or otherwise harmful constrictions of the blood vessels of their extremities by stripping the adventitia off short segments of the main distributing arteries leading to the parts concerned. The operation is known as a "periarterial sympathectomy." However, it did not generally prove to have a permanent effect. Woollard has since shown that the sympathetic fibers in the adventitia of the main distributing arteries do not extend to the peripheral branches of the arteries. He found the latter to be innervated chiefly by sympathetic fibers derived from the peripheral nerves that travel to the part. Woollard's work provides an anatomic basis for explaining why the periarterial sympathectomy operation performed on main distributing arteries so often failed to relieve arteriolar spasm in the extremity supplied by the artery.

MECHANISMS OF VASODILATATION. Since it has not been established that all arteries are innervated by parasympathetic vasodilator fibers, and since the great majority of sympathetic fibers in the vessels of man are vasoconstrictors (the arteries supplying muscles have more sympathetic vasodilator fibers than most), the problem of how vasodilatation is obtained when it is necessary or desirable is somewhat complex.

Two mechanisms which do not depend on the presence of vasodilator fibers may be involved in bringing about vasodilatation. Before considering the first of these, it should be recalled that in the medulla of the brain there is a vasoconstrictor center which controls the impulses that pass out along the sympathetic nerves to the musculature of the arteries. Afferent impulses arising as a result of the stimulation of the afferent nerve endings in the adventitia of vessels, or in other sites, could, on being conducted into and up the cord to the vasoconstrictor center, inhibit it. Inhibition of the center would be reflected in diminished tone in the smooth muscle of the vessels innervated by it.

Secondly, the afferent fibers in the adventitia of peripheral vessels are branches of fibers from which other branches go to other sites, for example, to the skin. Therefore, there is a possibility that impulses arising from the stimulation of endings in sites such as skin might travel along the fiber until they reach the bifurcation at which the arterial branch of the fiber originates. Here they might be reflected back along the sensory fiber of the vessel antidromically (against the usual direction of the current of impulses) to reach the endings in the vessel wall and there, perhaps through chemical mediation, inhibit the encircling smooth muscle cells of the vessel. Such a reflex occurring within 2 branches of a single nerve fiber is called an *axon reflex*.

Some authors believe that impulses may reach the afferent endings in arteries antidromically from the cord to bring about vasodilatation.

2. **Nervous Control of the Pressure in the Arterial System as a Whole.** Under normal conditions, variations in the arterial pressure are due chiefly to variations in (1) the degree to which arterioles are contracted and (2) the output of blood by the heart. The innervation of arterioles has already been explained. The heart has both sympathetic and parasympathetic innervation, but the parasympathetic fibers exert the greater regulatory influence. They are derived from the vagus nerve and they act to depress heart action continuously. For example, if the vagus is paralyzed, the heart rate may double. It is obvious that if afferent impulses from any part of the body were directed to the centers in the brain that control the tonus of arterioles and the heart beat, they could, by reflex mechanisms, control arterial pressure within wide limits.

While it is probable that afferent impulses from many blood vessels, and from other sites, find their way to these centers and so affect blood pressure, there are a certain few sites in the vascular system where vessels are richly provided with nerve endings that are especially receptive to pressure changes. In other sites there are complex nerve endings sensitive to changes in the chemical composition of the blood. The *carotid sinus* and the *carotid body*

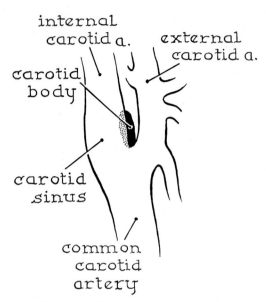

internal
carotid a.    external
carotid a.

carotid
body

carotid
sinus

common
carotid
artery

FIG. 22-8. Sketch of a carotid sinus and a carotid body.

serve as excellent examples of such structures, and we shall consider their structure.

**The Carotid Sinus and the Carotid Body.** The carotid sinus is the name given to a slight dilatation of one of the carotid arteries near the bifurcation of the common carotid artery. Usually the site of dilatation is the internal carotid artery immediately above its point of origin (Fig. 22-8). In the dilated part the tunica media of the vessel is relatively thin, and the tunica adventitia is relatively thick. Many nerve endings of afferent fibers from the carotid branch of the glossopharyngeal nerve are present in the adventitia. Since the media is thin at this site, the adventitia must bear more of the brunt of withstanding the pressure within the vessel than is usual in arteries; hence, the nerve endings within it are readily stimulated by pressure changes. Nerve impulses set up by pressure changes within the sinus are conducted over nerve networks to the centers in the brain that control the heart and the arteries.

Recently, Green and Boss and Green have demonstrated that, in addition to the carotid sinus, there are other areas along the common carotid artery of the cat that have *baroceptor* (*baros* = weight) activity. Boss and Green have studied the histology of these baroceptor areas and have found that basically it is simi-lar to that of the carotid sinus. In each area myelinated fibers ramify in the adventitia of the vessel in fibrillar arrangement. Furthermore, there are structural alterations in the arterial wall in each site in that there is generally less muscle and sometimes less elastin in the media, and the collagenic fibers of the adventitia are in the form of finer fibers than usual, and these are intricately interwoven.

The carotid body is a small condensation of tissue on the wall of the internal carotid artery (Fig. 22-8). It has a structure similar to that of an endocrine gland in that it consists of cords and clumps of epithelial-like cells and is abundantly provided with sinusoidal capillaries. The epithelial-like cells are richly supplied with nerve endings. These seem to be stimulated by changes in the concentration of carbon dioxide or oxygen tension in the blood. Nerve impulses arising from these endings, as a result of chemical changes in the blood, are also conducted to the centers in the brain that control the heart and the arteries.

Small structures similar to the carotid body are also present in the arch of the aorta, in the pulmonary artery and at the origin of the right subclavian artery. Delicate pressure receptors are also present in the walls of the great veins close to the heart.

## THE MICROSCOPIC STRUCTURE OF CAPILLARIES

To realize how capillary networks function, the student should examine living preparations, such as the web of the frog's foot, under the microscope, or at least see one of the motion pictures of capillary circulation. A visualization of capillary networks can also be gained from the study of thick, cleared sections of material in which the capillaries have been injected with a colored material (Fig. 20-20). Since capillaries are disposed in so many different planes in most tissues and since most of them pursue irregular courses, it is seldom that they are seen cut longitudinally in thin sections. Striated muscle is an exception, for in this tissue they parallel the muscle fibers; hence, longitudinal sections of striated muscle commonly reveal some capillaries cut in longitudinal section (Fig. 20-7). Contrariwise, the cross-section appearance of capillaries may be studied to great advantage in cross sections

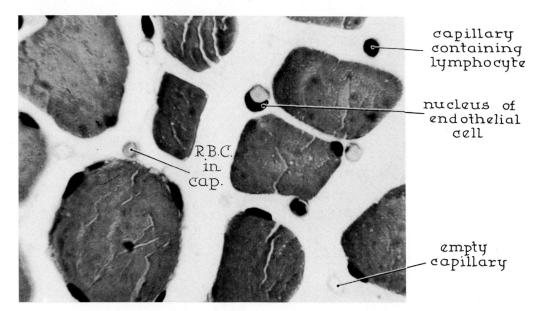

capillary
containing
lymphocyte

nucleus of
endothelial
cell

R.B.C.
in
cap.

empty
capillary

FIG. 22-9. Oil-immersion photomicrograph of a cross section of striated muscle, showing the various appearances presented by capillaries in cross section. In some instances the line of section passes through a capillary at a site where a nucleus of an endothelial cell is present; if so, the nucleus appears as a blue crescent, as may be seen above. If a capillary is cut at a site where no nucleus is present, it appears as a thin cytoplasmic ring. Either red blood cells or leukocytes may be present in capillaries at the sites where they are sectioned.

of striated muscle (Fig. 22-9). Such sections pass through most capillaries without passing through the nuclei of any of their endothelial cells; hence, these capillaries appear as cytoplasmic tubes (Fig. 22-9, *lower right*). However, in many instances, the nucleus of one of the endothelial cells making up a capillary wall will be cut, and, if so, it appears as a blue crescent partly encircling the lumen (Fig.22-9, *slightly above center*). In cross section, some capillaries are seen to contain red blood cells (Fig. 22-9, *left of center*) and some, leukocytes (Fig. 22-9, *upper right*).

**Similarities Between Capillaries and Venules.** Capillaries drain into an order of venules that differ from capillaries chiefly by being of a slightly greater diameter. Both capillaries and the venules into which they immediately drain probably serve in permitting fluid and cystalloids to diffuse through their walls. It seems probable, however, that venules permit leukocytes to pass through their walls (between endothelial cells) more readily than capillaries in sites of inflammation. Since true capillaries and venules have so much in common, it is convenient to discuss their fine

structure together and this will be done shortly after we have dealt briefly with the control of capillary circulation.

## CONTROL OF THE CAPILLARY CIRCULATION

The pink tinge to skin is due to blood in the capillaries and venules that lie below the epidermis. The fact that skin color changes under different emotional states (the white face of fear or the blush of embarrassment) proves that the flow of blood in the terminal vascular bed that lies beneath the epidermis must be under the control of the autonomic nervous system. Since the autonomic nervous system can regulate blood flow through vessels only by causing smooth muscle cells that surround blood vessels to contract or relax, there must be some place in the terminal bed where there are smooth muscle cells that surround vessels associated with the bed that can respond to nervous control (it is generally conceded that *endothelial lining cells* of capillaries or other vessels are not themselves contractile).

Years ago it was demonstrated that there

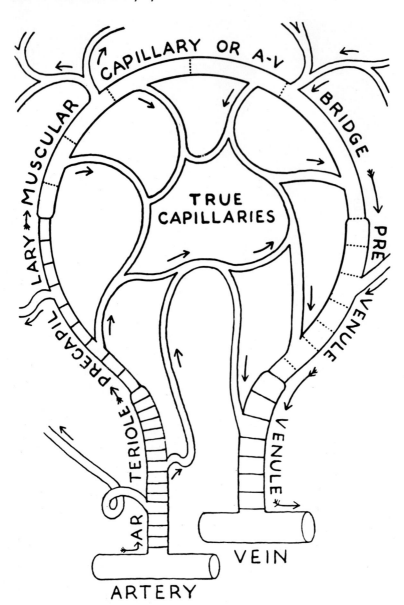

Fig. 22-10. Scheme showing the relationship between arterioles, muscular capillaries or A-V bridges, true capillaries and venules. (Zweifach, B. W.: Anat. Rec. *73*:478)

were at least occasional cells disposed along the sides of capillaries and venules, just outside the endothelium. These cells for a time were termed Rouget cells and for a time it was thought that these cells along the capillaries of mammals were comparable to contractile cells that could be demonstrated beside capillaries in certain sites in certain species and which were shown to be contractile. However, opinion soon changed, and it was generally conceded that such cells as could be seen just outside the endothelium of the capillaries and the venules of most of the bodies of mammals were not contractile. Moreover, the noncontractile cells in this location came to be known by the terms of *perivascular cells* or *pericytes*. We shall describe their fine structure presently.

As the circulation through the terminal vascular bed was studied further it was shown that cells in the same position, that is, close to the endothelium, but in vessels somewhat larger than capillaries or venules, were true smooth muscle cells and under the control of the autonomic nervous system. Zweifach made many studies on living preparations, studying the circulation through the terminal vascular

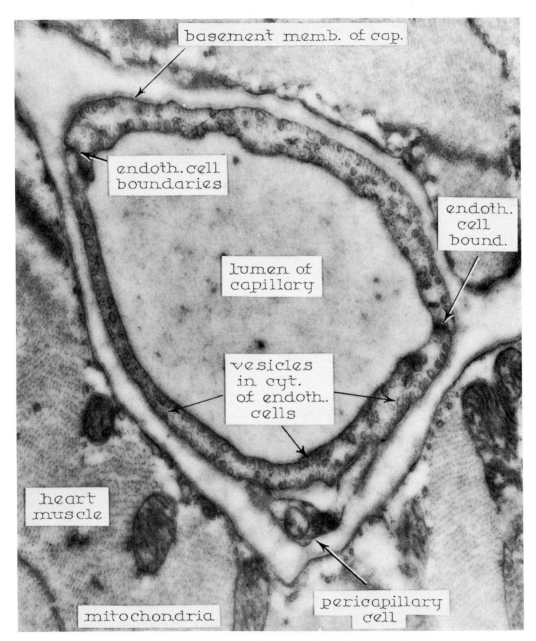

basement memb. of cap.

endoth. cell boundaries

endoth. cell bound.

lumen of capillary

vesicles in cyt. of endoth. cells

heart muscle

mitochondria

pericapillary cell

FIG. 22-11. Electron micrograph ($\times$ 57,000) of a section of heart muscle of a rat, showing a capillary cut in cross section and muscle fibers surrounding it. For further description see text. (Preparation by G. Palade, labeling added)

bed. He visualizes less direct and more direct routes through the terminal vascular bed. The more direct routes are composed of vessels of larger caliber. These larger vessels, first called A-V bridges, but more recently and more commonly, *preferred channels,* are contractile near their beginnings and at their endings. True capillaries branch off from the preferred channels to join others and so form loops. From these some branch off to empty back into a preferred channel near its end.

The general arrangement visualized by Zweifach that exists in the terminal vascular bed is shown in Figure 22-10. We would assume that contractile perivascular cells would be present only in the precapillary arteriole at the left and the largest venule shown on the right. Under ordinary conditions blood would flow mostly through the direct route (labeled A-V bridge). But, if the traffic became heavy, the side roads (the true capillaries) would open up more extensively and carry more of the traffic that was passing through the bed. The amount and the rate of blood passing through the bed would be regulated by the constriction or the dilatation of the larger vessels emptying into and draining the bed, respectively.

The role of the noncontractile pericytes disposed along the true capillaries and the smallest venules will be discussed presently.

## THE FINE STRUCTURE OF CAPILLARIES AND VENULES

**Types of Capillaries.** There are two types of capillaries, those in which the endothelial cells form a complete and continuous membrane and those in which the cytoplasm of the endothelial lining cells is fenestrated in that there are little holes 0.1 micron or less in diameter that extend through the cytoplasm from the inner to the outer surface of the endothelial tube. Fenestrated capillaries are found in some endocrine glands and a few other sites, but they are of particular importance in the glomeruli of the kidney where they will be considered further and in more detail.

Here we shall consider the capillaries that have continuous endothelium.

**Capillaries With Continuous Endothelium.** The fine structure of a capillary is illustrated in Figure 22-11 and that of a venule in Figure 22-12. The capillary in this illustration is cut in cross section. Two endothelial cells are required to encircle its lumen; the points where the cytoplasm of these come into contact are labeled in Figure 22-10 as *endothelial cell boundaries.* The type of junctional complex found here will be described in connection with venules. The lumen of the capillary contains fine granular material, which is probably precipitated blood protein, and dense round bodies, which are probably very small fat droplets that were present in blood. The inner and the

outer cell membranes of the endothelial cells are clearly apparent as dark lines. Between the inner and the outer membranes of the endothelial cells that surround the lumen is the cytoplasm of the endothelial cells; this is characterized by the presence of very numerous small smooth-surfaced pinocytotic vesicles of about 400 Å in diameter. These are mostly aggregated along the outer and the inner cell membranes of the endothelial cells. Some of the vesicles that abut on the outer and the inner cell membrane can be seen on close inspection (with a magnifying glass) to open onto the surface on which they abut, like little goblet cells. Such vesicles are, in effect, invaginations of the endothelial cell membrane into the cytoplasm of the endothelial cells. There is evidence indicating that there is a transport of fluid across the endothelial cell cytoplasm by means of small vesicles forming on one surface (where they phagocytose fluid) and then moving across the thickness of the endothelial cell to the other surface where the fluid is discharged. The taking up of fluid by vesicles which transport it through cytoplasm is, as has already been mentioned, termed *pinocytosis* (*pinein* = to drink). How great a part this mechanism plays in the formation and the absorption of tissue fluid is not yet established.

The capillary as a whole is wrapped in a basement membrane which is only a fraction of the thickness of the endothelial cells. With the EM it appears as a seemingly structureless (amorphous) band that rings the capillary (Fig. 22-11, *upper left*). The basement membrane is separated from adjacent muscle fibers by a space that contains some amorphous material. A small portion of a pericapillary cell may be seen at the lower border of the capillary.

The cytoplasm of endothelial cells contains mitochondria, but none are to be seen in this illustration.

**The Fine Structure of Venules.** As has been emphasized by Movat and Fernando, venules may prove to be the most significant of all the vessels of the terminal vascular bed with regard to the study of inflammation. Tissue fluid can form from venules. It is known that the migration of leukocytes can occur through the walls of venules, and they have also been shown to be sites where blood plasma passes

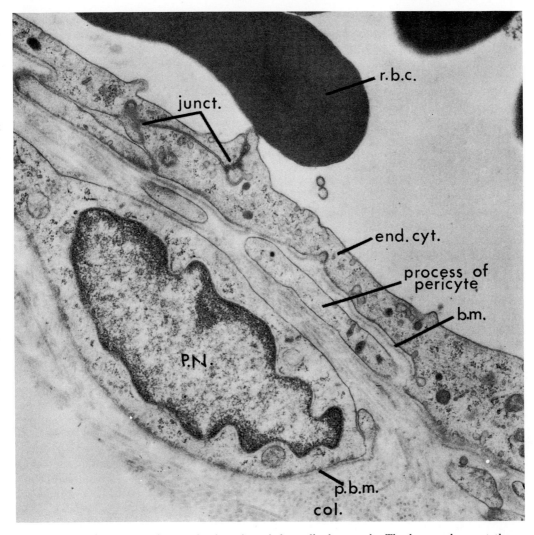

Fig. 22-12. Electron micrograph of section of the wall of a venule. The lumen, shown at the upper right, contains a red blood cell (r.b.c.). The cytoplasm (end. cyt.) of parts of two endothelial lining cells lines the lumen. The site of contact between the two endothelial cells is labeled *junct*. There are junctional complexes at the sites of contact. The basement membrane of the endothelium is labeled b.m. Passing outwardly from the basement membrane the process of a pericyte, labeled as such, is seen; farther outside is the nucleus of the pericyte. Basement membrane can be seen around the cell body of the pericyte (p.b.m.); outside this are some collagenic microfibrils (col.). (Preparation by N. S. Taichman and H. Z. Movat)

out into the tissues in the inflammatory process.

The venules are the smallest vessels on the venous side of the circulatory system. Venules are the vessels that collect the blood from capillaries. They have a larger diameter than capillaries. The walls of venules are best studied in the EM. As is shown in Figure 22-12,

they are lined by endothelial cells; parts of two endothelial cells are seen in this illustration. The site of their junction is labeled *Junct*. It is now believed that there is a fusion of the outer layers of the cell membranes of the two contiguous cells at a site near the lumen. The arrangement at this site of "tight junction" is the same as that in the zonula occludens seen between contiguous columnar epithelial cells which was described in detail in Chapter 8 and illustrated in Figure 8-14. In endothelium the zonula occludens is believed to form a belt that encircles the tube of endothelium. Except at this site where the outer layers of the cell membranes fuse, the cell membranes of the contiguous cells approach each other closely so that there is a space around 100 Å between them. It is possible that the zonula occludens may not completely encircle the endothelial tube and that small gaps may sometimes appear between contiguous endothelial cell membranes, and that these gaps permit some fluid leakage. As was shown in Figure 12-7, when endothelium is injured, leukocytes migrate through the walls of capillaries and venules, and to do so they effect a separation between the borders of contiguous cells and leave the vessels through the openings so formed.

The cytoplasm of the endothelial cells reveal some dark bodies which are probably lysosomes (Fig. 22-12). A few pinocytotic vesicles can also be seen in the endothelium of this venule.

Just outside the endothelium is a sheath of basement membrane (Fig. 22-12, bm). This is composed of an almost structureless fibrillar material. The basement membranes surrounding the endothelium of capillaries and venules are around 500 Å in thickness; they are thought to become thicker with age.

The large nucleus (Fig. 22-12, P.N.) at the lower left is the nucleus of a pericyte. The cytoplasm of the pericytes extends out from their main cell bodies, in the form of processes. The processes in thin sections are often cut in oblique or cross section as they extend along or around the endothelial tube of the capillary or venule. The pericytes and their processes are also enclosed with basement membrane which is continuous with the basement membrane that surrounds the tube of endothelium. In this sense the basement membrane of the endothelial tube splits so as to envelop the pericyte and its processes as well as the endothelial tube. Basement membrane can be seen on the pericyte at the site marked P.B.M.

Some collagen can be seen surrounding the endothelial tube and the pericytes. This is in the form of microfibrils that are mostly cut in cross section (Fig. 22-12, col.).

As venules become small veins, the character of the cells described as pericytes changes in that they become smooth muscle cells.

The function of the pericytes of capillaries and venules, unlike those of cells in a similar position in small veins and arterioles, is not generally believed to be contractile as was once believed. The pericytes of capillaries and small veins are now generally regarded as relatively undifferentiated mesenchymal derivatives. They have been shown to be phagocytic and in this way they resemble macrophages, and in the growth of new veins from venules it is thought that they can develop into smooth muscle cells. It has also been suggested that pericytes may help to make basement membranes or even collagen.

## VEINS

Venules have already been described.

**Veins of Small and Medium Size.** Their structure varies greatly. In general, their walls, like those of their corresponding arteries, consist of 3 tunics (Fig. 22-4, *right*). The intima consists of endothelium which rests either directly on a poorly defined internal elastic membrane (in which the fibers run longitudinally) or is separated from it by a slight amount of subendothelial collagenic connective tissue. The media is usually much thinner than that of a companion artery (Fig. 22-4). It consists chiefly of circularly disposed smooth muscle fibers. More collagenic fibers and fewer elastic fibers are mixed with them than in arteries. In some veins the innermost smooth muscle fibers of the media have a longitudinal course. In general, the media is much less muscular and hence thinner in veins that are protected, for example, by muscles or by the pressure of the abdominal contents, than in veins that are more exposed. The cerebral and the meningeal veins have almost no muscle in their walls. The adventitia of veins of medium size is often their thickest coat (Fig. 22-4, *right*). It usually consists chiefly of collagenic connective tissue.

The muscular media is well developed in the veins of the limbs, particularly in those of the lower ones. This is particularly true of the saphenous veins. Being superficial, these are not supported by the pressure of surrounding structures to the same extent as deeper

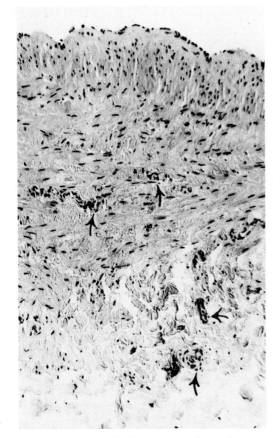

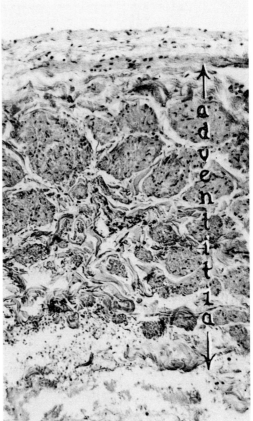

FIG. 22-13. Medium-power photomicrograph of the wall of the saphenous vein as it appears in a cross section. Note the inner layer of longitudinal muscle and note that the vasa vasorum, indicated by arrows, penetrate deeply into the media from the adventitia.

FIG. 22-14. Medium-power photomicrograph of the wall of the inferior vena cava, as seen in a cross section. Note the longitudinal muscle bundles in the adventitia.

veins. Furthermore, when a person stands erect, their walls must withstand the hydrostatic pressure generated by a long column of blood. For these two reasons their walls must be thicker than those of most veins. This is accomplished chiefly by a very substantial media. The innermost part of this consists chiefly of longitudinally disposed smooth muscle fibers associated with elastic fibers (Fig. 22-13) and the outermost and thicker part of circularly disposed smooth muscle fibers (Fig. 22-13).

**Large Veins.** The structure of different veins varies considerably. In general, the tunica intima resembles that of veins of medium size,

but the subendothelial layer of connective tissue is thicker. In most of the largest veins there is little smooth muscle in the media. The adventitia is the thickest of the three coats, and it contains both collagenic and elastic fibers. In many instances, for example, the inferior vena cava, its innermost part contains bundles of longitudinally disposed smooth muscle fibers (Fig. 22-14).

**Vasa Vasorum of Veins.** Veins are supplied much more abundantly with vasa vasorum than arteries. Since veins contain poorly oxygenated blood, the cells of the walls of veins probably need more oxygen on occasions than can be obtained by diffusion from the lumen of the vessel. Vasa vasorum carrying arterial blood into the substance of the walls of veins supply this need. Furthermore, since the blood in veins is under low pressure, vasa vasorum can approach the intima of the walls of veins without necessarily being collapsed by the pressure within the vein. Hence, the vasa vasorum of veins penetrate much closer to the intima than do those of arteries. They are seen to advantage in the thick walls of the saphenous vein (Fig. 22-13).

**Lymphatics.** Since the walls of veins do not have to withstand great pressures, as do the walls of arteries, lymphatics, as well as vasa vasorum, can be present in a patent state within the substance of their walls. Indeed, the walls of veins are supplied much more abundantly with lymphatic capillaries than

the walls of arteries. (This probably explains why tumors that spread by lymphatics invade the walls of veins but never the walls of arteries. Lymphatic capillaries may approach the inner surfaces of the veins so closely that the tissue fluid that enters them to become lymph is probably a filtrate or a dialysate of the blood in the lumen of the vein itself.

**Valves of Veins.** Many veins are provided with valves disposed so as to permit blood to flow toward the heart but not in the opposite direction. The valves of veins are of the flap (leaflet) type. Most valves have two leaflets, but some have only one. The leaflets are composed of folds of intima with some extra

SOME GENERAL DIFFERENCES BETWEEN DISTRIBUTING ARTERIES AND THEIR COMPANION VEINS

| ARTERIES | VEINS |
|---|---|
| Have a smaller over-all diameter and a smaller lumen. | Have a larger over-all diameter and a larger lumen. |
| Their walls are thicker because they must withstand pressure from the lumen. | Their walls are thinner because they have to withstand little pressure from the lumen. |
| The flow of blood is more rapid in them because the same amount of blood must pass through the narrower artery as passes through the wider vein. | The flow of blood is slower in them; the same amount of blood is handled as by companion arteries because of their larger lumens. |
| Their thicker walls do not collapse after death. | Their thinner walls collapse if blood drains out of them after death; hence, veins may appear as flattened structures in sections. |
| The oxygen content of blood in them is high. | The oxygen content of blood in them is low. |
| The inner parts of their walls contain no capillaries (low-pressure capillaries would be collapsed by the pressure from the lumen if they were present). | Low-pressure capillaries can be present and remain open in their walls because their walls do not have to withstand much pressure from their lumens. |
| No lymphatic capillaries are present in the inner layers of their walls for the same reason as above. | Lymphatic capillaries are present in the walls of veins. |
| The cells in the inner layers of their walls must be nourished by diffusion mechanisms that operate over long distances, from the blood in the lumen and from the vasa vasorum in the periphery. | The cells in their walls are nourished by diffusion mechanisms that operate only over short distances (from the vasa vasorum which permeate their walls and carry *arterial* blood). |
| The tunica intima is relatively thicker. | The tunica intima is relatively thinner. |
| The tunica media is muscular and considerably thicker. | The tunica media is generally a thin muscular layer. |
| The internal and the external elastic laminae are better developed. | The internal and the external elastic laminae are less well developed. |
| The tunica adventitia is about half the thickness of the media and has a high elastin content to assist in recoil during diastole. | The tunica adventitia is the thickest coat of the wall and is composed chiefly of collagen instead of elastin because no recoil effect is needed. |
| They have no valves. | Most of them have valves to prevent backflow. |
| Their structure is fairly constant. | Their structure is less constant—there are many variations related to particular positions, for example, saphenous veins. |

central reinforcements of connective tissue. Elastic fibers are disposed on the side of the valve that faces the lumen of the vessel.

Valves are especially abundant in the veins of the extremities, and they are generally absent from the veins of the thorax and the abdomen. Valves usually are placed immediately distal to sites where tributaries enter veins. Veins immediately proximal to the attachment of a valve are always dilated slightly to form a pouch or sinus. Hence, in distended superficial veins, localized swellings indicate the sites of valves.

The function of valves in veins is not completely understood. Obviously, valves must help to overcome the force of gravity by preventing backflow. But they may act in other ways. For example, valves in veins that are squeezed when surrounding muscles contract would enable the surrounding muscles to serve as pumps. Moreover, valves in such veins would prevent muscular contractions from creating back pressure on the capillary beds drained by the veins.

**Varicose Veins.** Superficial veins are relatively unsupported, and the force of gravity exerted through the blood within those below the heart is a more or less constant factor tending to cause their dilatation. Under conditions where there is obstruction to the return of blood from a part, or where the tissues of the walls of the veins are not as strong as usual, because of inheritance or disease, superficial veins gradually dilate. As dilatation proceeds, the valves become incompetent and, as a result, gravity exerts a still greater dilating force on their walls. Superficial veins that, under these conditions, become tortuous, irregular and wider than usual are called *varicose veins*.

## THE TRANSPLANTATION OF BLOOD VESSELS

The transplantation of segments of blood vessels to bypass or replace segments of vessels that are malformed, diseased and weakened or occluded is now a relatively common surgical operation. The discovery of anticoagulants, for example, heparin, has aided; these are commonly used locally to prevent agglutination and thrombosis from occurring at the sites where the new vessels are sutured to the old.

In the section on the transplantation of tissues, different kinds of transplants were described. A little thought is all that is required to realize that the use of autologous transplants of blood vessels would be very limited because there would be no source of autologous transplants for replacing any of the larger vessels of the body (except under certain circumstances when anastomoses are abundant). Some types of arterial defects can be repaired with autologous venous grafts, but the use of these is limited. Therefore, transplants of blood vessels must generally be of the homologous variety, and, as has already been explained, there is little use in hoping for the survival of cells in this type of transplant. However, homologous transplants of blood vessels are effective because the intercellular substance in them survives for the time while new tissue is growing into them. Elastin is probably the most important in this respect, and it has been shown experimentally that it will remain intact for at least 6 to 9 months.

A homologous transplant is invaded by cells from the host site. These grow into its substance and form collagen. It is not believed that new elastin is formed in vessel transplants. The inner surfaces of the transplant become paved with a modified connective tissue. Discontinuous patches of cells appear along the interior of a transplant; hence, it is considered that endothelium does not grow from the host vessels to line it, but that cells from outside the transplant grow through its walls to reach its interior where they differentiate into a type of lining cell to substitute for endothelium.

Since no cell survival can be expected in homologous transplants they may be stored and treated in a variety of ways which might destroy any cells they contain. Homotransplants may be stored in the deep freeze or be frozen and dried or treated in other ways.

Synthetic materials, formed into the shapes of blood vessels, are now widely used as substitutes for homotransplants. These are made of materials that do not stir up a tissue reaction, furthermore, they are made so that they are porous; this permits cells from the host to grow into their substance and fill the interstices of it with cells and intercellular substance. Since they are porous, cells can grow through them to reach their lumens and line them with living tissue.

Heterologous transplants of blood vessels have been studied experimentally to some extent but are not used very commonly in practice.

## ARTERIOVENOUS ANASTOMOSES

That arteriovenous anastomoses exist in many parts of the body, particularly in the distal parts of extremities, has been known for a very long time. Early evidence for their existence accumulated from two sources: (1) experiments in which particulate matter, too large to pass through capillaries, was injected into an artery and recovered from the corresponding vein and (2) histologic studies made on tissue, the vessels of which were injected with a colored material. However, comparatively little attention was paid to these important structures until some of the newer technics made their study possible in the living animal.

Grant first studied arteriovenous anastomoses in the living animal by subjecting carefully prepared rabbits' ears to direct microscopic observation by means of strong transmitted light. Grant and Bland later studied them in human skin and in the bird's foot. Clark and Clark, at almost the same time, studied them and their formation by means of transparent chambers inserted in rabbits' ears. Masson has described a special type of anastomoses seen in little organs in the skin called *glomi* (Fig. 23-18).

Arteriovenous anastomoses arise as side branches from arteries and arterioles and pursue either a tortuous or a fairly straight course to connect usually with the vein or the venule accompanying the arterial vessel from which they arise. Near the point where they empty into veins, their walls have the character of veins, and at their point of origin, their walls have the character of arteries but are slightly thicker. But, at the intermediate segment of transition, according to Grant, there is considerable muscular and adventitial thickening to be seen in the vessel. Moreover, this part of the anastomosis is particularly well supplied with nerve endings from the sympathetic division of the autonomic nervous system, and presumably it is more or less specialized to serve as a sphincter.

The dilatation of arteriovenous anastomoses in any part of the body permits a much greater amount of blood to pass through that part. It is obvious that arteriovenous anastomoses would serve a very important purpose in, for example, the tips of fingers or toes subjected to cold, because by their dilatation, they could permit greatly increased amounts of warm blood to pass through the extremities and so help maintain their temperature. It is very likely that arteriovenous anastomoses do serve a very important function in this way. Furthermore, it is not unlikely that they serve important functions in certain structures in the body that indulge in intermittent activities. Moreover, it is obvious that the dilatation of arteriovenous anastomoses in a normal body would have an effect in raising venous blood pressure and so aid the return of blood to the heart. Their closure under conditions of obstructed venous return similarly could help to diminish venous pressure. *Arteriovenous anastomoses are very different structures from A-V bridges, and to avoid confusion the latter are now commonly termed "preferred channels."*

## HEART

**Pericardial Cavity.** The heart is a hollow muscular organ of four chambers. It is covered with a fibro-elastic connective-tissue membrane, which, in turn, is covered with a single layer of mesothelium. This mesothelial-covered, fibro-elastic membrane is termed the *epicardium* (*epi* = upon). The heart, so covered, is surrounded by another fibro-elastic membrane, the *pericardium*. This is lined with mesothelium. Between the pericardium and the epicardium is a potential space, the pericardial cavity, which, in health, contains up to 50 ml. of fluid. This fluid is so distributed that it amounts to no more than a film in most places. The epicardium is continuous at the base of the heart with the pericardium. Sometimes the epicardium is referred to as the *visceral layer of the pericardium,* and what we have just described as the pericardium as the *parietal layer of the pericardium.* The lubricating film of fluid between the mesothelial lining of the pericardium and the mesothelial covering of the epicardium permits the heart to move freely during contraction and relaxation. In certain diseases the amount of fluid in the pericardial cavity becomes greatly increased;

in others, the epicardium becomes united by fibrous connective tissue to the pericardium. Both deviations from the normal greatly embarrass the action of the heart.

**Epicardium.** The character of the epicardium varies somewhat over different parts of the heart. Its more superficial layer consists of ordinary connective tissue. This is covered with mesothelium, and it contains some blood capillaries, lymphatic capillaries and some nerves. The deeper layer of the epicardium contains larger blood vessels and more fat and is continuous with the endomysium of the underlying cardiac muscle. Fat is particularly abundant along the course of the larger coronary vessels.

**Myocardium.** The muscular and thickest part of the wall of the heart lies deep to the epicardium. It is composed of cardiac muscle (this was described in Chap. 20). The arrangement of the various groups of fibers comprising the myocardium is considered in textbooks of gross anatomy.

**Endocardium.** This membrane forms a complete lining for the atrial and the ventricular cavities and covers all the structures that project into the heart (valves, chordae tendineae and papillary muscles). In general, the thickness of the endocardium varies inversely with the thickness of the myocardium it lines; for example, the endocardium in the atria is much thicker than that in the ventricles. The endocardium has 3 layers. The innermost consists of a delicate connective-tissue membrane lined with endothelium that is continuous with the lining of the blood vessels that leave the heart. The next (middle layer) is the thickest. It consists of dense connective tissue in which many elastic fibers are present, particularly in its inner part (Fig. 22-16). These commonly are disposed parallel with the surface, and in some sites where they are abundant, they alternate with layers of collagenic fibers. In the outer part of this layer some smooth muscle fibers may be present. The third and outermost layer of the endocardium consists of more irregularly arranged connective tissue. Fat may be present here. This layer contains blood vessels and cardiac muscle fibers of a special type (Purkinje fibers) (Fig. 22-20), to be described later. It is continuous with the endomysium of the myocardium.

**Skeleton of the Heart.** The aorta and the pulmonary artery arise from the left and the right ventricles, respectively. At its point of origin each is surrounded by a fibrous ring. The dense connective tissue of these rings is continuous either directly or indirectly, through the medium of a triangular mass of dense connective tissue with some cartilaginous qualities, the trigonum fibrosum, with the connective tissue of fibrous rings that surround the atrioventricular orifices. The fibrous rings surrounding the outlets of the atria and the ventricles prevent the outlets from becoming dilated when the muscular walls of the chambers contract and force their contents out through them. These fibrous structures, together with the fibrous (membranous) part of the interventricular septum, also provide a means for the insertion of the free ends of the fibers of the cardiac musculature. For this reason, these various fibrous structures sometimes are said to constitute the skeleton of the heart.

**Valves of the Heart.** Since each ventricle is of the nature of a one-cylinder pump, each requires an intake and an exhaust valve. The type of valve employed in the heart is the leaflet (flap) type (Figs. 22-15 and 22-16). The leaflets consist essentially of folds of endocardium. But, since 2 layers of endocardium would not be strong enough to withstand the pressures generated, each leaflet is reinforced with a flat sheet of dense connective tissue.

The intake valve of the right ventricle consists of 3 leaflets and is called the *tricuspid valve*. Since cusp means a *point* and, in particular, as any mathematics student will recall, a point at which 2 curved lines meet tangentially, it is highly probable that the valve was so-named because the curved free margins of the 3 leaflets meet tangentially at 3 points on the circumference of the valve to form 3 cusps. Although, strictly speaking, the points of meeting of the free margins of the leaflets are the cusps, it has become common for those not mathematically inhibited to speak of the leaflets themselves as cusps. The intake valve of the left ventricle consists of only 2 leaflets; hence, its opening is 2-pointed, and it is called the *bicuspid valve*. The leaflets of both of the atrioventricular valves have a similar histologic structure. They are covered on both sides with endocardium and have a middle supporting layer of dense collagenic connective tissue. On the ventricular side of the layer of collagenic tissue there are nu-

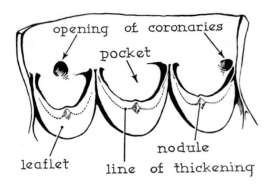

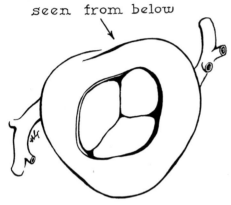

FIG. 22-15. (*Top*) The 3 leaflets of the aortic valve as they appear when the aorta is opened and spread out flat. (*Bottom*) The appearance of the closed valve as seen from below.

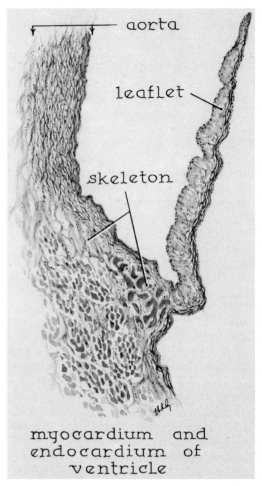

FIG. 22-16. Drawing of a longitudinal section of the heart (low-power) cut through the site where the wall of the ventricle continues an aortic valve leaflet. The tissue of the base of the leaflet merges into that of the skeleton of the heart.

merous elastic fibers. A few are also present beneath the endothelium on the atrial side of the leaflet.

At the bases of the leaflets, the middle collagenic supporting flat plate becomes continuous with the dense connective tissue of the rings surrounding the orifices. Smooth muscle fibers have been described at this site, and a sphincterlike action has been attributed to them. Capillaries may be present at the bases of the leaflets, where smooth muscle fibers are present, but capillaries do not extend into the valves proper in man. Such cells as are distributed throughout the dense connective tissue of the valves live in tissue fluid derived from the plasma of the blood that bathes the valves.

Tendinous cords of dense collagenic connective tissue (the chordae tendineae) covered by thin endocardium extend from the papillary muscles to connect with the ventricular surface of the middle collagenic supporting layer of each leaflet. It should be realized that the exhaust valves of the ventricles (the aortic and the pulmonary valves) open on ventricular contraction and that only the closed intake (atrioventricular) valves must withstand the full pressure of ventricular contraction. There is a danger, then, that unless they were specially protected, they might, on strong ventricular contraction, behave like umbrellas on windy days and be blown inside out. The chordae tendineae and the papillary muscles from which they arise limit the extent to which the portions of the valves near their free margins can be "blown" toward the atria. (See Fig. 22-17.)

The exhaust valve of the right ventricle is termed the *pulmonary semilunar valve* because of the shape of its leaflets. The exhaust valve of the left ventricle is termed the *aortic semilunar valve* and it too has 3 leaflets (Fig. 22-15). The leaflets of these valves are thinner than those of the atrioventricular valves. However, they are of the same general construction, being composed essentially of folds of endocardium reinforced with a middle layer of dense connective tissue; the folds of endocardium, at their bases, become continuous with the skeleton of the heart (Fig. 22-16). They have no chordae tendineae. The leaflets contain a considerable amount of elastic tissue on their ventricular sides (Fig. 22-16).

In a semilunar valve leaflet the dense middle layer becomes somewhat thickened along a line close to, and parallel with, its free margin, particularly near the middle of the leaflet. This is the line along which the leaflets touch one another when the valves close; hence, the tissue here must be relatively strong. Between this line of thickened tissue and their actual free margins, the leaflets are filmlike. The very pliable free margins permit a more perfect seal than could be obtained by stiffer tissue unless it were perfectly "machined."

For the free edges of 3 "patch" pockets bulging inwardly from the lining of a vessel toward its center to make a perfect seal requires that each leaflet, when the valve is

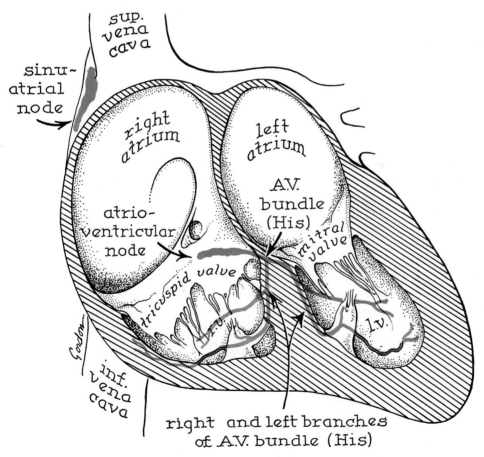

FIG. 22-17. Drawing of the cut surface (striped) and the interior of the heart, as seen from the front. The cut was made so as to expose and extend along, so far as was possible, the main parts of the impulse-conducting system, which is shown in red.

closed, must have the appearance, when seen from below (except for having a curved base), of a triangle with its apex reaching the center of the vessel (Fig. 22-15). Furthermore, the sum of the angles of the apices of the 3 triangular leaflets of a closed valve must be 360°. At the apex of each leaflet, the thickening along the line close to the free margin, described in the previous paragraph, is accentuated to form a nodule (Fig. 22-15). The free margin of a closed valve curves upward from both sides to a peak at this point; hence, this pointed portion of the free margin containing the nodule constitutes a true cusp (Fig. 22-15). However, as noted before, the whole leaflet is sometimes called a cusp.

Diseases affecting the valves of the heart may cause serious mechanical problems. In particular, in children suffering from rheumatic fever, the leaflets may become the seat of an inflammatory process. The healing of the leaflets often is associated with a considerable increase in their collagenic component; as a result, they may become stiffer and shorter or deformed in other ways. Leaflets sometimes become glued together with collagen. In any event, the end result is likely to be a valve that does not open or close properly. The student will see many examples of valves so affected in his clinical years.

## IMPULSE-CONDUCTING SYSTEM OF THE HEART

In a cardiac cycle, the blood enters the right and the left atria from the venae cavae and the pulmonary veins, respectively. Part of this blood flows directly into the relaxed right and left ventricles, while the rest fills the atria. The two atria then contract simultaneously, squeezing their contents into the partially filled ventricles to complete the filling process. Contraction of the ventricles then follows, which closes the atrioventricular valves and opens the aortic and the pulmonary valves through which their contents are discharged into the aorta and the pulmonary arteries, respectively. In the meantime, the atria are filling again.

The efficiency of the heart depends to a great degree on these different events following each other in orderly sequence. Unfortunately, in certain all too common diseases the orderly sequence of events is disturbed. For example, instead of a wave of contraction sweeping over the atria and later over the ventricles, the atria may begin to contract more or less independently of, and at different rates from, the ventricles. Or, the walls of the atria may only flutter instead of contracting properly. Indeed, there are far too many ways in which the normal order is disturbed to permit listing them here. But, since the student will soon be seeing examples of these conditions in the clinic, at this time he should become as familiar as possible with the mechanism that permits different events to be synchronized properly in the normal heart.

Long before the turn of the century, it was realized that the orderly sequence of contractions to be observed in the hearts of cold-blooded animals depended on a wave of excitation sweeping first along the muscular tissue of the atria and then along that of the ventricles. But the theory of muscular conduction of the impulse for contraction could not be applied at that time to the hearts of mammals because these were thought to have a continuous connective-tissue partition between the atria and the ventricles. However, in 1893, W. His, Jr., demonstrated that the partition in the human heart was pierced by a bundle of muscle which passes from the atrial septum to the upper border of the interventricular septum (Fig. 22-17). (Earlier in the same year, Kent had shown that the partition in the monkey heart was pierced by bundles of muscle fibers which were somewhat different from those of ordinary cardiac muscle.) The *atrioventricular* (A-V) bundle of muscle or, as it is often called, the *bundle of His*, provides a means whereby each wave of contraction that sweeps over the atria can be conducted by muscular tissue to the ventricles to institute their contraction at precisely the time when they have been properly filled with blood by the contraction of the atria. It is obvious that the fibers in the A-V bundle would be specialized to conduct (at a special suitable rate) rather than to contract and, as we shall see presently, they have a different microscopic appearance from the fibers of ordinary cardiac muscle (Fig. 22-19).

It soon became apparent that there was further muscle tissue in the heart that was specialized primarily for conducting, and even

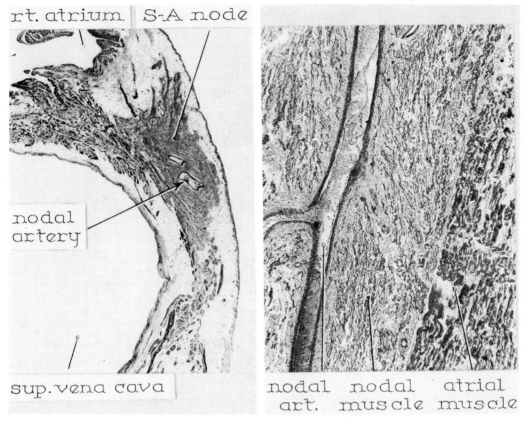

rt. atrium | S-A node

nodal artery

sup. vena cava | nodal art. | nodal muscle | atrial muscle

Fig. 22-18. (*Left*) Low-power cross section of the right wall of the superior vena cava at its junction with the right atrium, cutting through the sinu-atrial node. (*Right*) Low-power longitudinal section of the sinu-atrial node, showing the fine muscle fibers of the node, in contrast with the larger darker-staining atrial muscle. Note the nodal artery running through the center of the node. (Preparation by J. W. A. Duckworth)

some for initiating, the impulse for contraction. Indeed, it is now understood that the A-V bundle is only an important part of a whole system of fibers that are specialized for this purpose. These constitute what is termed the *impulse-conducting system of the heart,* and we shall now describe the various parts of this system and the microscopic structure of each representative division.

**The Sinu-atrial (S-A) Node.** This is a little mass of specialized cardiac muscle fibers that are contained in substantial amounts of dense fibro-elastic connective tissue. It is abundantly supplied with nerve fibers from both divisions of the autonomic nervous system. It lies in the right wall of the superior vena cava at the upper end of the sulcus terminalis (Figs. 22-17 and 22-18) and was first described, in 1907, by

Keith and Flack, who considered that the impulse for the contraction of the heart arose in it. This concept soon received support because it was found, in 1910, that the S-A node was the first region to become electronegative when a wave of contraction developed in the heart of the dog. It is now often described as the *pacemaker* of the heart, and it is generally believed that here nervous impulses make their influence felt by affecting the rate at which impulses for contraction develop in the node to sweep over the heart thereafter.

Duckworth has described the connective tissue content of the node becoming considerably increased immediately after birth and that at the same time the muscular elements in the node develop into their adult form. The adult

 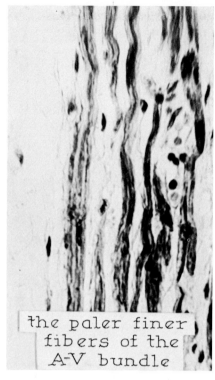

ordinary cardiac
muscle fibers

the paler finer
fibers of the
A-V bundle

FIG. 22-19. Two high-power photomicrographs of the same magnification of adjacent areas in a section of the uppermost part of the interventricular septum of the heart of a human adult (Hollande's chlorcarmine stain). (*Left*) The muscle fibers are those of ordinary cardiac muscle. (*Right*) The muscle fibers of the A-V bundle; they may be seen to be both narrower and paler than those of ordinary cardiac muscle. The striations which they clearly exhibit in many instances cannot be seen in this illustration. (Preparation by J. W. A. Duckworth)

nodal fibers are small cross-striated fusiform fibers about half the size of the ordinary atrial fibers and they lie parallel with the long axis of the nodal artery as it descends through the center of the node. These fibers are embedded in a relatively large amount of dense connective tissue which contains many capillaries (Fig. 22-18, *right*). Peripheral ganglia of the parasympathetic division of the autonomic system (of the vagus nerve) are present in close association with the node (Fig. 22-18, *left*), and, as has been noted already, the node is abundantly supplied with fibers from both divisions of the system. Parasympathetic stimulation slows the rate of the heart, while sympathetic stimulation increases it.

No pathways of special fibers have as yet been satisfactorily demonstrated in the walls of the atria; hence, it is assumed that the impulses that arise in the S-A node sweep through the ordinary muscle fibers of the atria

to reach the next part of the impulse-conducting system which is the atrioventricular node. This will now be described.

**The Atrioventricular (A-V) Node.** This was discovered in 1906 by Tawara, and it consists of a little mass of specialized tissue that is disposed in the lower part of the interatrial septum immediately above the attachment of the septal cusp of the tricuspid valve; anteriorly, it is continuous with the A-V bundle (Fig. 22-17). The cells of the node are cardiac muscle fibers but have fewer myofibrils than ordinary cardiac muscle fibers. The cells branch so extensively and in so many directions that the myofibrils of one cell are commonly seen to cross those of underlying or overlying cells at right angles.

**The A-V Bundle.** According to Duckworth the fibers of the bundle, during the first year of life become fine in caliber (Fig. 22-19). They become arranged parallel with one another with little connective tissue but with many capillaries between them. Many of the fibers are no wider than the capillaries. However, like the fibers of the S-A node, they anastomose freely.

**Purkinje Fibers.** In the human heart the two branches of the A-V bundle run about halfway down the two sides of the interventricular septum before their fibers enlarge to become continuous with what are called Purkinje fibers. These were first seen by Purkinje in 1845 in the subendocardial region in the ventricles of the ungulate heart. They resemble ordinary cardiac muscle fibers in that they have centrally disposed nuclei, cross striations and intercalated disks (Fig. 22-20). However, they differ from ordinary cardiac muscle fibers in that they are generally wider, and also because the myofibrils in each fiber tend to be disposed around its periphery; this leaves the central core of each fiber relatively empty of myofibrils, and their place is taken by considerable amounts of glycogen. In H and E sections the glycogen is not seen as such; hence, the central part of each Purkinje fiber appears to be empty except where nuclei are present (Fig. 22-20).

The Purkinje fibers, which arise from the branches of the bundle, spread from the interventricular septum direct to the papillary muscles (Fig. 22-17), before passing on to the lateral walls of the ventricles, up which they spread as a subendocardial network. These fibers, which conduct the impulse for contraction much more rapidly than the ordinary heart muscle, thus ensure that the papillary muscles will take up the strain on the leaflets of the mitral and the tricuspid valves before the full force of the ventricular contraction is thrown against them.

The fine structure of the cells of the bundle has been described by Rhodin and others. The cells contain short myofibrils which demonstrate cross striations similar to those seen in cardiac muscle. Most of the space in the cells is taken up by glycogen. The cells are joined together by much the same kind of arrangement that has been described under cardiac muscle (Chap. 20) in connection with intercalated disks. It is incorrect to refer to the specialized muscle of the heart as the Purkinje system when only a part of that system is made up of true Purkinje fibers.

**Electrocardiograms.** The passage of a wave

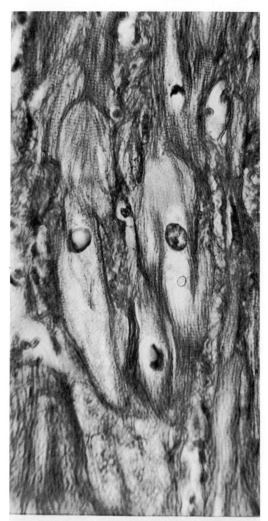

human Purkinje fibers from rt. ventricle

Fig. 22-20. High-power longitudinal section of human Purkinje fibers from the right ventricle. Note their large size and that the myofibrils occupy the periphery of the cell. (Preparation by J. W. A. Duckworth)

of excitation over either special or ordinary cardiac muscle fibers is associated with a changing electrical potential along the fiber. Essentially, the particular site over which the wave is passing at any given time is always negatively charged in relation to the parts of the fiber over which it has passed or which it has not yet reached. Hence, if a series of electrodes could be placed along the different parts

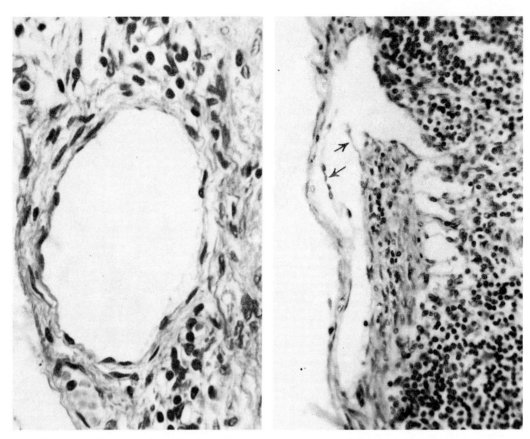

Fig. 22-21. (*Left*) High-power photomicrograph of a cross section of a small lymphatic vessel. The nuclei of a few smooth muscle fibers may be seen in its wall, but the layers of the wall are not clearly defined. (*Right*) High-power photomicrograph of an oblique section cut through the capsule of a lymph node and showing an afferent lymphatic vessel emptying into the subcapsular sinus. The 2 thin leaflets of a valve are indicated by arrows.

of the conducting system and connected to different galvanometers, the passage of the impulse for contraction over the system could be followed by watching the galvanometers. Similarly, if electrodes are taken from the intact heart and connected to galvanometers, the passage of the impulse for contraction, plus the changing potentials due to waves of contraction occurring successively in different parts of the heart muscle on their reception of the impulse, could be followed by watching the galvanometers. Indeed, to obtain a great deal of information about the passage of the impulse for contraction over the heart and the successive activation of the muscle of different parts of it, it is not even necessary to connect electrodes to the heart. Since the body tissues that surround the heart contain electrolytes,

they act as conductors; hence, if leads are taken off different parts of the body that are projections, as it were, of 3 widely separated points on the heart, they give somewhat similar information to leads taken directly from these 3 parts of the heart themselves. Originally, 3 standard leads were taken. The first is from the left and the right hands; the second, from the right hand and the left foot; and the third, from the left hand and the left foot. Each lead is connected to a galvanometer that is so arranged as to permit the changes in the electrical potential occurring in the 3 leads, as the impulse for contraction passes over the heart and successively activates different parts of it, to be recorded on a photographic film in relation to the passage of time. Such a record is called an *electrocardiogram*, and the various waves present in a normal one are a record of the passage of the impulse over, and the activation of the muscle of, different parts of the heart. If any disease condition exists which interferes with the proper conduction of the impulse for contraction over the heart or the proper activation of its different parts, a deviation from the normal pattern of waves is apparent in the electrocardiogram. Hence, electrocardiography is of great importance in helping to diagnose certain types of cardiac disease.

## THE LYMPHATIC DIVISION OF THE CIRCULATORY SYSTEM

**Lymphatic Vessels.** Lymphatic capillaries, from blind endings (Fig. 10-8), join together to form networks. The capillaries of these are generally of a greater diameter than blood capillaries, and the diameter of any given one varies more along its course than that of a blood capillary. Networks of lymphatic capillaries drain into somewhat larger lymphatic vessels. Both these and the larger lymphatic vessels into which they in turn drain are generally called *lymphatics*. The walls of the smallest of these—the kind into which the lymphatic capillaries empty—consist of a thin layer of connective tissue and an endothelial lining. When lymphatics become somewhere between one fifth and one half a millimeter in diameter, their walls show indications of being composed of 3 layers: an *intima,* a *media* and an *adventitia.* The 3 layers are not well defined in the walls of the smaller lymphatics (Fig. 22-21, *left*); however, they may be distinguished fairly clearly in the larger ones. The intima commonly contains elastic fibers. The media of the larger vessels consists chiefly of circularly and obliquely disposed smooth muscle fibers. The muscle fibers are supported by some connective tissue which contains elastic fibers. The adventitia is relatively well developed, particularly in the smaller vessels, and it contains smooth muscle fibers; these run both longitudinally and obliquely. Small blood vessels are present in the outer coats of lymphatics of a medium and a large size.

The lymphatics, which collect the lymph from the lymphatic capillaries and carry it to the larger lymphatic vessels that finally deliver it into the blood circulatory system, commonly pass through the tissue along with a vein and its companion artery. However, the lymphatic vessels do not show as much tendency to unite with one another to form a single large vessel as do small veins; hence, several lymphatics may be associated with a vein and its companion artery. The lymphatics, as they pass through the tissues, may unite with one another but they also branch again and so remain numerous.

The lymphatic vessels that collect the lymph from the lymphatic capillaries, before they drain into the terminal vessels of the system, empty into lymph nodes that are disposed along their course (Fig. 15-3). This permits the lymph, as it percolates through the reticuloendothelial mesh of the node, to be filtered; also, lymphocytes can be added to it. Lymph that has passed through lymph nodes contains lymphocytes; this fact, together with the absence of erythrocytes in the lumens of lymphatics, may assist the student to distinguish lymphatics from veins in sections. Lymph that is brought to the convex border of a lymph node by a set of *afferent* vessels leaves the concave border or hilus of the node in another set of efferent vessels (Fig. 15-3); these are the tributaries of the terminal vessels.

Lymphatic vessels, except the smallest ones, commonly, but not always, possess valves. These are more numerous and hence closer together than the valves of veins. Indeed, the valves of lymphatics may be so close together that a distended lymphatic appears to be beaded, because dilated sections between the numerous valves are so close together. The valves commonly have 2 leaflets; these consist of folds of intima, so they have delicate connective tissue plates in their middles and endothelial coverings (Fig. 22-21, *right*). The endothelial cells are said, like those of the valves of veins, to be orientated differently on the 2 surfaces of a leaflet, their long diameters being parallel with the stream on the side of the leaflet that faces the stream and at right angles to the stream on its sheltered side.

It is easy to understand how each segment of a lymphatic that is situated between 2 valves could act as a pump if (1) the wall of the lymphatic in that segment contracted or (2) that segment were squeezed because of compression developing outside the lymphatic. In frogs there are lymph hearts to propel lymph. It seems doubtful if lymph is propelled along the lymphatics of mammals by contractions of the smooth muscle in their walls. The compression of lymphatics occasioned by pulsating blood vessels in their vicinity, or by active or passive movements of the parts in which they are contained, may make lymphatic vessels serve as pumps to some extent and so aid in propelling lymph along them. This explains why massage may be employed to improve the lymphatic drainage of a part. It seems doubtful if there is very much lymph flow from normal tissues that are at rest. As we shall see when the intestine is studied, the lymphatics which drain it participate in the absorption of fat. After a fatty meal the lymph from the intestine is milky in color and is termed *chyle*.

The lymph that is collected in the body is finally returned to the bloodstream by means of 2 main terminal vessels; the *thoracic duct* and the *right lymphatic duct* (the latter may be represented by several vessels). At its beginning in the abdomen, the thoracic duct is somewhat dilated to form what is termed the *cisterna chyli*, and from here it extends for about 18 inches before it opens into the left innominate vein in the angle of its junction with the internal jugular and left subclavian veins. Sometimes it is represented by several smaller vessels which open separately into the great veins. The right lymphatic duct or, more commonly, several representatives of the right lymphatic duct, enter the great veins on the right side at sites comparable with those at which the thoracic duct enters the great vessels on the left side. The tributaries that flow into the thoracic duct and the right lymphatic duct (or their representatives), respectively, are described in textbooks of gross anatomy; here it is enough to point out that the thoracic duct receives all the lymph that forms in the abdomen; hence, it is much the larger vessel of the two.

**Fine Structure.** Perhaps the most important point that should be made about the fine structure of lymphatics is that lymph capillaries lack the surrounding basement membrane that ensheathes blood capillaries; this fact probably accounts in part for their ability to absorb macromolecules more readily than blood capillaries from tissue fluid and inflammatory exudates.

## REFERENCES

### REFERENCES ON ARTERIES, VEINS, LYMPHATICS AND THE TERMINAL VASCULAR BED

#### General

Abramson, D. I. (ed.): Blood Vessels and Lymphatics, New York, Acad. Press, 1962.

#### Special

Bennett, H. S.: The concepts of membrane flow and membrane vesiculation as mechanism for active transport and ion pumping, J. Biophys. Biochem. Cytol. 2:99, Supp. 1956.

Bensley, R. R., and Vimtrup, B.: On the nature of Rouget cells of capillaries, Anat. Rec. 39:37, 1928.

Buck, R. C.: The fine structure of endothelium of large arteries, J. Biophys. Biochem. Cytol. 4: 187, 1958.

Clark, E. R., and Clark, E. L.: Caliber changes in minute blood vessels observed in the living mammal, Am. J. Anat. 73:215, 1943.

————: Microscopic observations on the extra endothelial cells of the living mammalian blood vessels, Am. J. Anat. 6:1, 1940.

————: The relation of Rouget cells to capillary contraction, Am. J. Anat. 35:265, 1925.

Clark, E. R., Clark, E. L., and Williams, R. G.: Microscopic observations in the living rabbit of the new growth of nerves and the establishment of nerve controlled contractions of newly formed arterioles, Am. J. Anat. 55:47, 1934.

Cowdry, E. V.: Structure and physiology of blood vessels *in* Arteriosclerosis, p. 53, New York, Macmillan, 1933.

Fernando, N. V. P., and Movat, H. Z.: The smallest arterial vessels: Terminal arterioles and metarterioles, Exp. Molec. Path. 3:1, 1964.

————: The capillaries, Exp. Molec. Path. 3:87, 1964.

Florey, H. W., and Carleton, H. M.: Rouget cells and their function, Proc. Roy. Soc., London, s. B. 100:23, 1926.

Franklin, K. J.: A Monograph on Veins, Springfield, Ill., Thomas, 1937.

Hibbs, R. G., Burch, G. E., and Phillips, J. H.: The fine structure of the small blood vessels of normal human dermis and subcutis, Am. Heart J. 56:662, 1958.

Kampmeier, O. F., and Birch, C. L. F.: The origin and development of venous valves, Am. J. Anat. 38:451, 1927.

Kernohan, J. W., Anderson, E. W., and Keith, N. M.: Arterioles in cases of hypertension, Arch. Int. Med. 44:395, 1929.

Krogh, A., and Vimtrup, B.: The capillaries *in*

Cowdry's Special Cytology, ed. 2, p. 475, New York, Hoeber, 1932.

Majno, G., Palade, G. E., and Schoefl, G. I.: Studies on inflammation. II. The site of action of histamine and serotonin along the vascular tree: a topographic study, J. Biophys. Biochem. Cytol. *11*:607, 1961.

Movat, H. Z., and Fernando, N. V. P.: Small arteries with an internal elastic lamina, Exp. Molec. Path. *2*:549, 1963.

————: The venules and their perivascular cells, Exp. Molec. Path. *3*:98, 1964.

Nelemans, F. A.: Innervation of the smallest blood vessels, Am. J. Anat. *83*:43, 1948.

Palade, G. E.: Blood capillaries of the heart and other organs, Circulation *24*:368 (Part 2), 1961.

Sanders, A. G., Ebert, R. H., and Florey, H. W.: The mechanism of capillary contraction, Quart. J. Exp. Physiol. *30*:281, 1940.

Zweifach, B. W.: Character and distribution of blood capillaries, Anat. Rec. *73*:475, 1939.

————: The structure and reactions of the small blood vessels in amphibia, Am. J. Anat. *60*:473, 1937.

————: The microcirculation of the blood, Scient. Amer. *200*:54, 1959.

REFERENCES ON THE NERVOUS CONTROL
OF ARTERIES AND VEINS INCLUDING
BAROCEPTOR AREAS

Boss, J., and Green, J. H.: The histology of the common carotid baroceptor areas of the cat, Circulation Res. *4*:12, 1956.

Boyd, J. D.: Observations on the human carotid sinus and the nerve supply, Anat. Anz. *84*:386, 1937.

Clark, W. E. LeGros: The innervation of blood vessels *in* Tissues of the Body, ed. 2, p. 200, Oxford, Clarendon, 1945.

De Castro, F.: Sur la structure et l'innervation du sinus carotidien, Trav. du Lab-de Recherch. biol. Madrid *25*:331, 1928.

Nonidez, J. F.: Identification of the receptor areas in the venae cavae and pulmonary veins which initiate cardiac acceleration (Bainbridge's reflex), Am. J. Anat. *61*:203, 1937.

Woollard, H. H.: The innervation of blood vessels, Heart *13*:319, 1926.

Woollard, H. H., and Weddell, G.: The composition and distribution of vascular nerves in the extremities, J. Anat. *69*:165, 1935.
(See also textbooks of physiology.)

REFERENCES ON ARTERIOVENOUS
ANASTOMOSES

Clark, E. R.: Arterio-venous anastomoses, Physiol. Rev. *18*:229, 1938.

Daniel, P. M., and Prichard, M. M. L.: Arteriovenous anastomoses in the external ear, Quart. J. Exp. Physiol. *41*:107, 1956.

Prichard, M. M. L., and Daniel, P. M.: Arterio-venous anastomoses in the human external ear, J. Anat. *90*:309, 1956.

————: Arterio-venous anastomoses in the tongue of the sheep and the goat, Am. J. Anat. *95*:203, 1954.

REFERENCES ON THE HEART AND ITS
CONDUCTING SYSTEM

Bast, T. H., and Gardner, Weston D.: Wilhelm His, Jr., and the bundles of His, J. Hist. Med. Allied Sc. *4*:170, 1949.

Caesar, R., Edwards, G. A., and Ruska, H.: Electron microscopy of the impulse conducting system of the sheep heart, Z. Zellforsch. *48*: 698-719, 1958.

Davies, F., and Francis, E. T. B.: The conducting system of the vertebrate heart, Biol. Rev. *20-21*:173, 1946.

Duckworth, J. W. A.: The development of the sinu-atrial and atrio-ventricular nodes of the human heart, M.D. thesis, University of Edinburgh, 1952.

Gregg, O. E.: The coronary circulation, Physiol. Rev. *26*:28, 1946.

Herman, L., Stuckley, J. W., and Hoffman, B. F.: Electron microscopy of Purkinje fibers and ventricular muscle of dog heart, Circulation *24*: 954, 1961.

His, W., Jr.: Die Thätikeit des embryonalen Herzens, Arb. Med. Klin., Leipzig, 1893. Cited by Mall, F. P.: Am. J. Anat. *13*:278, 1912.

Kaylor, C. T., and Robb, J. S.: Observations on the differentiation and connexions of the specialised conducting tissue in the human heart, Anat. Rec. *97*:31, 1947.

Keith, A., and Flack, M.: The auriculoventricular bundle of the human heart, Lancet *2*:359, 1906.

Kent, S.: Researches on the structure of function of the mammalian heart, J. Physiol. *14*: 233, 1893.

Kistin, A. D.: Observations on the anatomy of the atrio-ventricular bundle (bundle of His), and the question of other atrio-ventricular connexions in normal human hearts, Am. Heart J. *37*:848, 1949.

Lewis, T., Oppenheimer, B. S., and Oppenheimer, A.: The site of origin of the mammalian heart beat; the pacemaker of the heart, Heart *2*:147, 1910.

Mahaim, I.: Les maladies organiques du faisseau de His-Tawara, Paris, Masson, 1931.

Mall, F. P.: On the development of the human heart, Am. J. Anat. *13*:249, 1912.

Muir, A. R.: Observations on the fine structure

of the Purkinje fibers in the ventricles of the sheep's heart, J. Anat. *91*:251-258, 1957.

Purkinje, J. E.: Mikroskopisch-neurologische Beobachtungen, Arch. Anat. Physiol. *22*:281, 1845.

Rhodin, J. A. G., Delmissier, P., and Reid, L. C.: The structure of the specialized conducting system of the steer heart, Circulation *24*:349-367, 1961.

Robb, J. S., Kaylor, C. T., and Turman, W. G.: A study of specialised heart tissue at various stages of development of the human heart, Am. J. Med. *5*:324, 1948.

Sanabria, T.: Recherches sur la différenciation du tissue nodal et connecteur du coeur des mammifères, Arch. Biol. *47*:1, 1936.

Shaner, R. F.: The development of the atrioventricular node, bundle of His and sino-atrial node in the calf, with a description of a third embryonic node-like structure, Anat. Rec. *44*: 85, 1929.

Stotler, W. A., and McMahon, R. A.: The innervation and structure of the conductive system of the human heart, J. Comp. Neurol. *87*:57, 1947.

Tawara, S.: Das Reizleitungssystem des Saugetierherzens, Jena, Fischer, 1906.

Walls, E. W.: The development of the specialized conducting system in the human heart, J. Anat. *81*:93, 1947.

(For Fine Structure of Cardiac Muscle *see* references for Chap. 20.)

# 23   The Integumentary System (The Skin and Its Appendages)

## INTRODUCTION

The skin is a membrane with many protective functions. It presents a barrier to disease organisms. The skin is nearly waterproof; this enables a relatively fluid body to exist in dry air. It likewise permits a body to be immersed in fresh water without becoming swollen and in salt water without becoming shrunken. The skin, particularly when it becomes pigmented, protects the body from the harmful effects of too much light. However, it is not impervious to all substances, for certain chemicals can be absorbed through it into the bloodstream. This may constitute an industrial hazard in certain trades (for example, in making certain kinds of explosives). But use may be made of this quality, for in treating certain diseases, some drugs may be administered by rubbing them on the skin, knowing that they will be absorbed.

The skin has other functions in addition to protective ones. It is important in regulating the temperature of the body. On hot days it facilitates heat loss and on cold days it acts as insulation. By sweating, the skin functions as an excretory organ. Vitamin D, the antirachitic vitamin, is made in skin exposed to ultraviolet light. Without vitamin D from other sources, children kept out of the sun develop rickets (Fig. 18-45). The skin contains nerve endings responsible for picking up stimuli that evoke many different types of sensation in consciousness (touch, pressure, heat, cold and pain). Hence, the skin is of the greatest importance in permitting man to adjust to his environment.

The peculiar importance of the skin in a physical examination should be realized by the student. No exploratory operations are necessary to see it; of all the important structures of the body, it alone is exposed so that it may be examined with the naked eye. Yet its appearance may reflect, just as truly as the appearance of deeply seated organs, the existence of a general disease. Its appearance often gives the doctor a more accurate estimate of a female patient's age than her own statement. The way hair is distributed helps in estimating inherent degrees of masculine and feminine personality components. The color of the skin may indicate a variety of conditions. Thus, it becomes yellow in jaundice, bronzed in certain glandular deficiencies, dry and hard in others and warm and moist in still others. Poisoning with silver may be revealed by the color of the skin. Cyanosis, already described, may give the skin a blue-gray appearance and so reflect impaired circulatory or respiratory functions. In vitamin A deficiencies, the skin of extensor surfaces may lose its hair and become rough, like sandpaper. In certain other vitamin deficiencies, the skin around the corners of the mouth may become cracked and scaly. Many infectious diseases that affect the whole body produce identifying rashes on the skin (for example, scarlet fever, measles, chickenpox, syphilis and others). The skin very commonly is affected when individuals are allergic (hypersensitive) to certain proteins and other substances, for example, some women develop rashes from certain kinds of face powder.

In addition to the involvement of the skin in conditions and diseases of a fairly general character, there are a whole host of skin diseases proper. The particular branch of medicine that deals with these and their treatment is called "dermatology."

Since the skin is the most exposed part of the body, it is peculiarly susceptible to various kinds of injuries. The treatment of cuts, abrasions, burns and frostbites are part of almost every doctor's life. So much skin is destroyed by accidents it is indeed fortunate that it can be grafted readily from one part of the body to another.

## GENERAL MICROSCOPIC STRUCTURE

The most important thing for the student to remember about skin is that it is a membrane

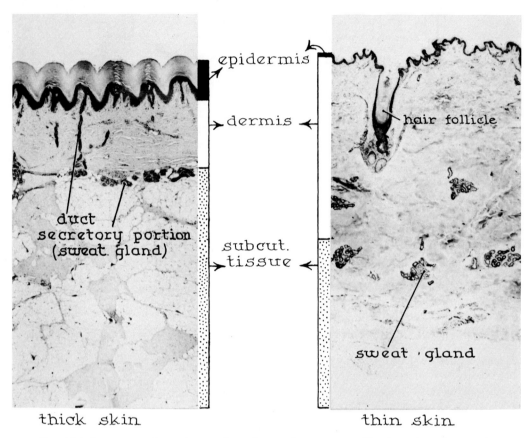

epidermis

dermis

hair follicle

duct
secretory portion
(sweat gland)

subcut.
tissue

sweat gland

thick skin                                                    thin skin

FIG. 23-1. Low-power photomicrographs, taken at the same magnification, of sections of thick and thin skin. The skin at the left was taken from the sole of the foot, and that on the right from the abdomen. Note that thick skin has a relatively thick epidermis that consists chiefly of keratin and that thin skin has a thin epidermis and a thick dermis.

consisting of *two* layers that are completely different in character and are derived from different germ layers. The outermost and thinner of these two layers, the *epidermis* (Fig. 23-1), is epithelial tissue and is derived from ectoderm. The innermost and thicker of the two layers, the *dermis* (Fig. 23-1), consists of dense connective tissue and is derived from mesoderm. These two layers are firmly cemented together to form a cohesive membrane—the skin—which varies in thickness from less than 0.5 mm. to 3 or even 4 mm. or more in different parts of the body. The skin rests on subcutaneous tissue which varies from areolar to adipose in character. This is the superficial fascia of gross anatomy. It is sometimes called the *hypodermis*, but it is not, like the epidermis, considered as part of the skin. Irregularly spaced bundles of collagenic fibers

extend from the dermis into the subcutaneous tissue to provide anchorage for the skin (Fig. 23-1, *left*). The subcutaneous tissue permits the skin over most parts of the body a considerable latitude of movement.

That the skin consists of an outer, epithelial and an inner, connective-tissue layer has certain implications. For example, very thin shavings may be cut from the surface of the skin without causing bleeding. The reason for this is that the very thin shavings consist entirely of epidermis, and epithelial membranes, it will be recalled, contain no blood vessels. Bleeding does not occur until shavings are taken deeply enough to cut into the dermis, where capillaries are situated. Hence, the cells of the epidermis live in tissue fluid derived from the capillaries of the connective-tissue dermis (refer to Figs. 10-1 and 10-8).

It will be recalled that glands generally develop as a result of the epithelial cells of a covering or lining membrane invading the supporting connective tissue of the region (review Fig. 9-1). During embryonic development, cells of the developing epidermis invade the developing dermis to form simple coiled tubular *sweat* glands (Figs. 23-1, *left,* 23-3 and 23-6). Other cells from the developing epidermis also grow into the dermis, or even somewhat deeper, to form "glands" that will in a sense "secrete" hairs, the *hair follicles* (Fig. 23-8). Epithelial cells from the sides of developing hair follicles grow out into the adjacent dermis to form *sebaceous glands* (Fig. 23-8). Similarly, near the tips of the fingers and the toes, epidermal cells invade the dermis to form grooves that will produce nails (Fig. 23-22). Sweat glands, hair follicles, sebaceous glands and nails constitute what are termed the *appendages of the skin,* and all develop, more or less like glands, by the invasion of the covering epidermis into the dermis.

Skin is commonly classified as *thick* and *thin*. Thick skin is found on the palms of the hands and the soles of the feet; thin skin covers the remainder of the body. However, these terms tend to give false impressions, for they refer to the thickness of the epidermis rather than to the thickness of the skin as a whole (compare the left and the right sides of Fig. 23-1). The skin of the palms of the hands and the soles of the feet has a thick epidermis with a particularly thick layer of keratin on its outer surface (Fig. 23-1, *left*). The skin covering the remainder of the body, although it has a thick dermis in some sites, as on the back, has a relatively thin epidermis, and the outer keratinized layer of this is relatively thin (Fig. 23-1, *right*). The particular structure of thick and thin skin will now be described.

## MICROSCOPIC STRUCTURE OF THICK SKIN

**Surface Ridges and Grooves.** In 1880, Henry Faulds, a Scottish medical missionary in Japan, published a note in *Nature* entitled "On the Skin Furrows of the Hand." He described these as "forever-unchangeable" and pointed out that "finger marks" might be used for the scientific detection of criminals. Indeed,

he reported some experience in this matter and described how some greasy finger marks had led to the identification of the individual who had been drinking their rectified spirits. This is the first reported instance of the use of fingerprints to detect a thief. From this beginning, fingerprinting has developed into a most useful tool in crime detection. More recently the dermal configurations have become a new area for medical research. For example, it has been shown that disturbances of fetal growth during the third and the fourth months of development may be permanently recorded in their patterns. Their study has also been proved useful with regard to deciding whether babies born at multiple births (twins, triplets, etc.) have their origin from the same or different ova.

**Significance and Development of Surface Ridges and Grooves.** If the palms of the hands (including the fingers) and the soles of the feet (including the toes) are examined with the naked eye or, better, with a magnifying glass, they are seen to be covered with ridges and grooves in a fashion reminiscent of a field plowed by the contour method. On the hands and the feet of the dark-skinned races the ridged area is clearly marked off by its lighter color.

Work by Cummins and others has shown that the ridges and the furrows develop during the third and the fourth fetal months. The pattern that then forms never changes afterward except to enlarge. The patterns are determined chiefly by hereditary factors, as is shown by the close similarity of those of one-egg twins and by the resemblances between those of the members of a family group. Racial differences are reflected in the patterns.

The patterns can be greatly modified by growth disturbances in the fetus during the third and/or the fourth months. This is strikingly shown in children that are born *mongoloid imbeciles* (this term originated because such children tend to have obliquely set eyes and certain other features that superficially resemble those of the Mongol race). Some 70 per cent of such children show combinations of patterns not seen in normal babies; hence, an analysis of the skin patterns of a newborn baby may give very important information as to whether or not it has been born an idiot, just as will the determination

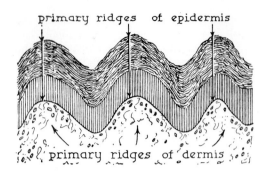

primary ridges   of epidermis

primary ridges  of  dermis

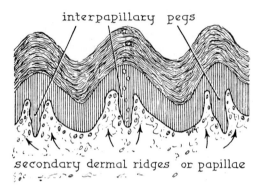

interpapillary pegs

secondary dermal ridges  or papillae

FIG. 23-2. Diagrams to show the relation between epidermal and dermal ridges. (*Top*) This diagram is not factual but is used to give the concept of a primary dermal ridge below each epidermal ridge. (*Bottom*) Actually, each primary dermal ridge is split into two secondary ridges as a result of the growth of the epidermis down into the primary ridge along its crest.

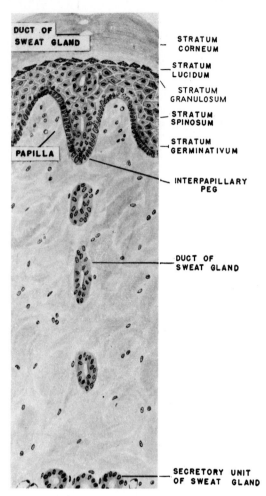

DUCT OF SWEAT GLAND

STRATUM CORNEUM

STRATUM LUCIDUM

STRATUM GRANULOSUM

STRATUM SPINOSUM

STRATUM GERMINATIVUM

INTERPAPILLARY PEG

PAPILLA

DUCT OF SWEAT GLAND

SECRETORY UNIT OF SWEAT GLAND

FIG. 23-3. Drawing of a section of thick skin (high-power) to illustrate the different layers of the epidermis, the way in which the duct of a sweat gland enters an interpapillary peg and how the wall of the duct thereafter is constituted by the cells of the different layers of the epidermis through which it passes. The thickness of the dermis is not in proportion; this was done to permit the secretory portion of the sweat gland to be shown.

of the number of chromosomes in its somatic cells.

The epidermal ridges are due to the epidermis following the contours of underlying dermal ridges. These may be studied in sections of skin cut at right angles to them. Sections of skin, so cut, would be easier to interpret if they appeared as is illustrated in the upper drawing in Figure 23-2, which shows clear-cut *primary dermal ridges* underlying the epidermal ridges. However, actual sections of skin do not appear this way but as is shown in the lower picture in Figure 23-2. This latter and real appearance is due to the fact that ridges of epidermis grow down into the peak of each primary dermal ridge so that the primary dermal ridges are each split into two ridges. The latter, from the appearance they

presented in single sections, were termed *papillae*, and, as a consequence, the epidermal downgrowth that lies between each pair is termed an *interpapillary peg*. (The structures termed papillae and interpapillary pegs are actually not cone-shaped papillae or pegs because they appear consistently in sections (Fig. 23-1, *left*). If they were true papillae and pegs they would be seen only on those occasions when the plane of the section happened to pass through one. (That they appear consistently proves that they are actually ridges; however, they are deficient occasionally along their courses.) As we shall see, the sweat glands of the skin open into the bottoms of the interpapillary pegs.

**Epidermis.** Since keratin is nonliving it cannot replace itself, and since it is continuously worn away or shed from the surface it must be continuously added to by means of the living cells beneath it turning into keratin. This requires that the living cells of the epidermis continuously proliferate to maintain their numbers. Storey and Leblond, by using colchicine and counting the mitotic figures in the epidermis, have shown that the living cells of plantar epidermis of rat are completely renewed every 19 days.

Many processes, then, are in more or less continual operation in the epidermis: (1) cell division in the deeper layers, (2) cells being pushed toward the surface as a result, (3) cells farthest from the dermis being transformed into keratin and (4) keratin desquamating from the surface. If these 4 processes are not synchronized properly—and in many skin diseases they are not—the character of the epidermis changes greatly.

Epidermis commonly is described as consisting of 5 layers or strata. The deepest of these abuts on the dermis. It consists of a layer of more or less columnar epithelial cells (Fig. 23-3). The borders of these are not distinct in the usual section, and the student must avoid thinking that their nuclei, which are distinct, are the cells themselves. This layer is called the *stratum germinativum* because it germinates new cells, which are pushed up into the next layer to be described.

The *stratum spinosum* or *prickle cell layer* is several cells thick (Fig. 23-3). The cells of this layer are of an irregular polyhedral shape. From appearances seen with the light microscope, such as the one illustrated in Figure 23-4, the individual cells of this layer often seem to be slightly separated from one another by tissue-fluid–filled intercellular spaces with adjacent cells being joined together only by fine lines (Fig. 23-4); the latter give the cells a prickly appearance and this accounts for cells of this layer being called *prickle cells*. In

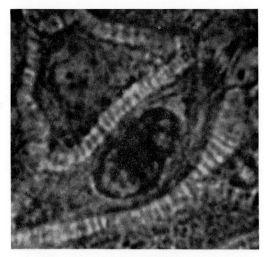

Fig. 23-4. Oil-immersion photomicrograph of section of thick human skin showing prickle cells. The fine lines that join adjacent cells, and which account for the prickly appearance of the cells, were once believed to be tonofibrils that passed from the cytoplasm of one cell into the cytoplasm of the next, and so anchored the cells together. It is now known that there is no cytoplasmic continuity between adjacent cells but that they are held together by desmosomes, the fine structure of which is illustrated in Figure 23-5.

the past it was believed that the fine lines were *tonofibrils* that actually crossed from the interior of one cell into the interior of the other. However, the EM has shown that the fine lines are actually very delicate strands of cytoplasm that extend out from each of two adjacent cells to meet and come into very close and firm contact at sites of *attachment plaques*, the basis of which is a form of desmosome which will be described presently (Fig. 23-5). Most of the substance of the fine lines that are seen with the light microscope is cytoplasm that has a considerable content of fibrillar material (black in Fig. 23-5); these condensed bundles of fibrillar material are in effect tonofibrils. The intercellular spaces are in part due to shrinkage artefact. If cells are separated slightly for any reason, the sites where cytoplasm is drawn out into fine lines are the sites where there are attachment plaques between the cytoplasm of adjacent cells; in other words, at the sites of desmosomes the cells do

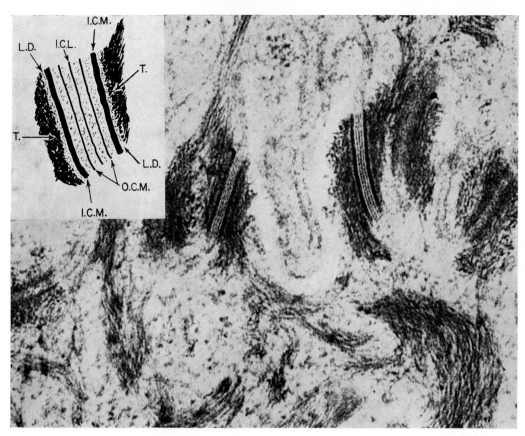

FIG. 23-5. Electron micrograph ($\times$ 85,000) of section of pig epidermis. Two good examples of desmosomes are clearly shown, one to the right and one to the left of the center of the picture. Each desmosome can be identified by 2 dark heavy parallel lines (I.C.M.) between which are 3 parallel fine dark lines. The middle fine dark line (I.C.L. for intercellular contact layer) represents electron-dense material at the site of contact between coatings which seem to be present on the outer layers of the cell membranes of the two adjacent cells. The fine dark line (O.C.M.) on each side of the middle line represents the outer layer of the membrane of each of the 2 cells that are joined by the desmosome. The heavy dark lines (I.C.M.) represent condensations of fibrillar material along the cytoplasmic side of the inner layer of the cell membrane of each of the 2 adjacent cells, and the dark fibrillar material (T.) which extends into the cytoplasm on each side from these condensations represents bundles of cell-web material large enough to constitute tonofibrils. (Wyllie, J. C., More, R. H., and Haust, M. D.: Lab. Invest. *13*:137)

(*Inset*) Diagram to help in the identification of what is seen in the main illustration.

not pull apart, so the cytoplasm in these sites is drawn out into the fine lines.

The desmosomes as seen in Figure 23-5 reveal lines of different densities. The inner layers of the cell membranes of the two cells that came into contact are represented by thick dark lines (I.C.M.). Between these, 3 thinner dark lines can be seen. The middle one is termed the intercellular contact layer (I.C.L.); this line would seem to be due to the cell membranes that approach each other in desmosomes being coated with some material that becomes electron dense along the line where the coatings meet and fuse. It would seem that in desmosomes it is the coatings on cell membranes that meet and fuse and not the cell membranes themselves, for the dark fine line (O.C.M.), seen on each side of the intercellular contact line, represents the outer layer of a cell membrane. As already noted, the heavy dark lines represent the inner thickened layers of cell membranes. Passing from the modified cell membranes that are seen in the desmosome to either side there is a narrow band of material of light density (L.D.) and then, after that, the dark heavy bundles of fibrillar material which is condensed into tonofibrils (T.).

The *stratum granulosum* is from 2 to 4 cells thick and lies just outside the stratum spinosum (Fig. 23-3). Its cells are roughly diamond-shaped, and they are fitted together with the long axis of each paralleling the contour of the overlying ridge or groove. The deepest cells of this layer resemble the cells of the stratum spinosum except for their cytoplasm which contains granules that stain deeply with hematoxylin (Fig. 23-3). These are called *keratohyalin* granules. However, the more superficial cells of this layer are considerably modified. Their nuclei are either broken-up or dissolved, and the number of cytoplasmic granules is greatly increased. It is in the stratum granulosum that the cells of the epidermis die. The nature of the keratohyalin granules that form in them is not thoroughly understood, but they are concerned in some phase of the process by which soft keratin is formed. The student should not make the mistake of thinking of these granules as a pigment, or of the stratum granulosum as a pigmented layer. True pigments possess color in their natural state; keratohyalin granules become colored only when stained.

The next layer is not always seen to advantage. When visible it is thin and appears as a clear, bright, homogeneous line. For this reason it is called the *stratum lucidum* (Fig. 23-3). It is said to consist of eleidin, which is presumed to be a transformation product of the keratohyalin observed in the stratum granulosum.

The fifth and outermost layer of the epidermis is termed the *stratum corneum* (*corneus* = horny) (Figs. 23-1 and 23-3). Here the eleidin of the stratum lucidum has become transformed into keratin, and what were once living epithelial cells have become horny scales that adhere to one another tightly, except at the surface where they desquamate.

It is of interest to inquire briefly into the cause of the differentiation or, as some prefer to think of it, the degradation of living epidermal cells into horny scales of keratin. Dehydration is probably not an all-important factor, because the cells of malignant tumors that arise from the epidermis and invade deeply the underlying connective tissue still continue to form keratin in sites far removed from the air. Likewise, epidermis transplanted into the subcutaneous tissue continues to form keratin. It is of interest that certain other types of specialized epithelium in the body, ordinarily not keratinizing, become so under conditions of prolonged vitamin A deficiency.

**The Junction Between Epidermis and Dermis.** The junction between the epidermis and the dermis is complex. First, there is an interdigitation of ridges and/or papillae. Next, it is believed that delicate processes from the basal cells of the epidermis extend into the dermis to form a ragged border between the two. This ragged border can be seen when separation occurs because of exudation (Fig. 23-19, *right*). Both the collagenic and the elastic fibers of the dermis seem to make very firm contact with the bases of the cells of the basal layers of the epidermis. A well-defined basement membrane such as is seen with the light microscope between epithelium and connective tissue, for example, in the intestine, is not seen in skin. However, a very delicate structureless basement membrane has been demonstrated with the EM at the bases of epithelial cells.

**Dermis.** This has 2 layers which are not sharply separated from one another. The outer is by far the thinner of the two and is called the *papillary* layer because the papillae are a prominent part of it. (Fig. 23-1). This layer extends only slightly below the bases of the papillae, where it merges more or less insensibly with the thicker *reticular* layer, which comprises the remainder of the dermis and is so-called because the collagenic fibers and bundles of fibers of which it is composed interlace with each other in a netlike manner.

Although both layers of the dermis consist of irregularly arranged fibrous tissue, the collagenic fibers in the papillary layer are not as coarse as those of the reticular layer; hence, the papillary layer has a finer and looser texture, being more of the order of loose connective tissue than dense. It contains a represen-

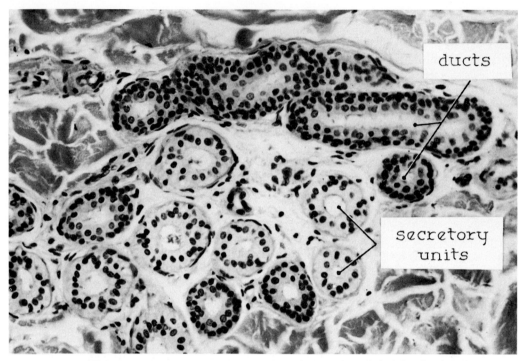

FIG. 23-6. High-power photomicrograph of an H and E section of dermis, showing the pale secretory units of sweat glands cut in cross section and the darker-staining ducts cut in both cross and oblique sections.

tation of the cells of loose connective tissue described in Chapter 11, except that plasma cells are infrequent in normal dermis. Some elastic fibers are interwoven with the collagenic fibers in both layers.

The cells of the dermis of thick skin are mostly fibroblasts, and these are scattered about sparingly. A few macrophages are also present. Fat cells may be present singly but are more commonly found in groups. The cells associated with the blood vessels, the lymphatics and the nerves of the skin will be described separately.

**Sweat Glands.** These are simple tubular glands. They are particularly numerous in thick skin; it has been estimated that there are 3,000 per square inch in the palm of the hand. Each one consists of a secretory part and an excretory duct. The secretory part usually is situated immediately below the dermis, in the subcutaneous tissue. The secretory part of the tubule is coiled and twisted on itself; hence, in sections it appears as a little cluster of cross and oblique sections of tubes (Figs. 23-3 and 23-6). The secretory cells are cu-

boidal or columnar in type, and they may exhibit pigment and vacuoles in their cytoplasm. The lumen of the secretory part is wider than its wall is thick. Spindle-shaped cells, resembling smooth muscle cells, are disposed obliquely and longitudinally around the secretory portions of the tubules. These are commonly called *myo-epithelial cells*, and it is thought that their contractions may assist in expelling sweat. Immediately outside these flattened cells, connective tissue is condensed so as to form a sheath around the secretory portions of the glands.

After pursuing a tortuous course in a very limited area, the secretory portion of the gland changes into a duct which passes toward the surface. The epithelial cells lining the duct stain more deeply than those of the secretory cells, and ducts can be distinguished readily in sections (Fig. 23-6). The lumen of the duct is much smaller than that of the secretory part of the gland; this is unusual, for in most glands the lumens of ducts are much wider than the lumens of secretory units. Duct walls consist of a double layer of thin cuboidal epi-

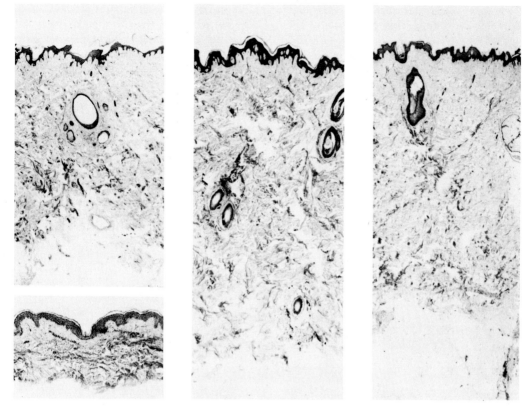

FIG. 23-7. The 3 large photomicrographs are all taken at the same magnification from sections of thin skin cut from different parts of the body. (*Left*) Skin from the inside of the leg. (*Center*) Skin from the abdomen which has been grafted to the wrist where it has been in position for some time. (*Right*) Skin from the lateral side of the thigh. (*Lower left*) Photomicrograph of a section cut from a split-skin graft that was cut at 18/1,000 of an inch in thickness. Notice that it contains a substantial content of dermis.

thelium. The ducts, which follow a somewhat spiral course through the dermis, enter the tips of the interpapillary pegs of epidermis that project down between the double rows of papillae (Fig. 23-3). The epithelium of the ducts at this site merges into that of the interpapillary pegs, and from this point on, the cells of the epidermis become the cells of the walls of the ducts. Ducts so constituted pursue a spiral course through the epidermis, and when the stratum corneum is reached, the spiral nature of their course becomes accentuated (Fig. 23-3). The ducts finally open on the surfaces of the ridges; their openings are obvious in a good fingerprint.

The blood and nerve supply of sweat glands will be considered later.

## MICROSCOPIC STRUCTURE OF THIN SKIN

Thin skin covers all of the body except the palms of the hands and the soles of the feet. As noted before, it should be understood that the adjective "thin" applies to the epidermis rather than to the skin as a whole. Actually, thin skin varies greatly in thickness in different parts of the body. These variations are due almost entirely to variations in the thickness of the dermis. The skin covering extensor surfaces is usually thicker than that covering flexor surfaces. The skin covering the eyelid is the thinnest in the body (0.5 mm. or less), and that covering the shoulders and the back is the thickest (up to 5 mm.) of the thin type.

Figure 23-7 illustrates some specimens of thin skin obtained from different parts of the body.

Thin skin contains sweat glands (Fig. 23-1, *right*) but they are not so numerous as those in thick skin. Thin skin differs from thick in that it contains hair follicles. These are highly developed in the scalp and in certain other regions, but they are present in the thin skin over the whole body, with a few minor exceptions (e.g., glans penis). Moreover, the surface of thin skin is not thrown into ridges and grooves like that of thick skin.

**Epidermis.** This has fewer layers than that of thick skin. The stratum germinativum is similar to that of thick skin, but the stratum spinosum is thinner. The stratum granulosum does not form a distinct continuous layer, but numerous cells containing cytoplasmic granules are scattered along the line where this layer might be expected. No stratum lucidum is present, and the stratum corneum is relatively thin (Fig. 8-20).

**Dermis.** The surface this presents to the epidermis is considerably different from that presented by the dermis of thick skin. Instead of papillae distributed regularly in the form of double parallel rows, the sites of which are indicated by epidermal ridges, the papillae of the dermis of thin skin are distributed more or less haphazardly, and their presence is not

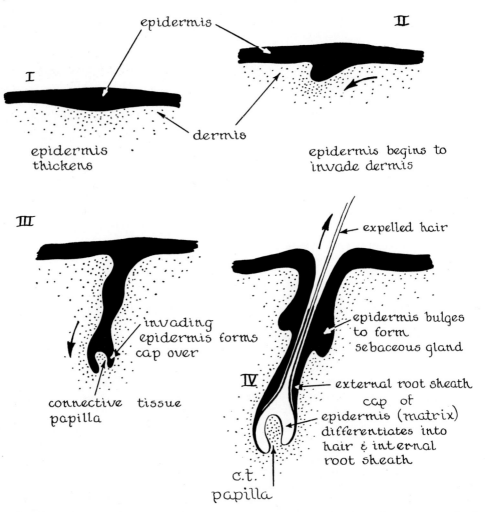

Fig. 23-8. Four sketches illustrating the development of a hair follicle and a sebaceous gland. (Redrawn and slightly modified from Addison: Piersol's Normal Histology, ed. 15, Philadelphia, Lippincott)

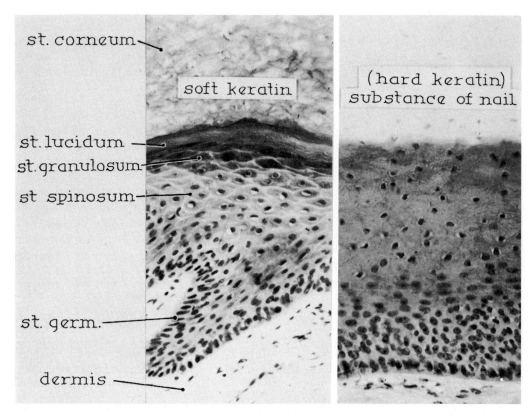

st. corneum

soft keratin

(hard keratin) substance of nail

st. lucidum
st. granulosum
st spinosum

st. germ.

dermis

Fig. 23-9. (*Left*) The process by which the soft keratin of thick skin is formed. Note keratohyalin granules in the stratum granulosum and that a stratum lucidum is present. (*Right*) The process by which the hard keratin of the nail is formed. Note the gradual transition of cells into nail substances with no stratum granulosum or lucidum and note that the hard keratin is more homogeneous than the soft.

reflected by any unevenness of the epidermal surface above them. The pattern of the epidermal surface is caused chiefly by lines that tend to connect the slightly depressed openings of the hair follicles.

## HAIR FOLLICLES

**Development.** Early in the third month of fetal life the epidermis begins to send downgrowths into the underlying dermis (Fig. 28-8, *I* and *II*). These develop first in the region of the eyebrows, the chin and the upper lip, but they are soon followed by others that develop in all parts of the body that later will be covered with thin skin. These epidermal downgrowths become hair follicles and give rise to hairs (Fig. 23-8, *III* and *IV*). By this means the fetus, at about the fifth or sixth month, has become covered with very delicate hairs. These constitute the *lanugo* (*lana* = wool) of the fetus. This coat of hair is shed before birth except in the region of the eyebrows, the eyelids and the scalp, where the hairs persist and become somewhat stronger. A few months after birth these hairs are shed and replaced by still coarser ones, while over the remainder of the body a new growth of hair occurs, and the body of the infant becomes covered with a downy coat called the *vellus* (fleece). At puberty, coarse hairs develop in the axilla and in the pubic region and, in males, on the face and to a lesser extent on other parts of the body. The coarse hairs of the scalp and the eyebrows and those that develop at puberty are termed *terminal hairs* to distinguish them from those of the lanugo and the vellus.

The human species, of course, is not very hairy. Most of the body is not covered with anything more than downlike vellus. Hair, then, is not a very important factor in keeping the body warm. It is, nevertheless, of the greatest importance that the skin of the human species should contain hair follicles. They, as we shall see, are instrumental in repairing epidermis injured by burns and abrasions, and they make split-skin grafting possible. We shall explain the reason for this presently.

**The Two Kinds of Keratin in Hair Follicles and Hairs.** From the work of Giroud, Bulliard and Leblond, Leblond, and Giroud and Leblond, it is apparent that there are two kinds of keratin. These, the *soft* and the *hard* types, can be distinguished by histologic means and they have different physical and chemical properties. Since both types are encountered in hair follicles we shall discuss the two types briefly so that their respective distribution in hair follicles can be described properly.

Soft keratin covers the skin as a whole; hard keratin is found only in certain of the skin appendages. The histologic changes that characterize the formation of soft keratin are seen most easily in thick skin (Fig. 23-9, *left*). The formation of soft keratin here, as everywhere else that it forms, is characterized by the epidermal cells that are becoming keratinized accumulating keratohyalin granules (or their counterparts) in their cytoplasm. Hence, an area where soft keratinization is occurring manifests a stratum granulosum or its counterpart. After this the cells become clear and glassy (stratum lucidum) before taking on the appearance which they characteristically present in the stratum corneum from which they continuously desquamate.

*To sum up:* Soft keratin is to be recognized histologically because in its formation the epidermal cells accumulate granules in their cytoplasm and because the keratinized squamous cells of which it is composed continuously desquamate from its surface (compare *left* and *right* of Fig. 23-9).

Hard keratin constitutes the nails and the cuticle and the cortex of the hairs of man as well as the feathers, the claws or the hooves of certain animals. Its formation is manifested histologically by the epidermal cells that form is not passing through a phase in which they demonstrate numerous granules of kerato-

hyalin in their cytoplasm or by their forming a stratum lucidum; instead, in the formation of hard keratin there is a gradual transition from the living epidermal cells into keratin (Fig. 23-9, *right*). Physically, hard keratin appears to be solid, and it does not desquamate; hence, it is a more permanent material than soft keratin (nails and hair must be cut if they are not to grow too long). Chemically, hard keratin is relatively unreactive and contains more sulfur than the soft variety.

**Structure of a Hair Follicle.** A hair follicle, as noted before, results from the growth of cells of the epidermis into the dermis or into the subcutaneous tissue. Therefore, it is an epithelial structure; indeed, it is much like a gland.

The deepest part of the epithelial downgrowth becomes a knobby cluster of cells and is called the *germinal matrix* of the hair follicle (Figs. 23-8 and 23-10) because, as we shall see, it germinates the hair. This cluster of epithelial cells (the germinal matrix) becomes fitted over a *papilla* of connective tissue (Figs. 23-8, *III* and 23-10) which brings capillaries, and hence a source of tissue fluid, into its central part.

The part of the epidermal downgrowth between the germinal matrix and the surface becomes canalized and thereafter is called the *external root sheath* of the hair follicle (Figs. 23-8, *IV;* 23-10 and 23-11). Near the surface of the skin, the external root sheath exhibits all the layers of epidermis of thin skin. This, of course, is to be expected since the external sheath represents a downward continuation of the epidermis. Therefore, the external sheath near the surface of the skin is lined with soft keratin that is continuous at the mouth of the follicle with the soft keratin of the epidermis of the skin (Fig. 23-10). But deeper down the follicle, the external root sheath becomes thinner and does not exhibit some of the more superficial layers of the epidermis. At the bottom of the follicle, where the external root sheath surrounds, and becomes continuous with, the germinal matrix, the external root sheath consists of only the stratum germinativum of the epidermis (Fig. 23-10).

For a hair to form in a follicle, the cells of the germinal matrix must proliferate. This forces the uppermost cells of the germinal matrix up the external root sheath. As the

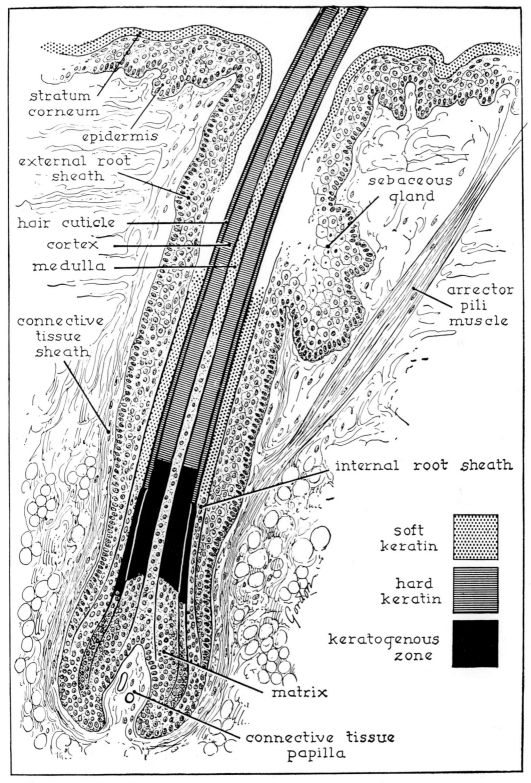

FIG. 23-10. Diagram of a hair follicle, showing the distribution of soft and hard keratin and the keratogenous zone in which hard keratin is produced. (Based on Leblond, C. P.: Ann. New York Acad. Sc. *53*:464)

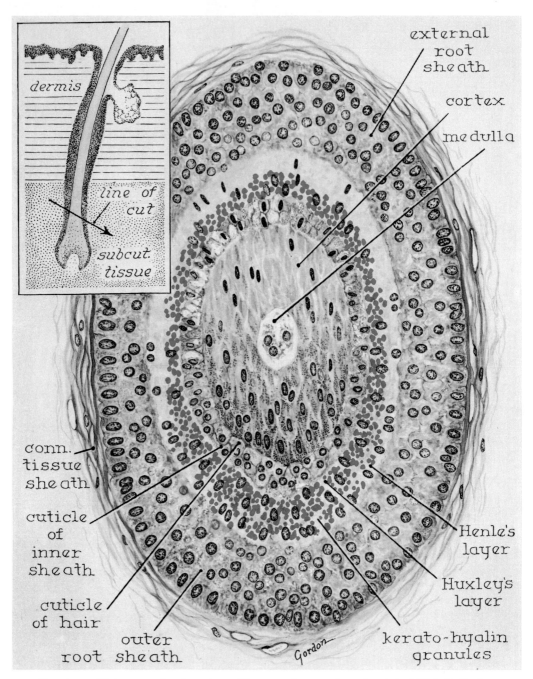

FIG. 23-11. High-power drawing of an oblique section cut through a hair follicle in the kera-togenous zone. The site and the plane of the section are shown in the inset at the upper left. (Hair follicles commonly extend into the subcutaneous tissue but usually not so far as the one shown in the inset.) Observe that the nuclei in both the internal root sheath and the hair are becoming pyknotic, and that red granules of trichohyalin (labeled kerato-hyalin) are present in the cells of the internal root sheath, thus indicating that it is forming soft keratin. No similar granules are to be seen in the cortex or the cuticle of the hair.

cells are pushed up they get farther and farther away from the papilla which is their
source of nourishment, and so they turn into
keratin. Those that turn into the cuticle and
the cortex of the hair, which are hard keratin,
show no keratohyalin granules, but instead a
keratogenous zone in which an even transition
into keratin occurs (Figs. 23-10, 23-12). Hairs
grow because of the continued proliferation of
the epidermal cells of the germinal matrix and
because of the successive conversion of these
cells into keratin as they are forced up the
follicle (Fig. 23-12).

However, the proliferating cells of the
matrix form another structure in addition to a
hair. This takes the form of a cellular tubular
sheath which is pushed up around the hair to
separate it from the external root sheath. This
is called the *internal root sheath* (Figs. 23-10
and 23-11). It extends only part way up the
follicle (Fig. 23-10). It is formed of soft keratin (Fig. 23-10); hence, granules of keratohyalin can be seen in its cells as they become
keratinized. In this region the granules are
generally called trichohyalin (*thrix* = hair,
*hyalin* = glass) granules, and instead of being
basophilic they stain a bright red (Fig. 23-11).

The inner root sheath has three layers: an
inner layer of cuticle, a middle Huxley's layer
and an outer Henle's layer (Fig. 23-11). The
student may have difficulty distinguishing
these but he should recognize the internal root
sheath by its content of acidophilic trichohyalin granules (Fig. 23-11).

As a hair follicle develops, cells from what
will become the external root sheath of the
upper third of the follicle grow out into the
adjacent dermis and differentiate into sebaceous glands (Fig. 23-8, *IV*). When these are
formed, their ducts open into the follicle at the
site from which the outgrowth occurred; hence,
the sebaceous glands empty into the upper
third of the follicle, below its mouth (Fig.
23-10). This part of the follicle often is called
the *neck*.

Most hair follicles slant somewhat from the
perpendicular. Therefore, the angle between
the hair follicle and the surface of the skin is
acute on the one side and obtuse on the other.
The sebaceous glands of a follicle usually are
disposed on the side of the obtuse angle (Fig.
23-10).

The hair follicle, it should be understood,

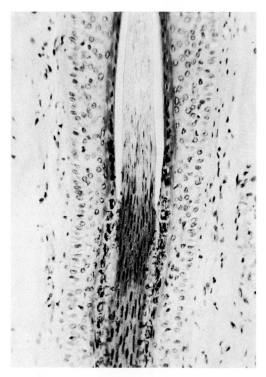

Fig. 23-12. Low-power photomicrograph
of a longitudinal section of a hair follicle at
the site where the cells from the matrix are
losing their nuclei and becoming converted
into keratin. The internal root sheath is
thicker at the bottom of the figure than it
is at the top.

is an epithelial structure. However, it is surrounded by a condensation of connective tissue which forms a *connective tissue sheath*
about it (Figs. 23-10 and 23-11).

A little bundle of smooth muscle fibers, the
*arrector pili* (erector of the hair), is attached
to the connective-tissue sheath of the hair
follicle (about halfway down the follicle or
deeper) and passes slantingly upward to reach
the papillary layer of the dermis a short distance away from the mouth of the hair follicle
(Figs. 23-10 and 23-13). This muscle, like the
sebaceous glands, is on the side of the follicle
that makes an obtuse angle with the surface.
This bundle of muscle makes a third side to a
triangle, the other two sides of which are the
follicle and the surface of the skin. The sebaceous glands are situated inside this triangle
(Fig. 23-10). When the arrector pili muscle
contracts, it not only pulls the whole hair

FIG. 23-13. Low-power photomicrograph of a section of thin skin at the site of an arrector pili muscle. The lumen and the upper part of the hair follicle do not show in this section. (Photomicrograph from Professor E. A. Linell)

follicle outward, but it also, by pulling on its deeper part from one side, makes the follicle more perpendicular (the hair "stands up"). Moreover, contraction of the muscle tends to "dimple in" the skin over the site of its attachment to the papillary layer of the dermis. The net result is a "goose flesh" appearance of, or "goose pimples" on, the skin. Moreover, the contraction of the muscle squeezes the sebaceous glands contained in the triangle previously described (Fig. 23-10), and this causes their oily secretion to be expressed into the neck of the follicle and onto the skin.

The arrectores pilorum, being smooth muscle, are innervated by the sympathetic nervous system. Cold is an important stimulus for setting off the reflex that leads to their contraction. The purpose of this reflex may be to express more oil onto the surface of the body from the sebaceous glands so that less evaporation, and hence less heat loss, can occur from the skin. Intense emotional states, as has been

pointed out, tend to energize the body through the medium of the sympathetic nervous system, and these too cause the arrectores pilorum to contract. Fear can make one's hair "stand on end." Lower animals often "bristle with rage." This response is useful in the porcupine.

### SOME POINTS OF INTEREST ABOUT HAIR AND HAIR GROWTH

For the interested, further and very practical information about hair is given in *The Hair and Scalp* by Agnes Savill. The conference on "The Growth, Replacement and Types of Hair," held by the New York Academy of Sciences and published in the *Annals* of the Academy *53*:464-751, 1951, covers almost every scientific aspect of the subject.

**Cyclic Activity of Hair Follicles.** It is only natural that any individual who notices that hairs come out in his brush or comb should wonder if baldness is imminent. Reassurance is to be obtained from the knowledge that hair growth is cyclic. This is more obvious in animals that live in the far north than it is in man, for these northern animals commonly grow a new coat for each winter and lose it for each summer. The hair follicles of man also exhibit cyclic activity in that they alternate between growing and resting periods. During the growing phase of the cycle, the cells of the germinal matrix continue to proliferate and to differentiate and, as a result, the hair is continually elongated. However, the growing phase merges into a resting phase as the germinal matrix becomes inactive and atrophies. The root of the hair then becomes detached from its matrix and gradually moves up the follicle, gaining for a time a more or less secondary attachment to the external root sheath as the lower end of the hair approaches the neck of the follicle. Meanwhile, in the deeper part of the follicle, the epidermal external root sheath has retracted upwardly toward the surface. Finally, the hair comes out of the follicle. Either before or after this event, the deeper parts of the external root sheath grow downward again to cover either the old papilla, which becomes rejuvenated, or a new one. A new germinal matrix develops, and this leads to a new hair beginning to grow up the follicle again.

The cyclic activity of the hair follicles of man differs in two ways from that of animals

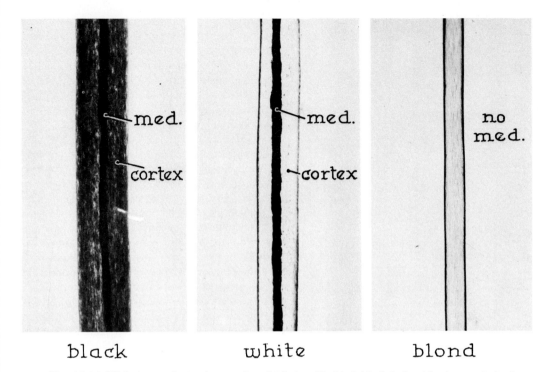

black　　　　　　　white　　　　　　　blond

Fig. 23-14. High-power photomicrographs of 3 hairs. (*Left*) A black hair with pigment in both its medulla and cortex. (*Center*) A white hair; it is to be observed that although no pigment is present in its cortex, it has pigment in its medulla. This shows that it is the pigment in the cortex that gives color to hair. (*Right*) This hair is of the blond variety, and it has no medulla; the black along each of its sides is due to refraction.

that form and lose a coat of hair each year. First, the cycles are longer in man. The hairs of the scalp probably last from 2 to 6 years. Secondly, different, even adjacent, hair follicles in man tend to be in different phases of their cycles at any given time. For example, Trotter found that at a time when 45 per cent of the hair follicles of the leg were in their growing phase, 55 per cent were in their resting phase.

**Common Baldness.** That baldness is very uncommon in women suggested for long that male sex hormone might have something to do with its cause, and Hamilton first provided evidence to show that it has. His studies indicate that castration, and hence a lack of male sex hormone production in the male, tends to hold in check the hereditary tendency to develop baldness, and that the administration of male sex hormone to individuals deficient in it, permits a hereditary tendency toward baldness to become operative, with baldness resulting. In other words, the genetic factors which tend to cause baldness can be fully effective only if male sex hormone is present in the bloodstream of the individual concerned. Although baldness is an obvious sign of male sex hormone activity, the compensating conclusion should not be drawn by balding men that they are necessarily more virile than those with good heads of hair. Male sex hormone does not cause baldness unless the hereditary disposition to develop baldness is present.

**The Effect of Cutting on the Growth of Hair.** Another question about hair, probably of more interest to women than to men, is whether or not shaving or otherwise cutting hairs encourages their growth. This has been the subject of much careful inquiry and has required long and painstaking experiments (see Trotter). The general conclusion from these experiments is that cutting or shaving hair has no effect on its growth.

**Structure of Hair.** The cross-section appearance and other features of hair vary in relation to race. In anthropology, three chief types of

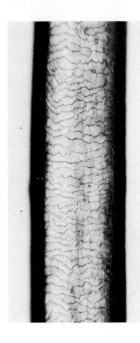

FIG. 23-15. Oil-immersion photomicrograph of the surface of a hair, showing its shinglelike cuticular scales.

hair are recognized: straight, wavy and woolly. Straight hair is found in the members of the yellow or Mongol races, the Chinese, the Eskimos and the Indians of America. Straight hair is characteristically coarse and lank and is round in cross section. Wavy hair is found in a number of people, including Europeans, and woolly hair on nearly all the black races. A cross section of a wavy hair is oval and that of a woolly hair, elliptical or kidney-shaped.

A hair consists of a central medulla of soft keratin (Figs. 23-10 and 23-11) and a cuticle and a cortex of hard keratin (Figs. 23-10 and 23-11). Many hairs contain no, or at least a very poorly developed, medulla (Fig. 23-14, *right*); hence, they show only a cuticle and a cortex of hard keratin.

The cuticle consists of very thin, flat, scale-like cells that are arranged on the surface of a hair like shingles on the side of a house, except that their free edges point upward instead of downward (Fig. 23-15). The free edges of these cells more or less interlock with the free edges of similar cells that line the internal root sheath and whose free edges point downward. The interlocking arrangement makes it difficult to pull out a hair without at least part of the internal root sheath coming with it.

The cortex consists of tapering cornified cells. It is the pigment in the cells of the cortex that gives color to hair (Fig. 23-14). This pig-

ment may be present as finely distributed granules or in clumps. It is also thought that pigment may sometimes be in solution in the cortex (fluid pigment).

The medulla consists of a central core of cornified cells that are commonly separated from one another. Air or liquid may be present between the cells of the medulla.

**Color of Hair.** The color of hair depends upon the quantity and the quality of the pigment present in the cortex. White hairs mixed with pigmented hairs give what is commonly called gray hair (true gray hair is rare). The pigment responsible for black or brown hair is melanin. How melanin is formed in hair will be considered after we deal with pigment in skin.

**Keratin and Its Properties.** The process by which the epithelial cells change into the hard keratin of the cuticle and the cortex of the hair is gradual (Fig. 23-12) and similar to that seen in the formation of the hard keratin of nails (Fig. 23-9, *right*). No keratohyalin granules are seen.

Keratin, like collagen and elastin, is a member of the albuminoid group of proteins and, like the others, is very resistant to chemical change. The hard type has a high content of sulfur.

## SEBACEOUS GLANDS

During the development of a hair follicle, epithelial cells, generally from the region of its neck and on the side of the follicle that makes an obtuse angle with the skin, grow out into the adjacent dermis (Fig. 23-8, IV) to form little pear-shaped glands (Fig. 23-16). Usually, several form from each follicle. These open by very short but wide ducts (Fig. 23-16) into the neck of the follicle. These glands secrete a fatty material called *sebum*; this oils the hair and lubricates the surface of the skin. Sebum is said to possess some bactericidal properties. However, its chief function is probably that of acting as a natural "cold cream." It prevents undue evaporation from the stratum corneum in cold weather and so helps to conserve body heat. In hot weather, by keeping the stratum corneum oiled, it helps to keep it from becoming cracked and chapped when sweat is evaporating from it.

Sebaceous glands are holocrine glands (see

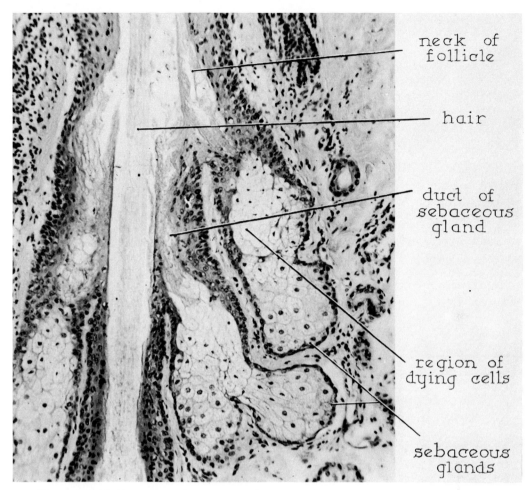

neck of follicle

hair

duct of sebaceous gland

region of dying cells

sebaceous glands

FIG. 23-16. Medium-power photomicrograph of a section of skin, showing a sebaceous gland opening into a hair follicle.

Fig. 9-3). As noted before, each little gland is pear-shaped with its body being the secretory portion of the gland and its neck the duct. The body of the gland is surrounded by a basement membrane which is covered on its outer surface by a delicate connective-tissue sheath. On the inner aspect of the basement membrane is the "stratum germinativum" or basal layer of the cells of the gland. This consists of thin, flat epithelial cells. On the inner aspect of this layer are cells that are derived from those of the basal layer but which are larger, more rounded and contain fat droplets (Fig. 9-3). Proceeding toward the central part of the gland, still larger cells containing more fat are seen. The nuclei of the cells in the central part of the gland are

pyknotic or absent (Fig. 9-3). Some granules of keratohyalin are present in some of the cells. Toward the neck of the gland (its duct), the cells break down completely, and a blend of fat, keratohyalin granules, keratin and cellular debris is formed (Fig. 23-16). This is sebum.

For a sebaceous gland to secrete sebum, many processes must be in progress more or less simultaneously. These are: (1) the proliferation of the cells of the basal layer of the gland, (2) the pushing of the extra cells formed as a result of the proliferation toward the center of the gland, (3) the accumulation of fatty material in the cytoplasm of these cells as they move away from the basal layer and (4) the necrosis of these cells as they are

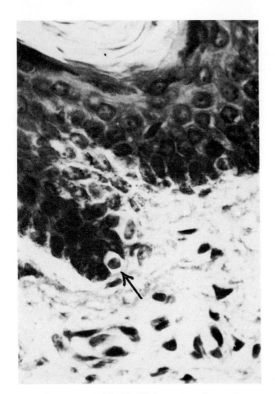

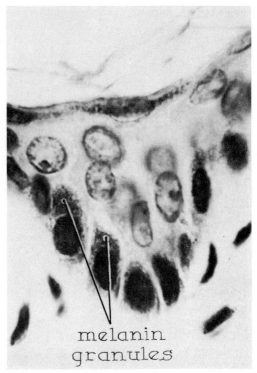

Fig. 23-17. (*Left*) High-power photomicrograph of a section of skin, showing a "clear cell" in the stratum germinativum. (*Right*) Oil-immersion photomicrograph of a section of pigmented skin, showing melanin granules in the cytoplasm of the cells of the stratum germinativum.

pushed still farther toward the center of the gland (because they are so far removed from sources of nourishment), by the continuing proliferation and differentiation of cells behind them. As noted before, contraction of the arrector pili muscle can cause formed sebum to be expressed quickly from the gland into the hair follicle.

That sebaceous glands develop from hair follicles explains why no sebaceous glands are found in the skin that covers the soles of the feet or the palm of the hands. However, in a few sites in the body sebaceous glands develop without hair follicles (eyelids, papillae of breasts, labia minora and corners of lips near the red margins in some people). And in some sites, and in particular in the skin covering the nose, the sebaceous glands that develop from hair follicles become much more prominent than the hair follicle itself; the hair follicle in these sites is, as it were, a means to an end.

## PIGMENTATION OF THE SKIN

The most important pigment in the skin is melanin. Its precise chemical constitution is not known, and it is likely that there are many melanins. These are widely distributed in the animal kingdom and range from yellow, through brown, to black in color. In man, melanin occurs chiefly in the epidermis, in the white race in the cells of the basal layers, where it tends to be disposed often, as a student once wrote on a histology examination on the sunny side of the nucleus (Fig. 23-17, *right*). Melanin occurs in the form of fine, brown to black granules but these commonly clump together if the pigment is abundant. The amount of melanin in the epidermis is responsible for the difference in the color of the skins of those of different races (black, brown, yellow and white). All have some melanin in their skins. An inherent inability in any individual of any race to produce melanin pigment results in an *albino* (*albus* = white).

Since the epidermis of white skin (unless tanned by the sun) contains relatively little melanin, it allows the color of the blood in those capillaries in the outer part of the dermis that are open to the circulation to show through it. If the blood in these capillary beds contains only a small amount of reduced hemoglobin, the blood is red and this shows through the skin to give it a pink color.

Increased amounts of melanin appear in the epidermis of white skin when it is exposed to ultraviolet light. It is the ultraviolet light in sunlight that causes suntan to develop. Brunettes tan more readily than blonds. In some individuals the skin tans evenly. However, in some individuals melanin tends to form in little patches (freckles).

**The Cells That Make Melanin Pigment.** The terminology regarding the cells that make melanin has been changed in recent years. In the older literature they were generally termed melanoblasts; now they are termed melanocytes.

The term melanoblast is now used for cells that in embryonic life develop in the neural crest and then migrate to the epidermal-dermal junction. Melanoblasts, as the term is now used, do not make melanin. As, or after, they take up a position at or in the basal layer of the epidermis, they differentiate into melanocytes, and these make melanin.

The cell bodies of melanocytes are disposed either just beneath or between the cells of the basal layer of the epidermis. Before they make melanin they may appear in the basal layer as "clear cells" (Fig. 23-17, *left*). The cell bodies of melanocytes in either position send out long processes which extend between or under epidermal cells, mostly those of the basal layer. The processes end on epidermal cells. In due course melanin granules, made by the melanocytes, pass into the epithelial cells via the long processes of the melanocytes. It is by this means that the ordinary epithelial cells of the basal layer come to contain melanin pigment. It follows therefore that melanocytes cannot be distinguished from true epidermal cells by, or because of, their containing pigment. Although it has been suggested that before they become functioning melanocytes they may appear as "clear cells"

(Fig. 23-17, *left*), functioning melanocytes can be distinguished from ordinary epidermal cells by a histochemical test which picks out cells that have the functioning metabolic equipment required to make pigment. This test, known as the "dopa reaction," is performed as follows.

The ability of melanocytes to produce melanin depends on their ability to synthesize the enzyme or the enzyme complex known as *tyrosinase*. If they possess this enzyme in active form, and are provided with the correct substrate, the tyrosinase will react with the substrate to form melanin. In man, however, the addition of tyrosine to preparations of epidermis does not lead at least immediately to the melanocytes of the preparation forming melanin (the reactions involved are complicated). However, if dihydroxyphenylalanine, which is referred to as dopa, and which is an oxidized product of tyrosine, is added to a suitable preparation of epidermis, the tyrosinase within the melanocytes converts the dopa of the solution that penetrates into these cells into melanin which then is seen in the cytoplasm of the melanocytes as a dark pigment. This test, which is termed the *dopa reaction,* can be used to distinguish cells that have the ability to make melanin from cells which have merely taken up melanin.

The dopa reaction has shown that melanocytes are very numerous in epidermis. According to Montagna, 1 out of every 4 to 1 out of 10 cells in the basal layer of the epidermis of man is a melanocyte. The dopa reaction has also been very helpful in demonstrating the complicated arrangements of processes that extend off from the cell bodies of melanocytes to intertwine with, and end on, epidermal cells and supply them with pigment. The processes are often termed dendrites, and in the past the cells that are probably now known as melanocytes were often termed dendritic cells.

The biosynthesis of melanin by melanocytes has been studied by many methods including electron microscopy. Seiji *et al.* have suggested a sequence of events which occurs in cells that are producing melanin. It could be expected that the rough-surfaced vesicles of endoplasmic reticulum are concerned at least in the early steps of the synthesis of the enzyme and that the protein products synthesized in rough-surfaced vesicles would be transferred to the Golgi region. Here, the product that arrives from the rough-surfaced vesicles is probably condensed and packaged in the form of smooth-surfaced membranous vesicles, the contents of which is now termed *pro-tyrosinase*. The contents of these smooth-surfaced membranous vesicles are now changed further, and the vesicles with their contents are now known as premelanosomes. When this occurs the contents become active; that is, active tyrosinase appears in the contents of the vesicles and this results in melanin being synthesized in or in association with these vesicles. When this happens the vesicles become known as melanosomes. Soon, or later, each melanosome becomes converted into a melanin granule, and when this has happened the structure no longer contains any demonstrable tyrosinase. The whole process is probably not unlike that which occurs in connection with the synthesis of zymogen granules, which was described in Chapter 7, except that the enzymes in membranous packages of secretion that appear in the Golgi region become active while the packages are still within the cytoplasm. In this respect the process is somewhat reminiscent of events that can occur in connection with the formation and the activation of lysosomes.

Such melanin-containing cells as are seen in the dermis, with one exception, are cells that have not made melanin but have phagocytosed it; hence they are called *chromatophores* (*phoreo* = I carry). However, in infants of the Mongol race there may be true melanocytes deep in the dermis of the sacral region. Seen through the tissue that covers them their pigment appears blue; this is the color seen when melanin is seen through overlying tissue. The blue spot thus apparent is called a Mongol spot. Melanocytes are seldom seen in this site in children of the white race.

Melanin protects the deepest layers of the epidermis and the underlying dermis from excessive ultraviolet light. The fact that a person becomes tanned is evidence of the formation of an increased amount of melanin for this purpose. Ultraviolet light on the skin is, of course, helpful to a point, because it irradiates ergosterol, a derivative of cholesterol, and irradiated ergosterol is one form of vitamin D, and this vitamin, which is absorbed from the skin, is an essential factor in a proper mineral metabolism. A lack of vitamin D can cause rickets in children. It is of interest that it was noticed years ago that Negro children who are brought up in northern regions where there is not so much sunlight as there is in more southern regions are more prone to develop rickets than children of the white race. Nowadays, of course, in order to prevent rickets, infants are given vitamin D preparations by mouth.

**The Pigmentation of Hair.** The pigment of hair, like that of the epidermis, is primarily due to its content of melanin. The melanin of hair is formed by melanocytes; these are distributed in the upper part of the bulb of a hair follicle. The melanocytes in this region, like those of the epidermis, send out cytoplasmic processes that reach, and provide melanin for, the epithelial cells that will, by undergoing keratinization, become the cortex and the medulla of the hair. As the cells that formed, by means of cell division, in the matrix of the follicle move upward, they take up melanin in the upper part of the bulb, and then move up farther and become keratinized to become the cortex and the medulla of the hair. The melanin they contain becomes incorporated into the keratin of the hair to give it color.

There is evidence to indicate that the melanocytes of the bulb of the follicle divide by mitosis and so perpetuate themselves.

As people become older their hair turns "gray." The lack of pigment in the hair of older people is ascribed to an increasing inability of the melanocytes of the bulbs of their hair follicles to make tyrosinase.

Although hair in the gross appears in different colors, hair pigments of only 3 colors can be seen with the microscope; these are black, brown and yellow. The yellow pigment is termed pheomelanin and its formation seems to be under the control of different genes from those that control the formation of black and brown melanin. The metabolic pathways concerned in its formation are not thoroughly understood but are different from those concerned in the formation of black and brown melanin.

For a comprehensive consideration of the nature of hair pigment, those interested will

find the chapter on this subject by Fitzpatrick, Brunet and Kukita in *The Biology of
Hair Growth,* edited by Montagna and Ellis,
most informative (see references).

## BLOOD SUPPLY OF THE SKIN

**Arteries.** The largest arteries of the skin
are arranged in the form of a flat network in
the subcutaneous tissue, immediately below
the dermis. This arterial network is called the
*rete cutaneum.* It receives blood from branches
of the larger arteries that run more deeply in
the subcutaneous tissue. From the rete cutaneum, branches pass both inwardly and outwardly. Those that pass inwardly supply the
adipose tissue of the more superficial parts of
the subcutaneous tissue and the parts of such
hair follicles as are disposed therein. Those
that pass outwardly supply the skin. They
generally pursue a curved course as they
penetrate through the reticular layer of the
dermis and they give off side branches to the
hair follicles and to the sweat and sebaceous
glands as they pass through it. On reaching
the outer part of the reticular layer of the
dermis, they form a second flat network, composed of smaller vessels, called the *rete subpapillare.* In the skin of the fingers and the
toes, and in certain other sites, arteriovenous
anastomoses are present in little bodies called
*glomi* that are disposed deep in the dermis
(Fig. 23-18).

**Capillary Beds.** It should be kept in mind
that the dermis, since it consists chiefly of the
relatively inert intercellular substance, collagen, does not require a very extensive capillary blood supply. Indeed, most of the dermis
is very sparingly supplied with capillaries. As
might be expected, the capillary beds of the
skin are extensive only in that portion of the
dermis that is in close association with epithelial cells that require abundant nourishment for their function and growth. The capillary beds of the skin, then, are confined to the
connective tissue that (1) immediately underlies the epidermis, (2) surrounds the matrix
of the hair follicles, (3) constitutes the papillae of hair follicles and (4) surrounds the
sweat and sebaceous glands.

The first capillary bed mentioned requires
some further comment. Arterioles from the
rete subpapillare pass toward the epidermis

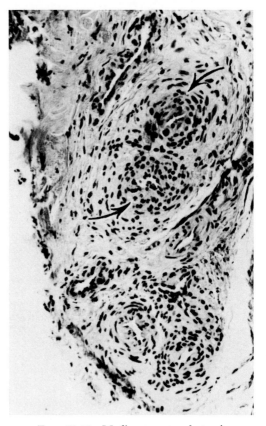

FIG. 23-18. Medium-power photomicrograph of a section of skin, showing a
glomus. The thick-walled arterial vessel in
the glomus (indicated by arrows) is coiled
or convoluted; hence, cross sections of it
appear in several sites.

and give rise to capillaries that extend as loops
up into the papillae (Fig. 23-19, *left*). These
efficiently supply tissue fluid to the basal cells
of the epidermis. However, the capillary loops
in the papillae are not the cause of the pink
color of skin. This is due to flat networks of
small thin-walled vessels (not the arterial
plexus) in the deeper part of the papillary,
and in the superficial part of the reticular,
layers of the dermis. These flat networks constitute the *subpapillary plexuses* of the skin.
Lewis has studied intensively the physiology
of these vessels. It is generally conceded that
most of them are independently contractile.
It is questionable if these small vessels should
be regarded as capillaries. The subpapillary
plexuses are often described as venous

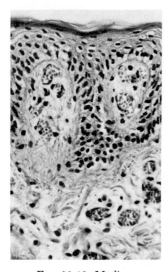 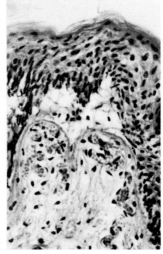 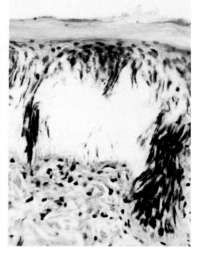

Fig. 23-19. Medium-power photomicrographs of sections of the skin of a pig, showing how a blister develops after a burn. (*Left*) Section taken from the skin 15 minutes after it suffered a light burn. Note that the capillaries in the dermal papillae, close to the epidermis, are dilated and congested with blood. (*Center*) Section taken 1 hour after the skin was burned lightly. The capillaries of the papillae are still dilated and congested, and, in addition, plasma has leaked from them and is accumulating between the dermis and the epidermis. (*Right*) Section taken 4 hours after the skin was burned lightly. It shows the epidermis lifted a considerable distance from the dermis by the plasma that has leaked from the injured capillaries of the dermis. (Ham, A. W.: Ann. Surg. *120*:692)

plexuses. Probably they are best thought of as consisting of both capillaries, venules and small veins, with most of them being sufficiently small to have walls thin enough to allow plasma to leak through them when they are injured. The capillaries in these plexuses are supplied by arterioles from the rete subpapillare. The small venules drain into larger ones, which, in turn, drain into small veins. In general, the veins leave the skin with the arteries.

**Function of the Superficial Capillaries and Venules.** In man, heat generated in the body is lost directly through the skin. If the temperature of the air is lower than that of the body, the rate of heat loss can be increased or decreased by the degree to which the capillaries and the venules of the papillary and the subpapillary regions of the skin are open to the circulation. If the temperature of the air is close to, or higher than, that of the body, the *effect* of a low outside temperature can be achieved by the sweat glands pouring fluid onto the surface of the body, where it evaporates and so cools the outer part of the skin.

Hence, blood circulating through the papillary and the subpapillary regions of skin from which sweat is evaporating is cooled, and by this mechanism heat can be lost from the body in hot weather. To keep down the temperature of an individual who performs violent muscular exercise on a very hot day and so generates a great deal of heat, both profuse sweating and dilatation of the superficial blood vessels are needed. Some unfortunate individuals are born with very few or no sweat glands. When the temperature rises sufficiently, such individuals, while at work, can maintain their body temperature at correct levels only by frequently changing into fresh wet clothing.

It should be pointed out that the skins of many animals cannot lose heat in this way in hot weather. The hairy coats of animals serve primarily as insulation. There is, then, no need for these animals to have sweat glands and extensive nets of capillaries and venules in the papillary and the subpapillary parts of their skins. For this reason, the blood supply of the skin of most laboratory animals

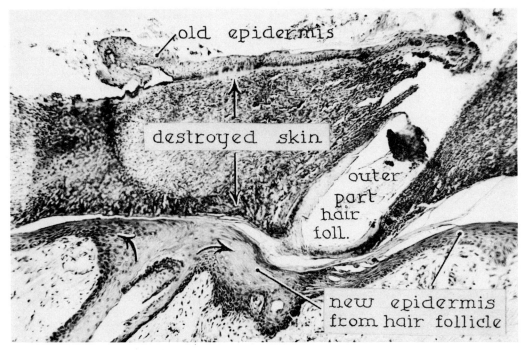

FIG. 23-20. Low-power photomicrograph of a section of the skin of a pig some days after it was burned sufficiently to destroy the epidermis and the outer part of the dermis. The original epidermis, now dead, may be seen in the upper part of the figure. Below it, a considerable layer of destroyed dermis, containing the destroyed outer part of a hair follicle, may be seen. Below the layer of dead dermis, a new, thin line of epidermis growing out from the deeper part of the hair follicle may be seen. The newly formed epithelial cells push along the line between the living and the destroyed skin. The destroyed skin eventually is extruded as a scab when the new epidermis forms a continuous covering for the living skin below. Subsequently, the epidermis becomes thick, and the dermis beneath it also thickens, so that the thickness of the entire skin is restored.

is very different from that of the skin of man. Therefore, deductions made from experiments performed on the skins of animals are not necessarily applicable to man. The common pig is an exception. It is not particularly hairy, and its skin is employed to lose heat in warm weather. The blood supply of the skin of the pig is similar to that of the skin of man. It is one of the few animals that becomes sunburned.

**Practical Application of Knowledge of Blood Supply.** A light burn, such as is commonly obtained on the first visit of the year to the beach, produces enough injury to cause the capillaries and the venules in the papillary and subpapillary layers of the skin to become widely open to the circulation (Fig. 23-19, *left*). This makes the skin red. An exposure to light or heat comparable with that which produces a red burn in man does not cause a reddening of the skin in most laboratory animals, for they lack the extensive papillary and subpapillary plexuses possessed by man and needed by man to disseminate heat.

In a slightly more severe burn, the capillaries and the venules of the papillary and the subpapillary regions, in addition to dilating, allow plasma to leak from them (Fig. 23-19, *center*). This causes an edema of the outer part of the skin and often results in blisters. In thin skin, blisters are the result of accumulations of plasma between the dermis and the epidermis (Fig. 23-19, *right*). In thick skin, blisters sometimes may be due to intraepithelial accumulations of plasma.

**The Regeneration of Epidermis.** If thin skin has been burned severely enough for blisters to have formed, it has been burned severely enough, we think, to have destroyed the epidermis. Under these circumstances, a new epidermis must be regenerated from the living epithelium that persists in the hair follicles. This grows out from them to cover the denuded dermis (Fig. 23-20). Even if a burn is severe enough to destroy the more superficial part of the dermis (as well as the epidermis), the epithelial cells from the deeper parts of the hair follicles will survive and grow out along the line between the living and dead dermis (Fig. 23-20) to form a new epidermis at this level.

If a burn is severe enough to destroy the epithelium deep in the hair follicles, the burned area can become epithelized naturally only by epithelium growing in from the edges of the injured area. This is a slow process, and if the burned area is large, it would take months or years to heal. In the meantime, the exposed dermis would become the seat of inflammatory process that, in all probability, would cause huge scars to form. Nowadays, such burns are treated promptly by skin grafting, as will be described presently.

**A Note on Thermal Burns.** In superficial burns, plasma leakage occurs chiefly from the dilated and injured capillaries and venules of the papillary and the subpapillary layers of the dermis. Such burns appear red because these superficial vessels become dilated by the injury (Fig. 23-19, *left*). In more severe burns these superficial vessels become coagulated by heat; hence, more severe burns may, at first, be white in color. In these, plasma leaks from deeper capillary beds associated with the hair follicles and sweat glands. In still more severe burns, plasma leaks from the capillary beds that supply the fat cells in the subcutaneous tissue. If a large area of skin is burned, even if the burn is not deep, enough plasma may leak from injured capillaries and venules to cause the death of the patient (see Hemoconcentration, Chap. 10). Consequently, in the modern treatment of burns, every effort is made to prevent hemoconcentration by administering blood plasma intravenously to the burned person. Extreme plasma leakage can be prevented, to a considerable degree, by applying pressure bandages (plasma cannot leak out of the circulatory system into tissues unless it can expand the tissues).

## SKIN GRAFTING

Skin may be grafted from one part of the body to another by two general methods. By one, the transplanted skin is never severed completely from its blood supply. By the second, the skin to be grafted is completely detached from its blood supply when it is transferred. This is called a *free graft*.

Grafting skin from one part of the body without ever severing it from a blood supply has led to the development of many ingenious operations by plastic surgeons. Without going into details, the general method, for example, by which skin from the arm can be transferred to the face, is as follows:

A flap of skin of the desired size is partly detached from the arm, and the wound so created is closed or covered with a free skin graft. If the flap has been cut properly, the blood vessels entering along its attached margin are sufficient to keep the whole flap alive. If the flap is protected (rolled up or otherwise treated), the blood vessels entering the flap from the attached margin respond to their increased duties by becoming larger and more numerous. After the flap is seen to have a satisfactory blood supply from its one attached margin, the arm is brought close to the site on the face where the new skin is needed and is fixed in this position. The free part of the flap then is sewed into the defect on the face. Blood vessels from the skin and the subcutaneous tissue of the face soon make connections with those in the flap. Soon the flap is being supplied by blood vessels from the site to which it has been transplanted. When the blood supply from this source becomes adequate, the original attachment of the flap to the skin of the arm, through which it has received blood up to this time, can be severed safely, and the repair of the facial defect can be completed.

The above-described method of skin grafting, though not necessarily using the arm as a source of skin, is employed particularly when reconstructions, such as the evolving of a new external ear to replace one that has been shot away, are necessary or when particularly good cosmetic effects are desired. However, under most conditions where skin grafting is required, for example, the covering of a large area where the skin has been completely de-

Fig. 23-21. The photographs illustrate how autogenous full-thickness skin grafts become vascularized. (These experiments were performed on pigs in collaboration with Dr. George Cloutier.) After death, the blood vessels of the animal on which the grafts had been made were injected with India ink in gelatin. In the photographs, the vessels containing black material are to be regarded as being open to the circulation. The striped band in each picture indicates the thickness of the graft. All the photographs are from thick sections that were cleared so that injected blood vessels could be seen readily.

The upper photograph illustrates an autogenous graft that was in position for 3 days. Blood is not yet circulating in its vessels; such black material as appears in the grafts is not the material injected into the blood vessels of the animal.

The middle photograph illustrates an autogenous graft that was in position for 7 days, and the bottom photograph one that was in position for 10 days. Large vessels filled with the injection material are present in both. These vessels are too large to have grown into the grafts in such a short time; indeed, sections showed that they were the original vessels that were in the skin that was grafted. They have become connected by capillaries with vessels in the bed of the graft. It is probable that blood is passing into the graft through the veins of the graft.

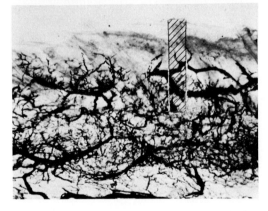

stroyed by a burn, *free* skin grafts, that is, grafts completely severed from their blood supply, are employed.

There are two kinds of free skin grafts: *split* grafts and *full-thickness* grafts. Although split grafts, which are thin shavings cut from the skin (Fig. 23-7, *lower left*), can be cut freehand, it is more common nowadays to cut them with a dermatome, a special instrument which quickly cuts a thin, even layer of skin from a broad surface. It was widely believed in the past, and sometimes it is still taught, that a split graft consists chiefly of epidermis and that the surface from which it is cut (the donor site) is left with the deeper parts of the interpapillary pegs of epidermis intact, and that these subsequently provide foci from which epidermal cells can grow out and quickly cover the denuded surface. For some reason there is widespread misconception about the thickness of the epidermis of thin skin and it is highly unlikely that split-skin grafts are commonly cut this thin. Split-skin grafts usually include a fairly substantial amount of dermis as well as epidermis (Fig. 23-7, *lower left*). Epithelization of the donor sites is brought about by a growth of epithelial cells, not from remnants of interpapillary pegs, but chiefly from the external root sheaths of the hair follicles (Fig. 23-20). The sweat glands do not participate in the repair of epidermis nearly so energetically as the hair

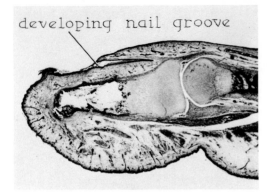

developing nail groove

FIG. 23-22. Photomicrograph of a longitudinal section cut through a terminal phalanx of a fetus, showing how the epidermis invades the dermis proximally to form a nail groove.

follicles. By this means, the surface of the donor site is soon covered with new epidermis, and, in the meantime, the underlying dermis, by means of the proliferation of fibroblasts and the formation of new intercellular substance, is quickly restored to its original thickness.

When a split graft is fastened in its new site and held in place with a little pressure, its constituent cells are kept alive by means of tissue fluid derived from the capillaries of the host tissue below. If the graft is thin, most of its cells can survive by this means until the graft becomes vascularized. Vascularization occurs when capillaries of the host make connections with capillaries of the graft (capillaries seem to be very adept at making such connections) and also by the growth of new capillaries from the host up into the graft.

In some instances, free grafts of the full-thickness variety are used. If the full thickness of the skin is removed from any site, no hair follicles are left to regenerate a new epidermal surface. For this reason, when a full-thickness graft is cut, the two edges of the donor site must be sewed together or, if this is not possible, it must, in turn, be covered with a split graft. However, many individuals are sufficiently plump to permit the suturing of the edges of the skin from which a full-thickness graft is removed.

Since full-thickness grafts are thicker than split grafts, it is somewhat more difficult for tissue fluid from the bed to which they are grafted to nourish them until they become vascularized. Vascularization of a free full-thickness graft is brought about by the abundant capillaries of the bed to which the graft is transplanted making connections with those in the graft. See Figure 23-21, *middle picture*. These connect with the larger vessels in the graft, so blood entering them soon flows again through the original blood vessels of the graft. The larger blood vessels of the graft begin to fill after 5 days (not shown in Figure 23-21) and are fairly well filled, and hence functioning to some extent, by 7 days (Fig. 23-21, *middle picture*).

Although skin may be grafted from one part of an individual to another, a graft taken from one individual and transplanted to another individual, with the exceptions described in Chapter 12, invokes a homograft reaction (Fig. 12-13) and is cast off.

## NAILS

Toward the end of the third month of embryonic life the epidermis covering the dorsal surface of the terminal phalanx of each finger and toe begins to invade the underlying dermis. The invasion occurs along a transverse curved line; hence, the invading epidermis has the form of a curved plate. Moreover, the invasion does not occur along a line at right angles to the surface but, instead, it slants proximally (Fig. 23-22). Later, the invading plate of epidermis splits so that it forms the nail groove (Fig. 23-22). The epidermal cells making up the deeper wall of this groove proliferate to become the matrix of the nail (Fig. 23-23). The cells in the matrix proliferate, and the upper ones differentiate into nail substance which is hard keratin (Fig. 23-9, *right*). With the continuing proliferation and differentiation of the cells in the lower part of the matrix, the forming nail is pushed out of the groove and slowly slides along the dorsal surface of the digit toward its distal part. Although it slides slowly over the epidermis of the dorsal part of the digit, it remains firmly attached to it all the while. The epidermis over which it slides is called the *nail bed* (Fig. 23-23). It consists of only the deeper layers of the epidermis; the nail, as it were, serves as its stratum corneum. The skin of the dorsal surface of the digits is formed into a groove along each side of the

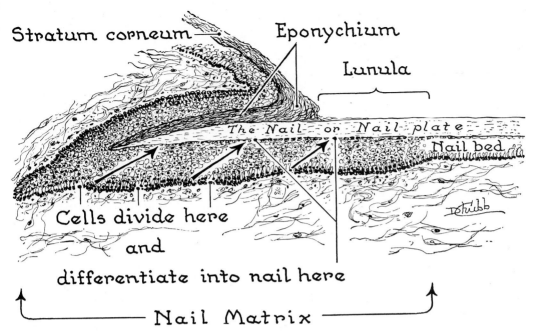

FIG. 23-23. Diagram of a longitudinal section (low-power) cut through the nail groove and the root of a growing nail.

nail (Fig. 23-24). With sufficient growth, the *free margin* of the nail will project beyond the distal end of the digit (Fig. 23-24).

The *body* of the nail is the part that shows. The part that is hidden in the nail groove is called the *root*. Seen from above, a crescent-shaped white area appears on the part of the body nearest the root. This is called the *lunule* (Fig. 23-24); it is seen to best advantage on the thumb and the first finger. It is usually absent from the little finger. The nail, except for the lunule, is pink because the blood in the capillaries of the dermis under the nail bed shows through. The lunule is white because the capillaries under it do not show through. There are different theories to explain this. Some authorities think the lunule indicates the extent of the underlying matrix (Fig. 23-23). Since the matrix is thicker than the epidermis of the nail bed, capillaries beneath it would not show through it as well as they would through the epidermis of the nail bed. However, the region of the lunule cannot always be correlated with the site of the matrix in sections. Hence, some authors think that its whiteness is due to the nail substance, when it is first formed, being more opaque than the more mature nail substance found over the bed.

At the proximal border of the nail, the stratum corneum of the epidermis of the skin of the dorsum of a finger or a toe projects over and is adherent to the nail. This, together with the stratum corneum of the epidermis that makes up the proximal and more superficial wall of the nail fold and is adherent to the proximal and outer surface of the nail root, constitutes the *eponychium* (*epi* = upon, *onyx* = nail) (Fig. 23-23) and it is soft keratin.

Infections in the region of the eponychium

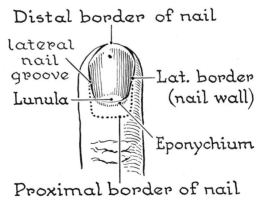

FIG. 23-24. Diagram of the end of a finger and a fingernail.

or along the lateral borders of the nail (Fig. 23-24) are not uncommon. Sometimes, in order to permit these infections to heal, it is necessary to remove the root of a nail. On being pulled out, the nail root will be seen to be shaped like the end of a curved chisel which does not extend into the nail groove as far as might be thought. Provided that the matrix is not destroyed, a new nail will grow out of the nail fold in due time. If the matrix is destroyed, a new nail will not form.

Sometimes, from wearing improper shoes, the curvature of toenails becomes accentuated, and they pierce the dermis along one of their lateral grooves (*a normal groove is shown in Fig. 23-24*). The condition is called an ingrown toenail. Sometimes it is necessary to cut away some matrix at one side of the nail groove to cure this condition. New nail will not grow from the region from which matrix is removed. Hence, the cutting away of matrix at one side of the nail groove results in the formation of a narrower nail, which, therefore, does not impinge on the skin at the bottom of the lateral groove, so the pierced skin at this point can heal.

The dermis beneath the epidermis of the nail bed is arranged in longitudinal grooves and ridges. In cross sections the ridges appear as papillae. The dermis in this site is very vascular. The ridges and the grooves of dermis present under the bed do not continue proximally under the matrix, but there are some papillae in this region.

On the average, nails grow about 0.5 mm. a week. Fingernails grow more rapidly than toenails, and both grow faster in summer than in winter. The rate of growth of nails is different at different ages. Nail growth may be disturbed when the body suffers from certain diseases. Even psychological upsets are said to be reflected sometimes by the pitting of nails. Certain hormone deficiencies and excesses affect the growth of nails; hence, the condition of the nails sometimes may help to indicate an endocrine gland disturbance.

## REFERENCES

### GENERAL REFERENCES ON THE SKIN AND PIGMENTATION

Montagna, William: The Structure and Function of Skin, ed. 2, New York, Acad. Press, 1962.

Riley, V., and Fortner, J. G. (eds.): Pigment cell, Ann. N. Y. Acad. Sci. *100*:1-1123, 1963.

Rothman, S.: Physiology and Biochemistry of the Skin, Chicago, Univ. Chicago Press, 1956.

### SPECIAL REFERENCES ON SKIN, INCLUDING FINE STRUCTURE AND PIGMENTATION

(References on fingerprints, hair and regeneration are given under separate headings)

Breathnach, A. S., Birbeck, M. S. C., and Everall, J. D.: Observations bearing on the relationship between Langerhans cells and melanocytes, Ann. N. Y. Acad. Sci. *100*:223, 1963.

Bertalanffy, F. D.: Mitotic activity and renewal rate of sebaceous gland cells in the rat, Anat. Rec. *129*:231, 1957.

Brody, I.: The keratinization of epidermal cells of normal guinea pig skin as revealed by electron microscopy, J. Ultrastr. Res. *2*:482, 1959.

Bullough, W. S., and Ebling, F. J.: Cell replacement in the epidermis and sebaceous glands of the mouse, J. Anat. *86*:29, 1952.

Charles, A.: An electron microscopic study of the human axillary apocrine gland, J. Anat. *93*:226, 1959.

Clark, W. H., and Hibbs, R. G.: Electron microscope studies of the human epidermis. The clear cell of Mason (dentritic cell or melanocyte), J. Biophys. Biochem. Cytol. *4*:679, 1958.

Edwards, E., and Duntley, S.: The pigments and color of living human skin, Am. J. Anat. *65*:1, 1939.

Fan, J., Schoenfeld, R. J., and Hunter, R.: A study of the epidermal clear cells with special reference to their relationship to the cells of Langerhans, J. Invest. Dermat. *32*:445, 1959.

Fitzpatrick, T. B., and Szabo, G.: The melanocyte, cytology and cytochemistry, J. Invest. Dermat. *32*:197, 1959.

Hibbs, R. G.: The fine structure of human exocrine sweat glands, Am. J. Anat. *103*:201, 1958.

Hibbs, R. G., and Clark, W. H., Jr.: Electron microscope studies of the human epidermis, J. Biophys. Biochem. Cytol. *6*:71, 1959.

Leuchtenberger, C., and Lund, H. Z.: The chemical nature of the so-called keratohyaline granules of the stratum granulosum of the skin, Exp. Cell Res. *2*:150, 1951.

Menefee, M. G.: Some fine structure changes occurring in the epidermis of embryo mice during differentiation, J. Ultrastr. Res. *1*:49, 1957.

Odland, G. F.: The morphology of the attachment between the dermis and the epidermis, Anat. Rec. *108*:399, 1950.

————: The fine structure of the interrelationship of cells in the human epidermis, J. Biophys. Biochem. Cytol. *4*:529, 1958.

Pease, D. C.: Electron microscopy of human skin, Am. J. Anat. *89*:469, 1951.

Porter, K. R.: Observations on the submicroscopic structure of animal epidermis, Anat. Rec. *118*:433, 1954.

Rhodin, J. A. G., and Reith, E. J.: Ultrastructure of keratin in oral mucosa, skin, esophagus, claw, and hair *in* Fundamentals of Keratinization, p. 61, Washington, D. C., Am. Assoc. Adv. Sci., 1962.

Rogers, G. E.: Electron microscope observations on the structure of sebaceous glands, Exp. Cell Res. *13*:517, 1957.

———: Some aspects of the structure of the inner root sheath of hair follicles revealed by light and electron microscopy, Exp. Cell Res. *14*:378, 1958.

Seiji, M., Shimao, K., Birbeck, M. S. C., and Fitzpatrick, T. B.: Subcellular localization of melanin biosynthesis, Ann. N. Y. Acad. Sci. *100*:497, 1963.

Storey, W. F., and Leblond, C. P.: Measurement of the rate of proliferation of epidermis and associated structures, Ann. N. Y. Acad. Sci. *53*:537, 1951.

Swanbeck, G.: On the keratin fibrils of the skin. An x-ray small angle scattering study of the horny layer, J. Ultrastr. Res. *3*:51, 1959.

Takagi, S.: A study on the structure of the sudoriferous duct traversing the epidermis in man with fresh material by phase contrast microscopy, Jap. J. Physiol. *3*:65, 1952.

Wyllie, J. C., More, R. H., and Haust, M. D.: Electron microscopy of epidermal lesions elicited during hypersensitivity, Lab. Invest. *13*:137, 1964.

SPECIAL REFERENCES ON FINGERPRINTS AND DERMIS

Cauna, N.: Nature and functions of the papillary ridges of the digital skin, Anat. Rec. *119*:449, 1954.

Cummins, H.: The topographic history of the volar pads (walking pads; tastballen) in the human embryo, Contrib. Embryol. *20*:103, 1929.

———: Dermatoglyphics: Significant patternings of the body surface, Yale J. Biol. Med. *18*:551, 1946.

Cummins, Harold, and Midlo, Charles: Finger Prints, Palms and Soles, New York, Blakiston Division of McGraw-Hill, 1943.

Faulds, H.: On the skin-furrows of the hand, Nature *22*:605, 1880.

Henry, E. R.: Classification and Uses of Fingerprints, London, Darling, 1905.

Herschel, W. J.: Skin furrows of the hand, Nature *23*:76, 1880.

Plotnick, H., and Pinkus, H.: The epidermal vs. the dermal fingerprint, Arch. Dermat. *77*:12, 1958.

Wilton, G.: Fingerprints: History, Law and Romance, London, Hodge, 1938.

SPECIAL REFERENCES ON THE BLOOD SUPPLY TO SKIN

Burton, A. C.: The blood flow, temperature and color of the skin, Am. Assoc. Adv. Sci., Publication No. 13, 1940.

Hibbs, R. G., Burch, G. E., and Phillips, J. H.: The fine structure of the small blood vessels of the normal human dermis and subcutis, Am. Heart J. *56*:662, 1958.

Lewis, T.: The Blood Vessels of the Human Skin and Their Responses, London, Shaw, 1937.

GENERAL REFERENCE ON HAIR

Montagna, W., and Ellis, R. A. (eds.): The Biology of Hair Growth, New York, Acad. Press, 1958.

SPECIAL REFERENCES ON HAIR AND KERATIN

Baker, B. L.: The relationship of the adrenal, thyroid, and pituitary glands to the growth of hair, Ann. N. Y. Acad. Sci. *53*:690, 1951.

Bear, R. S., and Rugo, H. J.: The results of x-ray diffraction studies on keratin fibers, Ann. N. Y. Acad. Sci. *53*:627, 1951.

Birbeck, M. S. C., and Mercer, E. H.: The electron microscopy of the human hair follicle. I. Introduction and the hair cortex, J. Biophys. Biochem. Cytol. *3*:203, 1957. II. The hair cuticle, J. Biophys. Biochem. Cytol. *3*:215, 1957. III. The inner root sheath and trichohyaline, J. Biophys. Biochem. Cytol. *3*:223, 1957.

Bissell, G. W.: Hirsutism, Ann. N. Y. Acad. Sci. *53*:742, 1951.

Butcher, E. O.: Development of the pilary system and the replacement of hair in mammals, Ann. N. Y. Acad. Sci. *53*:508, 1951.

Charles, A.: Electron microscope observations on hardening in the hair follicle, Exp. Cell Res. *18*:138, 1959.

Chase, H. B.: Growth of the hair, Physiol. Rev. *34*:113, 1954.

Chase, H. B., Montagna, W., and Malone, J. D.: Changes in the skin in relation to the hair growth cycle, Anat. Rec. *116*:75, 1953.

Danforth, C. H.: Physiology of human hair, Physiol. Rev. *19*:94, 1939.

Duggins, O. H., and Trotter, M.: Age changes in head hair from birth to maturity: II. Medullation in hair of children, Am. J. Phys. Anthropol. *8*:399, 1950.

————: Changes in morphology of hair during childhood, Ann. N. Y. Acad. Sci. *53*:569, 1951.

Forbes, T. F.: Sex hormones and hair changes in rats, Endocrinology *30*:465, 1942.

Garn, S. M.: Types and distribution of the hair in man, Ann. N. Y. Acad. Sci. *53*:498, 1951.

Giroud, A., Bulliard, H., and Leblond, C. P.: Les deux types fondamentaux de kératinisation, Bull. d'hisol. appliq. à la Physiol. *11*:129, 1934.

Giroud, A., and Leblond, C. P.: The keratinization of epidermis and its derivatives, especially the hair, as shown by x-ray diffraction and histochemical studies, Ann. N. Y. Acad. Sci. *53*: 613, 1951.

Hamilton, J. B.: Male hormone stimulation is prerequisite and incitant in common baldness, Am. J. Anat. *71*:541, 1942.

————: Patterned loss of hair in man: types and incidence, Ann. N. Y. Acad. Sci. *53*:708, 1951.

————: Quantitative measurement of a secondary sex character, axillary hair, Ann. N. Y. Acad. Sci. *53*:585, 1951.

Hardy, M. H.: The development of mouse hair *in vitro* with some observations on pigmentation, J. Anat. *83*:364, 1949.

Herrington, L. P.: The role of the piliary system in mammals and its relation to the thermal environment. Ann. N. Y. Acad. Sci. *53*:600, 1951.

Leblond, C. P.: Histological structure of hair, with a brief comparison to other epidermal appendages and epidermis itself, Ann. N. Y. Acad. Sci. *53*:464, 1951.

Matoltsy, A. G.: A study of the medullary cells of the hair, Exp. Cell Res. *5*:98, 1953.

Myers, R. J., and Hamilton, J. B.: Regeneration and rate of growth of hairs in man, Ann. N. Y. Acad. Sci. *53*:562, 1951.

Noback, C. R.: Morphology and phylogeny of hair, Ann. N. Y. Acad. Sci. *53*:476, 1951.

Parnell, J. P.: Hair pattern and distribution in mammals, Ann. N. Y. Acad. Sci. *53*:493, 1951.

Reynolds, E. L.: The appearance of adult patterns of body hair in man, Ann. N. Y. Acad. Sci. *53*:576, 1951.

Rogers, G. E.: Electron microscope observations on the glassy layer of the hair follicle, Exp. Cell Res. *13*:521, 1957.

Savill, A.: The Hair and Scalp, ed. 3, London, Arnold, 1944.

Trotter, M.: The hair *in* Cowdry's Special Cytology, ed. 2, p. 41, New York, Hoeber, 1932.

————: Hair growth and shaving, Anat. Rec. *37*:373, 1928.

————: The life cycles of hair in selected regions of the body, Am. J. Phys. Anthropol. *7*:427, 1924.

Whiteley, H. J.: Studies on hair growth in the rabbit, J. Anat. *92*:563, 1958.

SPECIAL REFERENCES ON BURNS AND
SKIN REGENERATION AND GRAFTS

Bishop, G. H.: Regeneration after experimental removal of skin in man, Am. J. Anat. *76*:153, 1945.

Gillman, T., and Penn, J.: Studies on the repair of cutaneous wounds, Med. Proc. (South African) *2*:93, 1956.

Ham, A. W.: Experimental study of histopathology of burns, with particular reference to sites of fluid loss in burns of different depths, Ann. Surg. *120*:689, 1944.

————: Experimental study of tannic acid treatment of burns, with particular reference to its effect on local fluid loss and healing, Ann. Surg. *120*:698, 1944.

Harkins, H. N.: The Treatment of Burns, Springfield, Ill., Thomas, 1942.

Johnson, F. R., and McMinn, R. M. H.: The cytology of wound healing of body surfaces in mammals, Biol. Rev. *35*:364, 1960.

McGregor, I. A.: The regeneration of sympathetic activity in grafted skin as evidenced by sweating, Brit. J. Plast. Surg. *3*:12, 1950.

McMinn, R. M. H.: The cellular anatomy of experimental wound healing, Ann. Roy. Coll. Surg. England *26*:245, 1960.

(See also references in Chapter 12 on Tissue Transplantation in section on Lymphocytes.)

# 24    The Digestive System

## INTRODUCTION

For practical purposes, the digestive system (Fig. 24-1) may be considered as consisting of: (1) a long muscular tube that begins at the lips and ends at the anus, at which two sites its epithelial lining becomes continuous with the skin; and (2) certain large glands situated outside the tube proper (salivary glands, liver, gallbladder and pancreas) that empty their secretions into the tube because they develop from its epithelial lining.

The first thing that a student should realize about the digestive tube is that the fluid and semifluid material in its lumen is as much outside the body as the water in which an ameba lives, and obtains its nourishment, is outside the ameba. Food must be absorbed from the lumen of the tube into the blood capillaries and the lymphatics of the wall of the tube before it can be said to have gained entrance into the body proper. However, most food taken in at the mouth is neither in a form suitable to be transported in the blood and the tissue fluid nor in a form suitable to be utilized by cells. For example, the carbohydrate of bread and potatoes is in the form of starch. Before this carbohydrate can be absorbed and used by cells it must be broken down to glucose. The process by which foods taken in at the mouth are converted into substances that may be safely absorbed and used by cells is known as *digestion*. Digestion occurs in the lumen of the digestive tube and is brought about by the food therein being acted upon by digestive juices that are secreted by the glands in the wall of the tube and by others situated outside the tube but emptying into it. The epithelial cells lining the tube are extremely selective in their absorptive functions; they absorb only the products of digestion. If they were not highly selective, and absorbed undigested substances, death would result.

The digestive tube consists of the mouth, the pharynx, the esophagus, the stomach, the small intestine and the large intestine (Fig. 24-1). These different parts of the tube serve somewhat different purposes. Before discussing the structure of each part in detail and how it relates to its function, we shall try to give a picture of the operation of the different parts of the tube by an analogy.

The operations that take place in the digestive tube are not unlike those that the biochemist performs when he wishes to extract a valuable material from some crude material. (1) He places the material in a mortar, adds some fluid to it, and then breaks up and mixes the mass with a pestle until it is fairly homogeneous. This operation corresponds roughly to what happens when food is taken into the mouth. Crude material here is ground with the teeth and mixed with saliva until it is brought to a reasonably homogeneous state. (2) The biochemist takes the homogeneous material from the mortar and puts it into a beaker, where he adds acid and enzymes and more fluid; he then stirs the mixture until the material is broken down into the simpler soluble compounds for which he is searching. This corresponds to what happens in the stomach and the first part of the small intestine. (3) The biochemist adds still more fluid to his mixture and puts it into a funnel provided with filter paper. The soluble simpler substances that have formed from the insoluble mass with which he began then pass through the filter paper into a separate container. This step is comparable with what happens in most of the small intestine. The simpler substances formed as a result of digestion are absorbed through the filtering inner lining of the intestine to enter the bloodstream and the lymphatics. (4) The biochemist does not unduly prolong the filtration because the material he is filtering may become contaminated with bacteria, with the result that poisonous products may form. So, he discards the residue held in the filter paper before contaminating bacteria have an opportunity to flourish in

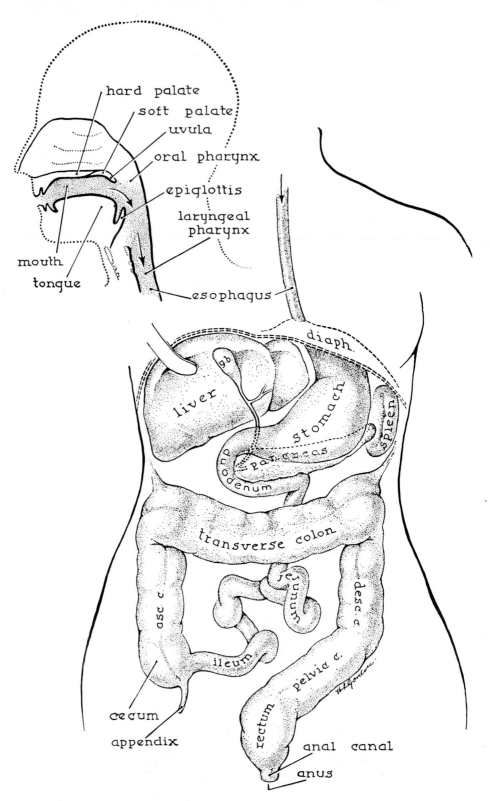

Fig. 24-1. Diagram of the parts of the digestive system. (Redrawn and modified from Grant, J. C. B.: A Method of Anatomy, ed. 4, Baltimore, Williams & Wilkins)

it. This step is roughly comparable with what happens in the lower end of the small intestine, for there the residue in its lumen is ejected into the large intestine, the lining of which is not adapted for absorbing the products of digestion. Here bacteria flourish and so are a conspicuous feature of the feces that are finally eliminated from the body.

Before attempting to learn the structure and the function of each part of the digestive tube, the student should understand thoroughly what is meant by the term *mucous membrane*. The wet epithelial lining of the digestive tube and (as we shall see) of other internal passageways that open to the surface constitutes, like the epidermis of skin, a barrier between the community of cells that comprise the body and the outside world. The problem of providing protection along the vast, wet epithelial surface of the digestive tube is considerably greater than that faced by the skin, because the epithelial membrane over considerable distances must be thin enough to be absorptive. One of the chief agencies ensuring the integrity of this wet epithelial membrane is its lubrication with mucus. From one end to the other, the digestive tube is richly provided with either individual cells or with glands that produce mucus. Wet epithelial membranes thus equipped are termed mucous membranes. Actually, the term mucous membrane usually refers to something more than an epithelial membrane alone; it includes the underlying connective tissue that supports the epithelial membrane and is usually termed the *lamina propria* or *tunica propria* of the mucous membrane. In some instances mucous membranes contain some smooth muscle in their deepest parts; if present, this also is considered as part of the mucous membrane and is called the *muscularis mucosae* (muscle of the mucosa).

## THE LIPS

The substance of the lips consists of striated muscle fibers and fibro-elastic connective tissue. The muscle tissue consists chiefly of the fibers of the orbicularis oris muscle and is distributed in the more central part of the lip (Fig. 24-2). The direction of the fibers and their attachments are discussed in textbooks of gross anatomy.

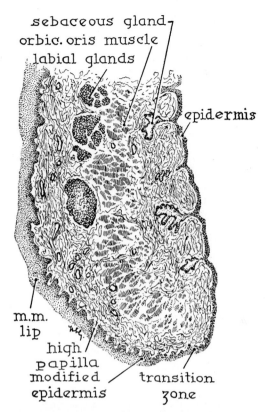

Fig. 24-2. Semidiagrammatic drawing of a sagittal section of a lip (low-power). (Redrawn from Huber: Piersol's Human Anatomy, ed. 9, Philadelphia, Lippincott)

The outer surface of each lip is covered with skin that contains hair follicles, sebaceous glands and sweat glands (Fig. 24-2, *right*). The red, free margins of the lips are covered with a modified skin which represents a transition from skin to mucous membrane. The epithelium in this site is covered with a layer of dead cells, like that of the skin, but it is said that there is a high percentage of eleidin, which is relatively transparent, in it. The connective tissue papillae of the dermis beneath it are numerous, high and vascular (Fig. 24-2), and, as a result, the blood in their capillaries readily shows through the transparent epidermis to make the lips appear red. No sweat or sebaceous glands or hair follicles are present in the skin of the red, free margins of the lips. Since the epithelium is not heavily keratinized and is not provided with sebum, it must be wetted frequently with the tongue if its integrity is to be preserved. "Chapped" and "cracked" lips are common under conditions which favor evaporation. The high papillae bring many nerve endings as well as capillaries close to the surface of the red margins of the lips; for this reason, they are very sensitive.

As the skin of the red, free margin passes onto the inner surface of the lip it becomes transformed into mucous membrane. The epithelium of this is thicker than the epidermis covering the outer surface of the lip (Fig. 24-2, *left*) and is of the stratified squamous nonkeratinizing type. However, some granules of keratohyalin may be found in the cells of the more superficial layers. High papillae of the connective tissue lamina propria (which, in mucous membranes, replaces the dermis of skin) extend into it. Small clusters of mucous glands, the labial glands, are embedded in the lamina propria (Fig. 24-2) and connect with the surface by means of little ducts.

### THE CHEEKS

The mucous membrane lining the cheeks has a fairly thick layer of epithelium of the stratified squamous nonkeratinizing type. This is the kind of epithelium that is characteristically found on wet epithelial surfaces where there is considerable wear and tear and from which no absorption occurs. The superficial cells of this epithelium are more or less constantly being rubbed off the surface and replaced from below. This, of course, requires that the cells in the deeper layers of the epithelium divide as rapidly as cells are worn away from the surface. If the ball of the finger is drawn across the inside of the cheek, many of the surface cells will be removed. If these are dabbed on a slide and stained with methylene blue, their flat bodies with their centrally disposed nuclei can be seen readily.

The lamina propria of the mucous membrane lining the cheek consists of fairly dense fibro-elastic tissue and extends into the epithelium in the form of high papillae. The deeper part of it merges into what is termed the *submucosa* of the lining of the cheek. This layer contains flat elastic fibers and many blood vessels. Strands of fibro-elastic tissue from the lamina propria penetrate through the fatty elastic submucosa to join with the fibro-elastic tissue associated with the muscle that underlies the submucosa and forms the chief substance of the wall of the cheek. These strands fasten the mucous membrane to the underlying muscle at intervals, with the result that when the jaws are closed, the relaxed mucous membrane bulges inward in many small folds instead of in one large fold that would project inward so far that it would be an inconvenience and frequently would be bitten inadvertently.

There are small mucous glands, some of which have a few serous secretory demilunes, in the inner part of the cheek.

### THE TONGUE

The tongue is composed chiefly of striated muscle, the fibers of which are grouped into bundles that interlace with one another and are disposed in 3 planes. Hence, if a longitudinal section is cut from the tongue, i.e., at right angles to the dorsal surface (a sagittal section), it will reveal both longitudinal and vertical muscle fibers cut longitudinally and horizontal fibers cut in cross section. Such an arrangement of striated muscle fibers is so unique in the body that finding it in any given section permits that section to be identified as having been cut from the tongue.

The individual muscle fibers inside the bundles are each surrounded by endomysium which tends to be somewhat more substantial than that seen in most striated muscle. The endomysium brings capillaries close to the muscle fibers (Fig. 20-17). The fibro-elastic tissue between the muscle bundles can be thought of as constituting the perimysium. It contains the larger vessels and nerves and, in many sites, adipose tissue; in some parts of the tongue, glands are embedded in it.

**Mucous Membranes.** That covering the undersurface of the tongue is thin and smooth. The lamina propria connects directly with the fibro-elastic tissue associated with the bundles of muscle. No true submucosa exists here.

The mucous membrane covering the dorsal surface of the tongue is of special interest (Fig. 24-3). Almost everyone can recall from his childhood being visited by a doctor and told to "put out his tongue" so that its dorsal surface might be examined. The dorsal surface of the tongue may give the physician information of two kinds. (1) If it is "coated"

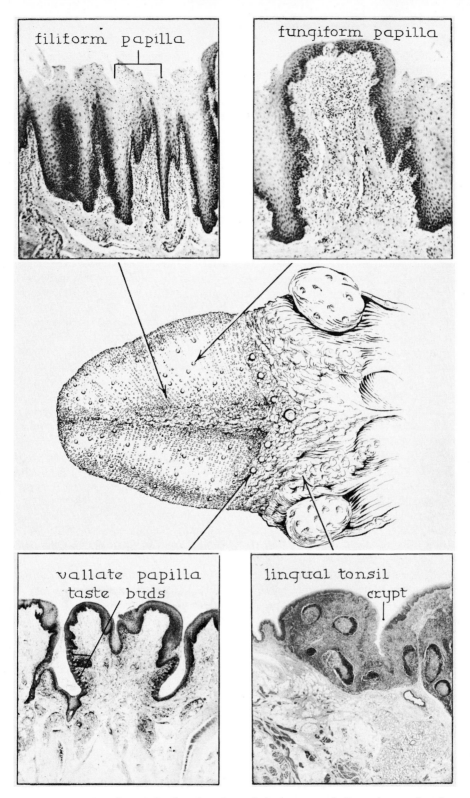

Fɪɢ. 24-3. Drawing of the dorsal surface of the tongue and photomicrographs of sections cut from its mucous membrane in 4 areas.

heavily it indicates that the general state of health of the individual, and perhaps particularly the operation of the digestive system, is not satisfactory. (2) Certain diseases, for example, scarlet fever and pernicious anemia, may cause certain specific alterations on the surface of the tongue, hence the detecting of these specific alterations may be a valuable help in making a diagnosis of one of these diseases.

The mucous membrane covering the dorsal surface of the tongue is divided into two parts: (1) that covering the anterior two thirds or oral part of the tongue (its body) and (2) that covering the posterior one third or pharyngeal part (its root). A V-shaped line, the sulcus terminalis, running across the tongue marks the border between these two parts (Fig. 24-3).

The mucous membrane covering the oral part of the tongue is very different from that covering the pharyngeal part. It is covered by little projections of the mucous membrane called *papillae*. There are three kinds of these in man—filiform, fungiform and vallate.

**Filiform** (*filum* = thread) **papillae** are relatively high, narrow, conical structures composed both of lamina propria and epithelium (Fig. 24-3, *upper left*). Each has a primary papilla of lamina propria from which secondary papillae of lamina propria extend toward the surface. The primary papilla is covered by a cap of epithelium which breaks up to form separate caps over each of the secondary papillae. Sometimes the epithelial caps over the secondary papillae break up into threads to justify the term filiform. The epithelium that caps the secondary papillae becomes very horny, but there is some question as to whether the surface cells become converted into true keratin in man. In some animals the horny filiform papillae make the dorsal surface of the tongue distinctly rasplike.

Filiform papillae are very numerous and are distributed in parallel rows across the tongue. Near the root these rows follow the V-shaped line that divides the body from the root of the tongue (Fig. 24-3).

**Fungiform papillae** are so-called because they project from the dorsal surface of the oral part of the tongue like little fungi which are narrower at their bases and have expanded smooth rounded tops (Fig. 24-3, *upper right*).

They are not nearly as numerous as the filiform papillae among which they are scattered; they are somewhat more numerous at the tip of the tongue than elsewhere. Each has a central core of lamina propria which is termed the *primary papilla,* and from this, secondary papillae of lamina propria project up into the covering epithelium. The epithelial surface does not follow the contours of the secondary papillae of lamina propria as it does in filiform papillae; hence, the secondary papillae of lamina propria bring capillaries very close to the surface of the epithelium. Since the covering epithelium is not keratinized, it is relatively translucent; this permits the blood vessels in the high secondary papillae to show through and, as a result, the fungiform papillae in life are red.

From 7 to 12 **vallate papillae** are distributed along the V-shaped line that separates the mucous membrane of the body of the tongue from that of the root (Fig. 24-3). The name (*vallum* = a rampart) suggests that each, like an ancient city, is surrounded by a rampart. Actually, each is like a turreted castle because it is surrounded by a moat or trench (Fig. 24-3, *lower left*). The moat that surrounds each is kept flooded, and so cleansed of debris, by glands disposed deep to the papilla but which empty by means of ducts into the bottom of the moat.

Each vallate papilla has a central primary papilla of lamina propria (Fig. 24-3, *lower left*). Secondary papillae of lamina propria extend up from this into the stratified nonkeratinizing epithelium that covers the whole papilla. Vallate papillae are narrower at their points of attachment than at their free surfaces, hence their shapes are not unlike those of papillae of the fungiform type.

**Functions of Papillae.** Animals in which filiform papillae are highly developed are capable of licking layers off solid and semisolid material with a sandpaperlike efficiency. Even though filiform papillae are not very highly developed in man, they permit children to lick ice cream satisfactorily. Such papillae contain nerve endings specialized for touch (tactile sense). Most fungiform papillae and all the vallate papillae contain taste buds in which there are special nerve endings which, on being stimulated, give rise to the nervous impulses that result in sensations of taste. Taste buds

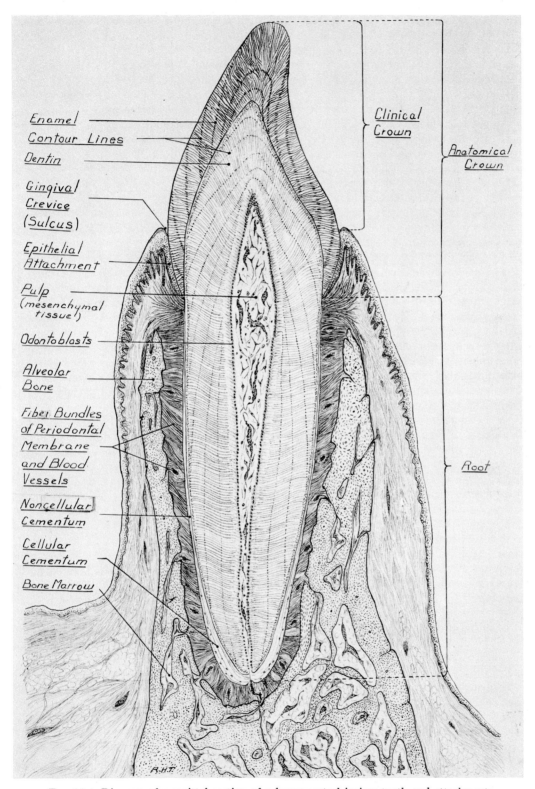

Enamel

Contour Lines

Dentin

Gingival
Crevice
(Sulcus)

Epithelial
Attachment

Pulp
(mesenchymal
tissue)

Odontoblasts

Alveolar
Bone

Fiber Bundles
of Periodontal
Membrane
and Blood
Vessels

Noncellular
Cementum

Cellular
Cementum

Bone Marrow

Clinical
Crown

Anatomical
Crown

Root

FIG. 24-4. Diagram of a sagittal section of a lower central incisor tooth and attachments.

will be described in detail in a subsequent chapter.

**Lingual Tonsil.** No true papillae are present on the mucous membrane covering the root of the tongue. The small humps seen over this part of the tongue are due to aggregations of lymphatic nodules in the lamina propria beneath the epithelium (Fig. 24-3, *lower right*). Such an arrangement, i.e., aggregations of lymphatic nodules in close association with stratified squamous epithelium, is generally called *tonsillar tissue*. That over the root of the tongue constitutes the *lingual tonsil*. Many of the lymphatic nodules in the lingual tonsil have germinal centers. Diffuse lymphatic tissue fills the spaces between them. Along with the lymphocytes there are many plasma cells. The stratified squamous nokeratinizing epithelium that overlies the lymphatic tissue extends down into it in many sites to form wells or pits (Fig. 24-3, *lower right*). These are called *crypts* (*kryptos* = concealed). Lymphocytes migrate through the epithelium covering these patches of lymphatic tissue, but more particularly through the stratified epithelial walls of the crypts, to gain entrance to their lumens. The superficial epithelial cells from the linings of the crypts desquamate into the lumens of the crypts, with the result that the lumens of crypts may show accumulations of debris formed from lymphocytes and desquamated epithelial cells. Ducts from underlying mucous glands open into the bottoms of many crypts; this arrangement, when present, serves to keep the lumens washed out and hence free from debris. For this reason, infected crypts are not so common in the lingual tonsil as in tonsillar tissue in other sites where there are no underlying glands that open into the crypts.

### THE TEETH

#### INTRODUCTORY DESCRIPTION OF AN ADULT TOOTH AND ITS ATTACHMENTS

In man the teeth function to reduce food that is taken into the mouth to small pieces and to mix it with saliva so that it is swallowed easily. They are arranged in two parabolic curves, one in the upper jaw and one in the lower. Each of these two curved rows of teeth constitutes a *dental arch*. The upper arch is slightly larger than the lower; hence, normally, the upper teeth slightly overlap the lower teeth.

The bulk of each tooth is made of a special type of calcified connective tissue called *dentin* (Fig. 24-4). Dentin generally is not exposed to the external environment of the tooth because it is covered with one or the other of two other calcified tissues. The dentin of that portion of the tooth that projects through the gums into the mouth is covered with a cap of very hard, calcified, epithelial-derived tissue called *enamel* (Fig. 24-4); this part of the tooth constitutes its *anatomic crown* (Fig. 24-4). The remainder of the tooth, the *anatomic root* (Fig. 24-4), is covered with a special calcified connective tissue called *cementum* (Fig. 24-4). There are two histologic types of cementum. That covering the coronal one half or one third of the root has no cells within its matrix and therefore is termed *noncellular cementum*. The rest of the cementum is called cellular cementum because it contains cells (cementocytes) within lacunae; the latter, like those of bone, have canaliculi extending from them. However, there are no haversian systems in cementum; normally, it is nonvascular as are all the other hard dental tissues. The junction between the crown and the root of the tooth is termed the *neck* or *cervix*, and the visible line of junction between enamel and cementum is termed the *cervical line*.

Within each tooth is a space that conforms to the general shape of the tooth; this is called the *pulp cavity* (Fig. 24-4). Its more expanded portion in the coronal part of the tooth is called the *pulp chamber*, and the narrowed part of the cavity that extends through the root is called the *pulp* or *root canal*. The pulp in the cavity consists of a mesenchymal-like connective tissue; this is what lay people call the "nerve" of the tooth because it is so sensitive. The pulp is well supplied with nerve fibers and small blood vessels. The sides of the pulp cavity are lined by modified connective tissue cells called *odontoblasts* (Fig. 24-4) whose function, as their name implies, is related to the production of dentin. The nerve and the blood supply of a tooth enters the pulp through a small hole (or holes) through the apex of the root called the *apical foramen* (Fig. 24-4, *not labeled*).

The lower teeth are set into a bony ridge that projects upward from the body of the mandible, and the upper ones into a bony ridge that projects downward from the body of the maxilla; these bony ridges are termed *alveolar processes*. In these processes are *sockets* (*alveoli*)—one for the root of each tooth. The teeth are suspended and held firmly in their alveoli by a connective tissue membrane called the *periodontal membrane* (Fig. 24-4). It consists chiefly of dense bundles of collagenic fibers running in various directions from the bone of the socket wall to the cementum that covers the root. The ends of the collagenic fibers are embedded in both the bone of the socket and the cementum of the tooth. The embedded fibers are called *Sharpey's fibers* (Fig. 24-17). The way in which Sharpey's fibers become embedded in bone and cementum will be explained later. The fibers are arranged so that when pressure is exerted on the biting surface of the tooth, the tooth, being suspended by them, will not be pressed farther into the narrowing socket (which could squeeze the blood vessels in the membrane), and at the same time the tooth is permitted some slight movement within its alveolus.

The mucous membrane of the mouth forms an external covering for the bone of the alveolar process; these coverings constitute the *gums*. That part of the gum tissue extending coronally beyond the crest of the alveolar process is the *gingiva* (Fig. 24-4).

The part of the tooth that extends into the mouth beyond the gingiva is called the *clinical crown* (as distinguished from the anatomic crown described previously). The clinical crown may or may not be identical with the anatomic crown of a tooth. Soon after the tooth erupts into the mouth, the gingiva is attached to the enamel somewhere along the anatomic crown, so the clinical crown is shorter than the anatomic crown. As eruption proceeds, there is a time when the gingiva is attached to the tooth at the cervical line; at this stage the clinical and the anatomic crowns are identical. As the gingiva recedes still farther, as generally occurs in older people, the gingiva is attached to cementum, so the clinical crown is longer than the anatomic crown.

## A General Description of Dentitions in Man

Two separate sets of teeth, or *dentitions*, develop during life. The first or *primary* dentition serves during the period of childhood. The teeth that develop in this dentition are called the *deciduous* (*decidere* = to fall down), *baby* or *milk* teeth. The primary teeth are shed progressively and are replaced by the permanent teeth that are intended to last the individual for the remainder of his life.

There are 20 teeth in the primary dentition—10 in the upper and 10 in the lower jaw. The shape of these is not the same; each is modified for different functions related to mastication. The first 2 teeth on each side of the midline in the upper and the lower jaws are called *incisors* (*incidere* = to cut into). These are shaped like chisels and can cut into food. The 2 incisors immediately next to the midline are the *central* incisors, and those next to them are the *lateral* incisors. The next teeth in order proceeding back from the incisors are the *canine* or *cuspid* teeth; the free-biting surface of these has only a single *cusp* (conical projection). These teeth (particularly in lower animals) serve to grasp and tear or shred food. Next in line, traveling posteriorly in a child's mouth, are 2 *molar* teeth on each side, the first and the second molars. Each molar tooth is modified for grinding food; hence, its biting surfaces are wider and flatter than the other teeth and have 3 or more cusps projecting from them. Each of the molars has more than one root; the lowers have 2, and the uppers have 3.

As has been mentioned already, the upper arch is slightly larger than the lower; hence, the upper teeth slightly overlap the lower. In addition, since the upper incisors are wider than the lower ones, each upper tooth not only meets its counterpart in the lower jaw but also contacts the next tooth behind that one.

The first of the primary teeth to erupt are the lower incisors that appear in the mouths of infants at about the age of 6 months. The last of the primary dentition erupts at approximately 2 years. This set of teeth serves the child for the next 4 years or so, at which time the primary teeth begin to be shed and replaced by the permanent ones. In addition to

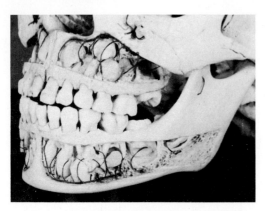

Fig. 24-5. Photograph of the jaws of a 5½-year-old child. The outer plates of bone have been removed from each jaw to show the roots of the primary teeth and the permanent teeth that are developing. (Preparation provided by K. J. Paynter)

replacing primary teeth, some of the permanent teeth erupt behind the last of the primary ones. This period of replacement of primary teeth extends over approximately 6 years, from about 6 through 12 years of age.

It should be realized that permanent teeth must be developing for some time prior to their eruption. Indeed, it takes several years (up to 12 for the upper cuspid) for a tooth to develop within a jaw. By the time a child is about 3 years of age, there are 48 teeth in the jaws that are either in function (the primary teeth) or in some stage of development. Figure 24-5 shows a dissected skull of a child of about 5½ years of age; the permanent teeth can be seen developing above and between the roots of the primary ones.

The permanent dentition consists of 32 teeth—16 in each jaw. Their shape is similar to the primary teeth but they are somewhat larger. The anterior or front teeth, as in the primary set, are the central and the lateral incisors and the cuspids. Immediately back of the cuspids are the 1st and the 2nd *bicuspids* or *premolars,* which are the teeth that occupy the spaces formerly occupied by the primary molars. Behind the bicuspids in each side of each jaw are 3 *molar* teeth. These are named the 1st, the 2nd and the 3rd molars; they have no predecessors in the primary dentition but erupt behind the last of the primary teeth in order. The 1st molar, or "6-year molar,"

erupts at about the age of 6 years. The 2nd molar erupts at about the age of 12 and is called the 12-year molar. The 3rd molar or "wisdom tooth" erupts considerably later, if it erupts at all. This tooth is subject to much variation in size and shape and all too frequently remains suppressed or impacted within the jaw. This may lead to disturbances later in life that can be relatively serious.

### THE DEVELOPMENT OF A TOOTH

The following description will be limited to the development of a lower primary incisor because of the relative simplicity of its development and because it is one of the first teeth to begin development in the fetus. It should be remembered that the other teeth develop in a similar manner in a regular chronologic sequence.

**Early Development.** To visualize the plane of section of the illustrations used to show the various stages of tooth development, the student should refer to the upper left sketch in Figure 24-6. This is a semidiagrammatic drawing of a sagittal section through the jaws and the tongue of an adult, cut in such a way as to permit the section to pass through both an upper and a lower incisor tooth. The remainder of the illustrations showing tooth development are all from within the rectangular area shown on this diagram.

To facilitate description, tooth development has been divided into various "stages" based primarily on the microscopic appearance of a tooth germ at various times during its growth. The student will realize, of course, that these "stages" pass from one to the next without interruption.

Teeth begin to develop early in embryonic life. At about 6 weeks after fertilization the first indication is apparent. At this time a section through the developing jaw would reveal a localized thickening of the basal cells of the oral ectoderm (Fig. 24-6, *upper right*). This thickening is apparent along the horseshoe-shaped line in a jaw, along which teeth will develop, and it has been called the *dental primordium* (*primus* = first; *ordior* = to begin). From this an epithelial shelf called a *dental lamina* grows into the mesenchyme (Fig. 24-6). From each lamina little epithelial buds develop where each primary tooth will form; these buds give rise to the primary teeth

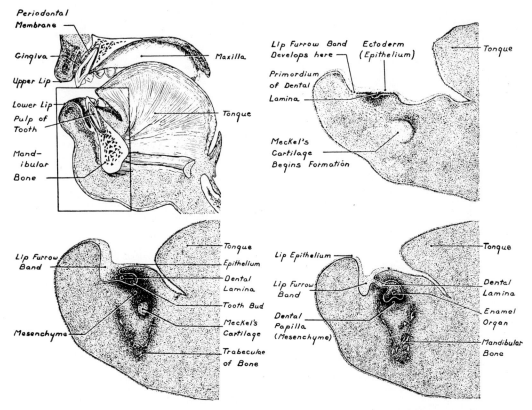

FIG. 24-6. (*Upper left*) This is to provide orientation for the succeeding figures. It shows the appearance of a sagittal section cut through the upper and the lower jaws of an adult in such a way as to pass through an upper and a lower incisor tooth. Note the rectangular area marked out by black lines. The appearance of this area, as seen in the developing embryo, is illustrated in the following figures. (*Upper right*) Diagram of a sagittal section of the developing lower jaw of an embryo at about the 6th week of development. The section passes through the area where a central incisor tooth will develop. (*Lower left*) Diagram of the same area in an embryo at about the end of the 7th week of development. The dental lamina has formed a tooth bud where the central incisor is to form. (*Lower right*) Diagram of the same area in an embryo toward the end of the 8th week. This illustrates the "cap" stage of development.

and their successors. Also it can be observed (Fig. 24-6, *lower left*) that at about this same time another invagination of epithelium occurs in front of (labial to) the dental laminae; eventually, this will split so as to separate the lip from the remainder of the mouth by a groove.

During the first few days of development, the dental lamina tends to grow in a slanted direction down (or up) and lingually (toward the tongue). Next, increased proliferation occurs in the cells of the lamina to form an epithelial bulge at each place where a tooth will develop; each bulge is directed deeply. Each

bulge is termed a *tooth bud*; one is shown in Figure 24-6, *lower left*.

As the tooth bud increases in size and penetrates deeper into the underlying mesenchyme, the lower surface of each becomes so indented that the lower concave surface of the bud comes close to the upper convex one. This makes the bud "cap-shaped." The "cap" stage of development is reached after about 2 weeks of development, and when it is reached the tooth bud is called the *enamel organ*, and the little papilla of mesenchyme over which the cap fits is called the *dental papilla*.

During the next several weeks, the enamel

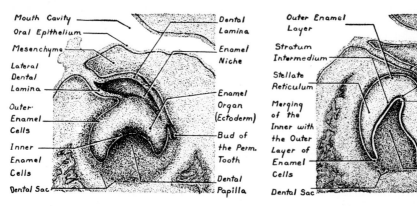

FIG. 24-7. (*Left*) Diagram of the same area in an embryo at about the 4th month. This illustrates the early "bell" stage of development. The bud of the permanent tooth has appeared. (*Right*) The same area later in the 4th month.

organ increases in size, and the bone of the jaws grows up to enclose it partly (Figs. 24-6 and 24-7). By the 4th month the enamel organ has grown almost to full size. At this time it appears, when seen in sagittal section (Fig. 24-7), to have the form of a bell, so this is termed the "bell" stage of development. During this period, i.e., the 4th developmental month, considerable cellular differentiation and specialization occurs within the enamel organ, as will now be described.

During the bell stage, the line of junction between it and the mesenchymal papilla assumes the shape and the size of the future line of junction between the enamel and the dentin of the adult tooth (Fig. 24-8). By the 5th month of development, the dental lamina

has been invaded and broken up by the surrounding mesenchyme, and the enamel organ loses any direct connection with the oral epithelium. Occasionally, some residual cells of the dental lamina may persist to give rise to cysts in later life.

At about this time the cells of the dental lamina, at the junction between the lamina and the enamel organ that formed from it, begin to proliferate; this results in a little bud of epithelial cells being formed on the lingual surface of the primary enamel organ. This is the bud of the *permanent tooth,* and later the succeeding permanent tooth will develop from it in this area (Fig. 24-7).

During this same stage of development, the mesenchymal cells surrounding the enamel

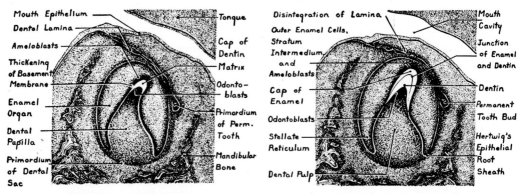

FIG. 24-8. (*Left*) Diagram of a sagittal section of a developing lower incisor tooth in an embryo between the 4th and the 5th months of development. This shows a cap of dentin at the tip of the papilla. (*Right*) The same area in the 5th month. Enamel, as well as dentin, has begun to form. The site where Hertwig's epithelial root sheath will form is indicated.

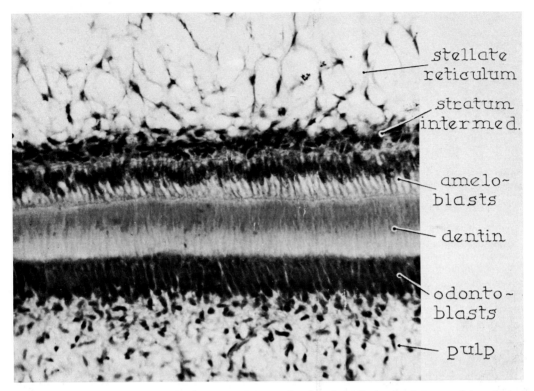

stellate
reticulum

stratum
intermed.

amelo-
blasts

dentin

odonto-
blasts

pulp

Fig. 24-9. High-power photomicrograph of a section cut through the dentino-enamel junction of a developing tooth shortly after dentin formation has begun.

organ become differentiated and form collagenic fibers, and the whole developing tooth becomes surrounded by a discernible loose fibrous connective tissue capsule. This is called the *dental sac* (Fig. 24-7, *right*), and it gives rise to the periodontal membrane—that dense connective tissue membrane that suspends the tooth in its socket.

The mesenchymal papilla that becomes enclosed by the enamel organ consists of a delicate network of mesenchymal cells connected to one another by thin protoplasmic strands and separated from one another by an amorphous intercellular substance. This tissue becomes increasingly vascular as development proceeds. Increased vascularization is also apparent in the connective tissue of the dental sac, and the outer (convex) surface of the enamel organ changes from being smooth to wavy as capillaries press onto its surface (but do not enter it).

**Cellular Differentiation Within the Enamel Organ and the Beginning of Hard Tissue Formation.** Up to the end of the "cap" stage of development all of the cells of the enamel organ appear the same. Considerable differentiation and specialization among these cells occurs during the bell stage. First, the cells immediately adjacent to the tip of the dental papilla become tall and columnar. At first their nuclei are at their bases, next to the connective tissue of the papilla, but before secretory activity begins in these cells their nuclei move to their opposite ends. These cells are called *ameloblasts* (*amel* = enamel; *blastos* = germ) (Figs. 24-7 and 24-9), and they are responsible for the production of tooth enamel. The single layer of cells forming the outer boundary of the enamel organ is known as the *outer enamel epithelium.* Between it and the ameloblasts are two distinct cell layers. The inner one immediately adjacent to the ameloblast layer is one or two cells in thickness and is called the *stratum intermedium*; the other, forming the bulk of the organ, is called the *stellate reticulum.* In the latter region the cells assume a star shape and are connected to one another by long protoplasmic extensions (Fig.

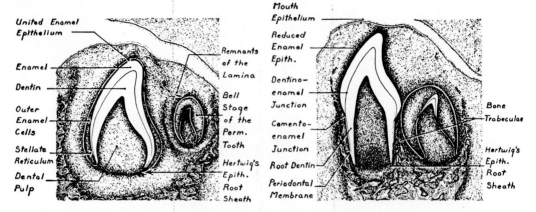

FIG. 24-10. (*Left*) Sagittal section of a developing lower incisor at about the time of birth. The development of the crown is almost completed. Hertwig's epithelial root sheath is beginning to develop. It should be noted that at this time the permanent tooth is developing in the same bony socket as the deciduous tooth. (*Right*) Diagram of the same area immediately before eruption. The crown is almost complete. The formation of the root is well advanced. Both dentin and enamel have appeared in the permanent tooth. Bone has formed to separate the two teeth, so the permanent tooth now has a separate socket.

24-9) similar to those of cells of mesenchyme.

While this differentiation is occurring in the enamel organ, some very important specialization also takes place in certain cells of the dental papilla. As was pointed out, the ameloblasts begin to differentiate at the tip of the developing cusp, or at the incisal edge of the tooth, and differentiation then proceeds down its sides, toward the base of the crown. As this occurs, the mesenchymal cells of the dental papilla immediately adjacent to the ameloblasts also become tall columnar cells; they are then known as *odontoblasts* (Fig. 24-8), for they will form dentin. The area where these two cellular transformations first appear in a tooth is termed its *growth center*. It is at this site that production of the hard tissues of the tooth first occurs. The actual mechanism of tissue production will be discussed in some detail below. It suffices to say here that the first tissue to appear is dentin; this is produced by odontoblasts at the tip of the papilla. After a thin layer of this is deposited, the ameloblasts begin to produce the matrix of enamel on it.

It should be pointed out here that the formation of dentin and enamel differs from bone formation in that no formative cells are trapped within the matrix that they produce. There is no such thing as an "odontocyte" or

an "amelocyte." Instead, the cells, as they produce the hard tissue matrix, retreat away from it—the ameloblasts outward, and the odontoblasts inward. Before discussing the formation of the hard tissues in more detail, the description of the development of the tooth as an organ will be completed.

**Formation of the Root.** During the "bell" stage of development of the enamel organ, the inner cells line up to assume the shape of the future line of junction between the enamel and the dentin of the adult tooth (Fig. 24-8, *right*). The deepest cells of the enamel organ differentiate to ameloblasts and produce enamel. But they also function to organize or induce the cells within the dental papilla to differentiate into odontoblasts. The inducting duties of these epithelial-derived cells seem to be all-important for the formation of odontoblasts and dentin. Since the roots of teeth, as well as their crowns, are largely composed of dentin, mesenchymal cells in the root region must be induced to become odontoblasts by epithelial cells of the enamel organ, even though the roots do not become covered with enamel. This is accomplished as follows:

After the formation of the hard tissues of the crown is well advanced, the epithelial cells around the base of the enamel organ begin to proliferate further. It should be realized that

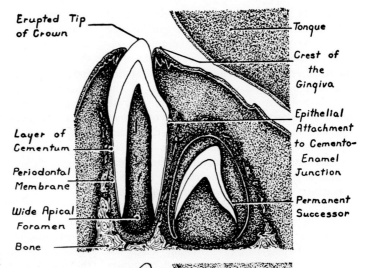

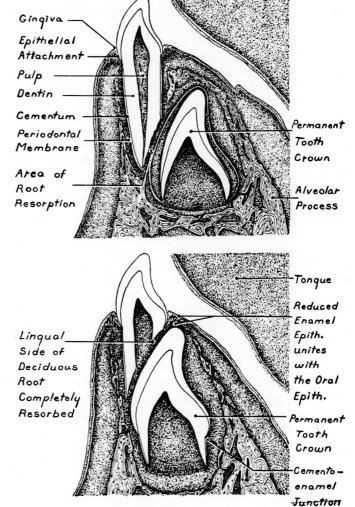

Fig. 24-11. (*Top*) Diagram of an erupting lower central incisor (6 to 12 months). The epithelium of the gingiva is attached to the enamel and continues down over it to the cemento-enamel junction. (*Center*) Diagram of a central lower incisor tooth 4 to 6 years after birth. The root becomes completed in the 2nd year, and its resorption begins after the 4th year. (*Bottom*) Diagram showing the shedding of a deciduous lower central incisor tooth. This usually occurs in the 7th year. The root has begun to form in the permanent tooth, which will erupt by the 8th year.

at this site (Fig. 24-8, *right*) the cells forming the inner layer of the enamel organ become continuous with those forming the outer layer, i.e., the ameloblast layer is continuous with the outer enamel epithelium. The cells at this line of junction—around the bottom of the "bell"—begin to proliferate and to migrate down into the underlying mesenchyme. Since the bottom of the bell is ring-shaped (if seen from below), the proliferating cells from the ring form a tube that surrounds further mesenchyme as it descends. The cells of the tube constitute *Hertwig's epithelial root sheath* (Fig. 24-10). As this sheath moves down it forms the pattern outlining the shape of the root of the tooth and it organizes the cells of the mesenchyme that it surrounds, which are immediately adjacent to it, to differentiate into odontoblasts. While the root is forming in this manner, the whole tooth is moving toward the oral cavity, and it erupts into the mouth before the root is fully formed. Indeed, most permanent teeth are in the mouth and in function for about 2 years before the end of the root is completely formed. As the epithelial root sheath approaches the end of the root it becomes narrower to form the typical conical shape of the apex (Fig. 24-11, *top*).

The root sheath grows downward by continued proliferation of the cells at its leading ring-shaped edge. The older part of it, toward the crown, having served its purpose, becomes detached from the root of the tooth, and the epithelial cells of it remain within the confines of the periodontal membrane surrounding the tooth. They may be observed histologically within the membrane at any age after the roots have formed. They are called the *epithelial rests of Malassez,* and under proper stimulus they may give rise to dental cysts at any time in life.

The root sheath separates from the formed root, and cells from the mesenchymal connective tissue of the dental sac deposit cementum on the outer surface of the dentin; this is laid down around the collagenic fibers of the membrane that the cells in this area are also forming.

While the primary tooth is developing and erupting into function, the tooth germ for its successor also is differentiating and laying down the substance of the permanent tooth (Figs. 24-10, *right,* and 24-11). As this oc-

curs, the tooth moves toward the oral cavity. The root of the primary tooth begins to resorb (Fig. 24-11, *middle*), and by the time the permanent tooth is ready to erupt, the root of the primary tooth has been completely resorbed. The crown becomes detached from the gum tissue, and the tooth is shed to be replaced by its permanent successor (Fig. 24-11, *bottom*).

## SOME FURTHER DETAILS OF THE FORMATION AND THE MICROSCOPIC STRUCTURE OF THE DENTAL TISSUES

In the foregoing section the way that teeth develop and take their places in the oral cavity has been described. In the following section the microscopic structure of the various tissues that form the dental organ will be described in more detail. Certain clinical observations, related to histology and thought to be of importance to the physician, will be included also.

The tissues with which we are concerned are both hard (calcified) and soft (uncalcified). They include dentin, enamel, cementum, dental pulp and periodontal membrane. With the exception of enamel, all are connective tissues.

### 1. Dentin

It will be recalled that after the enamel organ develops to a certain point, the epithelial cells lining its concave surface, adjacent to the dental papilla, become converted to tall columnar cells known as ameloblasts (Figs. 24-7, *right,* and 24-9). The presence of these cells apparently is necessary for the organization of cells within the dental papilla so that they are induced to develop into tall columnar cells called *odontoblasts* that play a leading part in the formation of dentin.

Odontoblasts begin to form dentin matrix very soon after they assume their typical form. At first they are separated from the ameloblasts by only a basement membrane. But soon a layer of intercellular substance is deposited by them; this separates them farther from the ameloblasts. The first intercellular substance to form is a complex of reticular fibers and an amorphous cementing material. The reticular fibers run in a characteristic corkscrew fashion through the odontoblast layer and parallel with the long axes of the cells of the layer until they reach the basement membrane; here they spread out in a fanlike manner to run parallel with, and become continuous with, the basement membrane. These bundles of reticular fibers that may be seen as the first predentin forms are known as *Korff's fibers*. The fibers that form later (as the production of intercellular substance continues) are collagenic rather than reticular.

The intercellular substance that is formed by the odontoblasts is similar to, but not identical with, the intercellular substance of bone. There are certain chemical differences between the two. For example, bone has both a higher organic content (24-26% vs. 19-21%) and, as might be expected, contains more collagen (25% vs. 18% for dentin). However, the processes by which dentin is formed and calcified are similar to processes already described in connection with bone. We shall elaborate:

It will be recalled that a piece of bone can become larger only by means of the successive addition of new layers of bone to one or more of its surfaces (Fig. 18-3). This is also true of dentin, except that the growth of this material is even more limited because odontoblasts are present only along the inner or pulpal side of dentin in a tooth. Hence, any new layers of dentin that are produced can be added only to the pulpal surface of such dentin as is present already. Therefore, the addition of layers of dentin must encroach on the pulp.

It will be recalled also that osteoblasts are provided with cytoplasmic processes that act as molds when the organic intercellular substance is laid down around them; these are responsible for canaliculi (Fig. 18-1). Odontoblasts are provided also with processes about which organic intercellular substance is deposited. However, these processes do not extend in all directions from their cell bodies as do those of osteoblasts, but mostly outward to reach the basement membrane that lines the concavity of the enamel organ. Thus, when intercellular substance is deposited between the layer of odontoblasts and the basement membrane, the deposited intercellular substance surrounds these cytoplasmic processes which, therefore, come to lie in tiny canals called *dentinal tubules*. The odonto-

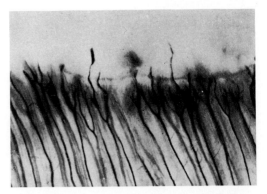

Fig. 24-12. The processes of odontoblasts lie in canals in the dentin. (Churchill, H. R.: Meyer's Histology and Histogenesis of the Human Teeth, Philadelphia, Lippincott)

blastic processes do not retract but remain within the tubules where they are called *Tomes' dentinal fibers* (Fig. 24-12). As more and more dentin is formed, the odontoblasts are displaced farther and farther away from the basement membrane that outlines the dentino-enamel junction. This requires that the dentinal processes, if they are to maintain a connection with the basement membrane, must become increasingly elongated, and that the dentinal tubules containing them must become increasingly elongated also.

It has been pointed out earlier in this text that two steps occur as bone is developing; the first is the manufacture of the organic intercellular substance, and the second is its calcification. For the formation of collagen in dentin see index. The calcification of the developing intercellular substance of dentin does not seem to take place as rapidly after its deposition as does the matrix of bone; hence, it is normal for the layer of most recently formed dentin in a growing tooth to be uncalcified for a short time. This uncalcified layer of dentin is called *predentin*. The oldest dentin in a growing crown is that next to the basement membrane that separates it from enamel. The youngest dentin is that closest to the odontoblasts. Thus, in a growing tooth it is normal for the older calcified dentin to be separated from the odontoblasts by a layer of (uncalcified) *predentin* (Fig. 24-13).

It is probable that the mechanism of calcification in dentin is very similar to that

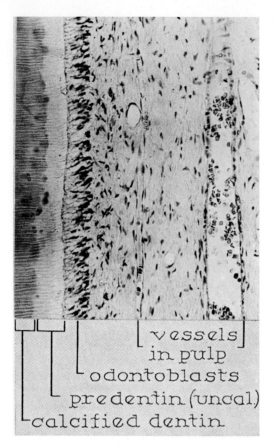

vessels
in pulp
odontoblasts
predentin (uncal)
calcified dentin

FIG. 24-13. High-power photomicrograph of a section of a child's tooth in which dentin was still forming. (Preparation by K. J. Paynter)

which operates in cartilage and bone. Phosphatase is involved in the mechanism. It has been established that, although its distribution varies somewhat, depending on the stage of development of the tooth, alkaline phosphatase is present in substantial quantities in the odontogenic cells of the dental papilla during the period of elaboration and calcification of the hard tissue. The enzyme has been observed also to a lesser extent in the predentin and the dentinal tubules.

As most of us are well aware, teeth may be extremely sensitive to stimuli arising on a dentin surface. The ability of dentin to be sensitive to stimuli is explained by the presence of the cytoplasmic processes of odontoblasts in the dentin, because nerve fibers have

not been demonstrated in dentin except very close to the pulpal border. This sensitivity of dentin generally decreases with age; the decrease in sensitivity is related to a calcification of the dentinal tubules and their filling in with calcium salts.

### 2. Enamel

It has been pointed out that the presence of ameloblasts, differentiated from the inner enamel epithelium of the enamel organ, are necessary to bring about a differentiation of the cells of the mesenchymal dental papilla into odontoblasts. After the odontoblasts have produced the first thin layer of dentin, the ameloblasts (Fig. 24-9) are, in turn, induced to make enamel. Enamel then forms and covers the dentin, but only over the anatomic crown of the tooth (Figs. 24-8, *right*, and 24-10). It forms first as a relatively uncalcified matrix, which later calcifies.

Just prior to the laying down of enamel matrix, the basement membrane between the ameloblasts and the newly formed dentin thickens. This is thought to be due to the formation of a cuticlelike material by the ends of the ameloblasts that are in contact with the basement membrane. Next, the character of the cytoplasm of the ameloblasts undergoes changes; adjacent to the basement membrane, it first becomes granular and then later it becomes homogeneous as it produces the material of enamel. The process of the formation of enamel is a very complex one, and there are differences of opinion as to whether the homogeneous material should be considered as a secretion of ameloblasts or as a transformation of their cytoplasm. There is much chemical and histochemical evidence to indicate that a type of keratin is produced in the process and that this constitutes a part of the organic material that is formed. It should be recalled at this time that ameloblasts are epithelial cells.

Individual ameloblasts have 6 sides, as may be seen in cross sections, and are separated from one another by thin partitions of intercellular material (Fig. 24-14, *left*). The material of enamel is produced in the form of rods. The enamel matrix retains the shape of the cell; both are prismatic (Fig. 24-14, *right*). The transformed ends of the ameloblasts have

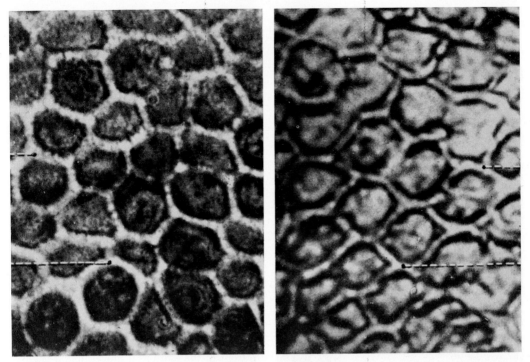

Fig. 24-14. (*Left*) This photomicrograph is from a cross section cut through ameloblasts; it shows the intercellular substance (indicated by leaders) between them. (*Right*) From a cross section of formed enamel, showing that interprismatic substance (indicated by leaders) has formed in the sites formerly occupied by intercellular substance. (Churchill, H. R.: Meyer's Histology and Histogenesis of the Human Teeth, Philadelphia, Lippincott)

been termed *Tomes' processes*; these are not to be confused with the Tomes' dentinal process described previously under dentin.

As enamel matrix is produced, the outer ends of ameloblasts migrate outwardly from their starting point—the basement membrane between them and the odontoblast layer. As they migrate they seem to do so rhythmically, i.e., they move in spurts—a certain distance each day; then they rest while preparing for the next day's work. This rhythmic production of matrix is manifest in ground undecalcified sections of adult teeth where it is indicated by lines visible in the enamel called the *striae of Retzius* (Fig. 24-15). Previously, it was thought that enamel matrix only partially calcified as it was produced and that it became fully calcified only after it was fully formed; the final step was termed *maturation*. Recent work using microradiography and the EM indicates that calcification does not occur

in two steps, but once it has begun it proceeds steadily to completion, proceeding from the dentino-enamel junction to the enamel surface (see Frank and Sognnaes).

Fully formed and calcified enamel is a very highly calcified material (approximately 95% inorganic) constructed of long hexagonal rods tied together with an interrod calcified cementing substance. Enamel is relatively inert; it has no cells in association with it because the ameloblasts are lost after they form all the enamel and the tooth erupts. Thus, enamel is completely incapable of repair if it is injured by decay, fracture or other means. However, there is a fairly rapid exchange of certain ions between enamel and saliva.

Phosphatase has been demonstrated in the nuclei and the cytoplasm of ameloblasts before enamel matrix formation takes place, and a high concentration of phosphatase is maintained both before and during elaboration of

FIG. 24-15. Low-power photomicrograph of a ground section of the enamel and a portion of the dentin of a tooth. The lines of Retzius may be seen curving from the left border upward and to the right. The irregular and slightly wavy structure that extends down from the surface at the upper right side and resembles an artefact is an enamel lamella. Enamel lamellae contain more interprismatic substance than ordinary enamel. Some dentin may be seen in the lower right corner. The tubules that extend from it into the enamel are called "enamel spindles."

the matrix (Fig. 24-16). The enzyme gradually disappears from the cells when calcification of the matrix is complete.

### 3. Cementum

Some cells of the mesenchyme of the dental sac in close proximity to the side of the developing root differentiate and become similar to osteoblasts. Here they are associated with the laying down of another special nonvascular calcified connective tissue called *cementum,* which buries in its substance the ends of the fibers of the periodontal membrane and so attaches them to the tooth (Fig. 24-17).

Cementum in the upper one third to one half the length of the root is noncellular (Fig. 24-17); the remainder has cells within its matrix. These cells are called *cementocytes* and they, like osteocytes, reside in small spaces within the calcified matrix called *lacunae* and communicate with their source of nutrition through canaliculi.

Under certain circumstances cementum may be subject to resorption, although this does not occur with the same ease or frequency as it does in bone. This fact is utilized clinically during the process of moving teeth slowly from one position to another in the jaw. Such treatment is indicated when teeth are badly aligned. Pressure on the tooth, when sustained long enough, brings about a resorption of bone in front of the tooth as it moves, and a deposition of bone occurs behind it. The cementum, on the other hand, does not resorb under such circumstances.

Cementum, like bone, can increase in amount only by additions to its surface.

### THE STUDY OF THE MINERALIZATION OF GROWING TEETH AND BONES BY THE RADIOAUTOGRAPHIC TECHNIC

Leblond, Bélanger, Greulich and others, using the radioautographic technic, have studied the development and the subsequent calcification of the matrix of the various hard tissues of the body. Animals have been injected with various radioactive materials, including sulfur, carbon, calcium and phosphorus, and then sacrificed at various time intervals following the injection. Then radioautographs have been made either by fluid coating the slide with emulsion or by preparing "inverted" autographs of the preparations.

These investigators have found that in the case of enamel there is a clear-cut distinction between the deposition of organic matrix and of minerals. The formation of the components of the matrix is indicated by the deposition of radioactive sulfur and carbon, and this occurs considerably in advance of the deposition of calcium and phosphorus. It was found

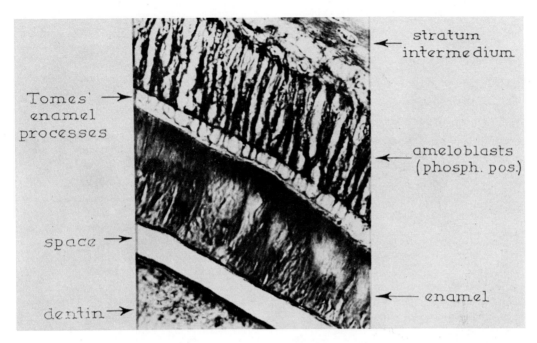

FIG. 24-16. Very high-power photomicrograph of a section from the cervical region of a 170-mm. pig canine tooth, decalcified by Kramer's and Shipley's method, and showing the cytoplasm of the ameloblasts to be phosphatase positive. (Bevelander, G., and Johnson, P. L.: Anat. Rec. *104*:125)

that the labeled sulfur and carbon disappeared from the matrix at the site of, and at the time of, the appearance of labeled calcium and phosphorus. In the case of dentin (and presumably also of bone) the matrix is elaborated in two steps. First, predentin is formed incorporating radioactive carbon; this probably is in the forming collagen. Radioactive sulfur enters into the formation of sulfated mucopolysaccharides. This complete matrix takes up calcium and phosphorus (Fig. 24-18).

### 4. Periodontal Membrane

As the root of the tooth forms and cementum is deposited on its surface, the periodontal membrane develops from the mesenchyme of the dental sac that surrounds the tooth during development and fills the space between it and the bone of the alveolar process. This tissue comes to consist of heavy bundles of collagenic fibers arranged in the form of a suspensory ligament between the root of the tooth and the bony wall of its socket (Fig. 24-4). The fiber bundles are em-bedded at the one end in the bone of the wall of the alveolus and at the other end in the cementum covering the root (Fig. 24-4). At both ends the parts of the fibers that actually are embedded in hard tissue are called *Sharpey's fibers* (Fig. 24-17).

**How Sharpey's Fibers Become Attached to Bone and Cementum.** It is most important for the student to understand clearly how collagenic fibers become embedded into either bone or cementum to become Sharpey's fibers. The fibers do not grow into the bone or the cementum. It should be understood that the cells of the developing periodontal membrane have the ability to produce not only collagenic fibers but also the organic matrix of both bone and cementum. At the bone border the cells of the membrane produce collagenic fibers and also the other elements of bone matrix; the latter materials are laid down around the bundles of collagenic fibers which, thereby, are embedded in bone matrix that becomes calcified and is cemented to the bone. The same phenomenon occurs at the tooth side of the membrane; here the cells of the developing periodontal

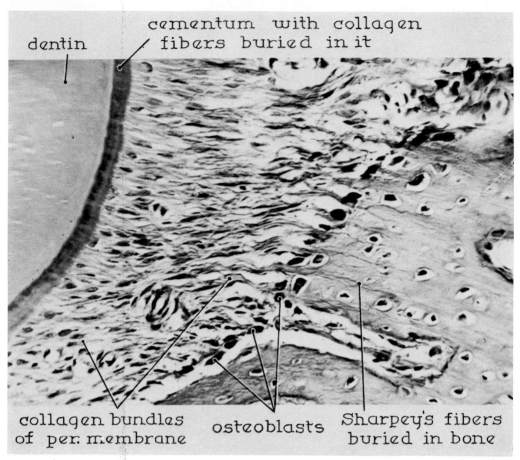

FIG. 24-17. High-power photomicrograph (lightly retouched) of a portion of a decalcified section of a tooth of a rat, showing how the collagenic fibers of the periodontal membrane continue into both the cementum and the bone to anchor the tooth firmly in its alveolus. (Section supplied by W. J. Linghorne)

membrane make collagenic fibers and also the other components of cementum. The latter materials are laid down around the fibers so as to embed them in a material that becomes calcified and is thus cemented to the dentin. It is important to realize that *cementum must be formed* if the collagenic fibers of the membrane are to be attached firmly to the tooth. Hence, if fibers become detached from the cementum, as occurs in some kinds of periodontal disease, they cannot be reattached firmly unless new cementum is formed.

The fibers of the periodontal membrane are generally a little longer than the shortest distance between the side of the tooth and the wall of the socket (Fig. 24-4). This arrangement allows for a certain limited movement of

a tooth within its alveolus. In addition to having a suspensory function, the periodontal membrane has other functions. Both the osteoblasts lining the bony wall of the socket and the cementoblasts associated with the side of the root are considered as cells of the membrane; hence, it has osteogenic and cementogenic functions. The blood capillaries within it form the only source of nutritive supply to cementocytes. The nerves of the membrane supply the teeth with their very important and remarkably sensitive tactile sense.

### 5. The Epithelial Attachment and Periodontal Disease

The gingiva surrounds each tooth like a collar, and under normal conditions the inner surface of the collar is attached tightly to the tooth. If the tooth and its surrounding gingiva are sectioned longitudinally, the gingiva appears to extend up each side of the tooth as a narrow triangle, the apex of which is termed the *gingival crest* (Fig. 24-4). The side of the triangle next to the tooth is covered with epithelium. This epithelium, as it extends down from the crest, is at first not adherent to the tooth; hence, there is a crevice between it and the tooth surface; this is called the *gingival crevice or sulcus* (this rings the tooth) (Fig. 24-4). At the bottom of the sulcus the epithelium of the gingiva becomes adherent to the tooth. In erupting teeth the epithelium, from here to the bottom of the anatomic crown, is attached to enamel. However, the epithelium extends a little below the enamel and is attached to the cementum of the root (Fig. 24-4). The attachment of the epithelium to the enamel is not nearly as strong as its attachment to the cementum because there is nothing on the surface of the enamel (except a little cuticle that is left over from the enamel organ) to which the epithelium can become firmly attached. However, the cementum in this region has been shown by Paynter to develop more

or less like a basement membrane (it is P.A.S. positive), so it provides the same means for a firm attachment of epithelium as does the material of basement membranes elsewhere.

It is obvious that the gingival sulcus would provide a site where debris might accumulate. Since there is calcium in saliva it is not surprising that calcified material, called *tartar or calculus,* accumulates in the gingival sulcus, and expanding accumulations of this tend to separate the epithelial attachment from the tooth. Once the epithelial seal around the tooth is broken it is obvious that bacteria could gain entrance to the connective tissue of the gingivae. Therefore, the gingival crevice is a danger zone.

For the reasons given above, or for other reasons (perhaps systemic factors) which are not yet understood, the epithelium of the gingivae may become separated from the cementum, and what are called *pockets* may develop down the sides of a tooth. Pockets commonly separate the cementum-covered root from the fibers of the periodontal membrane, and this, of course, loosens the tooth. The gingival epithelium generally grows down the outer side of pockets so that the pockets

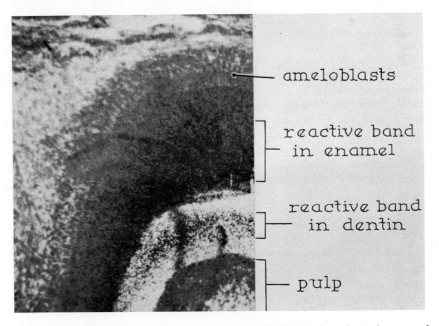

Fig. 24-18. Inverted radioautograph of an undecalcified section of a molar cusp of an 8-day-old hamster that was injected with radiophosphorus 4 days previously. (Preparation from L. F. Bélanger and C. P. Leblond)

are bordered on their outer aspects by epithelium and on their inner aspects by cementum-covered dentin. The pockets become infected. Unfortunately, the type of periodontal disease produced by the above described means is common in individuals in the middle and the older age groups; indeed, its prevalence in this age group is responsible for the loss of more teeth than any other condition. More research into the cause and the treatment of periodontal disease is badly needed.

### 6. The Dental Pulp and Dental Caries

The life of the tooth depends on the health of the dental pulp. The health of the dental pulp is threatened all too commonly by the development of dental caries, so before discussing the pulp in detail a few remarks will be made about this condition which is probably the most common of all diseases.

Dental caries causes cavities to develop on exposed tooth surfaces. The disease begins on the outer surface of the enamel, commonly in tiny pits or crevices, or between adjacent teeth—areas where food debris is not readily washed away by saliva or the toothbrush. The food in these tiny areas acts as a substrate for the metabolism of bacteria, which are abundant in the mouth. It is generally believed that the bacterial action leads to the formation of acid products which locally decalcify and destroy enamel. Cavities that thus develop tend to be progressive, for they retain food debris which continues to be acted on by bacteria. Unless such cavities are treated, sooner or later they will reach the dentin and continue to extend through it to reach the pulp of the tooth. When they near the pulp they are prone to cause inflammation of the pulp, and, as will be explained below, this can cause its death.

A developing cavity causes no pain when it is confined to the enamel. When it reaches the dentin it may or may not give rise to increased sensitivity of the tooth; the increased sensitivity may be related to certain foods, for example, sweet materials. The presence of cavities is best determined by regular dental inspections. To treat them, all the surrounding affected enamel and dentin must be drilled away or otherwise removed. Then the cavity is shaped so that it will retain a filling. Fill-ings must be used because there are no cells on the outer aspects of the tooth to make new enamel and dentin.

Dental pulp is a connective tissue derived from the mesenchyme of the dental papilla (Fig. 24-8, left), and it occupies the pulp chambers and the root canals of teeth (Fig. 24-4). It is a soft tissue which retains its mesenchymal appearance throughout life (Fig. 24-13). The bulk of its cells appear stellate in sections, being connected to one another by long cytoplasmic processes. Pulp is very vascular; the main vessels enter and leave it through the apical foramina. However, the pulpal vessels, even the large ones, have very thin walls (Fig. 24-13). This, of course, renders this tissue very susceptible to changes in pressure because the walls of the pulp chamber cannot expand. A fairly mild inflammatory edema often can lead to compression of the blood vessels and hence to the necrosis and death of the pulp. Following pulp death, sometimes the pulp can be removed surgically and the space it occupied filled with an inert sealing material. Such a tooth constitutes what is commonly called a "dead" tooth.

The pulp is richly supplied with nerves, and nerve endings have been observed in close association with the odontoblast layer between the pulp and the dentin. Some authors have reported finding nerves actually entering the dentinal tubules, but, as was mentioned above, there is no indication that they proceed more than a very short distance within the tubules.

It was explained before that any new dentin that is added to the walls of the tooth must be deposited on the surface of already existing dentin, and only on the surface abutting on the pulp, because this is the only place where odontoblasts exist. Dentin normally is produced throughout life, and under certain conditions it may form rapidly (for example, under a cavity), but under the latter conditions the dentin is of a more irregular character and is designated as *secondary dentin*. Dentin deposition leads to a gradual reduction in the size of the pulp chamber and the canals throughout life; hence, in older people the pulp is generally much reduced in size. Its character also changes in that it becomes more fibrous and less cellular.

The continuously growing incisor of the rat

has provided a valuable experimental tool in dental research. Schour in particular has exploited this to great advantage.

## THE SALIVARY GLANDS

**Introduction.** Three large paired glands— the parotid, the submandibular (submaxillary) and the sublingual—are usually considered as constituting the salivary glands. However, the secretions of numerous smaller glands, previously described as being scattered throughout the buccal mucosa, also contribute toward the saliva. Since these smaller glands have been described already, the following will deal only with the 3 large paired glands. These, like the liver and the pancreas, are situated outside the digestive tract proper. Their secretions are conveyed to the oral cavity through individual ducts.

**Saliva and Its Functions.** The mixed secretions of all the salivary glands are called *saliva*. Essentially fluid, it usually contains some cellular and bacterial debris and leukocytes. In man, the volume of saliva secreted in 24 hours varies from 1,000 to 1,500 ml. It may range from being thin and watery to viscous in consistency. Its composition varies with the type of stimulus that initiates its secretion. It is 99.5 per cent water. The remainder is made up of salts, gases and organic material. Two enzymes (*ptyalin* or *salivary amylase,* and *maltase*) and mucin make up part of the organic material.

Saliva has several functions: (1) It provides for the lubrication and the moistening of the buccal mucosa and the lips, thus aiding articulation. This function must be carried on continuously because of the evaporation and the swallowing of saliva, and the providing of a more or less steady supply of saliva for this purpose is probably the chief function of the buccal glands. (2) It provides a means whereby the mouth may be washed clear of cellular and food debris which otherwise might provide an excellent culture medium for bacteria. (3) Probably the most important function of saliva is to moisten food and transform it to a semisolid or liquid mass so that it may be swallowed easily. It may be noted here that animals such as the cow, which live on a fairly dry diet, may secrete up to 60 liters of saliva daily. Moreover, moisten-

ing the food allows it to be tasted. Taste buds are stimulated chemically, and substances that stimulate them must be in solution. (4) The role of the salivary enzymes in the digestion of food is questionable. Amylase breaks down starch to maltose in an alkaline or slightly acid medium. The food is retained in the mouth for much too short a time for any significant digestion to occur there, and when food reaches the stomach, the acid reaction therein, it might be thought, would inhibit any further amylase activity. But it has been shown that some of the starches that are consumed near the end of a meal may be broken down to maltose in the stomach because, being in the innermost part of the gastric contents, they are protected for a time from the gastric juice liberated from the stomach lining. (5) Some heavy metals and other inorganic and organic substances may be excreted in part in the saliva. (6) The secretion or lack of secretion of saliva indirectly aids in the control of water balance in the body. When too much fluid has been lost, the tissues, including the salivary glands, become dehydrated; this results in decreased secretion, hence, in a drying of the oral mucosa which, in turn, gives rise to a sensation of thirst.

**The Parotid Glands.** These are the largest of the 3 pairs of salivary glands proper. Each lies packed in the space between the mastoid process and the ramus of the mandible. It overflows onto the face below the zygomatic arch, and from this process of the gland, its duct (Stensen's), running parallel with and immediately below the arch, plunges through the buccinator muscle to open into the vestibule of the mouth opposite the 2nd upper molar tooth.

The gland is enclosed in a well-defined fibrous connective tissue capsule and is a compound tubulo-alveolar gland of the serous type. The microscopic details of the secretory units of such glands have been described in Chapter 9. In addition to the usual features to be seen in a gland of this type, it is specially characterized by many and prominent intralobular ducts (Fig. 24-19). Accumulations of fat cells in the connective tissue septa are also characteristic of this gland.

**The Submandibular Glands (Submaxillary).** These lie in contact with the inner surface of the body of the mandible, and their main

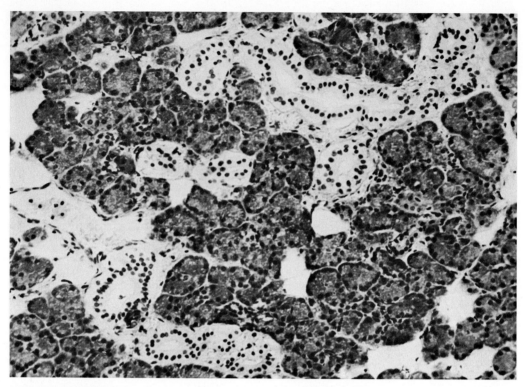

Fig. 24-19. Medium-power photomicrograph of a section of the parotid gland. The cytoplasm of the cells of the many ducts is light, and that of the cells of the secretory units, dark. The empty spaces represent fat, and a vein may be seen at the left.

ducts (Wharton's) open onto the floor of the oral cavity beside each other, anterior to the tongue and behind the lower incisor tooth. They are compound alveolar or tubulo-alveolar glands. Although of the mixed type, the majority of their secretory units are of the serous variety. Mucous units are usually capped by serous demilunes (see Chap. 9 for a description and illustrations of mixed glands). Like the parotid glands, the submandibular glands have well-defined capsules and fairly prominent duct systems.

**The Sublingual Glands.** Unlike the other salivary glands, the sublingual glands are not so definitely encapsulated. They lie well forward, near the midline, below the mucous membrane of the floor of the mouth, and their secretions empty by several ducts (Rivinus) that open along a line behind the openings of Wharton's ducts. They are compound tubulo-alveolar glands of the mixed type, but differ from the submandibular gland in that the majority of their alveoli are of the mucous

type. Their microscopic appearance is different in different parts of the gland. In some areas only mucus-secreting units and mucous units with serous demilunes may be found. The connective tissue septa are usually more prominent than they are in the parotid or the submandibular glands.

**Control of Salivary Secretion.** No hormone appears to have any effect on salivary secretion. Ordinarily, salivary secretion is controlled by nervous reflexes. Briefly, the efferent or secretory fibers to the salivary glands are derived from the cranial outflow of the parasympathetic system and the thoracic outflow of the sympathetic system. The parasympathetic preganglionic fibers to the submandibular and the sublingual glands run in the chorda tympani to the submaxillary ganglion, whence postganglionic fibers pass to the glands. The fibers ramify about serous units and supply vasodilator fibers to the vessels. The postganglionic sympathetic fibers are derived from the superior cervical ganglion and pass to the secretory cells and the walls of the blood vessels. The preganglionic parasympathetic fibers to the parotid gland travel by a devious route to the otic ganglion, from which post-ganglionic fibers arise. The sympathetic supply is the same as for the other salivary glands. There are many afferent pathways that may be concerned in salivary reflexes. The stimulus that evokes secretion reflexly may be mechanical or chemical. For example, the presence of food (or even pebbles or dry powders in the mouth) stimulates the ordinary sensory nerve endings and causes salivary secretion. The taste buds are receptive to chemical stimulation. Stimulation of many sensory nerves other than those of the oral cavity may initiate a salivary reflex, provided that the reflex has been conditioned (Chap. 21). The amount and the composition of the saliva depends on the nature of the stimulus that initiates the reflex and on whether sympathetic or parasympathetic fibers are predominantly involved in the efferent path. It has been shown that sympathetic stimulation of the submandibular gland gives rise to a thick, viscous, mucous secretion; parasympathetic stimulation gives rise to a copious, thin, serous secretion.

## THE HARD PALATE

It is desirable that the mouth (Fig. 24-1) should possess a strong roof so that the anterior part of the tongue, which is the part of the tongue that can move most freely, can bring force to bear against it in the process of mixing and swallowing food. It is also desirable that the mucous membrane lining the roof of the mouth in this site should be firmly fixed to the strong roof so that forceful movements of the tongue do not dislodge it, and that its epithelium should be capable of withstanding wear and tear. These desirable structural characteristics are realized by there being a bony roof over the mouth which is lined on its undersurface by a mucous membrane, the lamina propria of which is continuous with the periosteum of the bone above, and the epithelium of which is of the stratified squamous keratinizing variety.

Laterally, the mucous membrane is not so evenly adherent to the bony roof and is connected to it by strong bundles of connective

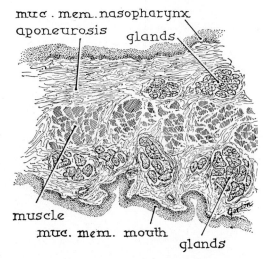

FIG. 24-20. Drawing of a section of the soft palate. (Redrawn and modified from Huber: Piersol's Human Anatomy, ed. 9, Philadelphia, Lippincott)

tissue. Fat cells are disposed between these anteriorly, and glands, posteriorly.

In the median line is a ridge of bone to which the epithelium is attached by a very thin lamina propria. This ridge is called the *raphe*. Rugae with connective tissue cores radiate out from this laterally. They are more prominent in early life than thereafter.

## THE SOFT PALATE

The soft palate continues posteriorly from the hard palate (Fig. 24-1). Its functions are different from those of the hard palate. It does not have to bear the thrust of the tongue. It must be movable so that in the act of swallowing it can be drawn upward so as to close off the nasopharynx and so prevent food from being forced up into the nose. This requires that it contain muscle. It must be reasonably strong, and this requires that it contain connective tissue which is disposed in it as an aponeurosis.

The soft palate projects backward into the pharynx from the hard palate (Fig. 24-1). Hence, the mucous membrane on its upper surface forms part of the lining of the nasopharynx, and the mucous membrane on its lower surface forms part of the lining of the oral pharynx. From above downward it ex-

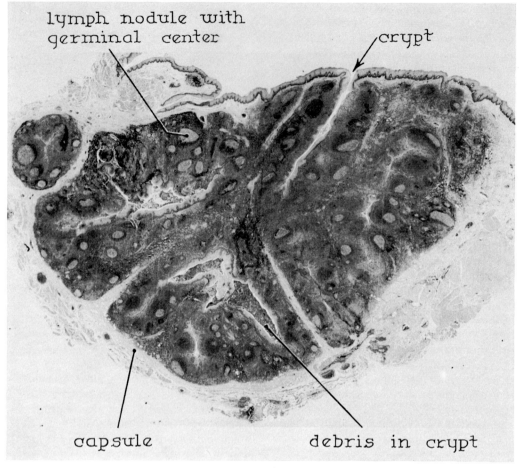

lymph nodule with
germinal center

crypt

capsule

debris in crypt

FIG. 24-21. Very low-power photomicrograph of a section of palatine tonsil.

hibits the following layers (Fig. 24-20); (1) stratified squamous or pseudostratified ciliated columnar epithelium; (2) a lamina propria which contains a few glands and, near the hard palate, has the form of a strong aponeurosis; (3) a muscular layer (posteriorly); (4) a thick lamina propria containing many glands; and (5) stratified squamous nonkeratinizing epithelium.

## THE PHARYNX

The pharynx is a somewhat conical-shaped chamber that serves as a passageway for both the respiratory and the digestive systems. Under conditions of nose breathing it conducts air between the nasal cavities and the larynx and to the eustachian tubes (Fig. 26-1). It also conducts food from the mouth to the esophagus, with which its apex is continuous

(Fig. 24-1). But, since it is common to both systems, it permits an individual whose nasal passages are obstructed to breathe through his mouth or, when his mouth is immobilized for surgical reasons, to be fed with a tube through his nose.

The pharynx is divided into 3 parts. The *nasopharynx* lies above the level of the soft palate (Fig. 24-1). The posterior limit of the mouth is indicated by the glossopalatine arches, and the part of the pharynx behind these is the *oral pharynx* (Fig. 24-1). The *laryngeal pharynx* is the part that continues from the oral pharynx, from below the level of the hyoid bone, into the esophagus (Fig. 24-1).

The pharynx is lined with epithelium. This varies in the different parts in accordance with their various functions. Where there is wear and tear, such as that occasioned by food

passing over a part or by parts rubbing together, the stratified squamous nonkeratinizing
type of epithelium is found. Where the lining
epithelium comes into contact only with air,
the pseudostratified columnar ciliated type is
present. Stratified columnar epithelium is
found in some sites, particularly in the transition zones between the other 2 types.

The lining of epithelium rests on a fairly
dense connective tissue membrane which contains elastic as well as collagenic fibers. At the
side of this farthest from the epithelium there
is usually a stout layer of elastic fibers. Outside this again is striated muscle—the longitudinal and the constrictor muscles of the
pharynx—and outside the muscle there is another fibrous layer that connects the pharynx
to adjacent structures.

Glands are present deep to the epithelium
of some parts of the pharynx, particularly near
the openings of the eustachian tubes. In some
instances the glands extend into the muscle
coat.

## THE PALATINE TONSILS

These ovoid masses of lymphatic tissue are
embedded in, and hence thicken, the lamina
propria of the mucous membrane that extends
between the glossopalatine and the pharyngo-
palatine arches. The epithelium here is of the
stratified squamous nonkeratinizing type and
dips into the underlying lymphatic tissue to
form 10 to 20 little glandlike pits (*primary
crypts*) in each palatine tonsil (Fig. 24-21).
The stratified squamous epithelium lining the
primary crypts may extend out into the adjacent lymphatic tissue to form secondary crypts.
Either primary or secondary crypts may extend deeply enough to reach the outer limits
of the tonsil.

The lymphatic tissue in the tonsil is mostly
arranged close to the epithelium; it lies directly deep to the covering epithelium and
extends down along the sides of the crypts.
It consists of primary nodules, with or without germinal centers, that may be so close
together that they melt into one another or
they may be separated by loose lymphatic
tissue. In addition to lymphocytes there are
generally many plasma cells in this tissue (Fig.
15-2).

The tonsillar tissue disposed near the beginnings of the digestive tube and the respira-

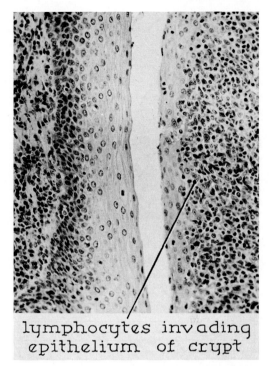

lymphocytes invading
epithelium of crypt

Fig. 24-22. High-power photomicrograph
of a section of palatine tonsil, showing
lymphocytes migrating through the epithelial lining of a crypt.

tory system would seem to be designed to
function as outposts, on the watch for infec-
tive agents against which antibodies should
be made as soon as possible. However, this is
a hazardous occupation, and often the infec-
tive agents conquer the outposts and become
so well established in the tonsils that the latter
must be removed.

Primary nodules may be very close to the
epithelium of the crypts. Many lymphocytes
formed in the tonsil leave it by migrating
through the crypt epithelium (Fig. 24-22).
Lymphocytes may so infiltrate the epithelium
that it becomes very difficult to establish its
deep border. The lymphocytes that escape
form degenerate bodies in the saliva called
*salivary corpuscles.*

Glands are associated with the palatine
tonsils, but their ducts open beside it and not
into its crypts; hence, the crypts are not
flushed out as they are in the lingual tonsil,
and debris can accumulate in them and dispose
them to infection.

## GENERAL PLAN OF THE
## GASTROINTESTINAL TRACT

A good understanding of the general plan on which the digestive tube is constructed is of assistance in learning the microscopic structure of the various parts of it which are now to be considered. Therefore, the general plan will be described in some detail before the particulars about different parts of the tract are given.

The wall of the gastrointestinal tube consists of 4 main layers (see Fig. 24-23, *lower right*): the mucous membrane, the submucosa, the muscularis externa and the serosa. The relation of the structure to the function of these 4 layers will now be described.

**Mucous Membrane.** This consists of 3 layers: an *epithelial lining*, a supporting *lamina propria* and a thin, usually double, layer of smooth muscle, the *muscularis mucosae* (Fig. 24-23).

EPITHELIUM. The type of epithelium varies in relation to the function of the part of the tube it lines. In some sites it is primarily protective, in others it is absorptive, and in still others, secretory. In most of the gastrointestinal tract the surface-lining epithelial cells are unable to provide all the secretions that are needed. To supplement the secretions supplied by surface-lining cells, vast numbers of glands are present. The commonest ones are short and extend outwardly only to the muscularis mucosae; therefore, they are wholly contained in the lamina propria of the mucous membrane (Fig. 24-23, labeled "gland in mucous membrane"). *The student, then, must expect to find the lamina propria of the mucous membrane of most parts of the gastrointestinal tract riddled with glands; indeed, in many parts the thin films of lamina propria between glands can scarcely be seen.* The second position occupied by glands that develop from the lining cells, to supplement their secretions, is the submucosa (Fig. 24-23, *middle left*). Glands in this position are found only in the esophagus and the duodenum. The third site occupied by glands that arise from the lining of the gastrointestinal tract is outside the tract altogether. The salivary glands, the liver and the pancreas are of this sort (Fig. 24-23, *upper left*). Since they all arise from the lining of the alimentary tract, they all drain into it by ducts which proclaim the sites of their origins.

LAMINA PROPRIA. This layer consists of connective tissue that is difficult to classify. It is what probably is best described as loose ordinary connective tissue with lymphatic tendencies.

The functions of the lamina propria are numerous. In order to support the epithelium and to connect it with the muscularis mucosae, it contains collagenic, reticular and, in some sites, elastic fibers. The frank lymphatic tissue with which it is sprinkled is of the nonencapsulated type and hence typical of lymphatic tissue that is commonly disposed under wet epithelial surfaces and which acts as a second line of defense against bacteria or other disease organisms that gain entrance to the tissues by invading the epithelial membrane, which, to be absorptive, must be relatively thin in much of the gastrointestinal tract.

The fact that lymphocytes are produced in great numbers in the lamina propria of the digestive tube and make their way through the lining epithelium to enter the lumen suggests that lymphocytes play some nutritive function in connection with the maintenance of the lining epithelium; possibilities in this connection have been suggested from time to time.

The lamina propria carries both blood and lymphatic capillaries close to the epithelial surface, particularly in the little fingerlike villi that project into the lumen from the small intestine (Fig. 24-23). Consequently, the products resulting from the digestion of carbohydrates, proteins and fats do not have to diffuse any great distance through the tissue fluid of the lamina propria in order to gain entrance to either type of capillary.

In villi (Fig. 24-23) particularly, smooth muscle fibers are present in, and are a constituent of, the lamina propria. These permit villi to sway from side to side and to shorten and lengthen. The latter movement may have a milking effect and so help to force lymph along their lymphatics.

MUSCULARIS MUCOSAE. This, the third and outermost layer of the mucous membrane, consists generally of 2 thin layers of smooth muscle fibers together with varying amounts of elastic tissue. In the inner layer of muscle the fibers are circularly disposed, and in the outer, longitudinally (Fig. 24-23). The muscularis mucosae probably permits localized movements of the mucous membrane. Increased tonus of the circular fibers would tend to throw

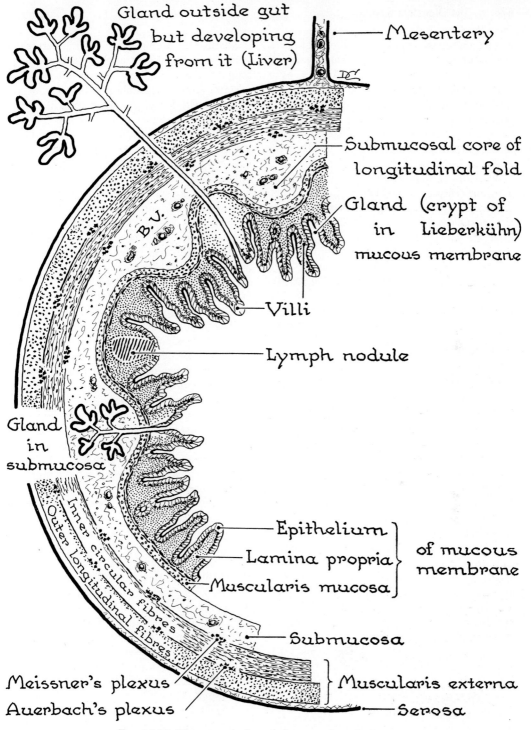

Gland outside gut but developing from it (Liver)

Mesentery

Submucosal core of longitudinal fold

Gland (crypt of Lieberkühn) in mucous membrane

B.V.

Villi

Lymph nodule

Gland in submucosa

Inner circular fibres

Outer longitudinal fibres

Epithelium
Lamina propria
Muscularis mucosa
} of mucous membrane

Submucosa

Meissner's plexus
Auerbach's plexus

Muscularis externa
Serosa

Fig. 24-23. The general plan of the gastrointestinal tract.

the mucous membrane into circular folds. The muscularis mucosae also could be visualized as acting on occasion to relieve the pressure on the veins in the submucosa caused by the tonus of the muscularis externa.

**Submucosa.** This coat connects the mucous membrane to the muscularis externa. It consists of a loose pliable type of connective tissue. It houses the plexuses of larger blood vessels (Fig. 24-23). The elastic fibers of these impart an elastic quality to the coat as a whole. This is augmented, particularly in the upper part of the gastrointestinal tract, by a considerable number of elastic fibers distributed throughout its substance. The elastic quality of the submucosa permits it to form the cores of such folds of mucous membrane as are present in different parts of the tract (Fig. 24-23, *upper right*).

A plexus of nerve fibers with which some ganglion cells are associated is present in the submucosa. This is called *Meissner's plexus* or the *submucosa plexus* (Fig. 24-23). The fibers in it are mostly nonmyelinated and are derived chiefly from the superior mesenteric plexus (a prevertebral plexus); hence, they are postganglionic fibers from the sympathetic division of the autonomic nervous system. The relatively few ganglion cells in the submucous plexus are of the nature of terminal ganglia of the parasympathetic division; the preganglionic fibers that synapse there are derived from the vagus nerve (cranial outflow).

**Muscularis Externa.** This coat consists characteristically of 2 fairly substantial layers of smooth muscle. The inner layer has circularly disposed fibers and is somewhat thicker than the outer layer, which has longitudinally disposed fibers (Fig. 24-23). However, it is probable that the fibers are not arranged precisely at right angles to, and parallel with, the tract, but that those of both layers tend to pursue a somewhat spiral course. By seeing whether the fibers in the inner and the outer coats are cut in cross or longitudinal section a student can tell whether he is examining a cross or a longitudinal section of any part of the tract (if in any section the fibers of the inner layer are cut in cross section, and the ones in the outer layer in longitudinal section, the section under view is a longitudinal section).

The muscularis externa is the primary instrument for propelling the contents of the tube downward from the pharynx to the anus. Gastroenterologists agree that the orderly functioning of the muscularis externa is an important requisite for health and happiness. The various kinds of actions it performs and their control are complex, and only elementary comment will be made on them here.

1. The smooth muscle of the muscularis externa constitutes a surrounding sheath for the tract. Smooth muscle, it will be recalled, is adapted to maintaining different states of tonus (sustained contraction). The state of tonus of the muscularis externa is a very important factor in regulating the size of the lumen of the bowel. In many individuals the tone of the muscle tends to be too high. In such individuals portions of the lower bowel can be felt at physical examination to be thin, hard and cordlike. On the other hand, in some individuals the tone of the muscle tends to be too low, so that portions of the bowel may be more or less chronically distended.

2. Smooth muscle has the inherent property of undergoing spontaneous and rhythmic contractions. Moreover, when smooth muscle cells are arranged in laminae, as they are in the muscularis externa, contractions so initiated can spread from one cell to another. Even without the help of nerves, the smooth muscle of the muscularis externa can exhibit rhythmic contractions which spread over short distances. How impulses are conducted between smooth muscle cells was described in Chapter 20.

3. The muscularis externa engages in *peristaltic movements*. These are the primary cause of food being moved along the bowel. They consist of waves of constriction that sweep downward, pushing the contents of the bowel ahead of them. There are two kinds: slow gentle ones and vigorous rapid ones called *peristaltic rushes*.

For waves of peristaltic contraction to sweep down the bowel, the help of a conduction system is required. This is provided chiefly by a plexus of nerve fibers, associated with numerous ganglia, that are situated chiefly between the circular and the longitudinal layers of the muscle. This plexus is called *Auerbach's plexus* or the *myenteric plexus* (Fig. 24-23). It contains preganglionic fibers of the parasympathetic division of the autonomic nervous system, which fibers (except in the distal part of the large intestine) are derived from the vagus nerve, and hence from the cranial outflow of the system. These fibers synapse with the cells of terminal ganglia in the plexus which are, therefore, parasympathetic cell stations. The postganglionic fibers given off by the ganglion cells terminate, for the most part, on muscle cells which they stimulate. Postganglionic fibers of the sympathetic division of the autonomic nervous system, most of which arise from ganglion cells of the prevertebral ganglia,

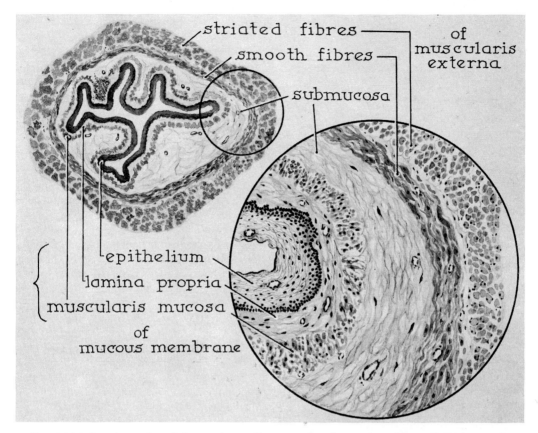

striated fibres ——
smooth fibres ——
of muscularis externa
submucosa
epithelium
lamina propria
muscularis mucosa
of mucous membrane

FIG. 24-24. A cross section of the esophagus (low-power) and a portion of its wall (high-power).

also contribute to Auerbach's plexus, though they have no cell stations there; they reach the muscle cells directly. Whether there are any different fibers in the myenteric plexus is a question that has been much discussed. Reflex actions seem to occur in the bowel, but there is little anatomic evidence to indicate a basis of afferent neurons to explain it. Perhaps something in the nature of an axon reflex, described in connection with the innervation of blood vessels, operates in this situation.

Although the chief function of the myenteric plexus is to assist in conducting waves of contraction down the bowel, it also provides a means whereby the activities of the bowel can be correlated with those of the body as a whole. Impulses traveling down the vagus nerve (parasympathetic division) tend to augment both the tone and the peristaltic movements of the muscularis externa. Impulses traveling down the sympathetic fibers from the prevertebral ganglia tend to inhibit both

tone and peristaltic movements. Unfortunately, the provision made for permitting the activities of the bowel to be correlated with those of the body as a whole is not wholly advantageous. Indeed, a vast amount of gastrointestinal malfunction seems to be due to emotional disturbances affecting the innervation of the bowel. Therefore, many frustrated individuals must suffer not only unhappiness for not having what they want but also gastrointestinal difficulties that develop as a result of their sustained emotional states.

**Serosa or Adventitia.** This, the fourth and outermost coat of the wall of the alimentary tube, must be termed *adventitia* in some sites because it is not of a serous character throughout the whole tract. It consists of areolar tissue, covered in those portions of the tube that are suspended freely by mesenteries, with a single layer of squamous mesothelial cells. In those portions of the tract that are affixed to adjacent tissues, the areolar tissue of the

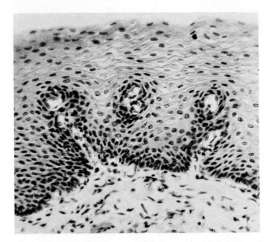

FIG. 24-25. High-power photomicrograph of a section of the lining of the esophagus. Notice a papilla of lamina propria extending up into the epithelium at the left. The light areas in the epithelium (*center and right*) are cross sections of papillae that ran into the epithelium at an angle.

adventitia merges into the connective tissue associated with the surrounding structures.

Sheets of mesentery are covered on both sides by mesothelium and have a core of areolar tissue containing varying numbers of fat cells together with the blood and lymphatic vessels and the nerves that it conducts to the intestine.

## THE ESOPHAGUS

The *esophagus*, known also as the *gullet*, is a fairly straight tube that extends from the pharynx to the stomach (Fig. 24-1). Its wall consists of the 4 layers described in connection with the general plan of the tract. Such variations from the general plan as are found in these layers are adapted to the special function that this part of the tract must perform. These will now be noted.

First, the speed with which food passes down the esophagus is considerably greater than that at which it is moved along the remainder of the tract. There is, then, no time for absorption to occur and hence no point in having absorptive columnar epithelium in the mucous membrane. Furthermore, since many individuals (from bad habit or lack of teeth) do not chew their food sufficiently, there is every reason to have a type of epithelium that is protective against the rough material often swallowed. Obviously, stratified squamous nonkeratinizing epithelium, or even the keratinized type, would be the logical choice for lining the esophagus. In man, the epithelium is of the nonkeratinizing type (Figs. 24-24 and 24-25), but in many animals, who swallow rough material even more hastily, the keratinized type is employed. Even in the epithelium of man, some keratohyalin granules sometimes may be seen.

The stratified squamous epithelium of the esophagus, like other such epithelia, undergoes renewal. The cells of the deeper layers undergo mitosis in man, while some of the superficial cells desquamate into the lumen. In the rat esophagus, mitosis occurs only in the basal layer, whereas in other species, 2 or even 3 of the deeper layers may show mitoses. In all cases, the deep layers of cells where mitosis occurs are composed of small, deeply basophilic cells with rare tonofibrils. As cells are displaced toward the lumen, they lose the ability to divide; and this is associated with loss of cytoplasmic basophilia and the appearance of tonofibrils in, and an over-all enlargement of, the cells. The differentiation of the cells is eventually followed by their desquamation.

The progeny of a mitotic division in a deep layer may take either of two courses. Some remain in the deeper layers to divide again, while others differentiate in the manner just indicated, so as to be eventually shed at the surface. The maintenance of such epithelia in the adult state requires that cell production is balanced by cell loss; that is, the epithelia are in "steady state" with regard to their cell population, as described by Leblond and Walker in 1956. There may, of course, be fluctuations in the rates of cell production and loss (e.g., diurnal variation), so that counts of the number of cells making up an epithelium might reveal minor periodic variations. But, on the average, the epithelium tends to be composed of a fixed number of cells. Therefore, for each cell that moves outward to be shed, one must be added which remains in situ. This conclusion implies that, since a given number of cells arise from mitosis, half of them will move outward, and the other half will remain in the epithelium where they will eventually divide again.

This theoretical requirement has been applied (see Rolshoven) in a consideration of individual dividing cells. As a result of work on the production of spermatogonia, he proposed that in all renewal systems the division of a stem cell provides two different daughter cells, one of which remains a stem cell, while the other differentiates. In the case of stratified squamous epithelia, the differentiating cell would be one that moves outward to be shed (see Mercer, 1962). The implication is that the dividing cell provides its two daughter cells with different amounts of material and thus leads them to different fates. This type of division has been referred to as *differential* (or unequal). However, the mapping of cells labeled by thymidine-H³ in the rat esophagus (Leblond, Greulich and Marques-Pereira, in 1964) made it possible to trace the two daughter cells from each mitoses. It was thus revealed that, while a few mitoses led to one daughter cell differentiating and another remaining in the basal layer (as if mitoses were differential), many others produced two daughter cells which both differentiated, and still other divisions resulted in two daughter cells, both of which remained in the basal layer. Indeed, the frequency of the three occurrences was just as expected if the decision of a cell for or against differentiation was entirely a matter of chance.

Since no absorption occurs through the lining epithelium, there is not the same need for lymphatic tissue to guard against the possible entrance of pathogenic organisms into the lamina propria as there is in other parts of the tract. The relatively little lymphatic tissue present is confined to those areas where the ducts of glands pass through the lamina propria.

Again, since there is no time for digestion to occur in the esophagus, and since the food that enters the esophagus is lubricated with saliva, there is little need for it to contain glands to secrete either mucus or digestive enzymes. Accordingly, few glands are found in this part of the tract. There are a few mucous glands scattered here and there in the submucosa; these are called the *esophageal glands*. In addition, there are some glands in the lamina propria of the mucous membrane; these are most common near the stomach and, since they resemble the glands in the cardiac portion of the stomach, they are called *cardiac glands*. A few glands also may be present at a higher level; these also secrete mucus.

The muscle associated with the pharynx is of the striated type. Striated muscle continues down into the upper part of the esophagus, where it forms the muscularis externa of the tube. In the middle third of the esophagus, smooth muscle makes its appearance in the muscularis externa and in the lower third generally comprises all of the muscle present. Hence, cross sections from the upper third of the esophagus generally show all the muscularis externa to be composed of striated muscle; those from the middle third show a mixture and those from the lower third show only smooth muscle. The section illustrated in Figure 24-24 was taken from the middle third and shows muscle of both types in the muscularis externa.

The striated muscle of the pharynx and of the upper part of the esophagus is an exception to the general rule that striated muscle is voluntary, that is, under the control of the will. That of the esophagus is innervated chiefly by parasympathetic fibers from the vagi. If the vagi are cut, the striated muscle fibers become paralyzed but, curiously enough, do not atrophy. This muscle, then, is under the control of the autonomic nervous system. Hence, swallowing is, at least in part, an involuntary act of the nature of a reflex action set in motion by the stimulation of afferent nerve endings distributed chiefly in the posterior wall of the pharynx. Although swallowing itself is a reflex action, an individual, because the striated muscles of the mouth are under the control of the will, can initiate swallowing but its continuation from the pharynx onward is involuntary because of the autonomic operation of the reflex. The pharynx, then, marks the site where the control of the movement of the alimentary tract is given over from the voluntary system to the involuntary.

In man, the muscularis externa of the esophagus is not thickened sufficiently at the point of entrance of the esophagus into the stomach (the cardia) to justify its being called the cardiac sphincter.

Since the esophagus is not covered with peritoneum, it has an adventitia rather than a serosa. This consists of areolar tissue and it connects the esophagus with its surrounding structures.

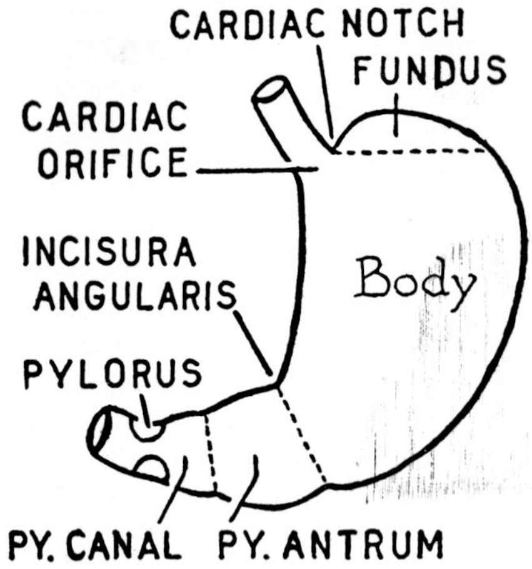

FIG. 24-26. Diagram of the parts of the stomach. (Grant, J. C. B.: A Method of Anatomy, ed. 4, Baltimore, Williams & Wilkins)

## THE STOMACH

The stomach is the considerably expanded portion of the alimentary tract between the esophagus and the small intestine (Fig. 24-1). It has several functions. It acts as a reservoir. This function is facilitated by the elasticity of its walls, which can stretch sufficiently to give it a capacity of from 1 to $1\frac{1}{2}$ quarts; its contents are retained by the well-developed sphincter at its outlet. The stomach does not merely store food; it is also a digestive organ. An ordinary meal remains in it from $3\frac{1}{2}$ to 4 hours, and during that time the meal undergoes considerable digestion. This is due to the action of the gastric juice that is secreted by the cells and the glands of the mucous membrane. Gastric juice contains 3 enzymes, hydrochloric acid and mucus. Of the 3 enzymes, *pepsin* is the most important. In an acid medium it begins the digestion of proteins. Hydrochloric acid, besides providing this acid medium for pepsin, has other beneficial actions. The other 2 enzymes are *rennin*, which curdles milk, and *lipase*, which splits fats. However, this last effect is probably not very extensive in the stomach. Since the gastric juice has such potent digestive properties, the mucous membrane must be protected from being digested by its own secretions. One factor in this is an abundant supply of mucus, which is provided by the mucous membrane.

The stomach acts as a mixer by virtue of its muscular movements, and it converts its contents, diluted with gastric juice, into a semifluid material of an even consistency called *chyme*. The stomach is also concerned in the production of the factor necessary to permit the absorption of vitamin $B_{12}$. The stomach may also serve to some extent as an absorptive organ, but its function in this respect is limited to the absorption of water, salts, sugar, alcohol and certain other drugs.

**Gross Characteristics.** The shape of the stomach and the extent and the position of its different parts are illustrated in Figure 24-26. The fundus is that part lying above a horizontal line drawn through the entrance of the esophagus. About two thirds of the remainder is called the *body of the stomach*. The third and last part of the organ is called the *pyloric antrum and canal*; these lead to the *exit* or *pylorus* (= gate).

If an empty, contracted stomach is opened, its mucous membrane is seen to be thrown into branching folds, most of which are disposed longitudinally. These are termed *rugae*. The cores of these consist of submucosa (Fig. 24-27, *top*). When the stomach is full, the rugae are almost completely "ironed out."

**General Microscopic Features.** The wall of the stomach is composed of the 4 layers described in the general plan of the alimentary tract. The mucous membrane of the stomach is relatively thick and contains millions of little simple tubular glands. In some sites the muscularis mucosae has 3 layers instead of the 2 described in the plan. There are no glands in the submucosa except in the pyloric part adjacent to the duodenum. The muscularis externa consists of 3 instead of 2 layers. The fibers of the innermost layer are disposed obliquely; those of the middle coat, circularly; and those of the outermost coat, longitudinally. A serosa is present.

It has been noted already that the gastric mucosa of the empty stomach is thrown into folds called rugae; these are substantial ridges easily seen on gross inspection or in sections with a very low-power objective (Fig. 24-27). If the gastric mucosa is examined with reasonably high magnification it is seen to be studded with tiny little openings through which the gastric juice wells up when the stomach is actively secreting. These little open-

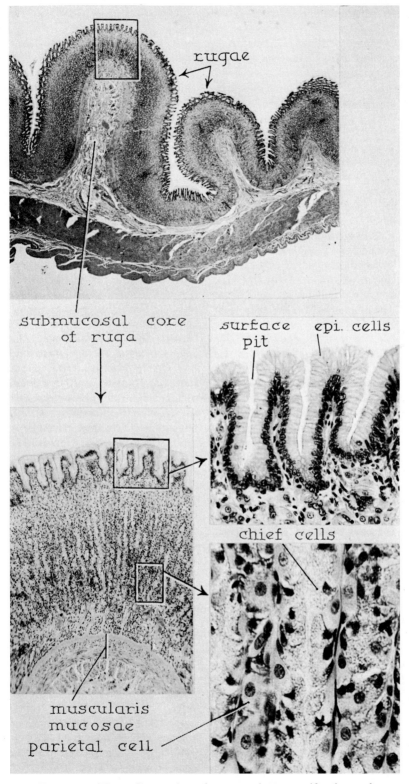

rugae

submucosal core
of ruga

surface
pit

epi. cells

chief cells

muscularis
mucosae

parietal cell

Fig. 24-27. Photomicrographs, taken at various magnifications, of a section of the body of the stomach of a cat.

ings are the openings of what are termed *gastric pits* or *foveolae*. The pits descend through the gastric mucosa to reach the glands which, therefore, open into the pits. The glands produce the secretion, deliver it into the bottoms of the pits, and the pits conduct it to the surface. There is not universal agreement about the shape of the pits. Sometimes they are depicted as having a tubular form and sometimes as being crevices. Probably both kinds exist, with the percentage varying in relation to species, but it is also probable that many crevices are interpreted as tubules, because a section that cuts along a crevice makes it appear as a longitudinal section of a tubule. Unless tubules were arranged in perfect rows it would be impossible to see so many in a single section as appear in Figure 24-27; the appearance shown here could result only from roughly parallel crevices being sectioned at right angles to their long diameters. The lamina propria between the bottoms of the pits and the muscularis mucosae is literally packed with simple tubular glands that open into the bottoms of the pits. In their deepest parts these glands reach or almost reach the muscularis mucosae. There are so many glands in the zone between the bottoms of the crevices and pits and the muscularis mucosae that the student may have difficulty in thinking of this zone as lamina propria. And, indeed, the tissue of the lamina propria itself is so broken up by the glands that it can be seen only as thin films between them (Fig. 24-27, *lower right*).

The inner surface of the stomach is lined by simple columnar epithelium (Fig. 24-27, *middle right*). This extends down to line the pits, and also into the isthmus, which is the region where gland becomes pit. The character of the surface epithelial cells will now be described.

**Surface Epithelium.** The chief function of the surface epithelium is to provide protection. In order to do this, its cells are tall and all alike; the fact that they are all alike enables the student to distinguish at a glance a section of stomach from a section of small or large intestine. (In the small and the large intestines goblet cells alternate with nonmucus-producing absorptive cells; this has a very different appearance from the lining cells of the stomach.) The surface epithelial cells form a membrane that, although it is only one cell thick, is fairly substantial. These cells also provide an indirect type of protection by producing the mucus which characteristically coats the lining of the stomach. They are unusual mucus-producing cells, however, for they do not have the usual shape of goblet cells (Fig. 24-27, *middle right*), and the mucigen granules in their cytoplasm stain only with certain of the mucus stains. As might be supposed, there is probably a fairly high rate of mortality among these surface cells, and they regenerate from those cells of the isthmus and deeper parts of pits, the cells of which seem to be somewhat less specialized in that they contain less mucigen than the cells that are more exposed.

Why the surface epithelial cells are not digested by the juices that well up into the pits and the crevices from the glands of the lamina propria in some parts of the stomach is not understood. Obviously, the protection against being digested, possessed by these cells, is a vital property, for they become digested immediately after death. Sections of stomach obtained from autopsies characteristically fail to demonstrate the surface epithelial cells to advantage since they have become digested during the interval between death and autopsy.

Ulcers of the mucous membrane are not uncommon. These sometimes extend into the other coats in the wall; they may even cause perforations. One might expect that if any surface epithelial cells were ever destroyed, the digestive juices present in the stomach would prevent healing. Yet wounds of the stomach under proper conditions heal rapidly; hence, the wall may be cut and sutured at operations with every confidence that the surface epithelium will regenerate and spread over the affected part to become a continuous membrane once more.

**Glands of the Lamina Propria of the Cardia.** The glands in the lamina propria in the area immediately surrounding the entrance of the esophagus into the stomach are somewhat different from those in the remainder of the organ. They are either simple or compound tubular glands composed of cells with pale cytoplasm. They secrete mucus and perhaps some enzymes. They are of little practical importance.

**Glands of the Mucous Membrane of the Fundus and Body.** These glands produce nearly all the enzymes and hydrochloric acid secreted in the stomach; they also produce some of the mucus. In the body of the stomach the pits are shallower than they are in the pyloric region and they extend into the mucous membrane for only about a quarter to a third of its thickness (Fig. 24-27, *lower left*). Therefore, the glands that extend from the bottoms of the pits to the muscularis mucosae are two to three times as long as the pits and the crevices are deep. The glands are straight except near the muscularis mucosae where they may be bent (Fig. 24-28). Since they are straight, they may be seen as reasonably complete longitudinal sections of tubules if sections are cut at right angles to the surface epithelium (Fig. 24-27, *lower left*).

According to Stevens and Leblond, each tubular gland of the body of the stomach consists of 3 parts or segments. The deepest part is the *base* (Fig. 24-28), the middle part is the *neck* (Fig. 24-28), and the upper part is the *isthmus* (Fig. 24-28). The isthmus is continuous with a pit. It should be understood that pits are not parts of glands; they are merely little wells and crevices sunk from the surface and lined by surface epithelial cells.

The gastric juice is secreted by the glands. The glands contain 4 kinds of secretory cells, but these are not evenly distributed in the different segments, as will now be described. The 4 types of cells can be demonstrated to advantage in sections stained by the P.A.S. method and hematoxylin, as has been shown by Stevens and Leblond.

The isthmus, according to these investigators, contains 2 types of cells, surface epithelial cells and parietal cells. The surface epithelial cells along the sides of pits have a considerable apical content of mucus that is represented as black in Figure 24-28. In the deepest parts of the pits the amount of mucus in the apical parts of the cell is considerably less (Fig. 24-28), and in the isthmus the surface epithelial cells demonstrate only a few granules of mucus in their apical parts. Scattered between the surface epithelial cells of the isthmus are large *parietal cells* that have relatively clear cytoplasm when stained by the P.A.S. method and hematoxylin. In good H and E preparations the cytoplasm of these cells is pink (Fig. 24-27). The parietal cells, as seen in a section, vary from being rounded to

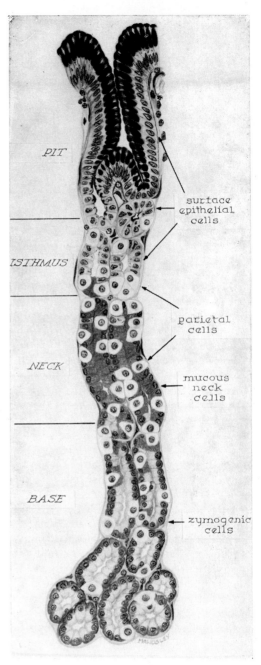

Fig. 24-28. Drawing of a section of the body of the stomach of a monkey, stained by the P.A.S. method and by hematoxylin. (Preparation by C. P. Leblond)

triangular in shape (Figs. 24-27 and 24-28). Their nuclei are dark and generally centrally placed.

The neck of a gland is made up chiefly of

cells that were first described by Bensley as *mucous neck cells*. These are very difficult to identify in H and E sections. With the P.A.S. method the cytoplasm of the mucous neck cells is seen to be literally stuffed with pink mucus (dark in Fig. 24-28) and to have a foamy appearance. The nuclei of these cells are generally pressed against their bases, where they often have a more or less triangular shape (Fig. 24-28). Parietal cells are scattered as individuals between groups of mucous neck cells in this part of the gland (Fig. 24-28).

The base or body of a gland is made up mostly of *zymogenic* (*chief*) *cells*. These have accumulations of chromidial substance near their bases. The cytoplasm between their nuclei and their free surfaces appears differently with different fixatives and stains. In an ordinary H and E preparation it appears vacuolated and reticular (Fig. 24-27) because the secretion granules it contains are not well fixed or stained. The P.A.S. and hematoxylin method demonstrates a similar appearance in it (Fig. 24-28). Parietal cells are sprinkled among the zymogenic cells. Not uncommonly a parietal cells will be seen with one of its three sides applied closely to the basement membrane of the gland and with two of its angles extending between the bases of adjacent chief cells and the basement membrane (Fig. 24-27). The apex of such a cell projects between the sides of the two chief cells that border it but not far enough to reach the lumen proper. The secretion from such a parietal cell then must pass between the two chief cells that almost cover it to reach the lumen proper of the gland. Parietal cells have centrally disposed, rounded nuclei and decidedly acidophilic cytoplasm. Hence, in H and E sections, they stand out as red cells among the paler chief cells. Under special conditions, secretory canaliculi may be seen in their cytoplasm. These open on the side of the cell closest to the lumen of the gland.

The zymogenic (chief) cells produce the enzymes of the gastric secretion, and the parietal cells produce the hydrochloric acid. The other types of cells produce only mucus.

## FINE STRUCTURE

All 4 types of cells described above have been studied with EM and described by different authors. Since these studies have often been made on different species, some of the inconsistencies in the various reports are probably due to this fact.

**Parietal Cells.** Under the EM the parietal cell is characterized by the presence of a branching caniliculus which extends into it from its apex and by which it delivers its secretion into the lumen of the gastric gland (Fig. 24-29). In addition to intracellular canaliculi there are intercellular canaliculi between adjacent parietal cells. A unique feature of the canaliculi, particularly the intracellular kind, is the tremendous number of microvilli which project into them (Fig. 24-29). The intracellular canaliculus takes up a considerable amount of space in a parietal cell and so encroaches on the cytoplasm, and the cytoplasm that remains is literally stuffed with mitochondria. Other components of the cytoplasm are present, but the striking feature of the cytoplasm is the abundance of mitochondria and the vast system of microvilli which project into the intracellular canaliculi. The cytoplasm does not reveal any secretion granules. Therefore, the EM appearance of the cell would not indicate that HCl is secreted in the form of a protein complex, as has been suggested in the past, because if it were one might expect to see many rough-surfaced vesicles of endoplasmic reticulum containing the protein secretory product. The intracellular canaliculi and the vast number of microvilli suggest that a vast area of cell membrane is involved in the secretion of HCl. Bradford and Davies, using a variety of dyes, have shown that there is sometimes a very low pH in the canaliculi in the parietal cells of frogs; their work suggests that HCl is secreted into the canaliculi as free acid. References to their work are given for those who wish to study this matter further.

**Zymogen Cells.** These cells are characterized by an abundance of rough-surfaced vesicles and cisternae of endoplasmic reticulum (Fig. 24-30). The way these are concerned in the formation of the many secretion granules that are also seen in these cells (Fig. 24-30) was explained in Chapter 7.

**Mucous Neck Cells and Surface Epithelial Cells.** Both of these cell types show many mucigen droplets, particularly near the end through which the secretion is delivered. The cells at the upper right in Figure 24-29 are probably mucous neck cells; they have short

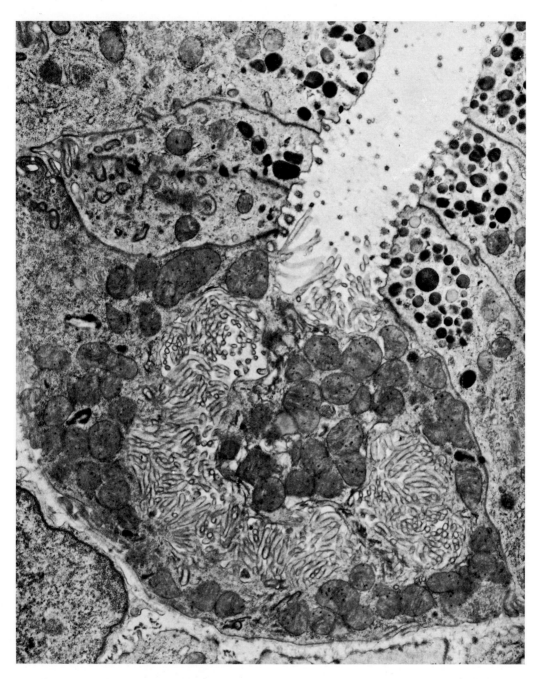

Fig. 24-29. Electron micrograph (× 9,500) of the bottom of a gastric gland of a bat. The clear area is the lumen of the gastric gland, lined on each side by mucous cells. Only the apical portions of these are shown. They contain many mucous granules and have short microvilli projecting into the lumen of the gland. The cell at the base of the gastric gland is a parietal cell. Its cytoplasm contains many round to ovoid mitochondria. Extending into this cell from the lumen of the gastric gland is a large C-shaped passageway which is an intracellular canaliculus. This does not appear empty, as might be expected, because it is filled with numerous microvilli projecting into it. These microvilli are cut in all planes, and more microvilli project from the surface of the parietal cell into the lumen of the gastric gland. (Preparation by Dr. S. Ito, Dr. R. J. Winchester and Dr. D. W. Fawcett)

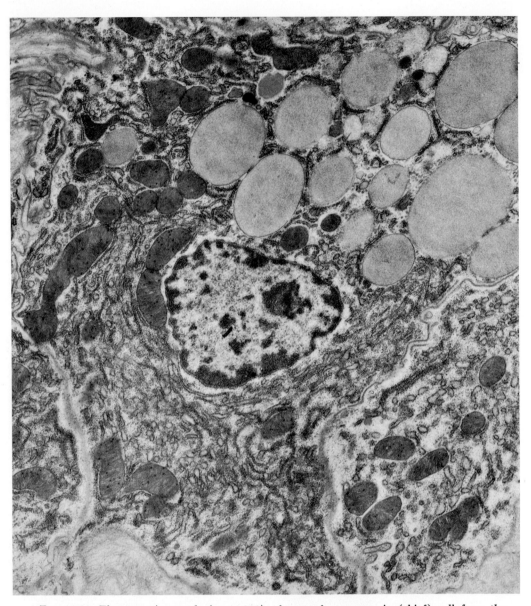

FIG. 24-30. Electron micrograph ($\times$ 14,000) of part of a zymogenic (chief) cell from the stomach of a bat showing nucleus, large secretory granules, granular endoplasmic reticulum and mitochondria. (Dr. S. Ito, Dr. R. J. Winchester and Dr. D. W. Fawcett)

microvilli on their free surfaces. Surface epithelial cells are similar but probably do not generally have so many secretory droplets in their cytoplasm.

**Renewal of Cells of the Gastric Mucosa.** Stevens and Leblond, using their cholchicine method, found that only the two mucus-containing types of cells showed any significant mitotic activity. They found that the surface epithelial cells are maintained by divisions of these cells occurring in the isthmus (where they contain less mucus). They estimated that 5.87 per cent of the surface epithelial cells enter mitosis every 4 hours. The mucous neck cells were found to divide less often; only 2.59 per cent enter mitosis every

4 hours. From the foregoing observations it would appear that the surface epithelium in the stomach is renewed (in the rat) every 3 days, and that this is done by cells in the isthmus dividing, and the new cells formed here push up the sides of the crypts and then over the surface to replace those that are constantly being lost by desquamation.

**Glands of the Pylorus.** The pits and the crevices in the pyloric portion of the stomach are deeper than those in the body and the fundus. Furthermore, the glands that open into the pits and the crevices are much shorter than those in the body and the fundus. Hence, there is a considerable difference between the ratio of the depth of the crevices and the pits to the depth of the glands in the pyloric portion of the stomach and that in the body and fundus (compare Figs. 24-27 and 24-31). This point should enable the student to distinguish readily sections of pylorus from those of body and fundus. Another point of difference between the glands of the two regions is that the pyloric glands are coiled; hence, they never are seen in longitudinal section (the glands of the body and the fundus are, if sections are cut perpendicular to the surface). Still another point of difference is that the pyloric glands, except near the pyloric sphincter and the body where a few parietal cells may be seen, consist of only one type of cell. In H and E sections, the cytoplasm of these cells is pale, but with special stains it may be shown to contain mucigen. The nuclei are more or less flattened and pressed against the bases of the cells (Fig. 24-31). The lumens of the glands are wider than those of the glands in the body and the fundus.

Many observers have commented on the similarity between the cells of the pyloric glands and the mucous neck cells of the glands of the body and the fundus. They have the same function, for the pyloric glands do not produce enzymes but only mucus.

At the pylorus, the circularly disposed smooth muscle fibers of the middle coat of the muscularis externa of the stomach are increased so as to form a thick bundle which encircles the exit of the stomach. This is called the *pyloric sphincter*. The stout band of muscle of which it is composed bulges the submucosa and the mucous membrane inwardly so that these are thrown into a circular fold. The chief

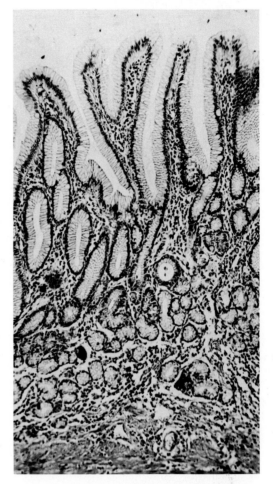

FIG. 24-31. Low-power photomicrograph of a section of the mucous membrane of the pyloric portion of the stomach of a man.

ingredient of the core of this fold, it should be noted, is the thickened middle coat of the muscularis externa. This fold differs from most folds in the alimentary tract, which have cores of only submucosa.

Peristaltic movements begin near the middle of the stomach and spread down to the pylorus. The pyloric sphincter automatically opens to permit such food as is sufficiently fluid and digested to enter the small intestine. At the same time it holds back solid undigested food. The precise way its operations are controlled is too complex a matter to discuss here.

**Control of the Secretion of Gastric Juice.** There is some difference between the secretion of gastric juice in experimental animals and its secretion in man. In dogs, the surface of

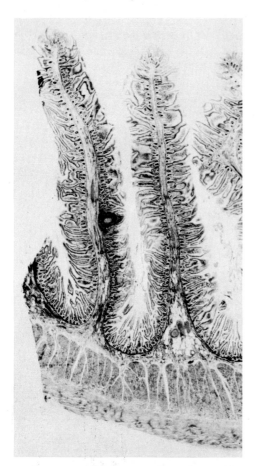

FIG. 24-32. Low-power photomicrograph of a longitudinal section of the wall of the jejunum of a dog, showing 2 plicae circulares cut in cross section. The plicae are studded with irregular villi.

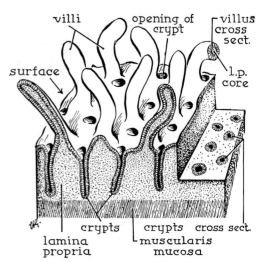

FIG. 24-33. Three-dimensional drawing of the lining of the small intestine. Observe that villi are fingerlike processes, with cores of lamina propria that extend into the lumen. Note also that crypts of Lieberkühn are glands that dip down into the lamina propria. Observe particularly the difference in the cross-section appearance of villi and crypts.

the resting stomach is coated with mucus; gastric juice wells up from the glands to flood the surface only when a meal is in prospect or is consumed. However, in man, Carlson has shown that there is a more or less continuous secretion of gastric juice, varying from 10 to 60 ml. per hour. This is augmented when food is about to be eaten or is eaten. Several factors are concerned in augmenting the secretion. Psychic factors, as shown by Pavlov, play an important part and so justify the imaginative cook. Psychic factors must operate through a nervous control of secretion by the vagus nerve. Certain foods, when they reach the stomach, have the ability to stimulate secretion further. These foods stimulate secretion even if the nerves to the stomach are cut.

Hence, if they stimulate secretion by means of a reflex initiated in the mucosa of the stomach, the reflex concerned must have something of the nature of a local one. Then, in addition to certain foods stimulating secretion, the breakdown products of a wide variety of foods also have this property, particularly when the breakdown products reach the small intestine, where they act on its mucosa possibly to make a substance that circulates by the bloodstream to reach the gastric glands. Accordingly, the gastric glands are said to secrete through 3 phases: (1) the cephalic (psychic factors), (2) the gastric, where consumed food either directly or indirectly stimulates the mucosa to induce secretion, and (3) the intestinal, where the breakdown products of digestion, and the gastric juice itself, reach and affect the intestinal mucosa to make it produce something that circulates by the bloodstream to stimulate further the gastric glands.

## THE SMALL INTESTINE

**Relation of General Structure to Functions.** The small intestine is about 20 feet long. Its first 10 to 12 inches constitute the *duodenum* (Fig. 24-1). This, except for its first inch or so, is relatively fixed in position, not being suspended by a mesentery. It pursues a horseshoe-shaped course around the head of the pancreas to become continuous with the *jejunum,* which constitutes the next two fifths of the small intestine (Fig. 24-1). The last three fifths is termed the *ileum* (Fig. 24-1). In general, the small intestine tends to become narrower throughout its course.

The small intestine has two chief functions: (1) completing the digestion of food delivered into it by the stomach and (2) selectively absorbing the final products of digestion into its blood and lymph vessels. In addition, it also makes some hormones.

The structure of the small intestine is specialized with regard to both its digestive and its absorptive functions. It will be more convenient to describe how its structure is specialized for absorption before describing how its structure is specialized for digestion.

To perform its absorptive function efficiently, the small intestine requires a vast epithelial surface, since it is through the epithelium of the mucous membrane that absorption occurs. The great length of the small intestine helps considerably in providing such a surface, but this is not enough, and provision is made in 3 other ways for increasing the absorptive surface still further.

1. Beginning about an inch beyond the pylorus, the mucous membrane is thrown into circularly or spirally disposed folds called the *plicae circulares* or *valves of Kerkring.* These folds are generally crescentic and extend from one half to two thirds of the way around the lumen. However, single folds may extend all the way around the intestine or even form a spiral of 2 or 3 turns; the highest ones project into the lumen for about a third of an inch. They all have cores of submucosa, are not ironed out if the intestine is full and, at first, are large and very close together (Fig. 24-32). In the upper part of the jejunum they become smaller and farther apart. In the middle or lower end of the ileum they disappear.

2. The surface of the mucous membrane over the folds and between the folds is studded with tiny leaf, tongue or fingerlike projections that range from $\frac{1}{2}$ to 1 mm. or more in height. These are called the *intestinal villi* (Fig.

24-33). Since they are projections of mucous membrane, they have cores of lamina propria. The muscularis mucosae and the submucosa do not extend into them as they do into the plicae circulares. The plicae could be likened to the ridges that cover a rough country and the villi to the trees that grow from the surface of both the ridges and the valleys between them (Fig. 24-32).

The villi of the duodenum are broader than those elsewhere, and many examples of leaf-like ones can be found in this region. In the upper part of the jejunum, the villi, in general, are said to be tongue-shaped. Farther down the jejunum they become longer and finger-shaped. There are fewer of them in the ileum, and those present tend to be narrower still. Villi, as will become apparent when their structure is described in detail presently, are highly specialized little absorptive organs.

3. The absorptive surface is made still greater by the microvilli that are present on the free surfaces of the absorptive cells (see numerous illustrations in Chapter 8).

In order to perform its other chief function (completing the digestion of food received from the stomach), the small intestine requires large supplies of digestive enzymes and considerable quantities of mucus to protect its epithelial lining from injury. The digestive enzymes are provided by glands; mucus is provided both by proper glands and by innumerable goblet cells that are intermingled with other cells along the mucous membrane. The glands that provide the digestive juices and the mucus necessary for the function of the small intestine are distributed in 3 general sites: (1) outside the intestine, but connected with it by ducts, (2) in the submucosa and (3) in the lamina propria.

The microscopic structure of the pancreas and the liver, the two glands that are situated outside the small intestine and deliver their secretions into it, will be considered later. Here we are concerned only with the effect of their secretions on the digestive process. Their ducts, usually conjoined, open into the duodenum about 3 inches from the pylorus (Fig. 24-1). The secretion of the pancreas, delivered into the duodenum at this site, is alkaline (and so helps neutralize the acid stomach contents), and it contains enzymes concerned in the digestion of proteins, carbohydrates and

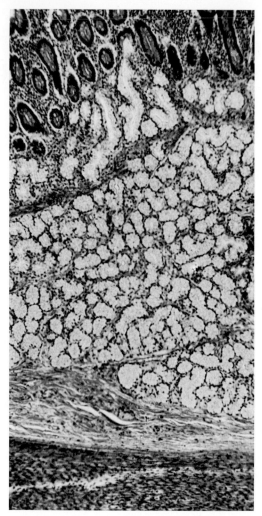

FIG. 24-34. Low-power photomicrograph of a section of the wall of the duodenum, showing Brunner's glands in the submucosa. The muscularis mucosae may be seen passing to the right and upward from above the middle of the left side. In the middle of the upper part of the figure, a gland of Brunner may be seen emptying into a crypt of Lieberkühn. The muscularis externa is seen at the bottom of the picture.

down starches to sugars. Some sugars, for example, maltose, must be acted on further by enzymes secreted by glands in the lamina propria and must be converted to monosaccharides before they are absorbed. The pancreatic juice also contains lipolytic enzymes that both emulsify fat and break down its structure. The effect of these enzymes is facilitated by the presence of bile, the secretion of the liver.

The second group of glands to consider are those situated in the submucosa. Glands are found in this position only in the duodenum. These are compound tubular in type and are called the *glands of Brunner* (Fig. 24-34). Their precise distribution varies considerably. They may extend into the pylorus for a short distance. Generally, they are most numerous in the first part of the duodenum and become less numerous and finally disappear in its more distal parts. Nevertheless, they have been observed on occasion in the first part of the jejunum.

The secretory portions of Brunner's glands are sufficiently expanded to have a somewhat alveolar appearance. The secretory portions are chiefly confined to the submucosa. The excretory ducts lead through the muscularis mucosae to empty into the crypts of Lieberkühn, to be described shortly. The muscularis mucosae does not always constitute a well-defined structure over them, for often it is so split up by glandular elements that it appears as a network of smooth muscle fibers whose interstices are filled with glandular elements.

The secretory cells are columnar and resemble those of the pyloric glands. Their nuclei are dark and flattened toward the bases of the cells. The cytoplasm is pale and finely granular in H and E sections (Fig. 24-34), but, with suitable stains, can be shown to contain mucigen.

There has been much discussion as to whether these glands produce proteolytic enzymes. The matter is complicated by the difficulty of obtaining pure extracts and by the fact that the glands of some experimental animals have different cellular components from those of man. There is some evidence to suggest that the secretion has some ability to activate other secretions concerned in protein digestion. But it has not been shown definitely that the Brunner's glands of man themselves

fats; several enzymes that effect different steps in protein digestion probably are elaborated. The enzymes are not active until they reach the intestine, where some agency renders them potent. In their totality they can break down proteins to amino acids; it is in this form that proteins are absorbed. The pancreatic juice also contains enzymes that break

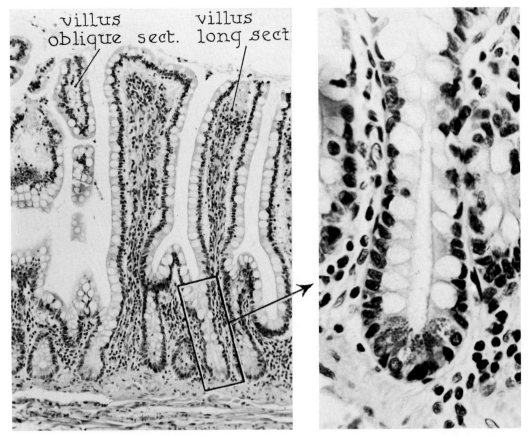

FIG. 24-35. (*Left*) Low-power photomicrograph of a section of the wall of the small intestine of a child, showing villi in longitudinal and cross section and crypts of Lieberkühn. (*Right*) High-power photomicrograph of a crypt of Lieberkühn, showing goblet cells along its sides and some Paneth cells with cytoplasmic granules at its deepest part.

produce a proteolytic enzyme. The glands are obviously useful in producing extra mucus at the site where the pancreatic enzymes are emptied into the intestine.

The third set of glands to consider are those called *crypts of Lieberkühn* and they dip down from the surface between villi to reach almost to the muscularis mucosae (Fig. 24-23). Their openings on the surface of the intestine is shown in Figure 24-33, but their openings are in reality difficult to see in the living animal, because their mouths are tightly closed. If the villi are likened to trees growing on ridges (plicae circulares), the crypts of Lieberkühn could be thought of as little wells that have been dug between each pair of trees. To avoid confusion, the student should realize that the villi *project* into the lumen from the mucous membrane of the small intestine and that the crypts of Lieberkühn *dip down* (like wells) from the surface into the mucous membrane (Fig. 24-33). It is known that some enzymes are secreted in the small intestine, particularly erepsin, which acts in the later stages of protein digestion to produce amino acids. Enzymes that convert disaccharides into monosaccharides and others that transfer nucleic acids into nucleosides are also secreted. Of the cells in the crypts only some cells at their bottoms, the Paneth cells to be described presently, show the features that are now associated with enzyme production. Yet there is some evidence that the cells of the villi elaborate disaccharidase.

The pancreas and the liver supply almost no mucus to the small intestine. Mucus is provided by the glands of Brunner and by innumerable goblet cells present both in the crypts of Lieberkühn and among the absorptive epithelial cells that cover the villi and otherwise line the interior of the intestine (Fig. 24-35).

## SOME DETAILS CONCERNING THE STRUCTURE OF THE MUCOUS MEMBRANE

**General Features of Epithelium of Villi.** It will be recalled that the surface epithelial cells of the stomach, although not typical goblet cells, all secrete mucus and are all alike. The cells of the epithelial membrane lining the small intestine do not all secrete mucus and are not all alike. Most of them are tall columnar in type, with each having a free border with numerous microvilli (Figs. 8-7, 8-9 and 8-12); these are primarily absorptive in function and they do not secrete mucus. However, true goblet cells that do secrete mucus are distributed among them (Fig. 8-5). Hence, there is a division of labor among the epithelial lining cells of the small intestine.

*Epithelium of Crypts.* The epithelium lining the glands that dip down into the mucous membrane (the crypts of Liekerkühn) varies in relation to depth. At the bottom of the glands there are columnar cells that are narrower at their apices than at their bases. Their nuclei are disposed close to the basement membrane, and the cytoplasm between the nucleus and the apex of each contains granules similar to zymogen granules (Figs. 24-35, *right,* and 24-37). These are the Paneth cells; they show the features characteristic of enzyme-secreting cells, although it is not known what enzyme they produce. The intestine is so long and the crypts of Lieberkühn so numerous, that the total number of Paneth cells in the body must be tremendous. It has been shown that Paneth cells are one of the few kinds of cells in the body to contain demonstrable amounts of zinc; the significance of this is not yet known.

Somewhat higher in the crypts, the lining cells are of a low columnar type with goblet cells interspersed between them. The columnar cells show features of immaturity in that they have numerous free ribosomes but only rare rough-surfaced vesicles of endoplasmic reticulum. Their microvilli are scarce and stubby. In contrast, the columnar cells of the villi are larger and have abundant rough-surfaced vesicles and tightly packed microvilli. Although the cells of the villi and the crypts differ, the study of their embryologic development reveals that the epithelium of both crypts and villi have the same origin and, furthermore, they transform into one another, as will now be described.

A salient feature of the crypts of Lieberkühn is the presence of abundant mitoses, even in the adult. The early German histologists believed that this mitotic activity was a repair process to regenerate the epithelium damaged by enzymes, food, and bacterial toxins. In 1948, however, Leblond and Stevens observed that fasting, which prevents damage due to food and also reduces enzyme secretion, affected mitotic activity in the crypts only slightly. Furthermore, mitotic activity was found to be equally abundant in germ-free animals. Moreover, mitosis occurs throughout the day and is, therefore, a constant *physiologic phenomenon.*

Early authors had wondered about the fate of the large number of cells produced. Bizzozero believed that under the pressure of increasing numbers of cells produced in the crypts, cells were pushed toward the villi to replace damaged ones. Ramond described desquamated cells in the lumen of the small intestine, which he thought came from the villus surface. Dias Amado in 1933 mentioned that the tips of the villi occasionally showed desquamated cells. In 1948 Leblond and Stevens described various types of "extrusion zones" at the tips of the villi, varying from small gaps to streamers of cells on their way out. They concluded that the cells produced in the crypts migrate along the sides of the villi to reach the extrusion zone at the tips of the villi.

The kinetics of the migration have been examined on the basis of a "steady state" being maintained in the cell population, and which requires that the mitotic rate be equal to the cell extrusion rate, and both be equal to the over-all turnover rate of the intestinal epithelium. With the colchicine technic, Leblond and Stevens found that the turnover rate of the intestinal epithelium (fraction of cells formed or lost per unit time) was more than 2 per cent per hour. The time necessary to replace a number of cells equal to that of

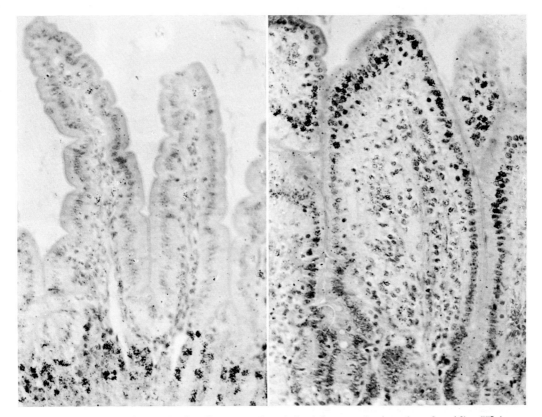

FIG. 24-36. H and E stained radioautographs of the jejunum of mice after thymidine-H³ injection (1 month exposure, × about 150). At left, mouse sacrificed 8 hours, and, at right, 72 hours after injection.

At left, many clusters of silver grains are seen in the region of the crypts (exclusively over nuclei). At right, the clusters of silver grains are seen only in the epithelium of the upper third of the villi. From this region, a decreasing gradient of reaction extends along the epithelium down to the crypts. These radioautographs illustrate that many of the cells present in the crypts at the early time interval (*left*) eventually migrate to the tips of the villi (*right*). (Preparation from C. P. Leblond and B. Messier)

the epithelium was therefore of the order of 2 days or less in the rat. Bertalanffy and Nagy in 1961 reached similar conclusions for the intestine of man.

So far the results were based on abstract reasoning. The development of radioautography made it possible to test whether the postulated cell migration took place. Since the daughter cells of a cell labeled with a radioactive precursor of DNA during the period of DNA duplication are both labeled (Figs. 6-24, and 6-26) the daughter cells may be traced. The first DNA precursor used to trace them was phosphate-P³², then adenine-C¹⁴ and finally thymidine-H³; the last gave

the most clear-cut results. Soon after labeled thymidine was injected into an animal, radioactivity was detected in a large proportion of the crypt cells (Fig. 24-36, *left*), but there was none in Paneth cells, or in the columnar cells of the crypt mouth. The location of the label was the same as that where mitotic figures are seen. By sacrificing animals at various times afterward and preparing radioautographs from these, the labeled crypt cells were found to migrate. First, they went up to the crypt mouth, later became part of the villous epithelium, later still ascended up to the villus tip (Fig. 24-36, *right*), and finally were extruded into the lumen where they could

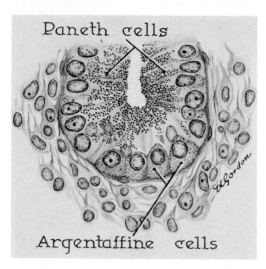

Paneth cells

Argentaffine cells

FIG. 24-37. Drawing of the bottom of a crypt of Lieberkühn (high-power). Both Paneth and argentaffine cells may be seen. It is unusual for argentaffine cells to be grouped together as they are in this section.

often be seen. The time taken for the migration of the front line of the labeled cells is an approximation to the turnover time of the covered area (about 2 days in the rat, 3 days in the mouse) because migration is accomplished by replacement of cells lying along the route (Leblond and Messier, 1958; Quastler and Sherman, 1959; Creamer et al., 1961; Lesher et al., 1961). Since the cell loss at the extrusion zone balances the cell production in the crypts, it appears that the familiar histologic picture of the intestinal epithelium is the result of this balance. As a result, when villi are short as in the ileum or long as in jejunum, the turnover time of the epithelium is respectively short or long (Altmann, 1964) because mitotic activity is about the same in both.

In man, the use of labeled precursors by Lipkin et al. has indicated a turnover time of the intestinal epithelium somewhat longer than in laboratory animals, that is, 3 to 4 days.

The mechanism of migration is not thoroughly understood. Grad and Stevens showed that migration persists when crypt mitoses are stopped by irradiation and therefore is not due to pressure resulting from cell production. After irradiation cells become fewer and flatten on the surface of the villi in an attempt, as it were, to keep them covered. Eventually the villus shrinks. Stunted broad villi or even a flattened surface is left, as has been shown by Wiernik et al. Hence, variations in cell turnover is an important factor in modifying the shape and the size of the villi as has been proposed by Creamer. As for the cause of cell extrusion, perhaps the muscle ribbon in villi, which extends from the muscularis mucosae to the basement membrane that covers the cells of the extrusion zone, should be implicated. Contraction of the muscle ribbon would loosen cells in the extrusion zone so they would fall into the lumen. The cells on either side of the resulting gap would then close in. The next cells would follow suit; and so would the cells farther down the villi and crypts, thus causing the whole epithelium to migrate in the direction of the villus tip. Mitosis would supply the cells required for the migration.

Goblet cells, like columnar cells, arise from mitoses in crypts and migrate from crypt to villus. In contrast, Paneth cells and the argentaffine cells next to be described seem to be stable and not change their location.

Disposed among the cells lining the crypts and those covering the villi are cells that are usually termed *argentaffine* or *enterochromaffine* cells because of the affinity of their cytoplasmic granules for silver and chromium salts. Two of these cells are seldom found together; almost invariably they are disposed in a solitary fashion between the other cells of the region. Figure 24-37 illustrates an unusual grouping of them. Their shape varies in relation to their position. On the villi they are columnar, but in the crypts they tend to be triangular (Fig. 24-37). Moreover, in the crypts, their apices tend to be withdrawn slightly from the surface, and their bases may crowd between the bases of adjacent cells and the basement membrane. Their position in this respect is reminiscent of that of parietal cells in the glands of the stomach. Their nuclei are round and may be disposed toward either end of the cell, although most commonly the nucleus is in the basal end of the cell but not far from its center. Their fine structure is illustrated in Figure 24-38.

Argentaffine (enterochromaffine) cells have been demonstrated in all parts of the alimentary tract, from the esophagus to the anus,

but they are more numerous in the small intestine, and for this reason they are described
here. They have also been seen in the bile and
the pancreatic ducts and in other sites. Similar
(perhaps identical) cells have been described
in other layers of the intestine. Curious little
tumors (carcinoid), not uncommon in the appendix, have been traced to cells of this or a
similar type. The precise origin of these cells
is not clear. It has long been suspected that
they develop from neuro-ectoderm and that
they might produce some secretion affecting
the autonomic nervous system. Relatively recently it has been established that they produce *serotonin;* the actions of this were
described in connection with platelets.

**Lamina Propria.** The cores of villi are composed of lamina propria. In this particular
site it consists of a loose connective tissue
which has many of the attributes of lymphatic
tissue. Its chief supporting element is a network of reticular fibers that extends throughout its substance and, at the sides and the tip,
unites with the basement membrane under the
surface epithelium. Branching cells with pale
cytoplasm are irregularly scattered over the
fibers in the reticular net. These are generally
thought to be reticular cells, and probably
both the undifferentiated and the reticuloendothelial types are represented. In the meshes of
the network, lymphocytes are common and
are probably of local origin (Fig. 24-35).
Plasma cells are sometimes fairly abundant.
Eosinophils that have migrated from the capillaries of the villus are also sometimes seen in
the reticular net. Furthermore, smooth muscle fibers with their long axes parallel with
that of the villus are characteristically disposed in its central part, usually around a
single, large, lymphatic capillary that begins
near the tip of the villus; this lymphatic capillary is usually termed the *lacteal* of the villus.

A single arterial twig from the submucosa
usually penetrates the muscularis mucosae
below each villus and ascends into it for some
distance and then breaks up into a capillary
network. The capillaries approach the epithelial cells very closely. Separate arterial twigs
break up into capillary nets surrounding the
crypts of Lieberkühn. Nerve fibers from
Meissner's plexus in the submucosa likewise
penetrate the muscularis mucosae to ascend
into each villus. Here they break up into net-

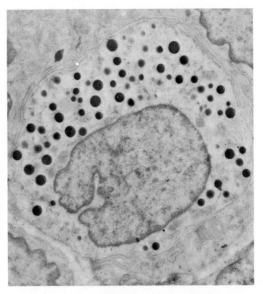

Fig. 24-38. Electron micrograph (×
8,000) of an argentaffine cell from the
stomach of a bat. The cytoplasm shows
dense granules each of which is surrounded
by a membrane. (Dr. S. Ito, Dr. R. J.
Winchester and Dr. D. W. Fawcett)

works that are said to extend throughout all
its substances. Frank nodules of lymphatic tissue are not uncommon in the lamina propria
of any part of the digestive tract but they are
relatively more numerous in the small intestine, particularly in the ileum. They appear
either singly, as "solitary" nodules, or in such
close association with others that "confluent"
masses are formed. The possible function of
lymphatic tissue in the lamina propria was
discussed in the general plan.

Solitary lymphatic nodules may be present
almost anywhere in the lamina propria in the
small intestine. They range from $\frac{1}{2}$ to 3 mm.
in width. The smaller ones are entirely confined to the lamina propria, but the larger
ones may bulge through the muscularis mucosae into the submucosa. The epithelium over
them and the other tissues about them are
usually infiltrated with lymphocytes derived
from these nodules. When nodules are numerous they tend to become confluent. The
larger confluent masses have an elongated oval
shape and are confined to the side of the intestine opposite the mesenteric attachment. They
vary from 1 to 12 cm. in length and from

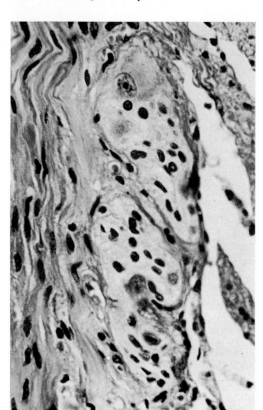

FIG. 24-39. High-power photomicrograph of a section of the small intestine of a child, showing a portion of Auerbach's plexus between the two layers of the muscularis externa. Note the large ganglion cell at the top. Its cytoplasm lies mostly above and to the right of its nucleus.

1 to 2½ cm. in width. They are called *Peyer's patches* after their discoverer. There are usually 20 to 30 of them, but more have been observed in young subjects. They are confined mostly to the lower part of the ileum, where they are largest, but they are also present in the upper part of the ileum and the lower part of the jejunum; they have even been observed in the lower part of the duodenum. Villi are usually absent over them. They were perhaps of more interest when typhoid fever was a prevalent disease, for in this condition they exhibit a profound inflammatory reaction and are common sites of ulceration, hemorrhage and even of perforation. Like the lymphatic tissue as a whole, both the solitary and

the confluent nodules become less prominent as an individual ages. In old age, Peyer's patches disappear almost completely.

The *muscularis mucosae* and the *submucosa* of the small intestine require no description other than that given in the general plan.

The *muscularis externa* of the small intestine exhibits no special features, but sections of the small intestine provide a good opportunity for the student to see and examine the ganglion cells and the nerve fibers of Auerbach's plexus which is to be seen between the two muscle layers (Fig. 24-39).

**Absorption from the Small Intestine.** Precise evidence regarding the particular cells that absorb the products of digestion and how they accomplish this function is difficult to obtain. However, it seems logical to suppose that in health most absorption is performed by the villi and, in particular, by the columnar cells which the EM has shown to be covered with microvilli (see numerous illustrations of microvilli in Chap. 8).

In our present state of knowledge, the laws of diffusion and osmosis cannot be applied to explain all aspects of intestinal absorption. As yet, obscure vital activities of the epithelial lining cells must be postulated to account for the selective action of the absorptive cells as well as for their ability to remove substances from sites of low concentration and to deliver them into sites of higher concentration.

Under normal conditions, carbohydrates are absorbed (as monosaccharides) through the absorptive epithelial cells and into the blood capillaries that are so close to them in the lamina propria. Proteins are absorbed as amino acids by the same route. Until recently, it was generally believed that fats were broken down in the lumen of the intestine to fatty acids and glycerol and absorbed as such by the epithelial lining cells, and that the fat droplets that reappeared in the cytoplasm between the striated border and the nucleus of the absorptive cells indicated a resynthesis of the fat in this site. More recently, Frazer has provided evidence showing that all fat is not split to the point where free glycerol is liberated from it before it is absorbed. This requires that some be absorbed as an emulsion. That this actually occurs has been proved recently by EM studies made by Palay and Karlin. They fed rats a fatty meal and then

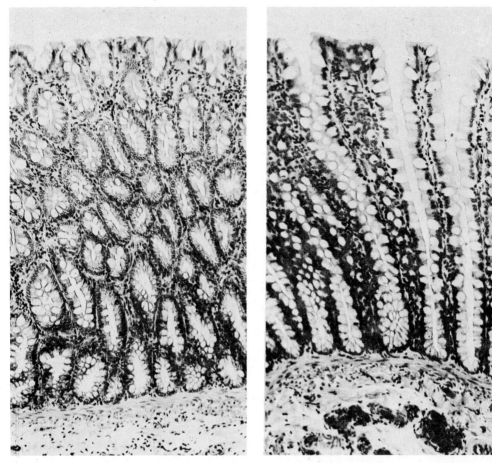

FIG. 24-40. Medium-power photomicrograph of sections of the wall of the large intestine, showing the mucous membrane. At the left, the crypts of Lieberkühn are cut in oblique section, and at the right, in longitudinal section. They are seen to extend down to the muscularis mucosae.

studied sections of the jejunum, taken at different times afterward, with the EM. They found that small fat droplets, between 300 and 500 Å in diameter, appeared between the microvilli 20 minutes after the animals had been fed. Moreover, at this time some droplets were found in the cytoplasm close to the bases of the microvilli. From ½ to 1 hour after the feeding, the fat droplets were seen deeper in the cytoplasm, and each could be shown to be surrounded by a membrane (this would seem to suggest that the mechanism operating here is similar to that already described for phagocytosis by macrophages and pinocytosis by endothelial cells). The fat droplets did not reach the basal parts of the absorptive cells but instead seemed to migrate to and through the sides of the cells so that

dense clusters of droplets came to lie between the borders of adjacent absorptive cells. From here the droplets seemed to pass through the basement membrane and so gained entrance to the lamina propria and its lymphatics.

The lymphatics that drain the intestine contain considerable amounts of emulsified fat after a fatty meal; this creamy lymph is termed *chyle*.

## THE LARGE INTESTINE

**Parts.** The large intestine consists of the cecum, the vermiform appendix, the ascending, transverse, descending and pelvic colons, and the rectum (including the anal canal). It terminates at the anus (Fig. 24-1).

**Function.** The unabsorbed contents of the

small intestine are emptied into the cecum in a fluid state. By the time the contents reach the descending colon they have acquired the consistency of feces. Absorption of water by the mucous membrane is an important function of the large intestine.

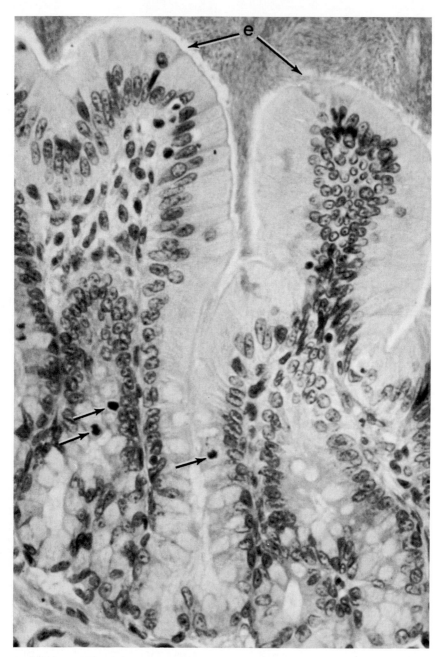

FIG. 24-41. H and E stained section of ascending colon. A crypt of Lieberkühn is visible in the center. At the bottom many goblet cells are seen; these seldom divide. Immediately above, there is a region of frequent mitoses (arrows) visible in both columnar cells and goblet cells. The cells migrate upward and, in so doing, the goblet cells release their mucus and tend to flatten out. The extrusion of cells balancing the cell production by mitosis takes place on the free surface (e). (Preparation from H. Warshawsky)

Although a great deal of mucus is present in the alkaline secretion of the large intestine, no enzymes of importance are secreted with it. Nevertheless, some digestion occurs in the lumen. Part of this is due to enzymes derived from the small intestine remaining active in the material delivered into the large intestine, and part is to be explained by the putrefactive bacteria that thrive in its lumen, breaking down cellulose, which, if consumed in the diet, survives to reach the large intestine because no enzymes that attack it are liberated by the intestine of man.

Many years ago, Metchnikoff (mentioned in connection with phagocytes) decided, for various reasons, that many of the ills of man were due to the absorption from the large intestine of the products of bacterial putrefaction. His ideas were responsible for a great number of people regularly consuming cultures of bacteria designed to supplant the putrefactive ones that normally flourish in the large bowel. Undoubtedly, poisonous materials *do* form in this location but they are probably not absorbed in sufficient quantities by healthy individuals to exert an adverse effect, particularly since special detoxifying mechanisms exist to deal with many of them. Furthermore, it has recently become apparent that some of the products of bacterial putrefaction are helpful, if not essential, to the organism. Vitamin K, spoken of in connection with the clotting of blood, is a product of the putrefactive process, as are certain members of the B complex.

Feces consist of bacteria, products of bacterial putrefaction, such undigested material as survives passage through the large intestine, cellular debris from the lining of the intestine, mucus and a few other substances.

**Histologic Structure.** The mucous membrane of the large intestine differs from that of the small intestine in many respects. It has no villi in postnatal life. It is thicker, hence the crypts of Lieberkühn are deeper (Fig. 24-40). The crypts, which are distributed all over the lining surface of the large intestine, contain no Paneth cells (except in the young), but they have more goblet cells than are present in the small intestine. The ordinary surface epithelial cells have striated borders like those of the small intestine, and some goblet cells are interspersed between them.

Cell migration occurs in the large as well as in the small intestine, although at a rate which is even more rapid, at least, in man (Lipkin *et al.* 1963). However, the cells present at the bottom of the crypts seldom divide, but those in the middle third often do (Fig. 24-41, arrows). From there the cells migrate upward and eventually reach the surface. The extrusion zones (Fig. 24-41, arrows, e) are on the surface about halfway between the openings of adjacent crypts.

The crypts of Lieberkühn disappear in the anorectal canal at the junction of rectal and anal epithelium. The stratified squamous anal epithelium is not keratinized and extends over about 2 cm. At its outer border it becomes continuous with the keratinized epidermis of the skin and on its inner border with the columnar epithelium that lines the remainder of the rectum. At the junction between anal and columnar epithelium, circumanal glands are present. These glands have a stratified columnar epithelium and are of the branched tubular type but do not seem to be actively functioning. They probably constitute an atrophic organ, reminding one of the actively functioning glands of certain mammals.

In the anorectal canal, the mucous membrane is thrown into a series of longitudinal folds known as the *rectal columns* or *columns of Morgagni.* Below, adjacent columns are connected by folds. This arrangement produces a series of so-called anal valves. The concavities of the pockets so formed are called rectal sinuses.

The muscularis mucosae continues only to the region of the longitudinal folds and in them it breaks up into bundles and finally disappears. Hence, there is not the same demarcation between lamina propria and submucosa in this region as in other parts of the tract. The merging lamina propria and submucosa contain many convolutions of small veins. A very common condition, *internal hemorrhoids,* is the result of the dilatation of these veins so that they bulge the mucous membrane inwardly and encroach on the lumen of the anal canal. External hemorrhoids result from the dilatation of veins at, and close to, the anus.

**Muscularis Externa.** In the large intestine, this layer differs somewhat from its arrangement in other parts of the tract. Beginning in the cecum, the longitudinally disposed fibers

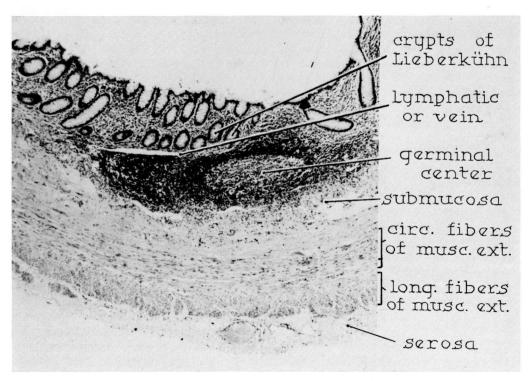

Fig. 24-42. Low-power photomicrograph of a portion of the wall of the appendix (cross section).

of the outer coat, though present to a certain extent over the whole circumference of the bowel, are for the most part collected into three flat bands, the *teniae coli*. These are not as long as the intestine along which they are disposed; hence, they are responsible for gathering the wall of this part of the bowel into sacculations or haustra (Fig. 24-1). If the teniae are cut or stripped away, the bowel immediately elongates and the sacculations disappear. The three teniae extend from the cecum to the rectum, where they spread out and fuse to some extent so as to form a muscle coat that is thicker on the anterior and the posterior aspects of the rectum than on its sides. The anterior and the posterior aggregates of longitudinally disposed smooth muscle are somewhat shorter than the rectum itself, and this results in a type of sacculation in this region; this causes the underlying wall of the rectum to bulge inwardly to form two transverse shelves, one from the right and a smaller one from the left, called the *plicae transversae* of the rectum. These help to sup-

port the weight of the rectal contents and so make the work of the anal sphincter less arduous.

The circularly disposed smooth muscle fibers of the inner coat of the muscularis externa form a thicker coat between sacculations than they do over the sacculations. In the anal canal they are increased to form a sphincter muscle, the internal sphincter of the anus.

**Serosa.** Along the colon and the upper part of the rectum, the serous coat leaves the surface of the intestine at irregular intervals to form little peritoneal sacs that enclose fat. These peritoneal redundancies hang from the external surface of the bowel and are termed *appendices epiploicae.* In some sites they contain only areolar tissue.

**Vermiform Appendix.** This wormlike appendage of the cecum (Fig. 24-1) is the seat of so much disease that it merits a separate description. Developmentally, it is the lower, blind end of the cecum that has failed to enlarge as rapidly as the remainder and, as a result, it appears as a diverticulum arising from the cecum an inch or less below the entrance of the ileum. In many lower animals it is larger than it is in man and so provides a good-sized pouch off the main track of the intestine where cellulose can be subjected to prolonged digestion. In man it is too short and has too narrow a lumen to serve a similar function. Indeed, its form is commonly so bent and twisted that there is grave danger of bacterial activity destroying not only the contents of the lumen but also the lining of the organ itself. As a result, organisms sometimes gain entrance to the tissues of its wall and lead to its infection. For this reason, surgical removal of the infected organ is one of the commonest abdominal operations.

The appendix usually is studied microscopically by means of cross sections (Fig. 24-42). In preparations of this sort, the lumen of the appendix of a young person often has a somewhat three-horned instead of a circular appearance. In adults, it is usually rounder, and in advancing years, it may be obliterated by connective tissue's replacing the mucous membrane as well as filling the lumen.

The epithelium of the mucous membrane is similar to that of the large intestine (Fig. 24-42). However, the lamina propria contains much more lymphatic tissue; indeed, confluent lymphatic nodules may completely surround the lumen, though the amount diminishes with age. The muscularis mucosae is not well developed and may be missing in some areas. A few eosinophils are normal constituents of the lamina propria but, if present in the submucosa, are considered as being of some significance in indicating a chronic inflammatory condition of the organ. Neutrophils in any numbers in the lamina propria or any other layer (Fig. 24-43) indicate an acute inflammatory lesion (acute appendicitis). The muscularis externa shows no deviation from the general plan found in the intestine, and the longitudinal fibers form a complete coat. The appendix has a rudimentary mesentery.

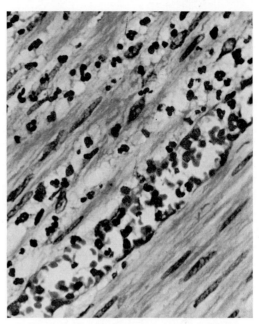

FIG. 24-43. High-power photomicrograph of a section through the muscular part of the wall of an appendix that was acutely inflamed and removed at operation. A small venule runs from the lower left corner to just above the middle of the right border. It contains both erythrocytes and leukocytes. Neutrophilic leukocytes can be seen migrating through the wall of the vessel out into the swollen spaces between the smooth muscle fibers. The neutrophils can be recognized by their lobed nuclei.

## REFERENCES

### GENERAL REFERENCE ON ORAL CAVITY AND SALIVARY GLANDS

Provenza, D. V.: Oral Histology, Inheritance and Development, Philadelphia, Lippincott, 1964.

### SPECIAL REFERENCES ON ORAL CAVITY EXCLUDING TEETH

Dewey, M. M.: A histochemical and biochemical study of the parotid gland in normal and hypophysectomized rats, Am. J. Anat. *102*:243, 1958.

Gairns, F. W.: The sensory nerve endings of the human palate, Quart. J. Exp. Physiol. *40*:40, 1955.

Jacoby, F., and Leeson, C. R.: The post-natal development of the rat submaxillary gland, J. Anat. *93*:201, 1959.

James, J.: Epithelium and lymphocyte in the development of the palatine tonsil, Acta anat. *27*:222, 1955.

Leeson, C. R., and Jacoby, F.: An electron microscopic study of the rat submaxillary gland during its postnatal development and in the adult, J. Anat. *93*:287, 1959.

Orban, B.: Atlas of Oral Histology and Embryology, St. Louis, Mosby, ed. 2, 1960.

Parks, H. F.: Morphological study of the extrusion of secretory materials by the parotid glands of mouse and rat, J. Ultrastr. Res. *6*: 449, 1962.

Scott, B. L., and Pease, D. C.: Electron microscopy of the salivary and lacrimal glands of the rat, Am. J. Anat. *104*:115, 1959.

Stormont, D. L.: The salivary glands *in* Cowdry's Special Cytology, ed. 2, p. 151, New York, Hoeber, 1932.

GENERAL REFERENCES ON TEETH

Kronfeld, R.: Histopathology of the Teeth and Their Surrounding Structures, ed. 4, Philadelphia, Lea & Febiger, 1955.

Orban, B.: Oral Histology and Embryology, ed. 4, St. Louis, Mosby, 1957.

Provenza, D. V.: Oral Histology, Inheritance and Development, Philadelphia, Lippincott, 1964.

Schour, I.: Oral histology and embryology *in* Noyes, F. (ed.): Oral Histology and Embryology, ed. 8, Philadelphia, Lea & Febiger, 1960.

Sognnaes, R. F. (ed.): Mechanisms of Hard Tissue Destruction, Washington, D. C., Am. Assoc. Adv. Sci., 1963.

SPECIAL REFERENCES ON TEETH

Bélanger, L. F.: Autoradiographic and histochemical observations on the mineralization of teeth in rats and hamsters of various ages, Anat. Rec. *114*:529, 1952.

————: Autoradiographic studies of the formation of the organic matrix of cartilage, bone and the tissues of teeth *in* Wolstenholme, G. E. W., and O'Connor, C. M. (eds.): Ciba Foundation Symposium on Bone Structure and Metabolism, p. 75, London, Churchill, 1956.

————: A method for routine detection of radiophosphates and other radioactive compounds in tissues: the inverted autograph, Anat. Rec. *107*:149, 1950.

Bélanger, L. F., and Leblond, C. P.: Mineralization of the growing tooth as shown by radiophosphorus autographs, Proc. Soc. Exp. Biol. Med. *73*:390, 1950.

Bélanger, L. F., Lotz, W. E., Visek, W. J., and Comar, C. L.: Autoradiographic visualization with Ca[45] of normal growth of the incisor of pigs and the effect of fluorine feeding, Anat. Rec. *119*:53, 1954.

Bevelander, G., and Johnson, P. L.: Alkaline phosphatase in amelogenesis, Anat. Rec. *104*: 125, 1949.

Frank, R. M., and Sognnaes, R. F.: Electron microscopy of matrix formation and calcification in rat enamel, Arch. Oral Biol. *1*:339, 1960.

Fullmer, H. M.: Observations on the development of oxytalan fibers in the periodontium of man, J. Dent. Res. *38*:510, 1959.

Glasstone, S.: The development of tooth germs on the chick chorio-allantois, J. Anat. *88*:392, 1954.

Gustafson, G.: The structure of the human dental enamel, Odontologisk Tidskrift. (Supp.), p. 53, 1945.

Kallenbach, E., Sandborn, E., and Warshawsky, H.: The golgi apparatus of the ameloblast of the rat at the stage of enamel matrix formation, J. Cell Biol. *16*:629, 1963.

Kumamoto, Y., and Leblond, C. P.: Radioautographic study of mineralization of growing teeth with labelled calcium, J. Dent. Res. *35*: 147, 1956.

————: Visualization of C[14] in the tooth matrix after administration of labeled hexoses, J. Dent. Res. *37*:147, 1958.

Leblond, C. P., Bélanger, L. F., and Greulich, R. C.: Formation of bones and teeth as visualized by radioautography, Ann. N. Y. Acad. Sci. *60*:629, 1955.

Lorber, M.: A study of the histochemical reaction of the dental cementum in alveolar bones, Anat. Rec. *111*:129, 1951.

Nuckolls, J., Saunders, J. B. de C. M., and Frisbie, H. E.: Amelogenesis: a further study of the development of Tomes' process and the enamel rod matrix in the molar and incisor teeth of the rat, J. Am. Coll. Dent. *10*:241, 1943.

Orban, B., Sicher, H., and Weinmann, J. P.: Amelogenesis, J. Am. Coll. Dent. *10*:13, 1943.

Reith, E. J.: The ultrastructure of ameloblasts from the growing end of rat incisors, Arch. Oral Biol. *2*:253, 1960.

————: The ultrastructure of ameloblasts during matrix formation and the maturation of enamel, J. Biophys. Biochem. Cytol. *9*:825, 1961.

————: The ultrastructure of ameloblasts during early stages of maturation of enamel, J. Cell Biol. *18*:691, 1963.

Sasso, W. S., and Castro, N. M.: Histochemical study of amelogenesis and dentinogenesis, Oral Surg. *10*:1323, 1957.

Schour, I.: Recent advances in oral histology, Internat. Dent. J. *2*:10, 1951.

————: The teeth *in* Cowdry's Special Cytology, ed. 2, p. 67, New York, Hoeber, 1932.

Schour, I., and Massler, M.: Studies in tooth development; the growth pattern of human teeth, J. Am. Dent. A. *27*:1778; *27*:1918, 1940.

Scott, D. B.: The electron microscopy of enamel and dentin, Ann. N. Y. Acad. Sci. *60*:575, 1955.

Shroff, F. R., Williamson, K. I., Bertaud, W. S., and Hall, D. M.: Further electron microscope studies of dentine, Oral Surg. 9:432, 1956.

Sognnaes, R. F.: Microstructure and histochemical characteristics of the mineralized tissues, Ann. N. Y. Acad. Sci. 60:545, 1955.

———: See also reference to "Mechanisms of Hard Tissue Destruction" under General References.

Stack, M. V.: The chemical nature of the organic matrix of bone, dentin, and enamel, Ann. N. Y. Acad. Sci. 60:585, 1955.

Symons, N. B. B.: The cells of the odontoblast, ameloblast, and internal enamel epithelial layers, Brit. Dent. J. 98:273, 1955.

———: Ribonucleic acid-alkaline phosphatase distribution in the developing teeth of the rat, J. Anat. 90:117, 1956.

Szabó, G.: Studies on the cultivation of teeth *in vitro*, J. Anat. 88:31, 1954.

Watson, M. L., and Avery, J. K.: The development of the hamster lower incisor as observed by electron microscopy, Am. J. Anat. 95:109, 1954.

Weinmann, J. P., and Sicher, H.: Bone and Bones, ed. 2, St. Louis, Mosby, 1955.

Wislocki, G. B., Singer, M., and Waldo, C. M.: Some histochemical reactions of mucopolysaccharides, glycogen, lipids and other substances in teeth, Anat. Rec. 101:487, 1948.

Wislocki, G. B., and Sognnaes, R. F.: Histochemical reactions of normal teeth, Am. J. Anat. 87:239, 1950.

### SPECIAL REFERENCES ON THE STOMACH

Bensley, R. R.: The gastric glands *in* Cowdry's Special Cytology, ed. 2, p. 197, New York, Hoeber, 1932.

Berger, E. H.: The distribution of parietal cells in the stomach; a histotopographic study, Am. J. Anat. 54:87, 1934.

Bowie, D. J.: The distribution of the chief or pepsin forming cells in the gastric mucosa of the cat, Anat. Rec. 78:9, 1940.

Bowie, D. J., and Vineberg, A. M.: The selective action of histamine and the effect of prolonged vagal stimulation on the cells of the gastric glands in the dog, Quart. J. Exp. Physiol. 25:247, 1935.

Bradford, N. M., and Davies, R. E.: Site of hydrochloric acid production in stomach as determined by indicators, Biochem. J. 46:414, 1950.

Challice, C. E., Bullivant, S., and Scott, D. B.: The fine structure of some cytoplasmic inclusions of oxyntic cells, Exp. Cell Res. 13:488, 1957.

Crane, E. E., Davies, R. E., and Longmuir, N. M.: Relations between hydrochloric acid secretion and electrical phenomena in frog gastric mucosa, Biochem. J. 43:321, 336, 1948.

Davenport, H. W.: Gastric carbonic anhydrase in dogs, Am. J. Physiol. 128:725, 1939-40.

———: In Memoriam: The carbonic anhydrase theory of gastric acid secretion, Gastroenterology 7:374, 1946.

Davenport, H. W., and Fisher, R. B.: Carbonic anhydrase in the gastro-intestinal mucosa, J. Physiol. 94:16, 1938-39.

———: The mechanism of the secretion of acid by the gastric mucosa, Am. J. Physiol. 131:165, 1940-41.

Davies, R. E.: Hydrochloric acid production by isolated gastric mucosa, Biochem. J. 42:609, 621, 1948. (Appendix by Davies, R. E., and Roughton, F. J. A.)

Davies, R. E., and Longmuir, N. M.: Production of ulcers in isolated frog gastric mucosa, Biochem. J. 42:621, 1948.

Davies, R. E., and Ogston, A. G.: On mechanism of secretion of ions by gastric mucosa and by other tissues, Biochem. J. 46:324, 1950.

Ferguson, A. N.: A cytological study of the regeneration of the gastric glands following experimental removal of large areas of the mucosa, Am. J. Anat. 42:403, 1928.

Grant, R.: Rate of replacement of the surface epithelial cells of the gastric mucosa, Anat. Rec. 91:175, 1945.

Hally, A. D.: The fine structure of the gastric parietal cell in the mouse, J. Anat. 93:217, 1959.

Helander, H., and Ekholm, R.: Ultrastructure of epithelial cells in the fundus glands of the mouse gastric mucosa, J. Ultrastr. Res. 3:74, 1958.

Hunt, J. N.: Gastric emptying and secretion in man, Physiol. Rev. 39:491, 1959.

Hunt, T. E.: Regeneration of the gastric mucosa in the rat, Anat. Rec. 131:193, 1958.

Ito, S., and Winchester, R. J.: The fine structure of the gastric mucosa in the bat, J. Cell Biol. 16:541, 1963.

Patterson, W. B., and Stetten, De Witt, Jr.: A study of gastric HCl formation, Science 109:256, 1949.

Sedar, A. W.: The fine structure of the oxyntic cell in relation to functional activity of the stomach, Ann. N. Y. Acad. Sci. 99:9, 1962.

———: Stomach and intestinal mucosa *in* Electron Microscope Anatomy, p. 123, New York, Acad. Press, 1964.

Sharples, W.: A note on the relatively high number of argentaffin cells in the mucosa of the human stomach, Anat. Rec. 91:237, 1945.

Stevens, C. E., and Leblond, C. P.: Renewal of the mucous cells in the gastric mucosa of the rat, Anat. Rec. 115:231, 1953.

Thomas, J. E.: Mechanics and regulation of gastric emptying, Physiol. Rev. *37*:453, 1957.

SPECIAL REFERENCES ON THE INTESTINE
EXCEPT THOSE RELATING TO CELL
TURNOVER WHICH ARE GIVEN
IN THE NEXT SECTION

Baker, J. R.: The free border of the intestinal epithelial cells of the vertebrates, Quart. J. Micros. Sc. *84*:73, 1942.

Clark, S. L., Jr.: The ingestion of proteins and colloidal materials by columnar absorptive cells of the small intestine in suckling rats and mice, J. Biophys. Biochem. Cytol. *5*:41, 1959.

Dalton, A. J.: Electron micrography of epithelial cells of the gastro-intestinal tract and pancreas, Am. J. Anat. *87*:109, 1951.

Dalton, A. J., Kahler, H., and Lloyd, B. J.: The structure of the free surface of a series of epithelial cell types in the mouse as revealed by the electron microscope, Anat. Rec. *111*:67, 1951.

Florey, H. W., Wright, R. D., and Jennings, M. A.: The secretions of the intestines, Physiol. Rev. *21*:36, 1941.

Frazer, A. C.: Differentiation in absorption of olive oil and oleic acid in the rat, J. Physiol. *102*:306, 1943.

———: Lipolysis and fat absorption, J. Physiol. *102*:329, 1943.

Frazer, A. C., Schulman, J. H., and Stewart, H. C.: Emulsification of fat in the intestine of the rat and its relationship to absorption, J. Physiol. *103*:306, 1944.

George, W. C.: The digestion and absorption of fat in lamellibranchs, Biol. Bull. *102*:118, 1952.

Granger, B., and Baker, R. F.: Electron microscope investigation of the striated border of intestinal epithelium, Anat. Rec. *107*:423, 1950.

Grossman, M. I.: The glands of Brunner, Physiol. Rev. *38*:675, 1958.

Hally, A. D.: The fine structure of the Paneth cell, J. Anat. *92*:268, 1958.

Hancox, N. M.: Alkaline phosphatase in the normal and explanted embryonic duodenum, Acta anat. *21*:18, 1954.

Irwin, D. A.: The anatomy of Auerbach's plexus, Am. J. Anat. *49*:141, 1931.

Kirkman, H.: The anal canal of the rhesus monkey with emphasis upon a description of bipolar, argyrophile cells in the zona columnaris, Am. J. Anat. *88*:177, 1951.

Landboe-Christensen, E.: The Duodenal Glands of Brunner in Man: Their Distribution and Quantity; An Anatomical Study, London, Oxford, 1944.

McMinn, R. M. H., and Mitchell, J. E.: The formation of villi following artificial lesions of the mucosa in the small intestine of the cat, J. Anat. *88*:99, 1954.

Palay, S. L., and Karlin, L.: Absorption of fat by jejunal epithelium in the rat, Anat. Rec. *124*:343, 1956.

———: An electron microscopic study of the intestinal villus, I. The fasting animal, J. Biophys, Biochem. Cytol. *5*:363, 1959.

Puchtler, H., and Leblond, C. P.: Histochemical analysis of cell membranes and associated structures as seen in the intestinal epithelium, Am. J. Anat. *102*:1, 1958.

Richardson, K. C.: Electron microscopic observations on Auerbach's plexus in the rabbit, with special reference to the problem of smooth muscle innervation, Am. J. Anat. *103*:99, 1958.

Verzár, F.: The absorption of fat, Am. J. Physiol. *90*:545, 1929.

SPECIAL REFERENCES ON CELL TURNOVER
IN THE INTESTINE

Altmann, G. G.: Cell number as a measure of growth and exfoliation of epithelium of the small intestine of rats, M.Sc. Thesis, Department of Anatomy, McGill University, 1964.

Bertalanffy, F. D., and Nagy, K. P.: Mitotic activity and renewal rate of the epithelial cells of human duodenum, Acta anat. *45*:362-371, 1961.

Bizzozero, G.: Regeneration des Elemente der schlauchförmigen Drüsen und des Epithels des Magendarmkanals, Anat. Anz. Cent. *3*:781-784, 1888.

———: Ueber die schlauchförmigen Drüsen des Magendarmkanals und die Beziehungen ihres Epithels zu dem Oberflächenepithel, Arch. mikr. Anat. *40*:325-375, 1892.

Creamer, B.: Variations in small-intestinal villous shape and mucosal dynamics, Brit. M. J. *2*:1371-1373, 1964.

Creamer, B., Shorter, R. G., and Bamforth, J.: The turnover and shedding of epithelial cells, Gut *2*:110-118, 1961.

Dias-Amado, L.: Un processus de régénération de l'épithélium intestinal, C. R. Assoc. anat. *28*:235-239, 1933.

Grad, B., and Stevens, C. E.: Histological changes produced by a single large injection of radioactive phosphorus ($P^{32}$) in albino rats and in $C_3H$ mice, Cancer Res. *10*:289-296, 1950.

Heidenhain, R.: Beiträge zur Histologie und Physiologie der Dünndarmschleimhaut, Arch. f. Physiol. *43*(Suppl.): 1-103, 1888.

Leblond, C. P., Greulich, R. C., and Pereira, J. P. M.: Relationship of cell formation and cell migration in the renewal of stratified squamous epithelia *in* Montagna, W., and Billingham, R. E. (eds.): Advances in Biology of Skin, vol. 5, pp. 39-67, New York, Pergamon, 1964.

Leblond, C. P., and Messier, B.: Renewal of chief cells and goblet cells in the small intestine as shown by radioautography after injection of thymidine-H³ into mice, Anat. Rec. *132*:247-259, 1958.

Leblond, C. P.. and Stevens, C. E.: The constant renewal of the intestinal epithelium in the albino rat, Anat. Rec. *100*:357-378, 1948.

Leblond, C. P., and Walker, B. E.: Renewal of cell populations, Physiol. Rev. *36*:255-275, 1956.

Lesher, S., Fry, R. J. M., and Cohn, H. I.: Age and degeneration time of the mouse duodenal epithelial cell, Exp. Cell Res. *24*:334-343, 1961.

Lipkin, M. Sherlock, P., and Bell, B.: Cell proliferation kinetics in the gastrointestinal tract of man, Gastroenterology, *45*:721-729, 1963.

Paneth, J.: Ueber die secernirenden Zellen des Dünndarm-Epithels, Arch. mikr. Anat. *31*:113-191, 1888.

Quastler, H., and Sherman, F. G.: Cell population kinetics in the intestinal epithelium of the mouse, Exp. Cell Res. *17*:420-438, 1959.

Ramond, M. F.: La desquamation de l'épithélium de l'intestin grêle au cours de la digestion, C. R. Soc. biol. *56*:171-173, 1904.

Rolshoven, E.: Ueber die Reifungsteilungen bei der Spermatogenese mit einer Kritik des bisherigen Begriffes der Zellteilungen, Verh. anat. Ges. *49*:189-197, 1951.

Wiernik, G., Shorter, R. G., and Creamer, B.: The arrest of intestinal epithelial "turnover" by the use of X-irradiation, Gut *3*:26-31, 1962.

# 25　Pancreas, Liver and Gallbladder

## THE PANCREAS

**Introduction.** The pancreas is a large and important gland. It lies in the abdomen with its head resting in the concavity of the duodenum and with its body extending toward the spleen, which its tail touches (Fig. 24-1). Grossly, a fresh pancreas is white with a pink tinge. With the naked eye its surface appears lobulated; it lacks a sufficiently substantial capsule to obscure the structure beneath it.

The pancreas is both an exocrine and an endocrine gland. The bulk of its cells are concerned with producing its exocrine secretion. This is collected and delivered by a duct system into the second part of the duodenum. The functions of the pancreatic secretion in digestion have already been described. The endocrine secretion of the pancreas is made by little clumps of cells, richly supplied with capillaries, that are scattered throughout its substance, and so surrounded by exocrine glandular tissue. Hence, these little endocrine units are appropriately termed *islets* and are named after Langerhans who described them. The known hormone produced by the *islets of Langerhans* is called *insulin* (*insula* = an island). The insufficient production of this hormone leads to the development of diabetes mellitus, a disease that will be described when the islets of Langerhans are discussed in detail in the chapter dealing with endocrine glands.

**Development.** The development of exocrine and endocrine glands is illustrated in Figure 9-1. The development of the pancreas offers examples of both the processes illustrated therein. Two diverticula (a ventral and a dorsal) arise from the epithelial (endodermal) lining of the developing duodenum and grow out and branch into mesoderm. Most of the pancreas (the tail, the body and the upper part of the head) arises from the dorsal outgrowth, while the lower part of the head arises from the ventral diverticulum. In some animals the fact that the pancreas arises from two different outgrowths is emphasized by the proximal parts of the outgrowths persisting to form two main ducts, each of which opens into the duodenum and drains the part of the pancreas originating from the particular outgrowth with which that duct is associated. However, in man, although two ducts persist in the majority of individuals, the dorsal and the ventral outgrowths fuse in such a fashion that the proximal part of the duct developing in the ventral outgrowth becomes continuous with the duct developing in the dorsal outgrowth, with the result that most of the secretion made by the part of the pancreas developing from the dorsal outgrowth actually comes to be conveyed, on the last part of its passage, into the duodenum by the duct that developed from the ventral outgrowth. This main duct, made up of parts of both embryonic ones, is known as the *pancreatic duct* (of Wirsung). The proximal part of the duct that develops from the dorsal outgrowth persists in the majority of individuals to form the accessory pancreatic duct (of Santorini).

The terminal portions of the two branching duct systems develop into exocrine secretory units. Although tending to be tubular in shape, these are sufficiently fat and rounded to resemble grapes hanging on stems, hence they are called *acini* (*acinus* = grape).

Some clumps of cells that arise from the developing duct system fail to develop a lumen. In many instances, though by no means always, these become completely detached from the duct system proper to become the islets of Langerhans—the endocrine units that are scattered through the pancreas. Moreover, there is reason to believe that some of the branches of the developing duct system fail to develop lumens or, if they do, that their lumens make no connection with those

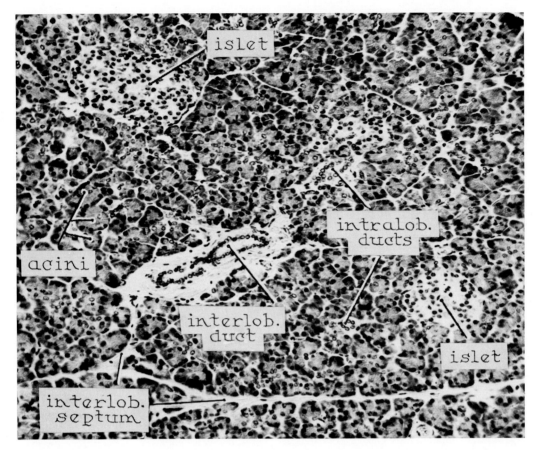

Fig. 25-1. Very low-power photomicrograph of a section of the pancreas, showing 2 islets, a large interlobular duct and smaller intralobular ducts, many acini and an interlobular septum.

of the duct system proper. By this means, an ill-defined network of cords or tubules of cells comes to be disposed irregularly through the substance of the pancreas in addition to the functional duct system. The cells of this network are relatively undifferentiated, and under certain circumstances they appear to give rise to new endocrine cells. This is the probable origin of those islet cells that are sometimes seen scattered singly among the acini.

### MICROSCOPIC STRUCTURE

It is not easy for the beginner to become oriented when sections of pancreas are first examined with the microscope. In order to facilitate orientation, the following account is so written that one feature of the tissue at a time may be identified and studied with the microscope.

**Capsule.** Most sections of the pancreas are cut at right angles to its surface, so, by looking around the periphery of a section with a low-power objective, the student should be able to find a capsule on one side. Here it will be seen that the connective tissue capsule that separates the pancreatic tissue from adjacent structures is remarkably thin; indeed, it scarcely merits being called a capsule. The pancreas, then, is poorly protected.

**Septa.** If the section as a whole is next studied by moving it about on the stage while it is examined with the low-power objective, it will be observed that partitions (septa) of connective tissue extend in from the capsule to divide it into lobules. These septa, like the capsule, are very thin (Fig. 25-1). Furthermore, separation commonly occurs along them when pancreatic tissue is fixed. Consequently,

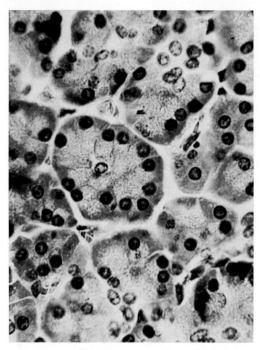

FIG. 25-2. High-power photomicrograph
of a section of the pancreas, showing an
acinus with the nucleus of a centro-acinar
cell appearing in its center.

the lobules commonly are clearly indicated because they are separated from one another by
fissures of the nature of artefacts.

The septa of the pancreas are so thin it
might be concluded that the pancreas is as
poorly provided with internal support as it is
with a protective covering. But this is not the
universal rule throughout the pancreas, for
considerable condensations of dense connective tissue are often present around the main
duct of the organ and its more immediate
branches (Fig. 25-1).

Acini. The tissue comprising the substance
of the lobules should be examined next. Most
of this consists of secretory units, the *pancreatic acini* (Fig. 25-1). These are packed
together in a most irregular way with only a
little reticular tissue between them, so that a
microtome knife, in cutting a section of pancreas, cuts acini in almost every conceivable
plane. Most, of course, are cut in oblique section. In many sections of pancreas the acini
do not stand out at all clearly as individual
structures. The student, then, may have diffi-

culty in deciding just what constitutes an
acinus. It may be helpful to realize that under
the high-power objective an acinus is approximately a tenth of the field in width. And, since
the nuclei of the secretory cells that make up
the acinus lie toward their bases, the nuclei in
a single acinus tend to be arranged so as to
form a rough ring of nuclei in its outer part
(Fig. 25-2). Individual acini would be easier
to recognize if their central parts were always
free of nuclei (the ring of peripheral nuclei
could then be observed more easily), but they
are not; this is because the ducts that lead
from acini do not always begin from their ends
but sometimes from their central part. A duct
may be more or less invaginated into the
lumen of the acinus. The duct cells that are in
this position are termed *centro-acinar* cells
(Figs. 25-2 and 25-3).

The sides of the more or less pyramidal
cells that are packed together to form acini
are so close together that cell boundaries between individual cells are not always distinct
in the light microscope (Fig. 25-2). The
apices of the cells of an acinus do not quite
come together in the central part of each
acinus; hence, a very small lumen is present
in this site (Fig. 7-18). The cytoplasm between the nucleus and the apex of each secretory cell contains acidophilic zymogen
granules which may be seen easily by partly
closing the condenser diaphragm (Fig. 25-2).
The nuclei are rounded and lie toward, but
not against, the bases of the cells. They exhibit prominent nucleoli, which are commonly
more acidophilic than those of most cells. The
cytoplasm between the nuclei and the bases of
the cells, as well as that on each side of the
nuclei, is commonly basophilic because of its
content of cytoplasmic RNA (Fig. 25-2).
This is an example of a cell which is synthesizing a great deal of protein (the zymogen
granules which are secreted, day by day, are
protein) having accumulations of ribonucleic
acid in its cytoplasm. In the bases of the
cells, the cytoplasmic RNA may present a
striated appearance because mitochondria are
disposed in this region in a plane parallel with
the long axis of the cell.

Fine Structure of Acinar Cells. The fine
structure of the secretory cells and the formation of zymogen granules is described in Chapter 7. The rough-surfaced vesicles of the

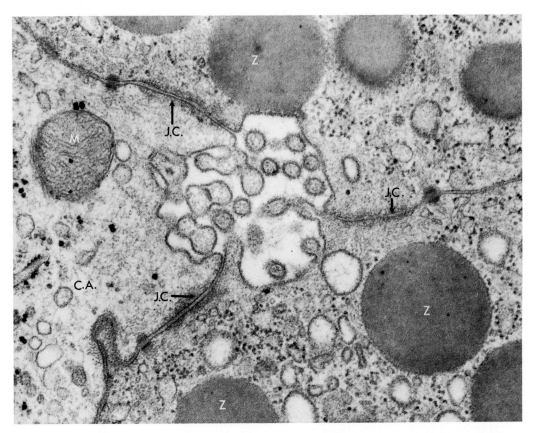

FIG. 25-3. Electron micrograph ($\times$ 50,000) of section cut through the lumen of a pancreatic acinus of a guinea pig. In the center, microvilli are seen projecting into the lumen. The cell at the left is a centro-acinar cell (CA); it is distinguished most readily by the fact that it contains no zymogen granules (Z) as do the other two cells whose apices abut on the lumen; it does, however, contain a mitochondrion. At the top a zymogen granule is about to be secreted. Junctional complexes (J.C.) are present at each site where the membranes of adjacent cells come into contact close to the lumen. (These are described in detail in Chap. 8.) (Farquhar, M. G., and Palade, G. E.: J. Cell Biol. *17*:375)

endoplasmic reticulum of acinar cells are illustrated in Figure 7-7. The mechanism of entry of the protein components of the secretion into microvesicles of the Golgi apparatus of acinar cells is illustrated in Figure 7-15. The process of secretion and the movement of secretions in the cell are both illustrated in Figure 7-16.

The junctional complexes between the borders of adjacent acinar cells, close to the lumen of an acinus, are illustrated in Figure 25-3. This same illustration shows zymogen granules about to be secreted in the apices of acinar cells and also that the centro-acinar cell in the illustration contains no zymogen granules; it is a duct type of cell.

A delicate, reticular connective tissue fills the space between individual acini and brings capillaries close to the bases of the secretory cells. Some of the capillaries have fenestrated endothelium. Nerve fibers are also conducted in this reticular connective tissue.

**Islets of Langerhans.** If enough lobules are inspected with the low-power objective, pale areas, considerably larger than cross or oblique sections of acini, will be seen (Fig. 25-1). These areas are *islets of Langerhans* and contain cords and irregular clumps of cells and

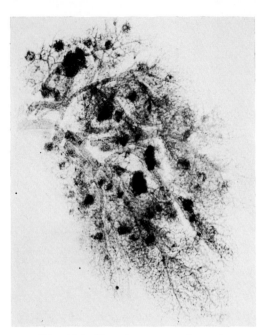

Fig. 25-4. Very low-power photomicrograph of a piece of a guinea pig's pancreas perfused with Janus green. The blood vessels subsequently were injected with carmine gelatin. The islets appear as dark patches, and the reticulated appearance of the background is due to the injected blood vessels. (Preparation of S. H. Bensley)

from a single section of any given pancreas has little more authority than a guess. A rough idea may be gained by the sampling method; that is, studying unselected sections cut from a dozen or so different parts of the organ. The total number of islets and the total extent of islet tissue can be determined by cutting a whole pancreas into serial sections of known thickness and measuring the area of islets seen in each and every section. This, of course, is an enormous task. Bensley, many years ago, described a much simpler method of determining the number of islets present in a pancreas. He perfused the blood vessels of the fresh organ with dilute solutions of either neutral red or Janus green. Both these supravital dyes stain the pancreas diffusely, but they stain the cells of the islets more or less specifically. Furthermore, as reduction occurs on standing, the dyes fade from the acinar tissue so that the islets stand out as either red or blue areas, depending on the dye used (Fig. 25-4). Pancreas so prepared is cut into little pieces that can be mounted on slides, and a group of observers can soon count the number of islets in all the pieces and so determine the number of islets in the pancreas. Haist and Pugh devised a more elaborate technic based on the same staining principles; this permits them to estimate not only the number of islets in a pancreas but also the total volume of islet tissue.

The different types of cells in islets and their appearance in different physiologic states will be described in the chapter on endocrine glands.

**Ducts.** Before describing the appearance of ducts seen in a section of pancreas under low-power magnification, a few words about their general arrangement are in order. The main duct of the pancreas, the duct of Wirsung, is enveloped by connective tissue and serves more or less as a "backbone" for the organ through which it runs. From this, side branches emerge regularly at angles, so that the duct system, stripped clean of other tissues, resembles a herring bone. The side branches of the main duct run between lobules and hence are interlobular ducts. These branch to give rise to intralobular ducts which enter the substance of lobules. Intralobular ducts are not nearly so prominent in the pancreas as they are in salivary glands.

capillaries. Red blood cells are present in the capillaries commonly enough for the capillaries to appear, even with the low-power objective, as pink or red streaks. However, with only the low-power objective, a beginner may confuse an islet with a duct or a little patch of connective tissue. With the high-power objective, the usual islet is a third to a half or more of the field in width and its characteristic structure of cords and clumps of cells separated by capillaries can be seen clearly. Islets are *not* encapsulated and so are separated from acinar tissue by only a film of reticular tissue. Internal support in islets is provided by reticular fibers that are associated with capillaries. But there is not much connective tissue in islets; otherwise, the secretion of the cells would have difficulty gaining entrance to capillaries.

Since the pancreas is a large organ and since the percentage and the size of the islets is not constant in all its parts, any estimate of the relative amount of islet tissue made

A relative absence of clean-cut intralobular ducts is then an important criterion by which the student can quickly distinguish a section of pancreas from that of parotid gland. The presence of islets of Langerhans in the lobules is, of course, another, but, in some preparations, considerable study is needed before islets can be identified with certainty.

The larger of the relatively few intralobular ducts can be seen, under low power, to be ensheathed by dense connective tissue derived from the septa from which they emerge (Fig. 25-1). The intralobular ducts give rise to very small ducts lined with flattened epithelium. These small ducts lead to the acini and are called *intercalated* (*intercalare* = to insert) *ducts* because they are inserted between the secretory units and the intralobular ducts proper. As noted before, the intercalated ducts often extend into the central part of acini to be known as centro-acinar cells (Figs. 25-2 and 25-3).

The lumen of the main duct may be as much as $2\frac{1}{2}$ mm. wide. It is lined by columnar epithelium. Goblet cells may be interspersed between the ordinary columnar cells. Near the duodenum, small mucous glands may be associated with the main duct. The interlobular ducts are lined by low columnar epithelium. In the intralobular ducts, the epithelium is low columnar to cuboidal, and in the intercalated ducts, flattened cuboidal.

### CONTROL OF EXOCRINE SECRETION

Since the pancreatic juice contains so many important enzymes needed to carry on the further digestion of food that has passed through the stomach, the need for some mechanism to regulate pancreatic secretion in accordance with deliveries of food into the duodenum from the stomach is obvious. Such a mechanism exists in the form of a hormone called *secretin.* It is made by the mucosa of the duodenum when the acid contents of the stomach are delivered into it. This hormone circulates by the bloodstream to the capillaries that surround pancreatic acini and there acts in some fashion to stimulate the secretory activity of the acinar cells. When enough alkaline pancreatic juice has been delivered into the duodenum to neutralize the acid chyme contained therein, the formation of secretin by the duodenal mucosa stops, and this in turn results in a cessation of pancreatic secretion. But when further acid chyme reaches the duodenal mucosa, more pancreatic secretion is delivered into the duodenum. By this mechanism a sufficient quantity of pancreatic juice to ensure further digestion is delivered automatically into the duodenum each time a fresh supply of chyme is received from the stomach.

Stimulation with secretin, particularly if it is prolonged, leads to some diminution in the number of granules in the acinar cells, but its effects are chiefly manifested by its stimulating the secretion of the nonenzymatic ingredients of pancreatic juice. Another hormone, *pancreozymin,* made by the duodenal mucosa, recently has been shown to be much more effective than secretin in stimulating the secretion of enzyme-rich pancreatic juice. Stimulation of the vagus nerve also causes the same effect. On the other hand, in starvation, when no appreciable amount of acid chyme is delivered into the duodenum and hence little secretin is made, the acinar cells accumulate granules.

### THE LIVER

**Some Gross Features.** The liver is the largest organ in the body, weighing, in the adult, about 3 pounds. It is an epithelial gland that performs both exocrine and endocrine functions. Its exocrine secretion is bile.

The liver is reddish brown. Most of it lies on the right side with its upper convex surface fitting the undersurface of the dome-shaped diaphragm (Fig. 24-1). It consists of two main lobes, the right much larger than the left (Fig. 24-1). The inferior surface is exposed in Figure 24-1, and shows the impressions of the several organs with which it normally comes into contact (parts of the alimentary tract and the right kidney which are separated from it in Fig. 24-1), so its inferior surface is often called its visceral surface. The visceral surface exhibits a short deep transverse fissure called the *porta* (door) of the liver (not shown in Fig. 24-1).

The liver is covered with a connective tissue capsule (of Glisson). At the porta, the trunk of a tree of connective tissue, which is continuous with the capsule, grows up, as it were, into the substance of the liver. In the substance of the liver the tree branches so extensively that no part of the liver substance is ever farther than a millimeter or two from one or, more generally, several of its branches.

The branching connective tissue tree provides internal support for the liver. It also performs another function, that of providing a means whereby branches of the portal vein (which brings food-laden blood to the liver from the intestine), the hepatic artery and the bile duct, as well as the lymphatic vessels, can reach all parts of the liver. At the porta the portal vein and the hepatic artery both *enter* the trunk of the connective tissue tree, and thereafter each of the vessels branches with every branching of the tree. Likewise, the lymphatic vessels and the bile ducts have branches in every branch of the tree. The main lymphatic vessels and the two main bile ducts, one from the right lobe and one from the left, *leave* the liver at the porta. The two main bile ducts soon join to form a single duct (Fig. 24-1). This is joined by the cystic duct from the gallbladder, and the common bile duct carries bile to the duodenum (Fig. 24-1).

Since the portal vein, the hepatic artery, the lymphatics and the bile ducts all branch along with the branching of the connective tissue tree, each branch of the tree that is seen in sections of human liver (and the branches are very numerous) reveals the presence of at least 4 vessels: a branch of the portal vein, a branch of the hepatic artery, a bile duct and one or more lymphatics (Fig. 25-10, *right*). Venous blood is brought to the liver by the portal vein, and arterial blood by the hepatic artery. Blood is drained away from the liver by hepatic veins. These do not travel in the branches of the connective tissue tree; their tributaries (called sublobular veins) and they themselves pursue lonely courses through the substances of the liver (where they are associated with only a little connective tissue) and empty into the vena cava as it comes into close contact with the back of the liver.

**Development.** The liver originates from the entodermal epithelium of the developing duodenum; the epithelium here first bulges outwardly to form what is termed the *hepatic diverticulum*. One branch of this forms the cystic duct and the gallbladder. The epithelial cells of another part grow in the form of pro-

jections into the splanchnic mesoderm and split it up. Branches from the veins which will become the portal vein grow into the area where the epithelium is splitting up the mesoderm, and the spaces between the developing epithelial projections become richly vascularized. The whole mass grows rapidly. The mesoderm provides a capsule for the organ and also the tree of connective tissue that forms in the interior of the organ.

In the development of exocrine glands the terminal outgrowths become secretory units, and the epithelial cells that connect these with the site from which the gland originates form the ducts (Fig. 9-1). As is shown in the two pictures in Figure 25-5, there is a difference in the way the cells of the outgrowth differentiate in forming the liver. The cell closer to the site of origin of the outgrowth begin to differentiate to form tubules; the lumens of some of these are cut in cross section and can be seen in the left picture in Figure 25-5. Farther away from the origin of the outgrowth the cells become arranged into thick irregular clumps and plates (Fig. 25-5, *right*). At this time there is no difference in the appearance of the cells that form the tubules or the plates. Later their appearance changes and the cells that in the left picture are forming tubules become the epithelial cells of bile ducts (ductular cells), whereas those shown in the right picture become the cells of the exocrine secretory units of the liver; these cells are called hepatic cells or *hepatocytes*. The thick plates in which the future hepatocytes are at first arranged become split up into plates that are only 1 cell thick with blood vessels between them; the latter become the sinusoids of the liver. The hepatocytes are responsible for both the exocrine and the endocrine secretions of the liver.

## SOME FUNCTIONS OF THE LIVER DEPENDENT ON ITS STRUCTURE AND POSITION

Since the liver has been shown to have over 100 functions, all that we can do here is to describe a few main functions performed by the organ; perhaps enough to give some clue as to why its structure and position are both adapted to carrying out the types of function it performs. The hepatocytes are very versa-

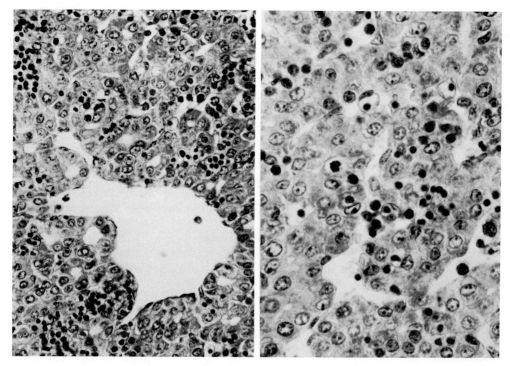

FIG. 25-5. Photomicrograph of sections of developing liver in human embryo of 8 weeks. The section at the left, which was taken closer to the source of the outgrowth, shows cells becoming arranged into tubules; these are future bile ducts. At the right, farther away from the source of the outgrowth, the cells are forming thick plates; these will later become split up to form liver plates only 1 cell thick. (Preparation from Dr. J. Steiner)

tile. They perform not only exocrine and endocrine secretory functions but many other functions as well. Their ability to carry out their many functions is dependent on their histologic arrangements, as will be described here briefly and in more detail later.

To perform both exocrine and endocrine functions, one side of each hepatocyte of the liver of an adult must abut on a blood passageway into which it can deliver its endocrine secretion, and another side must abut on a lumen into which it delivers its exocrine secretion. This arrangement (which in due course will be described in detail) is achieved by the hepatic cells being arranged in the form of anastomosing thin plates. Between the *plates* there are *blood sinusoids*. Within the plates, but *between adjacent rows of hepatic cells in the plates,* there are tiny passageways into which the exocrine secretion drains. These tiny passageways are called *bile canaliculi*. The canaliculi that drain different rows

of adjacent cells anastomose and eventually deliver the exocrine secretion into a duct system, as will be described later. We shall first comment briefly on the exocrine secretion of the liver.

The exocrine secretion of the liver is bile. About 500 to 1,000 ml. is formed and emptied into the intestine each day. Bile contains bile pigment (bilirubin), bile salts, protein, cholesterol and such crystalloids (dissolved in water) as are present in tissue fluid. Bilirubin pigment is primarily a waste product. It is formed not in hepatic cells but from the breakdown of the hemoglobin of erythrocytes in the reticuloendothelial cells that make up and are closely associated with the sinusoids of the spleen and the bone marrow. The non-iron-containing breakdown product of hemoglobin (bilirubin) passes into the blood and is absorbed from the blood by hepatocytes as blood flows through the liver. The hepatocytes change it slightly (by conjugation so as to make it water-soluble) and then secrete it as one component of bile. Bile salts, in contrast to bile pigments, are useful substances which in the intestine facilitate greatly the digestion of fats. Like cholesterol, a third component of bile, bile salts are produced in the hepatocytes.

Another component of bile is to be explained by the fact that many of the steroid hormones that are produced by the adrenal cortex and the sex glands are constantly absorbed from the blood that flows by the hepatocytes. In the hepatocytes the hormones are metabolized to different extents and the products so formed, or even active unchanged steroid hormones, are partly secreted into the bile. From the bile in the intestine some hormone may be reabsorbed again into the bloodstream. Hence, there is said to be an enterohepatic circulation of steroid hormones.

There is also an enterohepatic circulation of bile pigment, for when bilirubin reaches the intestine it is changed into urobilinogen and stercobilinogen by the action of bacteria that live in the intestine. Part of the urobilinogen is subsequently reabsorbed into the capillaries of the intestine. These, of course, drain into the portal system, and as the blood containing the reabsorbed urobilinogen passes along the sinusoids of the liver, the urobilinogen is taken up by hepatocytes and changed into bilirubin again, after which it is again secreted into the bile.

Although bile is secreted by the liver at a fairly regular rate it is delivered into the intestine irregularly, generally when it will do the most good; this requires it to be temporarily stored and concentrated in the gallbladder between meals as will be described later in connection with the gallbladder.

Having described the exocrine function of the liver, we shall now deal with some of its other functions before we consider its endocrine function. In considering these it is important to take into account the unique blood supply of the hepatocytes of the liver. As has already been noted, at least one side of every hepatocyte must abut on a blood passageway. The blood passageways between plates of liver cells are termed sinusoids and the cells that line the sinusoids, as we shall see, do not fit together perfectly, so that plasma with its large molecules can easily get through sinu-

soid walls to come into direct contact with hepatic cells. The blood that flows along the liver sinusoids comes from two sources. First, about 66 to 75 per cent of it is derived from the portal vein which, of course, drains the blood from the intestine and, as a consequence, this blood carries the food that has been absorbed from the intestine. The other 25 to 33 per cent of the blood that flows along sinusoids is derived from the hepatic artery and this is fresh (arterial) blood. Since the blood in the portal vein is under low pressure and that in the hepatic artery under much higher pressure, the delivery of both into the same sinusoids creates a problem in hemodynamics as will be described later.

The hepatocytes, since they come into close contact with food-laden blood, are *advantageously situated to perform the following functions*:

1. **Storage.** The hepatocytes can take sugar from the blood and store it as glycogen. They can take amino acids from the blood and build these into protein and so in a sense they can store protein. They can also store fat and some of the vitamins, for example, A and $B_{12}$.

2. **Performing Transformations and Conjugations.** Since the percentages of nutritive substances in the diet are not necessarily those that are the most desirable for the cells of the body, the hepatic cells within certain limits transform various substances into one another so that what the hepatic cells deliver into the blood is more suited for body cells to metabolize than the substances that were originally absorbed from the intestine. For example, if a person lived on a diet that was unbalanced, say because it was largely protein and contained almost no carbohydrate, the hepatocytes change some of the protein into carbohydrate so that the level of the blood sugar is maintained properly. Another type of transformation performed by hepatocytes concerns fat that is absorbed into the blood from the intestine and which is in the form of very small droplets called chylomicrons; the chylomicrons are taken up by hepatocytes and broken down into the components of fat, some of which are then combined with choline and phosphorus to form the extremely valuable phospholipids which are essential components of the membranes of cells.

Another function of hepatic cells that involves transformation and/or conjugation is that of detoxifying certain undesirable products that are absorbed from the intestine or formed in the body and which might otherwise exert a deleterious effect. For example, ammonia is formed in connection with the metabolism of amino acids, and ammonia is toxic in certain concentrations. The hepatocytes prevent such concentrations from being attained by using ammonia in the formation either of useful substances or urea; the latter substance is nontoxic (unless concentrations are excessive) and is eliminated from the body by the kidney.

3. **Syntheses.** The hepatic cells account for the formation of much of the blood protein. The hepatic cells produce the albumins, fibrinogen, and most of the globulins of the blood as well as other proteins concerned in blood coagulation. However, hepatocytes do not make the gamma globulins, which, as has been explained, are produced by plasma cells.

4. **Regulating the Concentration of Certain Substances in Blood.** Since man does not eat continuously but generally has 3 meals a day, the absorption from the intestine of sugar, fat and amino acids varies greatly at different times over a 24-hour period. The hepatic cells can take up sugar, fat, amino acids and certain other substances necessary for proper nutrition from the blood and deliver these back into the bloodstream as they are required. By performing this function the hepatic cells exert a delicate control over the level of the sugar in the blood. When much sugar is absorbed they keep the sugar level of the blood from rising by taking sugar from the blood and converting it to glycogen. Then, as sugar is utilized in the body between meals, so that its level in the blood would otherwise fall, the hepatic cells convert glycogen to glucose and deliver the latter back into the bloodstream. By this means the blood sugar level (in the presence of the hormones insulin and epinephrine which we shall discuss in a later chapter) is kept almost constant.

Although hepatic cells control the level of many substances in blood it is primarily because they deliver sugar (a useful substance) into the blood that the liver was originally designated as an endocrine gland (an endocrine gland was originally defined not as a gland that secretes hormones but as a gland that secretes a useful substance into the blood).

Having briefly described some of the functions of hepatic cells we shall now describe how they are arranged in relation to bile canaliculi and blood sinusoids; this requires that we first deal with what are called liver lobules.

## THE LOBULES OF THE LIVER

**Definition.** The term lobule means little lobe, so we must inquire into the meaning of lobe. This term seems to have been first used in anatomy to describe any projecting rounded part of a structure, for example, the lobe of the ear (its rounded lowermost part). When the term lobe came to be used in connection with glandular organs it was employed to designate any part that projected from the main mass of an organ or was separated from other parts of the organ by fissures, septa or indentations. The term lobule was used to designate smaller divisions that were detected within lobes which could be seen to be separated from each other by smaller fissures, septa or indentations. Hence, the first concept of a lobule was that a lobule is a portion of a lobe that is separated off from other portions by some kind of *obvious* boundary.

With the advent of the microscope, lobules of *exocrine* glandular tissue were generally seen to be parts that were not only separated from one another by partitions of connective tissue but also to be areas of glandular tissue in which the secretory units drained into a common duct or set of ducts. So a second definition for lobules came into being—that lobules are small divisions of an organ that are constituted of groups of closely adjacent secretory units that drain into a common duct or set of ducts. This second definition proved to be useful, for, as we shall see, it enables lobules to be identified in the kidney even though they are not separated from one another by fissures, septa or indentations. However, the advent of a second way of defining lobules caused some complications in connection with the liver because the areas of tissue in the liver that are separated from one another by partitions (and partitioned lobules are seen only in some species) are not constituted of exocrine secretory units that drain into the same duct, and the groups of secretory units that each drain into a common duct

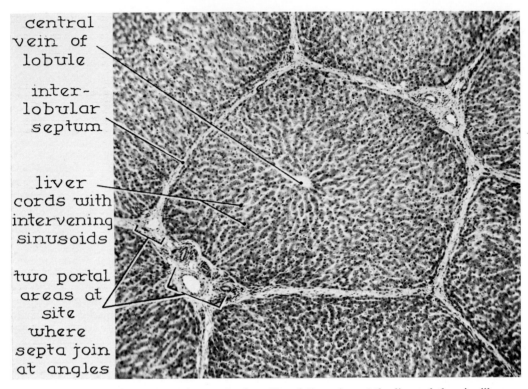

central
vein of
lobule

inter-
lobular
septum

liver
cords with
intervening
sinusoids

two portal
areas at
site
where
septa join
at angles

FIG. 25-6. Low-power photomicrograph of an H and E section of the liver of the pig, illustrating the classic hexagonal lobule.

(and which have been called *portal lobules* by those who believe lobules should be defined by this latter method) are not the same areas that are surrounded by partitions in those species in which partitions are present in the liver. As might be expected, there has been, through the years, some conflict about which definition (classic or portal) should be used for visualizing liver lobules, but most commonly the first definition of the term lobule is used and, as a result, anyone who now refers to liver lobules or hepatic lobules without further qualification is referring to little bodies of liver substance that in some species are surrounded (and so separated from similar bodies of liver substance) by partitions of connective tissue. This lobule is sometimes termed the *classic liver lobule* and hereafter when we use the term liver lobule we are referring to the classic lobule.

**The Liver Lobule of the Pig.** The pig is one of the animals in which liver lobules are demarcated by partitions of connective tissue, and so it is customary to begin the histologic study of liver lobules by examining sections of pig liver.

With the low-power objective, an area such as that illustrated in Figure 25-6 can soon be found. This figure shows a cross section of a hepatic lobule with parts of 6 other lobules ranged round its periphery. Each lobule is enclosed and separated from others by interlobular septa of connective tissue. The lobules in cross section generally reveal 5 or 6 sides. They are about 1 mm. in width and 2 mm. in length.

As was described under "Gross Features and Development," a branching tree of connective tissue extends into the substance of the liver from the porta, and carries the branches of the portal vein, the hepatic artery and the bile duct as well as lymphatic vessels to all parts of the liver. In the pig the terminal twigs of this tree give rise to broad thin leaves of connective tissue that ensheath each lobule; the leaves are the *interlobular septa* (Fig. 25-6). Since branches of the portal vein, the hepatic artery, the bile duct and the lymphatic

Bile in canaliculus flows on toward
   bile duct

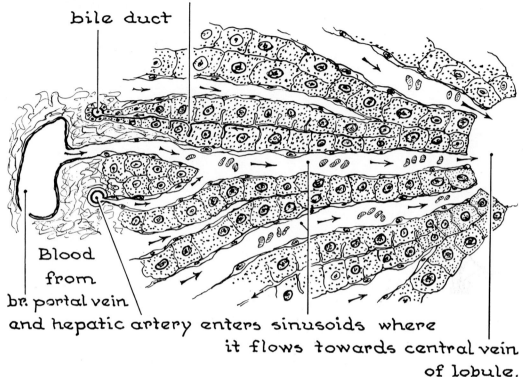

Blood
from
br. portal vein
and hepatic artery enters sinusoids where
         it flows towards central vein
                         of lobule.

Fig. 25-7. Drawing (at high-power magnification) to show how blood from the portal vein and the hepatic artery (*left*) flows into sinusoids, lined by reticuloendothelium, that lie between liver cords, and empties into the central vein (*right*). The way that bile travels in the opposite direction in canaliculi to empty into bile ducts in portal areas is also shown.

vessels are all carried in this branching tree of connective tissue, representatives of these 4 tubes are brought to the periphery of each lobule at several different points. Usually 4 tubes—vein, artery, duct and lymphatic—run close together in the connective tissue. Groups of 4 tubes are commonly seen in the septa at, or close to, the sites at which the septa join one another at angles. Such sites seen in cross section each reveal 4 different tubes, and each group of 4 tubes, together with the connective tissue that immediately surrounds the group, constitutes what is termed a *portal radicle* (*radicula* = a small root) *tract, canal* or *area*. Portal radicles (tracts) are generally found at the angles around lobules. Before describing how lobules are identified in the liver of man (where there are no interlobular septa) we shall briefly discuss liver cords and liver sinusoids.

**The Arrangement of Hepatic Cells in Lobules.** The substance of a liver lobule *seems* to consist of branching cords of hepatic parenchymal cells (dark in Fig. 25-6) that radiate from the center of the lobule to its periphery. Between these so-called *liver cords* are light spaces (Fig. 25-6); these are the *sinusoids* of the liver. The sinusoids receive blood from the branches of the portal vein and the hepatic artery that are in the periphery of the lobule in a way that will be described later, and they carry this blood from the periphery to the center of the lobule where they drain into the central vein of the lobule (see Fig. 25-7). The central vein runs longitudinally along the central (hepatic) axis of the lobule and drains into sublobular veins which are the tributaries of the hepatic veins which carry blood away from the liver.

Having established that blood flows along

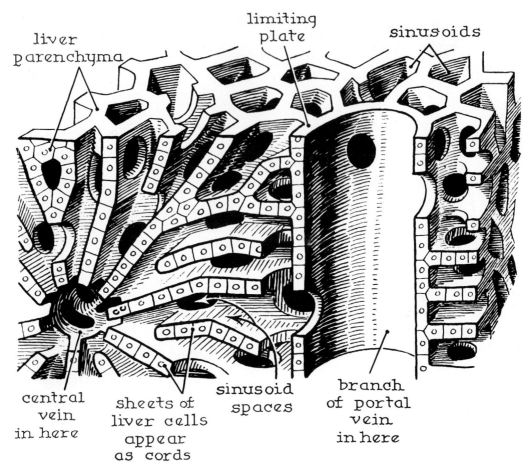

liver
parenchyma

limiting
plate

sinusoids

central
vein
in here

sheets of
liver cells
appear
as cords

sinusoid
spaces

branch
of portal
vein
in here

FIG. 25-8. Stereogram of a quadrant of a hepatic lobule. (Modified, to the extent that labeling was added, from Elias, H.: Am. J. Anat. *85*:379)

sinusoids between liver cords from the periphery of the lobule to its center, we can next investigate where bile is secreted and the direction in which it flows in the lobule. A consideration of this question requires that we briefly analyze the structure of liver cords.

It has been observed already in this book that many things studied in histology were originally named by the 2-dimensional appearance that they presented in sections when they were first seen. Their original names, many of which we continue to use, proved to be unsuitable or even misleading when these structures eventually came to be visualized in 3 dimensions. The term "liver cords" is an example. This name was given to what appeared in a 2-dimensional section to be single rows of hepatic cells that radiated from the central vein to the periphery of the lobule.

Between the "cords" there are blood sinusoids (Fig. 25-6).

Perhaps the first point to make here is that hepatic cells are exocrine secretory cells, and so, if they were arranged in single cords with the cord bounded on all sides by sinusoids, there would be no lumen into which they could discharge their exocrine secretion. Hence, a liver cord must always be at least 2 cells wide in some direction so that a cleftlike lumen (a bile canaliculus) can exist between the apposed cell membranes of the cells in the 2 rows that make up the cord, as is shown diagrammatically in Figure 25-7. This diagram shows how a double row of hepatic cells could be a secretory unit with a tiny cleftlike lumen between the cells of the 2 rows. If, however, what is shown here as a double row of cells were sectioned in another plane, this double row of cells could appear as a single row of cells (see right side of Figure 25-7 for example of single rows). So our first conclusion is that liver "cords" must be *at least* 2 cells wide or thick if they are to be exocrine secretory units. Actually, as Elias showed from making reconstructions of liver lobules, what appear as liver "cords" (single rows of cells) in any section are commonly much more than 2 cells wide because hepatocytes are arranged in the form of anastomosing plates that are many cells wide but commonly *only 1 cell thick*. Accordingly, since in the usual section these plates are cut at right angles to their broad surfaces, the plates in sections appear as single rows of hepatic cells (cords) bounded on each side by sinusoids. (A glance at the top of the 3-dimensional figure shown in Fig. 25-8 will show why this is true.)

The plates of hepatic cells are not evenly flat; more commonly they are curved. Furthermore, plates anastomose with each other and, finally, they have many holes through them (Fig. 25-8). All the spaces between the substance of plates are blood sinusoids, and it is into these spaces that the hepatic cells deliver their endocrine secretion. Their exocrine secretion *is contained within the plates*, because between adjacent rows of cells in the plates there are tiny cleftlike spaces (bile canaliculi) (Fig. 25-9, arrows) that run between rows of cells within the substance of the plates to eventually reach ductules in the portal areas into which they deliver their secretion. In other words, the sinusoids are spaces *between plates* and bile canaliculi are spaces *between the cells* of adjacent rows of hepatic cells *within* the plates.

The bile canaliculi between various rows of cells in plates anastomose freely with one another (Fig. 25-20) and the bile in this branching anastomosing system of canaliculi drains in the general direction of the periphery of the lobule where it empties into little canals that drain into the bile ductules and ducts that are in the portal tracts. Bile therefore drains from the central parts of lobules toward the periphery of lobules. Blood, on the other hand, is emptied into liver sinusoids from branches of both the portal vein and the hepatic artery at the periphery of lobules, and it drains from there to the central vein of the lobule. Hence, in a general way, bile and blood run in oppo-

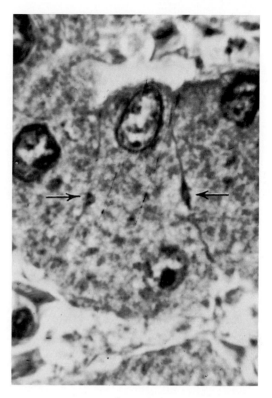

FIG. 25-9. Oil-immersion photomicrograph taken with the phase microscope of an H and E section of a liver plate, showing 2 bile canaliculi indicated by arrows.

site directions within lobules. This is illustrated in the very simple 2-dimensional diagram shown in Figure 25-7.

**The Lobule of the Liver of Man.** It has been explained already that a branching tree of connective tissue extends into the substance of the liver from the porta, and that each branch of the tree carries 4 tubes. In the pig the smaller branches of the connective tissue tree give rise to broad thin leaves of connective tissue which join adjacent end branches together, and the areas so enclosed are called *lobules* (Fig. 25-6). In man the branches of the tree do not sprout thin leaves of connective tissue to enclose lobules; hence, the branches (called portal tracts or portal radicles) are isolated from one another in the substance of the liver. Since the tube-containing branches are generally cut in cross or oblique section, they commonly appear in sections as tiny islands of connective tissue, each containing 4 tubes. As already noted, each of these

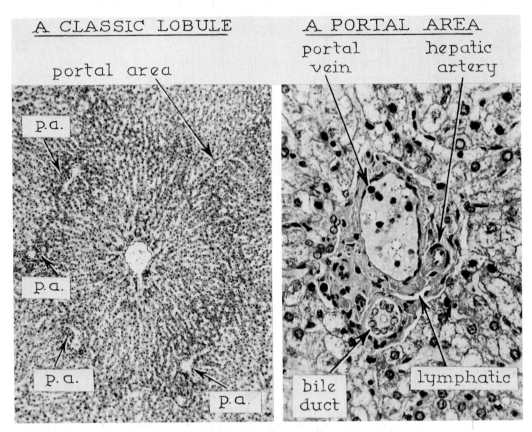

FIG. 25-10. (*Left*) Low-power photomicrograph of an H and E section of human liver, showing a classic lobule. (*Right*) High-power photomicrograph of a portal area, showing connective tissue and a branch of the portal vein, the hepatic artery and a bile duct and a lymphatic.

islands is generally called a *portal radicle* or *tract* (Fig. 25-10, *right*).

The classic lobule of the liver of man is the counterpart of the lobule that is outlined by connective tissue in the liver of the pig. Hence, to visualize the classic lobule of the liver of man, the observer first finds a central vein (Fig. 25-10, *left*). This is the center of a lobule. The periphery of the lobule is established by finding the 5 or 6 portal areas that generally lie nearest the central vein. These portal areas are then connected together with an imaginary continuous line so that the central vein lies in the center of a pentagon or a hexagon (or roughly polyhedral) figure. If a continuous line were drawn through the 5 portal areas indicated in Figure 25-10, *left*, where each is labeled p.a., it would outline a pentagonal lobule which would have a central vein in its center. As will be discussed later,

it is very difficult to find a perfect example.

**Portal Radicles (Tracts) Are of Different Sizes.** Since the trunk of a tree is larger than any of its branches, and since main branches are larger than the next order of branches, and so on, the size of portal areas varies in relation to whether they represent sections cut through major, intermediate or small branches of the connective tissue tree. When sections pass through the tree at sites where branching is occurring, the portal areas that appear may show double the number of tubes. Because branching occurs, the larger portal areas may show both large and small portal veins and both arteries and arterioles. The larger vessels seen under these circumstances are carrying blood to distant portions of the liver, and the smaller ones are branches from them that are designed to supply the surrounding parenchyma. The branches of the portal vein are the largest tubes seen in portal areas, and they exhibit the typical microscopic structure of veins except that, unlike veins in most parts of the body, they are not commonly collapsed because they are contained in fairly solid connective tissue (Fig. 25-10, *right*). The arteries and the arterioles have a typical structure. The bile duct can be recognized easily by its *cuboidal* or *columnar epithelial* lining; it is a typical duct (Fig. 25-10, *right*). The lymphatics appear as spaces lined with endothelium; they are often slitlike, as is shown in Figure 25-10, *right;* sometimes they are collapsed and cannot be seen with the light microscope.

### THE BLOOD SUPPLY OF HEPATIC CELLS IN DIFFERENT PARTS OF THE LOBULE

Nutritional deficiencies, toxins or an impaired circulation of blood may affect the liver, and the parts of lobules that are affected most is often dependent on the blood supply of that part of the lobule. In order to interpret many pathologic conditions of the liver properly, and to understand how they develop, it is necessary to appreciate that the blood supply of different parts of a lobule differs, and that as a result of difference in blood supply, indications of damage may appear in certain parts of lobules before it appears in others.

Speaking generally, blood from the branches of both the portal vein and the hepatic artery empty into blood sinusoids in the more peripheral parts of lobules. The blood then flows along the sinusoids to the central vein of the lobule. Since the hepatic cells along the way utilize oxygen and absorb food substances, the blood that reaches the hepatic cells that are close to the central vein of a lobule has less oxygen and food than blood that enters the periphery of lobules. Speaking generally, it can be said that the hepatic cells in the area surrounding central veins have the poorest blood supply of any part of the lobule. Conversely, it might be assumed that the hepatic cells closest to the periphery of lobules would all have the same and the best blood supply of any parts of lobules. However, as will be described next, the matter is not this simple, because the theoretical 6 points that are visualized as being distributed around a lobule (in any slice of liver tissue that is examined as a single section) are not necessarily present

or providing similar amounts of blood of the same quality to the cells that are seen in that section at various sites around the periphery of the lobule. In order to understand why the quality of the blood supplied to various peripheral parts of lobules is not the same, it is necessary to consider the existence of a smaller unit of structure than a liver lobule; a unit whose central core contains the terminal twigs that branch from the blood vessels of portal radicles. This smaller unit is termed the liver acinus (of Rappaport) and it will now be described in more detail.

### THE LIVER ACINUS

**Introduction.** As has already been noted, the cross-sectional appearance of an ideal lobule of the liver of man is commonly depicted as being hexagonal. An ideal lobule is a little longer than it is wide and has a central vein in its core, which therefore runs parallel with its long axis. Six portal radicles are commonly pictured as running longitudinally along the sides of the lobule, 1 at each of the 6 angles around its periphery.

The ideal, described above, is seldom realized for several reasons. Liver lobules are not stacked on their sides in an orderly honeycomb fashion but are more haphazardly stacked, pointing as it were, this way and that. Hence, any portal radicle, while it may be parallel with a lobule that is on one of its sides, may be disposed at an angle to the 2 lobules on its other side, and hence it would be "missing" from cross sections of those lobules. Any student who examines a few sections of liver soon realizes how difficult it is to find a cross section of a hexagonal lobule that has a central vein in its center and 6 portal tracts cut in cross section at the 6 points around its periphery; indeed, such a picture is very unusual because portal tracts that do not run longitudinally in relation to the lobule where the cross section is being studied may be "missing." The matter is complicated further by the fact that the vessels in portal radicles give off branches at various angles; such branches would not run parallel to the long axis of the stem vessels or to the lobules between which they run, and hence would not be cut transversely in cross sections of lobules. In view of the foregoing, it can be understood

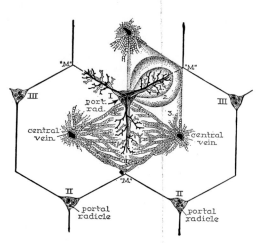

FIG. 25-11. Diagram illustrating the concept of liver substance being composed of units of structure called acini. So that the relation of acini to classic lobules can be visualized, lobules are outlined in the diagram. For details see text.

that attempts to interpret single sections of livers that have been subjected to damage from circulatory disturbances or other causes are hazardous because, although it can be assumed that the parenchyma around each central vein that is seen probably has the poorest blood supply of any part of the lobule, it is very difficult to know about the nearness of an arterial blood supply to the various parts of the visualized periphery of the lobule that is seen, because arterial vessels, running roughly in the plane of the section, but at right or other angles to the long axis of the lobule, may have been present immediately below or above any site around the periphery of a lobule that is seen in a single section.

The problems thus presented stimulated research for some smaller functional unit of liver tissue, the backbone of which would be the terminal vessels that empty into sinusoids. Rappaport has described such a unit; he terms it the *liver acinus*. Rappaport suggests that the observer is much more likely to find only 2, 3 or 4, instead of 6, well-defined triangular portal areas around the periphery of any hexagon (the reason for not finding the ideal arrangement of 6 portal radicles has been explained above). A lobule showing only 3 is illustrated in Figure 25-11; this figure also

indicates where portal radicles are "missing." Rappaport believes that distributing terminal branches extend out from these 3 main sets of vessels more or less at right angles to them (as is shown just above the center of Fig. 25-11), toward angular points around the hexagon where well-defined portal areas are "missing" (labeled M in Fig. 25-11). Since these smaller terminal vessels grow out in a tridimensional way, and roughly at right angles from the main vessels, they are not cut transversely in cross sections of lobules. However, they are sometimes cut obliquely because they pursue irregular courses. On their arched and irregular course toward the points of the lobule where triangular portal tracts are "missing" (Fig. 25-11, M), they may be cut repeatedly or not at all by the same plane of section and thus account for the appearance either of too many or of "missing," portal tracts around one central vein. In their course toward "missing" portal tracts or corners of an imaginary hexagon, the terminal portal and arterial branches, in association with the terminal bile ductules, form the backbones of small and irregularly shaped masses of hepatic parenchyma which constitute acini.

Two acini are shown in Figure 25-11. Just above the center of this illustration there is a typical portal tract. From it, small blood vessels descend vertically toward an M (a site where a portal tract is missing) to form the backbone of an acinus. The extent of this acinus (in 2 dimensions) is indicated in the illustration because the area occupied by the acinus is filled in with liver cords that extend out from its backbone toward both the left and the right, and on each side the liver cords converge on central veins. The acinus therefore includes liver parenchyma that is situated in parts of two different lobules (see Fig. 25-11).

The parenchymal cells closest to the vascular backbone of the acinus would have the best blood supply of any of its parts. This part, which Rappaport terms Zone 1 of an acinus, is shown by shading and is labeled 1 in the acinus that is shown just above and to the right of the center of the Figure 25-11. The liver parenchyma that surrounds Zone 1 has the next best blood supply; this is labeled Zone 2. The irregularly shaped outer part of an acinus that reaches to the central veins is termed Zone 3, and it has the poorest blood supply of any part of an acinus.

Since the vascular backbones of acini run more or less at right angles to the vessels in portal tracts the parenchyma at some sites in the periphery of a lobule seen in a single section may be part of Zone 1, 2 or 3 of an acinus whose vascular backbone runs parallel to the section but which might be considerably below or above the plane of the section. For this reason, what appears as a peripheral part of a lobule in any given section may not have a good blood supply because it may be relatively far off from the vascular backbone of an acinus.

**Connections Between Hepatic Artery, Portal Vein and Sinusoids.** The site and the manner of terminations of the hepatic arteries of the portal areas in the sinusoids in the liver of man are somewhat controversial. Knisely, Bloch and Warner have made an elaborate study of the circulation in the lobule of the frog liver in the living animal. In the living frog they found evidence of contractile arteriovenous anastomoses between the hepatic artery and the portal vein in the portal radicles (these, when open, would permit arterial blood to enter sinusoids through the portal vein inlets). They believe that almost every sinusoid is supplied by a separate end branch from both the portal veins and the hepatic artery, and that each sinusoid has a sphincter that controls the flow of portal blood into it at the periphery of the lobule, and another sphincter that controls the flow out of it into the central vein. They have shown that, because of all these various contractile structures, there can be great variations in the total flow of blood through the different lobules of the same liver, and also that the kind of blood that flows through lobules can vary greatly with regard to the proportions of arterial and venous blood it contains. However, it is very doubtful if the mammalian liver, and in particular, the liver of man, resembles that of the frog in these respects.

The circulation of blood through the liver is necessarily complex because its sinusoids receive blood from the portal vein under low pressure and blood from the hepatic artery under higher pressure. One very important factor to keep in mind is that the sinusoidal spaces in the liver constitute a vast sponge-

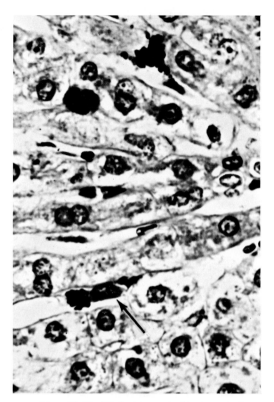

Fig. 25-12. High-power photomicrograph of a section of the liver of a rabbit that was previously injected intravenously with India ink. The arrow points to the nucleus of a reticuloendothelial cell that has phagocytosed India ink, which may be seen in its cytoplasm both to the left and the right of its nucleus. Two large masses of India ink in the cytoplasm of the R.E. cells may be seen in the upper part of the picture.

work that serves as a huge mixing receptacle for the two kinds of blood that enter it under two different pressures. Hence any reduction of the extent of the spongework brought about by disease of the liver reduces the capacity of the liver to soften the pressure exerted by the arterial blood that enters it, and hence a reduction in the size of the mixing receptacle can be a factor in raising the pressure in the portal circulation and thus causing portal hypertension.

### THE LINING OF THE SINUSOIDS AND ITS RELATION TO HEPATIC CELLS

The sinusoids of the liver, like those of the spleen and the bone marrow, are lined by

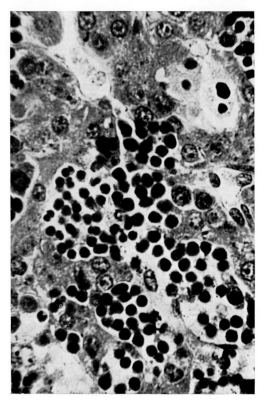

Fig. 25-13. High-power photomicrograph of a section of fetal pig liver, showing hemopoiesis in the sinusoids. The cells with the dark nuclei are mostly proerythroblasts and erythroblasts.

reticuloendothelium, which tissue has already been described in Chapters 15 and 16. The position of reticuloendothelial lining cells of liver sinusoids is illustrated diagrammatically in Figure 25-7, but the cells are not all alike; some are thin with somewhat flattened nuclei that have condensed chromatin, while others have larger, paler ovoid nuclei and more extensive cytoplasm of an irregular outline; these are called Kupffer cells or the stellate cells of Von Kupffer. If an animal is injected intravenously with a vital dye such as trypan blue, or finely particulate matter such as India ink, the Kupffer cells prove to be avidly phagocytic and soon accumulate dye or India ink in their cytoplasm (Fig. 25-12).

The Kupffer cells of the sinusoids are sometimes, for two reasons, described as constituting an ever-changing population. First, their tentaclelike processes shift position, thus open-

ing and closing tiny gaps in the reticulo-endothelial membrane. Secondly, they may become detached and washed away to the lung with new cells that develop from the smaller cells taking their places. The smaller flatter cells are often referred to as ordinary endothelial cells. However, the cells of ordinary vascular endothelium in most parts of the body do not, in our opinion, have the potentiality to develop into larger phagocytic cells. We think that it is better to think of the smaller cells as relatively undifferentiated members of the reticuloendothelial family. Some reasons for this view will now be considered briefly.

During part of prenatal life, the liver functions as a hemopoietic organ (Fig. 25-13), and occasionally, in postnatal life, it resumes this function. It is therefore assumed that in prenatal life there are cells of great mesenchymal potentiality distributed along sinusoids which can differentiate into free stem cells that are concerned in hemopoiesis. It is possible that the thinner cells with the darker nuclei that are interspersed between the more avidly phagocytic cells in postnatal life are the postnatal representatives of the mesenchymal cells of great potentiality which were present in this site in prenatal life. It should be pointed out, however, that postnatal hemopoiesis in sinusoids does not prove that these cells retain their original potentiality, for if hemopoiesis begins again in the liver in postnatal life it could be explained by circulating stem cells from bone marrow (colony formers–myeloblasts) settling out in this location.

In certain pathologic conditions associated with the excessive destruction of erythrocytes the Kupffer cells may assist reticuloendothelial cells of the spleen and the bone marrow in removing erythrocytes from the blood. However, under normal conditions they do not seem to perform this function.

**Fine Structure.** In the EM the sinusoidal lining cells show no special features (Fig. 25-14). Their nuclei are similar to those of other kinds of mesenchymal-derived cells. Their nucleoli are inconspicuous. Although their cytoplasm contains some free ribosomes the relatively little endoplasmic reticulum they contain is of the smooth-surfaced variety. Their mitochondria are smaller and fewer in number than those of hepatocytes. Golgi com-

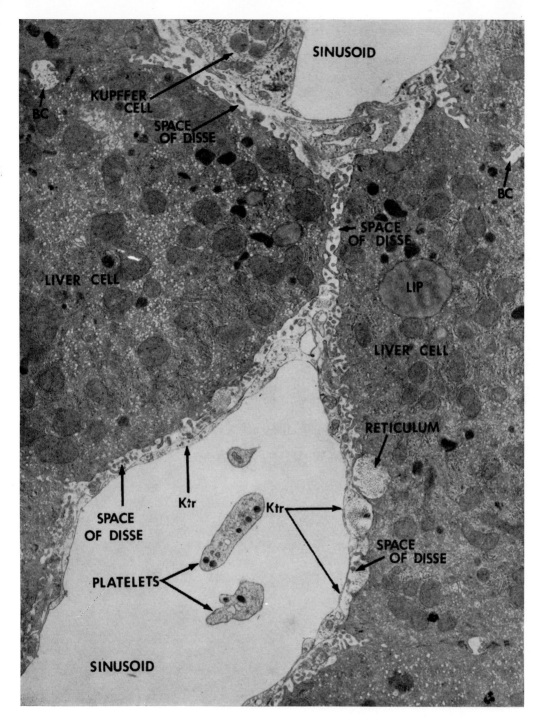

FIG. 25-14. Electron micrograph (× 8,800) of 2 liver cells and 2 communicating sinusoids. The sinusoids are surrounded by extremely thin trabeculae of Kupffer cell cytoplasm (Ktr) which separate the lumen of the sinusoid from the space of Disse into which microvilli (not labeled but obvious on careful scrutiny) of liver cells project. The space contains a few bundles of reticular fibers which occupy surface recesses of the liver cells (labeled RETICULUM). Note that the bile canaliculi (BC) are some distance away from the space of Disse and that there are no obvious communications between them. (Preparation by Dr. J. W. Steiner)

ponents are inconspicuous. From their fine structure it would therefore seem that their energy requirements are not great and that they have little or no function in connection with the synthesis or the packaging of secretory products.

**The Space of Disse.** When only light microscopy was available there was a good deal of discussion as to whether or not the reticuloendothelium of the liver sinusoids fitted firmly against hepatic cells (as for example is shown in the diagram, Fig. 25-7), or whether the reticuloendothelium of the sinusoids was separated slightly from liver plates by a space termed the *space of Disse*. Whether this space could be seen with the light microscope seemed to depend on the time after death when tissue was obtained and on the fixative used and other variable factors. However, the advent of the EM and its use in histology has shown clearly that such a space does exist. The EM has shown, moreover, that numerous microvilli extend from the borders of the hepatic cells that underlie the reticuloendothelium of sinusoids; these microvilli extend toward the sinusoid lining like pillars on which the reticuloendothelium can rest (Fig. 25-14).

Much evidence indicates that the reticuloendothelial lining of the sinusoids does not constitute a perfect membrane. Such interdigitations as exist between the processes of the reticuloendothelial cells seem to be sufficiently imperfect to allow for numerous small holes or slits in the reticuloendothelial membrane. The holes are usually small enough to keep blood cells but not blood plasma from entering the space of Disse. Furthermore, in most mammals there is no basement membrane beneath the reticuloendothelium to hinder plasma coming into direct contact with hepatocytes (the calf is an exception). The microvilli that project from the hepatocytes into the space of Disse provide an enormous surface over which hepatocytes are in contact with plasma (Fig. 25-14).

**Lymphatics.** The liver produces a great deal of lymph. There has been controversy about where it is formed. Lymphatics as yet have not been demonstrated with certainty in or around liver plates or sinusoids, but only in the connective tissue stroma of the liver, that is in: (1) the connective tissue of the capsule, (2) the tree of connective tissue that carries the branches of the portal vein, the hepatic artery and the bile duct to the sides of each lobule, and (3) to the sparse connective tissue associated with the hepatic veins. It might be thought that little lymph would form in this connective tissue, which is by no means abundantly supplied with capillaries. However, there is one concept to the effect that plasma could back up, as it were, in the spaces of Disse at sites where sinusoids begin—which is close to the connective tissue associated with portal tracts—and that the plasma would be under enough pressure in spaces of Disse in this area to form tissue fluid that would percolate into and through the delicate connective tissue at the edge of the tract to reach nearby lymphatic capillaries that begin in, or pass through, this delicate connective tissue. There is, however, another possible source of lymph in the liver. As was described in connection with veins in Chapter 22, it is possible for lymphatic capillaries to exist and function in the walls of veins where they can approach the intima closely. In the spread of cancer, cords of malignant cells (which characteristically grow along lymphatics) can sometimes be seen growing from the outside of veins in the liver into their walls to reach almost to their endothelial linings. There is, then, some reason for questioning if a substantial part of the large quantity of lymph that arises in the liver may not originate in the walls of branches of the portal vein. As yet the origin of lymph in the liver has not been definitely established.

## THE CYTOLOGY AND FINE STRUCTURE OF THE LIVER

### THE NUCLEI OF HEPATIC CELLS

Since nuclei were described in detail in Chapter 6, and since the nucleus of the hepatic cell was usually chosen in that chapter to illustrate points about nuclei in general, it would involve repetition to deal here in detail with the nuclei of hepatic cells. However, to provide continuity, and for the convenience of the reader who wishes to review this matter at this time, a brief summary with references to illustrations in Chapter 6 will be given here.

Hepatic cell nuclei are ovoid to round (Fig. 6-35). Binucleated cells are not uncommon. Under some conditions hepatic cells have more than 2 nuclei (Fig. 6-20). Polyploid nuclei are numerous (Fig. 6-19). Normally, mitotic figures are rare but they may be numerous if part of the liver is removed or injured. (Fig. 6-3).

**Chromatin.** The arrangement of chromatin in the interphase nucleus depends greatly on the fixative that is used. With glutaraldehyde fixation, and postfixation with osmium tetroxide, chromatin is distributed fairly densely in 3 main sites (1) peripherally, in association with the nuclear membrane (Fig. 6-35), (2) in islands that are scattered about in the nucleus (Fig. 6-35), and (3) around the nucleolus as the nucleolus-associated chromatin (Fig. 6-35). The dense arrangements of chromatin probably represent tightly coiled sections of chromosomes; this is positively heteropyknotic chromatin, and this, as was explained in Chapter 6, is probably heterochromatin. The less dense areas in the nucleus, in this type of preparation, probably contain the extended (euchromatic) portions of chromosomes. The fine structure of chromatin is described in Chapter 6 under the "Fine Structure of Chromosomes" and also under "Nuclear Sap."

**Nucleoli.** The fine structure of the nucleolus of a hepatic cell is illustrated in Figure 6-32; this shows the nucleolonema to be spongelike in character and to consist of fibrillar and granular components. The interstices of the nucleolonema are filled with pars amorpha which is probably nuclear sap containing extended and hence euchromatic portions of chromosomes. The nucleolus is more or less surrounded by the nucleolus-associated chromatin.

**Nuclear Membrane.** The nuclear membrane actually consists of 2 membranes separated by a space of about 200 to 300 Å. The outer membrane is commonly studded on its outer surface with ribosomes and connects with, and is part of, the rough-surfaced endoplasmic reticulum of the cytoplasm.

**Nuclear Pores and Pore Complexes.** Nuclear pores are holes in the nuclear membrane (Fig. 6-34). Pores are separated from one another by 0.1 to 0.2 microns and have a diameter of from 300 to 1,000 Å. They are circular in outline. A *pore complex* consists of a channel that passes through a pore (Fig. 6-34). On the nuclear side the channel is bounded by a condensation of chromatin and on the cyto-

plasmic side by a condensation of cytoplasm. Some pores may be covered with very thin diaphragms.

**Nuclear Sap.** The nuclear sap contains two types of granules, perichromatinic and interchromatinic; these are illustrated in Figure 6-36. Both kinds are probably ribosomal in nature. The extended portions of chromosomes that are assumed to be present in nuclear sap of interphase nuclei do not appear to advantage in the EM.

## THE CYTOPLASM OF HEPATIC CELLS

**Cell Membranes and Bile Canaliculi.** The cell membrane of each hepatic cell is modified in 3 sites. First, the membrane covering the part of a cell that abuts on the space of Disse projects into the space in the form of numerous microvilli (Fig. 25-14). Next, the line of contact between the cell membranes of adjacent hepatocytes in many mammals (but not in man) pursues an irregular course. Occasional projections and outfoldings of various shapes extend from one cell into corresponding depressions and infoldings on the surface of the adjacent cell; this makes the course of the two cell membranes that are in apposition very irregular in many species but, as noted above, not in man (Fig. 25-15). Thirdly, the cell membranes of adjacent cells at either side of the lumen of a bile canaliculus are tightly bound together by a junctional complex (Figs. 25-15 and 25-16). There is a fusion of the outer (adjacent) layers of the two cell membranes that are in contact just before the two cell membranes diverge to form the canaliculus; in other words, the junctional complex on each side of the canaliculus begins on the lumen side with a zonula occludens similar to those described in Chapter 8 and illustrated in Figures 8-13 and 8-14, and which is seen between the cells of columnar epithelium close to their free surfaces. Farther away from the lumen of the bile canaliculus the junctional complex on each side only occasionally shows a zonula adhaerens; therefore the next portion of the complex is generally a desmosome (Fig. 25-18).

The cell membranes that form the wall of a bile canaliculus project irregularly into the lumen of the canaliculus as short microvilli (see Figs. 25-15 and 25-17). Histochemical

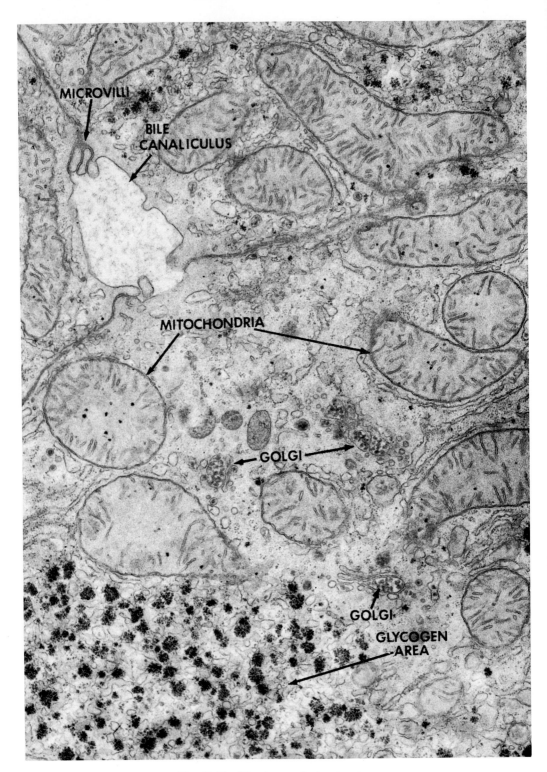

FIG 25-15. (*Caption on facing page*)

studies indicate that there is a substantial amount of ATPase at the border of the cytoplasm that abuts on the bile canaliculus. There is also some condensation of cell web material in this location.

**Endoplasmic Reticulum.** Hepatic cells contain aggregations of both rough-surfaced and smooth-surfaced endoplasmic reticulum.

Rough-surfaced endoplasmic reticulum characteristically appears in hepatic cells in the form of scattered groups of parallel and fairly closely packed flattened membranous vesicles (Fig. 25-17, ER). The position of these groups corresponds to the flakes of basophilic material that can be demonstrated in the cytoplasm of hepatic cells with special stains in the light microscope. As was described in Chapter 7, rough-surfaced vesicles are commonly found in cells where protein destined for secretion is being synthesized. It seems likely that the rough-surfaced vesicles in hepatic cells are therefore concerned with the synthesis of those proteins of the blood that are formed by hepatic cells. It is of course possible that they are concerned also with some of the other synthetic functions performed by the hepatic cells.

The smooth-surfaced endoplasmic reticulum of the liver commonly is in the form of tubules (Fig. 25-15, glycogen area); there is an association between these and sites of glycogen deposition (as is shown in Figure 25-15). Recently it has been shown in Leblond's laboratory that labeled glucose appears in hepatocytes over the smooth-surfaced tubules before glycogen make its appearance.

**The Golgi Apparatus.** Golgi components are most prominent in hepatic cells in the region between the nucleus and the bile canaliculus (Fig. 25-15, Golgi). However, some Golgi components may be scattered about in other parts of hepatic cells. It would seem therefore, from its position, that the Golgi apparatus is primarily concerned in the exocrine secretory function of hepatic cells but that it is also concerned to some extent with the secretion of some substance or substances into the bloodstream.

**Microbodies.** The cytoplasm of hepatic cells contains a number of bodies that are smaller, less numerous and denser than mitochondria (Fig. 25-18). Their granular content is very dense in their central regions where it may assume a crystalloid appearance. Like mitochondria, microbodies are each surrounded by a membrane. Indications of their function were first given by finding that a fraction could be separated from cell homogenates that contained many microbodies and yielded a considerable content of uricase, catalase and D-amino acid oxidase. The thought therefore arose that microbodies housed these 3 enzymes. More recently it has been shown that the crystalline structure that can be seen in the central parts of the microbodies of hepatocytes of certain mammals is identical with that of uricase. It is probable that this crystalline structure will be seen more readily in mammals other than man because uricase is concerned with metabolizing uric acid to a further stage which is eliminated from the body. In man this step does not occur, and that is why man has to excrete uric acid as such in urine and why those who do not do this efficiently may develop gout (which is associated with increased uric acid in the blood). At the time of writing it would seem questionable if the crystalline structure of uricase would therefore be found in the hepatocytes of man.

Fig. 25-15. Electron micrograph ($\times$ 30,000) of mouse liver cells. A bile canaliculus can be seen in the left upper corner. Its lumen contains a finely fibrillar material which is probably bile. Microvilli project into the lumen. Note that they vary considerably in size. This variability is often interpreted as being related to the functional state of the cells which constitute the lining. The cells show numerous mitochondria which are large and contain many cristae. Observe the rather prominent opaque granules in the matrix of the mitochondrion near the left center of the micrograph. Several Golgi zones are present, and their vesicles contain electron-opaque granules which are thought to be the excretion product of liver cells, possibly lipid in character. In the left lower corner is a group of glycogen granules which are arranged in rosettes of subunits. Between the glycogen particles are vesicles of the smooth-surfaced endoplasmic reticulum. (Preparation by Dr. A. M. Jézéquel)

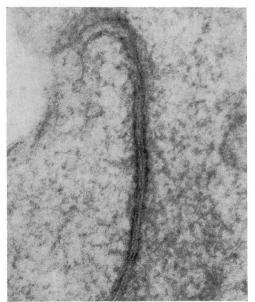

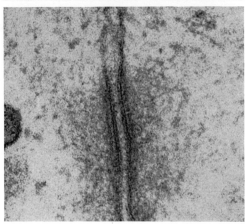

FIG. 25-16. (*Top*) Electron micrograph (× 160,000). A portion of a bile canaliculus is seen at the upper left. The outer layers of the cell membranes of the two hepatocytes that abut on the canaliculus have fused to form a dark line that is seen running along the middle of this part of the junctional complex; this part of the complex therefore represents a zonula occludens (described in detail in Chap. 8). (*Bottom*) Farther away from the bile canaliculus adjacent cell membranes are held together by desmosomes; in these, of course, the outer layers of the cell membranes are not fused with each other. (Biava, C. G.: Lab. Invest. *13*:840)

**Mitochondria** have been described in detail in Chapter 7. They are very numerous and well developed in hepatocytes (Figs. 25-15 and 25-17). Novikoff showed that the mitochondrial complement of hepatic cells differs in different parts of the liver lobule. Mitochondrial swelling may occur in hepatic cells under a variety of conditions. Giant mitochondria may develop by swelling alone or by the fusion of swollen mitochondria.

Mitochondria in living cells, as viewed with the phase microscope or darkfield illumination, appear to divide and even to re-form. With the EM appearances sometimes suggest that they divide by simple transverse fission. To study this, Lafontaine utilized the liver cells of animals that had been given a certain azo dye which, over a short time, increases tremendously the number of mitochondria in the liver cells. During this time, many mitochondria similar to the one indicated by the arrow in Figure 25-19 were seen. This illustration suggests that the mitochondria divide as the result of 2 membranes in a transverse cristae separating from one another with the outer membrane simultaneously dipping in to restore a double membrane over the 2 ends at the site of separation. It is also believed that new mitochondria can more or less bud off from pre-existing ones.

**Lysosomes.** As already noted in Chapter 7, dense membrane-surrounded bodies seen in the cytoplasm close to bile canaliculi (Figs. 25-17 and 25-18) were first described as pericanalicular dense bodies. These have now been shown to have the enzyme complement of lysosomes. Lysosomes can, of course, assume a variety of appearances (Fig. 25-21) depending on whether or not they are digesting materials taken into the cytoplasm from without or material that has arisen from the disintegration of some cellular component such as a mitochondrion (Fig. 7-24). As previously noted, lysosomes are characterized by a substantial content of hydrolytic enzymes. Since many waste products originate from the many metabolic processes carried on in hepatic cells, it seems very probable that lysosomes would play an important role in hepatic cells in variously coping with otherwise insoluble waste products by digesting them or otherwise eliminating them from the cytoplasm. Many may contain pigment as will be described when pigments in hepatocytes are considered below.

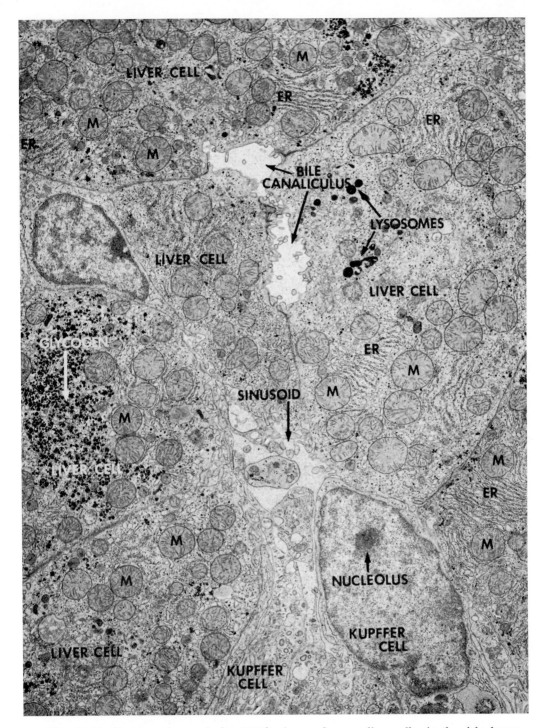

Fig. 25-17. Electron micrograph ($\times$ 5,000) of several mouse liver cells. At the right lower margin of the micrograph is a sinusoid, which contains a Kupffer cell. In this plane of section the lumen of the sinusoid can only be seen in a small area. The liver cells surround the bile canaliculus in the upper center of the micrograph. Note that the liver cells contain round mitochondria and abundant endoplasmic reticulum (ER), and that their glycogen stores vary in extent. The cells on the right of the micrograph contain virtually none. Lysosomes are prominent in the cell to the right of the bile canaliculus, but are almost totally absent from the other cells which form the canalicular wall. (Preparation by Dr. Kenjiro Arakawa)

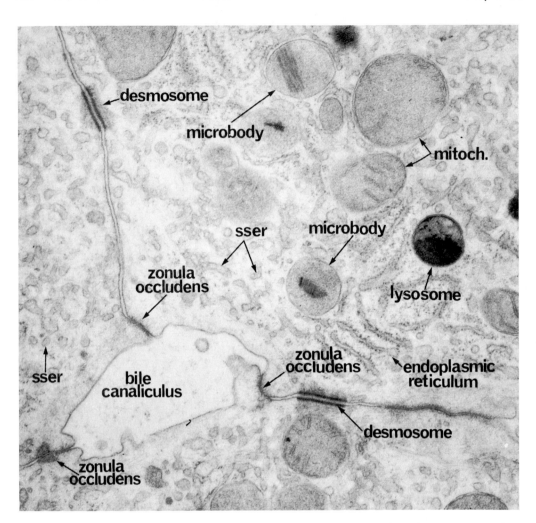

FIG. 25-18. Electron micrograph ($\times$ 17,550) of 3 liver cells of groundhog (*Marmota monax*) surrounding a bile canaliculus. The junctional complexes are seen as specializations of the cell membranes. The component of the junctional complex closest to the lumen is the zonula occludens, and some distance away from this is a desmosome. In the cytoplasm of the adjacent cells is some granular endoplasmic reticulum (ER), a lysosome and 2 microbodies which show the crystalline structure of their "nucleoid." On the left margin of the micrograph is an aggregate of agranular (smooth-surfaced) endoplasmic reticulum (sser). Compare the agranular reticulum with the ribosome-studded reticulum in the cell at the right margin of the micrograph. (Preparation by J. Steiner)

**Inclusions.** Hepatic cells contain many inclusions. Stored foods are prominent. Unless special staining methods are used, glycogen is seen in the EM as a pale amorphous material (Fig. 7-26). With suitable positive-staining procedures glycogen appears in the EM in the form of fine electron-dense particles (Figs. 25-15 and 25-17). With negative staining it is found to be in the form of small particles that commonly aggregate to form rosettes. (The light microscopic appearance of unstained and stained glycogen is illustrated in Figure 7-25.) Lipid inclusions may be of two sorts. Free fat appears in the form of droplets and after osmium tetroxide fixation these are black in electron micrographs (Fig. 25-14,

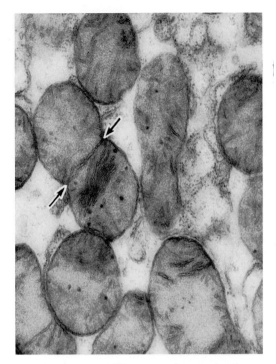

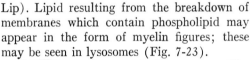

FIG. 25-19. Electron micrograph (× 30,000) of a section of a liver cell of a rat that was fed an azo dye that causes a great increase in the number of mitochondria in liver cells. The arrows indicate where a mitochondrion may be dividing. (Preparation by Dr. J.-G. Lafontaine)

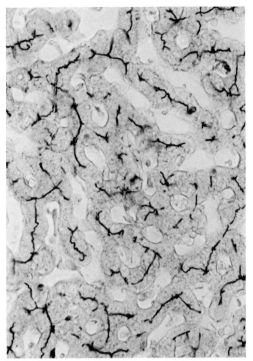

FIG. 25-20. Photomicrograph of section of liver. The anastomosing bile canaliculi are demonstrated here by the technic for alkaline phosphatase described in Chap. 4. (Preparation by Drs. M. J. Phillips and J. W. Steiner)

Lip). Lipid resulting from the breakdown of membranes which contain phospholipid may appear in the form of myelin figures; these may be seen in lysosomes (Fig. 7-23).

Pigment may be seen in hepatocytes. The common one is known as a lipofuchsin (lipochrome). This pigment is commonly considered to be a wear-and-tear pigment and its amount in cells generally increases with age. It is found in other cells besides hepatocytes, in particular in ganglion cells (Fig. 7-28) and in cardiac muscle cells; in the latter it commonly appears in the cytoplasm at each end of nuclei. With the light microscope, and in unstained preparations, it is yellow to brown in color. It becomes a deeper color after H and E staining because it takes up some eosin. The fact that one constituent of lipofuchsin is lipoid was first shown by the fact that the pigment is soluble in lipoid solvents. The EM confirmed this because the contents of what are termed

lipofuchsin bodies in material that has been fixed in osmium tetroxide are electron dense, which is due to the osmium tetroxide combining with a fatty material (Fig. 25-18). The lipofuchsin bodies seen in the EM are lysosomes that contain lipofuchsin; the EM has shown that lipofuchsin granules are always within lysosomes. There are, of course, lysosomes that do not contain lipofuchsin granules.

Normally bilirubin and hemosiderin, the two pigments that result from the breakdown of hemoglobin, are not present in sufficient concentrations to be seen in hepatocytes. They do, however, appear in hepatocytes in certain pathologic conditions.

**Bile Canaliculi and Their Connections With Bile Ducts.** Bile canaliculi can be demonstrated in the light microscope by different methods. Sometimes they can be seen in H and E sections, as in Figure 25-9; however, their demonstration without special treatment probably

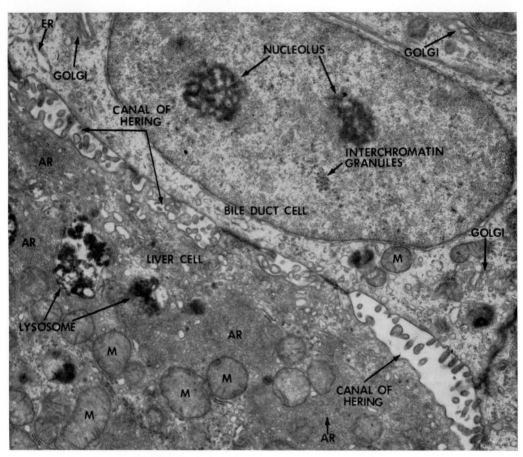

Fig. 25-21. Electron micrograph (× 13,300) of longitudinal cut of a canal of Hering in rat liver. These passages are difficult to find in normal liver. This picture is from an animal which received large doses of a chemical (alpha-naphthyl-isothiocyanate) which makes it easy to find them. In the left lower corner of the micrograph is a liver cell, and in the right upper corner is a bile duct cell. The channel between them, into which microvilli of both types of cells project, is the canal of Hering. Note that the mitochondria of the duct cell are somewhat smaller than those of the liver cell and that the structure of the duct cell is much simpler. The smooth-surfaced reticulum (AR) and the lysosomes of the liver cell are markedly increased in volume as a result of the effect of the chemical. (Preparation by Dr. J. W. Steiner)

depends on their being somewhat distended. Gomori showed that histochemical methods for alkaline phosphatase revealed them; alkaline phosphatase is known to be present in bile (Fig. 25-20). Bile canaliculi can be injected with opaque materials through the bile ducts and studied in cleared thick and thin sections.

Although it was once believed that bile canaliculi were structures with cuticular walls of their own, the EM has shown clearly that the bile canaliculi are merely spaces between the membranes of contiguous hepatic cells. As has already been noted there is, particularly in some species (but not much in man) a little condensation of cell web material around the cell membranes that border the canaliculi. This, together with firm union that occurs between the cell membranes in the junctional complexes on each side of the canaliculi (Fig. 25-16), permits canaliculi to withstand considerable pressures without rupturing and also

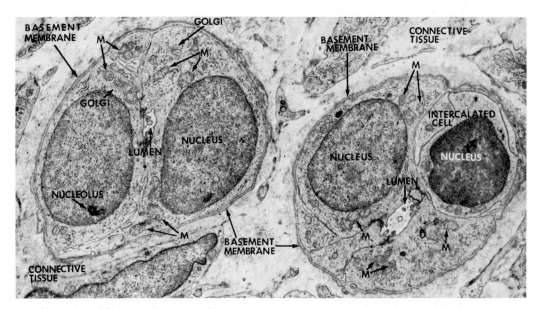

Fig. 25-22. Electron micrograph (× 8,320) of 2 bile preductules lying in the connective tissue of a portal tract. Each preductule is surrounded by a basement membrane. The lumen of the channel on the left side of the micrograph is lined by 2 biliary epithelial cells and the one on the right by 3. The channel on the right shows a cell which in this plane of section is not in contact with the lumen. Such cells are designated as intercalated cells. Note the rather simple structure of the cells with small, inconspicuous mitochondria, sparse Golgi vesicles and virtually no endoplasmic reticulum. This is thought to indicate that these cells are not metabolically very active. (Preparation by Dr. J. W. Steiner)

to remain more or less intact after the homogenization of liver cells or partial digestions of liver substance.

Bile canaliculi begin from blind endings in the hepatic plates in the central vein areas of lobules. As they pass along liver plates toward the periphery of lobules they anastomose freely (Fig. 25-20). The bile that flows along them drains finally into the bile ductules which are the smallest branches of the bile ducts that are surrounded by connective tissue in portal radicles (tracts). The connections between the bile canaliculi of the plates and the bile ducts in the portal radicles has been studied vigorously over the years and a certain amount of confusion about terminology has resulted. The use of the EM has clarified many of the points that were previously unsettled. The following description is based primarily on EM studies that have been made recently by Steiner and his associates.

First, the bile canaliculi in liver plates in man are bounded usually by 2 hepatocytes,

and in some instances by 3 hepatocytes (Figs. 25-9 and 25-17). At sites where plates approach and abut on portal tracts, the canaliculi of the plates empty into what are called the canals of *Hering*. The canals of Hering along their short courses (Fig. 25-21), are bordered in part by hepatocytes and in part by a different kind of cell which is not a secretory hepatocyte but a *duct type* of cell. The important point here is that there are no types of cells in the walls of the canals of Hering that represent transitions between hepatocytes and duct cells. There is, however, a mixture of clear-cut hepatocytes and clear-cut duct cells along the course of the canals (Fig. 25-21). The canals of Hering are very short and connect with the bile ductules (the finest branches of the bile duct system); these are present in the connective tissue of portal radicles. However, the canals of Hering are not the only channels by which bile from canaliculi reaches the bile ductules in the portal radicles, because leading off at angles from the canals of Hering there are little by-passes which are termed preductules, and these too drain into the bile ductules that are in the portal tracts. Preductules differ from canals of Hering because they have no hepatocytes along their course; their walls are made entirely of cells of the duct type (Fig. 25-22). The walls of the preductules are seen in cross sections to consist of no more than 2 or 3 cells of the duct type (Fig. 25-22). The bile ductules (small bile ducts) in the portal tracts, into which both the canals of Hering and the preductules drain, seen in cross section, always have more than 3 cells around their walls (Fig. 25-23). The bile ductules are merely the smallest branches of the branching tree of bile ducts that is contained in the connective tissue tree which sends its branches to the periphery of all liver lobules.

Cells of the duct type along the canals of Hering and in the walls of the preductules differ from hepatocytes in several ways. They are smaller and have much less cytoplasm in relation to their nuclei than hepatic cells (Figs. 25-21 and 25-22). Their cytoplasm contains only a few flattened rough-surfaced vesicles but does contain a moderate number of ribosomes. The Golgi apparatus is not particularly well developed and is commonly disposed between the nuclei of the cells and their apices that abut on the lumen. They contain no glycogen, and their mitochondria are smaller than those of hepatocytes. Basement membrane is present at the bases of cells of the duct type but not in association with hepatocytes. Junctional complexes are present to hold the cell membranes of contiguous cells firmly together at the sites of canaliculi. Elsewhere

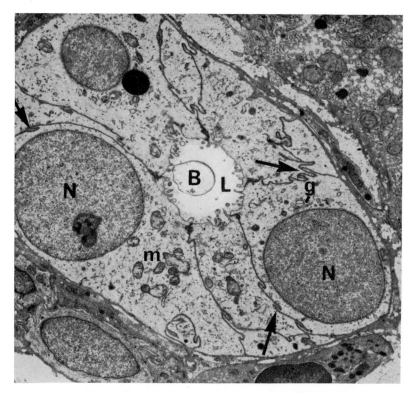

Fig. 25-23. Electron micrograph of section of portal tract in human liver showing a bile ductule. Notice the interlocking of folds along the cell membranes of the biliary epithelial cells; sites of these are indicated by arrows. Mitochondria are few. A bleb of cytoplasm (B) which is probably an expanded microvillus lies in the lumen. (Preparation by Dr. H. Sasaki and Dr. F. Schuffner; in Steiner, J. W., Phillips, M. J., and Miyai, K.: The pathology of the liver, Int. Rev. Exp. Path. 3:65)

the membranes of contiguous cells interdigitate to help hold the sides of contiguous cells together. Microvilli project into the lumens of bile ductules similarly to the way they project into canaliculi. All these points are shown by Figures 25-21 and 25-22.

### THE BILE DUCTS OF PORTAL TRACTS

In examining any section of liver, the student will observe that the bile ducts seen in different portal radicles are of different sizes. Generally, small bile ducts will be seen to be associated with relatively small arteries and veins and large ones with relatively large vessels. Furthermore, when the tubes are small, the amount of connective tissue surrounding them is considerably less than that which surrounds groups of larger tubes. The size of any bile duct, and portal tract in which it is contained, depends on the order of branch that is cut in the section.

The bile ductules, the smallest branches of the bile duct system, have walls of low cuboidal epithelium (Fig. 25-23). The slightly larger ducts seen in portal areas have walls of cuboidal epithelium (Fig. 25-10). Still larger bile ducts have columnar epithelium, so in general the height of the epithelium varies in relation to the size of the duct. The two main hepatic ducts which leave the liver at the site of the porta (the transverse fissure) unite to form the *hepatic duct*. The extrahepatic ducts require more support than the intrahepatic ones that are embedded in the connective tissue of the portal tracts. This is provided by dense connective tissue and smooth muscle arranged so as to surround the epithelial-lined lumen of the tube.

When bile ducts are large enough to be lined by columnar epithelium, fat droplets within the cytoplasm of their lining cells are not uncommon. In the larger intrahepatic bile ducts, and in the extrahepatic ones, tubulo-alveolar glands are present in a much-folded mucous membrane.

**The Problem About Possible Connections Between Bile Canaliculi and the Space of Disse.** The fact that certain substances injected into the bloodstream appear very quickly in bile has suggested the possibility that there might be some easier route for substances in the plasma in the space of Disse to reach bile canaliculi than by its having to pass

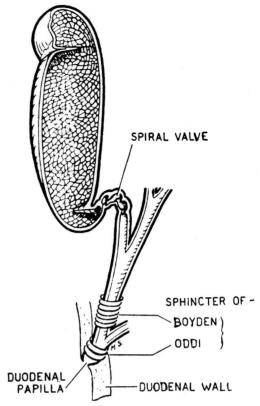

FIG. 25-24. Diagram of the gallbladder (showing its corrugated inner surface), the cystic duct, the bile duct and the sphincters of Boyden and Oddi. (Grant, J. C. B.: A Method of Anatomy, ed. 4, Baltimore, Williams & Wilkins)

through the substance of hepatocytes. Suggestions have been made regarding the possible passage of fluid between the cell membranes of adjacent hepatocytes. However, the demonstration of a zonula occludens in the junctional complex on each side of bile canaliculi would seem to make it less probable that there is any route of communication between adjacent cell membranes that connect canaliculi with the space of Disse.

### THE GALLBLADDER

A side branch (the cystic duct) extends from the hepatic duct to a somewhat elongated pear-shaped sac, the gallbladder (Fig. 25-24). The gallbladder is lined by a mucous membrane which is thrown into so many folds when

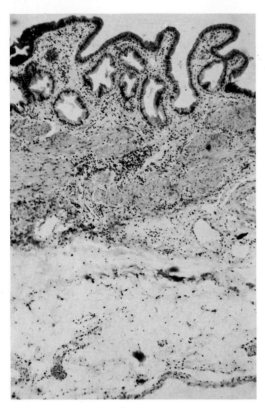

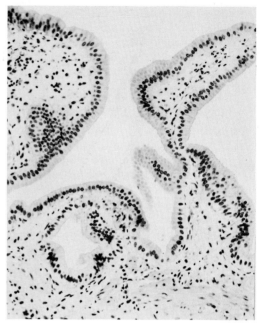

FIG. 25-26. High-power photomicrograph of H and E section of gallbladder showing the mucosal surface.

FIG. 25-25. Low-power photomicrograph of H and E section of human gallbladder.

the bladder is contracted (Fig. 25-24) that a student, on seeing a section of the wall of the organ, might think its mucosa was riddled with glands (Fig. 25-25). Actually, there are no glands in the mucosa of the gallbladder except near its neck, and if the organ is distended, most (but not all) of its mucosal folds that give the mucosa a glandular appearance disappear.

The epithelium of the mucous membrane of the gallbladder is high columnar (Fig. 25-26). Each cell in the membrane resembles the one beside it; in this respect it resembles the epithelium of the stomach. But the cells themselves are not like those lining the stomach. They resemble more closely the absorptive cells of the small intestine and, like them, are provided with microvilli. Secretory granules have been described in the more superficial parts of the cytoplasm of the cells, but the primary function of the lining cells is absorptive rather than secretory.

The epithelium rests on an areolar lamina propria (Fig. 25-25). There is no muscularis mucosae in the gallbladder; hence, the mucous membrane rests on a skimpy layer of smooth muscle comparable in position, but not in thickness, with the muscularis externa of the intestine (Fig. 25-25). Some of the smooth muscle fibers of which the muscularis externa is composed run circularly and longitudinally, but most run obliquely. Many elastic fibers are present in the connective tissue which fills the interstices between the smooth muscle bundles of this coat.

Outside the muscle coat is a well-developed perimuscular or subserosal coat (Fig. 25-25). This consists of areolar tissue, and it may contain groups of fat cells. It conveys arteries, veins, lymphatics and nerves to the organ. Along the side of the gallbladder that is attached to the liver, the connective tissue of its perimuscular coat (which here cannot be termed properly its subserosal coat) is continuous with the connective tissue of the liver.

The neck of the gallbladder is twisted in such a fashion that its mucosa is thrown into a spiral fold (Fig. 25-24). Somewhat similar crescentic folds of mucosa are present in the lining of the cystic duct. More muscle appears in the wall of the gallbladder at its neck, and in the wall of the cystic duct, than is present in the remainder of the gallbladder.

**The Bile Duct and the Sphincter of Oddi.** The duct that extends from the point of junction of the cystic and the hepatic ducts to the duodenum was, in the past, generally termed the *common bile duct*. In recent years there has been a tendency to omit the qualifying "common" from the term. This duct penetrates the outer coats of the duodenum close to the point of entry of the pancreatic duct. Part way through the duodenal wall the two ducts fuse, and the lumen of the fused duct is sufficiently expanded to be called an *ampulla* (*ampulla* = flask), the *ampulla of Vater*. The ampulla pursues an oblique course through the inner layers of the duodenal wall to open on the summit of a papilla that projects into the duodenal lumen, the *duodenal papilla*.

In the past, the muscle associated with the ampulla and the ends of the two ducts that enter the ampulla were said to constitute, collectively, the *sphincter of Oddi*. More recently, the development, the amount, the arrangement and the control of this muscle have been studied in detail by Boyden and his associates, whose papers (listed at the end of this chapter) should be consulted for full details. Briefly, these investigators have found that this muscle develops from mesenchyme independently and hence is not part of the muscle of the intestinal wall proper. That which develops around the preampullary part of the bile duct becomes strong and serves as a sphincter at the outlet of the bile duct; this may be called the *sphincter of Boyden* (Fig. 25-24). The muscle that develops around the ampulla itself and around the preampullary part of the pancreatic duct is not substantial enough to exert a very potent sphincteric action, except in a minority of individuals. The closure of the strong sphincter of Boyden, surrounding the preampullary part of the bile duct, prevents the secretion of the liver from entering the intestine and, as a result, bile formed during its closure is by-passed, by way of the cystic duct, to the gallbladder, where it is stored and concentrated. There are also smooth muscle fibers disposed parallel with the preampullary parts of the bile and the pancreatic ducts; their contraction shortens (and presumably broadens) the ducts so as to encourage flow through them.

**Functions of the Gallbladder.** The gallbladder stores and concentrates bile. Concentration is effected by the absorption of water and inorganic salts through the epithelium into the vessels of the lamina propria of its mucosa. This results in bile in the gallbladder coming to have an increased content of bile pigment, bile salts and cholesterol. Radiopaque substances of such a nature that they are excreted by the liver and so appear in the bile may be given to individuals. If the gallbladder is concentrating normally, these become sufficiently concentrated in the gallbladder to allow that organ to be outlined by x-rays. In this way, gallbladder function can be tested in the clinic. The reaction of bile becomes somewhat altered in the gallbladder; the absorption of the inorganic salts from it somehow results in its becoming less alkaline.

Both nervous and hormonal mechanisms are probably concerned in causing the gallbladder to empty. The feeding of fat is particularly effective in causing the gallbladder to empty. Boyden has shown that if the blood of a recently fed animal is injected into the veins of another animal, such blood will cause the gallbladder of its recipient to empty. It is probable that a hormone is made by the intestinal mucosa under the influence of digesting food, and that this travels to the gallbladder by the bloodstream to cause its contraction. Ivy and Oldberg have suggested "cholecystokinin" as a name for this hormone.

The muscle of the wall of the gallbladder is so thin that many investigators have doubted if its contraction could be an important factor in emptying it. However, considerable experimental work provides little ground for these doubts.

## A NOTE ON JAUNDICE

Jaundice means yellow. Under normal conditions the amount of bile pigment which is yellow that is present in blood is not enough to impart any color to the skin. But under certain conditions the amount in blood may become increased to the point where the skin, the mucous membranes and the eyeballs take on a yellow color. A person so afflicted is said to have jaundice.

Jaundice can occur from several causes. To explain these it should be reiterated that bile pigment is formed from the breakdown of hemoglobin in reticuloendothelial cells, after which it gains entrance to the bloodstream. On reaching the liver it passes between the lining cells of liver sinusoids and into hepatocytes. There it is made more soluble and is excreted into bile canaliculi and from there it passes into the duct system of the liver and is finally emptied into the intestine. Obviously, the amount in blood could become increased because of this orderly sequence of events being altered at any of three main points.

1. Normally the hepatocytes remove bilirubin from the blood at the rate at which it is produced by reticuloendothelial cells. But under conditions in which the rate of erythrocyte destruction becomes greatly increased, the uptake of bilirubin by hepatocytes may lag behind its rate of production by reticuloendothelial cells with the result that the concentration of bilirubin increases in the blood, sufficiently to cause jaundice. This type of jaundice is generally termed hemolytic jaundice because it is caused by the increased rate of hemolysis of red blood cells. (This is the mechanism responsible for the physiologic jaundice that occurs in the newborn, as all the nucleated red blood cells which still persist from prenatal life are quickly destroyed by reticuloendothelial cells.)

2. The ability of the liver to absorb bilirubin, handle it metabolically and secrete it into canaliculi may become impaired in various ways. First, in a rare condition there is a block at the cell membrane of the hepatocytes which become altered in such a way that bilirubin is prevented from entering them from the bloodstream as readily as it should. Next, hepatocytes may have hereditary enzyme defects which keep them from handling bilirubin properly, or hepatocytes may be injured from various causes so that there are not enough healthy cells to handle the bilirubin normally coming to them from blood. Finally, they may be injured in such a fashion that bilirubin

that they absorb is not properly secreted and leaks back into the sinusoids.

3. Finally, both the production of bilirubin and its uptake and secretion by hepatocytes may be normal but the bile secreted into the duct system is unable to flow to the intestine because of some obstruction to the duct system. The common obstruction is a stone in one of the main drainage ducts. Another cause of obstruction can be a malignant growth of cells in the head of pancreas which obstructs the duct entering the duodenum. Under these conditions bile regurgitates back through the hepatocytes into sinusoids.

**The Regenerative Capacity of the Liver and the Problem of Cirrhosis.** The liver is essentially a parenchymatous organ with over 60 per cent of its cells being hepatocytes. If a portion of the liver is excised from an experimental animal the hepatocytes soon undergo mitosis and restore the liver to its normal size and architecture in a few days time. The factors that operate to cause this rapid regeneration are not thoroughly understood. If, however, hepatocytes are injured because of nutritional deficiencies, toxic substances in the circulation or for other reasons, the problem of regeneration becomes much more complicated than it is when a portion of the liver is removed surgically; this is due primarily to the fact that all the structures essential for the regeneration of functional hepatic tissue may not be able to regenerate in a harmonious way so as to restore the normal complicated architecture of the organ. The situation with regard to the liver is more complicated than that which can occur in connection with the regeneration of bone at a fracture site. As has already been mentioned, if osteogenic cells fail to grow from one fragment to the other to effect an osteogenic type of union, fibroblasts from adjacent connective tissue may grow between the fragments at the fracture site and fill the gap with ordinary dense connective tissue and this in turn can prevent osteogenic cells from later growing across the gap to effect a bony union. Likewise, if the parenchyma of the liver is badly damaged with much cell death, the reticular and connective tissue framework which supports lobules collapses. Regeneration of hepatocytes may begin in isolated areas where some healthy cells have remained. The nodules of new liver parenchyma that develop from these sources are divorced from proper connections with the portal circulation and hence they lack a proper organization of sinusoids. Meanwhile, fibroblasts in the partially collapsed framework may variously proliferate and form much new connective tissue which interferes with new and normal connections being established by regenerating nodules of parenchyma with the system of bile ducts; the connective tissue also interferes with the development of proper connections being established between the sinusoids in regenerating parenchyma and the afferent venous and arterial vessels. Moreover, the increased amount of connective tissue prevents the liver from expanding as nodules of parenchyma become larger, and, furthermore, the connective tissue itself may shrink as it matures. For both these reasons the substance of the liver becomes compressed and hence blood flow through the affected liver is impeded.

As the student will learn, if he studies pathology, degeneration of hepatocytes can occur from many different causes and can begin in different sites within lobules. As a consequence the cirrhotic process can begin in different parts of the liver lobule.

## REFERENCES

### SPECIAL REFERENCES ON THE PANCREAS

Bensley, R. R.: Structure and relationships of the islets of Langerhans, Harvey Lect. 10:250, 1915.
———: Studies on the pancreas of the guinea pig. Am. J. Anat. 12:297, 1911.
Ekholm, R., and Edlund, Y.: Ultrastructure of the human exocrine pancreas, J. Ultrastr. Res. 2:453, 1959.
Farquhar, M. G., and Palade, G. F.: Junctional complexes in various epithelia, J. Cell Biol. 17:375, 1963.
Haist, R. E., and Pugh, E. J.: Volume measurement of the islets of Langerhans and the effects of age and fasting, Am. J. Physiol. 152:36, 1948.
Kuntz, A.: Effects of stimulation of the nerves of the pancreas on its exocrine secretory activity (abstr.), Anat. Rec. 100:55, 1948.
Munger, B. L.: A phase and electron microscopic study of cellular differentiation in pancreatic acinar cells of the mouse, Am. J. Anat. 103:1, 1958.
Opie, E. L.: Cytology of the pancreas in Cowdry's Special Cytology, ed. 2, p. 373, New York, Hoeber, 1932.

Palade, G. E., and Porter, K. R.: Studies on the endoplasmic reticulum. I. Its identification in cells in situ, J. Exp. Med. 100:641, 1954.
Saguchi, S.: Cytological Studies, No. 8, Kanazawa, Japan, Kanazawa Med. Coll., 1949.
Siekevitz, P., and Palade, G. E.: A cytochemical study on the pancreas of the guinea pig. II. Functional variations in the enzymatic activity of microsomes, J. Biophys. Biochem. Cytol. 4:309, 1958.
(See also references at end of Chap. 7 on the process of secretion in acinar cells; and references on islets at end of Chap. 28.)

### GENERAL REFERENCE ON THE LIVER

Rouiller, Ch. (ed.): The Liver; Morphology, Biochemistry, Physiology, 2 vols., New York, Acad. Press, 1963 and 1964.

### SPECIAL REFERENCES ON THE LIVER

Arey, I. B.: On the presence of the so-called portal lobules in the seal's liver, Anat. Rec. 51:315, 1932.
Biava, C. G.: Studies on cholestasis: A re-evaluation of the fine structure of normal human bile canaliculi, Lab. Invest. 13:840, 1964.
Bollman, J. L.: Studies of hepatic lymphatics in Tr. of 9th Conf. on Liver Injury, p. 91, New York, Macy, 1950.
Carruthers, J. S., and Steiner, J. W.: Fine structure of terminal branches of the biliary tree, Arch. Path. 74:117-126, 1962.
Deane, H. W.: The basophilic bodies in hepatic cells, Am. J. Anat. 78:227, 1946.
———: A cytochemical survey of phosphatases in mammalian liver, pancreas and salivary glands, Am. J. Anat. 80:321, 1947.
Dorfman, R. I.: The metabolism of androgens, Rec. Adv. Hormone Res. 2:179, 1948.
Elias, H.: Morphology of the stellate cells of Kupffer, Quart. J. Chicago M. Sch. 13:13, 1952.
———: A re-examination of the structure of the mammalian liver: I. Parenchymal architecture, Am. J. Anat. 84:311, 1949.
———: A re-examination of the structure of the mammalian liver, Am. J. Anat. 85:379, 1949.
Elias, H., and Petty, D.: Gross anatomy of the blood vessels and ducts within the human liver, Am. J. Anat. 90:59, 1952.
Elias, H., and Sokol, A.: Dependence of the lobular architecture of the liver on the portohepatic blood pressure gradient, Anat. Rec. 115:71, 1953.
Ernster, L., Siekevitz, P., and Palade, G. F.: Enzyme-structure relationships in the endoplasmic reticulum of rat liver, J. Cell Biol. 15:541, 1962.

Fawcett, D. W.: Observation on the cytology and electron microscopy of hepatic cells, J. Nat. Cancer Inst. *15*:1475, 1955.

Hard, W. L., and Hawkins, R. K.: The role of the bile capillaries in the secretion of phosphatase by the rabbit liver, Anat. Rec. *106*:395, 1950.

Harkness, R. D.: Regeneration of the liver, Brit. M. Bull. *13*:87, 1957.

Hartroft, W. S.: Accumulation of fat in liver cells in lipodiastaemata preceding experimental dietary cirrhosis, Anat. Rec. *106*:61, 1950.

———: The escape of lipid from fatty cysts in experimental dietary cirrhosis *in* Tr. of 9th Conf., p. 109, New York, Macy, 1950.

Howatson, A. F., and Ham, A. W.: Electron microscope study of sections of two rat liver tumors, Cancer Res. *15*:62, 1955.

Hruban, Z., and Swift, H.: Uricase, localization in hepatic microbodies, Science *146*:1316, 1964.

Irwin, J. W., and Macdonald, J., III: Microscopic observations of the intrahepatic circulation of living guinea pigs, Anat. Rec. *117*:1, 1953.

Knisely, M. H.: The structure and mechanical functioning of the living liver lobules of frogs and rhesus monkeys (abstr.), Proc. Inst. Med. Chicago *16*:286, 1947.

Knisely, M. H., Bloch, E. H., and Warner, L.: Selective phagocytosis: I. Microscopic observations concerning the regulation of the blood flow through the liver and other organs and the mechanism and rate of phagocytic removal of particles from the blood. Det. Kong. Dans. Videnskab. Selskab, Biol. Skr. *7*:1, 1948.

Lazarow, A.: Particulate glycogen: A submicroscopic component of the guinea pig liver cell; its significance in glycogen storage and the regulation of the blood sugar, Anat. Rec. *84*:31, 1942.

Lee, F. C.: On the lymph vessels of the liver, Contrib. Embryol. *74*:65, 1925.

Mall, F. P.: A study of the structural unit of the liver, Am. J. Anat. *5*:227, 1906.

Mosbaugh, M. M., and Ham, A. W.: Stimulation of bile secretion in chick embryos by cortisone, Nature *168*:789, 1951.

Novikoff, A. B., Beaufay, H., and de Duve, C.: Electron microscopy of lysosome-rich fractions from rat liver, J. Biophys. Biochem. Cytol. *2*:179 (Suppl.), 1956.

Novikoff, A. B., and Essner, E.: The liver cell, Am. J. Med. *29*:102, 1960.

Palade, G. E., and Siekevitz, P.: Liver microsomes, an integrated morphological and biochemical study, J. Biophys. Biochem. Cytol. *2*:171, 1956.

Paschkis, K. E., Cantarow, A., Walkling, A. A., Pearlman, W. H., Rakoff, A. E., and Boyle, D.: Secretion and excretion of carbohydrate-active adrenal compounds (oxysteroids), Fed. Proc. *7*:90, 1948.

Paschkis, K. E., and Rakoff, A. E.: Some aspects of the physiology of estrogenic hormones, Rec. Prog. Hormone Res. *5*:115, 1950.

Popper, H.: Correlation of hepatic function and structure based on liver biopsy studies *in* Tr. of 9th Conf., p. 9, New York, Macy, 1950.

Rappaport, A. M.: Anatomic considerations *in* Schiff, L.: Diseases of the Liver, Philadelphia, Lippincott, 1956.

———: The structural and functional acinar unit of the liver; some histopathological considerations (Monograph), Internat. Symp. Hepatitis Frontiers, Boston, Little, 1957.

———: The structural and functional unit in the human liver (liver acinus), Anat. Rec. *130*:673, 1958.

———: Acinar units and the pathophysiology of the liver *in* The Liver, vol. 1, *see* General Reference, 1963.

Rappaport, A. M., Borowy, Z. J., Lougheed, W. M., and Lotto, W. N.: Subdivision of hexagonal liver lobules into a structural and functional unit; role in hepatic physiology and pathology, Anat. Rec. *119*:11, 1954.

Rappaport, A. M., and Hiraki, G. Y.: The anatomical pattern of lesions in the liver, Acta anat. *32*:126, 1958.

———: Histopathologic changes in the structural and functional unit of the human liver, Acta anat. *32*:240, 1958.

Rich, A. R.: The formation of bile pigment, Physiol. Rev. *5*:182, 1925.

Steiner, J. W., and Carruthers, J. S.: Studies on the fine structure of the terminal branches of the biliary tree. I. The morphology of normal bile canaliculi, bile pre-ductules (ducts of Hering) and bile ductules, Am. J. Path. *38*:639-661, 1961.

Steiner, J. W., Carruthers, J. S., and Kalifat, S. R.: The ductular cell reaction of rat liver in extrahepatic cholestasis. I. Proliferated biliary epithelial cells, Exp. Molec. Path. *1*:162-185, 1962.

Steiner, J. W., Phillips, M. J., and Miyai, K.: Ultrastructural and subcellular pathology of the liver, Internat. Rev. Exp. Path. *3*:65, 1964.

Steiner, J. W., Jézéquel, A.-M., Phillips, M. J., Miyai, K., and Arakawa, K.: Ultrastructural pathology of the liver *in* Popper, H., and Schaffner, F. (eds.): Progress in Liver Disease, vol. 2, New York, Grune & Stratton, 1965.

Trump, B. F., Goldblatt, P. J., and Stowell, R. E.: An electron microscope study of early cytoplasmic alterations in hepatic parenchymal cells of mouse liver during necrosis *in vitro* (autolysis), Lab. Invest. *11*:986, 1962.

Wakim, K. G., and Mann, F. C.: The intrahepatic circulation of blood, Anat. Rec. *82*:233, 1942.

Wilson, J. W.: Liver, Ann. Rev. Physiol. *13*:133, 1951.

### References on the Gallbladder

Boyden, E. A.: An analysis of the reaction of the human gallbladder to food, Anat. Rec. *40*:147, 1928.

————: The sphincter of Oddi in man and certain representative mammals, Surgery *1*:25, 1937.

Jit, I.: The development of the unstriped musculature of the gall-bladder and the cystic duct, J. Anat. Soc. (India) *8*:15, 1959.

Ralph, P. H.: The surface structure of the gallbladder and intestinal epithelium of man and monkey, Anat. Rec. *108*:217, 1950.

Rhodin, J. A. G.: An Atlas of Ultrastructure, p. 74, Philadelphia, Saunders, 1963.

Yamada, E.: The fine structure of the gallbladder epithelium of the mouse, J. Biophys. Biochem. Cytol. *1*:445. 1955.

# 26   The Respiratory System

## INTRODUCTION

Blood that leaves the capillaries of the systemic circulatory system with a diminished oxygen and an increased carbon dioxide content must be provided, at some point on the rounds of the circulatory system, with an opportunity of ridding itself of carbon dioxide and taking on a fresh charge of oxygen. This opportunity is provided in the pulmonary circuit as blood passes through the lungs. The latter are two large organs, spongy because they contain innumerable little pockets of air. They are also provided with a vast number of capillaries which abut on the air pockets. Carbon dioxide, in the blood passing along the capillaries, diffuses from the capillaries into the air pockets, and oxygen from the air pockets diffuses into the blood that is circulating along the lung capillaries. This, of course, would soon cause the air in the pockets to become highly charged with carbon dioxide and depleted of oxygen if there were no provision for constantly changing the air in the pockets. The latter action is accomplished by respiratory movements: inspiration, by which act fresh air is drawn into the lungs; and expiration, by which vitiated air is expelled from the lungs.

Since the microscopic structure of the lung is commonly studied before the student has learned the gross anatomy of the thoracic cavity and the precise nature of respiratory movements, and since a proper understanding of the microscopic structure of the lung depends on some knowledge of how air is taken into and then expelled from lungs, we shall at this time give an elementary description of respiratory movements and their effects on the lungs.

**Respiratory Movements and Their Effects.** The lungs are contained in the thorax (Fig. 26-1). The thorax has a cagelike framework composed of the vertebral column, the ribs, the costal cartilages and the sternum. The bottom of the cage is a dome-shaped musculo- tendinous sheet, the diaphragm. The ribs are disposed in such planes, and articulate with the vertebral column and the sternum at such angles, that the contraction of the muscles attached to them makes the thoracic cage both deeper in its anteroposterior diameter and wider. Moreover, contraction of the diaphragm (and relaxation of the muscles of the abdominal wall, which permits the diaphragm to descend) elongates the cage. Hence, by the contraction and the relaxation of muscles, the thoracic cage can be made larger by becoming deeper, wider and longer.

The two lungs fill two large compartments in the thoracic cavity. Each compartment is lined with a fibro-elastic membrane, the *parietal pleura* (Fig. 26-1), which is provided with an internal layer of squamous mesothelial cells. Likewise, each lung is covered with a similar membrane, the *visceral pleura* (Fig. 26-1), the outermost layer of which consists of squamous mesothelial cells. A film of fluid is present between the parietal pleura that lines each cavity and the visceral pleura that covers each lung; this fluid has lubricating value and allows the visceral pleura covering the lungs—hence, the lungs themselves—to slide during respiratory movements along the parietal pleura that lines the cavities.

Except at its hilus, where a bronchus and blood vessels enter it (Fig. 26-1), each lung, because of the slippery pleural surfaces, is freely movable within its cavity. Around its point of attachment at the hilus, the visceral pleura covering each lung becomes continuous with the parietal pleura lining each cavity (Fig. 26-1). The space between the two layers of pleura contains, as was noted before, only a film of fluid; hence, it is only a *potential space* or *cavity*. Under certain abnormal conditions the amount of fluid becomes increased; this converts the potential cavity into a real one. The potential or real space between the two layers of pleura is known as the *pleural cavity*. It should be understood that, although a lung occupies a cavity in the thorax, it does not lie in the pleural cavity but outside it, just as the intestines occupy the abdominal cavity but lie outside the peritoneal cavity.

With these few points in mind we are in a position to discuss how respiratory movements change the air in the lungs. Everyone knows that opening a bellows draws air into it. Furthermore, one cannot open an airtight bellows if its spout is plugged. One cannot pull up the plunger of a large pump if its intake valve does not open. Likewise, the muscular movements involved in performing an inspiratory movement can be effective in enlarging the thoracic cage only if something (air, fluid or viscus) can be drawn into the cage to permit its expansion. Inspiratory movements are not powerful enough to create any significant degree of vacuum in the thoracic cage. If they were, sometimes they might accomplish the same result that was witnessed when, in the 17th century, Guericke first created a vacuum by exhausting the air from a large copper sphere with a strong, small pump. After prolonged pumping, the sphere suddenly collapsed, with what was said to be a great noise, inspiring terror in all who watched.

Normally the thoracic cage can be enlarged by inspiratory movements only to the extent to which air and blood can be drawn into it. Air, under normal conditions, is drawn only into the lungs, but extra blood is drawn both into the vessels of the lungs and into those outside the lungs but inside the thorax. The reason for air not being drawn into any other part of the thoracic cavity except the lungs is that there is no opening to the surface from these other parts of the thorax through which it can be drawn. If an opening is provided, for example, a deep knife wound in the chest, air may be drawn by an inspiratory movement into parts of the thorax other than the lungs.

**Some Fundamental Features of Lungs.** The lungs consist essentially of: (1) the spongy respiratory tissue in which gaseous exchange occurs between blood and air and (2) a branching system of air tubes called *bronchioles* and *bronchi* which "pipe" air into and from the pockets and passageways of the spongy respiratory tissue. The main bronchus from each lung connects with the trachea (Fig. 26-1), and this, in turn, by means of the larynx, the nasopharynx and the nose (or the

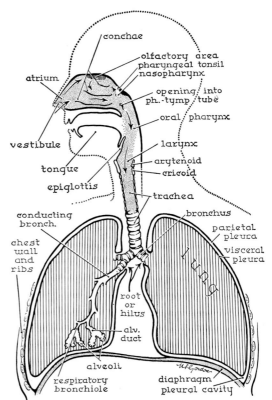

Fig. 26-1. Diagram of the parts of the respiratory system. (Redrawn and slightly modified from Grant, J. C. B.: A Method of Anatomy, ed. 4, Baltimore, Williams & Wilkins)

mouth if need be), connects with the outside air. Hence, on an inspiratory act, air is drawn through the nose, down the trachea, into the bronchial tree to its end branches and from there into the passageways and the pockets of the spongy, capillary-rich respiratory tissue, where, and only where, gaseous exchange occurs (Fig. 26-1, *alveoli*).

Before briefly considering the mechanism of expiration it is necessary to point out that the lungs would not fill the cavities in which they lie unless they were considerably stretched in all directions. A large amount of elastin is present in the visceral pleura that covers them, in the walls between the air pockets and in the bronchial tree. Since the lungs fill their respective cavities when they first develop in embryonic life, and since there is no easy way for fluid to be drawn into the pleural cavity during fetal life, the lungs are gradually stretched as the cavities containing them increase in size. The same process continues in the growing period of postnatal life. As a result, the elastic tissue of the lungs, under normal conditions, is always stretched, and the lung is always trying, as it were, to collapse and retract to the one point where it is attached (its root or hilus). Hence, if a hollow needle is inserted through the chest wall into the pleural cavity (between the parietal and the visceral layers of pleura), air immediately rushes through it into the pleural cavity, which thereupon, as the lung retracts toward the hilus, becomes a real (air-filled) cavity instead of being only a potential cavity. Letting air into the pleural cavity is a procedure sometimes used to put a lung at rest in the treatment of tuberculosis. The condition in which there is air in the pleural cavity is called a *pneumothorax*. In certain diseases the fluid in the pleural cavity which is normally no more than a film becomes greatly increased in amount. This, too, permits the lung to retract. This condition is known as a *hydrothorax.*

Since the elastic tissue of the lungs is normally stretched, it is scarcely necessary for an individual at rest to indulge in muscular movements to expel such air as is drawn into the lungs on inspiration. The elastic recoil of the lungs is enough, or almost enough, to expel the air out through the bronchial tree and draw in the sides and the bottom of the thoracic cage. But the elastic recoil of the lungs is not sufficient to expel large quantities of air as quickly as is necessary when one engages in violent exercise. Expiration is facilitated under such conditions, and probably to some extent in quiet breathing, by contractions of the abdominal muscles, which force the abdominal viscera against the undersurface of the diaphragm and so push it up into the thorax.

**The Conducting and Respiratory Portions of the System.** The system of cavities and tubes that conduct air from outside the body to all parts of the lungs constitutes the *conducting portion* of the respiratory system, and the pockets and the passageways of the respiratory tissue of the lung—the only sites where gaseous interchange occurs—are said to constitute the true *respiratory portion* of the system. The conducting part of the system

consists of the nose, the nasopharynx, the larynx, the trachea, the bronchi and the bronchioles (Fig. 26-1). It is to be noted that some of these structures lie outside the lung, and others (some bronchi and all the bronchioles) within it. It should be realized that those parts of the conducting system that lie without the lung must be provided with reasonably rigid walls; otherwise, a strong inspiratory act might collapse them, as sucking a soft drink through a wet straw (dry straws have rigid walls) collapses the straw. Rigidity is provided by cartilage or bone. Moreover, it should be kept in mind that the conducting part of the respiratory system performs functions other than conducting air to and from the lungs. The mucous membrane lining the conducting passageways strains, washes, warms or cools, as the case may be, and humidifies the air that passes along it toward the respiratory portion of the system. In other words, the conducting portion of the respiratory system is an excellent air-conditioning unit. Its different parts and their microscopic structure will now be described.

## THE NASAL CAVITIES

The nose contains two nasal cavities, one on each side, separated from one another by the nasal septum. Each cavity opens in front by a *naris* or *nostril* and behind into the *nasopharynx* (Fig. 26-1).

Bone and, to a lesser extent, cartilage and, to a small degree, dense connective tissue provide rigidity to the walls, the floor and the roof of the nasal cavities and so prevent their collapse on inspiration.

Each nasal cavity is divided into two parts: (1) a *vestibule,* the widened part of the passageway encountered just behind the naris, and (2) the remainder of the cavity, called its *respiratory portion.*

The epidermis of the skin covering the nose extends into each naris to line the front part of each vestibule. It is provided with many large hair follicles together with some sebaceous and sweat glands. The hairs are intended to strain coarse particles from air that is drawn through the nostrils. Farther back in the vestibule, the stratified squamous epithelium is not keratinized, and, still farther back, the epithelium becomes pseudostratified ciliated columnar with goblet cells. This type of epithelium lines the remainder of each nasal cavity.

The mucous membrane lining the respiratory portion of the nasal cavities is sometimes called the *schneiderian membrane* after the anatomist who first described it carefully. Typically, it consists of pseudostratified columnar ciliated epithelium with goblet cells and a lamina propria that contains both mucous and serous glands, which is adherent to the periosteum of the bone, or the perichondrium of the cartilage, beneath it. For this reason, the mucous membrane in this region is sometimes termed a *mucoperiosteum* or a *mucoperichondrium.*

The surface of the epithelium is normally covered with mucus provided by its goblet cells and by the glands of its lamina propria. Probably over a pint of fluid is produced by the nasal mucous membrane each day. The mucus, together with the particles of dust and

dirt that are picked up by it, is moved backward through the nasopharynx to the oral pharynx by means of the cilia with which the epithelial lining cells, excepting the goblet cells, are provided. Each cell has between 15 and 20 cilia that are about 7 $\mu$ in height and are anchored in the cytoplasm by rootlets. The drainage of the nose depends to a great extent on orderly ciliary action, and a loss of cilia from trauma or disease can interfere with the proper drainage of the nose.

The lamina propria contains both collagenic and elastic fibers. In some sites, and evidently by no means regularly, the lamina propria forms a well-developed basement membrane with elastic properties. Lymphocytes, plasma cells, macrophages and even granular leukocytes may be seen in the lamina propria. In general, it is a very vascular mem-

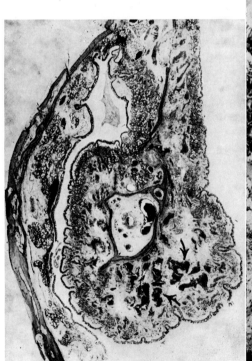
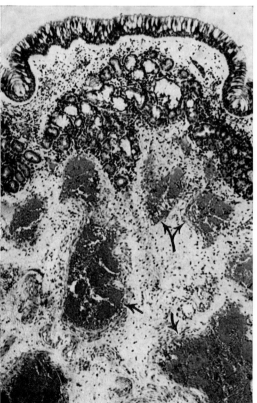

Fig. 26-2. (*Left*) Very low-power photomicrograph of a cross section of a concha. Thin bone may be seen in its central part. The blood in the venous spaces is dark. (*Right*) Medium-power photomicrograph of a section of the mucous membrane covering a concha. Glands may be seen in the upper region, and large venous spaces distended with blood may be seen in the lower part of the figure.

brane, and in cold weather it helps warm the air that is to be drawn into the lungs. In some sites lymphatic nodules appear; these are most numerous near the entrance to the nasopharynx.

The character of the mucous membrane of the respiratory portion of the nose has special characteristics in two places. That lining the upper parts of the sides and the roof of the posterior part of each cavity constitutes the organ of smell (the olfactory organ), and its special microscopic structure will be described in the chapter dealing with the system of sensory receptors (Chap. 31). The other site in which the mucous membrane is not typical will be dealt with now.

Three plates of bone, arranged one above the other like shelves, are disposed along the lateral wall of each nasal cavity. However, they are not flat like useful shelves; they are more like unsupported metal shelves which have had to bear too much weight, for they all curve downward. Since their curved form makes them look something like shells, they are called the *superior,* the *middle* and the *inferior conchae* (*concha* is Latin for shell), respectively (Figs. 26-1 and 26-2). They are also often referred to as the *superior,* the *middle* and the *inferior turbinate* (*turbinatus* = scroll-like) bones.

Although the mucous membrane of the nasal cavities is very vascular, containing many arteries, capillaries and veins, that of the lamina propria of the mucosa covering the middle and the inferior conchae has, in addition, a large number of venous structures which, under normal conditions, are collapsed. However, under certain circumstances, they can become distended with blood (Fig. 26-2), and this so increases the thickness of the mucosa that in some individuals it encroaches on the airway to such an extent that nose breathing is made difficult.

The term *erectile tissue* is usually used to designate any tissue that contains a large number of endothelial-lined cavities which, although they are on the circuit of the bloodstream, are usually collapsed and become distended with blood, to increase greatly the size of the tissue in which they lie, only as a result of special nervous stimulation. Most of the substance of the male copulatory organ, the penis, is erectile tissue; this accounts for the changes in the size and the consistency of this organ that can occur under conditions of erotic stimulation. The lamina propria of the nasal mucosa of the conchae is not as typically erectile tissue as that present in the penis, and some observers consider that it is not true erectile tissue at all. Perhaps it is better described as possessing a great many thin-walled veins along which smooth muscle fibers are both circularly and longitudinally disposed (Fig. 26-2, *right*). Nevertheless, it reacts like erectile tissue in that it can rapidly become turgid with blood. A further indication of its similarity to erectile tissue (which otherwise is limited to the genital systems of the male and the female) is that in certain individuals the mucosa covering the conchae is affected by erotic stimuli. Mackenzie, many years ago, wrote a most interesting and learned article about this relationship. From individuals encountered in his own practice he obtained many examples of erotic stimulation being associated with sneezing, with engorgement of the nasal mucosa covering the conchae and even with bleeding from this area; indeed, he even quotes one 16th century report of a youth who sneezed whenever he saw a pretty girl. It is difficult to understand the purpose served by having the erectile tissue of the nose linked nervously with that of the genital systems. The relationship probably hinges somehow on the fact that sex stimulation is so very dependent on the sense of smell in a large part of the animal kingdom. That a relationship exists between the erectile or pseudoerectile tissue of the nose and that of the genital system not only enlarges the number of possible factors that may be concerned in nasal congestions but also provides a basis for attempting to treat some atrophic states of the nasal mucosa with sex hormones.

## PARANASAL AIR SINUSES OF THE NOSE

The air *sinuses* (*sinus* = bay or hollow) are spaces in bones. There are 4 associated with each nasal cavity. They are named after the bones in which they are contained and hence are called the *frontal,* the *ethmoidal,* the *sphenoidal* and the *maxillary* sinuses, respectively. The maxillary sinus is the largest and is sometimes called the *antrum* (*antron* = a cavity) *of Highmore.*

The 4 sinuses on each side all communicate with the nasal cavity of that side. They are all lined by mucous membrane continuous with that lining the nasal cavity. The ciliated epithelium in the sinuses is not so thick as that in the nasal cavity itself, and it does not contain nearly so many goblet cells. A basement membrane is not present. The lamina propria is relatively thin and is continuous with the periosteum of the underlying bone. It consists chiefly of collagenic fibers and contains eosinophils, plasma cells and many lymphocytes in addition to fibroblasts. It has relatively few glands embedded in it.

The openings by which the sinuses communicate with the nasal cavities are not so large as to prevent their becoming closed if the mucosa at and around the opening becomes inflamed or sufficiently swollen for other reasons. Normally, the mucus formed in sinuses is moved to the nasal cavities by ciliary action. If the openings of the sinuses become obstructed, the sinuses may fill with mucus or, under conditions of infection, with pus. Drugs which act similarly to hormones of the adrenal medulla and cause contraction of the blood vessels of the part are often used locally to lessen the congestion about the openings of inflamed sinuses and so permit them to drain. Sometimes new openings must be made surgically to permit them to drain properly.

## THE PHARYNGEAL TONSIL

This consists of an unpaired median mass of lymphatic tissue in the lamina propria of the mucous membrane lining the dorsal wall of the nasopharynx (Fig. 26-1). A child who has an enlarged pharyngeal tonsil is said to have *adenoids* (*aden* = gland) because the enlarged lymphatic follicles of the tonsil give it a glandlike appearance. Adenoids may obstruct the respiratory passageway and lead to persistent mouth breathing. The muscular actions entailed in keeping the mouth always open, by changing the normal lines of force to which the bones of the developing face are subjected, may prevent the bones of the face from developing as they otherwise would, and the effect produced is usually unfortunate. For this reason, and also for the reason that an enlarged pharyngeal tonsil is usually more or less persistently infected, the removal of adenoids is a relatively common operation.

The pharyngeal tonsil resembles the pala-
tine tonsil in microscopic structure except that: (1) it is more diffuse, (2) its covering epithelium dips down into it as folds rather than as crypts, and (3) its epithelium may be pseudostratified, at least in some areas, instead of stratified squamous nonkeratinizing.

## THE LARYNX

The larynx is the segment of the respiratory tube that connects the pharynx with the trachea (Fig. 26-1). Its walls are kept from collapsing on inspiration by a number of cartilages that are contained in its wall and bound together with connective tissue membranes. Muscles that act on the cartilages are present both outside them (the extrinsic muscles of the larynx) and between them and the mucous membrane (the intrinsic muscles of the larynx). The larynx has many functions. It plays the most important part in phonation; however, this is phylogenetically a late development. A more fundamental function of the larynx is that of preventing anything but air from gaining entrance to the lower respiratory passages. It is said to be the watchdog for the lung, and if, in spite of its efforts, anything but air enters it, a cough reflex is set in motion immediately. It is of interest in this connection to note that some individuals who apparently have died from drowning are found at autopsy to have very little water in their lungs; they probably die from asphyxiation caused by laryngeal spasm induced by water gaining entrance to, and irritating, this organ.

The apex of a flaplike structure, the *epiglottis,* whose free portion projects upward and slightly backward, is attached anteriorly to constitute the uppermost part of the larynx (Fig. 26-1). In days past it was thought that the free part of this structure flapped down over the entrance of the larynx when food was swallowed and in this way kept food and fluid from gaining entrance to the larynx. Although this view has some modern supporters, it is now generally thought that the epiglottis plays a more subsidiary and passive role in keeping food and fluid out of the larynx during the act of swallowing and that the main factor responsible for this latter effect is the larynx being brought upward and forward in the act of swallowing so that the upper end of its tubular part is pressed against the pos-

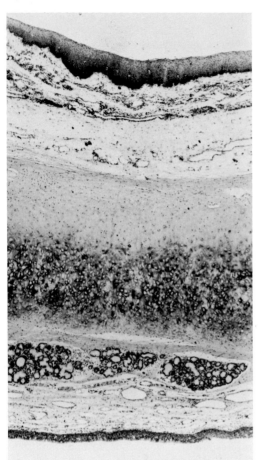

Fig. 26-3. Low-power photomicrograph of a section cut across the epiglottis. The anterior surface is above; the posterior below.

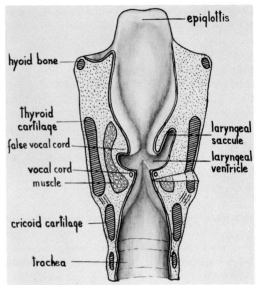

Fig. 26-4. Drawing of the anterior half of a coronally sectioned larynx as seen from behind. The cut is farther forward at the upper right side of the illustration so that the saccule is disclosed. (Redrawn and modified from Schaeffer, E. A.: Textbook of Microscopic Anatomy, published as Vol. 2, Part I of Quain's Elements of Anatomy, ed. 11, New York, Longmans)

terior aspect of the epiglottis, under the root of the tongue. Individuals who have had the epiglottis removed for one cause or another can still swallow without food entering the larynx.

A plate of elastic cartilage (Fig. 26-3) forms an internal support for the epiglottis. The perichondrium of this is continuous with the lamina propria of the mucous membrane which covers both its surfaces. The epithelium of the mucous membrane varies in relation to the function of the different parts of the epiglottis. On the anterior surface, where the epiglottis comes into contact with the root of the tongue in the act of swallowing, the epithelium is of the stratified squamous non-keratinizing type (Fig. 26-3) that is so well

adapted to cover wet surfaces subjected to wear and tear. The epithelium covering the upper part of the posterior surface comes into contact with things being swallowed and so is subjected to considerable wear and tear. It, too, is of the stratified squamous nonkeratinizing type. Taste buds are occasionally present in it. However, the epithelium covering the lower part of the posterior surface does not come into contact with food, and, since it constitutes the lining of part of the respiratory tube, it is lined with pseudostratified columnar ciliated epithelium with goblet cells (Fig. 26-3, bottom). The cilia beat toward the pharynx and wash mucus and particles picked up by the mucus in that direction. Mucous glands with some serous secretory units are present in the lamina propria under the posterior surface. They are said to be present also under the anterior surface. Glands are more numerous toward the attached margin of the epiglottis.

The lumen of the larynx is narrowed and

made more or less slitlike (the slit being directed in an anteroposterior direction) in two sites by folds of mucous membrane that projects into the lumen from each side. The upper pair of folds constitute the false vocal cords (Fig. 26-4). The second pair of folds lie below the first pair, and their cordlike free margins constitute the true vocal cords (Fig. 26-4). The opening between the two vocal cords is termed the *rima glottidis*. It is slitlike when the vocal cords are close together but somewhat triangular in shape, with the apex of the triangle being directed forward, when the vocal cords are farther apart. The expansion of the lumen of the larynx between the two sets of folds is called the *sinus* or *ventricle* of the larynx (Fig. 26-4). Anteriorly the sinus of each side is prolonged upward. Each cul-de-sac, so formed, is called the *laryngeal saccule* (Fig. 26-4). The cores of the folds that comprise the false vocal cords are composed chiefly of a somewhat loose lamina propria which contains glands. The cords of the second and lower pair of folds consist of connective tissue and muscle. The cores of the vocal cords themselves (the parts of the folds nearest their free edges) consist of connective tissue that is composed chiefly of elastic fibers. The aperture between the true vocal cords, and the tension under which the cords exist, is affected both by muscle fibers that act on the cords directly and by muscle fibers that affect the cords indirectly by shifting the tissues to which they are anchored.

The epithelium of the mucous membrane of the larynx varies in relation to the functions performed by its different parts. That covering the true vocal cords, which are subjected to considerable wear and tear, is of the stratified squamous nonkeratinizing type. All the epithelium lining the larynx below the true vocal cords is of the pseudostratified columnar ciliated type with goblet cells. Most of that lining the larynx above the true vocal cords is also of this type, although patches of stratified squamous nonkeratinizing epithelium may be present in some sites. The cilia beat toward the pharynx. Except over the true vocal cords the lamina propria of the mucous membrane contains mucous glands. Lymph nodules occur in the lamina propria of the mucous membrane. They are more numerous along the

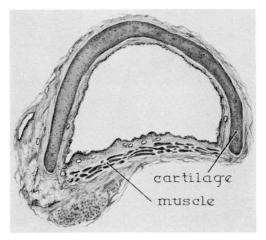

FIG. 26-5. Drawing of a cross section of the trachea of an adult (very low-power).

lateral and dorsal wall in the region of the ventricle and the false vocal cords.

## THE TRACHEA

The trachea is a tube continuous with the larynx above and ending below by dividing into two primary bronchi which pass toward the right and the left lungs, respectively (Fig. 26-1).

The trachea is prevented from collapsing by about 20 U- or horseshoe-shaped cartilages that are set in its wall one above the other so that each almost encircles the lumen. The open ends of these incomplete cartilaginous rings are directed backward (Fig. 26-5), and the gap between the two ends of each ring is bridged by connective tissue and smooth muscle (Fig. 26-5).

If a *longitudinal section* is cut from the wall of the trachea, the cartilaginous rings that encircle its wall are cut in *cross section*. The cross-section appearance of each ring is roughly ovoid (Fig. 26-6) with a greatest supero-inferior diameter of 3 or 4 mm. and a greatest mediolateral diameter of 1 mm. or thereabouts. The inner surface of each ring is convex, and its outer surface relatively flat (Fig. 26-6). The space between adjacent rings is considerably less than the supero-inferior diameters of the rings themselves and is filled with dense connective tissue which is continuous with that of the perichondrium of each ring (Fig. 26-6). The bundles of collagenic

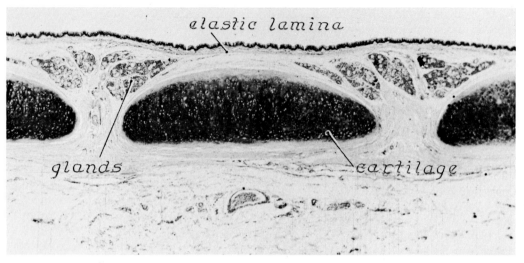

*elastic lamina*

*glands*

*cartilage*

FIG. 26-6. Very low-power photomicrograph of a longitudinal section of the anterior wall of the trachea of an adult.

fibers which make up this connective tissue are woven in such a way that some degree of elasticity is imparted to the tracheal wall. Some elastic fibers, distributed among the bundles of collagenic fibers, also may be of some importance in this respect.

The trachea is lined by a mucous membrane. The fine structure of mucous membranes of this type was described in Chapter 8. The membrane consists of pseudostratified ciliated columnar epithelium with goblet cells (Fig. 8-17). The lamina propria on which the epithelium rests is condensed to form a moderately distinct basement membrane. The remainder of the lamina propria contains a fairly high proportion of elastic fibers. A tendency toward a lymphatic character is indicated by the presence in the membrane of cells of the lymphocyte series and occasional true nodules. The deep border of the lamina propria is marked by a dense lamina or membrane of elastin (Fig. 26-6). The tissue just outside this is termed *submucosa*. The secretory portions of many mucous glands, with some serous secretory units, are embedded in the submucosa. In longitudinal sections of the trachea the secretory portions of these glands are seen to be disposed chiefly in the submucosa that fills in the triangular spaces between adjacent cartilages (Fig. 26-6). The ducts from these glands pierce the elastic lamina of the lamina propria to empty on the inner surface of the trachea. Some secre-

tory units may be present also in the lamina propria.

The posterior wall of the trachea is composed of interlacing bundles of smooth muscle fibers, arranged chiefly in the transverse plane and knitted together by connective tissue (Fig. 26-5). The inner surface of the posterior wall of the trachea is lined with a mucous membrane similar to that lining the remainder of its wall. The secretory units of glands are present in the mucous membrane, outside the mucous membrane in the interstices between the bundles of smooth muscle, and even outside the smooth muscle, in the connective tissue of the outer layers of the wall.

## THE BRONCHIAL TREE

The trachea ends by dividing into 2 branches, the 2 primary bronchi, which pass to the roots of the lungs (Fig. 26-1). The microscopic structure of the walls of these is the same as that of the wall of the trachea.

Usually the right lung is made up of 3 lobes and the left lung of 2. Each primary bronchus, in a sense, continues into the lower lobe of the particular lung to which it passes. The right primary bronchus, before doing so, gives off 2 branches to supply the middle and the upper lobes, respectively, of that lung. Likewise, the left primary bronchus, before continuing into the lower lobe of the left lung, gives off a branch to supply the upper lobe

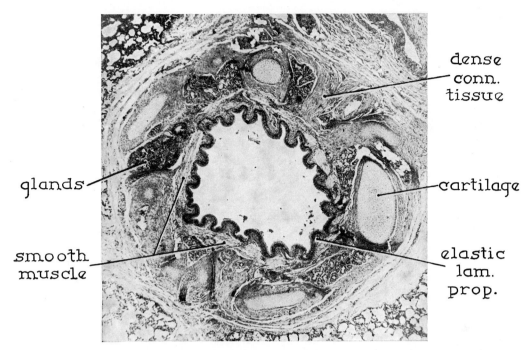

dense
conn.
tissue

glands

cartilage

smooth
muscle

elastic
lam.
prop.

FIG. 26-7. Very low-power photomicrograph of a cross section of an intrapulmonary bronchus.

of that lung. At the hilus of each lung the primary bronchus and its main branches become closely associated with the arteries which also enter the lung at this site and the veins and lymphatics which leave the lung, and all these tubular structures become invested in dense connective tissue. This complex of tubes invested in dense connective tissue is termed the *root* of the lung.

As stated above, a large bronchus enters each of the lobes of the two lungs. Within the lobes these branch to give rise to progressively smaller bronchi. The manner in which the first branchings occur to supply different parts of the different lobes of the lung is a matter of considerable interest, particularly with regard to the surgical treatment of certain diseases of the lung. Although there is some variation, certain parts or areas of each lobe tend to be supplied by certain main branches of the bronchus that enters the lobe. These parts or areas represent units of lung structure that may be dealt with surgically and are of a smaller order of size than whole lobes. The pattern and the bronchial connections of these constitute a matter too specialized to discuss here.

**Microscopic Structure of Intrapulmonary**

**Bronchi.** Although the bronchi that are within the lung have a microscopic structure similar to that of the trachea and the extrapulmonary portions of the 2 primary bronchi, they are somewhat different in a few respects which will now be described.

1. The U- or horseshoe-shaped cartilages of the trachea and the extrapulmonary parts of the primary bronchi are replaced in the intrapulmonary bronchi by cartilage plates of a most irregular shape. In a cross section of an intrapulmonary bronchus these appear as crescents (Fig. 26-7), and the impression is given that several are required to encircle the tube. But, as Miller has pointed out, this appearance is deceptive, for he found from reconstructions that what seemed to be several cartilages in a single section are only the various prolongations of a single large cartilage of irregular shape. In many instances he found the irregular cartilages to encircle the lumen completely. Since cartilages are disposed around all parts of the walls of these bronchi, the latter are not flattened on one surface like the trachea and the extrapulmonary bronchi. At sites of branchings Miller found that special saddle-shaped cartilages were often pres-

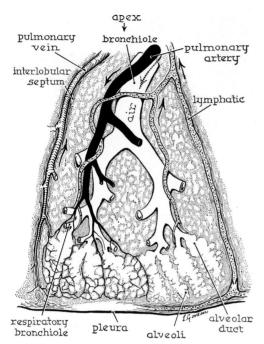

apex

pulmonary
vein

bronchiole

pulmonary
artery

interlobular
septum

air

lymphatic

respiratory
bronchiole

pleura

alveoli

alveolar
duct

FIG. 26-8. Diagram of a lobule of the lung
with its base abutting on the pleura. The
size of the bronchioles and the air passages,
as well as that of the blood vessels and the
lymphatics, is out of proportion. To make
it easier to follow the course of the blood
vessels and the lymphatics, the former have
been omitted from the right side, and the
latter from the left side.

ent to support the 2 branches at the site where
they make an acute angle with one another.
The spaces between different cartilages and
parts of the same cartilage which would otherwise be weak spots in the bronchial wall are
filled with collagenic connective tissue which
is continuous with the perichondrium of the
cartilages concerned.

2. The smooth muscle which is present only
in the posterior part of the trachea and the
extrapulmonary bronchi comes, in the intrapulmonary bronchi, to constitute a layer which
completely encircles the lumen. This layer of
muscle lies between the mucous membrane and
the cartilages (Fig. 26-7). It does not appear
as a complete layer in every section because
it is composed of 2 sets of smooth muscle
fibers that wind down the bronchial tree in
a left and a right spiral, respectively. The
arrangement of muscle can be roughly demon-

strated by winding 2 shoelaces down a broom-
stick in fairly close spirals, one clockwise and
the other counterclockwise.

3. The contraction of this muscle after
death, and perhaps to some extent during life,
throws the mucous membrane into the longitudinal folds that are characteristic of intrapulmonary bronchi seen in cross sections (Fig.
26-7).

4. The elastic lamina that marks the outer
limit of the mucous membrane of the trachea
is not present as such in the intrapulmonary
bronchi but instead elastic fibers are distributed in a way that will now be described. In
the bronchi, the cartilages are bound together
by coarse elastic fibers. Finer fibrils are present in the adventitia, between the muscle fibers
and in the lamina propria. The most remarkable feature, however, is the presence of several strong stripes of elastic tissue situated in
the lamina propria and running parallel to
each other for the full length of the bronchial
tree. They may easily be seen with the naked
eye on inspection of the mucosa. They branch
with the successive bronchial branches and are
continuous with the elastic components of the
terminal air passages.

The intrapulmonary bronchi are lined with
ciliated pseudostratified columnar epithelium,
and the secretion of the goblet cells disposed
in this membrane is augmented by that of
glands. The secretory portions of these are
disposed, for the most part, outside the muscular layer (Fig. 26-7), particularly in sites
where there are intervals between cartilages.

Both lymph nodes and individual nodules
are scattered along the bronchi in the outermost fibrous parts of their walls.

**Method of Branching.** In general, the
branching that occurs in the bronchial tree is
of the *dichotomous* (*dichotomia* = a cutting
in two) variety, with the total cross-sectional
area of the lumens of each 2 branches that
arise being greater than the cross-sectional area
of the lumen of the parent tube. This fact has
implications with regard to the relative speeds
at which air travels in the smaller and the
larger branches of the bronchial tree. Since
the same amount of air (per unit of time) can
pass through a parent tube as can pass through
its 2 branches (which have a greater total
cross-sectional area) only if it moves faster in
the parent tube, it follows that air moves slow-

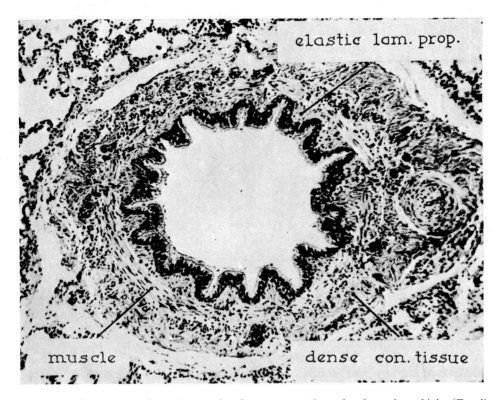

FIG. 26-9. Low-power photomicrograph of a cross section of a large bronchiole (Engel's bronchiolus) in the lung of a child.

est in the smallest tubes of the bronchial tree and fastest in the largest. Keeping this in mind is of importance in interpreting the breath sounds heard with a stethoscope.

**The Differences Between Bronchi and Bronchioles.** The continued branching of the bronchial tree results in the formation of successively narrower bronchi. The smaller ones differ in structure from the larger ones, chiefly because their cartilages are not so large and do not extend around their walls so completely.

As will be explained later, the lung develops like a gland and, as a result, its substance is made up of lobules. The bronchi of the lung are the equivalent of the extralobular ducts of glands because they are outside lobules. The branches of the bronchial tree that enter lobules, generally at their apices, are termed *bronchioles*; they are the counterparts of the intralobular ducts of glands. They differ in structure from bronchi in being smaller (generally bronchioles are less than 1 mm. in diam-

eter) and also by not having any cartilages in their walls. As will be explained later, bronchioles do not require cartilages in their walls to keep them from collapsing on inspiratory movements because they are inside the substance of the lung, which is opened up and hence expanded by inspiratory movements.

As is true of intralobular ducts, some connective tissue from interlobular septa extends along bronchioles to provide the larger ones particularly with support (Fig. 26-9).

**Lung Lobules.** Likening bronchioles to intralobular ducts is helpful because each of the bronchioles that arises from the branching of the smaller bronchi enters what is called a *lobule* of the lung to course thereafter, like an intralobular duct, through, and branch within, the substance of a lobule. Before discussing how the bronchioles connect with the air spaces where an interchange of gases between blood and air occurs, we shall discuss the structure of lobules in more detail.

Lung lobules, like pyramids, have apices and bases (Fig. 26-8). But here their resemblance to pyramids usually ends, for lobules are very irregular in shape. They vary greatly in size; their bases vary from somewhat less than 1 cm. to 2 or more cm. in diameter, and their height varies even more. Before considering how they are arranged within lobes, it may be helpful to compare each main bronchus with the trunk of a tree in that the bronchus "grows" from the root of the lung toward the central part of a lobe, and even beyond this point, branching as it grows. The smaller branches of the tree that are going to enter lobules and so become bronchioles mostly point outwardly toward the periphery of the lobe, but a considerable number of them point not outwardly, but inwardly, toward the central part of the lobe. The lobules fill the space that is available to them and this affects their shape. The peripheral lobules tend to have the shape of elongated pyramids as is illustrated in Figure 26-8, but the more central lobules in a lobe may be of irregular shapes and have angular contours. However, all the lobules are so arranged that their apices receive bronchioles (Fig. 26-8). This means that the bases of some lobules face the periphery of the lobe and those of others face its interior.

The bases of the peripheral lobules are visible as polygonal areas beneath the pleura. They are separated from one another by fibrous septa which in man extend for only a short distance (as complete septa) into the lung. In some animals, however, for example, the pig, the lobules are completely separated from each other by interlobular septa of dense connective tissue. This is continuous with the connective tissue of the visceral pleura at the base of the lobule (Fig. 26-20) and with the dense connective tissue that ensheathes the bronchi at the apex of the lobule. However, in other animals, for example, the rabbit, the lobules are not separated from one another by septa. In man the septa are incomplete.

**Microscopic Structures of Bronchioles.** A bronchiole on entering a lobule gives rise to many branches, and these extend in a treelike fashion to all parts of the lobule. Since bronchioles, like intralobular ducts, lie within the substance of lobules, they are attached on all sides to the elastic spongework of tissue that contains the air spaces where gaseous e. change

occurs (Fig. 26-9). There is, then, no tendency for them to collapse on inspiratory movements; indeed, on an inspiratory movement they are "pulled on," all around their circumference, as the elastic fibers of the respiratory spongework are stretched. Hence, there is no need for the walls of the bronchioles to be protected against collapsing on inspiratory movements by cartilaginous rings or plates, and they have none in their walls. They differ from bronchi also in not having any glands in their walls; perhaps they are so close to the respiratory spaces that secretions delivered into them from glands might be sucked into the respiratory spaces. Moreover, their epithelial lining is not as thick as that of bronchi. In the larger branches it is ciliated columnar, and in the final branches, nonciliated and high cuboidal in type. To sum up, the walls of bronchioles consist of epithelium that rests on a thin elastic lamina propria, and this layer, in turn, is surrounded by the muscular coat previously described for bronchi (Fig. 26-9). The muscle is supported by connective tissue.

**Orders of Bronchioles.** Once inside a lobule, the bronchiole that enters it gives off branches known as *terminal* bronchioles, the number of which varies according to the size of the lobule. There are often 5 to 7.

The next order of bronchioles arise, of course, from terminal bronchioles, and are called *respiratory* bronchioles (Figs. 26-8 and 26-10). The reason for their name is that as they branch and extend into lung substance they exhibit an increasing number of little delicate air-containing outpouchings from their walls. These little outpouchings are limited by capillary networks ensconced in delicate frameworks that will be described presently; the point to be made here is that gaseous exchange occurs between the blood in the capillaries in the walls of the outpouchings and in the air they contain. Because respiration thus occurs in the outpouchings from these bronchioles they are called *respiratory* bronchioles. The free terminations of the respiratory bronchioles flare out to some extent and open into what are called alveolar ducts.

**The Respiratory Portion of the Lobule; Alveolar Ducts, Alveolar Sacs (Saccules) and Alveoli.** Before commenting on alveolar ducts, into which the respiratory bronchioles open, it may be helpful to emphasize that the bronchi and the bronchioles are tubes with walls of their own and that they serve primarily to conduct air back and forth to the respiratory portions of the lobules. The terms that we shall now use to describe how air is conducted into all parts of the respiratory portion of the lobule (alveolar ducts, alveolar sacs [saccules] and alveoli), do not refer to structures that have walls of their own (as have bronchioles) but rather to spaces of various orders and shapes that exist in a huge elastic spongelike arrangement of capillary beds through which the right heart constantly pumps blood (Figs. 26-8 and 26-10). Alveolar ducts, alveolar sacs and alveoli all contain air that is more or less constantly being changed. The air in all these spaces is in close contact with the capillaries in the walls of the spongework that divide this portion of the lung into spaces, and since both the air and the blood are separated only by thin films of tissue through which diffusion occurs readily, a mechanism is provided for permitting blood to lose its carbon dioxide and take on oxygen as it passes through the capillary beds of the elastic spongelike respiratory portion of the lung.

**Alveolar Ducts, Alveolar Sacs (Saccules) and Alveoli.** The spaces into which the respiratory bronchioles directly open have the shape of long branching hallways along which there are many open doors of two general sizes. The long branching hallways are termed *alveolar ducts* (Fig. 26-10). The larger open doors communicate with rotundalike spaces which are termed *alveolar sacs* or *saccules*. Projecting inwardly from the periphery of the rotundalike saccules, spurlike partitions divide the peripheral zone of each saccule into a series of cubicles that open into the central part of the saccule. The cubicles are alveoli.

Before describing the histologic structure of the walls that separate the air spaces from one another we shall comment briefly on units of respiratory structure smaller than lobules; these are of importance in understanding certain pathologic conditions of the lung.

**Units of Structure Within the Lobule.** It has been stated already that one bronchiole serves a unit of lung structure called the lobule. However, there never have been any generally agreed upon terms for the units supplied by the succeeding divisions of the respiratory tree. The unit of lung served by a terminal bronchi-

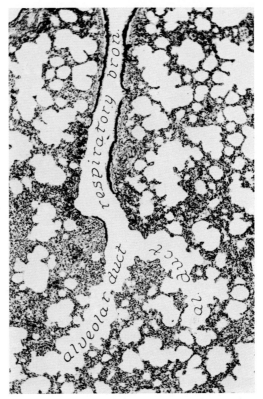

FIG. 26-10. Very low-power photomicrograph of a section of the lung of a very young child. A respiratory bronchiole is cut longitudinally and may be seen to be opening into 2 alveolar ducts.

ole is often termed an *acinus*. There are no standard names for the more distal units, but Barrie has recently suggested that they should be designated according to the channel which supplies them. Thus the unit supplied by a respiratory bronchiole could be termed a respiratory bronchiolar unit, and the unit supplied by an alveolar duct a ductal unit.

### THE MICROSCOPIC STUDY OF THE RESPIRATORY PORTION OF THE LUNG

The elastic fibers present in the spongework of the lung necessarily are stretched to enable a lung to fill the cavity in which it lies. Hence, when the pleural cavities are opened at autopsy the lungs collapse toward their roots. Sections cut from collapsed lungs do not give a representative picture of the structure of the respiratory spongework during life, for, when a lung collapses, the spaces in the spongework be-

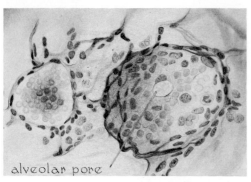

alveolar pore

Fig. 26-11. Drawing of a thick section (high-power) of the lung of the rabbit. A venule shows at the left, and the floor of an alveolus is to be seen on the right. The blood cells in the floor are in capillaries. At one site, the floor of the alveolus exhibits a defect, and alveolar pore.

come smaller, and the partitions between the spaces become thicker. A better impression of the structure of the lung during life can be obtained from the study of sections cut from lungs that have been redistended to their original size immediately after death by injecting fixative through a cannula into a stem bronchus and subsequently tying off the bronchus so that the lung cannot collapse again.

**Alveolar Walls or Septa vs. Interalveolar Walls or Septa.** Most of the partitions seen in the spongework of the lung separate adjacent alveoli from one another. Some partitions, of course, separate the passageways of alveolar ducts from alveolar spaces that are just outside the duct but which communicate with some other duct. In general, all of these partitions are called *alveolar septa* or *alveolar walls*. However, it should be understood clearly that the word alveolus has two meanings: it can be used to depict either *a little space* or *a little vessel* (structure). In the instance of the postnatal lung, the word is used to depict a space. The structure that is termed an alveolar wall contains many components and is actually an *interalveolar* wall or septum; it lies *between* two alveoli.

THE STRUCTURE OF INTERALVEOLAR
WALLS OR SEPTA

**The Use of Thick Sections.** In thin sections of distended lungs, interalveolar partitions are always cut in cross or oblique sections (Fig.

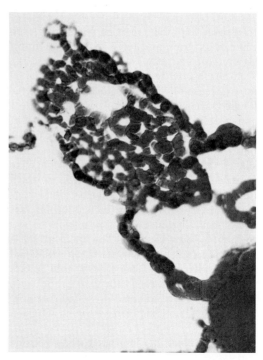

Fig. 26-12. High-power photomicrograph of a thick section of a lung, the blood vessels of which were injected with an opaque material. The figure shows the floor of an alveolus (an interalveolar partition in full face), and the injected capillaries may be seen to form an extensive and close mesh.

26-14). The reason for this is that, in distended lungs, interalveolar partitions are as thin as the sections themselves, and, since they are never perfectly flat (as sections are), it is impossible for a whole alveolar partition to be present in a thin section so that its full face may be examined. To see an interalveolar partition in full face it is necessary to cut sections of lung that are about as thick as the diameter of alveoli. In such sections, sites may be found where the top of one alveolus has been sliced off, together with the bottom of the alveolus immediately below it. One may then look down into an alveolus as one looks into a cup to inspect its bottom. In this instance the bottom of the cup is the interalveolar partition between the alveolus into which one is looking and the alveolus immediately below it (Fig. 26-11).

**The Capillaries of the Walls.** It is not easy to identify the various cells and structures in interalveolar walls seen this way. Many nuclei are seen; the various cells that contain these will be described presently. The extent of the capillary network in an interalveolar septum can scarcely be realized unless thick sections of lungs, the blood vessels of which have been injected with opaque material, are studied. Interalveolar walls seen in full face in such preparations show the networks in the interalveolar walls to be of a very close mesh (Fig. 26-12).

**Alveolar Pores and Lambert's Sinuses.** Some interalveolar partitions studied in full face in thick sections will be seen to be defective. The defects appear as little round or oval holes termed *alveolar pores* (Fig. 26-11). These have been studied extensively by Macklin. Where they are present they permit air to pass from one alveolus to another. Although some argue that pores are always the result of a previous disease process, they are so abundant in the interalveolar partitions of so many different kinds of animals that the view that considers them all to be pathologic defects seems unlikely. Interalveolar pores may be regarded as allowing interchange of air in alveolar sacs whose own supply routes have been obstructed. Recently, further intercommunicating channels have been discovered in the lung by Lambert. These are short openings in the walls of bronchioles or respiratory bronchioles leading into alveolar sacs belonging to the same or to a neighboring unit. These channels, called Lambert's sinuses, provide an alternative route for entry or escape of air into the terminal units and probably play an important role when parts of the lungs become fibrotic.

**How Interalveolar Walls Are Supported.** The capillary networks of which interalveolar walls are chiefly composed have little tensile strength. If they were not supported in some fashion, individual alveoli might become so overexpanded with air that the capillaries would be torn. However, such support as is provided for interalveolar walls cannot be too rigid, lest it interfere with their normal expansion. The matter seems to have been solved by interalveolar walls having two kinds of support, *basic* and *intimate*. The basic support consists of a skeleton of elastic fibers (Fig. 26-13). These are coarse and too infrequent to provide an intimate support for the many capillaries and cells in the walls; however, they

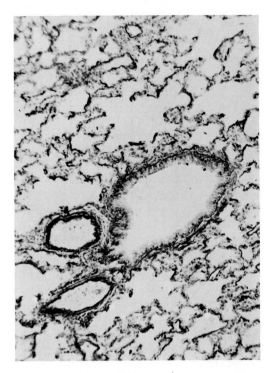

Fig. 26-13. Low-power photomicrograph of a section of rabbit lung stained with orcein to demonstrate elastic fibers. The elastic fibers appear as black lines and may be seen in the wall of the bronchiole, in the arteries, in the interalveolar partitions and along the alveolar ducts.

do provide a backbone that would resist overexpansion. In addition to the occasional fibers that course along in walls, there are, according to Short, elastic fibers around the free margins of alveoli (where they open into alveolar sacs or ducts).

As noted above, the occasional elastic fibers that run in interalveolar walls provide a backbone for them but no intimate support for the capillaries and the cells within the wall. Intimate support is provided for these by delicate fibrils of the reticular or the collagenic variety and by basement membranes, as will now be described. Some smooth muscle fibers may be seen along alveolar ducts particularly around their doorways.

Concepts of the microscopic structure of interalveolar walls have changed considerably over the last decade because of research along two different lines. First, studies with the EM, particularly the pioneer studies of Low, have

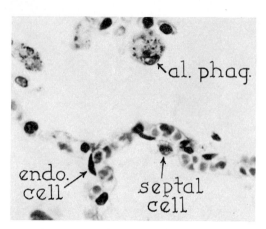

FIG. 26-14. High-power photomicrograph of a section of adult lung, showing an interalveolar partition cut in cross section. The capillaries of this lung were congested; hence, they are wider and contain more red blood cells than is normal. A septal cell and an alveolar phagocyte may be seen.

shown clearly that alveoli are lined with a continuous layer of epithelium which, except in sites where nuclei are present, is so thin that it would not be clearly visible in ordinary sections examined with the light microscope (Figs. 26-15 and 26-16). Secondly, the use of the PAS technic has made it possible, as has been shown so clearly by Leblond and Bertalanffy and their associates, to demonstrate the existence and the distribution of the basement membranes that underlie the epithelium and cover the capillaries in interalveolar walls (Fig. 26-15). From the evidence gained from these two lines of investigation it has become apparent that air in alveoli is separated from blood in the capillaries by: (1) the cytoplasm of the epithelial cells that line alveoli; (2) the basement membrane of the epithelium, which in some sites blends with the third component; (3) the basement membrane that covers the endothelium of the capillaries; and (4) the cytoplasm of the endothelial cells of capillaries. In some sites there are tissue spaces that contain fine fibrils between 2 and 3 (Fig. 26-16).

The Cells of Interalveolar Walls. The nuclei that are visible in alveolar walls are those of several types of cells. The largest number appear as flattened or bent ovoids with fairly condensed chromatin, these are the nuclei of the endothelial cells of the capillaries and the epithelial cells that line alveoli (Figs. 26-14, 26-15 and 26-16). The two kinds are similar in appearance, but the latter type can be distinguished from the former, according to Bertalanffy and Leblond, in PAS preparations, because they are outside the basement membrane that underlies the epithelium (Fig. 26-15).

*Alveolar (Septal) Cells.* The second most common kind of nuclei (about 30%, according to Bertalanffy and Leblond) are those of *alveolar (septal)* cells. The nuclei of these are ovoid but are somewhat larger, and they do not have as condensed chromatin as those of the first type discussed. The cytoplasm may be vacuolated because it contains numerous lipoid droplets or it may be of an even texture; hence, two types of alveolar or septal cells are described, the vacuolated and the nonvacuolated varieties (Fig. 26-15). Transitions are also seen. Alveolar cells of either types may be in alveolar walls, along the sides of alveolar walls or free in the alveoli. Both kinds are phagocytic, and, in general, the alveolar cells behave very much as do the macrophages of other parts of the body. The evidence suggests that new ones are formed in and along alveolar walls by the mitosis of pre-existing alveolar cells. Bertalanffy and Leblond, using the colchicine technic, estimated that the entire stock of alveolar cells in the lung is replaced about once a week. It has been suggested that alveolar cells may be concerned with maintaining the film of alveolar fluid that coats the inner surfaces of alveoli. Their obvious and pronounced function is that of serving as phagocytes so that any dust particles or other types of debris that gain entrance to alveolar spaces can be removed (Figs. 7-29 and 26-14). They are motile. Born in or along the sides of alveolar walls (those born in the walls would have to break through the epithelial basement membrane), they move up along the air passages to reach bronchioles where their further progress is aided by the cilia. Once alveolar cells become free of their attachments to alveolar walls they are generally termed *alveolar phagocytes* (Figs. 7-29 and 26-14). When lungs are congested with blood, because of an incompetent heart, blood often escapes into alveolar spaces where the alveolar phagocytes engulf the erythrocytes and form iron pigment from

FIG. 26-15. Schematic drawing of a thin section of 2 alveoli. In order to illustrate the modern concept of lung structure, the alveolar walls, the lining epithelium and the basement membranes all have been represented as being thicker, in relation to the size of the alveolar spaces, than they are. (Drawing based on illustrations provided by F. Bertalanffy and C. P. Leblond)

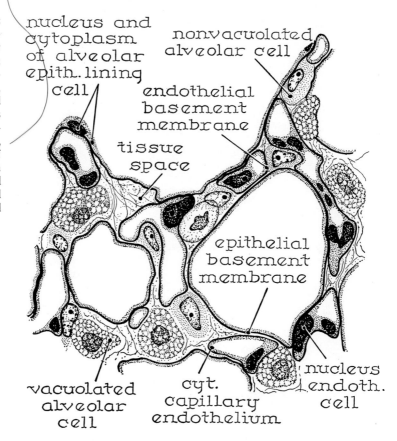

the hemoglobin they contain. The pigment-containing cells are commonly coughed up in large numbers under these conditions, and they give positive histochemical tests for iron. Such cells are called *heart failure cells*.

The origin of the alveolar (septal) cells is not certain. There are two main views about the matter. According to one school of thought, they are descendants of the epithelial cells that grow into mesenchyme to outline the bronchial tree and the alveoli of the lung. According to this view, they are members of the same family of cells as those that are flattened and line the alveoli. According to the other school of thought, they are of mesenchymal origin— macrophages that arise from the mesenchymal component of developing lung. According to this latter view, they could have their numbers supplemented readily by monocytes coming to the lung by way of the bloodstream.

Bertalanffy has recently dealt with the cells of alveolar walls in great detail (see references).

A third type of nucleus seen in interalveolar walls is that of leukocytes that are in the blood in the capillaries. Occasional leukocytes escape into other parts of the wall under normal conditions. In infections of the lung, for example, in lobar pneumonia, alveolar spaces may be packed solidly with fibrin and neutrophils.

**The Fine Structure of Interalveolar Walls.** The nuclei of the epithelial lining cells are surrounded by a relatively narrow rim of cytoplasm (Fig. 26-16) which from this region spreads out as a very thin sheet to form a cytoplasmic covering for the interalveolar wall (Fig. 26-16, *middle left*). Low estimates that the thickness of this sheet is approximately 0.2 $\mu$ in the rabbit, the guinea pig, the dog and in man. In the rat it is only about 0.1 $\mu$ thick. In the mouse the sheet is thinner still. Karrer, in particular, has studied the endothelium with the EM; in the mouse it averages about 0.15 $\mu$ in thickness, but in some sites it may become as thin as 0.01 $\mu$. In Figure 26-16 (man) it is seen to be slightly thicker than the

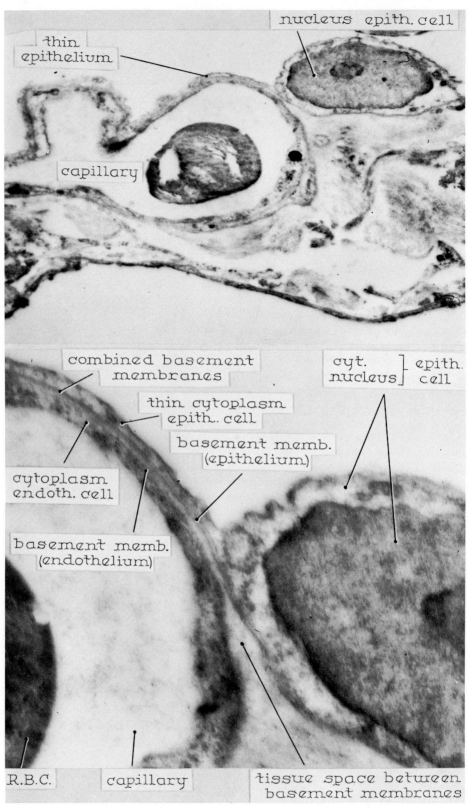

FIG. 26-16. Two electron micrographs ($\times$ 11,000, *top;* $\times$ 40,000, *bottom*) of the same area of a section of human lung. (Low, F. N.: Anat. Rec. *117*:241, with labeling added)

epithelium. The identification of the basement membranes of the epithelial and the endothelial cells in electron micrographs is somewhat difficult. They are only about 0.05 to 0.1 $\mu$ in thickness. According to Low, their electron density, when they are osmicated, is even, and their outlines are sharp (Fig. 26-16). Karrer describes the basement membranes of the lung as consisting of a rather homogeneous material of low electron density. A problem is created in interpreting what is seen in electron micrographs because at some sites the basement membrane of the epithelium and that of the endothelium approach one another and in all probability fuse to become a single homogeneous membrane (Fig. 26-16, combined basement membranes). However, at other sites, they diverge from one another to enclose tissue spaces (Fig. 26-16, tissue space between basement membranes). The tissue spaces contain fine fibrils of the collagenic or the reticular variety. If the tissue space labeled in Figure 26-16 is followed to the left it will be seen that it becomes so greatly thinned that the basement membrane of the epithelium is separated from that of the endothelium by a film of tissue that could only contain very fine fibrils. It could be argued that such thin films of tissue between basement membranes were actually parts of the basement membrane, but it seems preferable to consider them as parts of the fibrillar tissue that offers intimate support for the elements in alveolar walls, which becomes expanded in some sites and thinned in others and disappears altogether when the basement membranes of endothelium and epithelium come into direct contact (Fig. 26-16, combined basement membranes).

## THE DEVELOPMENT OF THE LUNGS

The lungs develop like exocrine glands. The outgrowth responsible for them arises from the epithelium of the anterior wall of the foregut. The epithelial outgrowth first assumes the form of a longitudinal bulge but this, before long, becomes pinched off from the foregut except at its cephalic end. The tube formed as a result of the pinching-off process is the forerunner of the larynx and the trachea. Its caudal end is closed, but cell proliferation at this site soon results in two hollow epithelial bulges forking out from it, one being directed toward the left, and the other to the right.

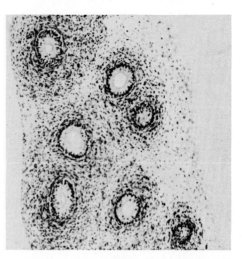

FIG. 26-17. Low-power photomicrograph of a section of the lung of a pig embryo in an early stage of development. Epithelial tubules (future bronchi) are growing and branching into the mesenchyme. (Ham, A. W., and Baldwin, K. W.: Anat. Rec. *81*:377)

These bulges are commonly termed the lung buds, but they are better termed the *primary bronchial buds* because they are the forerunners of the 2 primary bronchi.

The 2 primary bronchial buds, because of the continued proliferation of cells in their ends and walls, advance toward the sites at which lungs will develop. Bulges appear on these advancing tubes; these subsequently grow and elongate to give rise to the secondary bronchi. These, in turn, usually by pairs of bulges which appear at their blind ends, continue to branch and grow to give rise to the smaller bronchi (Fig. 26-17). The branching then becomes more irregular but continues to give rise to the forerunners of bronchioles.

Although it simplifies matters to say that the growing, branching, hollow epithelial tree that develops originally from the epithelium of the foregut gives rise to the bronchi and the bronchioles of the lungs and that these are comparable with the interlobular and intralobular ducts of exocrine glands, this is not the whole truth, for the epithelial outgrowth gives rise to only the epithelial lining and the glands of the bronchi and the bronchioles. The connective tissue and the smooth muscle of the walls of the bronchi and the bronchioles, and the cartilages of the bronchi, develop from the

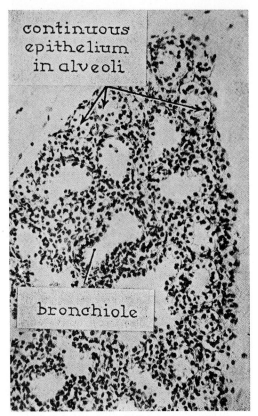

continuous
epithelium
in alveoli

bronchiole

FIG. 26-18. Medium-power photomicrograph of a section of the lung of a pig embryo about halfway through prenatal development. Notice that the developing bronchioles have given rise to epithelial alveoli, which are structures comparable with the secretory alveoli or glands.

mesenchyme that is invaded by the growing, branching, hollow epithelial tree. The mesenchyme, as it is invaded, becomes condensed around the epithelial tubes (Fig. 26-17) and there differentiates into the connective tissue constituents of their walls.

In the development of exocrine glands, secretory units sprout from the ends of the branching duct system. A comparable phenomenon occurs in the developing lung in the 5th month of development. The epithelium of what at this time are the terminal branches of the bronchial tree extends out into the mesenchyme to form epithelial structures comparable with alveolar ducts and alveoli. The soft cellular mesenchyme around these hollow epithelial outgrowths does not immediately

(although it may, much later in development) become condensed to make these outgrowths into bronchioles; hence, these outgrowths are comparable with the epithelial secretory units that develop from the terminal portions of the developing duct systems of exocrine glands (Fig. 26-18).

That the lung attains a stage of development, sometime during the 5th month, when it is clearly glandlike, possessing a branching duct system (the bronchial tree), the terminal branches of which connect with epithelial structures that are the equivalent of secretory units (alveolar ducts and alveoli), is generally accepted (Fig. 26-18). However, there has been a difference of opinion as to whether the lung remains glandlike throughout the remainder of prenatal development. It is sometimes said that the lung retains its glandlike character until the time of birth; that is, until the time of birth, the alveoli of the fetal lung are *rounded* hollow epithelial structures, being made of cuboidal to columnar epithelial cells firmly attached to one another. According to this view, the glandlike nature of the lung disappears only when respiratory movements begin after birth.

However, many investigations of lung development made with the light microscope, including our own, yielded results at variance with the concept described above. If glandlike refers to the alveoli remaining rounded, like secretory units, until the time of birth, the lung does not remain glandlike, for in the later stages of development the alveoli become angular, taking on the appearance that they have in postnatal life (Fig. 26-19, *top*). This fact has medicolegal implications, as will be described soon.

**Fetal Respiratory Movements and Their Possible Effects on Lung Structure.** It is interesting to question whether or not the change in the appearance of the fetal lung that occurs about two thirds of the way through pregnancy, which is reflected in the alveoli becoming angular and, in general, assuming an appearance similar to the one that they reveal in the postnatal lung (Fig. 26-19), is due to, or is facilitated by, fetal respiratory movements. Before considering this question it must be admitted that there is some question as to whether respiratory movements of any consequence occur in the fetus.

FIG. 26-19. (*Top*) Low-power photomicrograph of a section of the lung of a pig about two thirds of the way through prenatal development. It is not gland-like, and the alveoli are angular. (*Center*) Photomicrograph of a section of the lung of a pig killed 3 hours after birth. The alveoli are larger. (*Bottom*) Photomicrograph of another area of a section of the lung of a pig killed 3 hours after birth. The alveoli here are greatly expanded. (Ham, A. W., and Baldwin, K. W.: Anat. Rec. *81*:377)

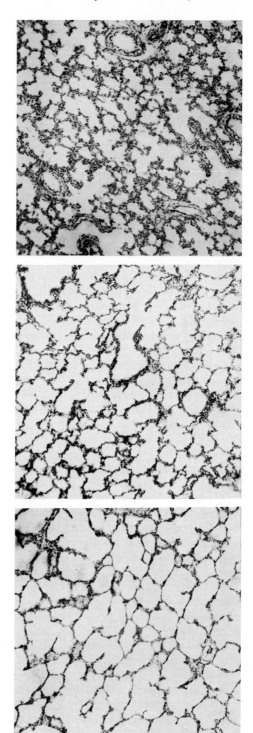

It should be understood that the thoracic cage can become larger in prenatal or postnatal life only if something can enter it to let it enlarge. For all practical purposes only two things can enter the thoracic cage in postnatal life to permit it to enlarge with inspiratory movements—air and blood. In prenatal life the only two things that can enter the cage to let it expand with fetal inspiratory movements are amniotic fluid and blood. Therefore, it is obvious that inspiratory movements in fetal life would draw amniotic fluid into alveolar ducts and alveoli, and so would let them expand, and blood into the capillaries of interalveolar walls to let them expand. It seems not improbable that inspiratory movements in fetal life assist in opening up alveoli so that they become angular rather than round, and that the movements also play a part in filling and expanding the capillary bed of the lungs, which may stimulate its growth, for it develops very rapidly in the interalveolar walls as the lung changes its character.

According to the more modern concept of the development of the lung, birth is not such an important milestone as it is according to the older view. According to the newer view, the developing lung ceases to be glandlike, not at birth, but approximately two thirds of the way through fetal life (Fig. 26-19, *top*). At this time it goes through most of the preparations for birth so that a baby born prematurely has a chance of living.

A fetus of 7 months is generally said to be *viable*; that is, it is capable of living by means of breathing air if it should be born. The great development of the capillary beds of the interalveolar walls that begins around two thirds of the way through fetal life is an obvious factor in permitting the fetus to attain this state.

**Some Medicolegal Aspects.** It has been observed already that it is sometimes of great importance to know whether a baby has breathed air after it was born, for it then would be considered as having been born alive. If a newborn baby has breathed air and subsequently dies, its lungs, when removed at autopsy, will not sink if they are placed in a pan of water, because the air they contain makes them lighter than water. If a baby has not breathed air, its lungs will sink. This test is probably much more reliable than that afforded by microscopic examination. There has been much confusion about this because certain of those who subscribe to the older view of the development of the lung may argue that a departure from the glandlike appearance is an indication that air has been breathed. Certainly, if sections of a fetal lung show it to be glandlike throughout, it can be assumed with much justification that the fetus concerned never breathed air. But, if a lung is not glandlike but instead, opened-up, as in Figure 26-19, *top*, it cannot be assumed that the fetus concerned has breathed air because such an appearance can be caused presumably by the fetus "breathing" amniotic fluid in fetal life. The medicolegal significance of interpretations of sections of lungs of the newborn with reference to whether the infants concerned breathed air or not has been thoroughly investigated and discussed by Shapiro in the light of the newer knowledge of lung development.

**Is There Continuous or Discontinuous Epithelium in the Fetal Lung?** Many light microscope studies made in the past seemed to indicate that the epithelial cells of alveoli and alveolar ducts became discontinuous in the later months of fetal life and that this permitted capillaries to bulge into the future air spaces. However, Krahl has extensively reviewed evidence from many fields and considers that the lining epithelium remains continuous throughout development and that it becomes greatly thinned as alveoli expand. Krahl also points out the importance of proper fixation for lung studies, and he shows that separation of epithelial cells in fetal lungs can be caused by improper fixation.

**Changes at Birth.** According to the newer view of the development of the lung, it is assumed that since the future air spaces of the fetal lung are filled with fluid at the time of birth, these spaces must be expanded further if air is to be taken into the lungs after birth.

Their greater expansion after birth (Fig. 26-19, *center, bottom*) is brought about by the greatly intensified respiratory movements that occur when a baby is born. It is of interest that these inspiratory movements, which are intensified over those that occur in intrauterine existence, not only draw air into the lungs but also more blood. This may explain why a newborn baby will increase its weight by several ounces if the umbilical cord is not cut too soon after a baby is born. Every effort is made by the doctor who delivers a baby to remove all the fluid that he can from the upper respiratory tract and so assist its displacement by air. However, it is questionable if all the fluid in the air spaces of the lung is drained away through the upper respiratory tract after birth; perhaps much of it is absorbed.

**Growth.** New alveoli could form in postnatal life by air being drawn into thicker alveolar walls so as to open up new spaces. In the later stages of prenatal life, as well as in the earlier stages of postnatal life, new generations of bronchioles, as well as new alveoli, develop in the lung. It is believed that new bronchioles develop as a result of the epithelium of respiratory bronchioles growing down alveolar ducts, after which the mesenchymal-derived connective tissue around the duct becomes increased and differentiates into the other constituents of a bronchiolar wall. It is believed that the fact that alveoli commonly open from the sides of respiratory bronchioles is evidence that the bronchiole concerned was once an alveolar duct which became converted into a respiratory bronchiole.

## BLOOD SUPPLY OF THE LUNG

Blood from the right ventricle is delivered, by the pulmonary artery and its branches, to the capillary beds of the respiratory tissue of the lung to be oxygenated there. Oxygenated blood is collected from the capillary beds of the lung by the branches of the pulmonary vein and delivered to the left atrium of the heart. It is to be kept in mind that, in the instance of the pulmonary circulation, the arteries carry what is ordinarily called venous blood, and the veins, arterial.

The pulmonary artery to each lung enters

it at its root and within the lung it branches along with the bronchial tree so that each branch of the bronchial tree is accompanied by a branch of the pulmonary artery. The small branches that reach the respiratory bronchioles break up into terminal branches which deliver blood into the capillary beds of the alveolar ducts, the alveolar sacs and the alveoli (Fig. 26-8, *left*).

Blood from the capillary beds of the respiratory tissue of the lungs is collected by the smallest branches of the pulmonary vein. These begin within the substance of lobules and in this region are supported by thin connective tissue sheaths. Supported in this fashion, they travel to, and enter, interlobular septa, where they empty into interlobular veins (Fig. 26-8, *left*). These in turn are conducted by the septa to the site where the apices of the lobules concerned meet. Here the veins come into close association with branches of the bronchial tree. From this point to the root of the lung, the veins follow the bronchi. In other words, except within lobules, the branches of the pulmonary artery and the pulmonary vein follow the branches of the bronchial tree, but within lobules, only the arteries follow the bronchioles.

Oxygenated blood is supplied to parts of the lung by the bronchial arteries. These also travel in close association with the bronchial tree and supply the capillary beds of its walls. They also supply the lymph nodes that are scattered along the bronchial tree. Moreover, branches of the bronchial arteries travel out along the interlobular septa and supply oxygenated blood to the capillaries of the visceral pleura.

### LYMPHATICS OF THE LUNG

General principles are easier to remember than details. It could be said that there is a rough general principle about the distribution of lymphatics in the lung: they are confined to the relatively dense connective tissue structures that prevent the spread of any air leakage that might occur into the delicate walls of alveoli. Hence, they are present in the visceral pleura, in the interlobular septa and in the dense connective tissue wrappings of the bronchioles, the bronchi, the arteries and the veins (Fig. 26-8, *right*). They are not pres-

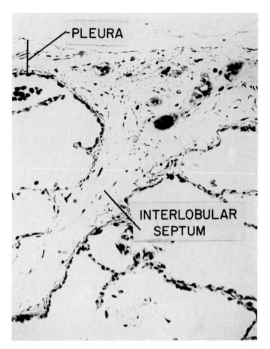

FIG. 26-20. Low-power photomicrograph of a section of the human adult lung showing the pleura at the top and the interlobular septum extending down from the pleura into the substance of the lung.

ent in the interalveolar partitions. However, Miller has described lymphatics in the tissue bordering the alveolar ducts. Lymphatic capillaries in alveolar walls might very well constitute a hazard.

It is customary to describe the lung as having a superficial and a deep set of lymphatics. The superficial ones are contained in the visceral pleura (Fig. 26-8, *bottom*). In city dwellers these are usually blackened by carbon particles which have become incorporated into their walls. The larger ones follow the lines where interlobular septa join the pleura; hence, the bases of those lobules which are projected onto the pleura are usually outlined by dark lines. Smaller lymphatics in the pleura form a pattern of closer mesh than those which surround the bases of lobules. The pleural lymphatics join up with one another to form vessels that are conducted by the pleura to reach and empty into the lymph nodes at the hilus of the lung.

The deep set consists of 3 groups: (1)

those in the outer layers of the walls of bronchioles and bronchi (Fig. 26-8), (2) those that accompany the branches of the pulmonary artery (Fig. 26-8)—these anastomose with those in the branches of the bronchial tree; and (3) those that run in the interlobular septa, particularly in association with the interlobular veins (Fig. 26-8, *right*). All 3 groups drain toward lymph nodes at the hilus of the lung.

The lymphatics of the interlobular septa (which belong to the deep set) communicate with those of the pleura (which belong to the superficial set) at sites where interlobular septa join the visceral pleura (Fig. 26-8, *lower right corner*). It has been taught for years, largely because of Miller's influence, that the lymphatics of the interlobular septa have valves that are disposed close to the pleura (Fig. 26-8, *lower right corner*) and that these valves prevent lymph from the pleural lymphatics from draining into the lymphatics of the septa. In other words, it has been generally conceded that although lymph could pass from the lymphatics of the interlobular septa outwardly into the pleural lymphatics, because of the direction of the valves it could not pass the other way, hence that lymph in the pleural lymphatics, to reach the hilus of the lung, would have to pass by way of the pleural lymphatics over the whole surface of a lobe to reach the hilus. Recently, however, Simer has shown that this older view is fallacious, and that the valves that were generally believed to prevent flow from the pleural lymphatics into the lymphatics of the interlobular septa (Fig. 26-8, *lower right corner*) are: (1) not always present, (2) if present, often poorly developed, and (3) do not always point toward the pleura. Simer showed that India ink injected into the pleural lymphatics does not usually pursue a course around the periphery of the lobe in order to reach the hilus, but instead passes into the lymphatics of the interlobular septa and from there into the lymphatic vessels associated with the bronchial tree and its vessels and so it takes a direct rather than a roundabout course to the hilus of the lung.

### Effects of Respiratory Movements on Lung Structure

The descent and the expansion of the lungs on inspiration require that the bronchial tree be elastic. Macklin has shown that bronchi become longer and wider on inspiration. The root of the lung also descends on inspiration. Recoil from these movements is accomplished chiefly by the already described elastic tissue of the tracheobronchial tree. Macklin's papers should be consulted for details of this and the recoil mechanism.

It is probable that the expansion of the respiratory tissue itself, that occurs on inspiration, is due more to the elongation and the dilatation of alveolar ducts than it is to expansion of alveoli.

### INNERVATION OF THE SMOOTH MUSCLE OF THE BRONCHI AND THE BRONCHIOLES

Fibers from both divisions of the autonomic nervous system pass to the bronchial tree. The parasympathetic supply is brought by branches of the vagus nerve. Stimulation of the efferent fibers causes the bronchiolar musculature to contract. Stimulation of the fibers of sympathetic nerves causes the bronchiolar musculature to relax. In the condition known as asthma, the smooth muscle of the smaller bronchioles contracts, and the mucous membrane of the affected tubes swells. This narrows the passages by which air can enter or leave alveolar ducts and makes breathing exceedingly difficult. Adrenalin, or a similarly acting substance, is often given to relax the bronchiolar musculature and so widen the lumens of the bronchioles of an individual suffering an attack. It is of interest that it is more difficult for an individual with asthma to expel air from his lungs than it is to draw it in; this is because inspiratory movements tend to expand such tubes as lie within lobules and so enlarge their lumens, while powerful expiratory movements, such as occur in asthma, tend, if air cannot be forced out freely through the bronchial tree, to compress such tubes as lie within lobules and so make their lumens still narrower.

### REFERENCES

#### General References on the Lung

Bertalanffy, F. D.: Respiratory tissue: structure, histophysiology, cytodynamics. I. Review and basic cytomorphology, Int. Rev. Cytol. *16*:233, 1964; II. New approaches and interpretations, Int. Rev. Cytol. *17*:213, 1964.

Engel, S.: The Child's Lung, London, Arnold, 1947.

Krahl, V. E.: Microscopic anatomy of the lungs, Am. Rev. Resp. Dis. *80*:24, 1959.

———: Anatomy of the mammalian lung *in* Handbook of Physiology, vol. 1 (Respiration), p. 213, 1964.

Miller, W. S.: The Lung, Springfield, Ill., Thomas, 1937.

von Hayek, Heinrich: The Human Lung, trans. by Vernon E. Krahl, New York, Hafner, 1960.

SPECIAL REFERENCES ON THE UPPER RESPIRATORY TRACT AND THE BRONCHIAL TREE

Arey, L. B.: On the development, morphology and interpretation of a system of cryptanalogues in the pharyngeal tonsil, Am. J. Anat. *80*:203, 1947.

Burnham, H. H.: An anatomical investigation of blood vessels of the lateral nasal wall and their relation to turbinates and sinuses, J. Laryng. Otol. *50*:569, 1935.

Jackson, C., and Jackson, C. L.: Diseases and Injuries of the Larynx, ed. 2, New York, Macmillan, 1942.

Karrer, H. E.: The fine structure of connective tissue in the tunica propria of bronchioles, J. Ultrastr. Res. *2*:96, 1958.

Lucas, A. M.: The nasal cavity and direction of fluid by ciliary movement in Macacus rhesus (Desm.), Am. J. Anat. *50*:141, 1932.

Mackenzie, J. N.: The physiological and pathological relations between the nose and the sexual apparatus of man, Johns Hopkins Hosp. Bull. *9*:10, 1898.

Macklin, C. C.: Bronchial length changes and other movements, Tubercle *14*:16 & 69, 1932.

———: The dynamic bronchial tree, Am. Rev. Tuberc. *25*:363, 1932.

———: The mechanics and dynamics of the human lungs and bronchi, M. Rec. *143*:89, 1936.

———: The musculature of the bronchi and lungs, Physiol. Rev. *9*:1, 1929.

Rhodin, J., and Dalhamn, T.: Electron microscopy of the tracheal ciliated mucosa in rat, Z. Zellforsch. *44*:345, 1956.

Schaeffer, J. P.: The mucous membrane of the nasal cavity and the paranasal sinuses *in* Cowdry's Special Cytology, ed. 2, p. 105, New York, Hoeber, 1932.

SPECIAL REFERENCES ON THE MICROSCOPIC STRUCTURE OF THE RESPIRATORY PORTION OF THE LUNG, INCLUDING REFERENCES ON FINE STRUCTURE

Barrie, H. J.: The acinus: The architecture of caseous nodules in the lung and the place of the word "acinar" in describing tuberculous lesions, Canad. M. A. J. *92*:1149, 1965.

Bensley, R. D., and Bensley, S. H.: Studies of the lining of the pulmonary alveolous of normal lungs of adult animals, Anat. Rec. *64*:41, 1935.

Bertalanffy, F. D., Glegg, R. E., and Eidinger, D.: Chemical confirmation of the abundance of reticulin in the lung, Canad. M. A. J. *70*:196 & 220, 1954.

Bertalanffy, F. D., and Leblond, C. P.: The continuous renewal of the two types of alveolar cells in the lung of the rat, Anat. Rec. *115*:515, 1953.

———: Structure of respiratory tissue, Lancet *2*:1365, 1955.

Bremer, J. L.: Evidence of an epithelial lining in the labyrinth of the avian lung, Anat. Rec. *73*:497, 1939.

Brettschneider, H.: Electron mikroskopische Untersuchungen an der Nasenschleimhaut, Anat. Anz. *105*:194, 1958.

Hartroft, W. S., and Macklin, C. C.: The size of the human lung alveoli expressed as diameters of selected alveolar outlines as seen in specially prepared 25 micron microsections, Tr. Roy. Soc. Canada, Sec. V (Biol. Sc.) *38*:63, 1944.

Hesse, F. E., and Loosli, C. G.: The lining of the alveoli in mice, rats, dogs and frogs following acute pulmonary edema produced by antu poisoning, Anat. Rec. *105*:299, 1949.

Josselyn, L. E.: The nature of the pulmonary alveolar lining, Anat. Rec. *62*:147, 1935.

Karrer, H. E.: The ultrastructure of mouse lung, J. Biophys. Biochem. Cytol, *2*:241, 1956.

———: The ultrastructure of mouse lung, J. Biophys. Biochem. Cytol. (Supp.) *2*:287, 1956.

———: The ultrastructure of mouse lung: the alveolar macrophage, J. Biophys. Biochem. Cytol. *4*:693, 1958.

Krahl, V. E.: The experimental production of pulmonary emphysema, Am. Rev. Resp. Dis. *80*:158, 1959.

———: Current concept of the finer structure of the lung, A.M.A. Arch. Int. Med. *96*:342, 1955.

———: The respiratory portions of the lung, Bull. Sch. Med. Univ. Maryland *40*:101, 1955.

Leblond, C. P., and Bertalanffy, F. D.: Reticulin membranes of the framework of the alveolar lung, tissue in the albino rat, Canad. M. A. J. *65*:263, 1951.

Loosli, C. G.: The rabbit's lung after phrenectomy and pneumothorax, Anat. Rec. *62*:381, 1935.

———: The structure of the respiratory portion of the mammalian lung with notes on the lining of the frog lung, Am. J. Anat. *62*:375, 1938.

Loosli, C., Adams, W. E., and Thornton, T. M.,

Jr.: The histology of the dog's lung following an experimental collapse with special reference to the nature of the alveolar lining, Anat. Rec. *105*:697, 1949.

Low, F. N.: Electron microscopy of the rat lung, Anat. Rec. *113*:437, 1952.

————: The electron microscopy of sectioned lung tissue after varied duration of fixation in buffered osmium tetroxide, Anat. Rec. *120*: 827, 1954.

————: The pulmonary alveolar epithelium of laboratory mammals and man, Anat. Rec. *117*: 241, 1953.

Low, F. N., and Sampaio, M. M.: The pulmonary alveolar epithelium as an entodermal derivative, Anat. Rec. *127*:51, 1957.

Macklin, C. C.: Pulmonic alveolar epithelium; report of a round table conference, J. Thoracic Surg. *6*:82, 1936.

Miller, W. S.: The epithelium of the lower respiratory tract *in* Cowdry's Special Cytology, ed. 2, p. 131. New York, Hoeber, 1932.

Ogawa, C.: The finer ramifications of the human lung, Am. J. Anat. *27*:333, 1920.

Rose, S. B.: The finer structure of the lung, Arch. Path. *6*:36, 1928.

Ross, I. S.: Pulmonary epithelium and proliferative reactions in the lungs; a study of the cellular response in lungs after intratracheal injections of toxic and nontoxic foreign substances, Arch. Path. *27*:478, 1939.

Swigart, R. H., and Kane, D. J.: Electron microscopic observations of pulmonary alveoli, Anat. Rec. *112*:93, 1952.

Woodside, G. L., and Dalton, A. J.: The ultrastructure of lung tissue from newborn and embryo mice, J. Ultrastr. Res. *2*:28, 1958.

SPECIAL REFERENCES ON THE DEVELOPMENT
AND GROWTH OF THE LUNG

Barnard, W. G., and Day, T. D.: The development of the terminal air passages of the human lung, J. Path. Bact. *45*:67, 1937.

Bensley, S. H., and Groff, M. B.: Changes in the alveolar epithelium of the rat at birth, Anat. Rec. *64*:27, 1935.

Clements, L. P.: Embryonic development of the respiratory portion of the pig's lung, Anat. Rec. *70*:575, 1938.

Cooper, E. R. A.: A histological investigation of the development and structure of the human lung, J. Path. Bact. *47*:105, 1938.

Flint, J. M.: The development of the lungs, Am. J. Anat. *6*:1, 1906.

Ham, A. W., and Baldwin, K. W.: A histological study of the development of the lung with particular reference to the nature of the alveoli, Anat. Rec. *81*:363, 1941.

Krahl, V. E.: The respiratory portions of the

lung, Bull. Sch. Med. Univ. Maryland *40*:101, 1955.

Loosli, C. G., and Potter, E. L.: Pre- and postnatal development of the respiratory portion of the human lung, Am. Rev. Resp. Dis. *80*:5, 1959.

Palmer, D. M.: Early developmental stages of the human lung, Ohio J. Sc. *36*:69, 1936.

————: The lung of a human foetus of 170 mm. C. R. length, Am. J. Anat. *58*:59, 1936.

Shapiro, H. A.: The limited value of microscopy of lung tissue in the diagnosis of live and stillbirth, Clin. Proc. *6*:149, 1947.

Short, R. H. D.: Alveolar epithelium in relation to growth of the lung, Phil. Tr. Roy. Soc. London *235*:35, 1950.

Stewart, F. W.: An histogenic study of the respiratory epithelium, Anat. Rec. *25*:181, 1923.

Willson, H. G.: Postnatal development of the lung, Am. J. Anat. *41*:97, 1928.

SPECIAL REFERENCES ON FETAL RESPIRATORY
MOVEMENT AND FETAL CIRCULATION

Barcroft, J.: Fetal circulation and respiration, Physiol. Rev. *16*:103, 1936.

Davis, M. E., and Potter, E. L.: Intrauterine respiration of the human fetus, J.A.M.A. *131*: 1194, 1946.

Potter, E. L., and Bohlender, G. P.: Intrauterine respiration in relation to development of the fetal lung, Am. J. Obst. Gynec. *42*:14, 1941.

Reynolds, S. R. M.: The fetal and neonatal pulmonary vasculature in the guinea pig in relation to hemodynamic changes at birth, Am. J. Anat. *98*:97, 1956.

Windle, W. F.: Physiology of the Fetus, Philadelphia, Saunders, 1940.

SPECIAL REFERENCES ON ALVEOLAR PORES
AND OTHER TYPES OF COMMUNICATION

Duguid, J. B., and Lambert, M. W.: The pathogenesis of coal miner's pneumoconiosis, J. Path. Bact. *88*:389, 1964.

Lambert, M. W.: Accessory bronchiolo-alveolar communications, J. Path. Bact. *70*:311, 1955.

————: Accessory bronchiolo-alveolar channels, Anat. Rec. *127*:472, 1957.

Loosli, C. G.: Interalveolar communications in normal and in pathologic mammalian lungs, Arch. Path. *24*:743, 1937.

Macklin, C. C.: Alveolar pores and their significance in the human lung, Arch. Path. *21*:202, 1936.

————: Pulmonic alveolar vents, J. Anat. *69*: 188, 1935.

————: Pulmonic interlobular air passages, Tr. Roy. Soc. Canada, Sec. V (Biol. Sc.) *28*:37, 1934.

SPECIAL REFERENCES ON ALVEOLAR (SEPTAL)
CELLS AND ALVEOLAR PHAGOCYTES

Bertalanffy, F. D., and Leblond, C. P.: The continuous renewal of the two types of alveolar cells in the lung of the rat, Anat. Rec. *115*: 515, 1953.

Bremer, J. L.: Postnatal development of alveoli in mammalian lungs in relation to the problem of the alveolar phagocyte, Contrib. Embryol. *25*:83, 1935.

Clements, L. P.: On the origin and relations of the pulmonary macrophages, Anat. Rec. *78*: 429, 1940.

Macklin, C. C.: Residual epithelial cells on the pulmonary alveolar walls of mammals, Tr. Roy. Soc. Canada, Sec. V (Biol. Sc.) *40*:93, 1946.

Sampaio, M. M.: The use of thorotrast for the electron microscopic study of phagocytosis, Anat. Rec. *124*:501, 1956.

SPECIAL REFERENCES ON SURGICAL
EMPHYSEMA AND THE LUNGS

Macklin, C. C.: The pattern of interstitial emphysema induced in the excised lung of the calf by overinflation, Tr. Roy. Soc. Canada, Sec. V *34*:69, 1940.

————: Pneumothorax with massive collapse from experimental overinflation of the lung substance, Canad. M. A. J. *36*:414, 1937.

————: Spontaneous mediastinal emphysema; a review and comment, M. Rec. *150*:5, 1939.

Macklin, C. C., and Macklin, M. T.: Pulmonic interstitial emphysema and its sequelae: an anatomical interpretation *in* Essays in Biology in Honor of Herbert M. Evans, Berkeley, Univ. California Press, 1943.

SPECIAL REFERENCES ON THE LYMPHATICS
AND BLOOD VESSELS OF THE LUNG
AND LUNG FLUID

Macklin, C. C.: Lung fluid, alveolar dust drift, and initial lesions of disease in the lungs, Canad. M. A. J. *72*:664, 1955.

————: Pulmonary sumps, dust accumulations, alveolar fluid and lymph vessels, Acta anat. *23*:1, 1955.

————: Terminal pulmonary venules in mammalian lungs, Tr. Roy. Soc. Canada, Sec. V *39*: 105, 1945.

Miller, W. S.: The lymphatics and the lymph flow in the human lung, Am. Rev. Tuberc. *3*:193, 1919.

Simer, P. H.: Drainage of pleural lymphatics, Anat. Rec. *113*:269, 1952.

Tobin, C. E.: Lymphatics of the pulmonary alveoli, Anat. Rec. *120*:625, 1954.

(*See also* Flint, J. M., p. 770)

# 27   The Urinary System

## SOME GENERAL CONSIDERATIONS

The combustion of coal results both in the production of energy and the formation of waste products. Some of the latter are gaseous and go up the chimney, but some are not so easily disposed of and remain in a furnace as ashes. Likewise, the metabolism of food by the cells of the body produces not only energy but also many waste products. These substances seep from cells through tissue fluid and into the bloodstream. From there an important waste product, carbon dioxide, goes up the chimney, as it were, by being eliminated from the lungs. Some of the others, particularly those that result from the metabolism of proteins, are not disposed of so easily; indeed, to eliminate these the body is equipped with two similar and specially constructed organs of substantial size—the kidneys—through which more than one fifth of the total blood of the body circulates every minute.

In the kidneys, waste products are eliminated continuously from blood and are concentrated in a fluid called *urine,* which is carried away from each kidney by a tube called a *ureter.* The ureter from each kidney leads to the *urinary bladder;* here urine can accumulate so as to be evacuated from the body periodically and at will through another, and single, tube, the *urethra.* The two kidneys, the two ureters, the urinary bladder and the urethra comprise the *urinary system.*

However, it should be emphasized that the kidneys perform other functions of very great importance in addition to that of ridding the body of the waste products of metabolism. For example, they can vary the amount of water that is lost from the body in urine. Hence, the kidneys play a very important part in regulating the *fluid balance* of the body. Likewise, the kidneys can vary the amounts and the kinds of electrolytes that are eliminated from the body in urine; thus they assist in maintaining a proper *salt balance* in blood and tissue fluid. The kidneys, in addition to eliminating waste products, act in many ways to maintain a fluid environment in the body which is suitable for the life of body cells. In maintaining this environment it should be understood that the kidneys act not only to *eliminate* waste and superfluous materials from the bloodstream but also to *conserve* fluid and/or dissolved materials that are needed to maintain a proper state of affairs in the bloodstream.

It should be obvious from the foregoing that kidney function is indispensable. However, the fact that over a fifth of the total blood of the body circulates through the kidneys every minute exposes them widely to injury should poisons or toxins be present in the blood. Fortunately, these organs possess a considerable measure of reserve so that a certain amount of impairment of function can be tolerated by the body. (Lehr and Churg showed that more than 80% of the total kidney mass had to be removed before any symptoms of kidney dysfunction appeared.) Since the kidneys perform so many different functions, kidney disease may be reflected by a lessened ability to perform any of their several functions as well as usual. Therefore, its diagnosis may require considerable study, and its proper management must be based on a sound knowledge of the microscopic structure of these organs and how their different parts perform their various functions in health and disease.

## THE BASIC MECHANISMS OF EXCRETORY TUBULES

Before attempting to learn the microscopic structure of the kidney, the student will find it helpful to know something about the simpler excretory organs of certain lower animals.

In simpler organisms, in which blood circulatory systems are not highly developed, tissue fluid is the dominant fluid. In it the waste products of metabolism tend to accumulate, and from it they must be excreted. A relatively simple mechanism for accomplishing this effect is present in the earthworm. Its segments are provided with tubules, both ends of which are open. One end of each tubule opens into the interior of the worm and the other onto its exterior. Tissue fluid enters the open internal end of each tubule and passes slowly along it to be eliminated at the exterior of the worm.

However, the tubules are not short and straight but long and coiled. Therefore, it takes some time for tissue fluid to pass along them. This provides an opportunity for the tissue fluid to be altered as it passes along the tubule by the epithelial cells lining the tubule either (1) *absorbing* certain valuable constituents of the fluid back into the organism or (2) *excreting* further things into the fluid in the tubule. It might be anticipated, then, that the fluid that finally emerges from the tubule onto the surface of the organism (and this, for all practical purposes, is urine) contains fewer valuable constituents than the tissue fluid that enters the tubule and also that it contains waste products in greater concentration. We shall see that in man, as in the earthworm, urine is *tissue fluid* that has been *modified* in the above-described fashion by passing along a tubule.

**Evolution of the Glomerulus.** As organisms became more complex the blood circulatory system became of increasing importance in distributing oxygen and food to cells in different parts of the body and in carrying away their waste products. This required some mechanism by which waste products could be removed from the blood more or less continuously. To accomplish this effect the excretory tubule was retained, but at one point along its course a cluster of thin-walled blood vessels was brought close to its wall, and the epithelial wall of the tubule at that site was bulged out to surround, more or less, the cluster of blood vessels. Under these circumstances, tissue fluid that is exuded by the blood vessels in the cluster has only to pass through the thinned wall of the tubule that bulges around the vessels to enter the lumen of the tubule. A little cluster of blood vessels of this sort is called a *glomerulus* (*glomus* = a skein), and the tissue fluid they exude into the tubule is called *glomerular filtrate*. Glomeruli greatly increase the amount of tissue

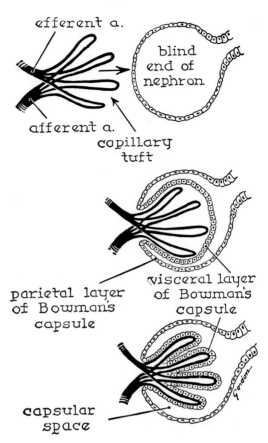

FIG. 27-1. Diagrams to show how capillary loops between afferent and efferent vessels are invaginated into the blind end of the excretory tubule. The visceral layer of Bowman's capsule at first covers the group of capillary loops as a whole; later it covers each loop (*lower picture*) and finally it almost completely surrounds the outgoing and the incoming arms of each loop (not shown here).

fluid that can be delivered into excretory tubules.

## THE NEPHRONS OF HIGHER ANIMALS AND HOW THEY FUNCTION

The arrangement of glomeruli being disposed along the sides of tubules was retained in only a few species. As evolution proceeded the innermost end of the tubule became closed; a glomerulus of capillaries was invaginated into it at this site (Fig. 27-1). The epithelial cells of the tubules at their blind ends, where the glomeruli of capillaries are invaginated, are very thin, so that at this site the lumen of a capillary is separated from the lumen of the excretory tubule by only two layers of living cells: the endothelium of the capillary wall and the thin squamous epithelium of the wall of the tubule (Fig. 27-1). An excretory tubule complete with a glomerulus invaginated into its blind end is termed a *nephron,* and there are over a million of these in each kidney of man.

Tissue fluid is formed only at the arterial ends of most capillaries in the body and resorbed at their venous ends (Fig. 10-8). The reasons for this are fully explained in Chapter 10. If the drainage of capillaries is impeded, as occurs, for example, in venous obstruction, tissue fluid is formed along the whole length of the capillary (Fig. 10-9). In most places in the body, extra tissue fluid produced this way results in edema. Arrangements are made in glomeruli so that the capillaries of glomeruli normally operate under conditions comparable with a certain amount of venous obstruction; hence, they produce tissue fluid along their whole lengths. This, of course, does not cause edema, because the tissue fluid, instead of accumulating in tissue spaces, as it would anywhere else in the body, enters the lumens of nephrons as glomerular filtrate.

The arrangement made in a glomerulus, so that its capillaries produce tissue fluid along their whole lengths, is that of having them drain, not into a wide unobstructed venule but into an arteriole. Since glomerular capillaries are supplied by an arteriole and also drained by an arteriole they represent, as it were, a tuft of capillaries interposed along the course of an arteriole. The arteriole that supplies the glomerular capillaries is termed the *afferent arteriole* of the glomerulus, and the arteriole into which the glomerular capillaries empty is termed the *efferent arteriole* of the glomerulus (Fig. 27-1). Since the lumen of the efferent arteriole is smaller than that of the afferent one (in contrast with what would be the case if the efferent vessel were a venule), a certain amount of resistance is offered to the free passage of blood from glomerular capillaries, enough to maintain a sufficiently high hydrostatic pressure throughout their whole lengths to permit them to exude tissue fluid along their whole lengths. The tonus of

the muscle in the walls of the efferent arteriole can change so as to vary the amount of resistance it offers.

According to Allen, from the 1,700 liters of blood that passes along the glomerular capillaries of the two kidneys every 24 hours, 170 liters of tissue fluid (glomerular filtrate) is formed. It follows, then, that every 24 hours 170 liters of glomerular filtrate are emptied into the tubular portions of nephrons. As this passes along the nephrons almost 169 liters of it are resorbed back into the bloodstream so that only about 1½ liters emerge from the ends of the nephrons each 24 hours to constitute the daily output of urine. Obviously, there must be as efficient a mechanism for the *tubular resorption* of fluid as there is in glomeruli for its production. A basic factor in the mechanism of resorption will now be considered.

The tubular portions of nephrons lie in a rich capillary bed (Fig. 27-19). This bed, as will be explained in detail later, is supplied almost entirely by the efferent arterioles of glomeruli. Hence, the blood that supplies the capillaries in which the tubular portions of nephrons lie has passed through glomerular capillaries where it has lost approximately 10 per cent of its fluid and crystalloid content, and, as a result, its colloid (protein) content has become relatively increased. Since the blood in the beds that surround the tubules drains into venules, which offer no substantial resistance to its flow, it is comparable with the blood in the venous ends of ordinary capillaries in that it has an increased osmotic pressure and is under a low hydrostatic pressure. Under these circumstances it might be expected that osmotic phenomena would be of great importance in tubular resorption, and later we shall describe some of the osmotic mechanisms involved.

To sum up the foregoing: The nephron— an epithelial tubule with a glomerulus of capillaries invaginated into its blind end— is the structural and functional unit of the kidney. The blood supply of its different parts is arranged so that so far as the production of tissue fluid is concerned, the capillaries of glomeruli function along their whole lengths as do only the arterial ends of capillaries in most parts of the body, and, so far as the resorption of tissue fluid is concerned, the capillaries that surround the tubular portions of the nephrons are similar to the venous ends of ordinary capillaries in that the hydrostatic pressure in them is low and, as a consequence, osmotic phenomena can operate readily to achieve resorption. However, it must not be thought that the relatively low hydrostatic pressure of the blood in the capillary beds that surround the tubular portions of nephrons is the only factor concerned in the resorptive process. Over most of the length of the nephron, its wall, though only one cell thick, is composed of cells of substantial thickness, a fact that suggests that these cells do additional vital work, the larger part of which is concerned with the resorption of valuable materials from the lumen of the nephron, and the smaller part, with the excretion of certain substances against a diffusion gradient into the lumen of the nephron.

The various specialized resorptive and excretory functions performed by the tubular portion of the nephron are not performed with equal facility along its whole length. The tubular portion of each nephron exhibits three consecutive segments which exhibit somewhat different structural features and perform somewhat different functions. These are termed the *proximal convoluted segment,* the *loop of Henle* and the *distal convoluted segment,* respectively. Their particular structure and functions will be described in some detail somewhat later when the nephron of the human kidney is considered.

## THE UNILOBAR (UNIPYRAMIDAL) KIDNEY

The gross and the microscopic anatomy of the multilobar kidney of man is a sufficiently difficult topic to justify its being approached by a somewhat circuitous route if that makes the understanding of its structure easier. It so happens that the kidneys of rats, rabbits and certain other animals consist of only a single lobe, and the structure of such a kidney is much simpler to discuss than the structure of a multilobar kidney. Accordingly, we shall first describe the gross and the microscopic structures of a unilobar kidney and then afterward the gross and the microscopic appearances of the multilobar kidney of man. In order to avoid undue repetition, the descrip-

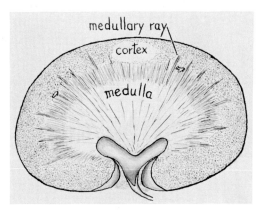

FIG. 27-2. Drawing of the cut surface of a split kidney of a rabbit. Notice that medullary rays appear to be extensions of the striated medulla into the granular cortex.

tion of the microscopic anatomy of the unilobar kidney will be confined to what can be seen with the low-power objective. Such details of the microscopic anatomy of the kidney as are seen to best advantage with the high-power and the oil-immersion objectives will be reserved for the discussion of the multilobar kidney of man, as will a discussion of the blood supply of the organ. However, the student should note that the kidney lobule is something that is best investigated with the low-power objective; hence, it will be considered in detail in connection with the unilobar kidney rather than with the multilobar kidney. The concept of the kidney lobule should be learned from, and reviewed in, the section dealing with the unilobar kidney.

**Some Gross Features.** The kidney of the rabbit or the rat is shaped like a lima bean; hence, if one is laid flat on a table and viewed from above, it is seen to have an extensive convex and a smaller concave border (Fig. 27-2). Considerable fat is generally present in its concavity or *hilus,* and a tube, the *ureter,* together with the renal artery and vein and a surrounding plexus of fine nerves, extend into the kidney through the fat at this site.

If a kidney from a rabbit or a rat is laid flat on a table and then cut in half by keeping the blade of a knife parallel with the surface of the table, the cut surface, when viewed with the naked eye, shows the kidney aside from its

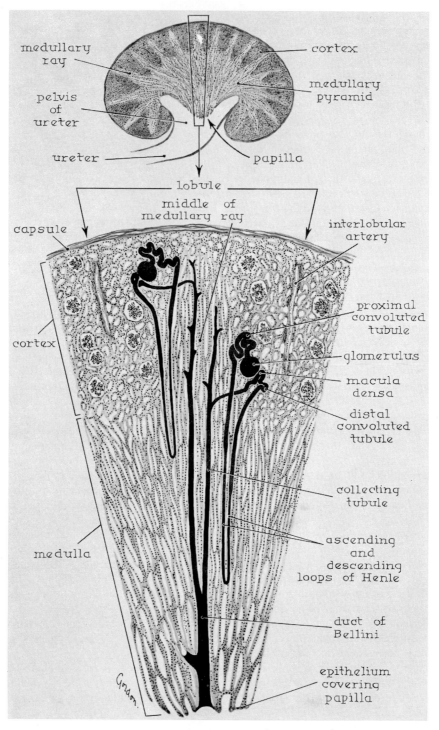

FIG. 27-3. Semidiagrammatic drawings of sections of a unilobar kidney. Two complete nephrons (in black) have been inserted into the drawings so that their course in the kidney may be followed. Of course, complete nephrons cannot be seen in any single section.

covering connective tissue *capsule* to consist of two chief parts. The first is called the *cortex,* and it consists of a broad red-brown granular layer of tissue that lies immediately beneath, and follows the contours of, the convex border of the organ (Fig. 27-2). The remainder of the kidney is shaped like a broad pyramid. The base of this is convex rather than flat and is fitted against the concave inner border of the cortex (Fig. 27-3). The apex of the pyramid points downward in Figure 27-2 and juts into the concavity or hilus of the kidney (Fig. 27-3). In contrast with the darker and granular cortex, the cut surface of the medulla is lighter and has a striated appearance, with the striations fanning out from the apex of the pyramid to all parts of its broad base (Figs. 27-2 and 27-3).

A pyramid of medullary substance, together with the cap of cortical substance that covers its base, constitutes a *lobe* of kidney tissue, and there is only one of these in the kidney of the rat or the rabbit. We shall now consider how nephrons are disposed in the lobes of kidneys; this will show why the cut surface of the cortex has a granular appearance and why the cut surface of the medulla has a striated appearance. It will also reveal the way in which kidney lobes are divided up into lobules.

**Disposition of Nephrons.** Most nephrons are so long that they can fit into a kidney only by pursuing a devious course in its substance.

All nephrons begin in the cortex; hence, *glomeruli are all confined to the cortex* (Fig. 27-3). The segment of the nephron that leads off from a glomerulus has fairly thick walls and pursues a very looped and tortuous course in the cortical tissue close to the glomerulus. This part of the nephron, for obvious reasons, is called the proximal convoluted segment or tubule (Fig. 27-3). In its next segment the nephron turns toward the medulla and pursues a straight course into it (Fig. 27-3). After having descended a certain distance into the medulla it loops back and follows a fairly straight course back to the glomerulus again. (Some nephrons whose glomeruli are in the outer part of the cortex loop back before they actually reach the medulla; compare the two in Fig. 27-3.) The segment of the nephron that loops down into or toward the medulla and

back again is termed the *loop of Henle.* Each loop has a descending limb and an ascending limb. In the lower part of the descending limb, the epithelial wall which, up to this time, has been relatively thick, becomes very thin and then, in the ascending limb, it becomes thick again (Fig. 27-3).

The ascending limb of the loop of Henle on reaching the glomerulus of the nephron curves in to touch its root between the site of entry of the afferent arteriole and the site of exit of the efferent arteriole. The portion of the wall of the tubule that comes into contact with the glomerular root becomes heavily nucleated and constitutes a thick spot known as the *macula densa* (Fig. 27-3).

The segment of the nephron that continues on from the macula densa is known as the *distal convoluted tubule.* It pursues a mildly tortuous course in the neighboring cortical tissue (Fig. 27-3). It then becomes continuous with a little side branch of one of the members of a branching system of long straight *collecting tubules* that extend from the cortex down through the medulla to open through its tip which is called the *papilla* of the pyramid (Fig. 27-3).

**Collecting Tubules.** The collecting tubules convey fluid from the nephrons into the pelvis and the ureter, thus bearing a relation to nephrons similar to that which ducts bear to secretory units of glands. Indeed, they have a different developmental origin from that of nephrons. A nephron develops from mesodermal cells which become organized into a tubule; this later becomes associated with blood capillaries that are forming a renal corpuscle in the kidney cortex. On each side of the body, a tube grows up from the developing bladder into the developing kidney where it branches. This tube becomes the ureter and the pelvis of the kidney, and each of its many branches becomes a collecting tubule which later connects with a nephron in such a way that the lumens of the two become continuous.

**Why the Cortex Is Granular and the Medulla Striated.** The cortex contains all the glomeruli and all the convoluted parts of the tubules; these constitute most of the bulk of the cortex (Fig. 27-3). If a slice is cut through a kidney, the proximal and distal convoluted tubules, being tortuous, are cut in cross and oblique section. Seen in the gross, tubules cut in this way, as well as the glomeruli scattered among them, appear to be granular.

The parts of nephrons in the medulla are the loops of Henle and the collecting tubules (Fig. 27-3). These run fairly straight courses so, if the medulla is sliced roughly parallel with them, it has a striated appearance with the striations fanning out from the apex of the medullary pyramid toward the base of the pyramid which, as has been noted before, fits into the concave border of the cortex.

**The Connection between the Ureter and the Kidney.** In a fresh unilobar kidney the ureter is seen to extend out from the kidney through the fat at its hilus (Fig. 27-2). If this tube is traced back up into the fat of the pelvis of the kidney it will be seen to become expanded to form a cap which fits over the papilla of the pyramid (Fig. 27-3). This expanded end of the ureter is called its *pelvis* (basin). Urine formed by nephrons passes into collecting tubules which carry it out through the papilla of the pyramid, and here it is collected by the caplike basin portion of the ureter. Urine here can only enter the lumen of the expanded end of the ureter because the epithelium that lines it is continuous with that covering the papilla of the pyramid, and this, in turn, is continuous with that lining the collecting tubules (Fig. 27-3). The papilla is so riddled with the collecting tubules that pass through it that it is called the *area cribrosa* (*cribrum* = a sieve). Smooth muscle has been described in the wall of the pelvis of the ureter, and it has been suggested that its contraction may exert a milking influence on the papilla and so squeeze urine out of the collecting tubules into the pelvis.

## LOBULES AND MEDULLARY RAYS

One of the commonest mistakes made in studying the kidney is that of confusing lobes with lobules. Therefore, this matter will be dealt with at some length.

A *lobe* of kidney tissue is a medullary pyramid with its cap of cortical tissue (Fig. 27-3). Accordingly, a unipyramidal kidney is a unilobar kidney. Each kidney of man consists of a dozen or more lobes; each of these lobes in itself greatly resembles a whole unipyramidal kidney.

As was explained in connection with the discussion of liver lobules (see index), a lobule can be defined as a small part of some organ that is separated from other parts by a connective tissue partition or by an indentation or by some other means. However, in connection with glandular tissue the small parts that are separated from one another by partitions are generally constituted of secretory units that drain into a single common duct that leaves the lobule. Hence parts of glands that each drain into single common ducts came to be called lobules even though they sometimes are not separated from one another by partitions or indentations. This last definition of a lobule is the one used to define lobules in the kidney; in this organ lobules are considered to be parts of the organ in which the nephrons all drain into the same collecting tubule. Such areas of tissue (lobules) are not separated from one another by partitions or indentations. Hence it is not easy to find the sides of kidney lobules; it is much easier to locate their central cores, which are known as *medullary rays*, and these will now be described.

The cortex of a freshly cut kidney has been said to be granular. But it is not *evenly* granular because *raylike* extensions of the light-colored striated medullary substance project up into it at intervals from the base of the medullary pyramid (Figs. 27-2 and 27-3). These raylike extensions of medullary substance that are *projected* into the cortex are termed *medullary rays,* and the student must take care to remember that these are not, as their name might be thought to imply, in the medulla but in the cortex.

In order to explain medullary rays it is necessary to amplify somewhat the description already given of the disposition of nephrons in the kidney. It has been explained previously that a proximal convoluted tubule leads off from a glomerulus and then after pursuing a tortuous course in the vicinity of the glomerulus it dips down toward the medulla as the descending limb of a loop of Henle. It then returns to the cortex as an ascending limb of the loop of Henle and after touching the glomerulus again at the macula densa becomes the distal convoluted tubule which pursues a tortuous· course and empties, together with many other nephrons, into a *common collec-*

*ing tubule* which, in turn, descends into and through the medulla to open through the papilla of the pyramid into the pelvis of the ureter. *Many nephrons drain into each collecting tubule* (Fig. 27-3).

The core of a lobule is a medullary ray, and the core of a medullary ray is the branched collecting tubule into which the distal convoluted segments of the many nephrons that surround it empty. The branched collecting tubule, in the kidney cortex, is the counterpart of a branched *intralobular* duct of an exocrine gland. In addition to a branched collecting tubule, a medullary ray contains the descending and the ascending limbs of the loops of Henle of the nephrons that, in the cortex, empty into the branched collecting tubule that the ray contains. The medullary ray, plus the surrounding glomeruli and proximal and distal convoluted tubules of the nephrons that empty into its branched collecting tubule, constitutes a *lobule* of kidney tissue (Fig. 27-3). It has been observed already that these lobules, like those of human liver, are not clearly delineated. However, when we study the blood supply of the cortex we shall find that interlobular arteries ascend into the cortex roughly between lobules, and these are seen occasionally in sections where they serve as landmarks to indicate the margins of lobules (Fig. 27-3).

The narrowest part of a medullary ray is the part that most closely approaches the capsule of the kidney. This is because medullary rays in the outer part of the cortex contain, in addition to relatively narrow collecting tubules, only the descending and the ascending limbs of loops of Henle of the nephrons whose glomeruli are in the outermost zone of the cortex. But as medullary rays descend in the cortex toward the medulla, they are added to by the descending and the ascending limbs of loops of Henle of the nephrons whose glomeruli are in the deeper parts of the cortex, and this, of course, makes the rays broader (Fig. 27-3).

A medullary ray, on entering the medulla, is no longer called a ray, because it does not stand out like a ray against a background of a different character; the substance of the medullary continuation of the ray is the same as that of medullary substance in general (Fig. 27-3). This leads to students visualizing kidney lobules as purely cortical structures. However, it should be remembered that the bundle of tubules that enters the medulla from each medullary ray, even though its limits can no longer be identified, is as much a part of the lobule as the bundle that projects into the cortex as the medullary ray. In other words, kidney lobules have medullary as well as cortical components.

## THE MULTIPYRAMIDAL OR MULTILOBAR KIDNEY OF MAN

**Some General Features.** The kidney of man contains from 6 to 18 lobes—individual pyramids of medullary tissue capped by cortical tissue. These are arranged within the kidney so that the tip of each pyramid points toward the pelvis (Fig. 27-4) of the ureter. In fetal life, and for at least part of the first year of postnatal life, the lobes are sufficiently distinct for their limits to be seen on the surface of the kidney. This condition occasionally persists into adult life and accounts for what is termed *fetal lobulation.* This term is not apt because *lobes,* not *lobules,* are demarcated. Normally, however, as growth continues, the surface distinctions between lobes is lost in early childhood, and the cortical tissue that covers each pyramid comes to merge smoothly into that which covers adjacent ones. However, a lobed appearance is retained in the medulla, for although some pyramids fuse during development and come to have a common papilla, many remain separated and provide the basis for a multilobar structure. Individual medullary pyramids, curiously enough, are separated from one another *by partitions of cortical substance* that extend down between them from the cortex proper. When a kidney is sliced, these partitions of typical cortical substance between pyramids appear as columns and are called the *columns of Bertin* (columni Bertini) (Fig. 27-4).

Medullary rays extend from the base of each pyramid of medullary tissue into cortical substance as they do in unipyramidal kidneys to form the cores of lobules (Figs. 27-3, 27-4 and 27-5). In sections of cortex a ray is seen to be surrounded by cortical substance composed of the convoluted tubules and glomeruli of the nephrons that empty into its branched collecting tubule (Fig. 27-5). Since convoluted tubules pursue such tortuous courses, the cortical substance of lobules that surrounds the medullary rays is termed the *labyrinth* (*laby-rinthos* = a maze) of the cortex (Fig. 27-5), to distinguish it from the substance of the ray.

Since the multilobar kidney has many medullary pyramids, each of which elaborates urine through its papilla, the pelvis of the ureter of the multilobar kidney is more complex than that of the unipyramidal organ. The ureter, on approaching the hilus of a multilobar kidney, becomes expanded into a pelvis as it does in the instance of a unipyramidal kidney. But, since there are many papilla from which urine must be collected, the pelvis of the ureter of the multilobar kidney divides into several large primary branches. Each of these, in turn, branches into a set of smaller tubes so that a separate tube (with an open end) is provided to fit over the papilla of each pyramid. Since these tubular branches from the pelvis fit over the individual papillae like cups they are termed *calyces* (*kalyx* = the cup of a flower). Each one that fits over a

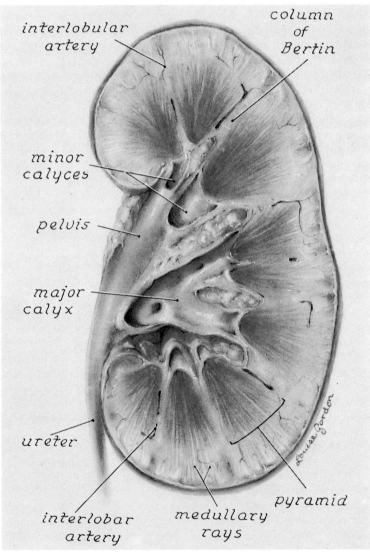

Fig. 27-4. Drawing of the cut surface of a human kidney. The granular cortex is streaked with medullary rays.

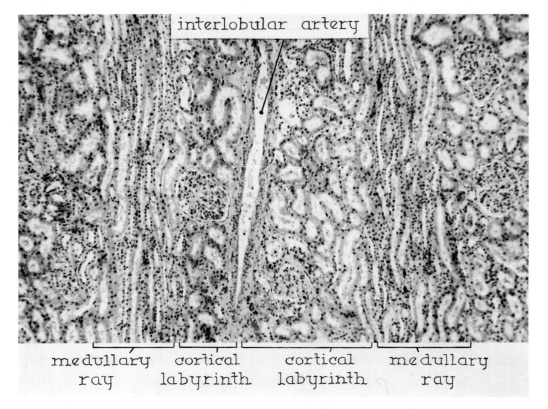

interlobular artery

medullary    cortical     cortical    medullary
   ray      labyrinth    labyrinth      ray

Fig. 27-5. Low-power photomicrograph of an H and E section of a human kidney showing 2 lobules separated by an interlobular artery. The 2 medullary rays that form the central cores for the 2 lobules are each surrounded by the glomeruli and convoluted tubules of the nephrons that empty into the collecting ducts of the ray; these comprise what is termed the cortical labyrinth.

papilla is termed a *minor calyx* (Fig. 27-4), and the main (primary) branches of the pelvis, from which the minor calyces arise, are termed *major calyces* (Fig. 27-4). Each papilla is, as it were, pushed for a short distance into the open end of its calyx. Of course, it cannot be pushed into the open end of the tubular calyx for any great distance because of its pyramidal shape (the tip of a sharpened pencil can be pushed into the open end of a glass tube for only a short distance). The walls of the open end of a calyx come into contact with the sides of the papilla a short distance up from its tip, and here the tissues of the wall of the calyx become continuous with those of the papilla. In particular, the epithelium that lines the calyx loops back to become the covering of the papilla.

## THE NEPHRON OF THE KIDNEY OF MAN: ITS PARTS AND THEIR FUNCTIONS

### SOME GENERAL FEATURES

Knowledge about the parts and the courses of nephrons was worked out, not by making reconstructions of nephrons from serial sections of kidneys which would be an almost impossible task, but by the method of maceration and dissection. This was employed around the turn of the century by both Huber and Peter, and our knowledge of the morphology and the course of the normal nephron stems from this work. More recently, Jean Oliver, by employing maceration and dissection, combined with staining technics, has investigated nephrons in many types of diseased kidneys

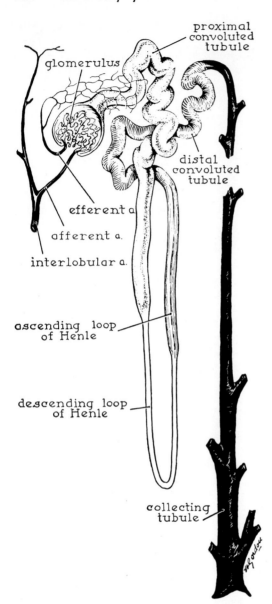

proximal convoluted tubule

glomerulus

distal convoluted tubule

efferent a.

afferent a.

interlobular a.

ascending loop of Henle

descending loop of Henle

collecting tubule

Fig. 27-6. To make this diagram less complex, the ascending limb of the loop of Henle is not shown in its normal relation to the vascular pole of the glomerulus; actually it should return to the glomerulus and fit into its vascular pole to form a macula densa before continuing on as the distal convoluted tubule.

and kidneys altered by experimental procedures and so has made an enormous contribution to an understanding of the pathology of this organ.

The nephrons of the kidney of man are similar to those of the unilobar kidney, the general features of which have been mentioned. However, in describing the nephrons of the kidney of man, we shall give considerably more detail than was presented in our preliminary description of nephrons of the unilobar kidney. It should be understood that most of this description applies to the nephrons of unilobar kidneys as well as to those of the kidney of man.

Nephrons of the kidney of man are said to be of an average length of from 50 to 55 mm. Those nephrons that begin from glomeruli situated in the zone of cortex that is close to the medulla (the juxtamedullary glomeruli) have longer loops of Henle than those nephrons that begin from glomeruli nearer the exterior of the kidney. There are probably about 1,300,000 nephrons in each kidney; some estimates run as high as 4,000,000. Allen gives the total length of all the tubules of both kidneys as approximately 75 miles. The nephron of the kidney of man consists of 4 chief parts: (1) the malpighian or renal corpuscle which contains the glomerulus, (2) the proximal convoluted tubule, (3) the loop of Henle and (4) the distal convoluted tubule (Fig. 27-6). The microscopic structure of each of these parts of the nephron will now be described and related, so far as is practicable, to its particular function.

### The Microscopic Structure of the Malpighian or Renal Corpuscle

**Definition and Development.** A glomerulus, as has been noted, is a tuft of capillaries supplied by an afferent arteriole and drained by an efferent arteriole—an arrangement admirably suited for the production of tissue fluid. When, during development, a glomerulus is invaginated into the blind end of an epithelial tubule (Fig. 27-1), the structure that comes into existence is known as a *malpighian* or *renal corpuscle*. This structure is composed of capillary networks plus the epithelium they push ahead of them which comes to cover them, plus the expanded blind end of the epithelial tubule into which the epithelial-covered capillary networks are pushed. The epithelium that is pushed ahead of the capillaries at first covers the tuft of capillaries as a whole (Fig. 27-1) and is known as the *visceral layer of*

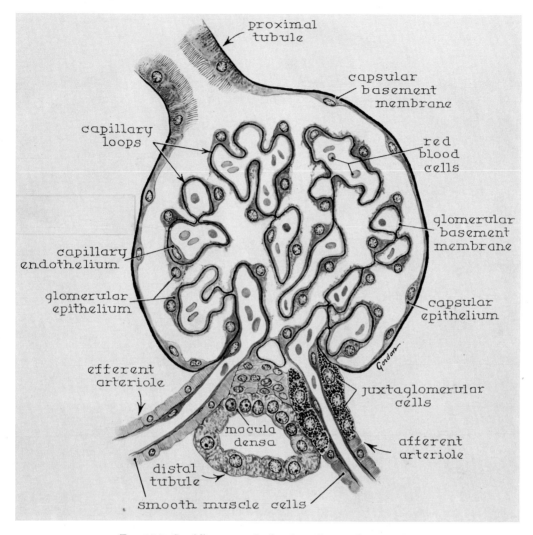

proximal
tubule

capsular
basement
membrane

capillary
loops

red
blood
cells

glomerular
basement
membrane

capillary
endothelium

glomerular
epithelium

capsular
epithelium

efferent
arteriole

juxtaglomerular
cells

macula
densa

afferent
arteriole

distal
tubule

smooth muscle cells

FIG. 27-7. Semidiagrammatic drawing of a renal corpuscle.

*Bowman's capsule* or, more commonly, as the *glomerular epithelium*. As development proceeds, the epithelium becomes apposed to all the individual capillaries in the network so that they will be completely covered with basement membranes, as will be explained in detail later. The epithelium of the bulged end of the nephron, into which the epithelial-covered glomerulus is invaginated, is known as the *parietal layer of Bowman's capsule* or, more commonly, as the *capsular epithelium* (Fig. 27-9). It is continuous with the glomerular epithelium. The lumen of the tubule, the spaces between the epithelial-covered capillaries and the parietal layer of Bowman's cap-

sule, constitutes *Bowman's* or the *capsular space* (Fig. 27-9).

Renal corpuscles range from around 150 to 250 $\mu$ in diameter. They are oval rather than spherical. The juxtamedullary corpuscles are generally larger than those nearer the capsule, probably because the juxtamedullary ones are the first to form during development and hence are the oldest.

**Course and Character of the Larger Glomerular Blood Vessels.** The over-all diameter of the afferent arteriole of a glomerulus is generally about twice that of the efferent arteriole. However, the lumen of the afferent arteriole of most glomeruli probably is not much larger

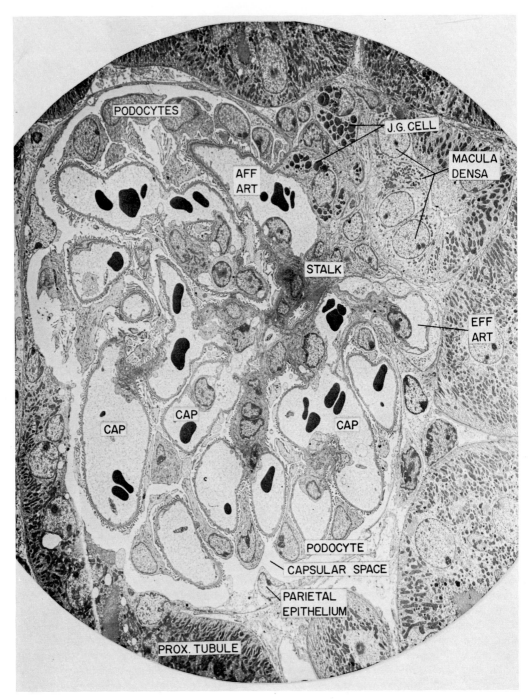

FIG. 27-8. Electron micrograph ($\times$ 2,200) is of a section of mouse kidney showing entire renal corpuscle. The vascular pole with afferent and efferent arterioles is in the upper right corner, and the urinary pole is in the lower left corner. The macula densa is wedged in between afferent and efferent arterioles, and JG cells are associated with the afferent arteriole. Numerous glomerular capillaries are sectioned, each being lined by endothelium and covered with small foot processes (pedicels) which are cytoplasmic extensions of the visceral epithelial cells or podocytes. The glomerular stalk contains some mesangial cells. (Preparation by Dr. J. Rhodin)

than that of the efferent one during life, because R. D. Bensley found that in preparations fixed by injection while under pressure, they were of about the same size. Indeed, more recently, Trueta and his associates have shown that the lumens of the efferent arterioles of the juxtamedullary glomeruli may even be wider than those of the afferent arterioles. Since the over-all diameter of the afferent arterioles is so much greater than that of the efferent arterioles, it is obvious that afferent arterioles must have thicker walls than those of efferent arterioles. Since the adventitia and the intima of afferent arterioles is poorly developed, it is obvious that the great difference in the thickness of the walls of the two vessels is due to the afferent arteriole's having a more substantial muscular media. The muscular media of the efferent vessel is not well developed, but Bensley has provided definite evidence of contractile cells in the wall of this vessel.

**Glomerular Root, Vascular Pole and Macula Densa.** Afferent and efferent arterioles generally pursue curved diverging courses as they respectively enter and leave glomeruli close to one another (Figs. 27-7 and 27-8). This site is termed the *vascular pole* or the *root* of the glomerulus. It has been mentioned that the ascending limb of the loop of Henle of each nephron returns to the glomerulus of that nephron, and before it continues on as the distal convoluted tubule it bends in between the afferent and the efferent arterioles at the vascular pole so that its wall, on one side, comes into close contact with the root of the glomerulus and also with the wall of the afferent arteriole (Figs. 27-7 and 27-8). The epithelial cells of the wall of the nephron, where it touches the root of the glomerulus and the afferent vessel, as has been mentioned before, exhibit a concentration of nuclei (Figs. 27-7 and 27-8). This relatively heavily nucleated portion of the wall of the nephron constitutes a structure which, although not sharply defined in ordinary sections, can be seen very clearly and measured in Oliver's preparations. This particular portion of the wall of the nephron is termed the *macula densa* (thick spot). Between it and the glomerulus proper, in the concavity between the afferent and the efferent arterioles, is a curious little aggregation of small cells with pale nuclei (Fig. 27-7).

This little area or group of cells is termed the *polkissen*. There is as yet no certainty about the nature or function of these cells.

**The Juxtaglomerular Complex.** The cells of the media of the afferent arterioles of glomeruli, in the region of the glomerular root, are distinctly different from ordinary smooth muscle cells. Their nuclei, instead of being elongated, are rounded, and their cytoplasm, instead of containing myofibrils, or as many as usual, contains granules (Figs. 27-7 and 27-8). The cells are known as JG (juxtaglomerular) cells. They have been found in all species that have been examined, including reptiles, birds and mesonephric fish. The cytoplasmic granules of JG cells are not visible with many of the usual histologic technics. The granules can be demonstrated with the PAS technic. However, the best method for their demonstration in the light microscope is the one evolved by Wilson working with the Hartrofts and is a modification of Bowie's neutral stain that has been commonly used for the demonstration of beta granules in the islets of Langerhans. The granules are, of course, clearly seen in the EM (Fig. 27-8).

There are several peculiarities about the position of the JG cells. (1) They are to be found only in the walls of afferent arterioles and not in the walls of the efferent ones. (2) The internal elastic lamina of the afferent arteriole disappears at the site where they are present; therefore, they are in very close contact with the endothelium lining the afferent arteriole and hence with the blood in its lumen. (3) They are in very close contact with the macula densa (Figs. 27-7 and 27-8), which, as has been described, nestles into the depression between the afferent and the efferent arterioles of the glomerulus. (4) McManus has shown that the basement membrane which otherwise surrounds the nephron throughout its whole length, which will be described presently, is absent at the macula densa; hence, the JG cells come into intimate contact with the cells of the distal convoluted tubule at this site. Finally, McManus has also shown that the Golgi network, which in the cell of a nephron generally is situated between its nucleus and the lumen, is situated, in the cells of the macula densa, between the nucleus and the outer border of most of its cells; in fact, on the side of the cell that faces the JG cells. Unfortunately, the reasons for these structural arrangements are not yet clear, and the problem remains, for the most part, a fascinating riddle yet to be solved. Some of the lines along which this riddle is being investigated will now be mentioned.

The student doubtless understands that a condition termed *high blood pressure* or *hypertension* is by no means uncommon in individuals who have passed the prime of life and that it may also occur, but less commonly, in younger people. Hypertension is due to the arterioles of the body becoming constricted; this raises the pressure within the arterial system. This, of course, puts more work upon the heart, which therefore tends to become hypertrophied. The arteriolar constriction may be due, at least for a time, to increased tonus or hypertrophy of the muscle cells of the arteriolar walls, with the cells of the wall remaining healthy. But in all too many instances the cells of the arteriolar walls become diseased, and deposits of abnormal materials accumulate in and beside them; these encroach on the lumens of the vessels and narrow them further. This type of hypertension is almost always associated with kidney disease; indeed, the relation between kidney disease and hypertension has been so noticeable through the years that each has been suggested as the cause of the other.

In 1939, Goldblatt made a brilliant discovery in this field; he showed that if the arterial blood supply of the kidneys was not entirely cut off, but only diminished, the blood pressure of an animal would rise. Moreover, he showed that this was due to the kidneys' liberating into the blood, under these ischemic conditions, a substance called *renin* (*renis* = kidney). In the bloodstream renin acts on another substance, *hypertensinogen* (also called *renin-activator*), to convert it to *hypertensin* (also called *angiotonin*), the substance which acts to raise the blood pressure. Renin can be extracted from kidneys; indeed, it was demonstrated in 1898, many years before Goldblatt's discovery.

It is only natural that it should have been suspected that the JG cells make renin, and that the granules in them (Figs. 27-7 and 27-8) are either renin or its precursor. Goormaghtigh, in Belgium, was the first to suggest that the JG cells make a hypertensive sub-

stance. Dunihue, in America, also found indications of hypertrophy of the JG apparatus in animals made hypertensive. However, Dunihue made a further and very important observation to the effect that the JG apparatus becomes more heavily granulated when the adrenal glands are removed. The Hartrofts have studied the apparatus extensively in rats under a variety of conditions and have made the striking observation that the JG cells both proliferate and become more heavily granulated when the sodium chloride intake of an animal is restricted and that they contain fewer granules if rats are given extra sodium chloride. Since the adrenal cortex, through some of its hormones, controls sodium metabolism, the Hartrofts' findings are in accord with Dunihue's findings that the JG apparatus becomes more heavily granulated in adrenalectomized animals.

There now are three types of evidence that JG cells elaborate renin. Pitcock and Hartroft have shown that there is a correlation between the amount of renin in the kidneys of man and the degree of granulation of their JG cells. Secondly, Bing and Kazimierczak, using microdissection technics, have demonstrated that the concentration of renin is highest in the region of the JG cells. The third type of evidence for secretion of renin by JG cells has been obtained by Edelman and Hartroft, using the immunofluorescence technic. Antiserum to renin prepared in the dog was coupled with a fluorescent dye and then used to locate renin in kidney sections. This showed that the fluorescent antibody attached itself chiefly to the JG cells. Therefore, the present-day evidence suggests that the JG cells elaborate renin and that, in addition to its pressor effect, renin stimulates the zona glomerulosa of the adrenal cortex to increase the secretion of aldosterone. As has already been noted, sodium depletion causes the JG cells to produce renin. Under the EM JG granules are osmophilic and spherical to oval in shape. They can be distinguished readily from the mitochondria of the JG cells (Fig. 27-8).

THE MICROSCOPIC STRUCTURE
OF GLOMERULI

**Glomerular Capillaries and Glomerular Lobules.** Through the years there have been different views held about the arrangements in which capillaries are disposed in glomeruli. One view that has had a considerable impact on kidney literature stemmed from the work of Vimtrup. According to him, an afferent arteriole, on entering a glomerulus, branches into from 2 to 4, or even more, primary branches; these either give rise to further branches that give off capillaries or they give off capillaries immediately. Each of the up to 50 capillaries formed in this way is visualized as pursuing a somewhat tortuous course before and as it loops back to join a primary branch of the efferent vessel. According to this view, capillaries in the glomeruli do *not* branch.

However, Vimtrup's views were not accepted by all, and some investigators, through the years, recorded examples of branching capillaries. Hall reinvestigated this matter by injecting glomerular vessels with latex and then macerating the tissue so that the injected material in the vessels could be dissected and examined under the light microscope. Hall's studies show that each afferent arteriole branches into a few main (basal) branches; each of these basal branches supplies a "lobule" of the glomerulus. Hall does not consider that anastomoses between lobules are common but anastomoses are common between the capillaries in any given lobule. The basal vessel in each lobule is thought to give rise to two or more major capillaries which act as preferred channels, and these follow a looped course, to return and empty into basal branches of the efferent system. Hall believes that capillaries are given off along the course of the preferred channels and that they anastomose with one another and with other preferred channels in the same lobule.

This concept of the glomerular vessels being disposed in lobules is in keeping with what is seen under the microscope (Fig. 27-9). Boyer, by reconstruction of injected glomeruli, has found that Vimtrup's concept of nonanastomosing capillary loops is no longer tenable. The glomerulus is composed of a capillary network comparable with all other capillary beds in the body. However, Boyer believes that there are some anastomoses between the structures that others would call lobules. This view has been confirmed recently by Lewis, and by Baringer.

**The Internal Support of Capillary Nets and**

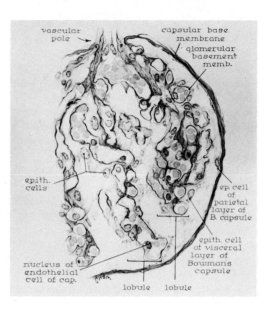

FIG. 27-9. Drawing of a portion of a renal corpuscle as seen under oil-immersion in a section of human kidney stained by the PAS method and by hematoxylin. Three lobules are to be seen hanging from the vascular pole. Note that the glomerular basement membrane surrounds each capillary in the lobules.

**Lobules: The Question of a Mesangium.** When only the light microscope was available there was a difference of opinion as to whether or not any connective tissue extended from the stalk of a glomerulus along its blood vessels so as to form a sort of mesentery for the capillary loops as well as an ensheathment for them in some sites. The investigation of this problem with the EM has disclosed that although capillary loops are not suspended by a true mesentery, there is indeed a delicate connective tissue to be found in association with the capillaries that are adjacent to one another in the substance of glomeruli. The cells of this delicate connective tissue seem to be similar both in their position and nature to the pericytes that are closely associated with the endothelium of capillaries and venules and which have been described and illustrated in Chapter 22. Evidence suggests that mesangial cells secrete a fibrillar material and also perhaps some mucopolysaccharide to provide a little intercellular substance which helps to support capillaries. The intercellular substance is considered to be more fibrillar than the material of basement membranes. Under some circumstances the mesangial cells demonstrate a capacity to produce collagen. Moreover, mesangial cells have been shown to have phagocytic capacities. In general, mesangial cells would seem to be mesenchymal cells which have various capacities for differentiation but do not exercise these to any great degree under ordinary circumstances.

**The Basement Membranes of Glomerular Capillaries: An Exercise in 3-Dimensional Visualization.** It will be recalled that basement membranes consist of a homogeneous amorphous material that is PAS-positive and that they are commonly interposed between epithelial membranes and the connective tissue on which the epithelium lies and from which it is nourished; the latter fact attests to the permeability of basement membranes.

Basement membranes are present in renal corpuscles exactly where they might be expected; they are interposed between the epithelial membranes and the mesenchymal-derived structures (capillaries develop from mesenchyme) that are covered or lined by the epithelial membranes. First, there is a substantial basement membrane between the parietal layer of Bowman's capsule and the stroma of the kidney cortex (Fig. 27-9). Secondly, there is a thinner basement membrane between the epithelial cells of the visceral layer of Bowman's capsule and the capillaries that they cover. The PAS method, which has been used to such advantage by McManus in studying the kidney, reveals these basement membranes both beautifully and clearly (Figs. 27-9 and 27-13).

Perhaps the most significant finding to take into account in attempting to visualize the arrangements of glomerular capillaries in 3 dimensions is the fact that *every capillary appearing in a cross, an oblique or an almost longitudinal section is seen in a good PAS preparation to be completely surrounded with a basement membrane* (Fig. 27-9). At first thought it might be assumed that these basement membranes are produced by the endothelial cells of the capillaries. But capillaries in other parts of the kidney are *not* covered with basement membranes that are readily demonstrated by the PAS method. Furthermore, pronounced basement membranes *are* found around all the epithelial tubules of the cortex of the kidney, between their epithelial walls and the connective tissue stroma in which they lie (Fig. 27-13). Therefore, the basement membranes in the kidney demonstrable with the light microscope seem to be disposed where there is interaction between epithelium and mesenchymal-derived tissue (connective tissue stroma or capillaries). This leads to the conclusion that the basement membranes seen around the capillaries in glomerular lobules must have formed under the influence of epithelial cells, and this leads to the further conclusion that the epithelial cells of the visceral layer of Bowman's capsule therefore must thoroughly permeate all the interstices that exist in the capillary networks of glomerular lobules to come into intimate contact with all capillaries.

The visceral layer of Bowman's capsule not only covers lobules as entities but in doing so it pushes into every cleft and space in the lobules and from all sides of the lobule so that in the middle of the lobule prongs of epithelium from one surface meet prongs that have pushed in from other surfaces. Everywhere throughout the lobule the epithelial cells apply themselves to the surfaces of capillaries to provide them with basement membranes (Fig. 27-9). Each capillary becomes covered with a basement membrane, one side of which may be produced by one epithelial cell and the other by another epithelial cell. Together with the mesangium the basement membranes provide support for the capillaries.

Since the basement membranes surround glomerular capillaries the endothelial cells of capillaries are always within rings of PAS-positive material while epithelial cells are outside the rings of basement membrane (Figs. 27-7 and 27-9).

**The Surface Area of Glomerular Capillaries.** The total surface area of the capillaries of a glomerulus has been both estimated and measured. The latter procedure requires the use of enlarged replicas of serial sections cut through a glomerulus and is so laborious and fraught with difficulties that few have attempted it. Book, when he was an associate of the author, and two of whose preparations are shown in Figure 3-2, injected the blood vessels of a kidney of a child of 6 and made replicas

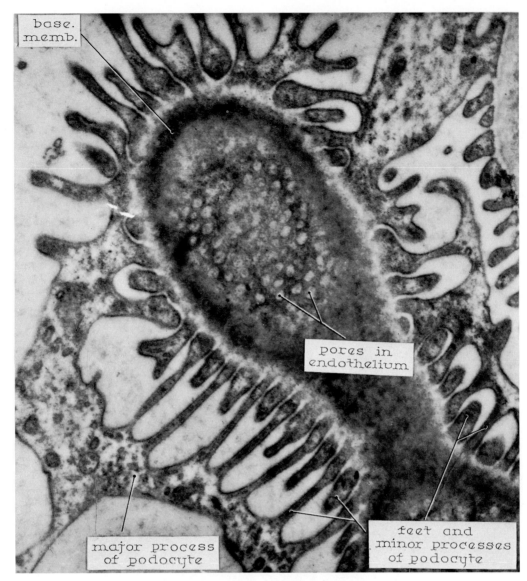

base.
memb.

pores in
endothelium

major process
of podocyte

feet and
minor processes
of podocyte

FIG. 27-10. Electron micrograph ($\times$ 40,000) of a tangential section through a glomerular capillary, showing pores in the endothelium as well as the interdigitating processes and the feet of podocytes. (Pease, D. C.: J. Histochem. *3:295*, with labeling added)

of each section cut through one glomerulus. On these replicas he measured the capillary surfaces. Allowing for certain corrections, he calculated the capillaries of the glomerulus to have a surface area of 0.3813 sq. mm. More recently, Kirkman and Stowell have measured painstakingly the capillary surface area of several rat glomeruli and find that it averages 0.19 sq. mm. They suggest that Book's illustrations indicate that the injection distorted

the capillary loops to some extent and that injected material is not suitable for this type of study. However, they state that his figure is the most reliable one available for the human glomerulus. Rat glomeruli are smaller than human glomeruli; hence, there is surprisingly good agreement between Book's findings and those of Kirkman and Stowell. Since it has been estimated that there are well over a million glomeruli in each human kidney, it seems probable that the total filtration surface of all the glomeruli of both kidneys is well over a square meter.

It has been estimated that the glomerular capillaries of all the renal corpuscles of the two kidneys produce from 170 to 200 liters of tissue fluid each 24 hours. As this fluid moves along through proximal convoluted tubules, loops of Henle and distal convoluted tubules, about 99 per cent of it is resorbed through the walls of the tubules back into the bloodstream. After considering the fine structure of the glomerulus we shall consider the structures of these parts of the nephron where resorption occurs and how their structure is related to their functions.

THE FINE STRUCTURE OF THE GLOMERULUS

The study of kidney glomeruli with the EM has been particularly rewarding. Two major findings of morphologic and physiologic interest have been made: one relates to the character of the endothelium of the capillaries and the other to the nature of epithelial cells of the visceral layer of Bowman's capsule. These findings will now be described.

The Fenestrated Endothelium of Glomerular Capillaries. The presence of nuclei in the endothelial cells of capillaries causes the cells to bulge into the lumen where nuclei are present (Fig. 27-12, *upper right*). Around the periphery of each bulged area the cytoplasm of an endothelial cell quickly attenuates (Fig. 27-12, *upper right*) and spreads out in a thin film to make up the remainder and major part of the wall of the capillary; hence, except where nuclei are present the capillary walls consist of only thin films of cytoplasm. From early studies with the EM, made before thin sectioning technics were well developed, it be-

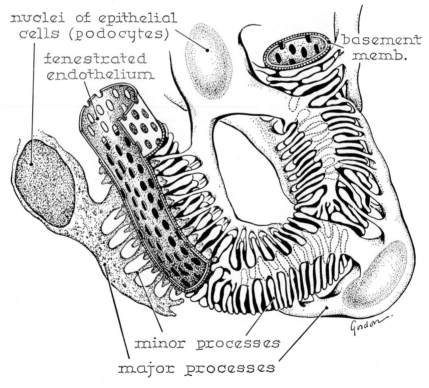

FIG. 27-11. Schematic diagram devised to give a 3-dimensional concept of part of a capillary loop in a glomerulus with its covering of podocytes and its fenestrated endothelium. At the upper left, part of a podocyte and part of a capillary have been cut away. (Based on electron micrographs from D. C. Pease and a diagram *in* Pease, D. C.: J. Histochem. *3*:295)

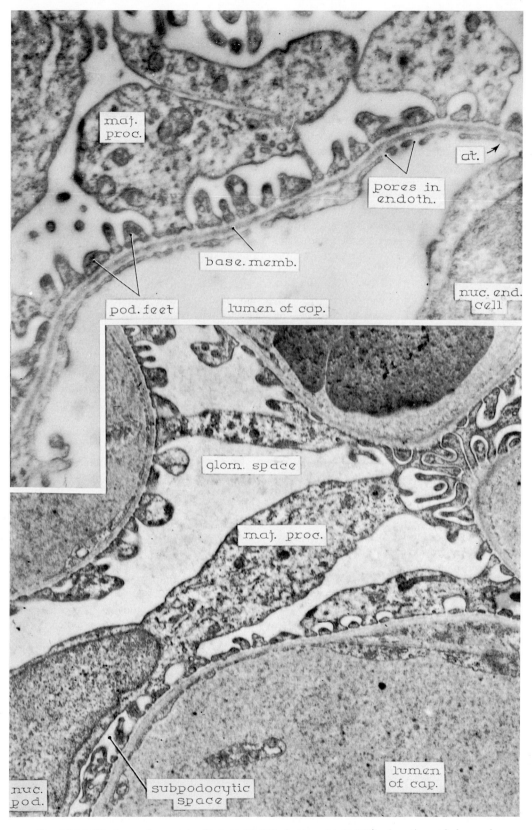

FIG. 27-12. Electron micrographs (*top*, × 30,000; *bottom*, × 22,000) of sections of glomerular capillaries and podocytes. (Pease, D. C.: J. Histochem. *3*:295, with labeling added)

came apparent that this endothelium is different from that of capillaries in most parts of the body in that it is riddled with pores (Figs. 27-10, 27-11 and 27-12). It was suspected for a time that the pores seen with the EM might be fixation artefacts, but from the persistent studies of Hall and subsequent studies by Pease and others it has become generally accepted that the pores are real and exist during life. The pores, although they are regularly arranged and close together, are not all of precisely the same size but measure on an average of around 0.1 $\mu$ in diameter. There is some evidence to indicate that their size varies somewhat in relation to the fixation procedures that are employed.

The Epithelial Cells of the Visceral Layer of Bowman's Capsule: the Podocytes. Although some histologists who have studied the kidney through the years with the light microscope have suggested that the epithelial cells that comprise the visceral layer of Bowman's capsule are of an unusual form, having many processes which are attached to the basement membranes that overlie the capillaries, not much attention was paid to their views, and there was a general belief that these cells are squamous in type and that they form a continuous covering for the capillaries. With the EM it has become evident that this view is incorrect on both counts, for the cells are not squamous in type, and they do not provide a continuous covering for the capillaries. They have a most unusual form and, because they have feet, are now generally termed *podocytes* (*podos* = foot).

The main cell body of a podocyte (which contains its nucleus) is separated from the capillary over which it lies by a *subpodocytic space* that is filled with glomerular filtrate (Figs. 27-8 and 27-12). Numerous arms of cytoplasm, which we shall call *major processes*, extend from the cell body (Figs. 27-11 and 27-12); these tend to run roughly parallel with the long axis or the circumference of the capillary, and they too tend to be separated from the capillary by spaces (Figs. 27-11 and 27-12). From the major processes, delicate minor processes extend in orderly array to the capillary (Figs. 27-10 and 27-11) where they terminate in *feet;* the soles of these are planted firmly on the basement membranes of the capillary (they are probably set in a cement substance) and follow its cur-

vature (Figs. 27-11 and 27-12). The minor processes and feet from different major processes interdigitate with one another as they approach and come into contact with the capillary (Figs. 27-10 and 27-11). The minor processes and feet that interdigitate with one another may be derived from two or more major processes of the same podocyte or from the major processes of two or more podocytes (Fig. 27-11). Such evidence as is available suggests that one podocyte can send processes to two capillaries, although generally their processes probably all go to one.

As may be seen in Figures 27-10, 27-11 and 27-12, the interdigitating feet do not come into contact with one another; there are tiny clefts between them. This means, of course, that the capillaries do not have a continuous epithelial covering and that it would not be necessary for glomerular filtrate to pass through the epithelial feet in order to enter the glomerular space in the normal.

Since the endothelium is fenestrated, and since there are clefts between epithelial feet, neither endothelium nor epithelium ordinarily act as perfect dialyzing membranes. This means that the basement membrane is *the* dialyzing membrane in glomeruli; it constitutes the only intact membrane between the blood and the glomerular filtrate in normal glomeruli. Having thus emphasized the importance of the basement membrane as the ultrafilter in the glomerulus it should now be added that some authorities consider that the clefts or slits between the feet of podocytes may not be as open as they seem but instead closed over by very thin diaphragms which conceivably could assist the basement membrane in its filtering capacity. Moreover, it has been shown that in some types of damage to glomeruli that result in protein macromolecules leaking through the basement membranes, the feet of the podocytes come close together and the cytoplasm of the podocytes take up escaped macromolecules to some extent at least.

A GENERAL ACCOUNT OF WHAT HAPPENS TO THE GLOMERULAR FILTRATE AS IT PASSES ALONG THE REMAINDER OF THE NEPHRON AND FINALLY ENDS UP AS URINE IN THE PELVIS OF THE KIDNEY

It is more interesting to study the microscopic structure of (1) the different parts of the nephron, (2) the collecting tubules and

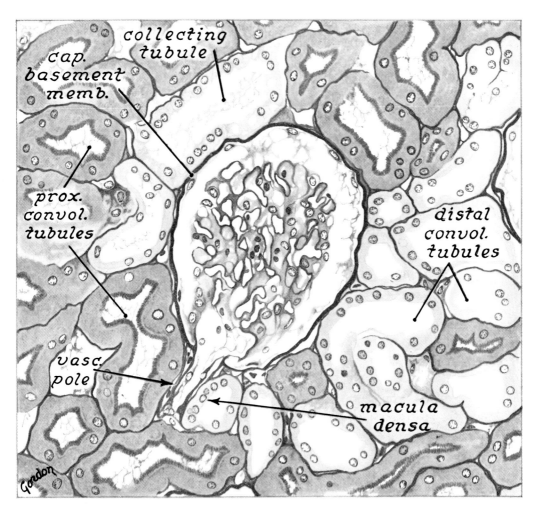

FIG. 27-13. Drawing of a section of human kidney fixed in formalin and stained by the PA-Schiff technic followed by hematoxylin. Note the PAS-positive brush borders of the proximal convoluted tubules and that the cytoplasm of the cells of these tubules stains more deeply than that of the cells of the distal convoluted or collecting tubules. Note the PAS-positive basement membranes that surround the tubules. Basement membrane is also present under both the visceral and the parietal layers of Bowman's capsule. The numerous capillaries that lie between adjacent tubules are collapsed and hence not seen in this preparation. The vascular pole of the glomerulus has been cut obliquely and is not as prominent as it otherwise would be.

(3) the capillary beds with which they are associated, if one has in advance some clue as to what function each performs; their structure and particularly their fine structure then takes on more significance. So we shall here describe something of what is now believed to happen as glomerular filtrate flows along the tubules mentioned above and which results in the reabsorption of most of the fluid and certain useful substances dissolved in the fluid.

As has already been mentioned, about 170 liters of glomerular filtrate (which is essentially tissue fluid) is formed each 24 hours. This literally enormous amount of fluid enters the proximal convoluted tubules. Of this 170 liters that begins the journey through the tubules only about $1\frac{1}{2}$ liters emerge as urine from the collecting tubules into the pelvis of the kidney. It is therefore obvious that there must be a reabsorption of glomerular fluid as the fluid passes along the tubules which conduct it to the pelvis of the kidney.

Along with the reabsorption of fluid there is of course reabsorption of substances that are dissolved in the glomerular filtrate. Some of the reabsorption is selective and some is not. For example, under normal conditions all the sugar in the glomerular filtrate is reabsorbed back through the walls of the tubular system (the reabsorption of sugar occurs in the proximal convoluted tubule). On the other hand, certain waste products of protein metabolism are not reabsorbed and so these become relatively concentrated in urine.

**Phenomena Involved in Reabsorption.** The reabsorption of some solutes such as glucose depend on specific enzymatic reaction which the cells of the proximal convoluted tubules are specially equipped to perform. In the following discussion, however, we are going to be concerned chiefly with water and electrolytes and discuss what accounts for water being reabsorbed from the tubules, the problem of the concentration of electrolytes inside and outside of tubules, and the factors that account for the urine that emerges in the pelvis of the kidney being hypertonic to tissue fluid. Accordingly, we shall have to concern ourselves to some extent with the permeability of certain of the tubule walls to water and electrolytes, respectively, and also with osmotic phenomena.

Many years ago Crane observed that only

animals that have loops of Henle in their nephrons excrete urine that is hypertonic to blood. It was therefore very tempting to assume that water must be selectively reabsorbed along the course of the loops of Henle with the result that electrolytes in solution in tubular fluid, for example sodium and chloride, became more concentrated as the fluid passed along the loops so that the fluid that was delivered into distal convoluted tubules would be hypertonic. But as matters have turned out, this assumption was wrong. When methods were evolved to provide information about the osmotic pressure of fluid along various parts of the nephron, and the osmotic pressure of the tissue fluid that is present between the tubules in various parts of medullary pyramids, some surprising results were obtained, and these have led to new hypotheses being formulated which will be described presently.

First, it is known that about $\frac{7}{8}$ of the fluid and about $\frac{7}{8}$ of the sodium is reabsorbed in the proximal convoluted tubule. The absorption of water here is termed obligatory reabsorption because the water must be reabsorbed in order for sodium to be reabsorbed. Since water and electrolytes are reabsorbed equally from the fluid in the proximal convoluted tubule there is no change in the osmotic pressure of the fluid that the proximal convoluted tubule delivers into the descending limb of the loop of Henle; the fluid therefore remains isotonic.

Before describing what is believed to occur in the loop of Henle we shall consider the state of the fluid that emerges from the ascending limb of the loop of Henle into the distal convoluted tubule. This turned out to be hypotonic (instead of hypertonic) and hence the concentration of electrolytes which is responsible for the urine of man becoming hypertonic does not occur in the loops of Henle. What does occur there will be described shortly.

Next, as the fluid passes along the distal convoluted tubule more water than salt is reabsorbed so in this tubule the fluid once more becomes isotonic. The reabsorption of fluid in the ~~proximal~~ distal convoluted tubule is controlled by the antidiuretic hormone of the posterior lobe of the pituitary (ADH). If the pituitary gland is removed, this reabsorption does not occur and hence an animal passes great quantities of dilute urine (as will be explained in connection with diabetes insipidus which will be discussed in connection with the posterior pituitary in Chap. 28).

Since the fluid becomes isotonic again in the distal convoluted tubule, the concentration of urine which accounts for it becoming hypertonic must occur as the fluid passes along the collecting tubules. In order to account for this we now have to consider what happens in the loops of Henle, for what happens in the loops of Henle is indirectly responsible for what happens in the collecting tubules.

The function of the loops of Henle is not, as was once assumed, that of actively reabsorbing water to make the urine hypertonic. Instead, their function is to create a hypertonic environment in the tissue fluid that surrounds them, so that the collecting tubules that pass through this same environment (consult Fig. 27-3) will have water drawn out of them into the tissue fluid that surrounds them. This extra water in due course passes into the capillaries and is thus taken back into the circulation. The way the loops of Henle create an extracellular hypertonic environment will now be described. It is easier to describe what happens in the loops of Henle if we begin with what happens as fluid passes up the ascending limb of the loop.

It would seem that the lining cells of the ascending loops have the ability to remove sodium (along with chloride) from the fluid in their lumens and deliver this sodium into the tissue fluid in which they and the descending loops are both bathed. It seems, moreover, that the walls of the ascending loops hold back water in their lumens but at the same time are permeable to water entering them from the tissue fluid that surrounds them. As a consequence, the fluid contained in the ascending loops would, since it is losing sodium, and gaining in water, become increasingly hypotonic as it ascends toward the distal convoluted tubule, and indeed this is what happens and why the fluid delivered into the distal convoluted tubule is hypotonic. However, what happens in the ascending tubule has another effect which we shall describe next.

As a result of the ascending limb of the loop of Henle pushing sodium and other ions out into the tissue fluid, the tissue fluid in this immediate area becomes hypertonic. The walls of the descending limbs of the loop of Henle, unlike those of the ascending limbs, can let water pass from their lumens out into this tissue fluid. Accordingly, the extra sodium chloride in this tissue fluid withdraws water from the fluid in the descending limb of the loop of Henle (it is possible also that along with losing water the descending limb of the loop may also take up some of the sodium from the tissue fluid), and as a result the fluid in the descending limb of the loop becomes hypertonic, increasingly so as it reaches the bottom of the loop and begins to ascend in the ascending limb of the loop. But, as already noted, as the fluid begins to ascend it begins to lose sodium and so it becomes not only isotonic but, by the time it reaches the proximal convoluted tubule, it has become hypotonic.

The whole purpose of these activities that occur in the thin loops of Henle and which are most marked near the bottoms of the loops (for orientation see Fig. 27-3) and which are relatively near the papillae of the medullary pyramids, would seem to be that of making the tissue fluid in this particular region more salty and hence hypertonic. Since the collecting tubules pass through this same territory (see Fig. 27-3) the hypertonic tissue fluid acts to draw water from the previously isotonic fluid in the lumens of the collecting tubules with the result that by the time the fluid in the collecting tubules has passed down through this hypertonic area it too has become hypertonic. Hence the urine delivered into the pelvis of the kidney by the collecting tubules is hypertonic. The antidiuretic hormone probably controls to some extent the permeability of the cells of the collecting tubules with regard to their permitting the hypertonic tissue fluid to draw water through their walls into the tissue fluid.

The capillary loops which are present in this area all contain blood that has passed through glomeruli (Fig. 27-19). Since blood in passing through glomeruli loses water and electrolytes but not its colloids, that part of its osmotic pressure that is due to its colloid content could be expected to be greater than that which exists in blood in ordinary capillaries. It seems possible that this could be a factor in helping these capillaries to cope with the hypertonic tissue fluid that is maintained near the papillae of the pyramids.

A more elaborate account of the mechanisms involved will be found in reference books on the kidney and in textbooks of physiology. In various accounts written about this subject the loop of Henle is commonly described as constituting a *hairpin countercurrent osmotic multiplier*.

### THE PROXIMAL TUBULE

The proximal convoluted tubule is about 14 mm. in length and has an over-all diameter of about 60 $\mu$. The first part of it, which leads off from the glomerulus, is sufficiently narrow and straight in some species to constitute a neck for the tubule. But, in man, this portion of the tubule differs so little from the remainder of the tubule that it does not merit a separate name or description. Proximal convoluted tubules get the convoluted part of their name because they pursue looped and tortuous courses in the immediate vicinity of the renal corpuscles from which they originate (Fig. 27-6). They then enter medullary rays (Fig. 27-5) and descend in these as the upper parts of descending limbs of loops of Henle. The descending limbs enter the medulla and extend into it for different distances before looping back as ascending limbs (Fig. 27-3). Aside from becoming straight, the character of the proximal convoluted tubule does not change materially as it becomes the first part of the descending loop of Henle. It is only after it has descended for some distance that the character of the tubule changes. Therefore, there is a segment of the descending loop of Henle which, though straight, has the same character and presumably performs the same function as the convoluted part of the tubule proper. This upper segment of the descending loop should be considered as part of the proximal convoluted tubule even though it is not convoluted.

**Some Aids to Recognizing and Studying Proximal Convoluted Tubules in Sections.** (1) For the most part they are seen in sections as oblique cuts through curved tubes (Fig. 27-13). Reference to Figures 3-3 and 3-4 may assist the student in understanding why they appear as they do. (2) Oblique and cross sections of proximal convoluted tubules are the most common sight in a section of kidney cortex (Fig. 27-13) and indeed they are the only kind seen between the outermost glomeruli and the capsule of the kidney in the normal. (3) The cells of proximal convoluted tubules become altered very rapidly as a result of postmortem degeneration; consequently, many of the features of them that are described for their appearance in well-fixed material cannot be seen in the usual H and E section obtained from autopsy material. (4) Even if the cells of the proximal convoluted tubules are altered as a result of postmortem degeneration, their cytoplasm is generally more acidophilic and more granular than that of other tubules; accordingly, proximal convoluted tubules are not only the most numerous tubules seen in an H and E section of kidney cortex; they are also the pinkest (Fig. 27-13).

The cells of the walls of proximal convoluted tubules are broader at their bases, which lie against a basement membrane, than at their free margins, which abut on the lumen. These cells are often described as being truncated in the sense that they resemble pyramids that have had their apices cut off. The boundaries between adjacent cells cannot be seen to advantage because the edges of any two cells that touch each other are serrated with the projections from the edge of one fitting into the notches of the other. In tissue fixed immediately after death and suitably stained, the appearance of proximal convoluted tubules varies between two extremes. At one the epithelium is low, and the lumen wide and round; at the other the epithelium is high, and the lumen small and triangular. These two extreme appearances, as well as intermediate ones, are to be explained by two factors: (1) the state of functional activity of the epithelial cells of the tubule, and (2) the degree to which the lumen of the tubule is distended by glomerular filtrate; the latter is affected by whether or not the glomerulus of the nephron is producing much or little filtrate. It is believed that the low epithelium and the wide round lumen is associated with the production of much filtrate.

The nuclei of the cells of proximal convoluted tubules are disposed toward the bases of the cells. They are large and spherical and possess nucleoli (Fig. 27-13).

Proximal convoluted tubules are ensheathed in a substantial basement membrane which is beautifully demonstrated by the PAS technic (Fig. 27-13).

**Fine Structure.** The fine structure of the proximal convoluted tubules has been investigated by many workers, notably Rhodin and Pease.

The cell surfaces that face the lumen are covered with thin microvilli about 1 $\mu$ long, which in many respects are similar to those of the lining cells of the small intestine (Figs. 27-14, *top*, and 27-15, *top*). However, there is one way in which these microvilli differ from those of the intestine; there appears to be a sort of matrix that fills in the spaces between them. Accordingly, in electron micrographs of cross sections of microvilli, the matrix between individual microvilli may appear as prominent as the microvilli themselves, and this appearance may suggest that the microvilli, instead of being fingerlike structures that project into the lumen from the cell surface, are actually pits, lined with cell membrane, that project inwardly into the cytoplasm from the free surface of the cell. This view was suggested in the past to explain the EM appearance of the brush border of the proximal convoluted tubule, but now it is accepted that the brush border consists of countless microvilli with some sort of jellylike matrix between them. Between the bases of adjacent microvilli the cell membrane sometimes extends down into the cytoplasm. The channels so formed may connect with vesicles. The number of microvilli is enormous, and obviously they increase the surface area greatly. In man, the total surface of the brush border of the proximal tubules of both kidneys is about 50 to 60 square meters and, as Fawcett has observed, the existence of such an enormous absorbing area goes a long way to explain the extraordinary capacity of the nephron for concentrating the glomerular filtrate.

At the base of a cell, the cell membrane shows many infoldings into the cytoplasm (Fig. 27-15, *bottom*). These infoldings or inflections are also seen in the distal convoluted tubule where they are more highly developed. They more or less divide the basal part of the cytoplasm into compartments which contain the characteristic long, large mitochondria of these cells. This system of infoldings of the cell membrane increases the surface through which fluid and dissolved materials can be resorbed by capillaries. Such resorption is known to require energy, and the close association of many mitochondria is a guarantee of a perfect enzymatic supply for the process. Ruska, Moore and Weinstock have studied this association of mitochondria and infoldings of the cell membrane and regard it as a functional unit for passing fluid resorbed from the lumen into the capillaries at the base of a tubule.

The basement membrane at the base of the cells is seen to advantage with the EM; it can be seen at the lower right in the bottom picture in Figure 27-15.

**Function.** The proximal convoluted tubules probably resorb about $\frac{7}{8}$ of the water and sodium of the glomerular filtrate that passes by them. Part of this absorption may be facilitated by the fact that the blood in the capillaries that are disposed between them is rich in colloid (protein) and is under a low hydrostatic pressure. But some of the selective absorption that occurs here is against an osmotic gradient and so requires that the cells perform special absorptive work. For example, in a healthy person all the sugar in glomerular filtrate is resorbed in the proximal convoluted tubules. The presence of the enzyme phosphatase may be demonstrated in proximal convoluted tubules in kidney sections by a histochemical technic.

*Cortical Capillaries.* Fluid and dissolved substances resorbed from the proximal (or distal) convoluted tubules must pass through the basement membranes that surround these tubules to gain access to the capillaries which are disposed in beds around the tubules. Pease has shown that the endothelium of the capillaries that lie between tubules in the kidney cortex is like that of the glomerular capillaries, fenestrated. However, the pores are somewhat smaller. Only patches of fenestrated capillaries occur in the medulla.

The cells of the proximal convoluted tubules can also perform excretory functions. Evidence has accumulated to establish the excretory capacity of tubular cells from several sources and procedures: (1) species whose kidneys have tubules but no glomeruli, (2) species in which the glomeruli and the tubules of the kidney have a different blood supply and so permit the glomeruli to be put out of action by experimental procedures, (3) by lowering the blood pressure of animals in whose kidneys the glomeruli and the tubules have a common blood supply below the point at which glomeruli continue to produce tissue fluid, and (4) from the study of tubules in tissue culture. But while proximal convoluted

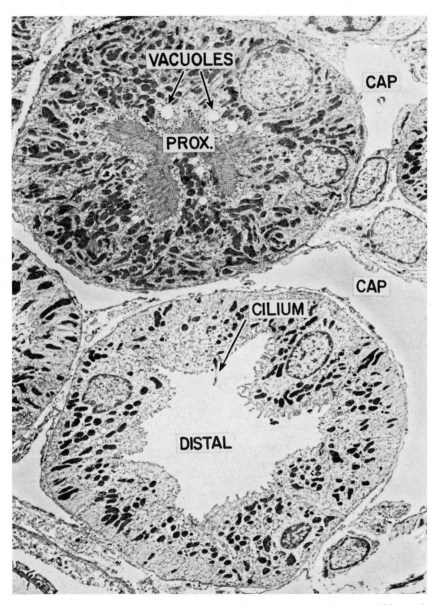

Fig. 27-14. Electron micrograph (× 3,000) of a section of mouse kidney. A proximal convoluted tubule (*top*) and a distal convoluted tubule (*bottom*) are cut in cross section. Their surrounding capillaries appear as empty spaces. Nuclei and mitochondria are obvious in the cells of both tubules. The lumen of the proximal tubule is filled with microvilli, while that of the distal tubule is open. Microvilli are sparse and short in the distal tubule cells, and occasionally a cilium can be seen. (One is visible here in the cell nearest to the proximal tubule.) (Rhodin, J.: *in* Clark, G. L. (ed.): Encyclopedia of Microscopy, New York, Rheinhold)

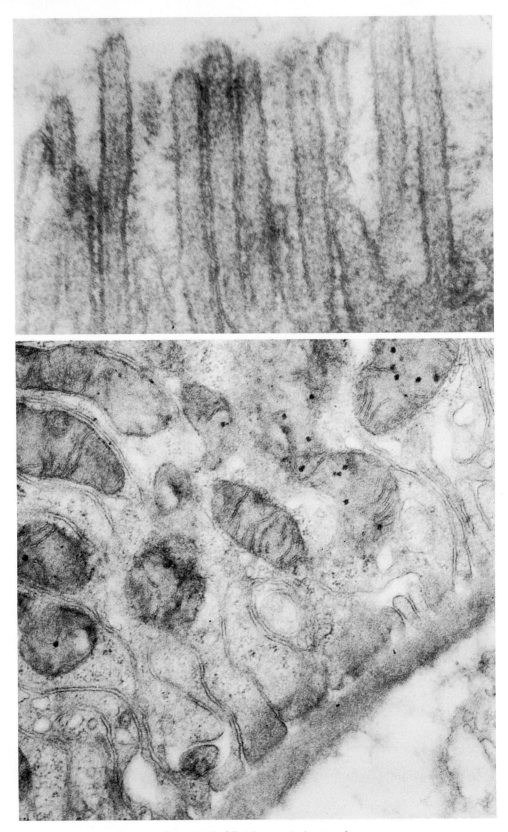

FIG. 27-15. (*Caption on facing page*)

tubules can indulge in excretory as well as resorptive functions, the modern physiologic view places more emphasis on the latter than on the former.

### Loop of Henle

Loops of Henle are either short or long. The majority of those nephrons, the glomeruli of which are in the outer part of the cortex, have short loops that do not extend for any great distance into the medulla; perhaps this is because they were the last nephrons to develop, and their loops had to accommodate themselves to such space as was available. The nephrons that arise from glomeruli near the medulla have long loops that extend well down into the medulla.

The first part of the descending loop is the straight continuation of the proximal convoluted tubules (Fig. 27-6). As it passes down into the medulla—a short distance in the instance of tubules that arise from glomeruli in the outer part of the cortex, and a greater distance in the instance of tubules that arise from glomeruli near the medulla—its lumen rather abruptly becomes narrower, and the cells of its walls squamous (Fig. 27-6). After this change has occurred the tubule is known as the *thin segment* of the descending limb of the loop of Henle. The thin segments of nephrons that arise from juxtamedullary glomeruli are much longer than those that arise from glomeruli in the outer part of the cortex (Fig. 27-3).

The appearance of this part of the nephron is so similar to a large capillary that the student may not be able to distinguish easily these tubules in the medulla from the capillaries that run between them (Fig. 27-16). It may be of help to understand that the tubules are wider than capillaries, but they may be partly collapsed. In general, the nuclei of the epithelial cells of the tubules bulge into the lumen of the tubule somewhat more than

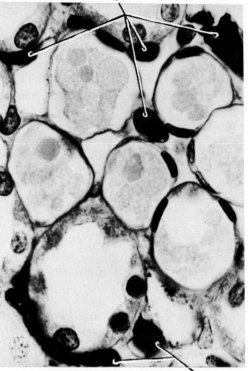

injected capillaries

injected capillaries

Fig. 27-16. High-power photomicrograph of a section of the medulla of a rat's kidney, showing thin loops of Henle cut in cross section. The capillaries are injected with india ink and hence are black. (Preparation and photomicrograph of Dr. W. S. Hartroft)

the nuclei of the endothelial cells of the capillaries. The nuclei of the squamous cells of the tubules are somewhat closer together than the nuclei of the endothelial cells of capillaries. Red blood cells in the capillaries may also be helpful toward identifying them, but artefact may lead to red blood cells being present in the tubules. The distinction between tubules

---

Fig. 27-15. Electron micrographs of a section of parts of a proximal convoluted tubule from a rat kidney. The upper one ($\times$ 120,000) is of microvilli of the brush border, and each is seen to be covered by an extension of the cell membrane which shows two thin dark lines separated by a light interval. The lower micrograph ($\times$ 47,500) is of part of the base of the proximal tubule cell. The homogeneous basement membrane is seen (*lower right*) and the cell membrane adjacent to it is inflected into the cytoplasm as a series of parallel double membranes. Mitochondria showing cristae and dense mitochondrial bodies lie in the cytoplasm between these membranes. (Preparation by Dr. H. Movat)

and capillaries is to be made more easily if
the blood vessels are injected with colored
injection mass, as is shown in Figure 27-16.

In the instance of long loops, the first portion of the ascending limb may be similar to
the thin portion of the descending limb. But
this soon gives way, in the ascending limb, to
a wider tubule with thicker walls; this is
known as the *thick segment* of the ascending
arm (Fig. 27-6). The character of the thick
segment is very similar to that of the distal
convoluted tubule, which will soon be described. In the instance of nephrons with
short loops of Henle, the epithelium may
change from the thin to that of the thick
type, even before the nephron has looped back
to begin its ascending arm.

**Function.** The function of the loops of
Henle in acting as a counter-current osmotic
multiplier has already been described.

### The Distal Convoluted Tubule

As has been described already, the thick
segment of the ascending loop of Henle returns to the glomerular root of the glomerulus
from which the nephron has its origin, and
there the part of its wall which comes into
contact with the glomerular root becomes
heavily nucleated and forms a thick spot, the
*macula densa* (Figs. 27-7 and 27-8).

Some authorities define the distal convoluted tubule as only that part of the nephron
which extends from the macula densa to a
collecting tubule. However, more authorities
classify the thick ascending arm of the loop
of Henle as part of it. Distal convoluted tubules differ from proximal convoluted tubules
in several respects which are listed below.

1. They are not so long; hence, cross and
oblique sections of them are not seen nearly
so often in a section of kidney cortex (Fig.
27-13).

2. Their cross-section diameters are generally not quite as great, but since the cells of
their walls are generally lower, their lumens
tend to be larger (Fig. 27-13).

3. The cells of their walls are smaller in all
directions; hence a cross section through a
distal tubule reveals many more nuclei than
similar sections of proximal convoluted tubules (Fig. 27-13).

4. The cells of their walls have no brush or
striated borders on their free surfaces, and

their cytoplasm is not nearly so acidophilic
(Fig. 27-13).

5. Since the borders between contiguous
cells do not interdigitate as extensively as
those of cells of the proximal tubules, cell
borders can be distinguished more clearly than
in proximal tubules.

Like proximal convoluted tubules, the distal
ones have a pronounced basement membrane
encircling them (Fig. 27-13).

**Fine Structure.** The cell surfaces that face
the lumen show only a few minor villous projections (Fig. 27-14, *bottom tubule*). The
basal parts of the cells show very highly developed infoldings of the cell membrane which
are even more highly developed than those
seen at the bases of proximal convoluted cells
and illustrated in the bottom picture of Figure
27-15; these more or less divide this portion
of the cytoplasm into compartments which
contain large long mitochondria. RNA granules are not nearly so numerous as in the cells
of the proximal convoluted tubules.

**Function.** Reabsorption here has been dealt
with in the general account.

### Other Features of the Kidney

**Collecting tubules** are not to be thought of
as parts of nephrons, even though they absorb
water, as has been described in the general account. They comprise a series of drainage
ducts into which urine is delivered by distal
convoluted tubules and conducted to medullary papillae where it is emptied into the
calyces of the ureter (Figs. 27-3 and 27-6).

The collecting tubules form a branched system. The largest ones are known as the *ducts
of Bellini*. These are easily seen in the apical
part of a medullary pyramid where they empty
through its papilla. They are large ducts with
wide lumens and thick walls composed of pale-
staining, high columnar cells with a thin cuticle on their free border. In contrast with the
different parts of the renal tubules, the borders
between the cells that make up the walls of
the ducts of Bellini and the smaller collecting
tubules that empty into them are distinct in
the ordinary section (Fig. 27-17). The pale
cytoplasm of these cells is illustrated in Figure 27-13. With the EM, the cells of the collecting tubules have been found to have only
moderately deep infoldings of the cell membrane from the base of the cell.

In the medulla, the ducts of Bellini branch at very acute angles (Fig. 27-3). Several generations of branches arise to provide a sufficient number of collecting ducts to supply each medullary ray in the kidney. In the rays, the ducts give off side branches. There each pursues a short arched course before becoming continuous with the termination of a distal convoluted tubule (Fig. 27-6).

Although each nephron is provided with an individual arched collecting tubule, several arched tubules empty into a single straight collecting tubule. Hence, there are not nearly so many straight collecting tubules as nephrons in the kidney.

**Casts.** A cast is a structure formed by the solidification of material that is poured into a mold. In connection with the kidney, the term is used to describe coagulated material, usually protein, that is seen sometimes in the lumens of the more distal parts of nephrons and in collecting tubules. Casts are not seen in the strictly normal kidney. But material obtained at autopsy and used for teaching kidney histology may not always be strictly normal; hence, some casts may be seen in the lumens of the tubules in it. There are many types of casts, but generally they form as a result of some kind of protein material gaining entrance to the lumens of nephrons, and then as the material becomes more concentrated, as resorption of fluid occurs along the length of the nephron, the material coagulates. The fact that enough protein gains entrance to the lumens of nephrons to form casts indicates altered kidney function. Under normal circumstances, either no protein or, as some believe, a very little escapes into the glomerular filtrate. Even if the latter view is true, the amount is so limited that it is all resorbed by the tubules and does not accumulate to form casts. As it is being resorbed it may appear in the form of hyalin droplets in the cells of the proximal convoluted tubules; these are normal in the rat.

**The Connective Tissue of the Kidney.** The kidney is covered with a thin translucent *capsule* that consists of fibrous connective tissue; the intercellular substance in it is chiefly collagen, but a few elastic fibers may be present. In health the capsule is smooth and glistening and can be stripped easily from the cortex. In some kinds of kidney disease fibrous connec-

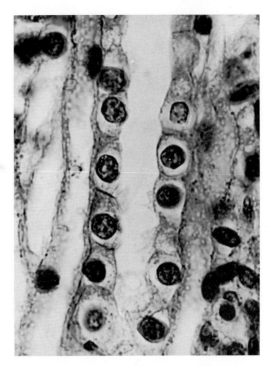

Fig. 27-17. Medium-power photomicrograph of a section of the medulla of a rat's kidney, showing a collecting tubule cut in longitudinal section. Notice that the adjacent borders of its cells are distinct. (Preparation and photomicrograph by Dr. W. S. Hartroft)

tive tissue forms in the parenchyma of the cortex and extends out to the capsule to bind it firmly to the organ. Under these conditions the capsule cannot be stripped readily from the organ, and this fact is noted at autopsy as an indication that the kidney has become diseased.

The basement membranes that surround the tubules are supported on their outer surfaces by delicate reticular fibers. As already noted, the latter do not extend into the glomeruli except perhaps for a short distance into their roots. More substantial fibrous types of intercellular substance may be found in association with the larger vessels of the kidney. But, all in all, the fibrous connective tissue of the kidney parenchyma, except between the ducts of Bellini in the papilla, where there is some loose connective tissue, is extraordinarily scanty, a fact which suggests that there is a great amount of osmotic activity requiring that only

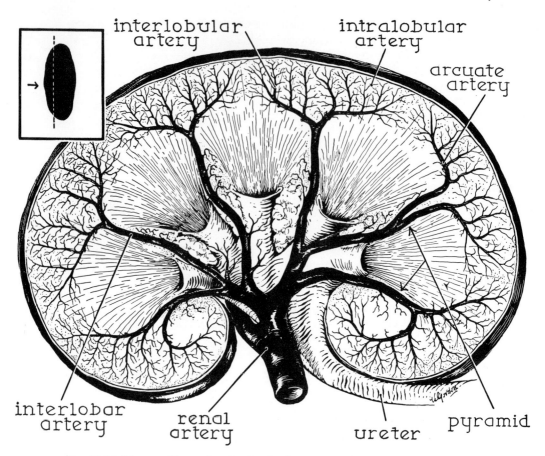

interlobular artery

intralobular artery

arcuate artery

interlobar artery

renal artery

ureter

pyramid

Fig. 27-18. Diagram illustrating the distribution of the arteries in a human kidney.

substances through which diffusion can occur (amorphous types of intercellular substances) be present between the tubules and the capillaries. Increased fibrous tissue in the kidney is a manifestation of past disease and in itself it can further interfere with function.

### THE CIRCULATION OF BLOOD THROUGH THE KIDNEY

Each kidney is supplied by a renal artery. These are relatively large vessels that arise from the aorta, so each kidney receives large amounts of blood delivered under a high pressure.

**Interlobar Arteries.** On reaching the hilus of a kidney the renal artery divides, usually into three branches. Two of these (the anterior branches) commonly pass toward the concavity of the kidney in front of the pelvis of the ureter, and one (the posterior branch), behind it. Before entering the substance of the organ

both the anterior and the posterior branches of the main vessel branch further. As a result of this branching, separate vessels are provided to penetrate the substance of the kidney between each pair of adjacent pyramids (Fig. 27-18). In addition, vessels are provided to extend up the outside border of the pyramids at the two poles of the kidney (Fig. 27-18). Since the pyramids represent lobes, the branches that ascend into the kidney substance between the medullary pyramids are called *interlobar arteries*. It is of interest that an interlobar artery does not ascend in the middle of a column of Bertin but at one of its sides, close to one of the pyramids that bounds the column (Fig. 27-18). The interlobar arteries, as they ascend in columns of Bertin, give off *small* branches to supply the perirenal fat, but the glomeruli in the columns of Bertin are supplied by branches from the next two types of artery to be described.

**Arcuate Arteries.** Some of the interlobar

FIG. 27-19. Diagram to show how the capillary beds of the cortex and the medulla are supplied with blood. (Based on Morison, D. M.: Am. J. Anat. *37*:93)

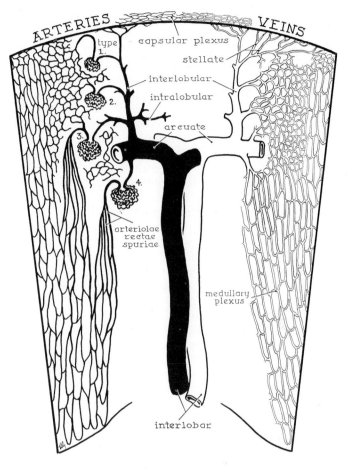

arteries break up into main branches as they ascend in the columns of Bertin, but most of them do so only when they have almost reached the corticomedullary border. Here their branches are given off at wide angles, nearly at right angles, and in all directions in this plane. These main branches, into which the interlobar arteries break up, arch over the bases of the medullary pyramids and are called *arcuate* (*arcuatus* = arched) arteries. Actually, the group of arcuate arteries that arise from each interlobar artery could be compared with the arching branches of an elm tree; the name arcuate was given to these vessels because *together* they form an arch. But as there is no continuity between the branches of adjacent trees, there is no continuity between the arcuate arteries that arise from adjacent interlobar arteries. Hence, there are no anastomoses between interlobar arteries through arcuate arteries (Fig. 27-18). Accordingly, if an interlobar artery becomes

plugged with a thrombus, a pyramidal-shaped segment of kidney tissue dies (the area supplied by the arcuate arteries from that particular interlobar artery); this area of dead tissue is called an infarct.

**Interlobular Arteries.** The arcuate arteries give off branches that ascend into the cortex (Fig. 27-18). These vessels run between lobules and are termed interlobular arteries (Figs. 27-18 and 27-19). They mark the boundaries between lobules and so alternate with the medullary rays that form the central cores of lobules (Fig. 27-5).

The interlobular arteries give off branches at wide angles on every side. Since these immediately enter the substance of surrounding lobules (the cortical labyrinth), they are called *intralobular arteries* (Fig. 27-19). These give rise to the afferent vessels of glomeruli. However, the terminal branches of the interlobular arteries continue on to the capsule to supply its capillary bed.

**How the Capillary Beds of Cortex and Medulla Are Supplied.** The efferent arterioles of glomeruli in different parts of the cortex deliver blood into different capillary beds. As may be seen in Figure 27-19, which is based on the study of Morison, the efferent arterioles from glomeruli in the outer part of the cortex (Fig. 27-19) empty their blood into the capillary beds that surround the proximal and the distal convoluted tubules in the cortex. Those from glomeruli somewhat deeper in the cortex (Fig. 27-19) contribute to the capillary bed of the cortex but also to long straight capillary-like vessels that descend into the medulla and are called *arteriolae rectae spuriae* (false straight arterioles) for reasons that will become obvious later. The efferent vessels from the deepest glomeruli in the cortex, some of which are below the level of the arcuate arteries, deliver most or all of their blood into the arteriolae rectae spuriae (Fig. 27-19).

The return of the blood from the capillary beds of the cortex and the medulla is illustrated on the right side of Figure 27-19. In general, the veins correspond to the arteries already described. It is to be noted that at the surface of the kidney little veins arise from the capillary beds of the capsule and the superficial part of the cortex to pass in a converging fashion to interlobular veins. Since these end branches radiate out in a starlike fashion from the ends of the interlobular veins, they are called *stellate veins* (Fig. 27-19).

Since the arteriolae rectae spuriae, which supply the capillary beds of the medulla, are all supplied by the efferent vessels of glomeruli in the deeper part of the cortex (Fig. 27-19), it follows that all the blood that is delivered into the capillary beds of the medulla, like that which is delivered into the capillary beds of the cortex, has passed immediately beforehand through glomeruli. However, this concept has been contested from time to time. It has been claimed by some who have investigated the circulation of blood through the medulla that arterioles arise directly from the arcuate and the interlobular arteries to pass directly to the capillary beds of the medulla. To distinguish these from the arteriolae rectae spuriae (the false straight arterioles) they are called the *arteriolae rectae verae* (true straight arterioles). If these exist it would mean that the medulla was supplied with blood that had

not passed through glomeruli. Most modern students of this matter do not believe that enough of these exist to be of any functional significance. Hartroft's study shows how some vessels, apparently of this nature, could arise through the fusion of the afferent and the efferent arterioles of the juxtamedullary glomeruli that undergo a physiologic atrophy during the growth of the kidney. Moreover, MacCallum's study shows how estimates of the number of arteriolae rectae verae present in normal kidneys might be overestimated because of their being investigated in kidneys that have been injured throughout life by disease. He has shown that the capillaries of glomeruli that are affected by certain disease processes tend to atrophy and disappear, and at the same time a more or less direct connection becomes established between their afferent and efferent vessels. Unless an observer looked very carefully, he might fail to see these atrophied glomeruli—and there are some, according to MacCallum, even in apparently normal kidneys (Hartroft's physiologic atrophy?)—and so the observer might conclude that what is really an afferent arteriole joined to an efferent arteriole at the site of a defunct glomerulus is an arteriole that has extended from an interlobular artery directly to the capillary bed of the medulla without there being a glomerulus inserted along its course. Therefore, general opinion is to the effect that for all practical purposes the blood in the capillary beds of the medulla has passed through glomeruli and has an increased colloid content over that of blood elsewhere and that this may be a factor in withdrawing interstitial fluid back into blood by osmotic phenomena.

It is possible that a small amount of blood that has not passed through glomeruli may be delivered to the capillary beds of the cortex by means of branches of afferent arterioles that have long been described as emptying into these beds. Such a branch of an afferent arteriole is known as a *Ludwig's arteriole*.

**The Two Circulatory Pathways Through the Kidney.** During World War II, attention was focused on the study of those unfortunate individuals who were partly buried by rubble when buildings collapsed from bombing. It was found that an individual whose legs had been crushed by a great weight but not necessarily irreparably injured would, in some instances and some days after the event, fail to excrete urine. Many injured in this fashion died after a short period of apparent recovery, not from their primary injuries but from kidney failure. This condition, termed *crush syndrome*, inspired Trueta, a surgeon, and his associates to make investigations which have thrown great light upon how the route taken by blood through the kidney may be altered in what is generally termed *shock*.

To understand this matter the student should refer back to Figure 27-19. This shows that the efferent vessels of the glomeruli in the outer part of the cortex (labeled 1 and 2) empty into the capillary bed of the cortical labyrinth, while those of the glomeruli near the border of the medulla, which Trueta terms the *juxtamedullary glomeruli* (labeled 3 and 4), empty almost entirely into the arteriolae rectae spuriae which supply the capillary beds of the medulla (the capillary beds of both the cortex and the medulla are, of course, continuous (Fig. 27-19). Furthermore, it is to be observed that the juxtamedullary glomeruli are larger than those nearer the surface of the kidney, and, as has been noted, the lumens of their efferent vessels may be larger than the lumens of their afferent vessels.

Trueta and his associates found that injuries, such as those occasioned when limbs are crushed, can reflexly cause spasm of certain blood vessels in the kidney. In general, the chief effect is on the peripheral two thirds of the interlobular arteries, which become constricted. Another factor that can have much the same effect as spasm of these vessels is a loss of plasma from the circulatory system, for the amount of fluid in the circulatory system is an important factor in keeping blood vessels open. Accordingly, it is easy to visualize that spasm in the smaller arterial vessels in the kidney and a lack of fluid in the circulatory system (as can occur in untreated shock) could result in the smaller arterioles becoming pinched off and this could lead to impaired function in, or even in the death of, kidney tissue. Since the greatest effect would be exerted on the smaller arterial vessels, the impairment of circulation would be greatest toward the periphery of the kidney. Conditions can arise, therefore, when it is possible for blood to continue to circulate through the

juxtamedullary glomeruli while ceasing to circulate through the glomeruli in the outer part of the kidney. Under these conditions, the whole outer part of the cortex becomes relatively pale and bloodless. Thus, all the blood that circulates through the kidney passes through the more deeply disposed glomeruli (the juxtamedullary ones), and since the efferent vessels of these empty almost entirely into the arteriolae rectae spuriae, the blood from them is conducted to the capillary beds of the medulla rather than to those of the cortex.

## LYMPHATICS OF THE KIDNEY

As was explained in Chapter 6, lymphatic capillaries, in most parts of the body, serve the purpose of draining away and returning to the bloodstream that portion of tissue fluid that is not absorbed by the venous ends of capillaries. Moreover, when blood capillaries are injured, so that they exude substantial quantities of colloid into the tissues (Fig. 10-10), the presence of lymphatic capillaries is particularly advantageous because they are permeable to the colloid and so help return it to the bloodstream.

The problem relating to the production and the absorption of tissue fluid, and hence to the role of lymphatic capillaries, in the kidney is considerably different from that in most parts of the body. Such tissue fluid is produced in the kidney by glomerular capillaries and passes into the lumens of nephrons as glomerular filtrate. Practically all of the other capillaries in the kidney are comparable with the venous ends of ordinary capillaries in that they are concerned with absorption and not with the production of fluid. Therefore, it is obvious that, except in glomeruli, tissue fluid is not produced in the parenchyma of the kidney; it is merely resorbed through the walls of nephrons back into capillaries. Furthermore, as has been pointed out, the blood that supplies the capillary beds of the tubular portions of nephrons has a relatively increased content of colloid and is admirably suited to draw fluid back into the capillaries.

Lymphatic capillaries, if they were present in glomeruli, would provide an alternative route of escape for tissue fluid; hence, if they were present, they would interfere with glomerular capillaries delivering tissue fluid into the lumens of nephrons. Therefore, it is not surprising that lymphatic capillaries have not been found in glomeruli. Since tissue fluid is not produced by capillaries elsewhere in the kidney parenchyma, but only absorbed, and since the blood in these beds has passed through glomeruli and so has an increased colloid content which makes it admirably suited to absorbing fluid, there does not seem to be much need for lymphatic capillaries here either, so it is not surprising that, with the possible exception of some of the medulla, lymphatic capillaries do not appear to be present in kidney parenchyma but only where there are substantial amounts of connective tissue, in particular that associated with the blood vessels.

The distribution of the lymphatics of the kidney has been investigated in recent years by Peirce and by Rawson. Peirce, using stab injections and other methods, could not satisfy himself that there were any lymphatics in the kidney other than those that accompany the blood vessels. He found that the periarterial plexuses were richer in lymphatics than the perivenous plexuses and that the lymphatics of the plexuses could be traced from the renal artery and vein along the interlobar, arcuate and interlobular vessels to the capsule of the kidney where they communicated with capsular lymphatics. However, they were not found to extend into the actual parenchyma of the cortex or the medulla from these vessels. He found valves in the larger lymphatics in the hilus of the kidney. Rawson, somewhat later, studied the lymphatics of a kidney which had been invaded by cancer cells, and he used their presence for mapping out the lymphatics. In general, Rawson found lymphatics in the same sites as those described by Peirce but he also found evidence of some lymphatic capillaries which began beneath the epithelium of the tip of the medullary pyramid and extended toward the base of the medullary pyramid where they emptied into the lymphatics associated with the arcuate vessels. However, none were found in the actual parenchyma of the cortex.

## POSTNATAL GROWTH OF THE KIDNEY

The growth of the kidney, in early postnatal life, has been investigated more extensively in the rat than in any other species; hence, most of the information given here relates to the studies made on this animal.

It has been shown both by Kittelson and Arataki that only about one third of the number of glomeruli that are to be found in the adult are present at birth. Glomeruli continue to be formed for about 100 days after birth, but the majority are formed in the first 3 to 4 weeks.

The first-formed glomeruli are in the region close to the medulla, and many of these undergo a physiologic atrophy (Hartroft) and disappear. However, in some instances their afferent and efferent vessels may remain and fuse to constitute a few arteriolae rectae verae. The oldest glomeruli, which are also the largest, are to be found near the arcuate vessels. At birth, the outer part of the cortex of the kidney is undifferentiated, and it is here that new nephrons are formed. After birth, renal corpuscles develop in the outer cortex of the kidney (the nephrogenic zone). The tubule of each new nephron then becomes connected to the duct system. The youngest nephrons are those situated in the outer cortex immediately beneath the capsule, and these are not fully differentiated for about 3 months after birth. The glomeruli of these nephrons are the smallest in the kidney. Figure 27-1 illustrates the classic theory of the development of the renal corpuscle. This theory has the advantage of being easily understandable, but recent work indicates that the renal corpuscle develops in situ and not by invagination by capillaries of the blind end of a previously formed tubule. In the renal cortex, a clump of cells is associated with the end of a developing tubule. Some of these cells become the parietal and visceral epithelial cells of Bowman's capsule, and others become endothelial cells. The capillaries so formed later connect with the vascular system.

The size of the kidneys in postnatal life is affected both by the diet and by hormones. High protein diets make the kidneys become larger. Injections of male sex hormone also make the kidneys of experimental animals become larger. The increase in size that occurs with high protein diets or male hormone treatment is brought about by nephrons increasing in size and not in number.

If one kidney is removed from adult animals the remaining kidney becomes larger. The increase in size is due to the nephrons becoming larger and not more numerous. However, in individual nephrons there is an increase in the number of cells of which they are composed, and mitotic figures can be seen in the nephrons of the remaining kidney for a period following the removal of the other. The kidneys also become larger during pregnancy; this is termed a physiologic hypertrophy, and mitotic figures have been found in the nephrons as they enlarge in this condition.

## THE URETER

The wall of the ureter has 3 coats: (1) a mucous membrane, (2) a muscular coat and (3) a fibro-elastic adventitia.

**Mucous Membrane.** This consists of only 2 layers, an epithelial lining and a lamina propria. The epithelium is of the transitional type (Fig. 27-21) and is from 4 to 5 cells in thickness, except in the pelvis, where it is somewhat thinner. Transitional epithelium is described in detail in Chapter 9, and information is given there on the polyploidy that occurs in it. The lamina propria consists of fairly dense connective tissue, except in its deepest part, next to the muscular coat, where it is of a somewhat looser texture. Some elastic fibers are mixed with the abundant collagenic ones. Occasional lymphatic nodules are encountered in it.

The mucous membrane of the ureter, except in the pelvis, is thrown into longitudinal folds which give its lumen a stellate appearance in cross sections (Fig. 27-20). The combination of transitional epithelium (which can stretch without rupturing) and longitudinal folds makes it possible for the lumen of the ureter to become considerably expanded without the mucous membrane's rupturing. This is an asset should concretions (kidney stones) form in the pelvis as they do under various abnormal conditions. These are sometimes "passed" by way of the ureter, the bladder and the urethra.

**Muscular Coat.** In approximately the upper two thirds of the ureter the muscular coat consists of 2 layers: an inner one of longitudinally disposed smooth muscle fibers and an outer one of circularly disposed fibers (Fig. 27-20). It may be helpful to remember that this is the reverse of the arrangement seen in

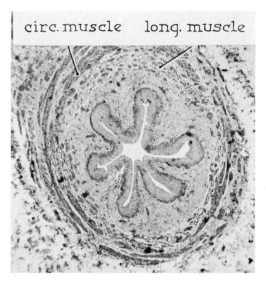

FIG. 27-20. Very low-power photomicrograph of a cross section of the ureter.

the intestine. Moreover, the layers of smooth muscle in the ureter are infiltrated by connective tissue from the lamina propria and adventitia; hence, they are not nearly so compact and distinct as those in the intestine. The amount of smooth muscle in the wall of the pelvis is less than that in the remainder of the ureter, except where the calyces are attached to the pyramids. At this site, the circularly disposed fibers are prominent, and it could be assumed that if this muscle contracted, the papilla it surrounds would be squeezed. A sustained, pronounced contraction of this muscle conceivably could shut off the flow of urine from the papilla concerned. However, occasional and not so severe contractions conceivably could have a "milking" effect on a papilla and squeeze urine out of the ducts of Bellini into the calyx concerned. It is likely that some action of the latter type is of physiologic importance.

In approximately its lower third, a third coat of muscle fibers is present in the ureter. This forms the outermost layer of the muscular coat, and its fibers are longitudinally disposed.

The ureters pierce the bladder wall obliquely. This, together with little valvelike folds of bladder mucosa that guard their entrance into the bladder, prevents contractions of the bladder wall from forcing urine back

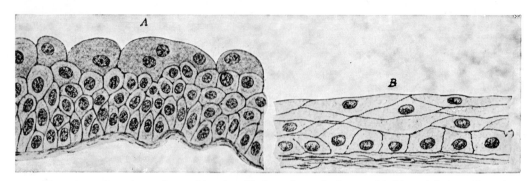

Fig. 27-21. Drawings of transitional epithelium from the human bladder: (*A*) in collapsed condition; (*B*) in distended condition. (Addison: Piersol's Normal Histology, ed. 15, Philadelphia, Lippincott)

up the ureters (the contraction of muscle fibers arranged in a thick sheet tends to close the lumen of a tube that passes through the sheet obliquely). As each ureter enters the bladder wall it loses its circularly disposed fibers. However, its longitudinal fibers continue through the wall to the mucosa membrane of the bladder, where they are attached. Urine does not drain from the kidney to the bladder because of gravity as at first might be thought; this is convenient for astronauts traveling through weightless space. Peristalticlike waves of contraction sweep down the muscle of the ureter and force urine into the bladder. The contraction of the longitudinal smooth muscle fibers in the part of the ureter that passes through the wall of the bladder helps open the lumen of that segment of the tube so as to permit urine to be delivered into the bladder.

**Adventitia.** This, the outermost coat of the ureter, consists of fibro-elastic connective tissue. At its periphery it merges into adjacent areolar tissue which, in turn, is connected to other structures.

### THE URINARY BLADDER

The wall of the urinary bladder is of the same character as that of the ureter but is considerably thicker. The transitional epithelium of its mucous membrane is about 5 cells thick in the empty bladder but only 2 or 3 in the distended one (Fig. 27-21). (See also Chap. 9 for details of transitional epithelium.) The lamina propria is collagenic in character and has only a few elastic fibers in it. Its deepest layer is somewhat looser in texture and has more elastic fibers in it than

are found in its more superficial part; this is sometimes termed the *submucosa layer* of the bladder. This extends up into such folds as form in the lining of the contracted organ. The muscular coat consists of 3 layers, but in sections these cannot be distinguished from one another to advantage. Their respective thicknesses vary in different parts of the bladder. In general, the middle coat is the most prominent one and its fibers are mostly circularly disposed. Around the opening of the urethra, muscle fibers are usually aggregated to form an internal sphincter. The adventitia is fibro-elastic in nature. Over part of the bladder it is covered with peritoneum. Over the remainder it blends into adjacent areolar tissue.

### THE URETHRA

The urethra is a tube which extends from the bladder to an external orifice and so permits urine contained in the bladder to be evacuated from the body. In the male, the urethra courses through the male genital copulatory organ, the penis; hence in the male the urethra is at times used for a second purpose, that of providing a pathway for semen (a suspension of spermatozoa in fluid) to be delivered from the body in the act of copulation. Since the urethra of the male is a part of both the reproductive and the urinary systems, its description may be postponed until the male reproductive system is considered. However, the urethra of the female serves no genital function but only a urinary one; hence, its structure will be described here.

The female urethra is said to vary in length

from 2 to 6 cm. There is some difference of opinion about its average length, different estimates ranging from about 3 cm. to about 4½ cm. It is a fairly straight muscular tube lined by mucous membrane. The musculature of its wall consists of 2 coats of smooth muscle fibers; those of the inner one are disposed longitudinally, and those of the outer coat, circularly. At its external orifice striated muscle fibers reinforce the smooth ones to form an external sphincter.

In cross section the lumen of the urethra is seen to be roughly crescentic. The mucous membrane is thrown into longitudinal folds. The epithelium of most of the urethra is stratified or pseudostratified columnar in type. However, transitional epithelium is present near the bladder and stratified squamous near the external orifice. The relatively thick connective tissue lamina propria, particularly in its deeper part, which is sometimes called the *submucosa*, is rich in elastic fibers and plexuses of veins; the latter are sufficiently extensive to give the deeper portions of the lamina propria a resemblance to erectile tissue.

In many sites the epithelium extends into the lamina propria to form little outpocketings. These little glandlike structures commonly contain mucous cells. In the aged, concretions may form in them. True glands, opening by fine ducts into the lumen of the urethra, have also been described as being present, particularly in its upper part.

## INNERVATION OF THE
## URINARY SYSTEM

Nerve fibers reach the kidney by way of the renal plexus. This is a network of nerve fibers that extends along the renal artery from the aorta to the kidney. The bodies of ganglion cells also may be present in the renal plexus; if so they are to be regarded as outlying cells of diffuse celiac and aortic ganglia. Most of the fibers in the renal plexus are those of the sympathetic division of the autonomic system and are derived from the cells of the celiac and the aortic ganglia. Parasympathetic fibers occur in the renal plexus in smaller numbers. These are derived from the vagus nerve, whose fibers, to reach the renal plexus, course through the celiac plexus without interruption.

The nerve fibers from the renal plexus follow the arteries into the substance of the kidney. Harman and Davies have recently described their distribution within the organ. They penetrate glomeruli to form extensive perivascular networks in these structures. They also supply the epithelium of the convoluted tubules the transitional epithelium of the pelvis and the walls of the arteries and the veins.

Since transplanted kidneys, which are necessarily removed from a nerve supply, and kidneys left in situ but with the nerves that supply them cut, both function in a fairly normal fashion, it is obvious that the functions of the kidney are not fundamentally dependent on nervous mechanisms. However, nervous mechanisms control kidney function to some extent. It seems likely that most of the control is mediated by way of the sympathetic fibers that terminate in the blood vessels. The way in which this nervous regulation can operate to cause the blood to circulate chiefly through the juxtamedullary glomeruli, as in crush syndrome, has already been described. The part played by the parasympathetic, vagus-derived fibers in the kidney is obscure. One might speculate as to whether they affect the secretory activities of the cells of the proximal convoluted tubules in some way. But it seems clear that the nervous regulation of kidney function is chiefly mediated through sympathetic vasomotor nerves.

Some nerve fibrils have been shown to end in the JG complex.

Afferent impulses travel over nerves in the renal plexus, for cutting the fibers of the plexus abolishes pain of renal origin.

Both sympathetic and parasympathetic fibers course along the ureter. But they do not seem to be particularly concerned with the normal peristaltic movements that sweep down the musculature of this tube, for the movements continue if these nerves are cut. Some of the nerves here carry afferent impulses.

The bladder is supplied by fibers from both the sympathetic and the parasympathetic divisions of the autonomic system. The parasympathetic fibers are derived from the sacral outflow. The terminal ganglia to which they lead are present in the bladder wall; hence, in sections of bladder the student may occasionally observe ganglion cells. Stimulation of the parasympathetic fibers to the bladder leads to relaxation of the sphincter and contraction of the muscle of the bladder; hence, the act of evacuating the bladder, called micturition, is brought about by impulses traveling along parasympathetic fibers from the sacral outflow. Obviously, impairment of the spinal cord above the level at which these fibers arise interferes with micturition. The sympathetic fibers exert an effect opposite to those of the parasympathetic, hence, their stimulation tends to relax the musculature of the bladder wall and constrict the sphincter.

The desire for micturition is not experienced in the normal individual until the bladder comes to contain a moderate amount of urine. The tonus of the smooth muscle of the bladder wall remains fairly constant as the bladder fills. It is only when the organ becomes well filled that the degree of tonus becomes increased to the point where afferent fibers are stimulated. In very young children micturition occurs reflexly when this point is reached. But as children become older they gain a considerable degree of voluntary control over this reflex. For example, an adult, on feeling the desire to micturate, may voluntarily postpone the act, and in so doing, may lose for a time the desire to micturate. This is probably accomplished by voluntary considerations somehow resulting in sympathetic stimulation which relaxes the tonus of the bladder wall so that the afferent impulses (set up by increased tone and responsible for the desire to micturate) are for a time abolished.

The fact that an individual can refrain from micturating, even though the desire to micturate is experienced, and the fact that an individual can micturate even though the desire for micturition (requiring afferent stimulation) is not present, both suggest the existence of a mechanism by which voluntary control is exerted over autonomic neurons. In considering this it should be kept in mind that the urethra is provided with a sphincter of striated muscle under voluntary control, as well as the internal sphincter of smooth muscle that is innervated by the autonomic system. It would not be surprising if reflexes controlling the smooth muscle sphincters were set up by the tightening or the relaxation of the voluntary sphincters so that both tended to act in harmony. In other words, perhaps what appears to be voluntary control over autonomically innervated smooth muscle sphinc-

ters is, at least in part, indirect rather than direct.

## REFERENCES

### GENERAL REFERENCES ON THE KIDNEY

Oliver, J.: New directions in renal morphology: a method, its results and its future, Harvey Lect. 40:102, 1944-45.

Smith, H. W.: The Kidney—Structure and Function in Health and Disease, ed. 2, New York, Oxford, 1956.

————: Principles of Renal Physiology, New York, Oxford Univ. Press, 1956.

Symposium: Histochemistry and the elucidation of kidney structure and function, J. Histochem. 3:243, 1955.

### REFERENCES ON GLOMERULI, INCLUDING THEIR FINE STRUCTURE

Bergstrand, A.: Electron microscopic investigations of the renal glomeruli, Lab. Invest. 6:191, 1957.

Book, M. H.: The secreting area of the glomerulus, J. Anat. 71:91, 1936.

Boyer, C. C.: The vascular pattern of the renal glomerulus as revealed by plastic reconstruction from serial sections, Anat. Rec. 125:433, 1956.

Dunihue, F. W.: Cellular components of the renal glomerulus, Anat. Rec. 127:286, 1957.

Elias, H.: The structure of the renal glomerulus, Anat. Rec. 127:288, 1957.

Farquhar, M. G., and Palade, G. E.: Glomerular permeability. II. Ferritin transfer across the glomerular capillary wall in nephrotic rats, J. Exp. Med. 114:699, 1961.

————: Functional evidence for the existence of a third cell type in the renal glomerulus. Phagocytosis of filtration residues by a distinctive "third" cell, J. Cell Biol. 13:55, 1962.

Farquhar, M. G., Wissig, S. L., and Palade, G. E.: Glomerular permeability. I. Ferritin transfer across the normal glomerular capillary wall, J. Exp. Med. 113:47, 1961.

Hall, B. V.: Studies of normal glomerular structure by electron microscopy, Proc. Fifth Ann. Conf. Nephrotic Syndrome, p. 1, New York, National Nephrosis Foundation, 1953.

————: Further studies of the normal structure of the renal glomerulus, Proc. Sixth Ann. Conf. Nephrotic Syndrome, p. 1, New York, National Nephrosis Foundation, 1954.

Huhn, Dieter, Steiner, J. W., and Movat, H. Z.: Die Feinstruktur des Mesangiums im Nierenglomerulum von Hund und Maus, Z. Zellforsch. 56:213, 1962.

Kirkman, H., and Stowell, R. E.: Renal filtration surface in the albino rat, Anat. Rec. *83*: 373, 1942.

Lewis, O. J.: The development of the blood vessels of the metanephros, J. Anat. *92*:84, 1958.

————: The vascular arrangement of the mammalian renal glomerulus as revealed by a study of its development, J. Anat. *92*:433, 1958.

McGregor, L.: The finer histology of the normal glomerulus, Am. J. Path. *5*:545, 1929.

McManus, J. F. A.: Structure of the glomerulus of the human kidney, Am. J. Path. *24*:1259, 1948.

McManus, J. F. A., Lupton, C. H., Jr., and Graham, L. S., Jr.: The demonstration of the intercapillary space of the human renal glomerulus, Anat. Rec. *110*:57, 1951.

Pease, D. C.: Fine structures of the kidney seen by electron microscopy, J. Histochem. *3*:295, 1955.

Pease, D. C., and Baker, R. F.: Electron microscopy of the kidney, Am. J. Anat. *87*:249, 1950.

Richards, A. N.: Urine formation in the amphibian kidney, Harvey Lect. *30*:93, 1934-35.

Rytand, D. A.: The number and size of mammalian glomeruli as related to kidney and to body weight, with methods for their enumeration and measurement, Am. J. Anat. *62*:507, 1938.

Smith, J. P.: Anatomical features of the human renal glomerular efferent vessel, J. Anat. *90*: 290, 1956.

Suzuki, Y., Churg, J., Grishman, E., Mautner, W., and Dachs, S.: The mesangium of the renal glomerulus. Electron microscope studies of pathologic alterations, Am. J. Path. *43*:555, 1963.

Trump, B. F., and Benditt, E. P.: Electron microscopic studies of human renal disease. Observations on normal visceral glomerular epithelium and its modifications in disease, Lab. Invest. *11*:753, 1962.

Vimtrup, B.: On the number, shape, structure and surface area of the glomeruli in the kidneys of man and mammals, Am. J. Anat. *41*: 123, 1928.

## REFERENCES ON THE VASCULAR POLE AND JG CELLS

Bing, J., and Kazimierczak, J.: Renin content of different parts of the periglomerular circumference, Acta path. microbiol. scand. *50*:1, 1960.

Dunihue, F. W.: The effect of adrenal insufficiency and desoxycorticosterone acetate on the juxtaglomerular apparatus (abstr.), Anat. Rec. *103*:442, 1949.

Dunihue, F. W., and Robertson, Van B.: The effect of desoxycorticosterone acetate and of sodium on the juxtaglomerular apparatus, Endocrinology *61*:293, 1957.

Garber, B. G., McCoy, F. W., Marks, B. H., and Hayes, E. R.: Factors that affect the granulation of the juxtaglomerular apparatus, Anat. Rec. *130*:303, 1958.

Goldblatt, H.: Experimental hypertension induced by renal ischemia, Harvey Lect. *33*: 237, 1937-38.

Goormaghtigh, N.: Existence of an endocrine gland in the media of the renal arterioles, Proc. Soc. Exp. Biol. Med. *42*:688, 1939.

————: Facts in favour of an endocrine function of the renal arterioles, J. Path. Bact. *57*: 392, 1945.

————: La fonction endocrine des arterioles renales, Louvain, Fonteyn, 1944.

————: Histological changes in the ischemic kidney with special reference to the juxtaglomerular apparatus, Am. J. Path. *16*:409, 1940.

Hartroft, P. M., and Hartroft, W. S.: The effects of dietary factors and administration of desoxycorticosterone acetate (DCA) on juxtaglomerular cells of the rat (abstr.), Anat. Rec. *112*: 39, 1952.

————: Studies on renal juxtaglomerular cells, J. Exp. Med. *102*:205, 1955.

Hartroft, P. M., and Edelman, R.: Renal juxtaglomerular cells in sodium deficiency *in* Moyer and Fuchs (eds.): Edema, pp. 63-68, Philadelphia, Saunders, 1960.

Hartroft, P. M., Newmark, L. N., and Pitcock, J. A.: Relationship of renal juxtaglomerular cells to sodium intake, adrenal cortex and hypertension *in* J. Moyer (ed.): Hypertension, pp. 24-31, Philadelphia, Saunders, 1959.

Marks, B. H., and Garber, B. G.: The juxtaglomerular apparatus as an extra adrenal site of ACTH action, Anat. Rec. *133*:306, 1959.

McManus, J. F. A.: Further observations on the glomerular root of the vertebrate kidney, Quart. J. Micro. Sc. *88*:39, 1947.

Pitcock, J. A., and Hartroft, P. M.: The juxtaglomerular cells in man and their relationship to the level of plasma sodium and to the zona glomerulosa of the adrenal cortex, Am. J. Path. *34*:863, 1958.

Pitcock, J. A., Hartroft, P. M., and Newmark, L. N.: Increased renal pressor activity (renin) in sodium deficient rats and correlation with juxtaglomerular cell granulation, Proc. Soc. Exp. Biol. Med. *100*:868, 1959.

Gottschalk, C., and Mylle, M.: Micropuncture study of the mammalian urinary concentrating mechanism: evidence for the countercurrent hypothesis, Am. J. Physiol. *196*:927, 1959.

Wirz, H.: Colston Symposium on the Neurohypophysis, pp. 157-166, London, 1957.

———: The production of hypertonic urine by the mammalian kidney *in* The Kidney, Ciba Foundation Symposium, p. 38, Boston, Little, 1954.

Selye, H., and Stone, H.: Pathogenesis of the cardiovascular and renal changes which usually accompany malignant hypertension, J. Urol. *56*:399, 1946.

Tobian, L., Janecek, J., and Tomboulian, A.: Correlation between granulation of juxtaglomerular cells and extractable renin in rats with experimental hypertension, Proc. Soc. Exp. Biol. Med. *100*:94, 1959.

Wilson, W.: A new staining method for demonstrating the granules of the juxtaglomerular complex, Anat. Rec. *112*:497, 1952.

### REFERENCES ON OTHER PARTS OF THE NEPHRON, INCLUDING FINE STRUCTURE

Bensley, R. R., and Steen, W. B.: The functions of the differentiated segments of the uriniferous tubule, Am. J. Anat. *41*:75, 1928.

Dalton, A. J.: Structural details of some of the epithelial cell types in the kidney of the mouse as revealed by the electron microscope, J. Nat. Cancer Inst. *11*:1163, 1951.

Edwards, J. G.: Functional sites and morphological differentiation in the renal tubule, Anat. Rec. *55*:343, 1953.

———: Studies on aglomerular and glomerular kidneys, Am. J. Anat. *42*:75, 1928.

Fawcett, D. W.: Structural specializations of the cell surface *in* Palay, S. L. (ed.): Frontiers in Cytology, pp. 19-41, New Haven, Conn., Yale Univ. Press, 1958.

Holton, S. G., and Bensley, R. R.: The function of the differentiated parts of the uriniferous tubule in the mammal, Am. J. Anat. *47*:241, 1931.

Huber, G. C.: Renal tubules *in* Cowdry's Special Cytology, ed. 2, p. 933, New York, Hoeber, 1932.

Longley, J. B., and Fisher, E. R.: Alkaline phosphatase and the periodic acid Schiff reaction in the proximal tubule of the vertebrate kidney, Anat. Rec. *120*:1, 1954.

Marshall, E. K., Jr.: A comparison of the function of the glomerular and aglomerular kidney, Am. J. Physiol. *94*:1, 1930.

Pease, D. C.: Electron microscopy of the tubular cells of the kidney cortex, Anat. Rec. *121*:723, 1955.

———: Fine structures of the kidney seen by electron microscopy, J. Histochem. *3*:295, 1955.

Rhodin, J.: Correlation of ultrastructural organization and function in normal and experimentally changed proximal convoluted tubule cells of the mouse kidney, Karolinska Institutet, Stockholm, Aktiebolaget Godvil, 1954.

———: Anatomy of the kidney tubules, Internat. Rev. Cytol. *7*:485, 1958.

———: An Atlas of Ultrastructure, Philadelphia, Saunders, 1963.

Richards, A. N., and Walker, A. M.: Methods of collecting fluid from known regions of the renal tubules of amphibia and perfusing the lumen of a single tubule, Am. J. Physiol. *118*:111, 1937.

Ruska, H., Moore, D. H., and Weinstock, J.: The base of the proximal convoluted tubule cells of rat kidney, J. Biophys. Biochem. Cytol. *3*:249, 1957.

Sjöstrand, F. S., and Rhodin, J.: The ultrastructure of the proximal convoluted tubules of the mouse kidney as revealed by high resolution electron microscopy, Exp. Cell. Res. *4*:426, 1953.

Smith, H. W.: The fate of sodium and water in the renal tubules, Bull. N. Y. Acad. Med. *35*:293, 1959.

Wirz, H.: Introduction—Tubular transport mechanism with special reference to the hairpin countercurrent *in* Duyff, J. W., *et al* (eds.): XXII International Congress of Physiological Sciences, Symposium VII, vol. 1, p. 359, New York, Excerpta Medica Foundation, 1962.

(For references on the function of different parts of the nephron consult textbooks on physiology and biochemistry.)

### REFERENCES ON THE CONNECTIVE TISSUE, THE LYMPHATICS AND THE NERVES OF THE KIDNEY AND OTHER PARTS OF THE URINARY SYSTEM

Barrington, F. J. F.: The nervous mechanism of micturition, Quart. J. Exp. Physiol. *8*:33, 1914.

DeMuylder, C. G.: The "Neurility" of the Kidney, Oxford, Blackwell, 1952.

Gruber, C. M.: The autonomic innervation of the genito-urinary system, Physiol. Rev. *13*:497, 1933.

Harman, P. J., and Davies, H.: Intrinsic nerves in the kidney of the cat and the rat, Anat. Rec. *100*:671, 1948.

Kirkman, H.: The number and distribution of macrophages and fibroblasts in kidneys of albino rats with emphasis on twenty-five day males, Am. J. Anat. *73*:451, 1943.

———: A comparative morphological and cytochemical study of globule leucocytes (Schollenleukocyten) of the urinary tract and of possibly related cells, Am. J. Anat. *86*:91, 1950.

Leeson, T. S.: An electron microscopic study of the postnatal development of the hamster kidney, with particular reference to intertubular tissue, Lab. Invest. *10*:466, 1961.

Marshall, E. K., Jr., and Krolls, A. C.: Studies on the nervous control of the kidney in relation to

diuresis and urinary secretion: II. The effect
of unilateral excision of the adrenal, section of
the splanchnic nerve and section of the renal
nerves on the secretion of the kidney, Am. J.
Physiol. *49*:302, 1919.

Peirce, E. C.: Renal lymphatics, Anat. Rec. *90*:
315, 1944.

Rawson, A. J.: Distribution of the lymphatics of
the human kidney as shown in a case of car-
cinomatous permeation, Arch. Path. *47*:283,
1949.

## REFERENCES ON THE DEVELOPMENT AND THE GROWTH OF THE KIDNEY

Andrew, W., and Pruett, D.: Senile changes in the
kidneys of Wistar Institute rats, Am. J. Anat.
*100*:51, 1957.

Arataki, M.: On the postnatal growth of the kidney, with special reference to the number and
size of the glomeruli, Am. J. Anat. *36*:399,
1926.

Clark, S. L., Jr.: Cellular differentiation in the
kidneys of newborn mice studied with the electron microscope, J. Biophys. Biochem. Cytol.
*3*:349, 1957.

Hartroft, W. S.: The vascular development of the
kidney of the pig, Tr. Roy. Soc. Canada, Sec.
V (Biol. Sc.) *35*:67, 1949.

Kittelson, J. A.: The postnatal growth of the kidney of the albino rat, with observations on an
adult human kidney, Anat. Rec. *17*:385, 1917.

Kurtz, S. M.: The electron microscopy of the
developing human renal glomerulus. Exp. Cell
Res. *14*:355, 1958.

Leeson, T. S.: Electron microscopy of the developing kidney: an investigation into the fine
structure of the mesonephros and metanephros
of the rabbit, J. Anat. *94*:100, 1960.

Leeson, T. S., and Baxter, J. S.: The correlation
of structure and function in the mesonephros
and metanephros of the rabbit, J. Anat. *91*:
383, 1957.

MacDonald, M. S., and Emery, J. L.: The late
intrauterine and postnatal development of
human renal glomeruli, J. Anat. *93*:331, 1959.

Rawlinson, H. D.: Compensatory hypertrophy of
the kidney of the young rat with special emphasis on the role of cellular hypoplasia, Anat.
Rec. *104*:263, 1949.

Sulkin, N. N.: Cytologic study of the remaining
kidney following unilateral nephrectomy in the
rat, Anat. Rec. *105*:95, 1949.

## REFERENCES ON THE RENAL CIRCULATION

Barclay, A. E., Daniel, P., Franklin, J. K.,
Prichard, M. M. L., and Trueta, J.: Records
and findings obtained during studies of the renal

circulation in the rabbit, with special reference
to vascular short-circuiting and functional cortical ischaemia, J. Physiol. *105*:27, 1946.

Baringer, J. R.: The dynamic anatomy of the
microcirculation in the amphibian and mammalian kidney, Anat. Rec. *130*:266, 1958.

Bensley, R. D.: The efferent vessels of the renal
glomeruli of mammals as a mechanism for the
control of glomerular activity and pressure,
Am. J. Anat. *44*:141, 1929.

Bialestock, D.: The extra-glomerular arterial circulation of the renal tubules, Anat. Rec. *129*:
53, 1957.

Daniel, P. M., Peabody, C. N., and Prichard,
M. M. L.: Cortical ischaemia of the kidney
with maintained blood flow through the medulla,
Quart. J. Exp. Physiol. *37*:11, 1952.

———: Observations on the circulation through
the cortex and the medulla of the kidney, Quart.
J. Exp. Physiol. *36*:199, 1951.

Daniel, P. M., Prichard, M. M. L., and Ward-
McQuaid, J. N.: The renal circulation in experimental hypertension, Brit. J. Surg. *42*:81,
1954.

Graves, F. T.: The anatomy of the intrarenal
arteries and its application to segmental resec-
tion of the kidney, Brit. J. Surg. *42*:132, 1954.

———: The anatomy of the intrarenal arteries in
health and disease, Brit. J. Surg. *43*:605, 1956.

Grollman, A., Muirhead, E. E., and Vanatta, J.:
Role of kidney in pathogenesis of hypertension
as determined by study of effects of bilateral
nephrectomy and other experimental procedures
on blood pressure of dog, Am. J. Physiol. *157*:
21, 1949.

MacCallum, D. B.: The arterial blood supply of
the mammalian kidney, Am. J. Anat. *38*:153,
1926.

———: The bearing of degenerating glomeruli on
the problem of the vascular supply of the mammalian kidney, Am. J. Anat. *65*:69, 1939.

Machado Simoes de Carvalho, A. A.: Contribuicao
para o estudo da circulacao renal, Coimbra,
Imprensa de Coimbra, 1954.

More, R. H., and Duff, G. L.: The renal arterial
vasculature in man, Am. J. Path. *27*:95, 1950.

Morison, D. M.: A study of the renal circulation,
with special reference to its finer distribution,
Am. J. Anat. *37*:53, 1926.

Pease, D. C.: Electron microscopy of the vascular bed of the kidney cortex, Anat. Rec. *121*:
701, 1955.

Trueta, J., Barclay, A. E., Daniel, P., Franklin,
K. J., and Prichard, M. M. L.: Renal pathology
in the light of recent neurovascular studies,
Lancet *2*:237, 1946.

———: Studies of the Renal Circulation, Oxford,
Blackwell, 1947.

# 28    The Endocrine System

## INTRODUCTION

**Development and General Structure.** As was explained in Chapter 9, some glands lose their connection with the epithelial surface from which they develop and so become islands of epithelium completely surrounded by connective tissue (Fig. 9-1). Since such glands possess no ducts, they are termed *ductless glands,* and since they must secrete into the substance of the body, rather than through a duct onto a surface, they are called *endocrine glands* or *glands of internal secretion.*

The functioning cells of endocrine glands must deliver their secretion into blood capillaries. For this to occur, the secretory cells must abut directly on blood capillaries. This leads to endocrine glands, in general, having a very simple microscopic structure; they consist of either cords or small clumps of cells, interspersed between capillaries and supported by delicate connective tissue (Fig. 9-1).

**Storage of Secretion.** In some endocrine glands secretion accumulates extracellularly in such a way that it is stored in the central part of a clump of secretory cells; this converts a clump of cells into a follicle (Fig. 9-9). But the clumps of cells in most endocrine glands do not develop into follicles; hence, in most endocrine glands there is no arrangement for the storage of more secretion than can be accommodated in the cytoplasm of secretory cells, where in some instances it may be demonstrated as secretion granules (Fig. 28-35).

**The Nature of Hormones.** The secretions of most endocrine glands are chemical substances called *hormones* (from *hormao* = I arouse to activity). The many different hormones made by the various endocrine glands exert numerous different effects. In general, however, these are all of the "arousing to activity" sort. The activity and, to a large extent, the normal microscopic structure of many parts of the body are dependent on these parts of the body being supplied more or less continuously by way of the bloodstream with small amounts of hormones made by endocrine glands. Only minute quantities of the various hormones are necessary in the bloodstream to keep different parts of the body roused to normal activity.

Although most endocrine glands make hormones, a gland can properly be termed endocrine even if it does not make a hormone provided that it secretes a useful product into the substance of the body. The liver, for example, secretes sugar into the bloodstream and for this reason is properly termed an endocrine gland. It is, of course, an exocrine gland as well, because it secretes bile into a duct system.

**The Endocrine System.** The hormone-producing endocrine glands are said to constitute the endocrine system because the functioning of one affects the functioning of others. The fact that the various endocrine glands interact with one another so extensively suggests that under normal conditions some sort of balance must be struck between their various activities. The particular balance that is struck probably differs in different individuals, and so different individuals are said to have somewhat different endocrine constitutions.

This chapter deals with all of the hormone-producing endocrine glands except the gonads (*gone* = seed) or sex glands of the female and the male; these will be considered in the next two chapters, which deal with the reproductive systems of the female and the male, respectively. With the exception of the gonads and the placenta of pregnancy, the hormone-producing endocrine glands are:

1. The pituitary gland (hypophysis cerebri)
2. The thyroid gland
3. The parathyroid glands
4. The adrenal glands
5. The islets of Langerhans of the pancreas

Little clusters of cells, scattered about in various parts of the body, and said to comprise the paraganglia, will also be considered in this chapter as will the pineal body. Both the paraganglia and the pineal body have been suspected of having an endocrine function.

**General Functions.** Some endocrine glands are essential to life. Others are responsible for growth and for such differences as exist between the male and the female forms and for most other male and female characteristics. Hormones play a very important role in the intermediate metabolism of carbohydrates, proteins and fats and in the mineral balance of the body. One hormone controls the metabolic rate of cells in general. In addition to affecting the growth and the form of the individual, hormones affect the temperament, the feelings and the emotions. Experimentally, they may be used to convert a fierce male animal into a motherly creature solicitous for the young. Indeed, the former fierce male, given the proper hormones, will feed the young at its breasts, for the development of the breasts and their capacity to produce milk are also due to hormones. It seems probable that a good many of the physical and emotional differences between people have their bases in people inheriting different types of endocrine constitutions.

**Diseases Are Caused by Hypofunction and Hyperfunction.** That different normal people have different endocrine balances suggests that what could be considered to be the normal production of most endocrine glands cannot be set very precisely. Obviously, the function of certain endocrine glands must be considered normal if it ranges within certain limits. But, as the physiologic limits of function are exceeded, either by the production of too little or too much hormone, pathologic states ensue. Hence, since there are many hormones, there is a large group of diseases that are caused by different hormone deficiencies and excesses. The study and the treatment of these constitute much of the subject matter of the branch of medicine termed *endocrinology.*

**Summary of How Knowledge Developed About Endocrine Glands and Hormones.** The first intimation of the function of the endocrine glands generally came from the observation that some clinical syndrome, observed during life, could be correlated after death with the diseased state of one of the bodies we now know to be endocrine glands. Next, the effects of too little secretion of each gland generally were determined by the experimental removal of the gland. This step depended on the development of modern surgical technics. The next step was the preparation of active extracts from the glands of animals. This step awaited the development of the proper chemical methods. When active extracts became available, the effects of the hyperfunction of any particular endocrine gland could be determined. By removing different glands from experimental animals it became possible to prove that some of the disease states seen in man were due to the hypofunction of a particular endocrine gland. Further, giving animals large doses of active glandular extracts made it possible to show that certain other disease states of man were due to the hyperfunction of certain endocrine glands. It became established that, in general, there are two different diseases that can result from the misbehavior of any one of the endocrine glands: one from its hypofunction and the other from its hyperfunction. Next, and this was of great importance for the clinical treatment of hypofunction, highly purified extracts were prepared, and in the instance of many hormones, the formula of the hormone was determined. This has permitted some hormones to be synthesized.

## THE PITUITARY GLAND OR BODY (HYPOPHYSIS CEREBRI)

**Some Gross Features.** The pituitary gland is ovoid. It measures about 1.5 cm. in the transverse plane and about 1 in the sagittal plane and is from 0.5 to 0.75 cm. or more thick. It becomes larger during pregnancy. It lies immediately below the base of the brain, to which it is attached by the pituitary stalk (Fig. 28-1). It rests in a depression in a bony prominence on the upper surface of the sphenoid bone. This bony prominence is shaped something like a Turkish saddle with a high back and a high front, and for this reason it is termed the *sella turcica.* The pituitary gland sits, as it were, in the saddle and so has bony protection in front, below and behind. The dura mater dips down to line the seat of the saddle and so envelop the pituitary gland. Furthermore, a shelf of dura mater, the diaphragma sellae, extends over most of the top of the gland to complete its enclosure (Fig.

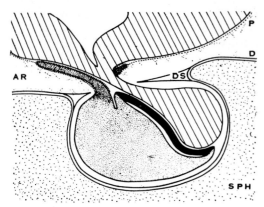

FIG. 28-1. Diagram of a sagittal section of the hypophysis cerebri, showing relation of the pars tuberalis to the meninges. *Lines,* brain floor and pars nervosa; *fine stipple,* pars anterior; *coarse stipple,* pars tuberalis; *solid black,* pars intermedia; SPH, sphenoid bone; P, pia mater; D, dura mater; DS, diaphragma sellae; AR, arachnoid spaces. (Atwell, W. J.: Am. J. Anat. *37*:174)

28-1, *DS*). The degree of protection that it is afforded is in relation to its importance.

In a sagittal section the pituitary gland of many animals can be seen to be separated into an anterior and a posterior lobe by a cleft which runs downward and posteriorly from near the attachment of the stalk. Such a cleft may be seen in the pituitary gland of a young child, but in the human adult it is replaced by a row of follicles. The 2 lobes so separated are divided into 4 parts. The main body of the gland anterior to the cleft or row of follicles is termed its *pars anterior* (Fig. 28-1, *fine stipple*). A projection from this, the *pars tuberalis* (Fig. 28-1, *coarse stipple*), extends up along the anterior and lateral aspects of the pituitary stalk. A rather narrow band of glandular tissue disposed along the posterior border of the cleft or row of vesicles comprises the *pars intermedia* (Fig. 28-1, *solid black*). The remainder of the gland (all that is posterior to the narrow cellular band that makes up the pars intermedia) is called its *pars posterior* or *pars nervosa* (Fig. 28-1, *lined*). The pars nervosa is not so wide as the pars anterior and more or less fits into a concavity on the posterior aspect of the pars anterior but is separated from it, of course, by the pars intermedia.

**Development.** The pars anterior, the pars tuberalis and the pars intermedia all have a microscopic structure fairly typical of endocrine glands. However, the pars nervosa does not; it resembles nervous rather than glandular tissue (Fig. 28-7). Its origin provides the reason. It develops as a downgrowth from the base of the brain. The other parts of the gland develop from an epithelial surface as do endocrine glands in general. We shall elaborate:

The anterior part of the mouth results from the inward bulging of ectoderm to form the oral fossa. Very early in development, before the bones of the skull have formed, the ectodermal lining of the roof of the oral fossa is in very close contact with the floor of the developing brain (which at this stage has a tubular form), and indeed it soon becomes adherent to it. This connection does not break as mesenchyme proliferates and gradually separates the developing brain from the developing mouth. As a consequence, the gradual separation of the brain and the mouth causes both the lining of the oral cavity and the floor of the brain to be drawn out into funnel-shaped structures with their tips in contact. The funnel-shaped extension of the roof of the oral fossa that points toward the brain is called *Rathke's pouch.* By the end of the second month of development this pouch breaks away from the oral ectoderm and thereupon becomes a hollow island of epithelium surrounded by mesenchyme except at its uppermost part where a peninsula is attached to the downward extension of the floor of the brain (Fig. 28-2). The main body of the hollow island of epithelium becomes more or less flattened around the anterior surface of the downgrowth of the brain. The cells of the anterior wall of the hollow epithelial island proliferate so that its anterior wall becomes greatly thickened. This becomes the pars anterior of the pituitary gland, and an upward extension of it becomes the pars tuberalis. The posterior wall of the island becomes the pars intermedia. The central cavity of the epithelial island between the pars anterior and the pars intermedia becomes flattened to form the cleft previously described, and the downward extension from the floor of the brain becomes the pars nervosa of the gland.

A residuum of cells of a character similar to those of the pars anterior may be present in the pharynx at the site from which the anterior lobe develops (Fig. 28-2). If so, they are said to constitute the *pharyngeal hypophysis*.

The part of the pituitary gland that develops from the epithelium of the pharynx (pars anterior, intermedia and tuberalis) is often referred to as the *adenohypophysis*, and the part that develops from the brain as the *neurohypophysis*.

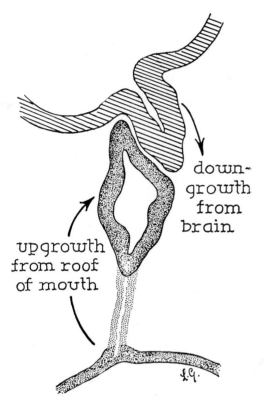

down-
growth
from
brain

upgrowth
from roof
of mouth

Fig. 28-2. Diagram illustrating the development of the pituitary gland from its two main sources.

### The Pituitary Gland as a Possible Link Between the Nervous and the Endocrine Systems

The experiencing of sensations, feelings, impulses, drives and emotions is a function of the nervous system. Likewise, the selection of the particular response that is to result from stimuli in the external or the internal environment of an individual is a function of the nervous system. Yet as we study the endocrine glands we shall see that hormones have a great effect on the way people feel and on the way they react to stimuli. Hormones are responsible for some of the "impulses" or "drives" that operate via the nervous system to motivate human activity. For example, what is generally termed sex "instinct" or "drive" depends fundamentally on certain hormones being, or at least having been, liberated into the bloodstream. However, the relation between the nervous and the endocrine systems is reciprocal because the activities of the nervous system affect the functioning of endocrine glands. When we study the adrenal medulla we shall find that under conditions of emotional stress it secretes a hormone into the bloodstream that reinforces the functioning of the sympathetic division of the autonomic nervous system. In addition, this hormone may affect indirectly the secretory activity of the anterior pituitary gland, and the hormones from this gland affect other glands. All in all, there is a very complicated interrelationship between the nervous and the endocrine systems, and the question arises as to what anatomic means are provided to permit these two systems to affect one another.

Most endocrine glands are not particularly well provided with nerves, and it is doubtful if such nerves as extend into them exert very pronounced effects on their secretory functions. However, there is one great exception to this rule. The medulla of the adrenal gland, as we shall see, has a unique and extensive innervation which permits the sympathetic division of the autonomic nervous system to exert control over its secretory functions. Moreover, the hormone that it produces reinforces the activities of the sympathetic division of the autonomic nervous system so that there is, in the medulla of the adrenal gland, a very important link between the nervous and the endocrine systems.

It might be expected from the fact that the pituitary gland develops from both ordinary epithelial and nervous tissue that it too would provide an important link between the nervous and the endocrine systems. It would be a suitable place for such a link because the pars anterior of the gland controls the secretory activities of most of the other endocrine glands of the body. That close contact between the adenohypophysis and the neurohypophysis is purposeful and does provide the means for a link between the two systems seems to be

most probable. But, contrary to what might
be expected, the link that is provided is not
a nervous one, because the adenohypophysis
is not innervated to any extent from the neurohypophysis. Instead, the link appears to be a
humoral (fluid) or a hormonal one and depends upon there being a curious arrangement
of blood vessels in the region which constitute what is termed the *hypophysioportal circulation* which permits blood from capillaries
in the median eminence and the neural stalk
(which are nervous tissue) to drain subsequently into the sinusoids that permeate between the secretary cells of the pars anterior.
We shall elaborate.

**The Blood Supply of the Pituitary Gland.**
Two main groups of vessels, the *superior* and
the *inferior hypophyseal arteries*, supply the
gland.

The *superior hypophyseal arteries*, of which
there are several, take origin from the circle
of Willis. They approach the gland as an anterior group and as a posterior group of vessels
(Fig. 28-3).

The arteries of the *anterior* group penetrate
the upper part of the pars tuberalis (Fig. 28-3)
and, in general, turn downward. As they pass
downward toward the pars anterior, they give
off numerous branches. The uppermost of these
pass into the region of the median eminence
(Fig. 28-3), and the ones at lower levels pass
into the neural stalk (Fig. 28-3). All of these
vessels end in clusters of tortuous wide capillaries; these have been a subject of study, in
particular, by Wislocki and by Green, who
should be read for details. Green describes
the arterial vessels and the capillary clusters
in which they terminate as being enclosed in

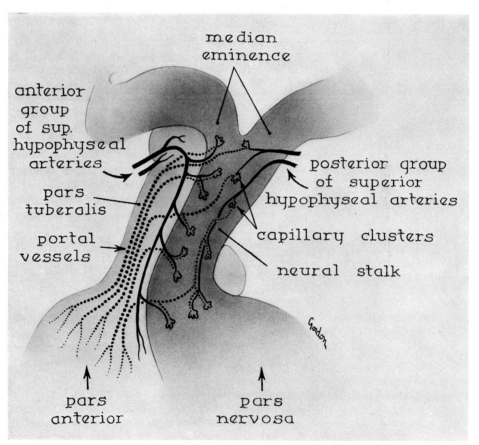

FIG. 28-3. Diagram illustrating Green's concept of the blood supply of the hypophyseal
stalk. The course of arterial blood is indicated by straight lines and that of venous blood by
dotted lines. (Redrawn and slightly modified from Green, J. D.: Anat. Rec. *100:273*)

a curious connective tissue sheath; this has also been described as a glial sheath. The capillary clusters empty into venules which run back in the same sheaths toward the pars tuberalis (Fig. 28-3, *dotted lines*) where they joint with one another to form larger venules (Fig. 28-3, *dotted lines*), which pass down to empty into the sinusoids of the pars anterior of the gland. Since the system of venules that drains the capillary clusters of the median eminence and the stalk contain venous blood which they empty into a second capillary bed, they constitute a *portal* system of vessels.

The *posterior* group of superior hypophyseal arteries penetrate the posterior aspect of the stalk (Fig. 28-3). The upper branches from these supply the median eminence, and the lower branches supply lower levels of the stalk. Here again the branches end in clusters of tortuous wide capillaries which, with the vessels that supply and drain them, lie in a connective tissue sheath. The venules from these capillary clusters pass forward to the pars tuberalis (Fig. 28-3, *dotted lines*) to drain down into the pars anterior; hence, these venules also constitute a part of the hypophysio-portal system.

The nerve fibers of the hypothalamohypophyseal tract (which will be described when the pars nervosa of the gland is considered) run in close association with the clusters of capillaries in the stalk but generally remain separated from them by the sheaths that surround the capillaries and the larger vessels. However, these connective tissue or glial sheaths are often thin, and it is possible that although the fibers of the hypothalamohypophyseal tract do not terminate here, some neurosecretory material (to be described later) may pass from fibers to capillaries in this region.

There appear to be no connections other than capillary anastomoses between the median eminence and the remainder of the hypothalamus. Therefore, the hypophysioportal circulation is not concerned with delivering blood from the bulk of the hypothalamus to the pars anterior but with delivering blood from the median eminence and the neural stalk into the pars anterior. According to Green, the portal circulation is not concerned with draining blood from the pars nervosa into the pars anterior. Accordingly, if any hormones or hormonelike substances are delivered into the pars anterior it would seem most probable that they gain entrance to this system from the median eminence and/or the neural stalk.

It is to be noted that not all of the blood that reaches the pars anterior from the superior hypophyseal arteries has passed through capillary clusters in the median eminence and/or stalk because some arterial branches pass directly down the pars tuberalis to the pars anterior (Fig. 28-3).

The second blood supply of the pituitary gland is obtained from the inferior hypophyseal arteries. There are two of these, one on each side. Each arises from the internal carotid artery (of the same side) as it lies in the posterior part of the cavernous sinus. Each inferior hypophyseal artery passes medially into the floor of the pituitary fossa and reaches the lower part of the gland at its inferolateral aspect. Here each gives off one or two small branches which enter the inferior aspects of the anterior and the posterior lobes. The main vessel on each side passes upwardly in the groove between the anterior and the posterior lobes, giving off numerous branches to the posterior lobe as it does so. At the upper part of each groove each main vessel passes forward between the corresponding lateral lobe and the stalk and then dips down into the lateral connective tissue cores of the anterior lobe. Therefore, the inferior hypophyseal vessels provide the chief blood supply for the pars nervosa of the gland and also the arterial blood for the pars anterior. There does not seem to be any evidence that the blood from this source enters the hypophysioportal system; in other words, the blood supplied to the pars nervosa by these vessels is collected into veins which do not empty into the pars anterior.

We shall discuss further the possible significance of the hypophysioportal system as a link between the nervous and the endocrine systems after the adrenal has been discussed.

FUNCTIONS OF THE PARS ANTERIOR

The pars anterior is composed of clumps and cords of cells intermingled with vascular channels. Before describing the different types of cells that are present we shall describe briefly the various hormones made by the gland so that when we describe the cells we shall be

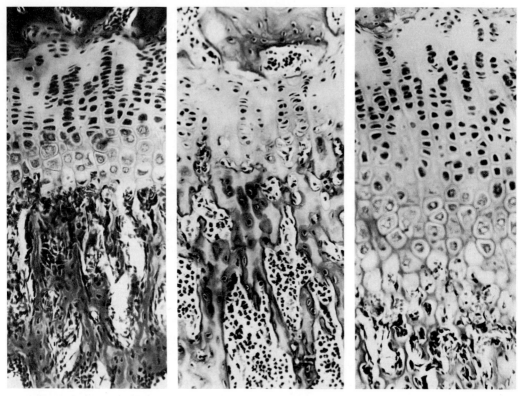

Fig. 28-4. (*Left*) Low-power photomicrograph of a longitudinal section of a metaphysis of the tibia of a rat nearing full growth. (*Center*) A similar photomicrograph of a metaphysis of a rat of the same age that received large injections of female sex hormone; the sex hormone suppressed the secretion of the growth hormone in the animal concerned. Observe that the epiphysial disk is thinner and that it lacks a zone of maturing cells. (*Right*) A similar photomicrograph of a metaphysis of the tibia of a rat of the same age as the other two but which received injections of anterior pituitary extract containing growth hormone. Observe that the epiphysial disk is thicker than at the left. High-power inspection shows many mitotic figures in the disk. (From experiments in collaboration with Dr. W. R. Harris)

able to relate their structures to their functions.

### The Hormones of the Pars Anterior

The cells of the pars anterior of the pituitary gland make several (probably 7) different hormones. These will now be described. Four pure hormones have been prepared from extracts of the gland, but these do not account for all the effects that are produced by crude extracts of the gland.

1. **Growth Hormone** (*Somatotrophin* = S.T.H.). A young animal stops growing after its pituitary gland is removed and thereafter remains a dwarf unless extracts of the pars anterior are given to it. Although the growth

of the body as a whole ceases when the pituitary gland is removed, the most striking, and perhaps the most significant, cessation of growth is that of the cartilage cells in the epiphysial disks of the long bones. When the young cells in the zone of proliferation stop dividing, no new cells are produced to mature and so add to the thickness of the zone of maturation. Since calcification does not cease, the zone of calcification continues to advance into the zone of maturation, and as a result the zone of maturing cells becomes greatly thinned (as in Fig. 28-4, *center*). Since this zone is an important factor in the thickness of the disk, a reduction in the thickness of this zone makes the disk as a whole thinner. The histologic changes that occur in the epiphysial disks after removal of the pituitary gland are described in detail by Evans and Simpson.

If an abnormal growth of the cells that make growth hormone occurs in an individual before full growth is attained and hence before the epiphysial disks of the long bones have been replaced by bone, the bones grow longer than usual, and so the individual becomes abnormally tall. This condition is termed gigantism. In a normal person, either the secretion of growth hormone ceases or that which is secreted becomes ineffective in the face of other developments at a certain time of life, and at that time the individual stops growing. Certain rare tumors evidently keep on secreting effectively beyond the time when the cells of a normal pars anterior would stop secreting enough hormone to cause more growth. Furthermore, as Evans and Long first showed, if the administration of growth hormone is begun before an animal has stopped growing, the animal will continue to grow; indeed, Evans and Simpson have shown that rats will continue to grow as long as pure growth hormone is administered.

If growth-hormone producing tumors develop after the epiphysial disks of the long bones have become replaced by bone, that is, after normal growth is over, or if growth hormone is given to a normal animal after its growth is over, no further growth in stature occurs. However, the bones, particularly those of the hands and the feet, tend to become thicker, and there is a great overgrowth of the mandible and a lesser growth of certain other bones in the face. Other tissues (e.g., the skin) are affected as well, but the condition as a whole is termed *acromegaly* (*akron* = extremity; *megas* = large) because the growth of the bones in the head, the hands and the feet makes these extremities large.

It may be of interest to know that the epiphysial disks of some laboratory animals are unusual in that they do not ordinarily become replaced by bone when their normal growth is over. For example, the epiphysial disks persist for a long time in the rat; hence, if female rats which have stopped growing (these are called plateaued rats because their growth curve has reached a plateau) are given growth hormone preparations, they will begin to grow again (Fig. 28-4, *compare left and right*).

Therefore, plateaued rats can be used for determining whether any given preparation contains growth hormone, but they are not as good for this purpose as hypophysectomized rats. They are, of course, much easier to obtain than the latter.

As we shall see, when the islands of Langerhans are considered later in this chapter, the growth hormone of the pars anterior has diabetogenic functions. If enough of it is injected into certain kinds of animals, permanent diabetes results. Growth hormone prepared from the pituitary glands of cattle and pigs produces growth and other metabolic effects in laboratory animals, but it is virtually ineffective in man and monkeys.

Recently, it has been shown that growth hormone prepared from pituitary glands of monkeys and from human pituitary glands obtained at autopsy is effective metabolically in man and monkeys.

2. **Lactogenic Hormone.** During pregnancy, as will be explained in detail when the female reproductive system is considered, certain hormones are produced which make the mammary glands of the female grow and develop greatly. Hence, by the time the offspring is born the mammary glands are large enough to supply the young with an adequate amount of milk. However, a particular stimulus is required for the glands to begin secreting milk and to continue performing this function. This stimulus is provided by a hormone called the *lactogenic hormone* or *prolactin* which is made by the pars anterior of the pituitary gland by cells that are believed to secrete large amounts of it at the termination of pregnancy. Thereafter they continue to secrete this hormone in quantities as long as the offspring is fed at the breast.

The lactogenic hormone has been prepared in crystalline form by White and associates. In addition to stimulating milk secretion, it arouses a maternal attitude in the individual exposed to its action; it will even do this if it is injected into males. It induces broodiness in hens.

In fowl, where the young are fed in part with the epithelial debris that desquamates from the lining of the crop gland of the mother, administration of the lactogenic hormone has been found to increase greatly the rate of epithelial proliferation of the thick lining epithelium of the gland. Indeed, the effect of the lactogenic hormone on the crop gland of the fowl constitutes a biologic method by which this particular hormone may be assayed.

As studies on the lactogenic hormone continued, it became obvious that it was concerned not only in causing fully developed breasts to secrete milk but that it was also concerned in bringing about the growth of the breasts that occurs as a preliminary to milk secretion. This matter will be discussed in more detail in the next chapter.

A third function that has been found for the lactogenic hormone is that of exerting what is termed a luteotrophic effect; that is, it has a function in activating the corpus luteum (to be described in the next chapter) and causing it to secrete the hormone progesterone (to be described in the next chapter). This function of the lactogenic hormone is clearly established in rats but it is not certain whether it has this effect in man.

3. **The Melanocyte-Stimulating Hormone (MSH), Also Called Intermedin.** It is difficult to know whether this hormone should be classed as a hormone produced by the pars anterior or by the pars intermedia. In certain species this hormone is clearly produced by the pars intermedia and in these species it causes a dispersion of the melanin granules in the pigmented cells of the skin. Evidence is now available to indicate that MSH may play a part in the skin color of man. However, it is probable that in man this hormone is primarily produced in the anterior lobe of the pituitary gland, perhaps because cells that in other species remain in the pars intermedia, migrate in man to take up their residence in the anterior lobe. However, the problem of ascertaining where MSH is produced and its precise role in the pigmentation of man is complicated by the fact that the amino acid sequences in the molecules of MSH and ACTH are very similar, so similar that it is easily conceivable that both hormones could be made by the same cell, and hence in the same lobe of the pituitary gland. It is now known that both MSH and ACTH can increase pigmentation of the skin in man under certain circumstances. Provisionally at least, it would seem that MSH should be considered as an anterior lobe hormone in man even though it is clearly a hormone of the intermediate lobe in some species.

4. **Trophic Hormones.** In addition to being able to secrete growth hormone and lactogenic hormone, the pars anterior can also secrete certain hormones that, in general, stimulate the growth and the function of many of the other endocrine glands; for this reason they are termed *trophic* (*trophe* = to nourish) hormones. (Some authors substitute *tropic* for *trophic*, and the student who encounters these different spellings of the word may wonder which is correct. This matter was the subject of an article in, and several subsequent letters to, "Science" in 1963. In the opinion of the author, *trophic* vanquished *tropic*.) Four trophic hormones have been identified by their effects, and they are named according to the particular gland that they affect: (1) thyrotrophin (TSH for thyroid stimulating hormone), which affects the thyroid gland; (2) adrenocorticotrophin (ACTH), which affects the cortex of the suprarenal (adrenal) glands; and (3 and 4) two gonadotrophins, the follicle-stimulating hormone (FSH) and the luteinizing hormone (LH). Both of the gonadotrophins are produced in females and also in males, and their actions on the respective gonads of the two sexes will be described in the next two chapters.

**The Push-Pull or Feed-Back Theory.** The equilibrium that is established between the activities of the different endocrines is achieved chiefly through the agency of the pars anterior. It is, as it were, chairman of the endocrine society. All the different members report to it regularly about their activities, and by secreting trophic hormones it controls the various members' structure and function. Should any particular endocrine gland become lazy, the pars anterior flogs it into activity by secreting the particular trophic hormone that arouses it. For example, should the thyroid gland produce too little thyroid hormone, the pars anterior promptly secretes some extra thyrotrophin, and this makes the thyroid gland work harder. How do the cells of the pars anterior know whether the thyroid gland is working or not? The simplest explanation for this is that they know by the amount of thyroid hormone that is present in the blood that courses through the sinusoids of the pars anterior along which they lie. Indeed, the cells of the pars anterior behave as if they performed regular chemical assays on the blood that passes by them to

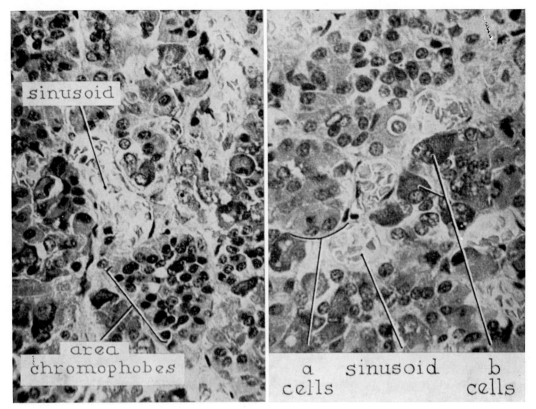

FIG. 28-5. Two high-power photomicrographs of an H and E section of the anterior lobe of the hypophysis. (*Left*) An area of chromophobes, with their nuclei close together. A sinusoid and some chromophils may be seen also. (*Right*) Acidophils, basophils and sinusoids (a = acidophils, b = basophils).

learn exactly how much of the various hormones the blood contains at these different times.

That the pars anterior is stimulated to secrete more of the specific trophic hormone concerned when the level of any particular hormone falls below its normal concentration in the blood is one of the generalizations of the push-pull or feed-back theory. A second generalization is that the secretion of any particular trophic hormone is suppressed when the concentration of the hormone of the gland it stimulates is raised to a high level in the blood. For example, the presence of a large amount of thyroid hormone in the blood acts to suppress the secretion of thyrotrophin by the pars anterior.

*Microscopic Structure of the Pars Anterior*

The glandular cells of the pars anterior are arranged in fairly thick irregular cords that branch with one another (Fig. 28-5). The cells are supported by delicate reticular fibers. Between the cords are vascular channels considerably wider than capillaries and lined by reticuloendothelium rather than by ordinary endothelium; for these two reasons they are classified as sinusoids rather than capillaries. The sinusoids are surrounded by a more substantial type of connective tissue than that which penetrates the cords to support the glandular cells (Fig. 28-5).

*The Parenchymal Cells of the Pars Anterior*

**Chromophils and Chromophobes.** The first step in the classification of the cells of the pars anterior is to separate them into two main kinds which are termed *chromophobes* and *chromophils*, respectively. This distinction can be made with H and E sections (Fig. 28-5); further distinctions require special staining as will be described later.

Chromophobes in H and E sections usually have less cytoplasm than chromophils. However, this is not the criterion that was used to name them; they were named chromophobes because their cytoplasm does not take up either acid or basic dyes with any avidity—it was their dislike of color that gave them their name. Chromophils, on the other hand, demonstrate relatively abundant cytoplasm which has an affinity for stain (but not always the same stain), and because of their liking for color, cells of this type were termed chromophils.

For reasons to be explained later, some cells cannot be readily classified as either chromophobes or chromophils because they represent transition stages between the two main types; they may be either chromophobes developing into chromophils or chromophils reverting to chromophobes.

**Chromophobes.** Perhaps the easiest criteria for the student to use in distinguishing chromophobes from chromophils in an ordinary section are that (1) chromophobes in general have less cytoplasm than chromophils and (2) they often appear in little groups in the more central parts of the clumps of cells that are disposed between sinusoids (Fig. 28-5, *left*). Since they have less cytoplasm than chromophils, the nuclei of the cells in a clump of chromophobes are much closer together than the nuclei of the cells of chromophils (Fig. 28-5, *left*), so looking for a group of nuclei that are close together makes it easy to find a group of chromophobes with the low-power objective.

Speaking generally, the chromophils are the functioning cells of the gland that secrete its various hormones. For this purpose, there is, as we shall see, considerable specialization among the chromophils. However, before considering chromophils and their functions further, we shall consider the function of chromophobes.

Chromophobes are the precursor cells that by differentiating give rise to the various types of functioning chromophils. Chromophobes vary in size because some may be in the process of differentiating into chromophils. Moreover, chromophobes probably differ from one another in another respect, because it seems probable that specialization exists at the chromophobe stage, so that at

least some chromophobes are destined to become only certain kinds of chromophils when they differentiate. It is possible that the least differentiated chromophobes are not specific in this respect and it is possible that there may be a reservoir of nonspecific chromophobe stem cells in the anterior lobe. However, this is difficult to establish *for mitosis is seldom seen in the gland,* and there is evidence indicating that after a chromophobe differentiates into a functioning chromophil, the chromophil in due course may stop working and revert back to being a chromophobe again, and so replenish the number of chromophobes.

**Types of Chromophils.** *Is there a separate kind of cell to secrete each hormone?* After it was established by endocrinologic studies that there were at least 7 anterior lobe hormones with different effects, the question arose whether or not there are 7 different kinds of chromophils to secrete these different hormones. There were two different problems associated with studying this matter. First, staining methods had to be evolved which would show that there were as many different types of chromophils as there were hormones, and, secondly, and which is more difficult, clinical or experimental findings to be found to relate the different types of cells distinguished by different staining methods to different hormones. We shall now describe some of the work that has been done in this area and the conclusions drawn from it.

The early types of staining methods used on the anterior pituitary showed that there were two types of chromophils; these can be distinguished in a good H and E preparation. The cytoplasm of one kind is acidophilic and the cytoplasm of the other kind is more or less basophilic; accordingly, these two cell types were long ago termed *acidophils* and *basophils*. Later, they were termed *alpha cells* and *beta cells* (Fig. 28-5, *right*). As will soon be described, the development of further staining methods in recent years has permitted subtypes with still different names to be demonstrated. However, before describing these, we should begin to consider the difficult problem of trying to establish which cell makes which hormone. This has to be done chiefly by indirect methods. We shall begin with acidophils.

Fig. 28-6. (Overleaf) Appearances of various cell types of the anterior lobe of the pituitary gland as they appear with the different staining methods listed on the left and, as is shown at the bottom, when they are partially degranulated. (Ezrin, C.: The pituitary gland, Ciba Clinical Symposia *15*:71)

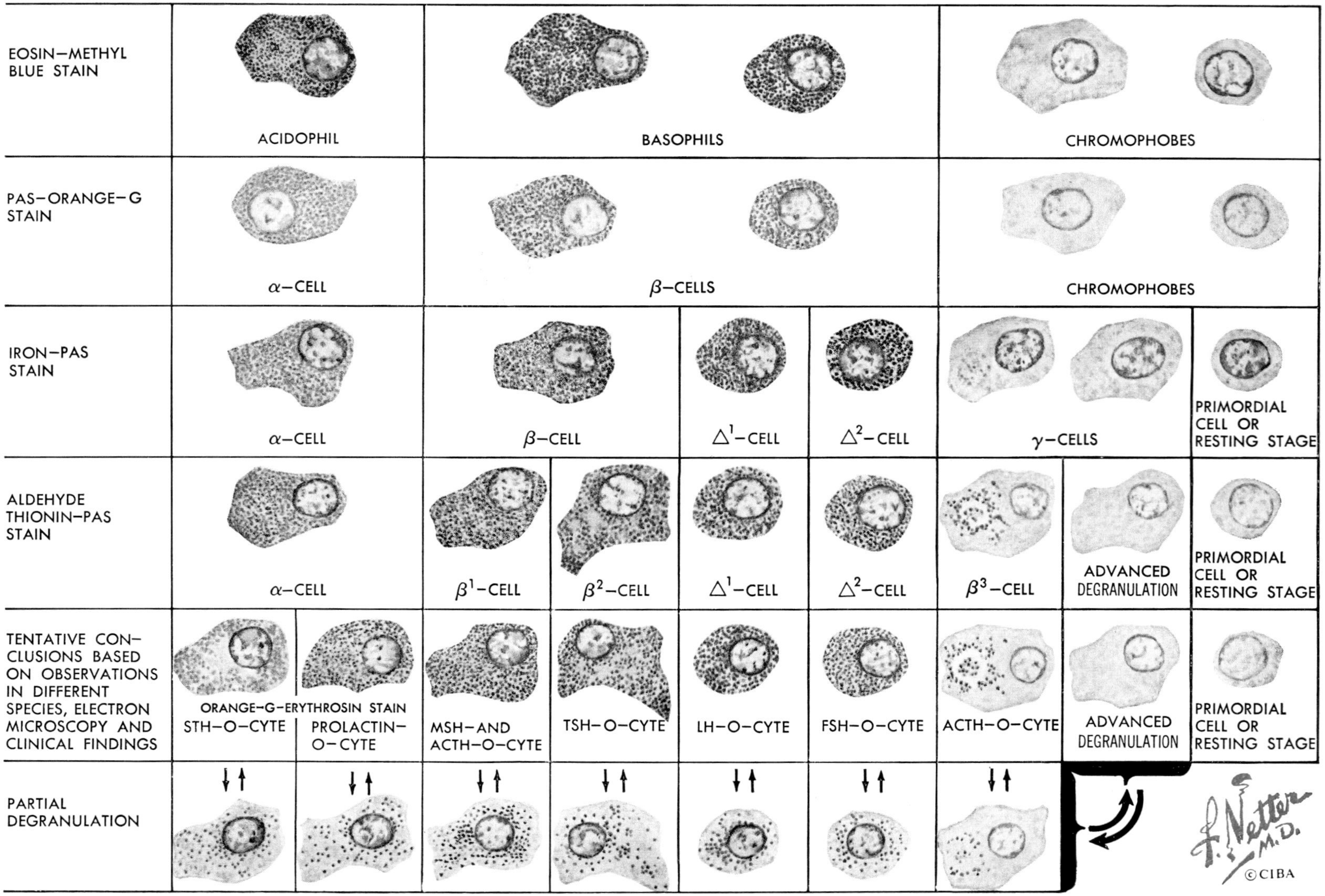

| | | | | | | | |
|---|---|---|---|---|---|---|---|
| **EOSIN–METHYL BLUE STAIN** | ACIDOPHIL | | BASOPHILS | | | | CHROMOPHOBES |
| **PAS–ORANGE–G STAIN** | α–CELL | | β–CELLS | | | | CHROMOPHOBES |
| **IRON–PAS STAIN** | α–CELL | β–CELL | β¹–CELL | β²–CELL | Δ¹–CELL | Δ²–CELL | γ–CELLS |
| **ALDEHYDE THIONIN–PAS STAIN** | α–CELL | | MSH– AND ACTH–O–CYTE | TSH–O–CYTE | LH–O–CYTE | Δ²–CELL | β³–CELL |
| **TENTATIVE CONCLUSIONS BASED ON OBSERVATIONS IN DIFFERENT SPECIES, ELECTRON MICROSCOPY AND CLINICAL FINDINGS** | ORANGE–G–ERYTHROSIN STAIN STH–O–CYTE / PROLACTIN–O–CYTE | | MSH– AND ACTH–O–CYTE | TSH–O–CYTE | LH–O–CYTE | FSH–O–CYTE | ACTH–O–CYTE |

Right-hand column (top to bottom): PRIMORDIAL CELL OR RESTING STAGE; ADVANCED DEGRANULATION (γ-CELLS, β³-CELL)

**PARTIAL DEGRANULATION**

©CIBA

**Functions of Acidophils. Two Different Types.** One way that this problem has been investigated and which has helped to establish the functions of acidophils hinges on the fact that tumors composed of acidophils sometimes develop spontaneously in the anterior lobe of the pituitary gland, and people who develop such tumors manifest certain body changes than can be attributed to a particular hormone or hormones. It has been known for a long time that acromegaly is due to the anterior pituitary gland secreting extra growth hormone and that this is often due to a tumor having begun to grow in that gland. When the anterior pituitary glands of acromegalics were studied histologically they usually revealed some overgrowth of the acidophils. This finding of course strongly indicated that acidophils secrete growth hormone.

Next, acromegaly in women is occasionally associated with persistent lactation; this is termed *galactorrhea* (*galactos* = milk; *rhoia* = flow), which may or may not be related to a previous pregnancy; this suggested that the cells that produce growth hormone may also produce lactogenic hormone. Furthermore, the pituitary glands of women, during the later stages of pregnancy and in the several weeks following childbirth, contain increased numbers of lightly granulated acidophils. These were originally termed pregnancy cells by Erdheim.

**Types of Acidophils.** The question then arose as to whether the same acidophils secrete both growth and lactogenic hormones or whether there are normally separate types of acidophils to secrete the two different hormones and that the reason for two hormones being secreted by acidophil tumors was that differentiation into both types may occur in tumors. The matter has been investigated by staining acidophils from normal glands by special methods to see if there are two different kinds of acidophils and it was found that there are. First, the cytoplasmic granules of one kind were found to contain relatively small granules that stain with the azocarmine technic, and others were found to contain larger granules that stain with the orange G technic (Fig. 28-6, lower left, second from bottom). In this staining reaction both kinds of granules stain with orange G, but the azocarmine displaces the orange G from the

smaller granules and so makes them red rather than orange. Subsequently it was found that a combination of erythrosin and orange G would distinguish between the two cell types even more clearly. With this combination the larger granules stain with the erythrosin and the smaller ones stain lightly with orange G. Tentatively then, it would seem that there are two types of acidophils in a normal pituitary. There is now evidence that suggests that the cells with the smaller granules are indeed specialized to secrete lactogenic hormone and those with the larger granules growth hormone. These two cell types are sometimes termed prolactin-o-cytes and STH-o-cytes respectively (prolactin is a synonym for lactogenic hormone and STH an abbreviation for somatotrophin which is another name for growth hormone).

**Different Types of Basophils.** The problem of distinguishing different kinds of basophils and correlating different types with different functions has been more difficult than it was with acidophils. We shall begin by commenting briefly on some of the staining methods that have been used and the types of cells they distinguish.

First, it became established from chemical studies that whereas the growth and the lactogenic hormones, and also ACTH, are proteins, the trophic hormones—TSH, FSH and LH—are *glycoproteins*. Accordingly, since the PAS method specifically stains certain reactive carbohydrate groups present in glycoproteins, it could be expected to stain specifically the granules of the basophils that produce these three types of glycoprotein hormones, and indeed it was found it did.

Once it was established that the granules of the basophils that made glycoprotein hormones could, by the PAS method, be distinguished with this "histochemical" approach from cells that made other types of hormones, attempts were made to see if further staining methods could be combined with the PAS method to distinguish subtypes of PAS-positive cells. For example, Ezrin *et al.* combined a dialized-iron-staining method with the PAS technic and showed that some PAS-positive cells continued to stain red (these were termed red beta cells) (Fig. 28-6), but others took on a purple color (these were named purple delta cells) (Fig. 28-6).

Another method that has distinguished sub-types in PAS-positive cells is the aldehyde thionin stain. This combination is termed the AT-PAS technic. By means of these combined staining technics, and also by taking the size and the shape of the cells that stain differently into consideration, it has been possible to postulate the existence of three different types of PAS-positive cells, one for every one of the glycoprotein hormones, TSH, FSH and LH (Fig. 28-6, *lower middle*). However, there seems to be one kind of cell that is PAS-positive but which probably does not make a glycoprotein hormone. There are other possible reasons for the cytoplasm of this cell being colored by the PAS method. This cell is the beta 1 cell shown just to the left and slightly below the center of Figure 28-6. This cell remains red when the PAS method is combined with the aldehyde thionin staining method. There is some evidence indicating that cells of this type produce ACTH and/or MSH (melanocyte stimulating hormone).

As might be expected, the nomenclature for naming the cells distinguished by these special methods became very confused, with different investigators using somewhat different terms. In the first place, the basophils came to be called beta cells. Then, when it was found that they could be classified into different groups, the term delta cell was introduced for one group. Then, when it was found that the beta cells and the delta cells could be each broken down into further groups, names such as beta 1 and beta 2 and delta 1 and delta 2 were used. Complicating matters is the fact that the cells of the pituitaries of different experimental animals differ somewhat in their staining reactions. So, instead of trying to distinguish the PAS-positive cells by the various terms that have been coined for them, we shall attempt to describe here the appearance of the different ones that are considered to have different specific functions.

Establishing the functions of different cell types among the PAS-positive basophils of the pituitary has not been as easy as it was with the acidophils. However, by studying the pituitaries of people who died with various clinical conditions due to special hormone deficiencies, and by removing various target glands of the different trophic hormones from animals (which leads to the cells in the pituitaries that produce the particular trophic hormones working harder), and by suppressing the secretion of different trophic hormones by giving the hormone made by the target gland to animals (this leads to a storage of the trophic hormone in the cells that make it), much information has been obtained to indicate the particular cells that make these three trophic hormones. It is now considered that the cell that makes TSH, and which is therefore termed a *thyrotroph,* is a large cell of irregular shape which, after PAS staining combined with one of the other methods mentioned above, reveals blue-purple granules (Fig. 28-6, TSH-o-cyte). The cell that makes FSH is rounded rather than angular, and its granules with the combined technics remain red (Fig. 28-6, FSH-o-cyte). On the other hand, the cell that makes LH, while rounded like the cell that makes FSH, has granules which with a combined technic are colored purple (Fig. 28-6, LH-o-cyte).

The type of cell that makes ACTH (a protein hormone) is more difficult to establish. There is some evidence that ACTH is produced by beta 1 cells. It is possible that ACTH is also produced by a cell that before the advent of the newer staining methods might have been termed a large chromophobe. Any large chromophobe may, of course, contain granules because of its beginning to develop into a chromophil, or because of its reverting from a chromophil into a chromophobe. However, it has been suggested that one kind of granule-containing "chromophobe" is not a transitional type of cell but is of a more consistent morphology and may be concerned with the production of ACTH (Fig. 28-6, *right side* ACTH-o-cyte). However, as has been pointed out already, the similarities in the molecular structure of MSH and ACTH make it less certain that there are two cell types for the respective production of these two hormones than is true of other anterior lobe hormones, and indeed there is less certainty about the cellular source of these two hormones than there is about the others. Further work is required before more than tentative beliefs can be held about the cellular source of ACTH and MSH.

As has been stressed by Ezrin, who has

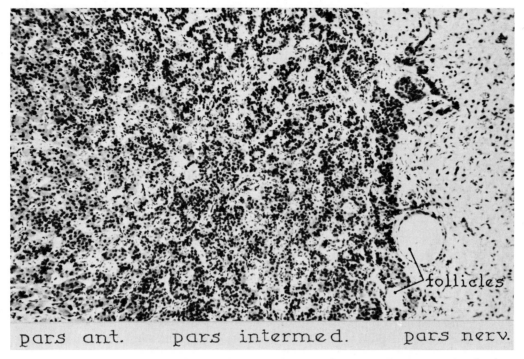

FIG. 28-7. Low-power photomicrograph of a section extending from the pars anterior (*left*) through the pars intermedia (*center*) into the pars nervosa (*right*) of the hypophysis cerebri.

studied histologically over 1,000 human pituitaries, the problem of allocating different hormones to particular cell types in man is complicated by the fact that most people die after an illness, and illness generally leads to a somewhat nonspecific degranulation and even exhaustion of many cells in the anterior lobe. A normal picture of the cells in the anterior pituitary of man can be anticipated only in instances of accidental and sudden death.

**Nuclei of Chromophobes and Chromophils.** The nuclei of the glandular cells of the pars anterior vary greatly in size and in the intensity with which they stain (Fig. 28-9, *lower left*). Many of the larger ones stain with only moderate intensity, and chromatin granules, lying in nuclear sap, can be seen within them. But in other nuclei, and these are generally smaller, the chromatin appears to be more condensed, and when this condition is accentuated, the nuclei appear pyknotic. It is probable, from the studies of Severinghaus, that the variations in the staining reaction and the size of the nuclei are to be explained by cells being in different stages of their secretory cycle. The nuclei of acidophils probably begin to stain more deeply when the cells that contain them become replete with granules and begin to discharge. As the cell discharges its granules, the chromatin of the nucleus becomes still more condensed and only begins to disperse as the cell once more begins to accumulate granules. The darker nuclei, then, are probably those of cells that are beginning to discharge or have discharged their granules, and the lighter, larger nuclei, those of cells that are accumulating granules.

**Fine Structure of Chromophils.** As might be expected, a chromophil possesses the usual characteristics that have already been described in detail for secretory cells: (1) rough-surfaced vesicles of endoplasmic reticulum where the protein secretion is synthesized, and (2) a well-developed Golgi apparatus that is concerned with packaging the secretion in the form of secretory granules and, in connection with the glycoprotein hormones, probably adding the carbohydrate component to the secretion. The granules are enclosed in membranous vesicles and their size differs in different chromophils, and with further work it might be expected that the EM will clarify further distinctions between the types of cells that have been distinguished by light microscopy and special staining and histochemical methods.

## OTHER PARTS OF THE PITUITARY GLAND

**Pars Tuberalis.** Although this is an upward extension of the pars anterior, it has a different microscopic structure. The cells it contains are roughly cuboidal in shape and contain no cytoplasmic granules. Their cytoplasm is diffusely and mildly basophilic. The pars tuberalis is fairly vascular. Its function, if any, is unknown.

**Pars Intermedia.** This is not nearly so well developed in man as in many other animals. In man, what is often interpreted as the pars intermedia consists chiefly of (1) an irregular row of follicles which contain pale-staining colloidal materials and are made of pale cells (Fig. 28-7), and (2) a few rows of moderate-sized cells with strongly basophilic granular cytoplasm (Fig. 28-7, *center*). (The granules disappear very quickly unless fixation is prompt.) These cells may extend into the pars nervosa for considerable distances (Fig. 28-7, *upper right*).

In certain species (for example fish and amphibia) the pars intermedia produces a hormone called the melanocyte stimulating hormone (MSH) or intermedin. This hormone causes the pigment granules which otherwise congregate around the nuclei of pigment-containing cells in the skin to become dispersed, and this causes the skin to become darker. Environmental factors seem to act variously to cause the release of MSH and so bring about color changes in these species. There is evidence to the effect that a melanocyte-stimulating hormone can be extracted from the pituitary glands of man. In man, MSH, as its name implies, stimulates pigment formation in melanocytes. As has been noted already, molecules of MSH and ACTH have very similar amino acid sequences, and it is not clear whether both hormones are made by the same cell type in the anterior lobe or not. It has been established that both ACTH and MSH can cause increased pigmentation in man, but as yet the respective roles of these two hormones in patients with increased pigmentation is not clearly established.

### THE PARS NERVOSA

The pars nervosa was investigated over the years in the same way as other endocrine glands. However, the results were not as clearcut as they were with other glands. Only relatively recently has information become available to explain why this gland has seemed to be so different from the others. But first we shall describe what has been known about the gland for some time.

It was known, for example, that a disease, *diabetes insipidus,* could result from lesions of the pars nervosa. (This is a very different disease from "sugar" diabetes, which will be described later in this chapter.) Diabetes insipidus is characterized by a great production of urine of a low specific gravity. For many years it was believed that this disease is due to the failure of the pars nervosa to make a hormone called the *antidiuretic hormone.* If the antidiuretic hormone is not present in the bloodstream in sufficient quantities the distal convoluted and collecting tubules of the kidney do not absorb their proper share of the glomerular filtrate; hence, the volume of urine is many times greater than normal.

However, there were many puzzling things about the relation of this disease to the pars nervosa. It was known, for example, that the disease could be caused by injuries to the hypothalamus and also by interrupting the nerve tract that leads from hypothalamic nuclei to the pars nervosa (Fig. 28-8). Nevertheless, the disease could be alleviated by means of extracts prepared from the pars nervosa. Hence, it was assumed that the antidiuretic hormone was made by the pars nervosa but that the pars nervosa required proper innervation from the hypothalamic region if it was to make its hormone.

In addition to containing an antidiuretic hormone, extracts of the pars nervosa, on being injected into animals, were found to cause much of the smooth muscle of the body to contract or develop increased tonus. As chemical extraction methods improved, Kamm and his associates were able to isolate two somewhat different and extremely active fractions from crude extracts. The first of these is termed *oxytocin* (*oxys* = swift; *tosos* =

labor) or *pitocin,* and, as its name implies, it acts chiefly on the smooth muscle of the wall of the uterus; so, by stimulating the uterus to contract, it may help in expelling a fetus. Oxytocin is also believed to be released under the stimulus of nursing (or milking), and it acts by causing myoepithelial cells that embrace alveoli to contract; this causes them to express the milk they contain into the duct system of the mammary gland. The second fraction that may be recovered from crude extracts is called *pitressin,* and it acts on the smooth muscle of the blood vessels (a hypertensive effect) and on that of the intestine. It also has the antidiuretic effect. Recently, the chemical structure of pitocin (oxytocin) and pitressin (vasopressin) has been elucidated by du Vigneaud and his associates, who have also achieved the remarkable feat of synthesizing these complex hormones.

A puzzle was presented by the fact that

although hormones could be extracted from the pars nervosa, its microscopic structure was not that of an endocrine gland.

**Neurosecretion.** Relatively recently, the answer to many of the hitherto puzzling features about the form and the function of the pars nervosa and its relation to the hypothalamus has been elucidated. It now seems to be established, particularly from Scharrer's work, that the hormones that can be extracted from the pars nervosa are not made in the pars nervosa at all but in the bodies of nerve cells in hypothalamic nuclei, the nerve cells of which produce a *neurosecretion* (Fig. 28-9, *top, left*). This neurosecretion passes from the cell bodies of the neurons in the supra-optic and the paraventricular nuclei of the hypothalamus down their axons in the hypothalamo-hypophyseal tract to the pars nervosa (Fig. 28-8). Here the neurosecretion (which contains the hormone activity) is absorbed into capillaries of

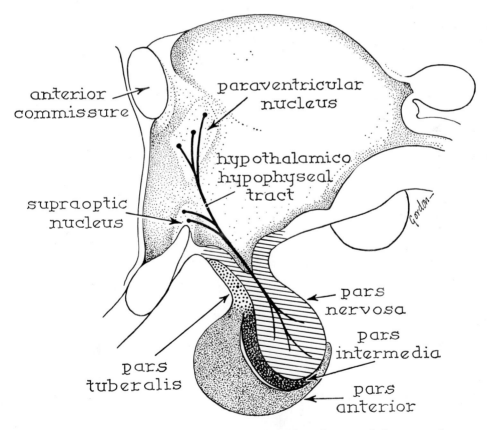

Fig. 28-8. Drawing showing the hypothalamico-hypophyseal tract and the course of neurosecretion from hypothalamic nuclei into the pars nervosa.

the septa of the pars nervosa (Fig. 28-9, *bottom, right*). If the hypothalamo-hypophyseal tract is interrupted, the neurosecretion cannot reach the pars nervosa to be absorbed, and diabetes insipidus results (unless new absorptive sites are built up).

By means of the chrome alum hematoxylin technic, neurosecretory granules have been observed in hypothalamic nuclei in every species studied, including man, where they were first seen by Scharrer and Gaupp. In mammals they are very small granules (see Palay) (Fig. 28-9, *top, left*). Neurosecretory cells are nerve cells that possess all the ordinary features of nerve cells, including Nissl bodies in their cytoplasm (Fig. 28-9, *top, left*). In addition, however, they produce secretory material that passes along their axons (Fig. 28-9, *top, right*) to nerve terminals from which it is discharged into the circulation (Fig. 28-9, *bottom, right*).

As has been mentioned, the neurosecretory material that accounts for the hormone activity of extracts of the pars nervosa is produced by nerve cells in the supra-optic and the paraventricular nuclei; it is only stored in, and absorbed from, the pars nervosa. This finding makes the structure of the pars nervosa more intelligible, as we shall see.

**Microscopic Structure.** In most species the pars nervosa does not exhibit a very well organized structure. However, the microscopic structure of the pars nervosa of the opossum is much more clear-cut, and this has been studied by Bodian in the light of recent knowledge about neurosecretion.

Bodian has shown that the pars nervosa of the opossum is divided into lobules by septa; the latter contain many small blood vessels, and it is into these that most of the neurosecretion is delivered (Fig. 28-10). The more central part of each lobule constitutes a hilus, and this is made up chiefly of bundles of fibers of the hypothalamo-hypophyseal tract. By means of Gomori's staining method, fine granules of neurosecretion can be seen in these nerve fibers. From the region of the hilus the fibers diverge to approach the septum that surrounds the lobule at right angles to it. Near their terminations each one is coated with a wrapping of neurosecretory substance; hence, near their terminations the fibers exist as the central cores of cylinders of neurosecretory material which come into contact with the septa more or less at right angles to them. The neurosecretory material is absorbed from the ends of these cylinders into the blood vessels of the septa. Bodian terms the zone which consists of cylinders that abut on the septa the *palisade zone* of the lobule (Fig. 28-10).

In the hilus of each lobule the nuclei of pituicytes can be seen (Fig. 28-10). Pituicytes are a type of neuroglia cell and probably serve a supporting function. However, some still believe that they have a hormone-secreting function. Their cytoplasmic processes (fibers) may extend out between the cylinders of neurosecretory material in the palisade zone (Fig. 28-10).

Bodies of material that stain with the Gomori technic, which have been known as Herring bodies, are to be seen in the pars nervosa. These are probably terminal bulb formations of fibers of the hypothalamo-

---

Fig. 28-9. (*Top, left*) Drawing of a nerve cell in the human hypothalamus, showing neurosecretory granules and Nissl bodies in the cytoplasm of the nerve cell. The section was stained with Klüver and Barrera's luxol fast blue-cresyl violet. (Prepared from a section provided by Louis Poirier) (*Center, left*) Drawing of a part of a section of the anterior pituitary of man, stained by the method employed by Ezrin and Wilson (see text). The acidophils are a yellow-orange color. Two types of basophils are to be seen: red and purple. The distinction between chromophobes and chromophils is not so distinct as with most stains. (Preparation supplied by W. Wilson) (*Bottom, left*) A section of the anterior pituitary of man, stained by the Gomori method. The acidophils are red, and the basophils are a light blue-purple. (*Top, right*) Section of the posterior lobe of the pituitary gland of man, stained by the Gomori method. The illustration shows the terminal branchings of a nerve fiber and neurosecretory material around them. A Herring body is also present. (*Bottom, right*) A section of the posterior pituitary of man, stained by the Gomori method. The termination of a nerve fiber, with an accumulation of neurosecretory material around it, is seen beside a capillary into which the neurosecretory material probably passes.

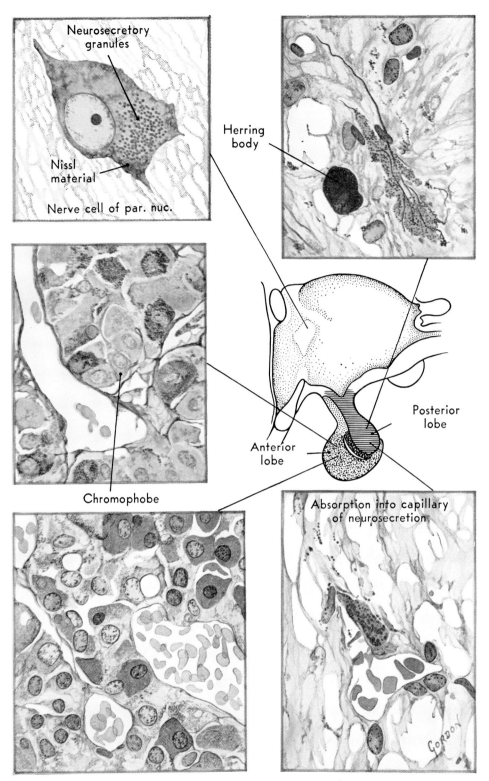

Neurosecretory
granules

Nissl
material

Nerve cell of par. nuc.

Herring
body

Chromophobe

Anterior
lobe

Posterior
lobe

Absorption into capillary
of neurosecretion

GORDON

FIGURE 28-9. (*See caption on page 830*)

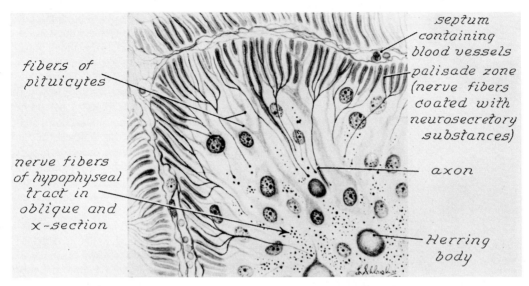

*septum containing blood vessels*

*fibers of pituicytes*

*palisade zone (nerve fibers coated with neurosecretory substances)*

*nerve fibers of hypophyseal tract in oblique and x-section*

*axon*

*Herring body*

FIG. 28-10. Schematic representation of the histologic organization of a lobule in the pars nervosa of the opossum. (Bodian, D.: Bull. Johns Hopkins Hosp. *89*:354)

hypophyseal tract that end within the substance of the gland, and in which there are accumulations of neurosecretory material (Fig. 28-9, *top, right*).

It seems probable that the microscopic structure of the pars nervosa of other species is basically similar to that of the opossum but not organized so clearly into lobules by orderly septa; hence, there is probably more absorption of neurosecretory material from the end regions of the fibers into blood vessels that are more irregularly disposed (Fig. 28-9, *bottom, right*).

## THE THYROID GLAND

### INTRODUCTION

**Gross Anatomy.** This gland was given by the name *thyroid* (*thyreos* = an oblong shield; *eidos* = form) because it is shaped like a certain type of shield (Fig. 28-11). It consists of two lobes of dark-red glandular tissue which are joined together by a broad band of similar tissue called the *isthmus* (Fig. 28-11). The isthmus lies over the second and the third cartilaginous rings of the trachea; and the two lobes, for the most part, fit over the front and around the sides of the trachea just below the larynx, but their upper parts extend for a short distance up its sides (Fig. 28-11).

**General Function.** It has been known for

a long time that the thyroid gland secretes the hormone thyroxine. More recently, the work of Gross in Leblond's laboratory led to the discovery of a second, even more potent, hormone secreted by the thyroid, namely triiodothyronine. Although the exact mode of action of these hormones is not known, it is well established that, speaking generally, they control the rate of metabolism in body cells. The basal metabolic rate of any individual can be determined by a breathing test which is based on determining the rate at which the individual, while at rest, uses up oxygen. This test, in the past, was much used to determine the state of thyroid function in people who were suspected of having altered thyroid function. However, determining the basal metabolic rate of a person gives only indirect information about the functioning of his or her thyroid gland; now, as will be explained presently, there are more direct methods for establishing how well the thyroid gland of any individual is functioning.

**Hypothyroidism and Hyperthyroidism.** Disorders of thyroid function may vary from the norm in either direction; the thyroid glands of some individuals secrete too little hormone while those of others secrete too much. The two conditions so-produced are termed *hypothyroidism* and *hyperthyroidism*, respectively. Both can vary in severity.

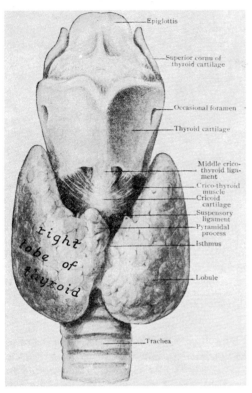

FIG. 28-11. The thyroid gland in situ. (Huber: Piersol's Human Anatomy, ed. 9, Philadelphia, Lippincott)

**Hypothyroidism.** If hypothyroidism occurs early in life, growth of the body is impaired. If the condition is severe it results in a type of dwarfism and general retardation known as *cretinism* (*cretin* = barely human). When hypothyroidism occurs after full growth is attained it results in a general slowing down of all bodily functions. In severe cases it results in an abnormal accumulation of mucopolysaccharides in certain of the connective tissues. Since the edematous condition of the connective tissues in this instance is not due to extra tissue fluid but to extra mucopolysaccharide, the edema that occurs is termed *myxedema* (*myxa* = mucus).

**Hyperthyroidism.** Too much thyroid hormone in the blood raises the metabolic rate to the point where an individual dislikes heat and bears cold readily. It also makes the heart go faster and the temperament excitable. People with hyperthyroidism are prone to become thin; their catabolism is so stimulated that they literally consume their own tissues.

**Factors Affecting Thyroid Function and Structure.** Disorders of thyroid function, in certain parts of the world, were much more common a few decades ago than they are today. The parts of the world where they were, or are, most common are those in which there is a relative lack of iodine in the soil or the water. The thyroid hormones both contain iodine, and if iodine is deficient in the diet the thyroid gland cannot make its proper quota of hormones. As might be expected, the thyroid glands of individuals whose diets are deficient in iodine react to the shortage by undergoing compensatory changes; they enlarge and work harder and as a result the thyroid glands of people where iodine is deficient sooner or later become so altered that even if the diet becomes adequate in iodine, the thyroid glands of these people always show structural changes that indicate that they once passed through a considerable period of iodine deprivation. The structural changes in the thyroid due to a period of iodine deficiency, and which commonly occurs in the first two decades of life, provide an unstable basis for normal function in later life, and, as a consequence, individuals who experience iodine deficiency for long periods when they are young are prone to develop disorders of thyroid function later in life.

The inclusion of iodine in salt in areas where iodine is deficient, a practice that began a few decades ago, has prevented an incalculable amount of illness from altered thyroid function. Moreover, by preventing much thyroid disease from this cause it has focused attention on the fact that there are other causes of altered thyroid function. It is now known that there are certain inborn errors of metabolism which manifest themselves in some individuals and which involve thyroid function. These inherited defects make it difficult or impossible for the thyroid gland to synthesize or secrete its hormones even if there is adequate iodine in the diet. There are other causes of altered function. The thyroid gland may be the seat of an infection and it is now believed that it may be the seat of an auto-immune reaction under certain conditions, as will be described later.

**Goiter.** As has been noted already, there is a push-pull arrangement between the thyrotrophic hormone secreted by the anterior pituitary and the hormones of the thyroid gland. If the content of thyroid hormones in the blood falls below normal levels, the pars anterior of the pituitary immediately responds by secreting more TSH. The extra TSH flogs the thyroid gland into increased activity, and under normal conditions the increased output of thyroid hormones so-induced suppresses the pars anterior from secreting further excess TSH. By this means thyroid hormones are kept at constant levels in the blood. But, because of iodine deficiency or for any other reason, the thyroid gland cannot respond to the increased stimulus of extra TSH by making more thyroid hormone. TSH secretion is not suppressed and so it continues. This results in the cells of the thyroid gland becoming more numerous and, as a result, the organ increases in size. A thyroid gland that is increased in size is called a *goiter*. The primary reason for most thyroid glands becoming enlarged so that they are goiters is that sometime in the life of the individual concerned there was prolonged excess stimulation of the gland by TSH. However, as time passes, other factors, as we shall see, can contribute to making such a gland even larger than it was when it was stimulated. Every altered thyroid gland tells a long story.

Although the history of most thyroid enlargements dates from a period of TSH stimulation, there is at least one kind of goiter that probably is an exception. This kind is called exophthalmic goiter because the eyes of individuals with this condition tend to protrude. It was assumed for a long time that this type of goiter also was due to the anterior pituitary secreting too much TSH and doing it persistently. But the thyrotrophs in the anterior pituitaries of people who die with this condition seem to be atrophic rather than hyperactive and, furthermore, although a thyroid-stimulating factor can be found in the blood of some people with this condition, it is different (a slower acting and much more long-lasting effect) from normal TSH. At the moment it is not known where this thyroid-stimulating factor that is in the blood of people with exophthalmic goiter comes from; however, it seems to disappear from the blood if most of the thyroid is removed surgically and only a little bit left.

As we shall show somewhat later, some kinds of goiters are associated with hypothyroidism and some with hyperthyroidism. But before dealing with variations in thyroid structure and function we shall first consider the microscopic structure of the gland and describe something of what is known about how the hormones of the gland are produced and secreted.

## Microscopic Structure of the Thyroid Gland

The gland is covered with two capsules. The outer one is continuous with, and is part of, the pretracheal fascia which, in turn, is part of the deep cervical fascia. The inner capsule is to be regarded as the true capsule of the gland. It consists of fibro-elastic connective tissue, and it sends septa into the gland, providing internal support and carrying blood vessels, lymphatics and nerves into its substance. The septa divide the gland into lobules, the limits of which may be dimly apparent on the surface of the gland (Fig. 28-11). However, the lobules are not discrete because the septa do not join with one another in the substance of the gland in such a way as to enclose completely limited areas of tissue; hence, the thyroid gland is not truly lobulated but pseudolobulated.

Figure 9-9 illustrates how a clump of cells in an endocrine gland can become a follicle, permitting its secretion to pour into a central lumen. Follicles are the units of structure of the thyroid gland, and the secretion product within them is called colloid. Each follicle is therefore not only a structural unit, but also a functional unit. In the thyroid there are no cords of secretory cells, as there are in so many endocrine glands.

In the normal gland, the follicles vary from being irregularly rounded to tubular in shape (Fig. 28-12). According to Marine, they measure from 0.05 to 0.5 mm. in diameter. In a section they appear to vary even more in size. This is due to the fact that in cutting a single section the knife passes through the centers of some follicles, through the edges of others, and through others at various levels between their centers and their edges. Those follicles whose edges are merely shaved by the knife appear in sections as solid clumps of cells (Fig. 28-12, *left*) for the same reason that a thin shaving cut from an orange shows

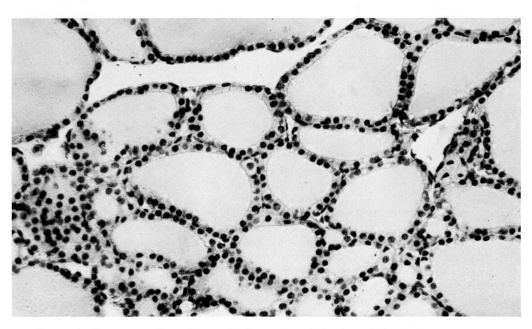

FIG. 28-12. Low-power photomicrograph of a section of the thyroid gland of a normal dog.

only skin and no pulp. However, some of the solid clumps of cells that are seen in sections are probably not to be explained as shavings from the sides of follicles. The cells in these clumps are larger than the typical follicular cells and have a clear cytoplasm. They have been called *light cells* or *parafollicular cells* because they are usually seen just beside follicles, occupying a space between the follicle and its basement membrane. These light cells are only found, or at least seen to advantage, in certain species. They give no evidence of being concerned in the formation or the secretion of thyroxine or tri-iodothyronine. Very recently some evidence has become available which seems to implicate them in secreting calcitonin, which is a hormone that acts to reduce the level of the calcium in the blood and which is secreted when the calcium level is high. Previously it was believed that calcitonin was secreted exclusively by the parathyroid gland. Calcitonin is discussed in more detail at the end of the section on the parathyroid gland. For references, see parathyroid.

Marine estimated that there are about 3 million follicles in the human thyroid. This is probably an underestimate; it is likely that there are ten times this number. Follicles are packed fairly closely together in a delicate reticular network that contains *an extensive capillary bed*. Each follicle is surrounded by

a basement membrane which is PA-Schiff positive. However, if careful reconstruction studies of the thyroid gland are made, it is possible, as Isler showed, to find apertures in the basement membranes of adjacent follicles where two neighboring follicles may be continuous. This feature makes it difficult to outline follicles and count them accurately.

Follicles are alike in that each consists of a single layer of epithelial cells surrounding a lumen filled with the colloid. The shape of the follicular cells of a follicle gives some clue to its functional activity. An inactive follicle tends to have walls of flattened cuboidal epithelium, while an active follicle has cuboidal-to-columnar epithelium. The normal epithelium is of a low cuboidal type (Fig. 28-12). Colloid contained within the follicles, after fixation, appears in sections as a solid, structureless, acidophilic material (Fig. 28-12). However, in sections of fixed tissue, the colloid is often seen to have shrunken away from the follicular epithelium in such a way as to present a serrated rather than a smooth outline. This is particularly true when the gland is very active (Fig. 28-18). Colloid, before fixation, is a viscous homogeneous fluid. The protein in colloid consists chiefly, if not exclusively, of a glycoprotein which becomes combined into a complex with iodine and is called *thyroglobulin*. Because of the carbohy-

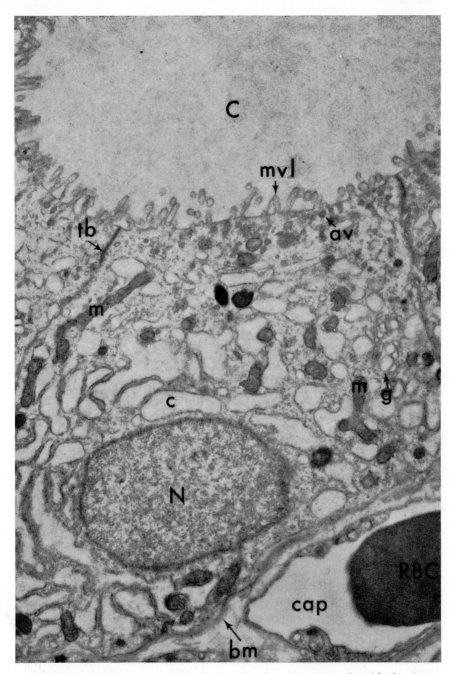

Fig. 28-13. Electron micrograph (× 9,000) of section of rat thyroid, showing a follicular cell. The basement membrane (bm) that is immediately below the base of the cell can be seen at the bottom of the picture along with a capillary (cap) that contains a red blood cell (RBC). The nucleus (N) lies close to the base of the cell. The most prominent feature of the cytoplasm that is near the nucleus is the presence of numerous more or less distended rough-surfaced vesicles of endoplasmic reticulum; one is labeled c. Some mitochondria are evident (m). Toward the right, parts of the Golgi apparatus can be seen (g). Close to the apex of the cell, numerous small vesicles filled with some moderately dense material are evident; these are apical vesicles (av). Numerous microvilli (mvl) extend from the inner border (the apex) of the cell into the colloid (C). (Nadler, N. J., Young, B. A., Leblond, C. P., and Mitmaker, B.: Endocrinology 74:333)

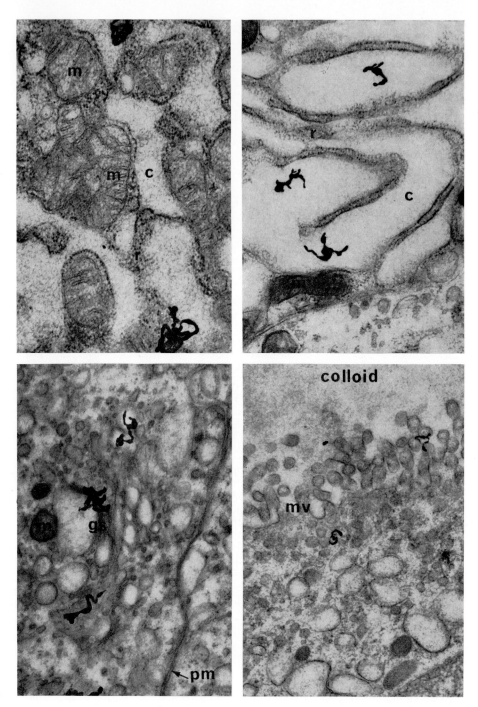

FIG. 28-14. Electron micrographs of radioautographs prepared from the thyroid glands of rats at various times after they were given a single injection of leucine labeled with tritium. (*Top, left*) Ten minutes after the injection, grains are seen over the ribosomes of the rough-surfaced vesicles of endoplasmic reticulum; this indicates that the incorporation of leucine into thyroglobulin is beginning to occur inside of 10 minutes. (*Top, right*) Thirty minutes after the injection the grains are seen over the lumens of rough-surfaced vesicles. (*Bottom, left*) One hour after the injection the grains are seen over the Golgi apparatus, thus indicating that thyroglobulin that was synthesized in association

(*Caption continued on facing page*)

drate content of thyroglobulin, colloid stains very well with PA-Schiff.

Colloid material is present not only in the central lumen of the thyroid follicle, but also as small droplets about 1 to 2 $\mu$ in diameter in the apical regions of the follicular cells (the parts of the cells closest to the lumen). These droplets possess the ordinary staining properties, as well as all the histochemical characters, of colloid. They are referred to as intracellular colloid droplets and are believed to represent colloid that is being resorbed from the lumen by the follicular cells. A full explanation of this and an interpretation of their functional significance will be given shortly. It is noted that the light cells, which constitute about 2 per cent of all the cells in the thyroid gland of the rat, do not abut on the lumens of the thyroid follicles but lie between the outer faces of the follicular cells and the basement membrane of the follicle concerned. Therefore, these light cells cannot resorb colloid from the follicular lumen and accordingly never contain colloid droplets. This feature affords the experimentalist the most positive means by which to identify light cells.

SOME GENERAL STEPS IN THE SYNTHESIS AND RELEASE OF THE THYROID HORMONE

The two important materials which enter into the composition of thyroid hormones are: (1) the amino acid tyrosine, and (2) iodine. However, the production of thyroid hormones is not a simple process in which iodine is linked directly with tyrosine. The tyrosine involved is actually in the form of a link or radical within the glycoprotein molecule of thyroglobulin; this glycoprotein, into which tyrosine is incorporated, is, as we shall see, synthesized in follicular cells. For the iodination of tyrosyl radicals in a glycoprotein molecule to occur, the iodide taken up by thyroid cells from the circulation must be oxidized to iodine. Then after the tyrosyl radicals in glycoprotein molecules have become iodinated, the next step is for two molecules of these radicals to com-

bine and form a single radical of thyronyl, still linked within the thyroglobulin molecule. Finally, the thyronyl radicals are dissociated from the glycoprotein and, in the process, become a free and relatively soluble substance that finally emerges through the bases of the follicular cells to enter capillaries. It is then the hormonal product. Some of the steps noted above occur in the follicular cells, while some occur in the colloid, as will become apparent as we consider (1) the fine structure of follicular cells and the synthesis of thyroglobulin, (2) the uptake of iodine and the iodination of tyrosine in thyroglobulin molecules, and (3) the breakdown of thyroglobulin and the release of thyroid hormones.

1. **The Fine Structure of Follicular Cells and the Synthesis of Thyroglobulin.** Figure 28-13 shows a follicular cell as it appears in the EM. Just below the base of the cell, which is at the bottom of the picture, a capillary (cap) containing a red blood cell (rbc) is present. Running along the base of the cell is a delicate basement membrane (bm). The nucleus (n) is near the base of the cell. The most prominent feature of the cytoplasm seen over a little more than the bottom half of the cell is the presence of many dilated rough-surfaced vesicles of endoplasmic reticulum; since dilated vesicles of this type are often termed *cisternae,* one in this illustration is labeled c. Toward the upper right side of the cell some smooth-surfaced vesicles of the Golgi apparatus (g) can be seen. Near the lumen there are many small vesicles that are filled with a material of slight-to-moderate electron density; these are termed apical vesicles (av). Microvilli (mvl) are seen on the surface that abuts on the colloid which is above and labeled C.

It is thus seen that follicular cells have a definite morphologic polarity; that is, there are a series of morphologic features which can be expected to be observed consistently as they are viewed from the basement membrane at the base of a cell to its apex that abuts on the colloid.

FIG. 28-14 (*Continued*)
with rough-surfaced vesicles has by this time moved to the Golgi region. (*Bottom, right*) Two hours after the injection, grains are seen over the apical vesicles, indicating that the thyroglobulin is being delivered by way of these vesicles into the colloid where the grains are seen shortly afterward. (Nadler, N. J., et al.: Endocrinology 74:333)

The synthesis and the passage through the cell of thyroglobulin was described by Nadler and co-workers, who have given animals a labeled precursor such as leucine which is built into thyroglobulin. They then obtained thyroid tissue at different times afterward, prepared radioautographs of thin sections of material taken at these different times and studied them in the EM. If this is done, radioautographs made from tissue taken as soon as 10 minutes after the labeled leucine is given show silver grains over the edges of the rough-surfaced vesicles (Fig. 28-14, *upper left*). After half an hour grains are seen over the lumens of the rough-surfaced vesicles (Fig. 28-14, *upper right*). After 1 hour the grains are seen over the Golgi vesicles (Fig. 28-14, *lower left*). After 2 hours the silver grains are seen over the apical vesicles that are close to the lumen of the follicle (Fig. 28-14, *lower right*). The process here, therefore, seems to be much like that which is concerned in the synthesis and the secretion of other proteins or glycoproteins in that the labeled amino acid is incorporated into a protein synthesized in association with rough-surfaced vesicles of endoplasmic reticulum. From these it is transported, probably by microvesicles, to the larger vesicles of the Golgi apparatus. Here the carbohydrate component of the glycoprotein is probably added and the glycoprotein thus formed is packaged into small vesicles and transported in these small secretory vesicles (the apical vesicles, a.v. in Fig. 28-13) to the inner surface of the follicular cell where the contents of the vesicles are discharged into, and so become part of, the colloid. As a result of all this activity, tyrosine, like leucine, enters the base of the cell and becomes incorporated into huge molecules of the thyroglobulin which are secreted into the lumens of the follicles where they help constitute the colloid.

**2. The Uptake of Iodide by Follicular Cells and the Iodination of Tyrosyl Radicals in Thyroglobulin Molecules.** A certain amount of iodine is present in the form of iodide in the normal individual; this constitutes what might be termed the *iodide pool* of the body. The iodide of this pool is derived from the iodine present in the diet and also from the breakdown of the iodine-containing thyroid hormones of the body. Iodine which enters the body from the diet may be in the form of organic or inorganic compounds; the iodine in these compounds is converted to iodide before entering the pool. Some iodine is continuously being lost out of the body into the urine, and the injection of sodium chloride into animals increases the amount of iodine wasted in this way. Axelrad and co-workers have shown that if the iodine intake is borderline, the eating of small amounts of salt will precipitate a condition of iodine deficiency resulting in goiter.

The cells of the thyroid follicles have a unique ability to trap iodide that passes by them in the blood of capillaries. As already noted, the thyroid gland has an extremely good blood supply, and hence much blood regularly courses by follicular cells which manifest a remarkable ability to extract iodine from the blood. If radioactive iodine is injected into an individual it is picked up and concentrated in the thyroid gland very quickly.

By some mechanism that is not as yet clearly understood, but perhaps through the action of an oxidizing enzyme, the iodide taken up by follicular cells from the bloodstream is converted to iodine which becomes bound to the tyrosyl radicals of the glycoprotein molecules. Within the framework of these molecules, the tyrosyl radicals forming mono-iodotyrosyl and di-iodotyrosyl unite to form tri-iodothyronyl and tetra-iodothyronyl radicals.

The site of iodination of the tyrosyl radicals in thyroglobulin molecules can be explored by giving animals radioactive iodine and then examining radioautographs made at different time periods after the radioactive iodine was given. Before this technic was more or less perfected it was thought, chiefly from the earlier radioautographs examined in the light microscope, that iodination began within the cytoplasm of the follicular cells; that is, *before* the thyroglobulin was secreted into the lumen of the follicle. But increasingly precise studies with the light microscope and newer studies made with the EM (Fig. 28-15, *bottom*) show that silver grains, which indicate incorporation of the labeled iodine into a product, are first seen not in cells but in the colloid, close to the lumen borders of the follicular cells, and that soon after, the label is seen throughout the colloid (Fig. 28-15, *top*). So this step in the formation of thyroid hormone occurs in the colloid.

**3. The Breakdown of Thyroglobulin and the**

**Release of the Thyroid Hormones.** The next and final step in the formation of the thyroid hormones involves the proteolysis of the thyroglobulin molecules with the release of its component amino acids. The latter step involves the liberation of free mono- and di-iodotyrosine and tri- and tetra-iodothyronine. Tri-iodothyronine and tetra-iodothyronine leave the thyroid gland to constitute the thyroid hormones; the first one is called tri-iodothyronine or $T_3$, and the second, thyroxine or $T_4$. On the other hand, free mono- and di-iodotyrosine do not leave the gland, for there is a dehalogenase enzyme or desiodase enzyme which acts specifically on these two substances. As a result, the iodine is detached from them and presumably goes back into the general iodide pool of the thyroid gland. A question arises whether this step occurs in the colloid or in the cytoplasm of the cells. There is evidence of two sorts to consider. First, De Robertis showed some time ago that there was an enzyme that was present in the colloid of follicles that could liquefy gelatin, and it seemed reasonable to think that such an enzyme could break down thyroglobulin in the colloid. However, as will be described presently, thyroid glands that are stimulated by TSH to release hormone have been shown to send out processes into the colloid that take up colloid droplets which are then carried into the cytoplasm where they are seen in large numbers. In the cytoplasm they disintegrate and disappear. At the moment it cannot be definitely stated whether the breakdown of the iodinated molecules of thyroglobulin with the consequent release of thyroid hormones occurs extracellularly in the colloid or intracellularly. Since it has been shown, however, that the process is influenced greatly by TSH, it would seem more probable that the mechanism is intracellular, for it is easier to conceive of a trophic hormone regulating hormone production and secretion as delicately as it does in the thyroid gland by controlling intracellular reactions than by controlling extracellular reactions. There is some evidence that lysosomes may be concerned in the proteolytic phenomenon, and they of course operate intracellularly.

It is to be emphasized that all processes involved in the synthesis and the secretion of thyroid hormones take place continuously and simultaneously. That is, while there is a synthesis of glycoprotein in the follicular cells,

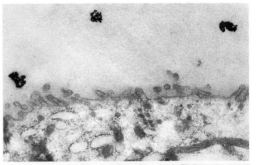

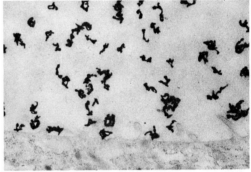

Fig. 28-15. Electron micrographs of radio-autographs prepared from sections of thyroid gland of animal injected with radio-active iodine ($I^{125}$). (*Top*) Section taken 2 minutes after the injection of radio-iodine. A few grains indicate that incorporation of iodine into thyroglobulin is beginning in the colloid close to the apical borders of the follicular cells. (*Bottom*) Section taken 12 hours after radio-iodine was given. Grains are now numerous and widely distributed in the colloid. (Preparation from Dr. H. E. van Heyningen)

there is also its secretion into the colloid, its iodination there and finally the breakdown of the iodinated thyroglobulin. The net result is a continuous release of thyroid hormone. By chance, some newly formed thyroglobulin molecules in the lumen may break down as soon as they are formed, while others may survive longer. In general, a measure of their mean survival is their turnover time. The faster the gland is working, the less is the turnover time of the average molecule in the thyroid follicle.

## FACTORS AFFECTING THE HISTOLOGY OF THE THYROID GLAND

In the embryo, follicles are small because they have little colloid in their lumens. During

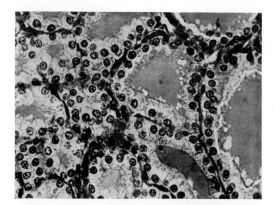

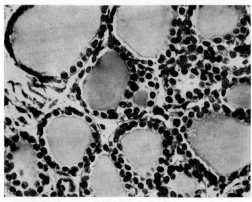

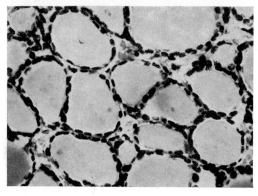

Fig. 28-16. Photomicrographs of sections of thyroid gland of rats. (*Top*) A 2-month-old rat. (*Middle*) Six days after hypophysectomy. (*Bottom*) Eighteen days after hypophysectomy. Note that after hypophysectomy the follicular cells become increasingly squamous while the round light nuclei of cells of the normal gland become thin, flattened and dark. (Preparation by A. Petrovic and C. P. Leblond)

vested in the hypophysis, the anterior lobe of which releases the thyroid-stimulating hormone, TSH. In the absence of the hypophysis the follicular cells become less active and change in appearance as indicated by comparing the top picture in Figure 28-16 with the lower two; this shows that without the stimulus of TSH the cells gradually change from cuboidal to squamous, and the nuclei flatten.

These various changes that occur in the thyroid gland after hypophysectomy can be repaired by giving the animals TSH. TSH augments the iodide-accumulating ability of the follicular cells, it increases the rate of synthesis and secretion of glycoprotein by the cells into the colloid, it increases the rate of iodination of glycoprotein in the colloid, and finally it increases the rate of breakdown of thyroglobulin and the liberation of hormones. Morphologically, the effect of TSH is to increase the size of the follicular cells, to decrease the volume of the colloid and to increase the number of intracellular colloid droplets. Recent experimental work by Nadler and collaborators demonstrated that colloid droplets make their appearance in the follicular cells as a result of pinocytosis (Fig. 28-17). Shortly after an injection of TSH, the follicular cells send out streamers of cytoplasm from the apical regions into the lumen of the thyroid follicles (Fig. 28-17, *upper left*). The streamers envelop small bits of colloid. The colloid droplets are then taken into the cytoplasm (Fig. 28-17, *upper right*). Thirty minutes after a large dose of TSH, nearly one half of the whole content of the colloid in the lumen of a follicle may be resorbed into the follicular cells in this fashion. After one half hour, the colloid droplets tend to disperse within the cytoplasm and disintegrate. After 4 hours most colloid droplets disappear and the follicular cells return to the normal condition.

growth, the thyroid gland increases in size because all the components of the thyroid follicles increase in size and also because of the occasional formation of new follicles. In the young, when all the follicles are small, the gland has a uniform appearance. However, with age, considerable variation appears in the size of follicles. In old age, previously spheroidal follicles often take on an irregular appearance.

The main control of the thyroid gland is

### PARENCHYMATOUS AND COLLOID GOITER

The action of the thyroid-stimulating hormone on the thyroid gland may become accentuated in a person because of a lack of iodine in the diet. If a person is on a low iodine diet, there is too little iodine available to the thyroid gland for it to make adequate amounts of hormone. As a result of the decreased amount of thyroid hormone in the blood there is a decrease in the inhibitory effect of thyroid hormone on the anterior pituitary gland so that it begins to secrete increased amounts of TSH. This stimulates the thyroid gland both to secrete and to grow. As a result of increased secretory activity the colloid content of the follicle becomes reduced, and the colloid itself becomes thin and pale-staining (Fig. 28-18). As a result of the stimulation of growth, the epithelial cells of the follicles become taller and increase in number by mitotic division. The follicles thus come to have thicker walls and to be composed of far

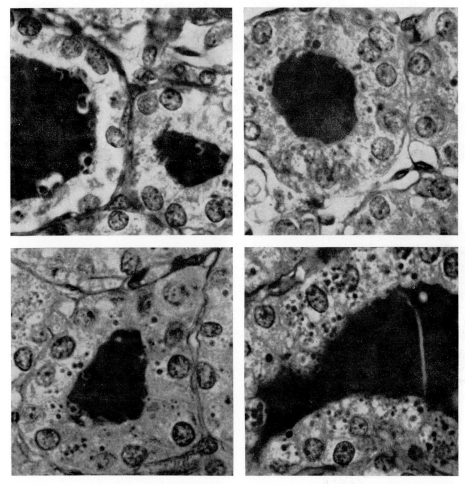

FIG. 28-17. Photomicrographs ($\times$ 1,000) of sections of central follicles of thyroid glands taken at various times after giving the animal T.S.H. Sections stained by the PAS method. (*Top, left*) Eight minutes after T.S.H. Note colloid droplets in lumen being taken up by streamers of cytoplasm from follicular cells. (*Top, right*) Twelve minutes after T.S.H. Colloid droplets have by now been taken into the apical halves of the cells. (*Bottom*) Thirty minutes and 4 hours, respectively, after T.S.H. Droplets of colloid have reached the basal parts of the cells and are disintegrating. (Nadler, N. J., Sarkar, S. K., and Leblond, C. P.: Endocrinology *71*:120)

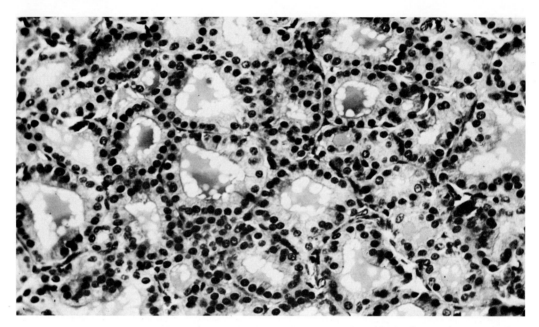

FIG. 28-18. Low-power photomicrograph of a section of the thyroid gland of a dog that had received 7 daily injections of anterior pituitary extract containing thyrotrophin. This is the type of histologic picture seen in parenchymatous goiter.

more cells than before (Fig. 28-18); this is reflected in an increase in the size of the gland as a whole, although the follicles, as they grow, lose most of their colloid, there being little within them to keep them distended. As a consequence, their walls become collapsed and infolded to a considerable extent. Since the enlargement of the gland is due chiefly to an increase in the number and the size of the epithelial cells of the follicles (the parenchyma of the gland) and not to an increased amount of colloid, the enlarged gland that results from thyrotrophic stimulation is termed a *parenchymatous* goiter. Before the days of iodized salt such goiters were common in many regions. This gross morphologic aberration may ultimately lead to the development of focal areas of benign or sometimes malignant tumors. Thus, low iodine diets have become an important experimental tool in the study of thyroid cancer.

A parenchymatous change, as described above, is probably the first change that occurs in iodine deficiency in people in areas where iodine is deficient in the diet. It seems that the need for thyroid hormone is increased at certain times, such as puberty and during pregnancy, and hence that parenchymatous goiters are more likely to develop at those times than others.

## FROM A PARENCHYMATOUS TO A COLLOID GOITER

Assuming that a parenchymatous goiter has developed in an individual at a time when the supplies of iodine were not adequate for the amount of hormone needed, for example, at puberty, and then that subsequently either the needs for thyroid hormone became less, or a little more iodine was taken in the diet, the microscopic structure of the thyroid would change once more. With a lessened demand for hormone, or with more iodine with which to make hormone, the gland would be able gradually to raise the concentration of hormone in the bloodstream. As the concentration of hormone in the bloodstream rises, the secretion of thyrotrophic hormone by the pars anterior would gradually be suppressed. With lessened thyrotrophic stimulation, the cells of the follicles of the thyroid gland would then revert to their former state; instead of being high cuboidal or columnar, they would become low cuboidal again (Fig. 28-19). It has been generally assumed that since the follicles would no longer be stimulated to secrete so much hormone into the bloodstream, they would be able to store more within their follicles, and as a result the follicles would increase in size (Fig. 28-19). It has been generally assumed further that since the follicles, as a result of the preceding proliferation of the cells of their walls, would have more cells in their walls than before, they would be much larger than before when they became distended with colloid. As a result, the gland as a whole would become larger than it was when it was primarily a parenchymatous goiter. Further, since its increase in size would now be due primarily to its large content of colloid (instead of parenchyma as previously), it would now be termed a *colloid* rather than a parenchymatous goiter (compare Figs. 28-18 and 28-19). The concept given above, of how a colloid goiter develops, elaborated by Marine, did not seem to lend itself to experimental verification in rats. However, Fallis has recently produced colloid goiters in hamsters by this means; this substantiates Marine's concept of how colloid goiters develop.

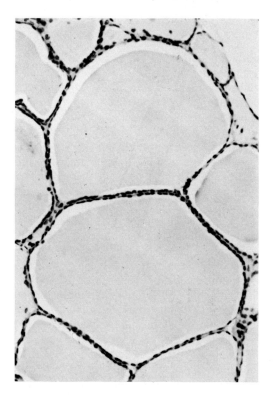

Fig. 28-19. Medium-power photomicrograph of a small area of a section of a simple colloid goiter.

### Drugs That Interfere With the Formation of Thyroid Hormones

It is now possible to treat certain kinds of hyperthyroidism with certain drugs. It was discovered that certain drugs, most notably thiouracil, prevent the thyroid gland from properly synthesizing thyroid hormone even if the diet contains adequate amounts of iodine. Therefore, the administration of thiouracil can cut down the production of hormone by the gland and so allay hyperthyroidism. It is of interest that thiouracil administered to a normal animal with an adequate iodine intake will soon cause its previously normal thyroid gland to assume the microscopic appearance of a parenchymatous goiter. The explanation for this is obvious.

### Other Causes of Hypothyroidism

It is now recognized that some goiters which are associated with hypothyroidism in man result from inherited defects. These defects are manifested by the existence of blocks in any of several of the various steps involved in the production of thyroid hormones or for

oxidizing iodide to the form in which it can link to the tyrosine groups of the glycoprotein precursor of thyroglobulin. The result is an accumulation of iodide in the thyroid but no synthesis of thyroglobulin, a situation similar to that produced by the administration of thiouracil.

Another similar condition appears to be due to the inherited absence of the system required for coupling iodotyrosines to make thyroxine and triiodothyronine. Mono- and di-iodotyrosine then accumulate in the thyroid. A third condition, inherited as an autosomal recessive and resulting in congenital hypothyroidism with goiter, is due to the absence of the enzyme discovered by Roche, which deiodinates the unused portion of iodotyrosines so that the iodide so released may be reutilized in the synthesis of thyroglobulin. This causes mono- and di-iodotyrosine to accumulate in the blood and to be lost as such in the urine.

### TESTING THYROID FUNCTION

As discussed earlier, one way of determining the extent of the activity of the thyroid is to estimate the effect that thyroid secretion is having on the oxidation processes in body cells by measuring the *basal metabolic rate*. Newer, more direct methods for determining the level of thyroid function are now available.

The thyroid hormones, upon leaving the gland, for the most part become linked to proteins of the globulin type in the blood. The iodine that is in this way attached to protein (serum protein-bound iodine, abbreviated to PBI) can be measured, and its level is an accurate indicator of the function of the thyroid gland. Therefore, it is now being widely used in the diagnosis of thyroid disorders.

Another method that owes its existence to the unique ability of the thyroid to concentrate iodine is known as the *radioiodine uptake*. Radioiodine in minute quantities is administered to patients and, at various time intervals thereafter, measurements are made of the rays emanating from their thyroids by means of an externally placed scintillation or Geiger counter, with no discomfort to the patients. This gives important information concerning the function of the thyroid gland because the rate of uptake is high in overactive glands and low in underactive ones.

Radioiodine in larger doses is used sometimes to treat certain pathologic conditions of the thyroid gland. Since it tends to become concentrated in the colloid of the thyroid follicles, attempts have been made in various centers to treat certain pathologic conditions of the thyroid gland by giving the patients sufficient doses of the material to permit destructive amounts of it to accumulate in the thyroid gland but not elsewhere. Concentration in only one site, with no harmful accumulations elsewhere, is probably a very difficult objective to attain with isotopes, but it is probably more feasible with radioiodine and the thyroid gland than with most isotopes and tissues.

### DOES THE THYROID GLAND PROVIDE AN EXAMPLE OF A SECLUDED ANTIGEN

As was mentioned in discussing the formation of antibodies in previous chapters, it is now known that the mammalian body may sometimes form antibodies against one of its own components; the antibodies so-formed are termed auto-antibodies, and the phenomenon itself, auto-immunity.

Knowledge in this field is as yet in its infancy. There is reason to believe that the further development of knowledge may elucidate the etiology of certain as yet ill-understood diseases of man; indeed, it is not inconceivable that part of what we now regard as some of the normal process of aging may eventually be found to be due in part to the immunity-producing mechanisms of individuals, as they grow older, reacting against themselves. In any event, the phenomenon of auto-immunity is of such interest and possible importance that it should be mentioned; and since a good example of it is sometimes provided by the thyroid gland, we shall discuss it here briefly.

As was explained in previous chapters, immunologic tolerance develops to macromolecules to which a fetus (or, in many species, a newborn animal) is suitably exposed and as a consequence of this the animal in postnatal life will lack the capacity for reacting against any of these macromolecules by producing antibodies against them. This is true of heterologous antigens which are injected into the fetus of the newborn animal, and it is reasonable to assume that it is also true of such macromolecules as develop normally in the fetus, and which would be antigens if they were injected into other hosts. Therefore, as a general rule, it would seem that an animal does not react against any of its *own* macromolecules in postnatal life, because it has been suitably exposed to them in fetal life and has become immunologically tolerant of them.

However, for a fetus to become tolerant to macromolecules that develop within it during embryonic life requires that these macromolecules either gain entrance to the tissue fluid, or the lymph or the blood of the fetus, so that somehow they can give information to the precursors of antibody-forming cells to the effect that antibodies are not to be made against them. As has already been explained, the period during which immunologic tolerance can be induced terminates around the time of birth. Accordingly, if any antigen forms in the fetus but is kept hidden from the tissue fluid, the lymph or the blood of the body, so that it does not come in contact with the precursor cells of the antibody-forming series, the latter will have no information about it, and so the body will not be immunologically tolerant to it. Hence, if previously *secluded antigens* gain entrance to one of the fluids of the body and so are able to reach antibody-forming cells in postnatal life, it could be expected that the body would react against them as it would against any foreign antigen.

The thyroid gland provides an example of a secluded antigen. Thyroglobulin or its precursor is a glycoprotein that is secreted by follicular cells into the lumens of follicles, and under normal conditions this glycoprotein does not as such enter any of the fluids of the body. Accordingly, an animal body may not be immunologically tolerant to the glycoprotein in the follicles of its thyroid gland. Experimental evidence provided by Witebsky and his associates and by others indicates very strongly that an animal injected with a suitable extract prepared from its own thyroid gland will make antibodies against it.

There is now some reason to believe that the development of auto-immunity against thyroglobulin or its precursor is a contributing factor in the development of a disease of the thyroid gland which is occasionally seen and is called Hashimoto's disease. In this disease the thyroid gland becomes enlarged; this is due primarily to the stroma of the gland becoming increased in amount and heavily infiltrated with lymphocytes and plasma cells and even giving birth to lymphatic nodules. The follicles become atrophic and contain little colloid, and thyroid function is generally impaired. Antibodies to some thyroid protein have been demonstrated in the blood of patients with this disease. Experimentally, it has been shown that if part of the thyroid gland of an animal is excised, disease can be produced in the remaining part by immunizing the animal with extracts prepared from the excised portion. Therefore, Hashimoto's disease would seem to have its origin in thyroglobulin or its precursor somehow gaining access to the stroma of the thyroid gland.

Another example of a secluded antigen is provided by the lens of the eye. Several factors are probably involved in keeping its proteins secluded: (1) its proteins are relatively in-

soluble; (2) the lens is enclosed by a capsule; and (3) the encapsulated lens lives in a bath of a special fluid, aqueous humor, which provides a more secluded environment than does ordinary tissue fluid. In any event there is evidence that if lens protein escapes, for example, during an eye operation, it can serve as an antigen in the body in which it was formed.

Spermatozoa (male germ cells, to be described in Chap. 30) provide another example of a secluded antigen, for they are formed inside tubules and hence are not in contact with tissue fluid, lymph or blood. It has been shown experimentally that a male can develop antibodies against his own spermatozoa. However, there is an additional reason for a body's not being tolerant to its own spermatozoa; it is that spermatozoa do not develop in the body until postnatal life and then not until the time of puberty. Hence, there is no opportunity for the body to become immunologically tolerant to spermatozoa in fetal life.

Secluded antigens are not the only cause for antibodies sometimes being developed against body components. Interesting as it would be to discuss possible mechanisms which may lead to antibodies being formed against various types of blood cells, and possibly also to some components of intercellular substance in the heart, the kidney and the joint capsules, it would not be proper to do so here.

## THE PARATHYROID GLANDS

**Introduction.** There are usually 4 parathyroid glands in each person, but there may be more. They are so named because they are *beside* the thyroid gland. More precisely, they are usually arranged 2 on each side, on the backs of the lobes of the thyroid gland, immediately outside the true capsule of the thyroid gland, but to the inside of its outer capsule of fascia. The upper parathyroids lie about midway between the upper and the lower poles of the lobes, while the lower ones are near the lower poles of the lobes. The upper ones are of a flattened ovoid shape, and the lower ones roughly that of a somewhat flattened sphere. Their length or greatest diameter is slightly more than half a centimeter. They are yellow-brown when seen in

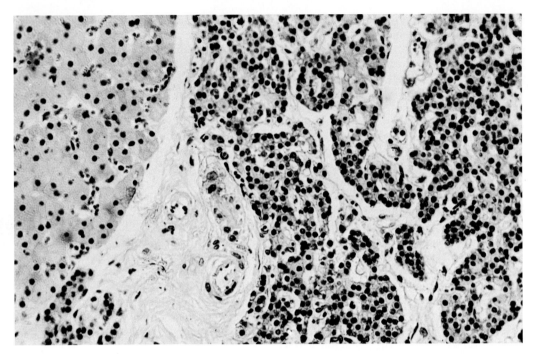

Fig. 28-20. Medium-power photomicrograph of a small area of a section of the parathyroid gland. An area of oxyphil cells may be seen at the left. The right side shows chief cells.

the fresh state. Both the upper and the lower parathyroids are supplied by twigs from the inferior thyroid artery, and it is said that these small glands can sometimes be found conveniently by tracing the arterial twigs that arise from the inferior thyroid artery to their terminations.

The numbers and the sites of parathyroid glands vary in different kinds of experimental animals. In the rat there are only 2 glands, and these lie buried in the substance of the thyroid gland, one in each lobe. In the dog, parathyroid glands may sometimes be found as far down as the bifurcation of the trachea. Even in man, aberrant parathyroid glands are not uncommon, and if a tumor develops in one of these it may be difficult to find.

In an early chapter of this book it was observed that the great disadvantage associated with the specialization of labor in a community, either of cells or people, is the fact that the whole community becomes dependent on each group of essential specialists continuing to live and work. The parathyroid glands illustrate very dramatically the dependence of the whole body on a small number of specialists,

for if the parathyroid glands are removed, the whole body, unless special therapy is instituted, perishes.

**Microscopic Structure.** Each parathyroid gland is covered by a delicate connective tissue capsule. Septa from it penetrate the gland to carry blood vessels and a few vasomotor nerve fibers into its substance. The septa do not divide the gland into distinct lobules. Until a few years before puberty, only one type of secretory cell is found in the gland. This is termed the chief or principal cell. It is smaller than the secretory cells of most endocrine glands; hence, *in the parathyroid gland the nuclei of the parenchymal cells are generally very close together* (Fig. 28-20). No granules can be seen in the cytoplasm of chief cells. Although their cytoplasm is never very dense or dark-staining, that of some chief cells is darker than that of others. Those with the darker cytoplasm are called *dark chief* cells; and those with very pale cytoplasm, *light chief* cells. Some light chief cells have no stainable substance in their cytoplasm whatsoever; these are called *clear* cells. Chief cells make the only hormone known to be secreted by the gland, and S. H. Bensley has related the different appearances that they present to different stages of a secretory cycle. Her paper should be consulted for details.

Although chief cells are smaller than the cells of most endocrine glands, they are arranged in clumps and irregular cords that are wider than those of most endocrine glands. The cells within the cords and the clumps are supported by reticular fibers. Large capillaries are present between the cords and the clumps.

A few years before puberty, clumps of cells with much larger amounts of cytoplasm than chief cells make their appearance in the gland. In contrast with that of chief cells, the cytoplasm of these contains granules. These are acidophilic; hence, the cells are termed *oxyphil* (*oxys* = acid) cells. The easiest way for the student to detect clumps of these is to look for sites in the gland where nuclei are more widely separated from each other than they are in areas of chief cells (Fig. 28-20). Such areas are more common in the periphery of the gland. Oxyphil cells are not nearly so numerous as chief cells. Oxyphil cells are not present in the parathyroid glands of most animals. In man, transitions between chief and oxyphil cells are commonly seen; since chief cells appear in the gland first, this suggests that oxyphil cells probably arise from chief cells. The function of oxyphil cells, if any, is unknown.

In the parathyroid glands of older people, occasional clumps of chief cells may form follicles. These probably represent attempts at storing secretion. In addition, the glands of older people often contain considerable amounts of fat.

**Function.** Although much is known about the effects of the parathyroid hormone, there is much uncertainty about how it produces these effects. We shall first consider some of the effects of too little and too much parathyroid hormone in the circulation, and then discuss how the hormone could produce these effects.

**Effects of Removal.** Removal of the parathyroid tissue from an animal causes it to develop a condition called tetany (this is not to be confused with tetanus which is an infection). Tetany is characterized by the development of prolonged or convulsive spasms of

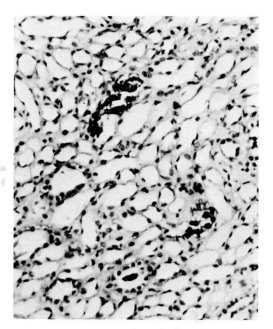

FIG. 28-21. Medium-power photomicrograph of a section of the medulla of the kidney of a dog that received large amounts of parathyroid hormone. The black material is calcium that has been deposited along the loops of Henle as a result of the kidney's having to excrete excess amounts of this mineral.

certain muscles. When it is very severe, spasms of muscles of the larynx or those responsible for respiratory movements may cause death. The immediate cause of tetany is a lack of a sufficient concentration of calcium ions in the blood; calcium ions routinely act to prevent undue irritability of nervous and neuromuscular mechanisms. Since the level of calcium in the blood falls when the parathyroid glands are removed, it is obvious that the parathyroid hormone in some way helps to maintain a proper level of calcium in the blood. This was not established until 1925 when Collip succeeded in making an extract of parathyroid glands that would raise the level of the blood calcium in dogs from which the parathyroid glands had been removed, and this prevented tetany from developing.

**Effects of Too Much Parathyroid Hormone.** Tumors of the chief cells sometimes occur. Moreover, sometimes parathyroid glands become hyperplastic without actually becoming tumors. In both conditions too much parathy-

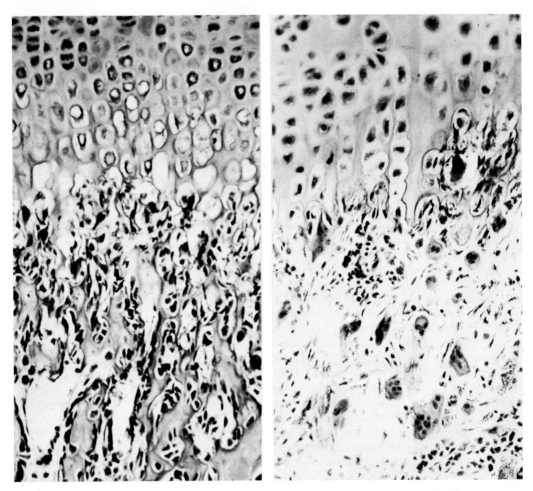

FIG. 28-22. (*Left*) Low-power photomicrograph of a small portion of a longitudinal section of the metaphysis of a long bone of a young, normal guinea pig. (*Right*) A similar preparation from a litter mate who was given a very large injection of parathyroid hormone 48 hours before. Note that the trabeculae on the diaphysial side of the epiphysial disk have melted away and that osteoclasts are left in their place.

roid hormone may be produced and liberated into the bloodstream; this is prone to cause grave effects in the skeleton. The bones become unduly fragile and are easily broken. Roentgenograms show that the amount of bone substance is greatly reduced, and histologic sections reveal a picture which suggests that the bony skeleton is being replaced with ordinary fibrous connective tissue and that bone resorption is greatly stimulated, as is indicated by increased numbers of osteoclasts. The condition is termed generalized osteitis fibrosa. The blood of individuals suffering from this disease usually contains increased

amounts of calcium, and urine examinations reveal that much calcium is being excreted in urine. The latter effect may lead to kidney stones and/or to the deposition of calcium precipitates in the kidney (Fig. 28-21), and these in turn may seriously damage the kidneys so that individuals with parathyroid tumors, if left untreated, may die of kidney disease.

**Effects of Administering Parathyroid Hormone to Normal Animals.** Different kinds of experimental animals vary in their responses to parathyroid hormone, but, in general, if large doses are given to young animals the blood calcium level is increased, and the trabeculae on the diaphysial sides of epiphysial plates are soon resorbed. Many osteoclasts are left in the sites previously occupied by trabeculae (Fig. 28-22).

**Effects of Parathyroid Hormone in Preventing Osteopetrosis in Certain Strains of Rats and Mice.** There are certain strains of mice and rats in which bone resorption does not proceed at a normal rate, and, as a consequence, the marrow cavities of long bones come to contain a greatly increased number of trabeculae (this condition is called *osteopetrosis*). The administration of parathyroid hormone to such animals results in the rate of bone resorption becoming more normal.

**A Primary Action of the Hormone.** From the foregoing the conclusion seems to be inescapable that the parathyroid hormone is concerned in controlling bone resorption. Normal growth is associated with bone formation and bone resorption remaining in balance. Much evidence, given above, suggests that the parathyroid hormone controls resorption and that if there is too much hormone in the blood, resorption becomes preponderant over formation.

**How Does the Parathyroid Hormone Control Bone Resorption?** The question now arises as to whether or not the parathyroid hormone affects the level of the calcium in the blood only because of its effect on controlling bone resorption or whether or not it has other effects that affect the level of calcium in the blood. First, we shall consider how the level of the calcium in the blood affects the parathyroid glands.

Years ago rickets was a common disease, and it was often observed that some rachitic children had enlarged parathyroid glands. However, rickets can be caused by a relative lack of either calcium or phosphorus in the blood; the latter is more common. The author, with Littner, Tisdall, Robertson and Drake, showed, some years ago, that the parathyroid glands become greatly enlarged in rachitic rats when the rickets was caused by a low content of calcium in their blood, but they did not become enlarged in rachitic rats that had a normal calcium, but a depressed phosphorus, level in their blood. Accordingly, it would seem that the secretion and the growth of the parathyroid glands is regulated by the amount of calcium that is in the blood; that blood calcium and parathyroid secretion are involved in a simple push-pull arrangement.

It has also been noticed that individuals with certain kinds of kidney disease had hypertrophied parathyroid glands. The kidneys of such individuals cannot excrete phosphorus properly, so the amount of phosphorus in their blood becomes increased. This led to the view that an increased amount of phosphorus in the blood causes the parathyroids to enlarge; this, in turn, suggested that the parathyroid hormone controls phosphorus excretion. However, there is a very curious reciprocal relation between the amounts of calcium and phosphorus in the blood, so that if the level of one increases, the level of the other falls. So, a high blood phosphorus could cause parathyroid hypertrophy because it depresses the blood calcium level.

It has also been suggested that a primary action of the parathyroid hormone is that of stimulating phosphorus excretion by the kidneys. An argument in favor of this view was the experimental finding that parathyroid hormone does not seem to be effective in raising the blood calcium level in animals from whom the kidneys had been removed. However, Grollman has shown that if nephrectomized animals are kept alive by means of peritoneal lavage, parathyroid hormone, administered to them, will increase their blood calcium levels. This would seem to show that the action of parathyroid hormone is not exclusively on the kidneys.

SOME CONCLUSIONS ABOUT THE GENERAL FUNCTION AND MECHANISM OF ACTION OF THE PARATHYROID HORMONE

The parathyroid glands are extraordinarily sensitive to the concentration of calcium in the blood. By secreting more hormone when the calcium concentration in the blood begins to fall, and by secreting less when it begins to rise, the glands achieve a very delicate control over the blood calcium level, keeping it normally at an extraordinarily constant level.

It appears then, and much evidence indicates, that the secretory functions of the parathyroid gland are controlled by the level of the calcium of the blood. It more or less follows that the hormone of the gland must act somehow to control the level of the calcium of the blood. Problems arise in establishing how it performs this latter function.

Although there may be other effects of the hormone that indirectly affect calcium levels in the blood, the one effect that has been established most clearly is that parathyroid hormone acts as a controlling factor in the mechanisms which relate to calcium being deposited in, and calcium being removed from, bone. As a result of its affecting these mechanisms, the amount of calcium in the blood of a person with a normal calcium intake is kept constant; this requires that not too much calcium be deposited in bone at the expense of the blood or that not too much be taken from the bone to increase the content in the blood (which results in its being wasted because of its being lost from the body via the urine).

The next question we must consider is how a hormone could regulate the balance between calcium deposition in bone and calcium removal from bone.

In considering ways and means whereby parathyroid hormone could conceivably act to release calcium from the intercellular substance of bone it should be mentioned that it seems most improbable that this could be the result of a direct action of the hormone on the intercellular substance. Hormones, which are present in blood only in very minute amounts, must surely all act by influencing some metabolic process that takes place in living cells. Therefore, experiments in which implants of parathyroid gland have been placed beside bone, and observed to cause resorption, should not be interpreted as proving that the hormone acts directly on nonliving bone intercellular substance. As was noted in Chapter 18 in the discussion there on bone resorption, the presence of living cells on bone surfaces, if they are metabolically acting cells of a different kind from those that normally clothe and protect bone surfaces, could be expected to cause bone resorption. Malignant tumors that invade bone cause bone resorption.

If it can be assumed therefore, that parathyroid hormone acts by affecting cells, we might ask what kind of cells it affects in, or on, bone. There are two possibilities here. First, it could affect the cells that normally cover or line bone surfaces or it conceivably could affect the osteocytes that are buried in bone substance and connected to surfaces only by canaliculi. We shall deal with the latter possibility first. Recently there have been experimental studies which have been thought to yield some evidence that resorption can occur around the deeply buried osteocytes and that parathyroid hormone may play some part in stimulating deeply buried osteocytes to dissolve bone in their immediate neighborhood. While it is important to keep an open mind, it seems to the author that it would be extremely difficult for parathyroid hormone to percolate along the extremely fine canaliculi of compact bone to reach deeply buried osteocytes. It likewise would be very difficult for any calcium liberated deep within the lamellae of haversian systems to ever move outward through canaliculi to a bone surface in order for it to be carried away in the blood. It is of course known that deeply buried osteocytes may die, and indeed examples of empty lacunae are often seen in compact bone, deep within its substance. But it seems doubtful if there could be any removal of the substances of which calcified bone intercellular substance is composed from any site deep within compact bone until a resorption tunnel was eroded into the area, whereupon the removal of bone substance from the area could take place at a surface and the dissolved materials could be carried away by capillaries. Therefore, our opinion is that parathyroid hormone acts on the cells that cover and line bone surfaces.

Certainly a very clear-cut finding, when a large amount of parathyroid hormone is given a growing experimental animal, is that there is a great deal of bone resorption instituted on bone surfaces. As was explained in Chapter 18 (Bone), all bone surfaces are normally covered with cells of a special lineage. Most of those on the surfaces of resting bone are flattened osteogenic cells. On surfaces where bone is being formed, the osteogenic cells proliferate and some differentiate into osteoblasts and form the organic intercellular substance of bone which is thereupon deposited on that surface. The organic intercellular substance takes up calcium from the tissue fluid and so becomes calcified. Surfaces from which bone is being resorbed, and from which calcium is being liberated into the tissue fluid, are generally covered at least in part by osteoclasts. The obvious effect of excess parathyroid hormone is to change the character of the kinds of cells that cover and line bone surfaces. Excess parathyroid hormone affects both resting osteogenic cells and osteoblasts so that they fuse into the multinucleated masses that we know as osteoclasts. The bone surfaces beneath these show every evidence of resorption which of course is associated with the liberation of calcium.

It would seem therefore that a primary action of parathyroid hormone is to convert the cells that cover or line bone surfaces, and which normally function by protecting or adding to that surface, into osteoclasts which neither protect nor add to the surface and indeed probably act to erode bone and hence free calcium which then is available to enter the blood.

A distinction should be made here. It is sometimes said that parathyroid hormone stimulates osteoclast function. In the opinion of the author this is not the important point to make. The important point is that it changes cells which protect and build bone into cells that fail to protect, and which actually destroy bone; the hormone thus stimulates the *formation* of osteoclasts. It changes the balance between the number of cells that are either protecting bone or building bone and those that do not protect or build but destroy bone. The change is effected in covering and lining cells in some sites more easily than in others; the cells covering the trabeculae on the diaphysial sides of the epiphysial plates of growing animals are particularly sensitive as is shown in Figure 28-22.

**The Parathyroid and Osteoporosis.** Osteoporosis, as mentioned in Chapter 18, is an all too common condition that develops in older people and is characterized by a loss of bone substance. Compact bone becomes riddled with resorption tunnels and this of course reduces the number of intact haversian systems in the substance of compact bone. Curiously enough, there is some evidence that giving patients with osteoporosis extra calcium improves the condition, even though the cause is not that of an impaired calcification of bone but instead an inability of the body to make the organic intercellular substance of bone as fast as bone is being resorbed. It is

possible, however, that the parathyroid glands are involved in the causation of osteoporosis even though there is no evidence of a hypercalcemia which would indicate hyperfunction of the glands. It is possible that if a person was on a diet deficient in calcium for a long time that the parathyroids would secrete extra hormone over a long period in order to maintain a proper level of calcium in the blood over that period of time. If the calcium required to maintain a proper blood calcium level was not available from the diet, the parathyroid hormone would therefore cause more or less continuous bone resorption. The rate of resorption would exceed the rate of bone formation and hence in due course the bones might be expected to become less dense. The beneficial effects of extra calcium in such individuals could possibly be explained by the extra calcium slowing parathyroid function, and this in turn could result in the rate of bone resorption being diminished to the point where new bone formation could compensate for it. However, much further research is needed before the serious problem of osteoporosis will be fully clarified and the role of the parathyroid glands, if any, in its etiology, understood.

**Calcitonin.** In 1961 Copp and his associates obtained experimental evidence indicating that the parathyroid glands could secrete a second hormone, one that acts to depress the blood calcium instead of raising it, as does the hormone that was previously believed to be the only hormone secreted by the gland. Copp and his associates named this second hormone *calcitonin* and showed that the stimulus for its secretion was a high blood calcium level. More recently, Hirsch and his associates have found evidence indicating that the thyroid gland can secrete calcitonin. It seems improbable that the follicular cells of the thyroid that secrete thyroxine and tri-iodothyronine would also secrete calcitonin, and it has been suggested that the parafollicular (light) cells described in the previous section on the thyroid, and which hitherto have had no function ascribed to them, could be responsible for secreting calcitonin.

The author has thought for some time that superficially at least the light (parafollicular) cells of the thyroid resemble the cells of the parathyroid more than they resemble the

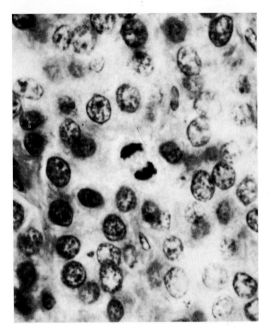

FIG. 28-23. High-power photomicrograph of a section of the parathyroid gland of a dog that had received several daily injections of anterior pituitary extract. A mitotic figure in a chief cell is to be observed.

follicular cells of the thyroid, and that adenomas of the parafollicular cells of the thyroid which can be produced by dietary means resemble parathyroid tissue more than they resemble thyroid tissue. It seems conceivable, therefore, that both the parafollicular cells of the thyroid and the parathyroid cells may share in the same function, and hence that both the thyroid and the parathyroid glands could secrete calcitonin. Work in this area is being actively prosecuted, and in due course more precise information on the source of calcitonin and its role in regulating the blood calcium level will become available.

**The Question of Pituitary Control.** There is some evidence to show that the parathyroid gland is affected by the anterior pituitary gland. Under ordinary conditions, mitotic figures are rare in the parathyroid gland. After injections with extracts of the pars anterior we observed numerous mitotic figures in the gland (Fig. 28-23). Other observers have shown that the blood calcium level is raised after injections of anterior pituitary extracts. Certainly, the pars anterior is able to stimu-

late the parathyroid glands; but whether it does this by means of a special parathyrotrophic hormone is by no means certain.

## THE ADRENAL (SUPRARENAL) GLANDS

### SOME GROSS CHARACTERISTICS

The adrenal glands are paired, flattened, yellow masses of tissue that lie, as their name implies, in contact with the upper poles of the kidneys (Fig. 28-24). The right gland—sometimes described as having the shape of a cocked hat—is wedged in the interval between the upper pole of the right kidney and the adjacent inferior vena cava; the left gland—roughly crescentic—occupies the medial border of the left kidney from pole to hilum. Each gland is about 5 cm. long, 3 to 4 cm. wide and somewhat less than 1 cm. in thickness. In many animals the glands, although situated close to the kidneys, do not lie above them; hence, the term *adrenal* (*ad* = to) has a more general application than suprarenal.

Each gland consists of a cortex and a medulla. These two parts have different origins, characters and functions. Therefore, each suprarenal gland is to be thought of as two glands in one. Indeed, in some animals, cortical tissue and medullary tissue form separate bodies no more related to one another anatomically than they are functionally. Many investigators have suspected that there is some reason for the close anatomic association of the two parts of the gland in so many animals, but, although there has been much speculation about this matter, the reason, if any, for the arrangement has not yet been ascertained.

### DEVELOPMENT

The first intimation of the development of the cortices of the glands is a thickening that occurs in the mesoderm near the root of the dorsal mesentery. Two substantial masses of cells, one on each side, form in this region and come to lie close to the developing kidney. It seems likely, from the studies of Keene and Hewer, that, as development proceeds, the original mass of cells making up the cortex becomes capped and then surrounded by a second mass of cells derived approximately from the same site as the first. The original or

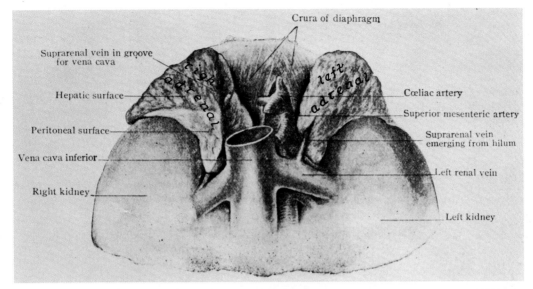

FIG. 28-24. Anterior aspect of adrenal glands hardened in situ. (Huber: Piersol's Human Anatomy, ed. 9, Philadelphia, Lippincott)

inner mass forms what is called the *provisional* or *fetal cortex of the gland,* and the second or outer mass that subsequently covers it, the *permanent cortex.*

In the meantime, ectodermal cells have migrated from the neural crests (or from the neural tube itself—the source of these cells is somewhat uncertain) to form the celiac ganglia. However, some of these ectodermal-derived cells, instead of developing into ganglion cells, migrate further afield and into the substance of the cortical tissue to take up a position in its central part. A continuous migration of cells from the developing celiac ganglia proceeds almost until the time of birth (and perhaps later), so that by this time a substantial number of cells have taken up a position in the central part of the adrenal gland to comprise its medulla. The relation of the cells of the medulla to the sympathetic nervous system will be described in detail when we consider the adrenal medulla somewhat later.

The provisional or fetal cortex—derived from the first group of mesodermal cells to separate from the celomic epithelium—becomes arranged into cords of cells separated by blood vessels, and the structure as a whole reaches a high state of development during fetal life. Not only do the cells of the provisional cortex comprise the bulk of the cortical tissue that exists at this time, but also they are so numerous as to make the adrenal cortex of the fetus an organ of impressive size. The cells of the permanent cortex do not develop to any great extent during this time. However, after birth, the provisional cortex—so highly developed during fetal life—undergoes a rapid involution. As this occurs, the cells of the permanent cortex begin to differentiate, but for a few years they do not become organized into the 3 zones that characterize the adult cortex.

The fact that the provisional cortex has a somewhat different origin from the permanent cortex and is enormously developed in fetal life but involutes after birth suggests strongly that this provisional cortex should be regarded as an endocrine gland in its own right, having a special function in fetal life. Since it involutes after birth, it could be reasoned that the trophic hormones that cause its great development during fetal life are perhaps the gonadotrophiclike hormones (to be described in the next chapter) made by the placenta during pregnancy. One difficulty in determining the function of the adrenal cortex in fetal life is that a comparable development of the gland does not occur in the fetuses of the common experimental animals; hence, the experimental study of the phenomenon is correspondingly restricted.

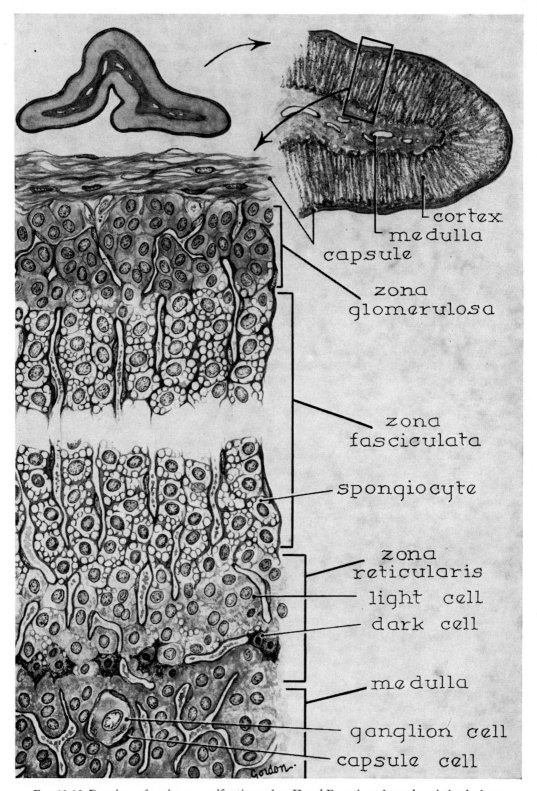

FIG. 28-25. Drawings of various magnifications of an H and E section of an adrenal gland of man.

## General Microscopic Appearance of the Gland as a Whole

A general preliminary inspection of a section of the gland should be made with the low-power objective in order to establish certain prominent landmarks. First, the gland will be seen to have a relatively thick capsule of connective tissue (Fig. 28-25). Next, in the central part of the gland, large veins may be seen (Fig. 28-25). These are the veins of the medulla, and a moderate amount of connective tissue is associated with them. Between this connective tissue and that of the capsule is the parenchyma of the gland. Most of this is cortex. Although the medulla occupies the more central part of the gland and so is surrounded by cortex, the gland is so flattened that the medulla generally appears in a section as a rather thin "filling" in a sandwich of cortex (Fig. 28-25). Moreover, the medulla is not very sharply demarcated from the cortex. However, the cytoplasm of the cells of the medulla is more basophilic than that of the cortical cells; hence, even in a casual low-power inspection of an H and E section, the medulla may generally be identified as a muddy blue layer between two lighter layers of cortex.

With more detailed study it will be observed that the parenchymal cells of both the cortex and the medulla follow the general plan seen in endocrine glands; that is, they are arranged in clumps or cords with vessels between them (Figs. 28-25 and 28-28, *right*). The vessels in the cortex have been described by some authorities as capillaries and by others as sinusoids; certainly some of their lining cells are phagocytic and so belong to the reticuloendothelial system. Both narrow capillaries and wider venous channels are found between the clumps and the cords of cells of the medulla; these drain into the large veins mentioned previously.

With this preliminary description of the gland as a whole we are more prepared to consider some details about the structure and the function of its two main parts.

## The Adrenal Cortex

**Microscopic Structure.** The arrangement of the parenchymal cells differs at various levels between the capsule and the medulla. Three different arrangements are seen; hence, the cortex is said to be composed of three different layers or zones. Immediately beneath the capsule the parenchymal cells are grouped into little, irregular clusters (the *zona glomerulosa*) with capillaries between the clusters (Fig. 28-25). Beneath this is a thick layer (the *zona fasciculata*) in which the cells are arranged in fairly straight cords which run at right angles to the surface and have straight capillaries between them (Fig. 28-25). Between the zona fasciculata and the medulla is a relatively thin layer (the *zona reticularis*) in which the cells are disposed in cords which run in various directions and anastomose with one another (Fig. 28-25). Sinusoidal capillaries occupy the interstices between the cords. The student should keep in mind that the three zones described above usually are not sharply defined; hence, such borders as may be set between them are only approximate.

The parenchymal cells of the zona glomerulosa tend to be columnar. Their nuclei are somewhat smaller and darker than those of the next zone; likewise, their cytoplasm is of a more even texture, but it contains some lipid droplets.

The cells of the zona fasciculata are roughly polyhedral. Their nuclei are larger and less dense than those of the zona glomerulosa. Their cytoplasm, in H and E sections, appears to be extensively vacuolated, because in life it contains large numbers of lipid droplets (Fig. 28-25). Indeed, this feature of the cells of this zone is so pronounced that the cells here are sometimes termed *spongiocytes*. Cholesterol is said to be more concentrated in these cells than in any other part of the body. With appropriate technics these cells can also be shown to contain considerable quantities of ascorbic acid (vitamin C). The adrenocorticotrophic hormone (ACTH), if given in sufficient amounts, rapidly depletes these cells of much of their cholesterol and ascorbic acid. Both tests—the depletion of these cells of either ascorbic acid or cholesterol—have been used in experimental animals to assay the potency of solutions of ACTH. The cells are rich in mitochondria; the EM has shown these to differ from mitochondria in most cells in the respect that their cristae tend to be tubular villi instead of relatively flat shelves. There has been much discussion as to whether or not histochemical methods identify adrenal cortical hormones in these cells, but it is by no means agreed that this can be done at all accurately.

The cells of the zona reticularis vary in appearance. Some have small dark nuclei and acidophilic cytoplasm and appear to be degenerating. Others have lighter nuclei and cytoplasm. Some cells here contain considerable quantities of pigment (Fig. 28-25).

**Functions.** The active crystalline substances that have been recovered from cortical tissue belong to a group of substances called *steroids*. They all have a basic 4-ring structure (the cyclopentenophenanthrene nucleus). The sex hormones, to be described in the next 2 chapters, have the same nucleus. Many other compounds having potent biologic effects, as well as the hormones of the adrenal cortex and the sex hormones, are built around this nucleus. It seems extraordinary that the particular groupings that are attached to certain positions in this nucleus alter so profoundly the type of biologic effect produced by the compound.

The various steroids that have been recovered from the adrenal cortex have been found to have one of three types of effects.

1. Those of the first group are called the mineralocorticoids, and they control the sodium and potassium balance in the body. The most potent is called aldosterone. That it is one function of the adrenal cortex to control sodium and potassium balance is evidenced in Addison's disease, which condition is caused by diseased adrenals, for in this condition, or in adrenalectomized animals, sodium is lost from the body into the urine, and potassium accumulates in the blood. Some amelioration of this state of affairs, which, if prolonged, leads to death, can be accomplished by the administration of extra sodium chloride; for example, adrenalectomized rats can be kept alive for long periods of time by putting sodium chloride in their drinking water. The giving of mineralocorticoids to such animals will, of course, restore their ability to retain salt.

2. Those of the second group are called the glucocorticoids. It seems probable that the chief active one produced in the body is cortisol (hydrocortisone). Cortisol exerts a great many effects in the body. The precise way it produces these effects is not well understood. To some extent it exerts an effect similar to the hormones of the first group in that it tends to cause sodium retention and potassium excretion. But this is not nearly so pronounced or distinctive an effect as the one it exerts on protein and carbohydrate metabolism. So far as protein is concerned, hydrocortisone is a catabolic hormone which tends to stimulate the conversion of protein and protein precursors into carbohydrate. This effect can be demonstrated very easily by giving hydrocortisone (or cortisone, which probably becomes converted into hydrocortisone in the body) to suitable experimental animals because it causes increased amounts of glycogen to form in the parenchymal cells of the liver. Insulin also causes liver cells to accumulate glycogen, so it should be explained that the ways in which hydrocortisone and insulin exert this effect are quite different. Insulin acts to cause liver cells to take up glucose from the blood and to store it as glycogen; in other words, the glycogen that appears in liver cells as a result of insulin activity lowers the blood sugar level. On the other hand, hydrocortisone acts to cause the production of carbohydrate in liver cells from protein or protein precursors; hence, hydrocortisone can cause glycogen to be laid down in liver cells without taking glucose from the blood and so lowering the blood sugar level; indeed, its action in causing the formation of carbohydrate from protein provides extra sugar for the blood and tends to raise the level of sugar in it. Hence, insulin has an antidiabetogenic effect in that it tends to lower the blood sugar level, and hydrocortisone has a diabetogenic effect in that it tends to raise the blood sugar level. Normally, of course, these two effects are nicely balanced, but in the absence of either hormone the effects of the other are manifested.

The catabolic effect of hydrocortisone is manifested by its effect on lymphatic tissue also; the administration of the hormone leads to a rapid reduction in the size of the thymus gland, the spleen and other depots of lymphatic tissue, it is believed that in sufficiently large doses it actually causes a breakdown of lymphocytes. Hydrocortisone acts to bring about a reduction in the size of lymphatic organs and tissues in another way also, by causing a reduction in the rate of mitosis in these organs and tissues.

In addition to affecting lymphatic tissue, hydrocortisone affects other connective tissues as well. Its administration, while fractured bones are healing, leads to the formation of less callus tissue than usual. Hydrocortisone also inhibits the proliferation of fibroblasts in the healing of wounds in ordinary fibrous connective tissue. Given in sufficient amounts it slows the growth of the epiphysial disks of young rats. Hydrocortisone can also inhibit the production of antibodies. All of these effects could be explained at least in part by the fact that amino acids that, under ordinary conditions would be synthesized into proteins, are diverted, under conditions where there is excess hydrocortisone, into the formation of carbohydrate and thereafter metabolized to provide energy. Hence, under conditions of excessive hydrocortisone, protein synthesis is slowed because of there being a deficiency of amino acids for that purpose.

The easiest effect to observe when hydrocortisone is administered is the effect that it has in causing eosinophils to leave the blood vascular system, presumably to enter the substance of the connective tissues; so it produces an *eosinopenia*. In many species it causes lymphocytes also to leave the blood stream in a similar way.

3. The third group of steroid hormones made by the adrenal cortex are of the sex variety. Three main types can be isolated from the cortex: (1) weak androgens called 17 ketosteroids, (2) progesterone and (3) estrogens.

*Pseudohermaphroditism.* Tumors or hyperplasias sometimes occur in the adrenal cortex in women and produce much male sex hormone. Women developing tumors of this type become masculinized. Although they are fundamentally females, they gradually develop the secondary sex characteristics of the male. Even their genitalia may be profoundly affected. If severe, the condition is termed *pseudohermaphroditism*. It differs from true hermaphroditism in that the individual concerned does not possess gonadal tissue of both sexes; she has only ovaries, and such male hormone as appears in her bloodstream is derived from the adrenal gland. Many of the bearded women of circuses are examples of

women who have developed masculine traits as a result of tumors or hyperplasias of the adrenal cortex. However, the role of the adrenal cortex in sex is not simply one of manufacturing male hormone; in some instances, adrenal tumors in males are said to exert feminizing effects. Nevertheless, the production of significant amounts of male hormone by the adrenal glands of females would seem to be a more common phenomenon than the production of significant amounts of female hormone by the adrenal glands of either sex.

Other effects produced by the cortex have also been described; for example, it is necessary for lactation.

**Functions of the Three Zones of the Adrenal Cortex.** There are two possible reasons for there being three zones in the adrenal cortex.

First, it can be shown, at least in some species, that the zona glomerulosa is the germinative zone and that nearly all of the new cells that are produced in the adrenal cortex are produced in it by mitosis. Thereafter, the cells so formed are pushed into the zona fasciculata. Then, after leading a useful life in the zona fasciculata, because of the continued proliferation in the zona glomerulosa, the cells are finally pushed into the zona reticularis, where they degenerate and die. According to this theory the zona reticularis is regarded more or less as the graveyard of the cortex.

A second theory represents the three zones as specializations for the production of the three types of hormones. According to this theory the cells of the zona glomerulosa produce the mineralocorticoids, the cells of the zona fasciculata, the glucocorticoids and the cells of both the zona fasciculata and reticularis, the sex hormones.

An important reason for matters not being as clear-cut as they might be with regard to the functions of the three zones is that there are considerable differences with regard to the way the adrenals of different species react to the removal of the pituitary gland and to the administration of ACTH. However, there are certain observations which we think are worth noting.

First, it has been shown clearly in rats that the transplanted capsule of an adrenal gland

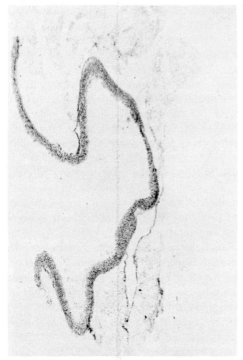

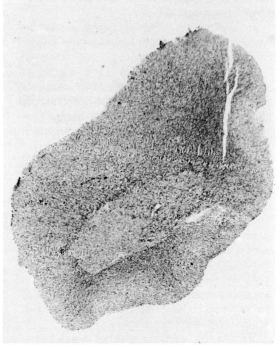

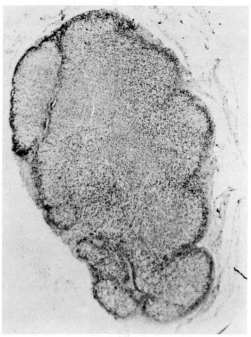

FIG. 28-26. (*Top left*) Very low-power photomicrograph of a section of the capsule and some of the zona glomerulosa of what is left of an adrenal gland of a rat after the contents of the capsule (*top right*) have been squeezed out from the gland through a hole in the capsule. (*Top right*) Very low-power photomicrograph of a section of the contents of the capsule that may be squeezed out through a hole in the capsule. On transplantation this does not regenerate. (*Bottom left*) Very low-power photomicrograph of the mass of cortical tissue that regenerates in 10 days when the tissue illustrated at the upper left is transplanted either into muscle or into subcutaneous tissue in the rat. (From experiments performed in collaboration with Dr. M. I. Armstrong)

to which some of the zona glomerulosa is still attached (Fig. 28-26) will regenerate a new cortex and also that rats with these transplants will live. Moreover, it has been shown that transplants of the gland minus its capsule and zona glomerulosa do not grow and survive (Fig. 28-26). Therefore, transplantation experiments in rats suggest that the zona glomerulosa is the regenerative zone of the adrenal cortex.

Secondly, there is evidence indicating that the zona glomerulosa of some animals, particularly rats, is not affected to any great

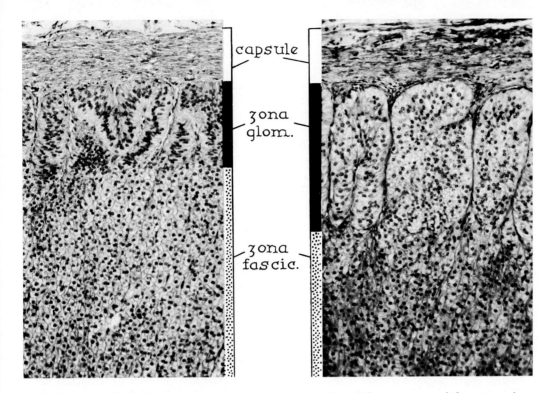

capsule

ʒona
glom.

ʒona
fascic.

FIG. 28-27. (*Left*) Low-power photomicrograph of a section of the outer part of the cortex of the adrenal gland of a normal dog. (*Right*) Photomicrograph, at the same magnification, of a similar section of the adrenal cortex of a dog that had received several daily injections of an anterior pituitary extract containing adrenocorticotrophin. Observe the great thickening of the zona glomerulosa. High-power inspection shows many mitotic figures in this zone under these conditions.

extent by ACTH, and that it makes mineralocorticoids. Hypophysectomized rats show little atrophy of the zona glomerulosa but much atrophy in the zona fasciculata. Moreover, their ability to retain salt is not seriously diminished. However, in our experience in following the day-to-day histologic changes in the adrenal glands of dogs given crude anterior pituitary extracts, we (Ham and Haist) found literally enormous numbers of mitotic figures in the zona glomerulosa (Fig. 28-27) but only occasional ones in the zona fasciculata. So, although the zona glomerulosa may be concerned chiefly with secreting mineralocorticoids, we think that it also serves as the chief regenerative zone for cells of the fasciculata that secrete glucocorticoids.

**Effects of ACTH on the Adrenal Cortex.** Trophic hormones, as has been explained, exert two fundamental effects on the glands they affect: they stimulate both secretion and growth in them. In the thyroid gland the same cells are stimulated both to grow and to secrete. However, in the adrenal cortex the effect of ACTH seems to differ with different species; in some it causes growth primarily in the zona glomerulosa but in others at the site of junction between the two zones, or even some in the zona fasciculata. However, the secretory effect of ACTH is exerted chiefly on the cells of the zona fasciculata; here the effects of a large dose of ACTH are manifested histologically by the cells becoming depleted of much of their cholesterol and ascorbic acid content. Of course, they can adapt themselves to a sustained increase in ACTH by increasing their usual rate of production of cortical hormones. We shall consider the control of the secretion of ACTH itself after we have considered the medulla of the adrenal gland.

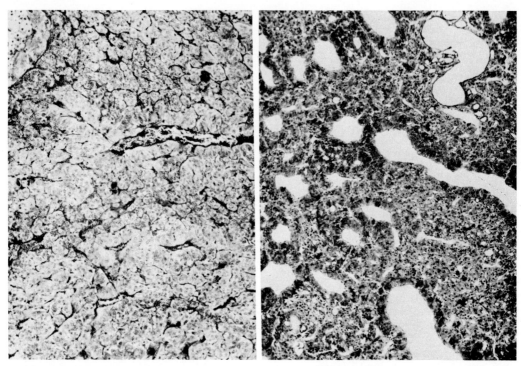

Fig. 28-28. (*Left*) A section from the medulla of an adrenal gland fixed by immersion in formol-dichromate. The blood vessels, for the most part, are collapsed, and the arrangement of cells as columnar epithelium about the veins is obscured here. The appearance of "cords" and "whorls" of medullary cells is noticeable in some places, but, for the most part, the cells seem arranged irregularly (× 77). (*Right*) A section from the medulla of a gland fixed by perfusion with formol-dichromate, with the blood vessels fixed in a state of distention. The true arrangement of cells as columnar epithelium about the veins is brought out clearly in many parts of the section. Naturally, it will not be apparent unless the vein and its surrounding cells are cut in a favorable plane. A true columnar arrangement about vessels not shown in this section is brought out in serial sections, even in areas which seem irregular between the vessels in this particular picture. Note that the cells are not arranged as columnar epithelium about the small capillaries nor about the tortuous artery seen in the upper right-hand corner (× 77). (Bennett, H. S.: Am. J. Anat. *69*:373)

## The Adrenal Medulla

**Microscopic Structure.** The cells of the medulla are of a large, ovoid, columnar type and are commonly grouped together in clumps and irregular cords that are arranged around the blood vessels in a special manner (Fig. 28-28, *right*) that will be described when the relation of their structure to their function is considered. Many of them contain fine granules that are colored brown with chrome salts (Fig. 28-29). This is called the *chromaffin reaction,* and it can be observed in the gross by exposing the freshly cut surface of the gland to a weak solution of chrome salts or chromic acid, whereupon the medulla of the gland becomes brown.

The same reaction can be observed in a test tube if the two hormones of the gland are mixed with chrome salts or chromic acid which indicates that the reaction observed in cells is caused by the presence in the cells of granules of hormone that are destined for secretion. When this reaction was first observed it was called the chromaffin reaction because it was assumed that it was due to a specific affinity of the granules in the cells for chromic acid or chrome salts. However, it was shown later that the reaction was due to the hormone-containing granules in the cytoplasm of the gland cells being oxidized by chromic acid or chrome salts and that the same reaction could be produced if other oxidizing agents were used instead of chromic acid.

The adrenal medulla was the first endocrine gland from which an extract was prepared that was active when it was injected into other animals. This was accomplished by Oliver and Schafer in 1894. It was also the first gland from which a pure crystalline hormone was prepared; this was accomplished in 1901. The hormone was named epinephrine. A proprietary name for it is Adrenalin. Only a relatively few years ago it was shown that what were believed to be pure extracts of the gland actually contain two substances: epinephrine and norepinephrine (noradrenaline). The latter substance is a precursor of epinephrine. However, the two substances have somewhat different effects.

Because the medulla of the gland is so closely associated with the cortex and because the cortex is essential to life, some time elapsed before it was established that the medulla of the adrenal is not essential to life. Indeed, as experimental work progressed it became obvious that animals deprived of their medullary tissue (provided that their cortical tissue remained intact) suffered little, if any, inconvenience.

Although there has been some controversy about the matter, it now seems to be established that the medulla does not secrete its two hormones rapidly enough to raise their concentration in the bloodstream to the point where they produce major physiologic effects under ordinary conditions but only under extraordinary conditions. We shall elaborate:

**How Secretion by the Medulla Is Affected by Emotional and Physical Stress.** As was explained when we dealt with the development of the gland, the parenchymal cells of the adrenal medulla are derived from the same group of cells as those that become the sympathetic ganglion cells of the celiac plexus. However, after migrating into the central part of the adrenal cortex, most of these young developing cells do not differentiate into ganglion cells proper; instead, they differentiate into secretory cells. Nevertheless, they occupy the same position on the two neuron sympathetic chains as do ganglion cells themselves; therefore, they are innervated by preganglionic fibers rather than by postganglionic fibers as are the other types of secretory cells in the body.

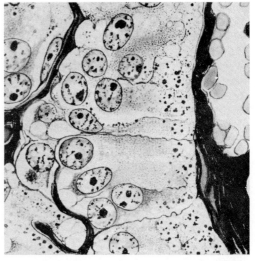

FIG. 28-29. A group of medullary cells along a vein in an adrenal gland fixed in formol-dichromate and then subjected to silver intensification before counterstaining with hematoxylin and eosin-azure. The vein is to the right and shows plasma containing a reducing substance thought to be epinephrine. The capillaries at the other pole of the cells also contain a similar reducing substance. Note that the nucleus is at the capillary pole of the cell and that the secretion droplets are most abundant at the venous pole of the cell but are also found in smaller numbers at the capillary pole and along the sides of some cells. (Bennett, H. S.: Am. J. Anat. *69*:379)

From the foregoing it is obvious that, developmentally, the secretory cells of the adrenal medulla and postganglionic neurons of the sympathetic division of the autonomic nervous system should be very much alike, and it is not surprising that they should function similarly. How they function similarly will now be explained somewhat further.

From our study of the autonomic nervous system it will be recalled that it has a sympathetic and a parasympathetic division which more or less oppose one another in their actions. It will also be recalled that the nerve endings in the autonomic nervous system stimulate or inhibit the activities of smooth muscle or gland cells by means of chemical mediators of the nervous impulse which act locally to stimulate or inhibit the muscle or gland cells with which the postganglionic fibers connect. The nerve endings of postganglionic fibers of the parasympathetic division of the autonomic nervous system are called *cholinergic* endings, and those of the sympathetic division, *andrenergic* endings. The reason for this is that the chemical mediator for the cholinergic (parasympathetic) endings is acetylcholine and the chemical mediator at the adrenergic (sympathetic) nerve endings is norepinephrine. The ordinary sweat glands are an exception, for, although they have sympathetic innervation, their chemical mediator is acetylcholine.

In view of the above it seems reasonable to assume that if there were a sudden secretion of medullary hormones into the circulation the action of the chemical mediator of the nervous impulse at sympathetic nerve endings would be reinforced with the result that the sympathetic division of the autonomic nervous system would temporarily dominate the parasympathetic division. We might now ask what would cause this to happen, and what useful purpose would be achieved by such a happening. It should next be observed that when an individual suffers a severe frustration, for example, if he is kept from obtaining something he wants very badly, or prevented from running away from a situation that he considers very dangerous, he experiences an emotional reaction (rage or fear). The development of rage or fear is generally associated with an increase of sympathetic activity over parasympathetic. The increased sympathetic activity not only results in more noradrenaline being produced at sympathetic nerve endings, but it also results in the parenchymal cells of the adrenal medulla, with their very direct sympathetic connections, being stimulated to produce their hormones more rapidly than usual. Enough enters the bloodstream to reinforce the noradrenaline effect at sympathetic nerve endings all over the body.

Therefore, a discharge of adrenal medullary hormones enhances the effect of the increased sympathetic activity that occurs in association with emotional states. Both norepinephrine and epinephrine do many things to the body that more or less supercharge it temporarily to help it to fight harder or run away faster. The body becomes geared for "fight or flight." The heart beats faster and stronger, the blood

pressure becomes increased, and the spleen contracts and adds more blood to the circulatory system. More blood is diverted to striated muscles and less to the viscera. The glycogen of the liver is converted to glucose and liberated into the bloodstream. There are effects on activities of the central nervous system. Some of these result in increased secretory activity on the part of the cells of the pars anterior of the pituitary gland. Indeed, a great many more changes occur which temporarily aid the body to greater efforts. (The effects of the two hormones differ considerably with regard to their effects on the heart rate and increasing the peripheral resistance in the circulatory system, and also in their calorigenic effects and their ability to release sugar into the blood as will be explained in detail in pharmacology and physiology courses.)

An effective secretion of epinephrine and norepinephrine by the cells of the medulla occurs not only as a result of emotional states but also reflexly as a result of the afferent stimulation involved in severe cold, pain and other stress conditions.

All medical students, but particularly those interested in the relation between mental and physical health (psychosomatic medicine), should read the various books written by Cannon. He showed conclusively the profound effects of emotional states on the function of the sympathetic nervous system and the structures innervated by it, and he formulated the "emergency" theory of medullary function. Psychologists have shown how an emotional state can be produced by a "drive" being frustrated. For example, one does not experience the emotion of fear if one can run away from a dangerous situation but only if something, for example, an ideal, prevents and so frustrates one from running away. This helps to explain how emotional states can be prolonged. Furthermore, the psychoanalysts have suggested that one may not be aware of a drive that is being frustrated or of what is frustrating a drive. It is obvious that much skill, insight, knowledge and patience may be necessary to determine why in a patient the mechanism that was designed primarily to operate only occasionally to help to overcome obvious frustrations is kept operating over prolonged periods.

Recently, it has become obvious that what

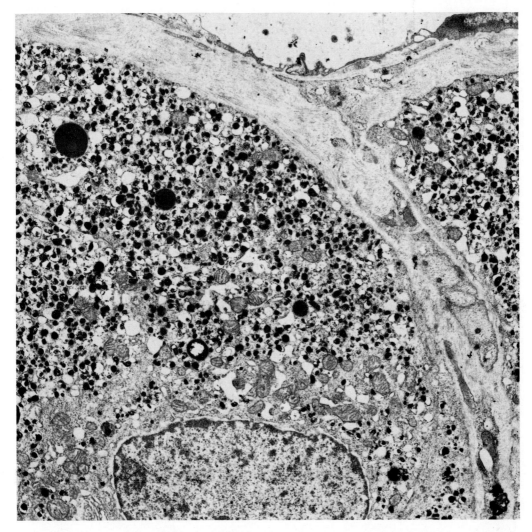

Fig. 28-30. Electron micrograph ($\times$ 9,000) of adrenal medulla of rat, showing parts of 2 cells believed to be of the kind that secrete norepinephrine which is probably represented by the numerous very dark spherical to oval granules that are loosely enclosed in membranous vesicles in the cytoplasm. Many mitochondria are also present, particularly near the nucleus which is below. (Preparation by Dr. W. R. Lockwood)

might be termed stress situations are reflected in parts of the central nervous system being stimulated in such a way as to cause humoral factors to be formed which flow via the portal circulation to the pars anterior of the pituitary gland, causing it, for example, to produce increased amounts of ACTH. One of these effects is probably mediated through the hypothalamus (which has some claim for being considered the seat of the emotions) by its making an ACTH-liberating hormone. The increased secretion of ACTH causes increased amounts of cortical hormones to appear in the body. It has been noted already that the medullary hormones exert many effects which gear the body for flight or fight. Many of these effects are of such a nature that more fuel would be required for the cellular activity involved for their performance. Extra secretion of the carbohydrate-protein-affecting cortical hormones would supply this extra fuel. But, here again, the long-continued operation of a mechanism

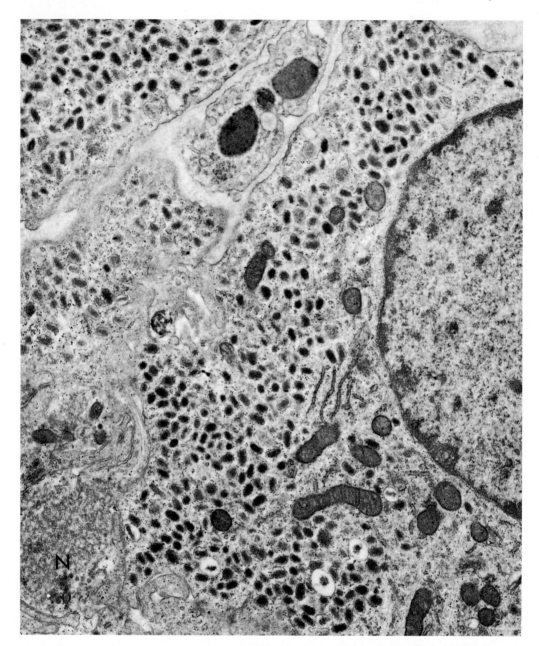

Fɪɢ. 28-31 A. Electron micrograph (× 18,000) of adrenal medulla of rat, showing cells believed to secrete epinephrine. The granules believed to be epinephrine are less dense than those believed to be norepinephrine and shown in Figure 28-30. Moreover, the epinephrine granules more completely fill the rounded vesicles in which they lie. At the lower left, and labeled N, a nerve ending can be seen.

designed to operate only temporarily for emergencies could conceivably injure certain parts of the body. Selye has given elaborate consideration to the effects of stress on the organism and the cause of what he terms "diseases of adaptation."

**Relation of Microscopic Structure to Function.** Bennett and Kilham, and Bennett have

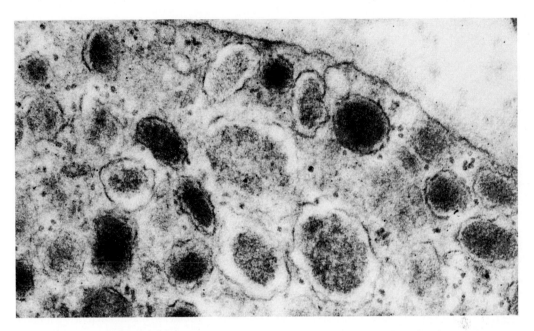

FIG. 28-31 B. A higher-power electron micrograph showing what are believed to be membrane-enclosed epinephrine granules that are about to be discharged from the cytoplasm. (Preparations by Dr. W. R. Lockwood)

shown that the appearance presented by the medulla of an adrenal gland which has not been perfused by way of the veins so as to expand them is misleading (Fig. 28-28), and that the cells of the medulla, instead of being arranged as is commonly said, in haphazard clumps and cords, are arranged in a very special way in relation to the blood vessels. There are two kinds of the latter: (1) a system of branching veins into which the blood from the cortical sinusoidal capillaries empties and (2) a system of capillaries that are supplied directly by arterioles that penetrate the cortex from the capsule. Bennett has shown that in the distended medulla of the cat the parenchymal cells resemble columnar epithelial cells (Fig. 28-28, *right*) and are arranged in whorls and cords in such a way that one end of each cell abuts on a vein, and the other on a capillary (Fig. 28-29). The nuclei of the parenchymal cells are disposed toward the ends of the cells that abut on capillaries, and the secretion granules, which he terms globules, tend to accumulate at the ends of the cells that abut on veins (Fig. 28-29). This latter fact, together with the position of the Golgi network in the cells, indicates that the cells dis-

charge epinephrine and norepinephrine into the veins rather than into the capillaries. However, the nerve fibers that stimulate the secretory functions of the cells reach their capillary ends (see N in Fig. 28-31 A).

The two hormones of the adrenal medulla, epinephrine (adrenaline) and norepinephrine (noradrenaline) are described chemically as catecholamines or as the catechol hormones, because they are amines with a catechol group in their molecular structure. Both act as reducing agents, but norepinephrine forms a darker pigment than adrenaline when sections are treated with oxidizing agents, and this has led to the finding that the pigment formed in response to oxidizing agents is darker in some cells than in others and hence to the concept that there is specialization in the adrenal medulla with some cells producing noradrenaline and some, adrenaline.

Chemically the building block of both hormones is tyrosine. This first becomes converted to dopa (dihydroxyphenylalanine), then to dopamine, and then to norepinephrine. The formation of epinephrine involves the methylation of norepinephrine.

**Fine Structure.** The most striking feature of

the medullary cells is their content of dark granules (Figs. 28-30 and 28-31). Each granule is enclosed by a smooth-surfaced membrane (Fig. 28-31) and is denser in its core than in its periphery. Granules are of an average· diameter of around 200 millimicrons. In different cells the number of granules varies somewhat; this is probably due to the fact that cells are in different stages of secretory activity. Another factor accounting for differences in the granules in different cells is that there are two types of cells, one specialized to secrete norepinephrine (Fig. 28-30) and the other specialized to secrete epinephrine (Fig. 28-31). The site of formation of the granules in the cells is complicated because the problem of the formation of these granules is different from that of the synthesis of a protein because granule formation does not involve linking amino acids together in specific sequences, but merely bringing about successive changes in an amino acid. The fact that the granules are enclosed by smooth-surfaced membranes would suggest that a packaging process at least occurs in the Golgi apparatus. Membrane-enclosed granules move to the surface of the cell where their contents are discharged. Empty membranous shells that are left behind have been seen at the cell membrane. The other features of the cytoplasm are not remarkable. The medullary cells do not have an abundance of rough-surfaced vesicles as would be expected if the cell synthesized protein for secretion. However, they do contain a moderate content of free ribosomes.

The endothelium of both the capillaries and the venules that are in contact with medullary cells is fenestrated.

**Paraganglia.** The cells of the adrenal medulla, it has been noted, are the result of a migration of developing sympathetic ganglion cells from the site of the developing ganglion to a point some distance from it. This is probably not the only example of the migration of developing sympathetic ganglion cells that occurs, for there are many little clusters of cells that probably originate in the same way to be found behind the peritoneum in various sites. The cells in these little bodies are arranged in clumps and cords and are provided with an extensive blood supply. Since these little bodies are associated with ganglia, they are said to constitute the *paraganglia* of the

body. Furthermore, since the cells in these bodies give the chromaffin reaction, the medullary tissue of the adrenal glands and the paraganglia together are often said to constitute the *chromaffin system*. However, the cells of paraganglia produce only norepinephrine.

BLOOD VESSELS, LYMPHATICS AND NERVES

Usually each suprarenal gland is supplied by 3 arteries that come from different sources. These break up into many branches as they approach the gland. Some of these supply the capillary beds of the capsule. Others penetrate directly into the medulla to supply the capillary bed of that region with arterial blood. However, the majority empty into the sinusoidal capillaries that run from the zona glomerulosa to the zona reticularis, where they empty into the venous radicles of the medulla. It is said that in the zona fasciculata most cells abut on 2 capillaries, one at each of their ends. However, in ordinary sections, the capillaries of the cortex are often collapsed and hence do not show to advantage. The capillaries of the medulla also empty into the venous radicles of the part. These unite to form a large central vein which emerges from the hilus of the gland. The central vein has numerous longitudinally disposed smooth muscle fibers in its wall. Veins also arise from the capsule. Lymphatics have been described only where substantial amounts of connective tissue are present in the gland; that is, in association with the larger veins and in the capsule.

Fibers from the parasympathetic system reach the suprarenal gland, but their function, if any, is unknown. Little is known about the functions of the sympathetic fibers that are distributed to the capsule and to the cortex. The significant innervation of the gland is that provided by the preganglionic sympathetic fibers that run directly to the parenchymal cells of the medulla. True ganglion cells are also present in the medulla (Fig. 28-25).

## THE ISLETS OF LANGERHANS

### INTRODUCTION

The general features of the islets of Langerhans of the pancreas have already been described (Chap. 24). Here we shall discuss the cytologic structure of their cells in more detail and in particular how it varies in relation to different functional states.

*Diabetes* (*diabetes* = a syphon, or running through) was the name used by the Greeks to designate diseases characterized by a great production of urine (polyuria). In the 18th century it was proved that the urine in most cases of diabetes contained sugar; hence, this kind of diabetes was called *diabetes mellitus* (*mellitus* = honeyed) to distinguish it from the other kind in which polyuria was not associated with glycosuria. It was also realized at this time that it was an ill omen for anyone to begin passing large quantities of sugar-containing urine, for, almost invariably, their health would decline steadily from then onward. Many so afflicted literally wasted away, being particularly susceptible while doing so to the development of a great variety of infections and degenerative diseases.

In 1869, Langerhans discovered the islets in the pancreas that now bear his name. However, he did not suspect that they were little organs of internal secretion. Soon afterward, Kuhne and Lea pointed out that the islets contained extensive capillary networks; this was to help later in making other investigators suspect that they had an endocrine function.

Although Cowley, an English physician, had suggested a full century before that there was some relation between diabetes and the pancreas, it was not until 1889 that this was positively established. At this time, von Mering and Minkowski removed the pancreas from each of a group of experimental animals and found subsequently that the animals upon which they had operated were passing increased amounts of urine and that it contained sugar.

Von Mering's and Minkowski's experiments could be interpreted logically as indicating that a lack of some pancreatic function is responsible for diabetes. But what function? The obvious function of the pancreas known

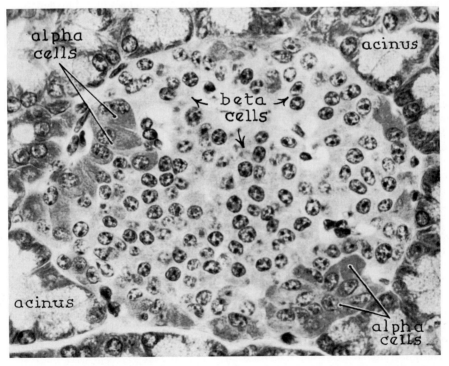

FIG. 28-32. Oil-immersion photomicrograph of an islet of Langerhans in a section of a guinea pig's pancreas stained by Gomori's method. Alpha cells, with cytoplasm that appears darker than that of the beta cells, may be seen in the periphery of the islet. Most of the interior of the islet is made up of beta cells ranged along capillaries. (Photomicrograph from W. Wilson)

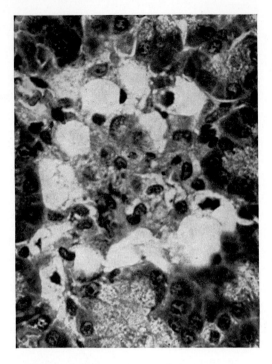

Fig. 28-33. Oil-immersion photomicrograph of an islet of Langerhans in a section of pancreas of a dog that had been given 11 daily injections of anterior pituitary extract that exerted a diabetogenic effect. The beta cells contain large droplets of fluid. This histologic picture is called hydropic degeneration and is an indication of severe overwork on the part of the beta cells. (Ham, A. W., and Haist, R. E.: Am. J. Path. *17*:812)

of that time was that of making an external secretion. Nevertheless, the concept of Claude Bernard—that certain bodily functions depend on internal secretions—had by this time made a considerable impression on the scientific world, so further work was done in an attempt to discover whether diabetes results from the pancreas failing to make a proper external or internal secretion. To determine this point, Hedon performed a very ingenious experiment. He showed that a piece of pancreas grafted back into a depancreatized animal would keep the animal free from diabetes even though the graft had no duct connections. In other words, he showed that the antidiabetic principle made by the pancreas was absorbed into the blood—it was an internal secretion.

The foregoing experiments resulted in his-tologists becoming increasingly interested in the microscopic structure of the pancreas. Laguesse, in particular, studied its development and structure in great detail. He came to the conclusion that the islets were little organs of internal secretion and suggested that they should be investigated in the pancreases of those who died from diabetes. However, he did not believe that islet cells were fundamentally different from acinous cells.

At this time, then, although it was established that diabetes was the result of the lack of an internal secretion, it was not at all clear as to whether acinous cells or islet cells made the secretion; indeed, it was not clear as to whether islet cells were fundamentally different from acinous cells. However, this matter was settled soon afterward by Ssobolew and Schultze. They tied off the pancreatic ducts of experimental animals and found that after a time the acinous tissue of the pancreas all became atrophied and that only islet tissue was left. Animals that had this operation performed on them, while they suffered from impaired digestion and certain other complaints, did not develop diabetes.

Only one thing more, it appeared, required to be established to lead to the universal acceptance of the islet theory of diabetes: proof that the islets were diseased in those who die of the disease. This was first provided by Opie. At the turn of the century he found that diabetes in most instances was associated with either a lack of islets or with degenerative changes in such islets as were present. Following the studies of Opie and others on the same matter, all but the very skeptical conceded that diabetes mellitus is due to a deficiency of normal islet cell secretion. The theoretical hormone made by the cells and deficient in diabetes was even given the name *insulin*.

**Two Kinds of Islet Cells Are Discovered.** In 1908, Lane, working under the direction of R. R. Bensley, established by means of histochemical methods, not only that the granules of islet cells had different histochemical properties from those of zymogen granules (hence, that islet cells were fundamentally different from acinous cells), but also that two kinds of islet cells could be distinguished by the different chemical properties of their granules. In short, he found that certain alcoholic fixatives dissolved the fine cytoplasmic granules from the majority of the cells of the islets but preserved the granules in a minority of the cells. Conversely, fixatives of the same type made up with water instead of alcohol preserved the granules in the majority of the cells but dissolved those from the minority. The numerous cells with the alcohol-soluble granules he termed *beta cells*, and the scarcer ones with alcohol-resistant, water-soluble granules, *alpha cells*. This led to many different staining technics being devised for coloring alpha and beta cells differently (Fig. 28-32).

Although not so common as certain other types of degenerative lesions observed in the islets of diabetics, there was one curious type of islet lesion called hydropic degeneration that was sometimes seen. It was given this name because the cytoplasm of islet cells showing this change appeared to be swollen with a watery fluid and contained little stainable substance (Fig. 28-33). (More recently it has been shown that the clear fluid in hydropic beta cells contains a considerable amount of glycogen.) Between 1912 and 1914, both Homans and Allen showed that if most of the pancreas of an animal was removed and the animal thereafter was fed carbohydrate or protein liberally: (1) hydropic degeneration occurred in the islets of the part of the pancreas that had been left intact and (2) diabetes developed. However, if the animal was given a minimal diet, the islet cells showed no disease, and the animal remained healthy. Using stains based on the findings of Lane and Bensley, both Homans and Allen each showed that hydropic degeneration occurred only in the beta cells of the islets and that this change was preceded by a degranulation of the cells concerned.

These experiments and many others performed by Allen led to the development of what is called the overwork hypothesis. Allen showed that if from four-fifths to nine-tenths of the pancreas were removed from a dog, the remaining portion had enough islets to keep the animal free from diabetes provided that the dog's diet was restricted. However, he found that if such an animal were fed additional carbohydrate or protein, the beta cells in the fragment of pancreas it possessed would become degranulated and hydropic. He assumed that the extra carbohydrate and protein fed the animals placed increased secretory demands on the beta cells and that their consequent degranulation and hydropic degeneration were to be interpreted as evidences of exhaustion through overwork. When the increased food intake was continued, he found that the islet lesions became permanent and that there was no recovery.

The experiments of Allen had, and still have, great implication with regard to the treatment of diabetes. In particular, they have great implication for those who are in danger of developing diabetes, for they show that if any individual overstrains his beta cell capacity by eating too much carbohydrate or protein (fat has a sparing effect on the beta cells), beta cells will be destroyed from overwork and this, of course, will decrease the individual's beta cell capacity and make those that remain more susceptible to overstrain than before.

Although the overwork hypothesis led to better treatment, diabetes remained a widespread and usually fatal disease. It could be expected that many investigators would make attempts to recover the islet hormone from the pancreases of animals so that substitution therapy could be employed in man. Some of these earlier attempts to extract the antidiabetic hormone gave some tantalizingly promising results, but this was as far as they went, and the world remained without substitution therapy for diabetes until the time of Banting and Best.

On the afternoon of October 30, 1920, Banting, then a young medical graduate, read in a medical journal an article about the pancreas in which the findings of Ssobolew and others who had tied off the ducts of the pancreas were described. Banting was very much impressed with the fact that the acinous tissue atrophied after duct ligation, and it is generally believed that he began to suspect that previous attempts to obtain an active extract of islet tissue had failed because the enzymes of the acinous tissue destroyed the islet hormone before it could be extracted. In any event, before going to bed that night he had decided to try making extracts from pancreases after their ducts had been tied off for 6 or 8 weeks so that they presumably would contain only islet and not acinous tissue. The events that occurred between the inception of the idea and the accomplishment of insulin, the collaboration of Best and later of Collip,

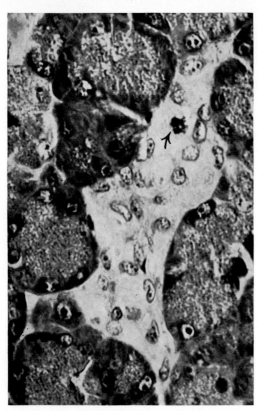

FIG. 28-34. High-power photomicrograph of an islet of Langerhans in a section of pancreas from a dog which had been given 11 daily injections of a diabetogenic anterior pituitary extract and, in addition, enough insulin to protect the beta cells from becoming hydropic from overwork. Observe the mitotic figure in a beta cell.

the inevitable succession of encouraging and discouraging results, the lack of funds and above all the dogged persistence of Banting, make an inspiring story.

At the conclusion of his **Harvey Lecture** on the islets of Langerhans in 1915, R. R. Bensley observed: "One of the most inviting fields, apart from the investigation of diabetes, is undoubtedly the investigation of the interrelation of the various internal secreting organs." Fifteen years were to elapse before the wisdom of this prediction was appreciated. In 1930, Houssay and Biasotti showed that diabetes produced in animals by removing the pancreas could be ameliorated by removing the pituitary gland as well, and that such animals, instead of steadily declining in health, as do those from which the pancreas only is

removed, would live, free from diabetes, for long periods.

Some intimation that the pars anterior of the pituitary gland can exert a diabetogenic function had, of course, been given previously by the finding that individuals with certain types of anterior lobe tumors tended to develop diabetes. Furthermore, in 1927, Johns, O'Mulvenny, Potts and Laughton had produced signs of diabetes in dogs by giving them injections of anterior pituitary extract. By 1932, several investigators had also observed this phenomenon. However, one group of investigators, Evans and his collaborators, noted something additional. Whereas all the others had noted signs of diabetes only while injections were continued, Evans and his group observed that two animals continued to have diabetes after the course of injections of anterior pituitary extract had been finished. One animal recovered after 2 months, but the second was still diabetic 4 months after the last injection. The importance of this finding was not realized until Young, in 1937, showed that a sufficiently prolonged course of injections of anterior pituitary extract would make dogs permanently diabetic. Richardson and Young made histologic studies of the islets of these dogs. In some islets they found histologic pictures similar to those observed in long-standing cases of diabetes in man; in others they found degranulation and hydropic degeneration of beta cells and in some mitotic figures. Subsequently, the author (with Haist) showed that anterior pituitary injections given daily to dogs caused a progressive degranulation of beta cells, and that this was followed by hydropic degeneration, usually between the 7th and the 11th days (Fig. 28-33). Subsequently, further studies, in collaboration with Best, Campbell and Haist, showed that if enough insulin were administered along with anterior pituitary extracts, the degranulation and hydropic degeneration of beta cells was largely prevented (Fig. 28-34). The similarity between the findings with anterior pituitary extracts and those observed by Allen after partial pancreatectomy and liberal feeding was so obvious it was realized that anterior pituitary extracts injure the beta cells by making them overwork to the point of exhaustion and death.

How crude anterior pituitary extracts accomplish this effect has been the subject of much study. It is obvious that they greatly increase the need of the organism for insulin. This effect is produced in different ways. Anterior pituitary extracts containing adrenocorticotrophic hormone of the anterior pituitary stimulate the adrenal cortex to make more of the cortical hormone that furthers the conversion of protein and protein precursors to sugar in the body. Long and Lukens and their collaborators have shown clearly the effectiveness of the diabetogenic effect of this cortical hormone. In addition, anterior pituitary extracts stimulate the thyroid gland; this also increases the need of the animal for insulin. Furthermore, there is evidence that the anterior pituitary extracts act in some manner to render insulin relatively ineffective.

It is questionable if anterior pituitary extracts contain a pancreatrophic hormone. Certainly, in addition to all the other effects they produce, anterior pituitary extracts stimulate cell division in the acini, the small ducts and the islets (Fig. 28-34) in the pancreas. It seems most probable that the chief diabetogenic factor made by the anterior pituitary gland is the growth hormone. An argument against there being a pancreatrophic hormone is the fact that islets do not atrophy if the pituitary gland is removed. Yet one gets the impression that anterior pituitary extracts contain something that stimulates beta cells in some direct way so that they become exhausted more easily under pituitary stimulation than they would in the absence of anterior pituitary stimulation. The matter is too complex to discuss further here.

The foregoing indicates that many diabetogenic influences are normally at work in the body and that they do not produce diabetes because they are opposed successfully by adequate amounts of the antidiabetogenic hormone, insulin, made by the beta cells of the islets. Diabetes develops when the diabetogenic influences are greater than the beta cell potential of the pancreas. In other words, diabetes depends on something positive as well as on something negative. It may now be of interest to comment briefly on the action of the beta cell hormone.

## The Action of Insulin

In a normal individual on a normal diet the amount of sugar in the blood remains at a fairly constant level, varying between 0.08 and 0.11 per cent. Since it is dissolved in the blood plasma, sugar, in this concentration, is present in the glomerular filtrate. However, at this concentration, all the sugar in the filtrate can be resorbed as the filtrate passes along the remainder of the nephron. Hence, in a normal individual on a normal diet sugar does not appear in the urine. However, in an untreated diabetic the blood sugar rises above the normal level (*hyperglycemia*) to the point where the increased amounts in the glomerular filtrate cannot all be resorbed as it courses along the remainder of the nephron; hence, sugar appears in the urine (*glycosuria*). The point at which the kidney cannot resorb all the sugar filtered through its glomeruli is said to be its *threshold* for sugar.

The most obvious action of insulin is that it reduces the blood sugar level. It will do this if it is injected either into a diabetic with hyperglycemia or into a normal person. A sufficiently large dose of insulin will reduce the blood sugar level to the point where convulsions and unconsciousness occur. This is called insulin shock. Enough insulin can lower the blood sugar level to the point where death ensues. A certain amount of sugar is required in the blood if life is to be supported. Occasionally islet-cell tumors occur; these may cause hyperinsulinism and hypoglycemia.

Insulin acts to lower the blood sugar level by acting at several sites. In a normal individual the sugar absorbed from a hearty meal would raise the blood sugar level substantially were it not for the fact that some of the sugar taken into the blood is stored as glycogen in the parenchymal cells of the liver and in muscle cells. Insulin facilitates this storage phenomenon. Excess sugar that has been absorbed may also be removed from the blood by being converted into fat and stored in the fat depots. Insulin facilitates this change also. Then, insulin, in addition, facilitates the metabolism of carbohydrate in muscle cells. In this way, it tends to reduce the level of sugar in the blood by speeding up the utilization of carbohydrate. Finally, as has been noted before, insulin opposes the catabolic and antianabolic effects of adrenal cortical hormone.

In view of the foregoing, it is easy to realize that the blood sugar level of an untreated diabetic on an unrestricted diet would exceed the kidney threshold because (1) sugar would not be removed from the blood and stored properly, (2) it would not be metabolized so quickly and (3) extra amounts would be delivered into the blood by virtue of the conversion of protein or protein precursors to sugar by the parenchymal cells of the liver.

**Cell Characteristics.** Under normal conditions, only about 1 to 2 days' supply of insulin is stored in the cytoplasm of the beta cells of the pancreas. However, this is an amount sufficient, or almost sufficient, to cause death if it were all discharged into the bloodstream at once. Indeed, a phenomenon much like this actually occurs if an animal is given suitable amounts of alloxan. This chemical exerts a very specific and rapid lethal effect on the beta cells of the islets (Fig. 6-38, *right*). As soon as they are destroyed, their content of stored insulin is almost immediately washed into the bloodstream, and unless sugar is given the animals at this time they may die of hypoglycemia. If the animal survives this preliminary hypoglycemia, it goes on, of course, to develop hyperglycemia.

The fine cytoplasmic granules which are either insulin itself or the immediate precursors of insulin may be demonstrated in fresh pancreas by the supravital methods devised by Bensley for enumerating the islets (Fig. 25-4). In our experience these granules do not appear to advantage in sections stained by many of the special stains that are used to distinguish alpha from beta cells. But we think that the very fine blue granules that are revealed in beta cells by means of Bowie's neutral ethyl violet-Biebrich scarlet stain are representative of the insulin content of the cell. With Haist, we have observed that the number of beta granules revealed by this method become reduced if animals are starved, given insulin or fed a high proportion of fat. It is obvious that the reduction in the number of granules under these circumstances is not the result of degranulation from overwork but, instead, to a lack of synthesis due to a lack of work stimulus. Therefore, a reduction in the granule content of beta cells can be caused either by overwork or underwork.

The cytoplasmic granules of alpha cells are larger than those of beta cells. A course of injections of a diabetogenic extract of the anterior pituitary gland, which will cause degranulation of the beta cells, does not commonly cause degranulation of the alpha cells.

In some species, for example, in the rat, the alpha cells tend to have a peripheral distribution in islets. In other species, including man and the dog, the alpha cells are scattered throughout the islets but generally show some tendency to form little groups in the more central parts of islets.

The reticular fibers of normal islets are so delicate and sparse that they are scarcely demonstrable. Reticulum that is easily demonstrated is suggestive of pathologic change.

By means of special staining technics, cells which have been termed delta cells and C cells have been demonstrated in the islets of animals of some species. These cells are not numerous, and their functions are unknown.

The nuclei of alpha and beta cells are different in some species, for example, in the guinea pig, but not in most species. Hence, alpha and beta cells cannot generally be distinguished in sections by the morphology of their nuclei.

The mitochondria of islet cells are fine in contrast with the coarser ones of acinar cells. Islet cells have Golgi nets in their cytoplasm; these are present between the nuclei of the cells and the surfaces of the cells through which secretion takes place. Well-defined negative Golgi images can be seen with the light microscope in cells that are actively secreting.

**Control of Insulin Secretion.** There is much evidence to show that insulin secretion tends to vary in relation to the blood-sugar level and that the blood-sugar level controls insulin secretion.

**Alpha Cells and Their Possible Functions.** It is difficult to know how alpha cells are related to beta cells. They both arise from the same stem cell in fetal development. In some animals (rats) beta cells develop first, but in others (rabbits) alpha cells develop first. Alpha cells appear to be unaffected when diabetes is produced either by partial pancreatectomy, anterior pituitary extracts or alloxan. Islets composed only of alpha cells may be encountered in the pancreases of diabetics.

There is reason to believe that the insulin requirement of an animal in which the beta cells have been destroyed is greater than that of an animal from which the entire pancreas has been removed. A possible explanation for this is that the pancreas makes some hormone that has an action opposite to that of insulin and raises the blood-sugar level; indeed, a ma-

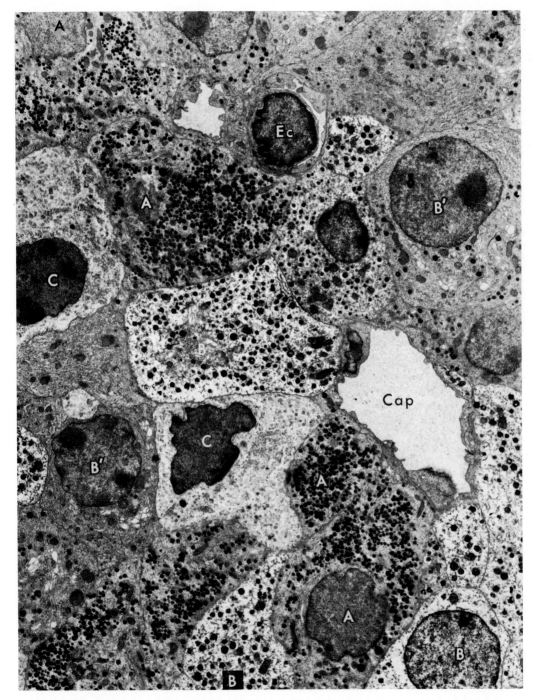

FIG. 28-35. Electron micrograph (× 3,000) of an islet of Langerhans in a guinea pig, showing alpha cells containing alpha granules (A), beta cells filled with granules (B), beta cells in the stage of synthesizing insulin (B′), a chromophobe (C), a capillary (Cap), and another capillary in which the nucleus of an endothelial cell is present in the section (Ec). (Preparation from L. Herman)

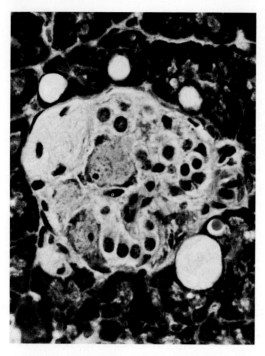

FIG. 28-36. High-power photomicrograph of a section of a rat's pancreas, showing a neuro-insular complex. Note the large ganglion cells in association with islet cells. (Dr. W. S. Hartroft)

terial called *glucagon*, which raises blood sugar levels, has been found in certain pancreatic extracts. Much evidence has been obtained which indicates that the alpha cells produce glucagon; for example, Bencosme has shown that it is not present in extracts of pancreas that have no alpha cells. Glucagon has many effects similar to hydrocortisone in that if it is administered to an animal in sufficient quantities it tends to raise the blood sugar and inhibit protein synthesis. However, its physiologic role in the normal individual is not yet clear.

**Fine Structure of Granules of Alpha and Beta Cells.** The granules of alpha cells are similar in different species, being round, dense and homogeneous, and filling the membranous vesicles in which they lie (Fig. 28-35, *bottom*).

The granules of the beta cells differ in different species.

In the rat and the mouse they are round and homogeneous and enclosed in smooth-surfaced membranous vesicles. However, they can be distinguished from alpha granules because they, in contrast with alpha granules, do not, generally, completely fill the membranous vesicles in which they lie; hence, a space can be seen between the edges of beta granules and the membranous vesicles that contain them.

In the dog, beta granules often appear as rectangular crystalloid structures. The plate-like granules do not fill the rounded membranous vesicles which contain them; hence, a comparatively large space can be seen between the long surfaces of the granules and the rounded vesicles in which they lie. In the cat also the beta granules have a crystalloid appearance; but in this species the central part of each granule contains a dense rhomboidal or prismatic structure.

In the guinea pig the beta granules have a rounded shape (Fig. 28-35).

In man the beta granules vary from being round to crystalloid in appearance. Here, again, the beta granules, whatever their shape, tend to be withdrawn from the membranous vesicles in which they are contained.

Insulin is a protein which is secreted by the beta cells that produce it. It might therefore be expected that the cells that synthesize and secrete it would have well-developed rough-surfaced vesicles of endoplasmic reticulum and a well-developed Golgi apparatus. However, rough-surfaced vesicles do not appear to advantage in the cytoplasm of beta cells that are well filled with granules. On the other hand, it is easy to find some cells in islets that have cytoplasm that has a great content of rough-surfaced vesicles and few granules (Fig. 28-35, B[1]). Herman, Sato and Fitzgerald suggest that beta cells pass through two stages, one in which there is much rough-surfaced endoplasmic reticulum and during which insulin is being synthesized and then a second stage in which their energies are devoted, not to synthesis, but to processes concerned in the delivery of their secretion into the bloodstream, and to the author this explanation seems to explain what is seen. Since beta cell granules are packaged in smooth-surfaced vesicles, it seems most probable that they, like so many types of secretory granules, are packaged in the Golgi apparatus in secretory vesicles which become detached from flattened vesicles and move toward the surface of the cell that abuts on a capillary.

**Other Cell Types in Islets.** Further cell types have been described in islets. One type in particular is sometimes called a chromophobe (Fig. 28-35, C) because it lacks the distinguishing granule content that permits alpha and beta cells to be distinguished by staining reactions. Its function is not known.

**Problem of Beta Cell Regeneration.** In the light of Allen's overwork experiments, it was anticipated, when insulin was discovered, that the administration of the hormone would lessen the strain on a diabetic's beta cells and so allow them to recover their health and functional capacity. This hope was realized, and there are countless examples of the insulin requirements of diabetics having become reduced as their own beta cells recovered and functioned more normally. But, although there is much evidence to indicate that tired beta cells are often restored, there is not much to indicate that new beta cells are regenerated in any number in the pancreas of the treated diabetic. Hence, most diabetics will remain diabetics until someone discovers some way to make their beta cells regenerate. In this sense, the cause of persisting diabetes is the inability of the beta cells of the pancreas to regenerate. How to induce beta cells to regenerate, or how to induce the ductules of the pancreas to produce beta cells, is a challenging problem for the research worker.

**Nervous Control of Islet Cells.** The extent to which insulin secretion is affected by the autonomic nervous system, and hence by severe emotional states, has not been worked out as satisfactorily as might be wished, but there is some indication that parasympathetic fibers, traveling by way of the right vagus nerve, stimulate insulin secretion. Furthermore, it has been shown that there are intimate associations between islet cells and ganglion cells in the pancreas. These little aggregates are termed *neuro-insular complexes* (Fig. 28-36). They have been studied most intensively in recent years by Simard, whose papers should be consulted for further details of their microscopic structure and for a discussion of their significance.

## THE PINEAL BODY

The pineal body, also called the epiphysis, is a little cone-shaped body about 1 cm. in length. Although it originates from, and remains connected to, the posterior end of the roof of the third ventricle, it projects backward so that it lies dorsal to the midbrain.

Its development begins early in embryonic life. At this time the roof of the diencephalon, behind the site of origin of the choroid plexus of the third ventricle, bulges dorsally as a diverticulum. As development proceeds, the walls of the diverticulum thicken so that the lumen of the outgrowth is gradually obliterated. In postnatal life a lumen is to be seen only at the base of the pineal body, where it is called the pineal recess of the third ventricle.

The outgrowth of the roof of the diencephalon that gives rise to the pineal body contains two types of cells. First, the roof itself contains neuro-ectodermal cells; secondly, the pia mater, which covers the outgrowth, contains mesenchymal cells. Both types of cell participate in the formation of the pineal body. The neuro-ectodermal cells give rise to the parenchymal cells of the body and also to neuroglial cells. The mesenchymal cells give rise to the connective tissue of the capsule of the body and to the incomplete partitions of connective tissue that more or less divide the body up into lobules.

On viewing a section of the pineal body, lobules of parenchymal cells may be seen to be incompletely separated from one another by septa of connective tissue that extend into the body from the capsule and carry blood vessels into the substance of the gland (Fig. 28-37). Delicate support for the parenchymal cells within lobules is provided by neuroglial tissue. The parenchymal cells (Fig. 28-37) are probably of several types. They are not nerve cells. By special staining methods, del Rio-Hortega has shown that they have complicated arrangements of processes.

The pineal body of mammals is the vestige of the median eye which was probably a functioning organ in certain amphibia and reptiles that are now extinct. Like other vestigial organs in man, it tends to reach its greatest development relatively early in life and thereafter to degenerate. One evidence of the latter process is the formation of calcified bodies of a laminated appearance in the organ. These constitute what is called brain sand (Fig. 28-37).

The function of the pineal body has been

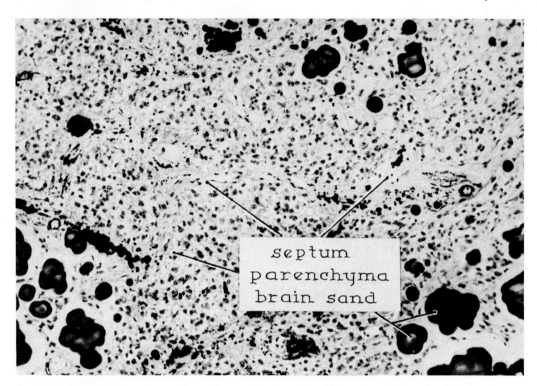

septum
parenchyma
brain sand

Fig. 28-37. Medium-power photomicrograph of an H and E section of the pineal body of an adult, showing parenchyma, septa and brain sand.

studied by the same means that have been employed for the study of endocrine glands. The effects of the removal of the pineal body from young animals have been investigated, as have the effects of grafting a series of pineal transplants into animals. Various types of extracts made from pineal bodies have been fed or injected into animals. The effects of pineal tumors on men and women have been noted. The net result of all this study is difficult to assess. The experimental results are conflicting. Nevertheless, there is some evidence to suggest that there is some association between the sexual development of the male and the pineal body. However, the nature and significance of this association is still obscure.

Giving pineal extracts to invertebrates affects their ability to react by color changes to light. It might therefore be questioned if some product of the pineal gland in vertebrates has an effect on melanocytes. In this connection a substance called *melatonin* has been extracted from ox pineal glands and has been shown to cause the opposite of the dispersion of pigment in melanocytes that is effected by

MSH in frogs in that the pineal extract causes the pigment of melanocytes to congregate around their nuclei. However, there are other substances (for example the catechol hormones) that act similarly but not so profoundly, and hence it is difficult to know if these findings are in any way indicative of any normal function of the pineal gland in this respect in mammals.

## REFERENCES

SOME GENERAL REFERENCES ON ENDOCRINE GLANDS

Pincus, G. (ed.): Recent Progress in Hormone Research, New York, Acad. Press (continuing series).
Pincus, G., and Thimann, K. V. (eds.): The Hormones, vols. 1-5, New York, Acad. Press, 1948, 1950, 1955.
(*See also* textbooks on endocrinology.)

THE PITUITARY GLAND AS A WHOLE: ITS DEVELOPMENT AND BLOOD SUPPLY

Atwell, W. J.: The development of the hypophysis cerebri in man, with special reference to the pars tuberalis, Am. J. Anat. *37*:159, 1926.

Bailey, P.: The structure of the hypophysis cerebri of man and the common laboratory mammals *in* Cowdry's Special Cytology, ed. 2, p. 771, New York, Hoeber, 1932.

Ezrin, C.: The pituitary gland, Ciba Clinic. Symp. *15*:71, 1963.

Green, J. D.: The comparative anatomy of the hypophysis, with special reference to its blood supply and innervation, Am. J. Anat. *88*:225, 1951.

————: The histology of the hypophyseal stalk and medium eminence in man, with special reference to blood vessels, nerve fibers and a peculiar neurovascular zone in this region, Anat. Rec. *100*:273, 1948.

Green, J. D., and Harris, G. W.: Observation of the hypophysio-portal vessels of the living rat, J. Physiol. *108*:359, 1949.

Harris, G. W.: The hypothalamus and regulation of ACTH secretion *in* Ralli, E. P. (ed.): Proc. Third Conf. on the Adrenal Cortex, p. 54, New York, Macy, 1952.

————: Neural control of pituitary gland, I and II, Brit. M. J. *2*:559, 627, 1951.

Popa, G. T., and Fielding, U.: A portal circulation from the pituitary to the hypothalamic region, J. Anat. *65*:88, 1930.

Shanklin, W. M.: Lymphocytes and lymphoid tissue in the human pituitary, Anat. Rec. *111*:177, 1951.

Van Dyke, H. B.: Physiology and Pharmacology of the Pituitary Body, 2 vols., Chicago, Univ. Chicago Press, 1936.

Wislocki, G. B.: The meningeal relations of the hypophysis cerebri: II. An embryological study of the meninges and blood vessels of the human hypophysis, Am. J. Anat. *61*:95, 1937.

————: The vascular supply of the hypophysis cerebri of the cat. Anat. Rec. *69*:361, 1937.

————: The vascular supply of the hypophysis cerebri of the rhesus monkey and man, Proc. A. Res. Nerv. Ment. Dis. *17*:48, 1938.

## THE ANTERIOR PITUITARY GLAND

Benoit, Jacques, and Da Lage, Christian (eds.): Cytologie de l'Adenophypophyse, Colloques Internationaux du Centre National de la Recherche Scientifique, Paris, 1963.

Briseno-Castrejon, B., and Finerty, J. C.: An azocarmine stain for differential cell analysis of the rat anterior hypophysis, Stain Technol. *24*:103, 1949.

Catchpole, H. R.: Distribution of glycoprotein hormones in anterior pituitary gland of rat, J. Endocrinol. *6*:218, 1949.

Ezrin, C., and Murray, S.: The cells of the human adenohypophysis in pregnancy, thyroid disease and adrenal cortical disorders, Colloques Internationaux du Centre National de la Recherche Scientifique, vol. 15, 1963.

Halmi, M. S.: The effects of graded doses of thyroxine on the anterior pituitary of hypothyroid male albino rats, Anat. Rec. *112*:17, 1952.

————: Two types of basocells in the rat pituitary, thyrotrophs and gonadotrophs vs. beta and delta cells, Endocrinology *50*:140, 1952.

————: Two types of basophiles in anterior pituitary of rat and their respective cytophysiological significance, Endocrinology *47*:289, 1950.

Koneff, A. A.: Adaptation of the Mallory-azan staining method to the anterior pituitary of the rat, Stain Technol. *13*:49, 1938.

Ladman, A. J.: Mitotic activity in the anterior pituitary of the pregnant mouse, Anat. Rec. *120*:395, 1954.

Pasteels, J. L.: Recherches morphologiques et expérimentales sur la sécrétion de prolactine, Arch. biol. *74*:439, 1963.

Pearse, A. G. E.: The cytochemistry and cytology of the normal anterior hypophysis investigated by the trichrome-periodic acid—Schiff method, J. Path. Bact. *64*:811, 1952.

————: Histochemistry, Theoretical and Applied, London, Churchill, 1953.

————: Observations on the localisation, nature and chemical constitution of some components of the anterior hypophysis, J. Path. Bact. *64*:791, 1952.

Purves, H. D., and Griesbach, W. E.: The significance of the Gomori staining of the basophiles of the rat pituitary, Endocrinology *49*:652, 1951.

————: The site of thyrotrophin and gonadotrophin production in the rat pituitary studied by McManus-Hotchkiss staining of glycoprotein, Endocrinology *49*:244, 1951.

————: Specific staining of the thyrotrophic cell of the rat pituitary by the Gomori stains, Endocrinology *49*:427, 1951.

————: Morphology of the hypophysis related to its function *in* Young, W. C. (ed.): Sex and Internal Secretions, vol. 1, p. 161, Baltimore, Williams & Wilkins, 1961.

Rasmussen, A. T.: Changes in the proportion of cell types in the anterior lobe of the human hypophysis during the first 19 years of life, Am. J. Anat. *86*:75, 1950.

Rinehart, J. F., and Farquhar, M. G.: The fine vascular organization of the anterior pituitary gland, Anat. Rec. *121*:207, 1955.

Ritter, H. B., and Oleson, J. J.: Combined histochemical staining of acid polysaccharides and 1, 2 glycol groupings in paraffin sections of rat tissues, Am. J. Path. *26*:639, 1950.

Saffran, M., Schally, A. V., and Benfey, B. G.:

Stimulation of the release of corticotropin from the adenohypophysis by a neurohypophyseal factor, Endocrinology, *57*:439, 1955.

Selye, H.: Stress, Montreal, Acta, Inc., 1950.

————: Stress and general adaptation syndrome, Brit. M. J. *1*:1383, 1950.

Severinghaus, A. E.: Cellular changes in the anterior hypophysis with special reference to its secretory activities, Physiol. Rev. *17*:556, 1937.

Siperstein, E., Nichols, C. W., Jr., Griesbach, W. E., and Chaikoff, I. L.: Cytological changes in the rat anterior pituitary from birth to maturity, Anat. Rec. *118*:593, 1954.

Spagnoli, H. H., and Charipper, H. A.: The effects of aging on the histology and cytology of the pituitary gland of the golden hamster (Cricetus auratus), with brief reference to simultaneous changes in the thyroid and testis, Anat. Rec. *121*:117, 1955.

Van Dyke, H. B., *et al.*: Protein hormones of the pituitary body, Ann. N. Y. Acad. Sci. *43*(6): 253-426, 1943.

White, A.: Preparation and chemistry of anterior pituitary hormones, Physiol. Rev. *26*:575, 1946.

Wilson, W. D., and Ezrin, C.: Three types of chromophil cells of the adenohypophysis, Am. J. Path. *30*:891, 1954.

Wolfe, J. M., and Cleveland, R.: Cyclic histological variations in the anterior hypophysis of the albino rat, Anat. Rec. *55*:233, 1933.

Wolstenholme, G. E. W. (ed.): Ciba Foundation Colloquia on Endocrinology, Anterior Pituitary Secretion, London, Churchill, 1952. (See papers by J. R. Brobeck, J. W. Everett, C. Fortier, J. DeGroot and G. W. Harris, G. W. Harris, G. W. Harris and D. Jacobsohn, D. M. Hume, and V. N. E. Long.)

GENERAL REFERENCE ON THE PARS INTERMEDIA AND CONSIDERATIONS RELATING TO THE MELANOCYTE-STIMULATING HORMONE AND COLOR CHANGES IN VERTEBRATES

Barrington, E. J. W.: An Introduction to General and Comparative Endocrinology, Chap. 11, Oxford, Clarendon Press, 1963.

THE POSTERIOR LOBE OF THE PITUITARY GLAND AND NEUROSECRETION

Bargmann, W., and Scharrer, E.: The site of origin of the hormones of the posterior pituitary, Am. Scientist *39*:255, 1951.

Bodian, D.: Nerve endings, neurosecretory substance and lobular organization of the neurohypophysis, Bull. Johns Hopkins Hosp. *33*:354, 1951.

Duncan, D.: An electron microscope study of the neurohypophysis of a bird, Gallus domesticus, Anat. Rec. *125*:457, 1956.

du Vigneaud, V., Ressler, C., Swan, J. M., Roberts, C. W., Katsoyannis, P. G., and Gordon, S.: The synthesis of an octapeptide amide with the hormonal activity of oxytocin, J. Am. Chem. Soc. *75*:4879, 1953.

Green, J. D., and van Breemen, V. L.: Electron microscopy of the pituitary and observations on neurosecretion, Am. J. Anat. *97*:177, 1955.

Palay, S. L.: An electron microscope study of the neurohypophysis in normal, hydrated and dehydrated rats, Anat. Rec. *121*:348, 1955.

————: Neurosecretory phenomena in the hypothalamo-hypophyseal system of man and monkey, Am. J. Anat. *93*:107, 1953.

Rennels, E. G., and Drager, G. A.: The relationship of pituicytes to neurosecretion, Anat. Rec. *122*:193, 1955.

Scharrer, E., and Scharrer, B.: In Handbuch der mikroskopischen Anatomie des Menschen, vol. 6, p. 953, Berlin, Springer, 1954.

————: Neurosecretion, Physiol. Rev. *25*:171, 1945.

————: Neurosecretion, Recent Prog. Hormone Res. *10*:183, 1954.

Scharrer, E. A., and Wittenstein, G. J.: The effect of the interruption of the hypothalamo-hypophyseal neurosecretory pathway in the dog, Anat. Rec. *112*:387, 1952.

THE THYROID GLAND

Axelrad, A. A., Leblond, C. P., and Isler, H.: Role of iodine deficiency in the production of goiter by the Remington diet, Endocrinology *56*:387, 1955.

Barker, S. B.: Thyroid, Ann. Rev. Physiol. *17*: 417, 1955.

————: The Thyroid, Brookhaven National Laboratory, Upton, N. J., Associated Universities Inc., 1955.

Bélanger, L. F., and Leblond, C. P.: A method for locating radioactive elements in tissues by covering histological sections with a photographic emulsion, Endocrinology *39*:8, 1946.

DeGroot, L. J.: Current views on formation of thyroid hormones, New Eng. J. Med. *272*:243; *272*:297; *272*:355, 1965.

Dempsey, E. W.: The chemical cytology of the thyroid gland, Ann. N. Y. Acad. Sci. *50*:336, 1949.

De Robertis, E.: Cytological and cytochemical bases of thyroid function, Ann. N. Y. Acad. Sci. *50*:317, 1949.

————: Proteolytic enzyme activity of colloid extracted from single follicles of the rat thyroid, Anat. Rec. *80*:219, 1941.

De Robertis, E., and Nowinski, W. W.: **Mecha-**

nism of therapeutic effect of iodine on thyroid gland, Science *103*:421, 1946.

Dziemian, A. J.: Proteolytic activity of the thyroid gland, J. Cell. Comp. Physiol. *21*:339, 1943.

Follis, R. H., Jr.: Experimental colloid goiter in the hamster, Proc. Soc. Exp. Biol. Med. *100*: 203, 1959.

Gersh, I., and Caspersson, T.: Total protein and organic iodine in the colloid and cells of single follicles of the thyroid gland, Anat. Rec. *78*: 303, 1940.

Gorbman, A.: Some aspects of the comparative biochemistry of iodine utilization and the evolution of thyroidal function, Physiol. Rev. *35*: 336, 1955.

Gross, J.: Thyroid hormones, Brit. M. Bull. *10*: 218, 1954.

Gross, J., and Leblond, C. P.: The presence of free iodinated compounds in the thyroid and their passage into the circulation, Endocrinology *48*:714, 1951.

Gross, J., and Pitt-Rivers, R.: Experimental study of thyroid metabolism with radioactive iodine, Brit. M. Bull. *8*:136, 1952.

————: Tri-iodothyronine in relation to thyroid physiology, Recent Prog. Hormone Res. *10*: 109, 1954.

Harington, C. R.: The Thyroid Gland; Its Chemistry and Physiology, London, Oxford Univ. Press, 1933.

Leblond, C. P., and Eartly, H.: An attempt to produce complete thyroid deficiency in the rat, Endocrinology *55*:26, 1952.

Leblond, C. P., Fertman, M. B., Puppel, I. D., and Curtis, G. M.: Radio-iodine autography in studies of human goitrous thyroid glands, Arch. Path. *41*:510, 1946.

Leblond, C. P., and Gross, J.: Thyroglobulin formation in the thyroid follicle visualized by the "coated autograph" technique, Endocrinology *43*:306, 1948.

Levitt, T.: The Thyroid: A Physiological, Pathological, Clinical and Surgical Study, Edinburgh, Livingstone, 1954.

Marine, D., *et al.*: The relation of iodine to the structure of the thyroid gland, Ann. Int. Med. *1*:349, 1908.

Means, J. H., *et al.*: Thyroid function as disclosed by newer methods of study, Ann. N. Y. Acad. Sci., vol. 50, 1949.

Michel, R.: Thyroid, Ann. Rev. Physiol. *18*:457, 1956.

Nadler, N. J., and Leblond, C. P.: The site and rate of formation of thyroid hormones, Brookhaven Sympos. Biol. No. 7, p. 40, 1955.

Nadler, N. J., Sarkar, S. K., and Leblond, C. P.: The origin of intracellular colloid droplets in the rat thyroid, Endocrinology *71*:120, 1962.

Nadler, N. J., Young, B. A., Leblond, C. P., and Mitmaker, B.: Elaboration of thyroglobulin in the thyroid follicle, Endocrinology *74*:333, 1964.

Pitt-Rivers, R., and Tata, J. R.: The Thyroid Hormones, 2 vols., International Series of Monographs on Pure and Applied Biology, London, Pergamon Press, 1959.

Rawson, R. W., Rall, J. E., and Sonenberg, M.: The chemistry and physiology of the thyroid *in* Pincus, G., and Thimann, K. V. (eds.): The Hormones, ed. 3, p. 433, New York, Acad. Press, 1955.

Roche, J., and Michel, R.: Nature, biosynthesis and metabolism of thyroid hormones, Physiol. Rev. *35*:583, 1955.

————: Thyroid hormones and iodine metabolism, Ann. Rev. Biochem. *23*:481, 1954.

Roche, J., Michel, R., Tissitzsky, S., and Michel, Mme. Odette: Sur la formation d'iodures a partir de la diiodotyrosine dans le corps thyroide et sur leur reutilisation, C. R. Acad. Sc. *232*:2148, 1951.

Sugiyama, S.: Studies of the histogenesis of the thyroid gland of the guinea pig: I. The thyroid cells (follicle cells and parafollicular cells), Anat. Rec. *120*:363, 1954.

Sugiyama, S., and Sato, T.: Studies of the histogenesis of the thyroid gland of the guinea pig: II. Quantitative measurements of the follicles and correlation with function, Anat. Rec. *120*: 379, 1954.

Young, B. A., and Leblond, C. P.: The light cell as compared to the follicular cell in the thyroid gland of the rat, Endocrinology *73*:669, 1963.

## THE PARATHYROID GLANDS

Albright, F., and Reifenstein, E. C.: The Parathyroid Glands and Metabolic Bone Disease, Baltimore, Williams & Wilkins, 1948.

Barnicot, N. A.: The local action of the parathyroid and other tissues on bone in intracerebral grafts, J. Anat. *82*:233, 1948.

Bartter, F. C.: The parathyroids, Ann. Rev. Physiol. *16*:429, 1954.

Bensley, S. H.: The normal mode of secretion in the parathyroid gland of the dog, Anat. Rec. *98*:361, 1947.

Bhaskar, S. N., Schour, I., Greep, R. O., and Weinmann, J. P.: The corrective effect of parathyroid hormone on genetic anomalies in the dentition and the tibia of the *ia* rat, J. Dent. Res. *31*:257, 1952.

Bhaskar, S. N., Weinmann, J. P., Schour, I., and Greep, R. O.: The growth pattern of the tibia in normal and *ia* rats, Am. J. Anat. *86*:439, 1950.

Burroughs, R. B.: Variations produced in bones of growing rats by parathyroid extracts, Am. J. Anat. *62*:237, 1937-38.

Castleman, B., and Mallory, T. B.: The pathology of the parathyroid gland in hyperparathyroidism, Am. J. Path. *11*:1, 1935.

Chang, H.: Grafts of parathyroid and other tissues to bone, Anat. Rec. *111*:23, 1951.

De Robertis, E.: The cytology of the parathyroid gland of rats injected with parathyroid extract, Anat. Rec. *78*:473, 1940.

————: The cytology of the parathyroid and thyroid glands of rats with experimental rickets, Anat. Rec. *79*:417, 1941.

Drake, T. G., Albright, F., and Castleman, B.: Parathyroid hyperplasia in rabbits produced by parenteral phosphate administration, J. Clin. Invest. *16*:203, 1937.

Foster, C. L.: Studies on the parathyroid of the mouse, J. Anat. *80*:171, 1946.

Grafflin, A. L.: Cytological evidence of secretory activity in the mammalian parathyroid gland, Endocrinology *26*:857, 1940.

Greep, R. O., and Kenny, A. D.: Physiology and chemistry of the parathyroids *in* Pincus, G., and Thimann, K. V. (eds.): The Hormones, ed. 3., p. 153, New York, Acad. Press, 1955.

Grollman, A.: The role of the kidney in the parathyroid control of the blood calcium as determined by studies on the nephrectomized dog, Endocrinology *55*:166, 1954.

Ham, A. W., Littner, N., Drake, T. G. H., Robertson, E. C., and Tisdall, F. F: Physiological hypertrophy of the parathyroids, its cause and its relation to rickets, Am J. Path. *16*:277, 1940.

Howard, J. E.: Present knowledge of parathyroid function, with especial emphasis upon its limitations *in* Wolstenholme, G. E. W., and O'Connor, C. M. (eds.): Ciba Foundation Symposium on Bone Structure and Metabolism, p. 206, London, Churchill, 1956.

McLean, F. C.: The parathyroid glands and bone *in* Bourne, G. H. (ed.): The Biochemistry and Physiology of Bone, p. 705, New York, Acad. Press, 1956.

Pappenheimer, A. M., and Wilens, S. L.: Enlargement of the parathyroid glands in renal disease, Am. J. Path. *11*:73, 1935.

Patt, H. M., and Luckhardt, A. B.: Relationship of a low blood calcium to parathyroid secretion, Endocrinology *31*:384, 1942.

Raybuck, H. E.: The innervation of the parathyroid glands, Anat. Rec. *112*:117, 1952.

Schour, I., Bhaskar, S. N., Greep, R. O., and Weinmann, J. P.: Odontome-like formations in a mutant strain of rats, Am. J. Anat. *85*:73, 1949.

Thomson, D. L., and Collip, J. B.: The parathyroid glands, Physiol. Rev. *12*:309, 1932.

(*See also* references on Bone Resorption and Osteoclasts in Chap. 15.)

SPECIAL REFERENCES ON CALCITONIN

Baghdiantz, A., Foster, G. V., Edwards, A., Kumar, M. A., Slack, E., Soliman, H. A., and MacIntyre, I.: Extraction and Purification of Calcitonin, Nature *203*:1027, 1964.

Cameron, E. C., and Copp, D. H.: Parathyroid control of hypercalcemia due to injection of parathyroid extract in the rat, Proc. Soc. Exp. Biol. Med. *114*:278, 1963.

Copp, D. H., Cameron, E. C., Cheney, B. A., Davidson, A. G. F., and Henze, K. G.: Evidence for calcitonin—a new hormone from the parathyroid that lowers blood calcium, Endocrinology *70*:638, 1962.

Copp, D. H., and Henze, K. G.: Parathyroid origin of calcitonin—Evidence from perfusion of sheep glands, *75*:49, 1964.

Foster, G. V., MacIntyre, I., and Pearse, A. G. E.: Calcitonin production and the mitochondrion-rich cells of the dog thyroid, Nature *203*:1029, 1964.

Hirsch, P. F., Voelkel, E. F., and Munson, P. L.: Thyrocalcitonin: Hypophosphatemic principle of the thyroid gland, Science *146*:412, 1964.

Talmadage, R. V., Neuenschwander, J., and Kraintz, L.: Evidence for the existence of thyrocalcitonin in the rat, Endocrinology *76*: 103, 1965.

THE ADRENAL GLAND AS A WHOLE

Grollman, A.: The Adrenals, Baltimore, Williams & Wilkins, 1936.

Hartman, F. A., and Brownell, K. A.: The Adrenal Gland, Philadelphia, Lea & Febiger, 1949.

Hewer, E. E., and Keene, M. F. L.: Observations on the development of the human suprarenal gland, J. Anat. *61*:302, 1927.

Jayne, E. P.: Cytology of the adrenal gland of the rat at different ages, Anat. Rec. *115*:459, 1953.

Kitchell, R. L., and Wells, L. J.: Functioning of the hypophysis and adrenals in foetal rats: Effects of hypophysectomy, adrenalectomy, castration, injected ACTH, and implanted sex hormone, Anat. Rec. *112*:561, 1952.

Swinyard, C. A.: Growth of human suprarenal glands, Anat. Rec. *87*:141, 1943.

THE ADRENAL CORTEX—GENERAL

Gaunt, R., *et al.:* The adrenal cortex, Ann. N. Y. Acad. Sci. *50*:509-678, 1949.

Jones, I. C.: The Adrenal Cortex, London, Cambridge Univ. Press, 1957.

Moon, H. D. (ed.): The Adrenal Cortex, New York, Hoeber, 1961.

Noble, R. L.: Physiology of the adrenal cortex *in* Pincus, G., and Thimann, K. V. (eds.): The Hormones, ed. 3., p. 685, New York, Acad. Press, 1955.

Yoffey, J. M. (ed.): The suprarenal cortex *in* Proc. of the Fifth Sympos. of the Colston Res. Soc., London, Butterworth, 1953.

## THE ADRENAL CORTEX—SPECIAL

Addison, T.: On constitutional and local effects of disease of suprarenal capsule, M. Classics 2:244, 1937.

Bennett, H. S.: Life history and secretion of cells of the adrenal cortex of the cat, Am. J. Anat. 67:151, 1940.

Broster, L. H., and Vines, H. W. C.: The Adrenal Cortex: A Surgical and Pathological Study, London, Lewis, 1933.

Deane, H. W., and Greep, R. O.: A morphological and histochemical study of the rat's adrenal cortex after hypophysectomy, with comments on the liver, Am. J. Anat. 79:117, 1946.

Feldman, J. D.: Endocrine control of the adrenal gland, Anat. Rec. 109:41, 1951.

————: Histochemical reactions of adrenal cortical cells, Anat. Rec. 107:347, 1950.

Glick, D., and Biskind, G. R.: The histochemistry of the adrenal gland: I. The quantitative distribution of vitamin C, J. Biol. Chem. 110:1, 1935.

————: Studies in histochemistry: IX. The quantitative distribution of vitamin C in the adrenal gland at various stages of development, J. Biol. Chem. 115:551, 1936.

Hench, P. S., Kendall, E. C., Slocumb, C. H., and Polley, H. F.: The effect of a hormone of the adrenal cortex (17-hydroxy-11-dehydrocorticosterone: compound E) and of pituitary adrenocorticotrophic hormone on rheumatoid arthritis, Ann. Rheum. Dis. 8:97, 1949.

Hoerr, N.: The cells of the suprarenal cortex in the guinea pig: their reaction to injury and their replacement, Am. J. Anat. 48:139, 1931.

Holmes, W. N.: Histological variations in the adrenal cortex of the golden hamster with special reference to the X zone, Anat. Rec. 122:271, 1955.

Lever, J. D.: Electron microscopic observations on the adrenal cortex, Am. J. Anat. 97:409, 1955.

Long, C. N. H.: Pituitary-adrenal relationships, Ann. Rev. Physiol. 18:409, 1956.

Miale, J. B.: Connective tissue reactions—a critical review: I. The effects of ACTH and corti-sone on allergic reactions and the collagen diseases, Ann. Allergy 9:530, 1951.

Ralli, E. P. (ed.): Proceedings of Third Conference on the Adrenal Cortex, New York, Macy, 1952.

Schaberg, A.: Regeneration of the adrenal cortex *in vitro*, Anat. Rec. 122:205, 1955.

Selye, H.: Physiology and Pathology of Exposure to Stress, Montreal, Acta, Inc., 1950.

van Dorp, A. W. V., and Deane, H. W.: A morphological and cytochemical study of the postnatal development of the rat's adrenal cortex, Anat. Rec. 107:265, 1950.

Williams, R. G.: Studies of adrenal cortex: Regeneration of the transplanted gland and the vital quality of the autogenous grafts, Am. J. Anat. 81:199, 1947.

## THE ADRENAL MEDULLA

Bennett, H. S.: Cytological manifestations of secretion in the adrenal medulla of the cat, Am. J. Anat. 69:333, 1941.

Bennett, H. S., and Kilham, L.: The blood vessels of the adrenal gland of the adult cat, Anat. Rec. 77:447, 1940.

Cannon, W. B.: Bodily Changes in Pain, Hunger, Fear and Rage, New York, Appleton, 1920.

Cannon, W. B., and Rosenblueth, A.: Autonomic Neuroeffector Systems, New York, Macmillan, 1937.

Cori, C. F., and Welch, A.: The adrenal medulla, J.A.M.A. 116:2590, 1941.

Hagen, P., and Welch, A. D.: The adrenal medulla and the biosynthesis of pressor amines, Recent Prog. Hormone Res. 12:27, 1956.

Krayer, O.: Symposium on the catecholamines, Pharmacol. Rev. 11:241, 1959.

Lands, A. M.: The pharmacological activity of epinephrine and related dihydroxy phenylalkylamines, J. Pharmacol. Exp. Therap. 96:279, 1949.

Tepperman, J.: Metabolic and Endocrine Physiology, Chicago, Year Book Pub., 1962.

Vane, J. R., Wolstenholme, G. E. W., and O'Connor, M.: Andrenergic Mechanisms, Ciba Foundation Symposium, Boston, Little, 1960.

## THE ISLETS OF LANGERHANS

Allen, F. M.: Diabetic experiments, Tr. A. Am. Physicians 53:320, 1938.

————: Studies Concerning Glycosuria and Diabetes, Cambridge, Harvard, 1913.

————: Pathology of diabetes: I. Hydropic degeneration of islands of Langerhans after partial pancreatectomy, J. Metabolic Res. 1:5, 1922.

Banting, F. G., and Best, C. H.: The internal

secretion of the pancreas, J. Lab. Clin. Med. 7:251, 1922.

Bencosme, S. A.: The histogenesis and cytology of the pancreatic islets in the rabbit, Am. J. Anat. 96:103, 1955.

Bencosme, S. A., and Lazarus, S. S.: Glucagon content of pancreatic tissue devoid of alpha cells, Proc. Soc. Exp. Biol. Med. 90:387, 1955.

Bencosme, S. A., and Liepa, E.: Regional differences of the pancreatic islet, Endocrinology 57:588, 1955.

Bencosme, S. A., Mariz, S., and Frei, J.: Studies on the function of the alpha cells of the pancreas, Am. J. Clin. Path. 28:594, 1957.

Bensley, R. R.: Structure and relationships of the islets of Langerhans, Harvey Lect. 10:250, 1915.

Bensley, S. H.: Solubility studies of the secretion granules of the guinea pig pancreas, Anat. Rec. 72:131, 1938.

Bensley, S. H., and Woerner, C. A.: The effects of continuous intravenous injection of an extract of the alpha cells of the guinea pig pancreas on the intact guinea pig. Anat. Rec. 72:413, 1938.

Best, C. H., Campbell, J., Haist, R. E., and Ham, A. W.: The effect of insulin and anterior pituitary extract on the insulin content of the pancreas and the histology of the islets, J. Physiol. 101:17, 1942.

Bowie, D. J.: Cytological studies of the islets of Langerhans in a teleost, *Neomaemis griseus*, Anat. Rec. 29:57, 1924.

Bryans, F. F., Kinash, B., Ashworth, M. A., and Haist, R. E.: The effect of hypophysectomy on the growth of the islets of Langerhans, Diabetes 1:358, 1952.

Campbell, J., Davidson, I. W. F., and Lei, H. P.: The production of permanent diabetes by highly purified growth hormone, Endocrinology 46:558, 1950.

Campbell, J., Haist, R. E., Ham, A. W., and Best, C. H.: The insulin content of the pancreas as influenced by anterior pituitary extract and insulin, Am. J. Physiol. 129:328, 1940.

Dohan, F. C., and Lukens, F. D. W.: Persistent diabetes following the injection of anterior pituitary extract, Am. J. Physiol. 125:188, 1939.

Evans, H. M., Meyer, K., Simpson, M. E., and Reichert, F. L.: Disturbance of carbohydrate metabolism in normal dogs injected with hypophyseal growth hormone, Proc. Soc. Exp. Biol. Med. 29:857, 1931-32.

Gomori, G.: Observations with differential stains on human islets of Langerhans, Am. J. Path. 17:395, 1941.

————: Studies on the cells of the pancreatic islets, Anat. Rec. 74:439, 1939.

Ham, A. W., and Haist, R. E.: Histological effects of anterior pituitary extracts, Nature 144:835, 1939.

————: Histological studies of trophic effects of diabetogenic anterior pituitary extracts and their relation to the pathogenesis of diabetes, Am. J. Path. 17:787, 1941.

Hédon, E.: Physiologie normale et pathologique du pancréas, Paris, Masson, 1901.

Hellerström, C., Hellman, B., Petersson, B., and Alm, G.: The two types of pancreatic A-cells and their relation to the glucagon secretion *in* The Structure and Metabolism of the Pancreatic Islets, p. 117, New York, Pergamon Press, 1964.

Herman, L., Sato, T., and Fitzgerald, P. J.: The pancreas in Kurtz, Stanley (ed.): Electron Microscopic Anatomy, chap. 3, New York, Academic Press, 1964.

Homans, J.: The relation of the islets of Langerhans to the pancreatic acini under various conditions of secretory activity, Proc. Roy. Soc. London, s.B. 86:73, 1912-13.

Houssay, B. A.: Diabetes as a disturbance of endocrine regulation, Am. J. M. Sc. 193:581, 1937.

Houssay, B. A., and Biasotti, A.: Le diabète pancréatique des chiens hypophysectomisés, C. R. Soc. biol. 105:121, 1930.

————: Hypophysectomie et diabète pancréatique chez le crepaud, C. R. Soc. biol. 104:407, 1930.

————: The hypophysis, carbohydrate metabolism and diabetes, Endocrinology 15:511, 1931.

Johns, W. S., O'Mulvenny, T. O., Potts, E. B., and Laughton, N. B.: Studies on the anterior lobe of the pituitary body, Am. J. Physiol. 80:100, 1927.

Lacy, P. E.: Electron microscopic identification of different cell types in the islets of Langerhans of the guinea pig, rat, rabbit and dog, Anat. Rec. 128:255, 1957.

————: Electron microscopic and fluorescent antibody studies on islets of Langerhans, Exp. Cell Res. (Suppl.) 7:296, 1959.

————: Electron microscopy of the beta cells of the pancreas, Am. J. Med. 31:851, 1961.

Lacy, P. E., and Hartroft, W. S.: Electron microscopy of the islets of Langerhans, Ann. N. Y. Acad. Sci. 82:287, 1959.

Lane, M. A.: The cytological characters of the areas of Langerhans, Am. J. Anat. 7:409, 1907.

Lawrence, R. T. B., Salter, J. M., and Best, C. H.: The effect of insulin on nitrogen retention in the hypophysectomized rat, Brit. M. J. 2:437, 1954.

Long, C. N. H., Katzin, B., and Fry, E. G.: The adrenal cortex and carbohydrate metabolism, Endocrinology 26:309, 1940.

Long, C. N. H., and Lukens, F. D. W.: The effects of adrenalectomy and hypophysectomy upon experimental diabetes in the cat, J. Exp. Med. *63*:465, 1936.

Long, C. N. H., Lukens, F. D. W., and Dohan, F. C.: Adrenalectomized depancreatized dogs, Proc. Soc. Exp Biol. Med. *36*:553, 1937.

Mering, von, J., and Minkowski, O.: Diabetes mellitus nach Pankreasextirpation, Arch. exp. Path. u. Pharmakol. *26*:371, 1889.

Munger, B. L.: A phase and electron microscopic study of cellular differentiation in the pancreatic islets of the mouse, Am. J. Anat. *103*:275, 1958.

O'Leary, J. L.: An experimental study on the islet cells of the pancreas *in vivo*, Anat. Rec. *45*:27, 1930.

Opie, E. L.: Histology of the islands of Langerhans of the pancreas, Bull. Johns Hopkins Hosp. *11*:205, 1900.

———: Pathological changes affecting the islands of Langerhans of the pancreas, J. Exp. Med. *5*:397, 527, 1900-01.

Richardson, K. C.: The influence of diabetogenic anterior pituitary extract on the islets of Langerhans in dogs, Proc. Roy. Soc. London, s.B. *128*:153, 1939-40.

Richardson, K. C., and Young, F. G.: Histology of diabetes induced in dogs by injection of anterior-pituitary extracts, Lancet *1*:1098, 1938.

———: The "pancreatropic" action of anterior pituitary extracts, J. Physiol. *91*:352, 1937.

Salter, J., and Best, C. H.: Insulin as a growth hormone, Brit. M. J. *2*:353, 1953.

Schulze, W.: Die Bedeutung der Langerhansschen Inseln in Pankreas, Arch. mikr. Anat. *56*:491, 1900.

Sergeyeva, M. A.: Microscopic changes in the islands of Langerhans produced by sympathetic and parasympathetic stimulation in the cat. Anat. Rec. *77*:297, 1940.

Simard, L. C.: Le complexe neuro-insulaire du pancréas chez les mammifères adultes, Rev. canad. biol. *1*:2, 1942.

Ssobolew, L. W.: Zur normalen und Pathologischen Morphologie der inneren Secretion der Bauchspeicheldrüse, Virchows Arch. path. Anat. *168*:91, 1902.

Thomas, T. B.: Cellular components of the mammalian islets of Langerhans, Am. J. Anat. *62*:31, 1937-38.

Woerner, C. A.: Studies of the islands of Langerhans after continuous intravenous injection of dextrose, Anat. Rec. *71*:33, 1938.

Young, F. G.: Experimental investigations on the relationship of the anterior hypophysis to diabetes mellitus, Proc. Soc. Exp. Biol. Med. *31*:1305, 1938.

———: Permanent experimental diabetes produced by pituitary (anterior lobe) injections, Lancet *2*:372, 1937.

———: The pituitary gland and carbohydrate metabolism, Endocrinology *26*:349, 1940.

### THE PINEAL BODY

Bailey, P.: The pineal body *in* Cowdry's Special Cytology, ed. 2, p. 787, New York, Hoeber, 1932.

Gladstone, R. J., and Wakeley, C. P. G.: The Pineal Organ, London, Ballière, Tindall & Cox, 1940.

Kelly, D. E.: Pineal organs: photoreception, secretion and development, Am. Scientist *50*:597, 1962.

Kitay, J. I., and Altschule, M. D.: The Pineal Gland, Cambridge, Mass., Harvard Univ. Press, 1954.

Quay, W. B.: Effect of dietary phenylalanine and tryptophan on pineal and hypothalamic serotonin levels, Proc. Soc. Exp. Biol. Med. *114*:718, 1963.

———: Circadian rhythm in rat pineal serotonin and its modifications by estrous cycle and photoperiod, Gen. Comp. Endocrinol. *3*:473, 1963.

Wurtman, R. J., Axelrod, J., and Chu, E. W.: Melatonin, a pineal substance: Effect on the rat ovary, Science *141*:277, 1963.

# 29    The Female Reproductive System

## INTRODUCTORY REMARKS ABOUT SEX

Under normal conditions, the embryo that forms when a female germ cell (an ovum) is fertilized by a male germ cell bearing an X chromosome develops the form and the organs of a female. Correspondingly, the embryo that forms when a female germ cell is fertilized by a male germ cell bearing a Y chromosome develops the form and the organs of a male. Hence, under normal conditions, the reproductive system that develops in any given embryo is determined by the chromosome complement of the male germ cell that fertilizes the ovum.

However, the chromosome complement of the fertilized ovum does not control the formation of the reproductive system of the embryo in the way that at first might be thought; that is, by limiting the embryo's potentiality to form the organs of one specific system. Hence, an embryo that forms from an ovum fertilized by a male germ cell bearing an X chromosome is not limited to forming a female reproductive system, for, as we shall see, such an embryo, under certain abnormal environmental circumstances, may develop male rather than female organs. Indeed, it appears that every young embryo, no matter which chromosome complement is present in the ovum from which it arises, has the *potentiality* to develop either type of reproductive system. Nevertheless, since under normal conditions the one of the two potentialities realized in any given embryo is determined by the chromosome complement of the fertilized ovum, it may be concluded that the chromosome constitution, while it does not limit, exerts a profound *directing* influence on development.

The way that the chromosome complement of a fertilized ovum directs the development of a male or a female reproductive system in an embryo is not understood. As we shall see, sex hormones probably play some part in the matter, but there are other factors involved. Before discussing the matter further we shall describe something of the development of the sex glands of the embryo and discuss some of the factors that affect their development.

**Indifferent Nature of the Early Gonad.** The fundamental organ of either reproductive system is the *gonad* (*gone* = seed) or *sex gland*. There are 2 of either sex in each individual. Those of the female are termed *ovaries*; those of the male, *testes*. The gonads have a dual function in each sex. During the period of sexual maturity the ovaries of females regularly produce mature female germ cells that are capable of being fertilized. They also produce female sex hormone. The testes of males produce male germ cells and male sex hormone.

In the early embryonic development the gonads of both sexes are said to be indifferent. A histologic examination of one made at this time gives no indication as to whether it will later become an ovary or a testis. However, as development proceeds, the organization of cells within the previously indifferent glands becomes indicative of whether they will develop into ovaries or testes. Certain features of the indifferent gonad become suppressed, and others accentuated. As a result of these processes, the embryonic gonads of the 2 sexes soon come to have different microscopic appearances.

On rare occasions both male and female gonads, or parts of gonads, develop and remain in a single individual. For example, the left gonad may develop into a testis, and the right one into an ovary, or both testicular and ovarian elements may develop in the same gonad. The development of both male and female gonadal tissue in the same individual is associated with a disturbed development of the other parts of the reproductive system. Instead of developing only male or female organs and structures, such individuals develop various mixtures of both. Such individuals, then, cannot be classified as either males or females, either by their gonads or by the other organs and structures of their reproductive systems. Therefore, such individuals are called *hermaphrodites* (*Hermēs* = Mercury; *Aphroditē* = Venus). By using Barr's technic, hermaphrodites can be shown to be chromosomal males or chromosomal females. If one is the latter, the cells of the male organs that develop in it will reveal the sex chromatin of the female.

**Effects of Sex Hormones on the Differentiation of the Indifferent Gonad.** That a genetically determined female embryo may be induced by environmental factors to become a hermaphrodite was shown many years ago by Lillie in his classic study of freemartins in cattle. Moreover, Lillie's study gave some intimation of the factors that direct differentiation within the developing reproductive system along one line or another. It had long been known that when cows gave birth to twins of opposite sex, the male calf would grow into a normal male but the female calf often, though not always, would develop a mixture of male and female organs, including male and female gonads. Such an altered female was termed a *freemartin*. Lillie showed that this condition was due to the fusion of the membranes that surround each of the two developing embryos in the uterus of the cow, so that blood could circulate freely between the developing genetically determined male and the genetically determined female. Under these circumstances, the male hormone derived from the developing male embryo circulates through the female, and this stimulates the development of male gonads and other male organs in the female. Such female hormone as is made in the genetically determined female which passes into the circulation of the male does not affect it materially, for the male twin is born normal.

**Potentialities for the Development of Characteristics of the Opposite Sex in Adults.** In many lower animals, and even in some vertebrates, sex reversal can occur. For example, it has been described in the fowl, and there are reports of hens that, for a time, have laid perfectly good eggs and have then undergone a sex reversal and have become fertile cocks. However, sex reversal is not so complete in these vertebrates in which it has been reported as it may seem, for it does not entail the devel-

opment of the ability to make sex chromosomes other than those provided for by the original genetic constitution of the animal concerned.

In the mammals the potentiality for developing either type of gonad does not seem to persist throughout later development to the same extent as it does in certain lower animals. Hence, if large amounts of male sex hormone are given a mature female mammal, a true sex reversal does not occur, for a testis does not develop. However, a limited potentiality for forming the other organs and structures of the male genital system persists, and this is exercised. Moreover, under these conditions, female organs and structures may regress. The secondary attributes of the male (hair distribution, voice, attitudes, etc.) develop. This condition, to distinguish it from true hermaphroditism, is called *pseudohermaphroditism*. As noted previously, this condition occurs in females who develop adrenal tumors of the kind that secrete masculinizing hormones.

*To sum up:* The somatic cells of any embryo have the same chromosomal constitution as the fertilized ovum from which they develop in so far as they all contain either 44 autosomes plus an XX or an XY combination of sex chromosomes. Nevertheless, either chromosomal male or female embryos have the potentiality to form the reproductive system (including the gonads) of either sex. However, any testicular tissue that forms in chromosomal females is not able to produce germ cells with Y chromosomes.

Sex hormones can influence which kind of reproductive system develops in an embryo but they cannot change the chromosomes. Hence, cells of male organs, if the latter develop in chromosomal females under the influence of male hormones, would have XX combinations of sex chromosomes in them. Both true and pseudohermaphrodites are either chromosomal males or females, and which they are can be determined by the microscopic examination of suitable somatic cells.

## THE PARTS OF THE FEMALE REPRODUCTIVE SYSTEM

The female reproductive system, as may be seen in Figures 29-1 and 29-2, consists of 2 ovaries, 2 oviducts (also called uterine tubes

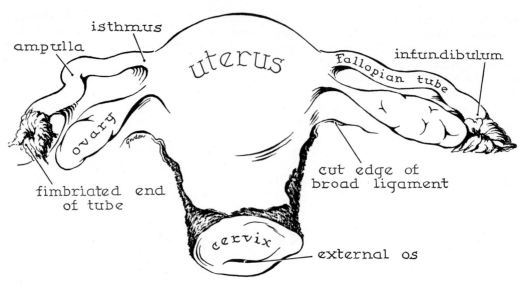

Fig. 29-1. Drawing of the uterus, the oviducts and the ovaries, as seen from behind.

or fallopian tubes), a uterus, a vagina, external genitalia and 2 mammary glands (breasts). In the following account the gross and the microscopic structure of the various parts of the system will be described in a general way. Further details regarding microscopic structure will be presented later.

In the sexually mature woman the ovaries are somewhat flattened, solid, ovoid bodies, roughly of the shape and the size of unshelled almonds (Fig. 29-1). The anterior wall of each is attached to the back of the broad ligament, close to the lateral wall of the true pelvis, by means of a short fold of peritoneum called the mesovarium (Fig. 29-1), which conducts vessels and nerves to and from the hilum of the ovary. A rounded ligament, *the ligament of the ovary*, connects the medial end of each ovary with the uterus (Fig. 29-1). The ovary itself is not covered with typical peritoneum but with germinal epithelium (Fig. 29-9). The cut surface of the ovary shows a cortex and a medulla; the latter contains many blood vessels and hence sometimes is called the zona vasculosa.

The surface of a mature ovary is scarred and pitted; this is due to its having shed many ova (germ cells). As we shall see, these are contained within the cortex in little epithelial bodies called follicles (to be described later). In a nonpregnant sexually mature woman a follicle of one ovary matures and ruptures

through the ovarian surface (and in doing so liberates an ovum) approximately every 28 days. The phenomenon is known as *ovulation,* and since each time ovulation occurs an egg cell, surrounded by some epithelial cells, plus some fluid, has to burst through the surface of the ovary, each ovulation results in a break on the ovarian surface which has to heal. Immediately beneath the break the remaining cells of the follicle from which the egg cell was liberated become transformed into a little endocrine gland called a *corpus luteum.* If pregnancy does not occur the corpus luteum functions for only around 10 to 12 days after which it degenerates and is replaced by a gradually contracting scar in the ovary immediately beneath the site where the rupture occurred. Scars forming this way from repeated ovulation result in the surface of the ovary becoming increasingly wrinkled and pitted over sites where ovulation has occurred. As we shall see the fact that the covering (germinal) epithelium of the ovary dips down in the crevices that form in this way is important, for the epithelium at the bottom of a crevice may become pinched off from the surface and form a small inclusion cyst.

If pregnancy occurs after an ovulation the corpus luteum that forms at the ovulation site continues to develop and function for several months and by the time it finally degenerates

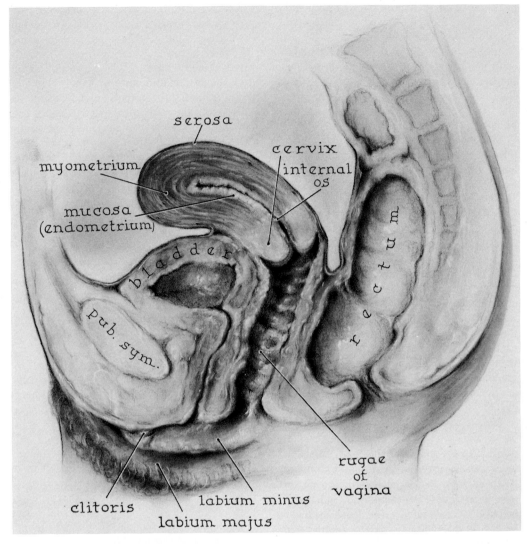

FIG. 29-2. Semidiagrammatic drawing of the parts of the female reproductive system, as seen in a sagittal section.

it has become large enough to leave a relatively large scar in the ovary.

When a follicle ruptures through the surface of an ovary, an ovum, surrounded by some of the cells of the follicle that still adhere to it, is extruded directly into the peritoneal cavity (Fig. 29-9). As is illustrated in Figure 29-1, the open end of each oviduct is funnel-shaped, and the wide end of the funnel is more or less fitted over the aspect of the ovary from which ova are liberated. Figure 29-1 reveals that the expanded open end of the oviduct is fimbriated (*fimbriae* = fringe), and the

fringelike processes that extend from the open end of the tube permit much of the ovarian surface to be encompassed in such a way that a liberated ovum is led into the lumen of the oviduct.

The oviducts (Fig. 29-1) are the tubes that connect the ovaries to the uterus, whose side walls they pierce; each is covered with peritoneum (the broad ligament is its mesentery). Each oviduct has a muscular wall and is lined with a mucous membrane equipped with ciliated epithelium which will be described later. An ovum cannot move by its own efforts;

hence, an ovum, delivered into the open end of the oviduct, must be moved to the cavity of the uterus by actions performed by the walls of the oviduct. It is probable that peristaltic contractions that sweep from the open end of the oviduct toward the uterus are chiefly responsible for moving an ovum to the uterus, although the action of the cilia of the epithelial lining of the tubes may assist.

The mucous membrane of the oviduct is thrown into an extraordinary arrangement of longitudinal folds (Fig. 29-15, *left*). Each fold has a core of lamina propria. These folds probably ensure that an ovum that enters the open end of the tube is kept in close contact on almost all its sides with living cells and compatible fluids as it passes along the tube. These folds probably also provide a similar protection for male germ cells, should these have been introduced into the vagina (Fig. 29-2) of the female, for male germ cells make their way up the cervical canal into the cavity of the body of the uterus (Fig. 29-2), through which they pass to enter the oviducts. It is in the maze created by the folds of mucous membrane in the oviduct that the fertilization of an ovum by a male germ cell occurs (Fig. 29-11).

The uterus (womb) is a hollow muscular organ with thick walls. It occupies a central position in the pelvis (Fig. 29-2). In shape it resembles an inverted pear that is somewhat flattened from before backward. Its narrower part is the body. The uppermost part of the body—that part above the level of the entrance of the oviducts—is the fundus. Since the body of the uterus is somewhat flattened from before backward, its central cavity is slitlike, with its anterior and posterior walls in apposition. In its upper part, this slitlike cavity is continuous at each side with the lumen of an oviduct. The cavity of the body narrows below and is continuous with the cervical canal. This, in turn, opens into the vagina (Fig. 29-2).

The body of the uterus is lined by a special kind of mucous membrane termed *endometrium* (*metra* = womb) that is pitted with simple tubular glands. It will be described in detail later. In the sexually mature (but not old) nonpregnant woman the innermost (and thicker) part of this layer breaks down and is exfoliated into the cavity of the uterus approximately every 28 days. The process of exfoliation usually takes about 4 days before its course is run, and during these 4 days the raw surface created by the continuing exfoliation bleeds. The mixture of blood, glandular secretion and broken-down endometrium delivered into the cavity of the uterus and passed out through the cervical canal and the vagina constitutes the *menstrual* (*mensis* = monthly) *flow*, and the phenomenon is called *menstruation*. Following menstruation the endometrium regenerates. Ovulation also, it will be recalled, occurs every 28 days. Ovulation, although there is much variation, does not coincide with menstruation but tends rather to occur about halfway between menstrual periods.

The liberation of an ovum from an ovary, its fertilization in the oviduct, the changes that occur in it as it passes along the oviduct to the uterus and its implantation into the endometrium—and this marks the beginning of pregnancy—are all illustrated diagrammatically in Figure 29-11.

The further development of the fertilized embedded ovum to form an embryo constitutes the separate subject of *embryology* and hence is dealt with in textbooks of embryology. However, the formation of the *placenta*, an organ which permits interchange of dissolved substances between the bloodstreams of mother and embryo, is described later in this chapter.

Menstruation does not occur after a fertilized ovum becomes implanted in the endometrium; hence, a "missed" menstrual period is a time-honored, though by no means invariable, sign of pregnancy. Menstruation does not occur throughout pregnancy. When the fetus has reached full term, parturition (*parturire* = to be in labor) occurs, and a baby is born. The muscle wall of the uterus, which has become very thick during pregnancy, contracts, and the cervix (Fig. 29-2)—the outlet of the uterus—dilates, whereupon the fetus, usually head foremost, slips through the dilated cervix and vagina to reach the outside world. The placenta then separates, and the baby begins its independent existence.

The vagina (L. = sheath) is a flattened tube; it serves as a sheath for the male organ in sexual intercourse. Its walls consist chiefly of smooth muscle and of fibro-elastic connective tissue; they are a few millimeters thick.

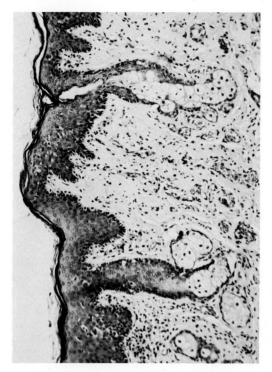

FIG. 29-3. Low-power photomicrograph of a section cut at right angles to the surface of a labium minus. Observe that there are only rudimentary hair follicles; these produce no hairs but are associated with sebaceous glands.

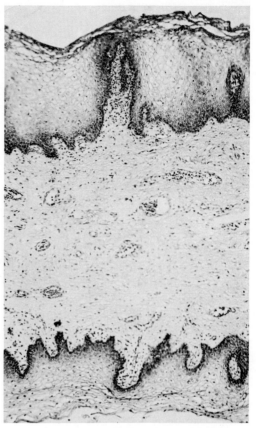

FIG. 29-4. Low-power photomicrograph of a portion of a section cut through the hymen. Observe that both surfaces are covered with stratified squamous nonkeratinizing epithelium and have high papillae.

It is lined with a mucous membrane that is thrown into transverse folds known as *rugae* (Fig. 29-2). The epithelium is of the stratified squamous nonkeratinizing type. This type of epithelium also covers that part of the cervix that projects into the vagina.

The external genitalia consist of several structures (Fig. 29-2). A collection of fat deep to the skin that covers the symphysis pubis causes the skin to be raised here in the form of a rounded eminence; this is called the *mons pubis* or *mons veneris*. At puberty this eminence becomes covered with hair. Two folds of skin, the *labia majora* (Fig. 29-2), originate just below the mons pubis. They separate from one another as they pass backward and approach one another again (but do not actually meet) a short distance behind the external opening of the vagina; hence, the vagina opens into the cleft which they enclose. Each of these folds has 2 surfaces covered with skin.

The epidermis covering the outer surface of each tends to be pigmented and is equipped with many large hair follicles and sebaceous glands. That of the inner surface also has hair follicles and sebaceous glands, but the hairs are delicate. Sweat glands are also present. The cores of the folds contain fat and some smooth muscle.

Near the anterior end of the cleft between the labia majora is a small body of erectile tissue, the *clitoris* (Fig. 29-2). This is the homologue of the penis of the male. Two delicate folds of skin, the *labia minora*, arise just anterior to it. After investing part of the clitoris between them they pass backward, following much the same course as the labia majora to which they lie medial. The labia

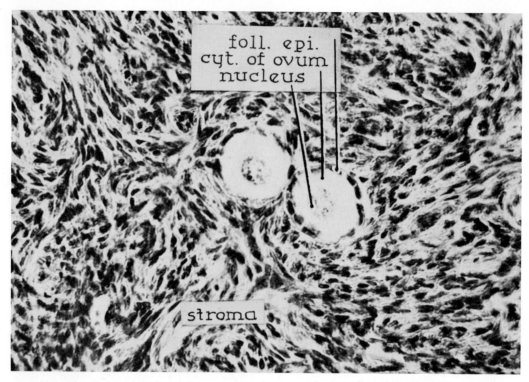

FIG. 29-5. High-power photomicrograph of a section of an ovary of a mature woman, showing "swirly" stroma at 2 primitive follicles. The germ cell which is labeled ovum is more accurately termed an oogonium at this stage.

minora consist of thin folds of skin but possess no hairs (Fig. 29-3). Sebaceous and sweat glands are found on both their surfaces (Fig. 29-3). Although the inner surface of each fold consists of skin, it exhibits the pink color of a mucous membrane.

The labia minora enclose the vestibule of the vagina. In the virgin, an incomplete membranous fold, the *hymen* (Fig. 29-4), projects centrally from the rim of the vestibule and partially occludes the vaginal entrance. Two small glands, the *glands of Bartholin*, which are tubulo-alveolar in type and secrete mucus, are present, one on each side of the vestibule. Each drains into a duct that empties into the groove between the hymen and the labium minus on the side on which the gland is situated. Two elongated masses of erectile tissue, constituting the bulb of the vestibule, are disposed beneath the surface along each side of the vestibule. These two masses approximate each other in front. Many mucous glands are present beneath the surface around the vestibule. The urethral orifice is in the midline between the labia minora and between the opening of the vagina and the clitoris (Fig. 29-2).

The external genitalia are richly provided with sensory nerve endings.

## THE OVARY: OVULATION AND HORMONE SECRETION

**Basic Microscopic Features.** The ovary is covered with a single layer of *germinal epithelium.* In young women this is cuboidal (Fig. 29-9) but it becomes flattened later in life over parts of the ovary but it remains cuboidal in the pits and crevices seen on its surface.

The connective tissue substance of the ovary is called its *stroma.* It consists of spindle-shaped cells and intercellular substance. Most of the stroma of the cortex contains a high proportion of cells to intercellular substance; hence, in sections it appears heavily nucleated (Fig. 29-5). Moreover, the bundles of cells and fibers that make up most of it run in various directions; hence, in sections the stroma of the cortex has a characteristic "swirly" appearance (Fig. 29-5). However, the layer immediately beneath the germinal epithelium differs from the bulk of the stroma in that it has a higher proportion of intercellular substance, and its fiber bundles and cells are both arranged more or less parallel with the surface. This special layer is called the *tunica albuginea*, and the white appearance that its name suggests is due to its great content of intercellular substance and lack of vascularity.

In contrast with the dense texture of the stroma of the cortex, that of the medulla is loosely arranged. It differs further from that of the cortex in containing more elastic fibers, some smooth muscle cells and, in addition, extensive convolutes of blood vessels, particularly veins. The veins may be so large and contain so many blood cells that in a section the student may mistake one for an area of hemorrhage or a hemangioma (a blood vessel tumor). Small blood vessels extend from the medulla into the cortex.

**The Development of the Ovary and the Origin of Follicles.** Since we shall spend some time discussing the cyclical events that occur in the ovary during the time when a woman is fertile and which involve follicles regularly maturing just below the surface of the ovary and just as regularly rupturing and releasing female germ cells into the oviduct, it is essential that we should know how follicles are formed in the ovary; this in turn requires that we consider briefly the development of the ovary.

The ovaries develop from ridges, termed gonadal or genital ridges, which bulge from the surface of the intra-embryonic coelomic cavity. The two ridges are located one to either side of the mid-line of the embryo between the dorsal mesentery and the mesonephros. Eventually the tissue of these two ridges evolves into the two almond-shaped bodies that are present in later life.

The histologic picture seen in sections taken from the developing ovaries of the developing embryo is not easy to interpret and it is not surprising that through the years different interpretations have been placed on the sequences of events that occur. We shall now consider some of the views that have been and are held and their bases.

First, the mesodermal cells at the surface

of the developing ovary differentiate into a layer of epithelial cells to form a covering for the organ and hence a lining for the cavity. In other sites in the coelomic cavity surface cells differentiate into the thinner mesothelial cells which line the peritoneal cavity.

Secondly, beneath the covering epithelium, cords of cells which have an epithelial appearance similar to the covering epithelial cells, appear among the stromal cells. The histologic picture here is reminiscent of that seen in the development of epithelial glands and as a result a commonly held view has been to the effect that the cords of cells that appear in the cortex of the ovary represent downgrowths from the surface epithelium.

Thirdly, around the time when the developing cords of cells are seen, primordial germ cells make their appearance in the cortex of the ovary along with the cells of the cords. One view that has often been held through the years is that the primordial germ cells develop from cells of the cords. This was thought to happen as a result of the cords being broken up into clumps by stromal cells after which the central cell of the clump became a primordial germ cell. The cells of the clump that surrounded the germ cell were believed to constitute a complete layer that enclosed the germ cell.

Although there is uncertainty about how they form, there is no doubt about the fact that little bodies, each consisting of a central cell which is a primordial germ cell, enclosed by a single layer of epithelial cells, make their appearance in the ovary. Such structures are termed *primordial follicles* and many thousands of them develop (it has been estimated that there may be up to 400,000 follicles in the two ovaries at the time of birth). The central cell of the primordial follicle becomes known as an *oogonium*. The single layer of cells that surround the oogonium are termed *follicular epithelial cells* or, more commonly, *granulosa cells* (why they should be termed granulosa cells is not clear, but this is the common term used for them in pathological and clinical circles).

According to the view described above there would be good reason to term the epithelium that covers the ovary *germinal* epithelium because this view interprets it as giving rise both to the cords of cells that appear in the cortex during early development and also the germ cells themselves. However, there are reasons for thinking that the term germinal is a misnomer, and these will now be described.

First, it has now been established by tracing cells by their histochemical features that the primordial germ cells do not develop in the ovary but instead elsewhere, probably in the endoderm of the yolk sac from which they migrate to the developing ovary and somehow enter its substance at around the time the cords are forming in the cortex. Hence, the epithelium of the ovary is *not* germinal in the sense that it gives rise to the primordial germ cells.

Secondly, it may be questionable if the covering epithelium is germinal with regard to the cords and/or the granulosa cells that surround the primordial germ cells. If the covering epithelial cell of the ovary is ever germinal in this respect it subsequently must lose a great deal of its potentiality, for it is now known that cysts or even tumors that develop from covering epithelial cells that may become pinched off in crevices on the surface following the repair of a site of rupture of a follicle are of a different character from cysts or tumors that develop from the granulosa cells that are supposed to originate from cord cells that in turn are supposed to develop from the covering epithelium.

In considering this question it should be observed that the situation with regard to the relation between the covering epithelium and the underlying stroma in the ovary is very different from the usual situation in the body where there is an epithelium derived from ectoderm or endoderm supported by connective tissue that develops from a very different origin. In the ovary the stromal cells and the covering epithelial cells have the same origin. Next, around the time when the cords appear, primordial germ cells are arriving in the ovary and proliferating. It might be expected that the primordial germ cells would exert potent inducing effects that could result in adjacent cells assuming an epithelial appearance and surrounding them as follicular epithelial (granulosa) cells. It is therefore a distinct possibility that the follicular cells are not necessarily derived from downgrowths of the covering epithelium but instead from stromal

cells that are immediately adjacent to them. As we shall see, as follicles develop further, another surrounding layer is added to them (known as a theca) and this layer is clearly derived from stromal cells, and later both granulosa cells and thecal cells (unlike the cells of the covering epithelium) become hormone producers.

The foregoing is of practical importance because conceiving of the covering epithelium of the ovary as a germinal epithelium is a handicap in understanding pathologic lesions that may develop in the ovary. Having noted this we should now say that the term germinal epithelium of the ovary is so firmly entrenched in the literature that it has become a matter of habit to use it, and if we do so in the following pages it is only because of convenience and habit, and not because we think of it as germinal as it was once believed to be.

By the end of the third month some of the oogonia have started to develop into larger cells which are termed primary oocytes. Soon after they develop, the oocytes begin to enter the prophase of their first meiotic division and by the time of birth they are all in a late stage of prophase of their first meiotic division and rest in that stage. They only complete their first meiotic division after puberty and in follicles that are about to rupture at the surface of the ovary (Fig. 29-9) as will be described later. Follicles that consist of primary oocytes surrounded by epithelium are termed primary follicles. These all lie in the stroma of the ovary.

**Changes That Occur at Puberty and Their Cause.** In early childhood the pars anterior of the anterior pituitary, while producing growth hormone, produces very little gonadotrophic hormone. As a consequence, the ovary develops only in keeping with the remainder of the body. But as the time of puberty approaches, the pars anterior (one group of basophils) begins to produce gonadotrophic hormone. This causes the ovaries to begin liberating an ovum into an oviduct approximately every 28 days. Moreover, the ovary, under gonadotrophic stimulus, begins to function as an endocrine gland. It makes 2 hormones.

The primary hormone made by the ovary is *estrogen*. This is the basic female sex hormone. On being liberated into the bloodstream at puberty, it brings about the development of the secondary sex characteristics of the female. The breasts enlarge and become rounded. Increased amounts of fat appear under the skin of the hips and the buttocks. The growth of hair is stimulated in certain parts of the body, particularly in the pubic region; its distribution here is somewhat different from that of the male in that its upper border forms a straight line rather than running up to a middle point as it does in the male. The larynx does not increase further in size as it does in the male. Libido is aroused; this soon becomes directed toward the opposite sex. Other effects of estrogen will be described presently.

The secondary hormone made by the ovary at puberty is *progesterone* (progestin). This is made by the corpus luteum that develops each time an ovum is liberated (Fig. 29-9). Since corpora lutea do not persist for more than 2 weeks after ovulation in the nonpregnant female, progesterone is not made continuously except during pregnancy. In the nonpregnant woman the chief function of progesterone is to prepare the uterus for the reception of a fertilized ovum. It does this anew each month even in a virgin. The preparation consists of making the endometrium grow thick and succulent so that a fertilized ovum may easily become embedded in it and be nourished adequately. It has been believed also that it tends to make the uterine muscle quiescent so that it does not contract and expel the developing embryo. However, recent work has cast doubt on this hypothesis. Unless a fertilized ovum becomes implanted in the endometrium (or elsewhere), the corpus luteum of the ovary does not continue making progesterone for more than 12 days after ovulation has occurred. If the corpus luteum had a mind, one might visualize its thinking at this time that, "unless fertilization has occurred by now it won't occur this month, for this month's ovum, by this time, will have died; hence, there is no point in maintaining the endometrium in a special state any longer." And, drawing these conclusions, the corpus luteum fails and soon stops making progesterone. As a result, the endometrium, brought to a high state of development by this hormone, disintegrates, desquamates and bleeds; this constitutes menstruation, and, as may be

concluded, menstruation is caused primarily by the failure of the corpus luteum to continue making progesterone. After the next ovulation, of course, a new corpus luteum will develop in the ovary and make more progesterone but, unless pregnancy occurs, the same sequence of events will be repeated. If pregnancy occurs, the corpus luteum does not degenerate; hence, menstruation does not occur. The reason for the corpus luteum's persisting when pregnancy occurs will be explained presently. The need for a persisting corpus luteum, and the continued secretion of progesterone, when pregnancy occurs, is obvious.

From the foregoing it may be concluded that the secondary sex characteristics that develop in the female at the time of puberty are due to the ovaries' secreting the primary sex hormone, estrogen, at this time. It may also be concluded that menstruation, which begins at the time of puberty, is due to the ovaries regularly secreting, and as regularly ceasing to secrete, the secondary hormone of the ovary, progesterone. The third conclusion that may be drawn is that the ovary begins to liberate ova and to function as an endocrine gland only because it is stimulated to do so by the gonadotrophic hormone secreted by the pars anterior of the pituitary gland. Hence, puberty is caused primarily by an anterior pituitary hormone appearing in the circulation. Experimentally, sexual maturity can be induced in very young animals by injecting them with gonadotrophic hormone.

Why the anterior pituitary should begin to secrete gonadotrophic hormone at a certain time of life is not definitely known. Age, temperature, other hormones, physical activity, afferent impulses from the stimulation of light and other types of sensory receptors, and even psychological factors, have all been suspected of stimulating gonadotrophic secretion. The matter is complex; Matthews found that although a virgin pigeon will ovulate in the spring if it is placed in a cage with a male, or, after a slightly longer time, if it is separated from a male by a glass partition, or, after a considerably longer time if it is placed in a cage with another female, it will not ovulate if it is kept in a cage by itself unless it is provided with a mirror.

Before describing the histologic changes that

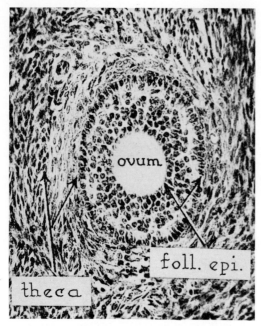

FIG. 29-6. Low-power photomicrograph of a section of an ovary of a mature woman, showing a follicle surrounded with stratified epithelium which has not yet begun to secrete fluid. The plane of section was such that the knife did not pass through the nucleus of the primary oocyte which is labeled "ovum." The theca may be seen indistinctly separated from the ovarian stroma.

occur in the ovary when it is stimulated by gonadotrophic hormone which result in its liberating an ovum from its surface and variously producing 2 hormones, we should deal briefly with the fact that the gonadotrophic hormone does not appear to be a single substance, but, instead, a complex of 2 fractions. These have different effects and are secreted in different quantities and at different times throughout the menstrual cycle. The first fraction is called the *follicle-stimulating hormone*; and the second, the *luteinizing hormone*. From now on, as is common practice, these 2 hormones will be referred to as FSH and LH, respectively. We shall now describe the effects that these 2 hormones produce on the ovary, particularly with regard to their respective effects on maturation of follicles, liberation of ova and hormone secretion.

**The Development of Follicles.** Of the hun-

dreds of thousands of primary follicles present in the 2 ovaries at birth, only from 300 to 400 come to maturity and liberate oocytes from the surfaces of the ovaries after puberty. Most of the primary follicles of the ovary degenerate either as they are or after some degree of spurious development. The spurious development and the death of a follicle is termed *atresia*, and follicles showing the histologic changes of degeneration or death are termed *atretic follicles*. Their microscopic appearance will be described after we have considered those associated with the normal development of follicles.

A ~~primary~~ follicle is from 40 to 50 $\mu$ in diameter. It consists chiefly of a relatively large oogonium which is wrapped with a single layer of flattened follicular epithelial cells (Fig. 29-5). The nucleus of the oogonium is large and centrally disposed. Its membrane stains with moderate intensity. Chromatin granules are not prominent in it, so its interior is pale except for the nucleolus which is well-stained and prominent (see left follicle in Fig. 29-5). The cytoplasm is pale and contains yolk granules which are spread throughout it evenly.

The earliest sign indicating that a primary follicle is beginning to develop is given by the follicular epithelial cells. At first these become cuboidal, some columnar, and then, as a result of their proliferation, stratified (Fig. 29-6); the follicle is then known as a secondary follicle. In the meantime, the primary oocyte that it contains increases in size, but its growth is not proportional to that of the follicular epithelium; hence, this latter tissue soon comes to constitute the bulk of the follicle. When the primary oocyte has become somewhat more than twice its original diameter, a thick membrane that stains deeply, the *zona pellucida* (Fig. 29-8), develops around it. Probably both the oocyte and the innermost follicular epithelial cells contribute to its formation.

After the follicular epithelial cells, by their continued division, have come to constitute a covering for the primary oocyte, many cells thick, fluid begins to accumulate in little pools between them (Fig. 29-9). These pools of fluid are at first small and are seen roughly halfway between the periphery of the ovum and the border of the follicle. The precise origin of this fluid, which is called *follicular*

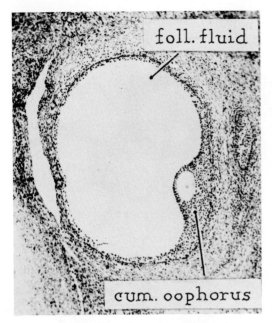

FIG. 29-7. Very low-power photomicrograph of a section of an ovary of a mature woman, showing a developing follicle distended with follicular fluid and the ovum contained in a cumulus oophorus.

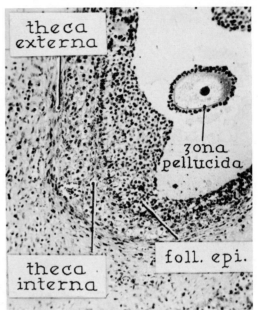

FIG. 29-8. Low-power photomicrograph of a section of an ovary of a mature woman, showing a developing follicle. The secondary oocyte, with some surrounding follicular epithelial cells, appears to be free in the follicle, but this appearance is probably due to the plane of the section. The oocyte shows a well-developed zona pellucida, and the 2 layers of the theca are apparent.

*fluid,* is not known; its composition suggests that it is something more than tissue fluid, hence that it must be at least modified by the follicular cells among which it accumulates. The follicle continues to enlarge because the follicular epithelial cells continue to proliferate by mitosis and because fluid continues to accumulate between them. The smaller pools fuse with each other so that larger ones are formed, and the continuance of this process leads eventually to the bulk of the follicle coming to be composed of a large more or less central pool of fluid which is not spherical because the oocyte, which now is termed a secondary oocyte, together with the follicular cells that cover it, projects into the single large pool of fluid, like a little hill, from one side (Fig. 29-7). The little hill of follicular cells that contains the ovum is known as the *cumulus oophorus* (*cumulus* = a heap; *oon* = egg; *phorus* = bearer).

While the follicle is developing, as described above, the ovarian stroma that immediately surrounds the follicle becomes organized into a membrane called the *theca* (*theke* = a box). This more or less spherical box of stroma

ensheathes the epithelial follicle closely. As development proceeds, the cells of the theca become differentiated into 2 layers. The innermost layer, the *theca interna,* is relatively cellular and is provided with many capillaries (Fig. 29-8). The outer layer, the *theca externa,* is more fibrous and not so vascular (Fig. 29-8). However, the line of demarcation between the 2 layers is not usually very distinct.

A fully developed follicle is so large in relation to the thickness of the cortex that it causes a bulge on the surface of the ovary (Fig. 29-9). Moreover, as the follicle develops, the cortex between the outermost part of the follicle and the surface of the ovary becomes very thin.

All the changes described up to this time, relating to the development of a primary follicle into a mature one that bulges from the surface of the ovary, are brought about by FSH and can be demonstrated easily in

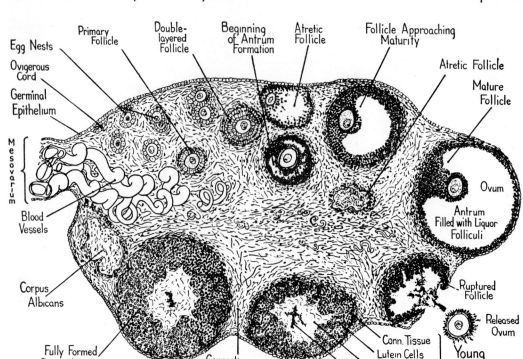

FIG. 29-9. Schematic diagram of an ovary, showing the sequence of events in the origin, the growth and the rupture of an ovarian (graafian) follicle and the formation and the retrogression of corpus luteum. Follow clockwise around ovary, starting at the mesovarium. (Patten, B. M.: Human Embryology, New York, Blakiston Division of McGraw-Hill)

young animals by administering FSH to them. If FSH administration is continued after mature follicles reach the surface, ovulation occurs, but this is due to the FSH having stimulated estrogen production in the ovary and the estrogen in turn having stimulated the anterior pituitary to secrete LH; this is shown by the fact that the same dose of FSH that will cause ovulation in intact animals will not cause ovulation in hypophysectomized animals (which have no pituitary glands to make LH).

LH has two actions. Its first one is to cause the follicle to burst; how it does this is not known precisely; but its causing increased vascularity in the theca interna with increased tissue fluid production is probably a factor. When the follicle bursts, the secondary oocyte, which is still surrounded by some follicular cells which comprise a *corona radiata* for it, is liberated into, or close to, the open end of the oviduct (Fig. 29-9).

Before considering the second action of LH we shall consider briefly some changes that occur in the oocyte that at this point is liberated into the oviduct.

At this time the oocyte, which was in late prophase of its first meiotic division, quickly passes through the other stages of this division. The division of cytoplasm that occurs in this division is very unequal, for one cell, which is now termed the secondary oocyte, retains almost all of the cytoplasm of the primary oocyte, and the other, which is known as a polar body, receives almost none (Fig. 29-11). A second meiotic division then begins in the secondary oocyte, but this is not completed unless fertilization occurs and this does not normally occur until the oocyte is passing along the oviduct (Fig. 29-11). The second meiotic division is also associated with a most uneven distribution of cytoplasm, with another polar body being formed. All polar bodies are discarded. The secondary oocyte,

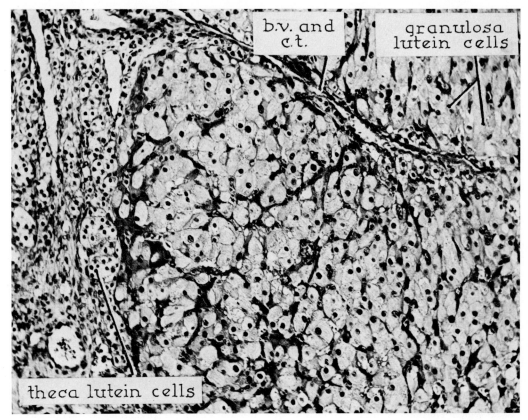

FIG. 29-10. High-power photomicrograph of a portion of a section of a corpus luteum of pregnancy. Observe the large, pale granulosa luteal cells with vacuoles in their cytoplasm. The theca luteal cells are smaller.

because of the meiotic divisions, has only 23 chromosomes of its own and on fertilization it receives another 23 from the male germ cells that brings about its fertilization. As a result each pair of its chromosomes thereafter has a member from each side of the family.

The second action of LH is that of its stimulating the formation of a functional corpus luteum in the follicle from which the ovum is extruded. However, there is another school of thought which subscribes to the idea that after having acted to cause ovulation, LH only starts a corpus luteum on its way, and that the further growth of the corpus luteum is caused by a third anterior hormone, *luteotrophin* (which is probably the same thing as lactogenic hormone), being secreted at this time. While the role of luteotrophin is well established in the rat, it is by no means clear that it is the hormone that makes the

corpus luteum grow and secrete progesterone in man. Therefore, we shall assume that LH is the hormone that is instrumental in bringing about the formation of a functional corpus luteum in man.

After the ovum and part of the follicular fluid have been extruded at ovulation, the follicle collapses sufficiently to permit the edges of the wound made on the surface of the ovary by the rupture of the follicle to come together (Fig. 29-9). Moreover, the reduction in size of the follicle causes the remaining follicular cells and those of the theca interna to be thrown into folds (Fig. 29-9). Only the theca externa retains its original shape. The rupture and subsequent collapse of the follicle usually results in some bleeding (though in man this is not so much as has generally been thought in the past). The escaped plasma and red blood cells become mixed with such follicular fluid as remains in the central part of the follicle. Strands of fibrin then form from the fibrinogen of the escaped plasma.

Under the continued stimulus of LH, the follicular epithelial cells that remain in the follicle enlarge greatly (Fig. 29-10) to become what are called *follicular* or *granulosa lutein* cells. Their cytoplasm becomes abundant as a result of its accumulating lipoid. Lutein pigment also forms in their cytoplasm, but somewhat later. When enough of this accumulates it imparts a yellow color to the corpus luteum. The cells of the theca interna, that before ovulation had become enlarged, also become lutein cells and contribute to the size of the corpus luteum. These are called *theca lutein* cells (Fig. 29-10), but although they are of a connective tissue origin, they develop many of the characteristics of granulosa lutein cells.

Capillaries from the theca interna grow in among the cords and the clumps of lutein cells as the latter develop; hence, the corpus luteum comes to have a fairly typical endocrine gland structure (Fig. 29-10). Fibroblasts from the theca interna grow into the more central part of the corpus luteum and there form an undifferentiated type of connective tissue which contains a high proportion of amorphous intercellular substance. This connective tissue tends to surround the remains of the follicular fluid and clotted blood that are still present in the central part of the corpus luteum (Fig. 29-9).

Following ovulation, under the continued stimulus of LH, the corpus luteum develops for about 10 days, attaining a diameter of from 1.5 to 2 cm. (Fig. 29-9). The growth that it manifests over this period is probably due to its cells becoming increasingly hypertrophied and not to their undergoing mitosis. As noted before, unless the ovum, liberated from the follicle before it becomes a corpus luteum, is fertilized, the anterior pituitary gland secretes only enough LH to sustain the corpus luteum for about 10 days. After the secretion of LH fails, the corpus luteum begins to involute; this is associated with its vessels collapsing. Moreover, when LH fails, the corpus luteum no longer continues to secrete enough progesterone to maintain the endometrium in a luxuriant condition, so that it begins to show signs of impending

disintegration and it is soon mostly cast off.

The failure of the corpus luteum, in addition to precipitating menstruation, has another effect. Previous to its failure, the corpus luteum has secreted enough progesterone into the bloodstream to inhibit the anterior pituitary from secreting FSH. With little FSH in the bloodstream, the development of follicles in the ovary is not encouraged; hence, during the periods in which progesterone is secreted, follicular development comes to a standstill in the ovary. But when the progesterone level falls as a result of the failure of the corpus luteum, the anterior pituitary begins to secrete FSH again; hence, follicles again begin to develop in the ovary, so, in about 2 weeks after the failure of the corpus luteum, another follicle has matured and reached the surface of the ovary. Moreover, under the stimulus of FSH, the ovary has also been stimulated to produce estrogen. This encourages the repair of the endometrium following menstruation, but, as its concentration in the bloodstream increases, it also stimulates the anterior pituitary to begin again the secretion of LH. When enough LH is secreted, ovulation occurs, and another corpus luteum forms. If pregnancy does not ensue, the whole series of events described above is repeated.

## Summary of Hormonal Factors Concerned in the 28-Day Cycle

1. At the time of menstruation the anterior pituitary begins to secrete FSH.

2. FSH causes follicles to develop in the ovary and makes the ovary secrete estrogen. After being stimulated by FSH for about 2 weeks, a follicle matures at the surface of one ovary.

3. The estrogen secreted by the ovary during these 2 weeks keeps the sex organs of the female in a developed state and aids libido. Toward the end of the 2-week period, the concentration of estrogen in the bloodstream becomes sufficient to stimulate the anterior pituitary to begin secreting LH.

4. The anterior pituitary continues to secrete LH for about 10 days. The first effect of LH is to cause the mature follicle at the surface of the ovary to rupture; it then causes

a corpus luteum to develop from the remains of the follicle and to secrete progesterone for about 10 days.

5. The progesterone, in general, quiets the uterine muscle and builds up the endometrium so that it is suitable for the reception and the nourishment of a fertilized ovum. It also keeps the anterior pituitary from secreting effective amounts of FSH, so follicular development in the ovary is stilled, and estrogen production is diminished.

6. The anterior pituitary secretes LH for less than 2 weeks. It stops probably because the falling blood estrogen level fails to stimulate it, and the rising progesterone level inhibits it. When it ceases secreting LH, the corpus luteum stops making progesterone, and menstruation occurs.

7. The decreased amount of progesterone in the blood is not sufficient to inhibit the anterior pituitary, so it begins again to secrete FSH. The cycle is then repeated (see 1).

It should be kept in mind that the foregoing is only a working hypothesis that appears reasonable in the light of our present knowledge. Since methods for estimating the blood content of all the various hormones mentioned are not yet available, it is obvious that much in the hypothesis is based on inference from animal experiments. Another point that should be mentioned is that some investigators have questioned if there are actually 2 gonadotrophic hormones. Nevertheless, the hypothesis given above is the one that is generally adopted, and a knowledge of it has proved to be useful in the understanding and the treatment of ovulatory and menstrual disorders. However, the student will find it worth while to investigate this hypothesis a little more deeply by learning something about the sex cycles of the females of other families of the animal kingdom. These are more easily understood than those of the human female, and some knowledge of them facilitates greatly the development of a proper perspective on the cause and the nature of the changes that succeed one another in the human cycle. For this reason, and also to enable the student to keep in mind the bases for the biologic assay of hormones and the bases for pregnancy tests, the sex cycles of certain common laboratory animals will now be described.

## SEX CYCLES IN LOWER ANIMALS

**The Estrous Cycle.** Anyone with a little knowledge of the breeding habits of domestic or wild animals knows that the mating impulse of the female is dormant for most of the year and becomes aroused only at certain seasons. At these times the female is said to have come into *heat* or *estrus* (*oistros* = mad desire), and only at these times will the female mate with a male. There is a wide variation among the females of different kinds of animals with respect to the number of times they come into estrus each year. In some kinds, estrus occurs only once a year, in many it occurs 2 or 3 times a year, and in still others it occurs every few days.

The phenomenon of estrus is caused by the ovaries of an animal more or less suddenly secreting a large amount of estrogen. The ovaries are stimulated to do this by the anterior pituitary secreting FSH. The latter hormone, as well as stimulating the ovary to secrete estrogen, also stimulates follicular growth in the ovary and brings a crop of mature follicles to its surface. In other words, FSH not only prepares the stage for ovulation but, at the same time, stimulates the ovary to secrete estrogen and so makes the female eager to mate at the very time when a mating could be expected to be fertile. This is the basic reason for the dual action of FSH.

Estrus, as such, does not occur in the human female. However, its counterpart does occur at about the time of ovulation, because, at that time, FSH has acted on the ovary both to make it secrete estrogen and to bring a follicle to its surface. But, although the amount of estrogen made by the ovary of the human female is greater at this time than at other times in the cycle, the proportional increase is not nearly so great as that which occurs in lower animals at the time of estrus. In lower animals, a greatly increased concentration of estrogen in the bloodstream is the dominant factor in arousing the mating impulse of the female and in causing it to mate.

That estrogen plays a basic role in arousing the mating impulse in the human female is obvious from the changes that occur in the average girl's interests after puberty. But, although estrogen provides the physiologic basis for the development of a mating impulse in the human female, the strength of that impulse thereafter does not ebb and flow in relation to the amount of estrogen present in the bloodstream to anything like the same extent that it does in the lower animals. It is true that some surveys have shown that if all other things remain constant (and they seldom do), the mating impulse of some women is somewhat enhanced at the time of ovulation and, more commonly, a short time before menstruation. The first of these examples is probably to be explained by an increased estrogen content in the blood and the second by an increased progesterone content, which acts to augment the estrogen effect. But the changes in the intensity of the impulse caused by ordinary hormonal variations are not comparable with those that are caused by psychological factors (for example, by falling in love). Indeed, the psychological factors become so much more important than the hormonal that a woman who has been happily married for many years does not necessarily experience any substantial decrease in libido if her ovaries are removed. In other words, estrogen is necessary to establish the basis on which mating reflexes of various types may be built in the human female, and after these are well established they tend to remain.

**Pseudopregnancy.** The events that follow estrus in the females of various kinds of animals differ considerably (provided that the female does not mate with a male). A comparison of the events that follow estrus in the rabbit, the rat and the dog families is of interest.

When an isolated female rabbit comes into estrus, ovulation does not occur automatically; instead, the female rabbit remains in estrus until it mates. However, on mating, ovulation occurs. Since ovulation depends upon the anterior pituitary secreting LH, it is obvious that some factor other than a relatively high blood estrogen level is necessary in some animals to cause the anterior pituitary to secrete enough LH to cause ovulation. If a female rabbit is mated with a sterile male, ovulation still occurs; therefore, it is obvious that ovulation does not depend on male germ cells being introduced into the female but upon such nervous stimulation as is involved in the female's mating with the male. That this nervous factor is instrumental

in causing ovulation by stimulating the anterior pituitary to secrete LH has been shown by the fact that if the anterior pituitary is removed immediately after a female rabbit mates, ovulation does not occur. It is not known to what extent sexual excitement or the nervous stimulation involved in the mating procedure stimulates the secretion of LH in the human species, but the fact that it is so fundamental to LH secretion in some animals suggests that it could conceivably play some part in modifying the time of ovulation in the human female. However, most authorities are doubtful that it does.

If a female rabbit is mated with a sterile male, not only does ovulation occur, but corpora lutea also develop in the ovary from which the ova are liberated. These, for a time, grow and develop and make progesterone, and, as a result, the animal begins to exhibit all the signs of pregnancy except that its uterus does not contain any embryos. This false pregnancy that develops in the rabbit after it mates with a sterile male, which is due to corpora lutea growing and secreting progesterone, is called *pseudopregnancy*. It continues for a considerable time, though not for so long as a true pregnancy. Its maintenance is due presumably to the anterior pituitary continuing to secrete LH for a considerable time after the act of mating. However, after a time the anterior pituitary "discovers" that true pregnancy has not occurred and it ceases to secrete LH, and, as a result, the corpora lutea in the ovaries involute and the pseudopregnancy comes to an end. It is to be kept in mind that the termination of a pseudopregnancy in the rabbit has many points in common with menstruation as it occurs in the human female.

The estrous cycle of the rat is different from that of the rabbit, for the isolated female rat remains in estrus for only a few hours and then begins a new estrous cycle. A new cycle is repeated approximately every 4 days. The rat ovulates spontaneously at the time of estrus. Nevertheless, if it does not mate, functional corpora lutea do not develop in its ovaries; hence, no progesterone is made to inhibit the anterior pituitary from secreting FSH, and so, after estrus, the anterior pituitary begins again to secrete FSH. This brings a new crop of follicles to the surface of one of the ovaries in 4 days' time and stimulates the production of enough estrogen to put the rat into estrus by the time the follicles mature.

If a female rat mates with a sterile male at the time of estrus, the sexual excitement and the nervous stimulation associated with the mating procedure cause the anterior pituitary to secrete enough LH to make functional corpora lutea develop in the ovary. These secrete enough progesterone into the bloodstream to cause pseudopregnancy and to prevent the anterior pituitary from secreting FSH and so causing a new estrous cycle to begin. Therefore, the mating of a female rat with a sterile male upsets its estrous cycle. When the pseudopregnancy has run a course of several days it terminates because the anterior pituitary ceases to secrete enough LH to maintain the corpora lutea. When these involute and cease making progesterone, the anterior pituitary thereupon is permitted once again to secrete FSH, so a new estrous cycle begins.

The estrous cycle of the female of the dog family is different still. An isolated bitch normally comes into estrus twice a year. Ovulation occurs spontaneously at estrus; evidently the high level of estrogen in the blood at the time of estrus is sufficient to cause the anterior pituitary to secrete LH and cause ovulation. Moreover, the anterior pituitary, following ovulation, continues to secrete LH for a considerable time, and, as a result, pseudopregnancy automatically follows estrus in the isolated bitch. This continues approximately half as long as a real pregnancy. Under the influence of progesterone the uterus enlarges, the belly droops, and the mammary glands begin to enlarge. Observing these phenomena, most owners of bitches who are not familiar with the phenomenon of pseudopregnancy begin to wonder if the isolation they imposed on their pets at the time of estrus was as efficient as they thought. But at about this time the pseudopregnancy terminates. The endometrium, previously built up by the action of progesterone, reverts back to its normal thickness; this is accomplished usually without any external bleeding, although some slight hemorrhages into the substance of the endometrium have been observed.

However, the bitch does bleed externally at the time of estrus, and for many years this led medical men to assume that menstruation in the human female was comparable with estrus in lower animals. However, from many different kinds of investigation, it has now become obvious that ovulation does not commonly occur at the time of menstruation but, most commonly, a few days before the halfway point between 2 menstrual periods. The time of ovulation seems to be rather inconstant, and the evidence suggests that there are instances of its having occurred very early and very late in the cycle. It is of interest that a slight amount of bleeding occurs from the endometrium of some women at the time of ovulation; it is this rather than the bleeding of menstruation that is comparable with the estrous bleeding observed in some lower animals.

Moreover, it should be clear from the foregoing that menstruation in the human female is the counterpart of the termination of a pseudopregnancy in lower animals. It is of interest that the human female is representative of the type of animal in which ovulation occurs spontaneously; the nervous stimulation involved in mating, though it may conceivably affect the time of ovulation to some extent, is not essential for a functional corpus luteum to develop and institute pseudopregnancy. The reason for the termination of pseudopregnancy in the human female being associated with such a severe and prolonged event as menstruation, when pseudopregnancy terminates in so many lower animals with almost no disturbance, is probably to be explained by the special pattern of the blood vessels that supply the lining of the uterus in human females; these will be described later.

A little reflection on the foregoing facts should emphasize the importance of progesterone to the institution and the continuance of pregnancy. In some animals Nature is so economical that corpora lutea do not form following estrus unless the animal mates. However, in others Nature takes no chances and has arranged for functional corpora lutea to develop following ovulation even if the female does not mate at this precise time. It is of interest that if the human female were not a representative of this type of animal it would be necessary in those instances when artificial insemination is performed to adopt measures

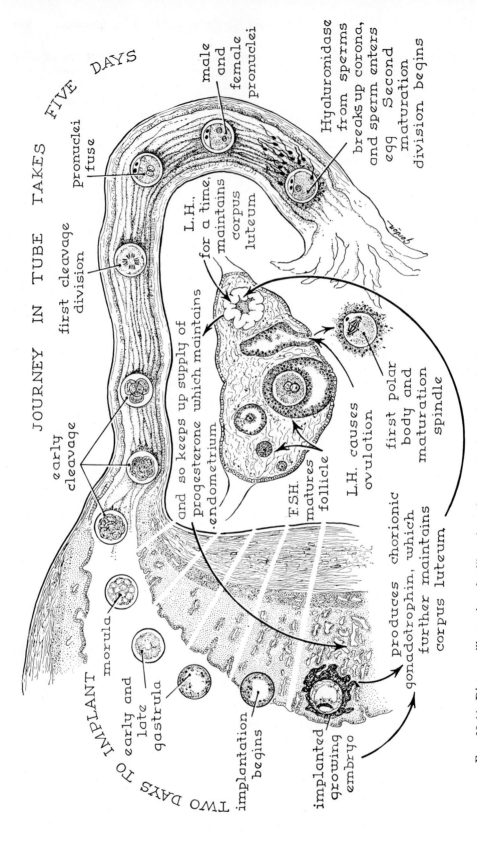

JOURNEY IN TUBE TAKES FIVE DAYS

Pronuclei fuse

first cleavage division

male and female pronuclei

Hyaluronidase from sperms breaks up corona, and sperm enters egg  Second maturation division begins

early cleavage

L.H. for a time, maintains corpus luteum

and so keeps up supply of progesterone which maintains endometrium

F.S.H. matures follicle

L.H. causes ovulation

first polar body and maturation spindle

morula

early and late gastrula

implantation begins

produces chorionic gonadotrophin, which further maintains corpus luteum

implanted growing embryo

TWO DAYS TO IMPLANT

Fig. 29-11. Diagram illustrating the liberation of an ovum from the ovary, its entrance into the oviduct, its fertilization, its passage through the oviduct and its implantation in the endometrium. Study in an anticlockwise direction. The 5 segments of uterine wall that are shown represent from above down the changes that occur in the endometrium from the time of ovulation to the time of implantation. (Redrawn and modified from Dickenson, R. L.: Human Sex Anatomy, Baltimore, Williams & Wilkins)

to ensure that functional corpora lutea would develop in the ovaries.

### ANOVULATORY CYCLES

In the foregoing, menstruation has been described as the result of the termination of a pseudopregnancy. However, occasionally both women and higher monkeys experience bleeding from the endometrium at the time of menstruation without previous ovulation and thus without the development of a corpus luteum in the ovary. These unusual instances of menstrual bleeding without previous ovulation (anovulatory menstruation) are probably due to preceding variations in the level of blood estrogen. We shall elaborate:

If estrogen is withdrawn, for example by removal of the ovaries from a sexually mature woman, the endometrium may bleed as a consequence. Furthermore, if estrogen is given to a female at a standard rate for a time and then the dosage is considerably reduced, but not entirely stopped, bleeding from the endometrium will occur not immediately but *only* after an interval of some days. Therefore, it is believed that the bleeding that occurs in anovulatory menstruation is to be explained as a delayed response to the reduction in the estrogen output of the ovary that occurs following the maturation of a follicle.

Anovulatory cycles in women are not rare; de Allende has shown that a perfectly healthy woman may have 3 or 4 anovulatory cycles a year with a higher proportion near puberty and the menopause.

### THE CORPUS LUTEUM IN PREGNANCY

That progesterone is essential for the continuance of pregnancy already has been explained. We shall now comment briefly on how the production of progesterone is maintained when pregnancy occurs.

If pregnancy does not occur, a corpus luteum persists in the ovary of the human female for only about 10 to 12 days and reaches a diameter of from 1.5 to 2 cm. It then begins to involute because its growth and function are no longer stimulated by LH. Its capillaries collapse and the lutein cells disintegrate; this is shown by their becoming vacuolated. As its characteristic cells degenerate further, it shrinks in size, and it finally becomes a small white scar called a *corpus albicans* (Figs. 29-9 and 29-12).

FIG. 29-12. Very low-power photomicrograph of a section of an ovary of a mature woman, showing a corpus albicans that has formed as a result of the degeneration of a corpus luteum of menstruation.

If pregnancy occurs, the corpus luteum continues to grow and function and attains a diameter of about 5 cm. in the third month of pregnancy. At that time, or somewhat later, it begins to involute. However, the involution of a corpus luteum of pregnancy at this late date does not cause menstruation, because by this time the placenta has begun to manufacture progesterone and hence the involution of the corpus luteum of pregnancy does not cause a progesterone deficiency. Indeed, it appears that the ovary containing the corpus luteum of pregnancy may be removed much earlier than has been generally believed without interrupting the pregnancy because of the placenta soon becoming competent to make enough progesterone to support pregnancy. The involution of a corpus luteum of pregnancy leaves a substantial scar in the ovary.

Why should pregnancy prevent a corpus luteum in an ovary from involuting 2 weeks after ovulation? A corpus luteum begins to involute in the nonpregnant female because LH fails. It might be assumed, then, that

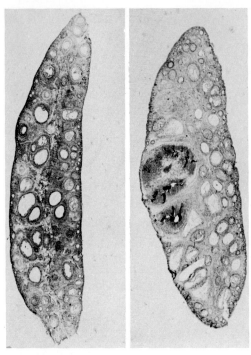

FIG. 29-13. (*Left*) Very low-power photomicrograph of a section of an ovary of a virgin rabbit that was injected with urine from a nonpregnant woman. Mature unruptured follicles may be seen close to the surface. This is the picture seen in a negative test. (*Right*) Very low-power photomicrograph of a section of the ovary of a virgin rabbit that was injected with urine from a pregnant woman. Notice that two of the surface follicles at the left side are very large and are filled with blood as a result of the occurrence of ovulation. On high-power examination, each of these may be seen to have a lining of typical granulosa luteal cells. This is the picture seen in a positive test.

pregnancy somehow prevents an LH failure. Actually, this is not quite what happens, but something very similar does occur. A new hormone that acts very much like LH is made, by the trophoblastic cells of what will become the placenta, soon after the ovum becomes implanted in the endometrium (Fig. 29-11, *lower left*). This hormone is usually called *chorionic* or *placental gonadotrophin*. It differs from LH chiefly in that it cannot do everything that LH can do in an animal from which the anterior pituitary gland has

been removed. However, if such an animal is given some anterior pituitary gonadotrophic hormone, chorionic gonadotrophin then exerts an LH effect. In other words, given a little collaboration by the anterior pituitary, chorionic gonadotrophin acts similarly to LH.

**Pregnancy Tests.** Chorionic gonadotrophin is made in abundance in pregnancy, and it is responsible for making the corpus luteum continue to grow and secrete progesterone (Fig. 29-11). So much chorionic gonadotrophin is made in pregnancy that it is excreted in the urine. Indeed, so much of this hormone is excreted that the urine of a pregnant woman, injected into an animal, causes profound biologic effects. This is the basis for many of the animal tests for pregnancy. An excellent and commonly employed one is the Friedman modification of the Aschheim-Zondek test. This will now be described.

It will be recalled that the virgin rabbit, on coming into estrus, remains in estrus, with mature follicles present at the surface of an ovary, until it mates with a male (Fig. 29-13, *left*). In other words, in the rabbit, ovulation awaits the secretion of LH, which occurs normally only as a result of the sexual excitement and the nervous stimulation associated with the act of mating (sometimes the presence of a male in the vicinity is enough to cause enough LH secretion to cause ovulation; hence, males should be excluded from the testing laboratory). It is obvious that if some LH were injected into a virgin rabbit in estrus, ovulation would immediately occur, and it would be easy, on inspecting the ovaries of the rabbit soon afterward, to see that it had occurred, from finding hemorrhagic follicles (Fig. 29-13, *right*) and young corpora lutea. Likewise, if chorionic gonadotrophin were injected into a vein of a rabbit, the same results would be obtained, for this hormone, in an animal with an intact anterior pituitary gland, acts like LH. There is so much chorionic gonadotrophin in the urine of a pregnant woman that a relatively small amount of urine injected into a vein of a virgin rabbit in estrus will cause ovulation and corpus luteum formation (Fig. 29-13, *right*). Since there is no chorionic gonadotrophin in the urine of a nonpregnant woman and not enough LH to have any effect on a rabbit, it is obvious that the injection of urine

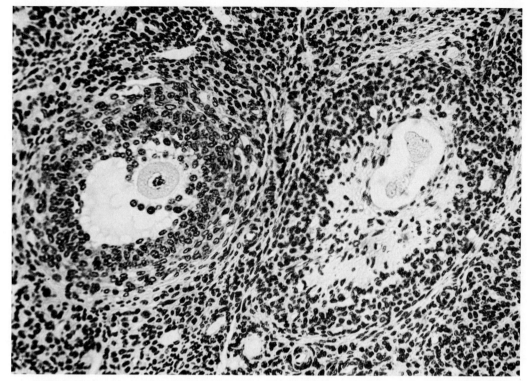

Fig. 29-14. Low-power photomicrograph of a section of an ovary of a guinea pig, showing a normal, developing follicle at the left and an atretic follicle at the right. Observe that the oocyte has degenerated in the atretic follicle and that fibroblasts have grown into the central part of the follicle.

into a virgin rabbit in estrus permits a decision to be made as to whether the urine was obtained from a pregnant or a nonpregnant woman (Fig. 29-13).

### ATRETIC FOLLICLES

It can now be understood that the cortex of the ovary of a sexually mature nonpregnant woman who, however, has borne children, may contain a great variety of structures: primary follicles, normal follicles in various stages of development, follicles in various stages of atresia, perhaps a functioning corpus luteum of menstruation and scars of old corpora lutea of menstruation and of pregnancy. We shall now describe some of the features of some of these structures in more detail so that the student may have some general principles for differentiating among them in sections.

It is to be remembered that, out of many large follicles that are brought close to the surface of the ovary of a woman at the time

of ovulation, only one usually appears to survive and liberate an oocyte. It seems probable, according to Allen, Pratt, Newell and Bland, that the other large ones all undergo atresia. They do not, then, remain in a state of suspended animation, waiting for an opportunity to ovulate in a subsequent month, but die. For ovulation to occur in another month requires that a new set of follicles develop and approach the surface.

In a given section of ovary, there may be, then, many large atretic follicles and, if they are just beginning to undergo atresia, it may be difficult to distinguish them from normal follicles. If atresia has proceeded for any length of time, the student's task is easier, for later on, in atresia, fibroblasts grow into the breaking-down follicle and replace it with connective tissue (Fig. 29-14, *right*). But before this occurs the detection of atresia requires the use of less obvious criteria. Two early signs of the condition are the pulling away of the follicular epithelium from the theca interna (or a break in the follicular epithelium) and pyknotic nuclei in the follicular epithelial cells. Allen *et al.* note that the cumulus oophorus becomes detached in atresia, but this, of course, cannot be established from the study of a single section. The histologic signs of cell death may, of course, be observed in the ovum in atresia, but the ovum may not be seen in the part of the follicle through which the section under view has been cut.

In distinguishing old atretic follicles from degenerate corpora lutea it is helpful to keep in mind that the term atresia is reserved for follicles that degenerate before they mature, and hence that there has been no reason for bleeding to have occurred in them. On the other hand, old corpora lutea, whether of menstruation or pregnancy, usually contain blood pigment that remains behind in them to indicate that they were once the site of a hemorrhage.

### The Ovary After the Menopause

After functioning for 30 odd years, both with respect to liberating ova and secreting hormones, the ovaries appear to become exhausted and, after a short period during which they function sporadically, they finally cease liberating ova and producing hormones. When they fail to liberate oocytes there are, of course, no new corpora lutea formed, and, as a result, the endometrium thereafter neither becomes greatly thickened nor collapses each 28 days. The most obvious sign of ovarian failure, then, is that the menses cease; and, indeed, it is for that reason that this time in a woman's life is described as the *menopause* (*mēn* = month; *pausis* = cessation). The menopause usually occurs somewhere between the ages of 45 and 50, and it marks the end of the reproductive life of a woman. Actually, fertility declines rapidly during the 10 years before menopause. An artificial menopause occurs earlier if the ovaries are removed or if their function is otherwise destroyed as, for example, by irradiation or disease.

The onset of the menopause is usually indicated, though not always, by other signs and symptoms. Commonly, the function of the vasomotor nerves becomes disturbed, and women suffer from what are called "hot flushes." Moreover, they may find it more difficult, for a time, both from physiologic and psychological reasons, to maintain their usual adjustment to life; hence, some women exhibit a certain amount of emotional instability at this time. Indeed, in the very badly adjusted, the menopause may precipitate serious mental illness. Other symptoms, such as headache, insomnia and alterations in the rate of the heart beat, are sometimes experienced. Much can now be done to alleviate the more distressing symptoms that occur at this time by the judicious administration of sex hormones.

It should be clearly understood that the hormonal disturbances that occur at the menopause are due to ovarian failure and not to the failure of the anterior pituitary. Indeed, as the estrogen level of the blood falls after the menopause, the push-pull arrangement between estrogen and FSH leads to FSH being secreted in such increased amounts that fairly large quantities of it appear in the urine. Hence, if the urine of a woman who has passed the menopause is injected into a young animal, it will stimulate follicular development and estrogen production in that young animal and so bring about a precocious puberty in it. There is no point, then, in giving a woman gonadotrophic hormone at this time to stimulate her ovaries. On the other hand, the administration of estrogen to a women at the time of the menopause could be expected to suppress, to some extent, the increased FSH secretion that ordinarily occurs at this time, as well as to produce other beneficial effects.

The ovary of a woman who has recently passed the menopause is to be distinguished by the relative absence of: (1) primary follicles, (2) follicles in various stages of normal development or showing early atresia and (3) recent corpora lutea. As the years pass, the ovary becomes increasingly shrunken, consisting almost altogether of old fibrous tissue.

It seems probable that the falling-off in progesterone production is more abrupt at the menopause than the falling-off in estrogen production. New corpora lutea are necessary if progesterone production is to be carried on for any great length of time. Estrogen production by the ovary, though diminished, may be carried on for some time after the menopause. It is probable that estrogens are made by thecal cells. So, as long as theca elements persist in the ovary, some estrogen might be produced. Moreover, it is probable that there are some, though not very important, extra-ovarian sources of estrogen in the body.

The great decrease in estrogen production that occurs at the menopause may be reflected sooner or later in substantial tissue changes in certain parts of the body. Those parts of the female reproductive tract that are dependent on this hormone for the maintenance of their structure tend to become atrophic. For example, the functional capacity of the glands associated with the external genitalia becomes diminished; the external genitalia themselves tend to atrophy, and the vaginal lining may become very thin and increasingly susceptible to infection. Substitution therapy can do much to relieve these conditions when they occur.

### SOME THEORETICAL CONSIDERATIONS· ABOUT THE MECHANISMS CONCERNED IN THE PREVENTION OF CONCEPTION BY HORMONE PREPARATIONS

For a woman to become pregnant it is of course essential for ovulation to occur so that the ovum of a mature follicle is liberated from the ovary into the female reproductive tract where it is available for fertilization. It follows therefore that a basis for the prevention of pregnancy could be the adoption of measures that prevent ovulation.

Since the development, maturation and rupture of ovarian follicles depend primarily on the successive actions of two trophic hormones of the anterior pituitary gland, namely FSH and LH, ovulation will not occur if adequate amounts of these two hormones are not present in the circulation for proper lengths of time. Female animals from whom the pituitary glands have been removed do not ovulate even though their ovaries are intact.

FSH and LH are secreted by the anterior lobe more or less in a sequential order. Next, as was described at the beginning of the previous chapter in connection with trophic hormones, there is a push-pull arrangement between the secretion of trophic hormones of the anterior pituitary and the secretion of the hormones of the target glands they affect. For

example, the administration of thyroid hormones to an individual by mouth results in increased amounts of thyroid hormone being absorbed from his intestine into his bloodstream and the increased amount in his bloodstream inhibits the secretion of TSH (thyrotrophin) by the thyrotrophs of the anterior pituitary gland. Further, as was explained in this present chapter, there is a push-pull arrangement between the secretion of FSH by the anterior pituitary and estrogen by the ovary. Likewise, there is a push-pull arrangement between the secretion of LH by the anterior pituitary and progesterone by a corpus luteum. The operation of these two push-pull arrangements will now be reviewed.

It was explained in a preceding section that following menstruation the anterior pituitary begins to secrete FSH; this causes a follicle to mature at the surface of the ovary and it also causes the cells of the wall of the follicle (apparently the theca cells) to secrete estrogen. As the estrogen secretion continues, the estrogen in the bood begins to push back, as it were, on the anterior pituitary and by about half-way through the cycle it suppresses the further secretion of FSH. The anterior pituitary then secretes LH and this causes the ovarian follicle to rupture and it also causes the corpus luteum to produce progesterone. The increasing amounts of progesterone in the bloodstream then begin to push back against the cells in the anterior pituitary that secrete LH and so after about 10 days activity the secretion of LH by the cells of the anterior pituitary is suppressed.

Since the maturation of follicles at the surface of the ovary is dependent on the secretion of FSH and since the rupture of the follicle with the release of the ovum is dependent on the secretion of LH, it follows that if a woman took by mouth daily, over roughly the interval that would occur between two menstrual periods, adequate amounts of a proper preparation of estrogen and progesterone, it would be possible for her to absorb enough estrogen and progesterone into her bloodstream to inhibit the anterior pituitary from secreting either FSH or LH. As a result of the activities of the anterior pituitary in this connection being inhibited, no follicle would mature at the surface of the ovary, ovulation would not occur, and no corpus luteum to make progesterone would develop. This then is the basis for the use of hormone preparations for preventing conception; the preparations are designed to inhibit the secretion primarily of FSH and, to a lesser extent, LH and are taken daily over the period of time during which FSH and LH would ordinarily bring about the maturation of a follicle, its rupture, and the formation of a corpus luteum.

Since the secretion of estrogen by the ovary (as well as the maturation of follicles) is dependent on FSH stimulation, it follows that the regular use by a woman of hormone preparations that suppress FSH secretion, would have the second effect of diminishing the output of estrogen by her ovaries. Since female nature is basically dependent upon estrogen, an important function of a hormone preparation that is used to suppress FSH secretion is that it should supply sufficient estrogen to take the place of that which is not formed by the woman's ovaries because they lack FSH stimulation. Likewise, since corpora lutea are not formed, progesterone secretion is stopped. Accordingly, such progesterone as is required by a woman who takes one of these hormone preparations must also be supplied by the preparation. Accordingly, hormone preparations used to prevent conception have to serve two purposes, first, prevent ovulation, and secondly, supply the sex hormones which are not made in the woman taking the preparation because the cycles of activity in her ovaries are stilled.

The next question that might be asked about the use of these preparations is what happens about menstrual periods. As is explained elsewhere in this chapter, there are two primary factors concerned in causing menstruation. The more important is a cessation of progesterone secretion; this acts promptly to institute menstruation. The second factor is estrogen withdrawal, this acts somewhat more slowly. So, if a woman who is taking hormone preparations that contain estrogen and progesterone stops taking the preparation shortly before she would normally menstruate, the conditions of estrogen and progesterone withdrawal are both realized and so she menstruates. So the occurrence of menstruation in a woman taking these hormone preparations is dependent on her not taking the preparations for a brief period over the 28-day cycle so that menstruation can occur.

From much of the foregoing it is apparent that dosage of these preparations must be regulated with great care both with regard to amounts taken and timing.

A woman who, during the fertile period of her life, takes one of these hormone preparations for some time and then stops will resume her normal cycles, and the evidence indicates that she is just as fertile as she was before, if not more so. It would seem, moreover, that if a woman continued taking hormone preparations of this type beyond the time when she would ordinarily have passed through the menopause, she would perhaps be unaware that she had reached this period of her life because she, under the influence of the preparation she was taking, would continue to menstruate and, since her sex hormones would not be dependent on the output of her ovaries, she conceivably would experience fewer of the symptoms that can arise from the diminished sex hormone production of the ovaries that occurs normally at that time of life. In due course, it will be known whether the advantages gained would be outweighed by disadvantages which may, in due course, be discovered. Finally, it is interesting to question whether or not a woman who took one of these preparations most of her life and so suppressed ovulation through most of her life, and stopped taking the preparation when she had passed the time of life when she normally would have experienced the menopause, would still be fertile. Would the primary follicles in her ovaries whose development had been suppressed through the years then respond to FSH stimulation and mature and liberate ova capable of being fertilized? From what we now know about the ovary this possibility seems unlikely. There is a superabundance of follicles in the ovary, and holding a few in abeyance through the years would increase the total number that the ovary contains only very slightly. From what we now know, it could be thought that primary follicles in the ovary have only a certain life expectancy and that by the time a woman reaches menopause age, follicles in her ovary have lived out their span.

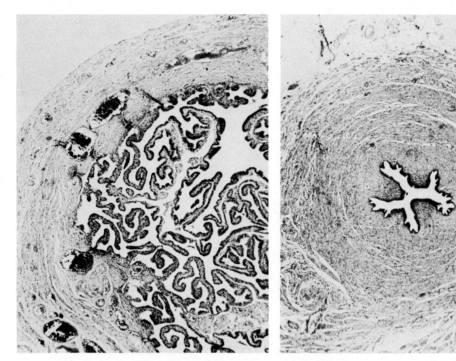

Fig. 29-15. (*Left*) Very low-power photomicrograph of a portion of a cross section of the ampulla of an oviduct of a mature woman. The dark areas in the muscle coat are congested veins. Observe the complex longitudinal folds that are cut in cross section. (*Right*) Very low-power photomicrograph of a cross section of the isthmus of an oviduct.

A FURTHER NOTE ABOUT THE PUSH-PULL
MECHANISM FOR REGULATING SEX HORMONE
SECRETION

As was noted in the preceding chapter, there is evidence to the effect that the nervous system may be involved in the regulation of hormone secretion by means of certain parts of it releasing humoral factors which act as releasing factors with regard to cells of the anterior pituitary which make certain trophic hormones. It was mentioned that there was evidence indicating that an ACTH-releasing factor under certain circumstances could be liberated from the hypothalamic region and flow to the cells of the anterior lobe where it acts to cause the cells that make ACTH liberate their secretion. There is likewise growing evidence that indicates that there may be hypothalamic factors released which can cause the liberation of secretion from the cells of the anterior lobe that make FSH and those that make LH, and further-

more, that the suppression of the secretion of these two anterior lobe hormones may be due at least in part to the hormones whose secretion they control not pushing back directly on the cells that secrete FSH and LH but on the nervous centers that produce the hormone-releasing factors. The involvement of the nervous system, and particularly emotional centers, in the mechanisms involved in the release of hormones that control the secretion of sex hormones is, of course, of great interest.

THE OVIDUCTS

Each oviduct (Fig. 29-1) is about 12 cm. long and consists of 4 parts: (1) an intramural part—that portion of the tube that extends through the wall of the uterus; (2) an isthmus —the short narrow part of the tube next to the uterus; (3) an ampulla—the longest part of the tube, about the diameter of a pencil and extending from the isthmus to, (4) an infundibulum—the flared termination of the tube

**Tube**

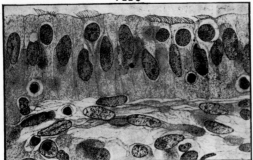

**Mid-interval**

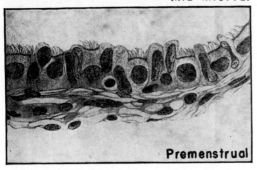

**Premenstrual**

FIG. 29-16. (*Top*) Human oviduct about midinterval stage. (*Bottom*) Tube at premenstrual stage. (Camera lucida drawings; × 700). (Snyder, F. F.: Bull. Johns Hopkins Hosp. *35*:146)

provided with processes or fimbriae. The wall of the oviduct is made up of 3 layers, a mucous membrane, a muscular coat and an adventitial serous coat (Fig. 29-15).

**Mucous Membrane.** The epithelium consists of a single layer of columnar cells. There are 2 types of these, ciliated and secretory, and they alternate irregularly with one another (Fig. 29-16, *top*). Their relative and absolute heights vary in relation to different times in the menstrual cycle. Beginning shortly after menstruation, according to Snyder, they both increase in height, and at the time of ovulation they are both about 30 μ high (Fig. 29-16, *top*). Following this, however, the ciliated cells become much shorter, and the nonciliated secretory cells, though they too become somewhat shorter, come to project between the ciliated cells into the lumen of the tube, thus making the free epithelial surface somewhat irregular (Fig. 29-16, *bottom*). A few clear cells with dark-staining nuclei may be scattered about in the epithelial mem-

brane close to the basement membrane. They are probably young secretory cells. In addition occasional lymphocytes are found in this site. It is not believed that the nonciliated cells become ciliated or vice versa. The cilia beat toward the uterus. Their fine structure is shown in Figure 8-18. The nature of the secretion of the secretory cells is not known; Novak and Everett found that it did not become colored with stains for mucin or glycogen. However, Siegler indicates that glycogen may form in the lining cells of the oviducts of immature monkeys if the animals are injected with one of the gonadotrophic hormones. Probably the watery secretions in the tube, whatever they may be, are in some way nutritive or otherwise helpful for the ovum and that the hormonal stimulation of the cells concerned in making secretions occurs at a time when an ovum would be likely to be passing along the tube.

The lamina propria of the mucous membrane is of the ordinary connective tissue type except that its cells have potentialities similar to those of the endometrial stroma, for they react similarly if a fertilized ovum inadvertently becomes implanted in the mucosa of the oviduct.

As described in the general account of the parts of the reproductive system, the mucous membrane of the oviduct is thrown into extensive longitudinal folds (Fig. 29-15, *left*). These become reduced in size and extend in the isthmus (Fig. 29-15, *right*) and amount to little more than ridges in the intramural portion of the tube.

**Muscle Coat.** This consists of 2 layers: an inner one of circularly or somewhat spirally disposed smooth muscle fibers and an outer one of longitudinally disposed fibers. However, the line of demarcation between the 2 layers of muscle is by no means clear-cut, and since some connective tissue extends between the bundles of muscle fibers, the muscle coats may be difficult to identify in anything more than a general way. The inner coat of circular fibers is thickest in the intramural portion of the tube and least prominent in the infundibulum. Peristalticlike movements of the muscle are believed to be accentuated around the time of ovulation. The tonus, as well as contractions of the muscle, has been shown to be affected by hormones.

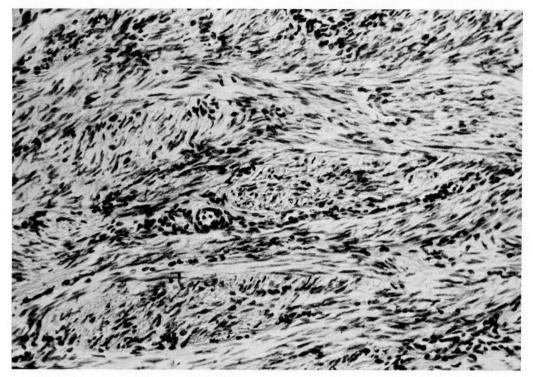

FIG. 29-17. Low-power photomicrograph of a section of the myometrium. Observe the interlacing bundles of smooth muscle fibers.

The histologic structure of the serosa is typical.

## THE BODY AND THE FUNDUS OF THE UTERUS

The wall of a uterus (Fig. 29-2) varies in thickness from 1.5 cm. to slightly less than 1 cm. It consists of 3 coats, which from without in, are (1) a thin serous coat or *serosa,* (2) a thick muscle coat or *myometrium,* and (3) a mucous membrane or *endometrium.*

The serosa—in reality the peritoneal investment of the organ—consists of a single layer of mesothelial cells supported by a thin connective tissue membrane; it is continuous at each side of the organ with the peritoneum of the broad ligament and is deficient in the lower half of the anterior surface (Fig. 29-2).

The myometrium consists of bundles of smooth muscle fibers separated from one another by connective tissue (Fig. 29-17). The bundles are arranged so as to form 3 rather ill-defined layers. The outermost and innermost layers are thin and consist chiefly of longitudinally and obliquely disposed fibers. The middle layer is much thicker, and in it the smooth muscle fibers tend to be disposed circularly. The larger blood vessels of the wall of the uterus are mostly contained in this middle layer; hence, it is sometimes called the *stratum vasculare.* The smooth muscle fibers in this layer, in the uterus of the nonpregnant woman, are about 0.25 mm. in length. They become 10 times as long and many times as thick during pregnancy. The great increase in the thickness of the myometrium in pregnancy is brought about not only by a hypertrophy of previously existing fibers but also by an increase in the number of fibers; the new ones being derived, in all probability, both from the division of pre-existing fibers and from the transformation of undifferentiated cells in the connective tissue between the bundles into smooth muscle cells.

### THE ENDOMETRIUM

This, the mucous membrane that lines the body and the fundus of the uterus, consists of an epithelial lining and a connective tissue

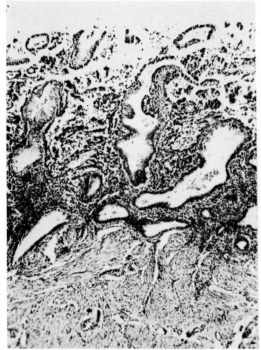 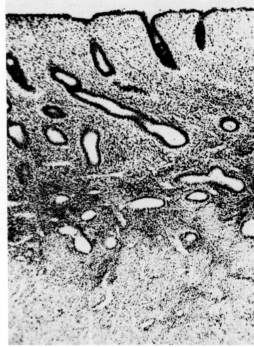

Fig. 29-18. (*Left*) Low-power photomicrograph of a section of the endometrium and the adjacent myometrium near the end of menstruation. Observe the raw inner surface and notice that all but the most deeply situated parts of the glands and the stroma associated with them are degenerating and being cast away. (*Right*) Low-power photomicrograph of the same region in a section taken from a uterus in which the endometrium was in an early proliferative phase. Observe that the previously raw surface has become epithelized and that the glands are straight.

lamina propria which is continuous with the myometrium. Customarily, the lamina propria is referred to as the *endometrial stroma,* and hereafter we shall use this term. The stroma is beset by simple tubular glands whose mouths open through the epithelial surface into the lumen of the uterus and whose deepest parts almost reach the myometrium (Fig. 29-18, *right*). The glands are composed of columnar epithelium similar to that which lines the cavity of the uterus.

It is helpful to describe the endometrium as consisting of 2 chief layers: a thick superficial one, called the *functional* layer, and a thin deep one, called the *basilar* layer. The functional layer is so-called because its character changes greatly during the menstrual cycle; indeed, at menstruation it is mostly shed (Fig. 29-18, *left*). The character of the basilar layer does not change to any great extent during the menstrual cycle, and it remains through menstruation to regenerate

another functional layer after the menstrual flow ceases.

**Endometrium During the Menstrual Cycle.** In the first part of this chapter, the menstrual cycle was stated to be a 28-day one. As might be supposed, it is by no means constant; it may be a few days shorter or several days longer. Furthermore, the length of the cycle may vary in the same individual from time to time. It is usual to number the days in the cycle from the first day of menstruation; this is a concession to medical practice because the first day of menstruation is a date which a patient can set with exactitude. Most commonly, menstruation lasts for 4 days, but periods a day shorter or a day longer are common.

It is usual to describe the endometrium as passing through several different phases in each menstrual cycle. For example, the endometrium from days 1 to 4 is said to be in its *menstrual phase* (Fig. 29-18, *left*). From

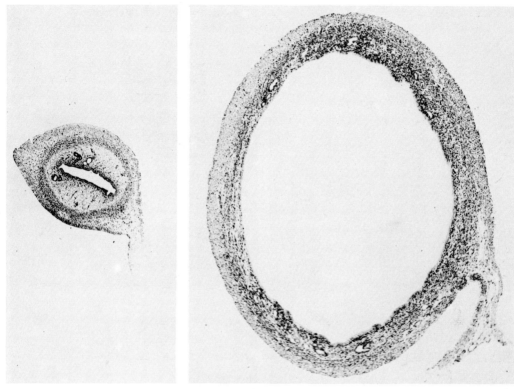

FIG. 29-19. (*Left*) Very low-power photomicrograph of a cross section of one horn of the uterus of a rat a month after its ovaries were removed. The uterus has atrophied as a result of estrogen deficiency. (*Right*) Photomicrograph, at the same magnification, of the same type of preparation made from a rat treated identically, except that the rat from which this specimen was obtained was given large doses of estrogen for a few days before the specimen was recoverd. This illustration shows not only that estrogen makes the cells of an atrophied uterus grow but also that estrogen makes its epithelial cells secrete, for this uterus is enormously distended with secretion.

day 4 until a day or two after ovulation the endometrium is said to be in its *estrogenic, proliferative, reparative* or *follicular phase* (Fig. 29-18, *right*). During this time it grows from something less than 1 mm. to 2 or 3 mm. in thickness. Its growth during this period is encouraged by the estrogen that is being secreted by the ovary as a follicle matures and approaches the surface (hence the terms estrogenic and follicular). Figure 29-19 illustrates how potently estrogen can affect the growth of the uterus. After ovulation occurs it probably takes the corpus luteum that develops a day or two to secrete enough progesterone to affect the endometrium, and since the estrogenic phase lasts until the progestational phase begins, the estrogenic phase can be considered to last a day or two past the

time of ovulation. The last day of the estrogenic phase cannot be set with any exactitude because of the variability of the time of ovulation. Such evidence as exists is somewhat conflicting, but ovulation probably occurs somewhere between days 8 and 20 and rarely before or after this period (see Siegler: *Fertility in Women*). With the understanding that the time of ovulation varies considerably, for convenience we shall say that it occurs at day 14 and, therefore, that the endometrium is in its estrogenic phase from days 4 to 16. In some part of the endometrium this phase probably begins even before day 4. The latter part of the estrogenic phase is often termed the *interval phase*. This term is used to depict that period that ensues after the endometrium has become thoroughly repaired but has not

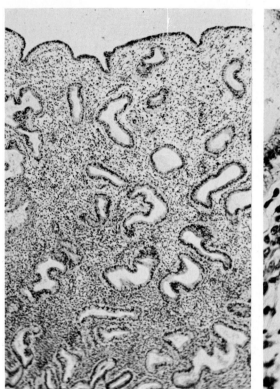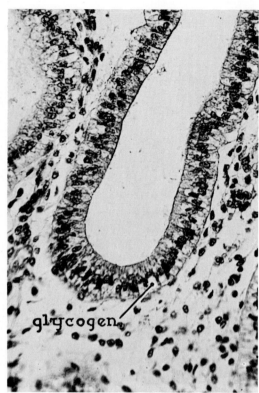

glycogen

FIG. 29-20. (*Left*) Low-power photomicrograph of the inner portion of the endometrium in the early progestational phase. (*Right*) High-power photomicrograph of one of the glands. At this stage glycogen is present between the nuclei and the bases of their cells.

yet begun to be affected by progesterone. The last phase of the menstrual cycle is called either: (1) the *progestational phase,* because the changes that occur in the endometrium during this phase are due to the action of progesterone, or (2) the *progravid (gravid =* heavy, pregnant) *phase,* because pregnancy, when it occurs, begins in this phase, or (3) the *secretory phase,* because the epithelial cells of the glands actively secrete at this time. This phase begins about 2 days after ovulation and lasts normally for 12 to 14 days. That the corpus luteum develops and functions for about 10 to 12 days seems to be a much more constant phenomenon in the menstrual cycle than the time of ovulation. The last day or two of the progestational phase is sometimes called the *ischemic (ischo = I keep back; haima = blood) phase* because the vessels that supply the more superficial parts of the functional layer of the endometrium become shut off for variable periods

during this time, and the endometrium suffers from a lack of blood supply, as will be described in more detail later.

**Details of Microscopic Appearance in Different Phases.** It is convenient to describe first the structure of the endometrium in the later stages of the estrogenic phase (the interval phase). The endometrium at this time is from 2 to 3 mm. thick. The epithelial cells that line the surface and comprise the glands are columnar and often piled up on one another because of active proliferation. The small amount of mucus they secrete at this time is thin and watery. Patches of ciliated columnar cells are scattered about among the secretory cells. The glands in the functional layer of the endometrium tend to be narrow and straight. The stroma consists of star-shaped mesenchymal cells whose cytoplasmic processes connect with each other. The cells are adherent to a network of reticular fibers. Metachromatically staining amorphous intercellular substance is not so abundant at this time as somewhat earlier. Leukocytes are not common in the stroma in this phase.

In the progestational phase the endometrium becomes more than twice as thick as it was in the interval phase. The increase in thickness is partly due to increased amounts of tissue fluid in the stroma (edema), partly due to the glands accumulating increased amounts of secretion and partly due to the increase in the size of stromal cells. Except in the more superficial part of the functional layer and in the basal layer, the glands become wide, tortuous and sacculated (Figs. 29-20, *left,* and 29-21). Their cells come to contain considerable amounts of glycogen. At first this accumulates between the nuclei and the bases of the cells (Fig. 29-20, *right*), but later it appears between the nuclei and the free borders of the cells; the latter thereupon become ragged in appearance (Fig. 29-21). The secretion in the glands becomes much thicker and more abundant than formerly. The cells of the stroma are enlarged, undergoing what is called a *decidual reaction* (the word decidua, *deciduus* = a falling off, refers to the membrane into which the functional zone of the endometrium becomes transformed during pregnancy and is cast off at the time of birth). Stroma cells evidence this reaction by becoming large and pale, and their cytoplasm comes to contain glycogen and lipoid droplets. If pregnancy occurs the decidual reaction is intensified and persists.

The changes that occur in all but the latter part of the progestational phase are due to the action of progesterone, working in collaboration with such estrogen as is still present in the circulation. It is presumed that, in general, these changes are designed to make the endometrium nutritive for a fertilized ovum; for example, the glycogen that forms may serve as a readily available form of carbohydrate.

The changes that occur toward the end of the progestational phase, provided that pregnancy does not occur, have been described by Markee. This investigator studied them by implanting bits of the endometrium of monkeys into the anterior chambers of their eyes, where they became vascularized and could be observed directly for hours. Markee found that the endometrium, toward the end of what we have termed the progestational phase, begins

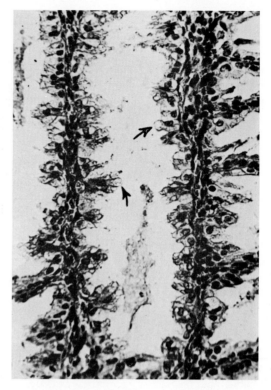

FIG. 29-21. Medium-power photomicrograph of a section of endometrium in the late progestational phase. Observe the ladderlike appearance of the gland photographed and note that the free borders of the cells of the gland are ragged because there is glycogen at this site.

to regress (shrink). Regression, according to Markee, always precedes menstrual bleeding. In order to explain how the regression of the endometrium, which in all probability occurs because of the decreasing stimulation of both estrogen and progesterone at this time, may act to institute bleeding in, and the breakdown of, the functional layer of the endometrium, we must first describe the special features of the blood supply of the endometrium. As regression begins leukocytes invade the endometrium.

**Blood Supply of the Endometrium.** Daron has studied the arterial supply of the endometrium of the monkey in the various phases of the menstrual cycle by injecting the blood vessels of the animal and then freezing and fixing the uterus *in situ*. Both cleared thick

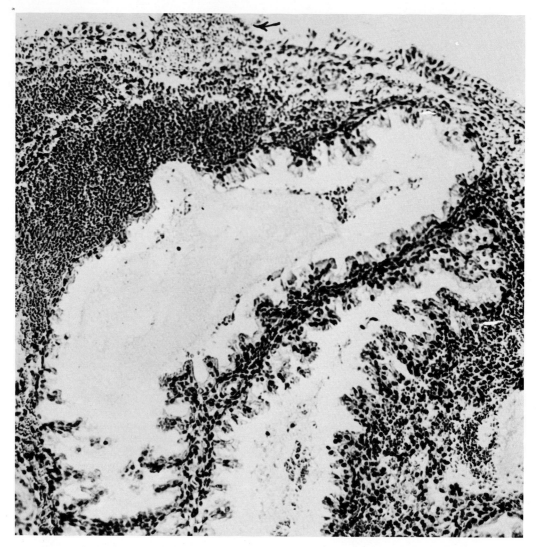

Fig. 29-22. Medium-power photomicrograph of a section of endometrium at the beginning of menstruation. Observe that a pool of blood has formed in the stroma (*upper left*), that the epithelial lining of the uterus has become discontinuous in the upper middle part of the picture, and that red blood cells are entering the lumen of the uterus at the site indicated by the arrow.

sections and ordinary serial sections were used in his study. Essentially, he found that 2 types of arteries lead from the stratum vascularis of the myometrium to the endometrium. Those of the first type, on approaching the endometrium, assume a coiled form and, without branching to any great extent, maintain their coiled form as they extend through the endometrium to its superficial part; there they terminate in a fountainlike arrangement of precapillary arterioles which supply the capillary beds of the inner part of the endometrium.

The second type of artery that Daron describes extends from the stratum vascularis of the myometrium to end, after pursuing a straight course, in the deeper (outer) layer of the endometrium. The blood supply of at least the more superficial (inner) part of the functional layer of the endometrium, then, is derived from the coiled arteries.

**Ischemic and Menstrual Phases.** The coiled arteries are of the greatest importance in menstruation; indeed, the phenomenon of menstruation occurs only in those few members of the animal kingdom in which the endometrium of the female has this particular type of blood vessel. Markee has paid particular attention to the changes that occur in these vessels in the latter parts of the progestational phase. He finds that, as the endometrium regresses, the coiled arteries become increasingly coiled to accommodate themselves to the thinning endometrium. As menstruation approaches, the circulation in them slows, and beginning the day before menstruation, the coiled arteries, one by one, become constricted for prolonged periods of time so that the endometrium that lies over them becomes blanched. After a coiled artery has remained constricted for a time, it dilates, and as blood once more reaches the arterioles and capillaries supplied by the artery (these have suffered from a lack of blood supply during the period of vasoconstriction) it escapes through their walls into the stroma. By this means little pools of blood accumulate beneath the endometrial surface (Fig. 29-22). These soon rupture through the epithelium into the uterine cavity (Fig. 29-22, *top*). Meanwhile, the coiled artery concerned has become constricted again, and its terminal portions die. The same sequence of events is repeated in other arteries. As small pieces of endometrium become detached, <u>arterioles</u> may bleed directly onto the surface rather than into the stroma. As the deeper parts of the functional layer become involved, veins become opened, and they too slowly bleed. Eventually, over a few days, most of the functional layer of the endometrium is lost.

The cause of the progressive disintegration of the endometrium appears to be a lack of blood supply. That the functional layer of the endometrium is supplied by coiled end-arteries facilitates the effectiveness of vasoconstriction in causing an almost complete ischemia of the inner part of the endometrium. That the endometrium regresses and so causes the coiled arteries to become more or less buckled before menstruation, probably further facilitates the effectiveness of the vasoconstriction process in causing the necrosis of the endometrium. The reason for the basal layer's not being lost during menstruation lies in its different blood supply.

The cause of the regression of the endometrium in the latter stages of the progestational phase, and the vasoconstriction of the coiled arteries that follows in its wake, is hormone-deficiency. Although both estrogen and progesterone are deficient at this time, progesterone failure is the more important precipitating factor; indeed, menstruation can be delayed by the administration of extra progesterone. The student, then, may find it helpful to think of menstruation as the result of the termination of a pseudopregnancy in the uterus of an animal in which the more superficial parts of the endometrium is supplied by coiled arteries. Nevertheless, it is to be kept in mind that a reduction in the blood estrogen from the level attained in the midpart of the cycle plays some part in the process, for in anovulatory cycles (which are less common in women but occur commonly in some seasons in monkeys), bleeding occurs at the regular time for menstruation without ovulation having occurred, without a corpus luteum having formed, without progesterone having been secreted and without the endometrium having passed through a proper progestational phase. Hence, estrogen withdrawal, as it is often termed, can, by itself, cause retraction of the endometrium and bleeding from coiled arteries. Nevertheless, in women it is commonly progesterone failure that precipitates the endometrial breakdown.

**Early Part of Estrogenic Phase.** The basal layer of the endometrium, with its separate arterial supply, is left intact throughout the cycle (Fig. 29-18, *left*). When the menstrual phase has run its course, the epithelium from the glands grows out over the denuded surface and rapidly covers it again (Fig. 29-18, *right*). Mitotic figures become numerous both in the gland and in the stroma cells. Amorphous intercellular substance is formed in noticeable amounts in the stroma; according to both S. H. Bensley and Sylvén, this precedes the substantial formation of reticular fibers, and the amount of it decreases as the fibers develop. Repair is so rapid that an interval type of endometrium is soon produced.

## THE PLACENTA

**Some General Considerations.** The placenta is an organ that develops during pregnancy in the lining of the uterus. When fully developed it has the shape of a flat cake (*placenta* = cake), approximately 15 cm. in diameter and 3 cm. thick. It is fundamentally of fetal origin. Its primary function is to permit substances dissolved in the blood of the mother to diffuse into the blood of the fetus and vice versa. Its design permits this to occur over a vast area. Under normal conditions the blood of the fetus and the blood of the mother neither mix nor come into direct contact with one another. They are always separated by what is termed the placental barrier; this, as we shall see, is a membrane composed of certain tissues. In the placenta, food and oxygen, dissolved in the mother's blood, diffuse through the placental barrier into the bloodstream of the fetus, and by this means life and growth are supported in the fetus until it is born. Likewise, waste products dissolve through the barrier from the blood of the fetus to that of the mother and are eliminated by the mother's excretory organs. Blood passes to and fro from the fetus to the placenta by means of blood vessels in the umbilical cord; the latter structure connects the fetus to the placenta during pregnancy. At birth the fetus is expressed from the uterus, still connected by means of the umbilical cord to the placenta. One task of the attending physician is to tie the umbilical cord, for soon after the delivery of the baby the placenta is expressed from the uterus; hence, it can no longer perform its function.

**Development.** Fertilization of the ovum usually occurs in the uterine tube (Fig. 29-11). The ovum then passes along the tube, taking about 4 days to reach the uterus. By this time several cell divisions have occurred, and it consists of a clump of cells. Since it now resembles a mulberry (Fig. 29-23 A) it is called a *morula*. A cavity then appears in this previously solid mass of cells after which it is called a *blastocyst* ("cyst" because it has a cavity and "blasto" because it will form something) (Fig. 29-23 B). The blastocyst remains free in the uterine cavity for only 2 or 3 days (Fig. 29-23 B), after which it becomes *implanted* in the wall of the uterus (Fig. 29-23 C and D). Usually, therefore, implantation begins 6 or 7 days after fertilization. At this time, the endometrium (Fig. 29-20) has been under the influence of progesterone for several days; hence, it is "receptive" toward the ovum. The site of implantation may be anywhere on the wall of the uterus but usually is high up toward the fundus on the anterior or the posterior wall (Fig. 29-23 E).

The wall of the blastocyst (Fig. 29-23 B and C) is, at first, composed of a single layer of cells called the *trophoblast* (*trephein* = to nourish, *blastos* = germ) because the cells of this layer obtain nourishment for the embryo that will develop inside the blastocyst (Fig. 29-23 C) from a mass of cells called the *inner cell mass* (Fig. 29-23 B). In describing the formation of the placenta we shall not concern ourselves with the further history of the inner cell mass; this is done in textbooks of embryology.

The trophoblast of the blastocyst becomes fixed to the free surface of the endometrial epithelium. At the point of contact the cells of the trophoblast proliferate to become several cells thick (Fig. 29-23 C). The uterine epithelium breaks down at this point, probably because of the enzymatic activity of the trophoblast. This leaves a gap in the uterine lining which permits the blastocyst to sink into the endometrial stroma (Fig. 29-23 C and D). The defect in the endometrium is closed temporarily by a plug of fibrin and cellular debris called the closing coagulum (Fig. 29-23 D). Later, the endometrial epithelium grows over the embedded blastocyst to restore the uterine lining. The blastocyst then lies surrounded by stromal cells in the superficial layer of the endometrium (Fig. 29-24).

By the 11th day after fertilization the cells of the trophoblast have divided and formed 2 layers. The cells of the inner layer are well defined; this layer is called the *cytotrophoblast* because it is clearly composed of many individual cells (Fig. 29-25, *top*). The outer layer is much thicker and does not consist of well-defined cells but of a continuous mass of cytoplasm containing many nuclei (Fig. 29-25). Since the cells of this layer are joined together, this layer constitutes a syncytium (*syn* = together), and the layer itself is called the *syncytiotrophoblast* (Figs. 29-23 D, 29-24 and 29-25). At this stage there are a few small spaces, called *lacunae* or *lakes* in the syncytium. By the 15th day these have increased in size and often become confluent. Moreover, they are filled with blood from the uterine veins and the venous sinuses which the trophoblast has eroded. Only later does the trophoblast erode maternal (spiral) arteries so that these too deliver blood into these spaces.

As the lacunae enlarge, the strands of trophoblast left between them are called *pri-*

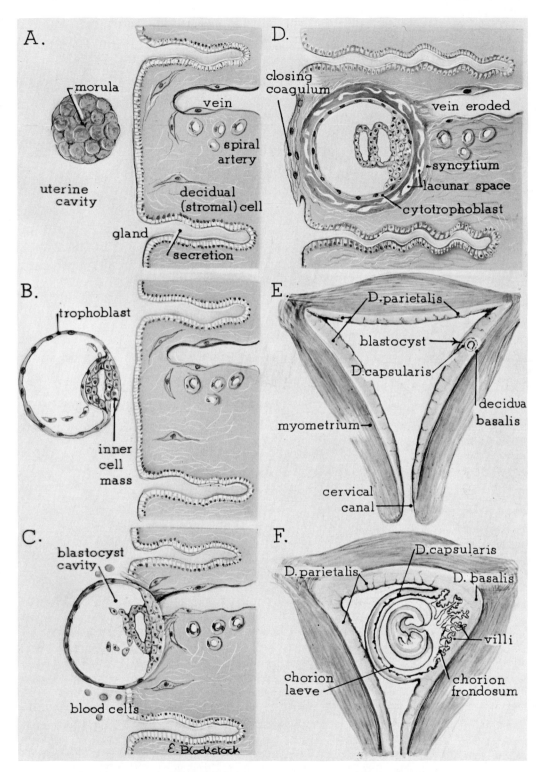

FIG. 29-23. Diagrams A, B, C and D illustrate the stages in the formation of the blastocyst and the embedding of the blastocyst in the uterine wall. The relationships of the growing embryo to the uterus are shown in diagrams E and F.

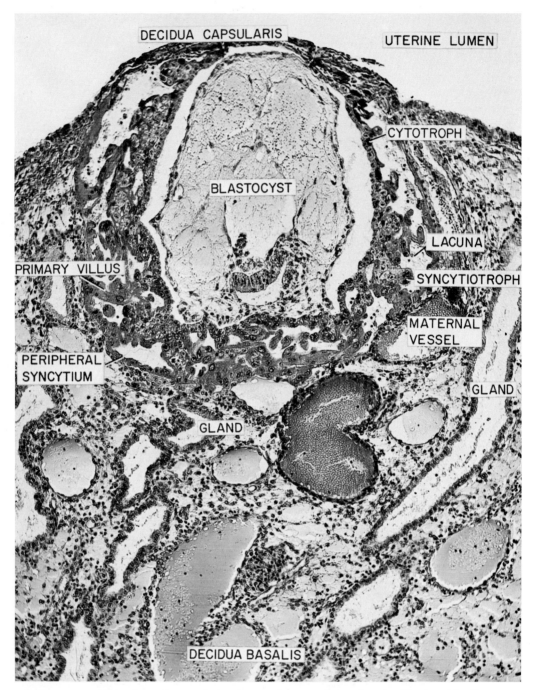

FIG. 29-24. This photomicrograph is of an embryo 12 days after fertilization (the Barnes embryo) embedded in the uterine wall. Primary villi, lacunae, blastocystic trophoblast and inner cell mass are shown. (There is an artefactual space between the trophoblast and the developing mesoderm.) In the uterine mucosa (decidua), glands and maternal blood vessels are seen with decidual cells in the stroma. (This embryo is approximately at the stage illustrated diagrammatically in Figure 29-23 D.) (From Prof. W. J. Hamilton)

*mary trophoblastic villi* (Fig. 29-24). Each villus consists of a core of cytotrophoblast covered with an outer irregular layer of syncytiotrophoblast. The villi that extend out from the blastocyst around its whole periphery come into contact with the endometrium in which the blastocyst is buried, and cells from the villi apply themselves to the endometrium to form a lining for the cavity in the endometrium in which the blastocyst lies (Fig. 29-23 D). This lining of the cavity is peripheral to the blastocyst, and so it is called the peripheral syncytium. Hence, at this time, trophoblast cells form a covering for the blastocyst and a lining for the cavity in which it lies, and between the two are strands of cells, the villi, which partially separate lacunar spaces (Fig. 29-23 D), which are filled with maternal blood. The cytotrophoblastic component proliferates rapidly at the tips of the villous structures that are forming.

The villi thus consist of cytotrophoblast covered by syncytiotrophoblast. Mitoses are common in cytotrophoblast but not very common in the syncytiotrophoblast. It would seem that the latter grows by cells of the cytotrophoblast fusing to become syncytiotrophoblast.

The structure of the villi begins to change around the 15th day. By this time the different germ layers are forming in the embryo, and mesoderm has grown out from the developing embryo to form a lining for the trophoblast that surrounds the blastocyst. When the trophoblast has gained a lining of mesoderm it is called the *chorion* (*chorion* = skin). The mesoderm from the chorion then extends into the villi to provide them with mesodermal cores; when this happens the villi are called *secondary* or *definitive villi*. These grow and branch. Fetal blood vessels develop in the mesoderm in their cores, and later these vessels become connected with the fetal circulation.

So far the changes that have been occurring in the trophoblast have taken place all around the periphery of the blastocyst. From here on, developments differ in various sites around the circumference of the blastocyst. To explain these we must introduce some further terms.

The endometrium that lies between the blastocyst and the myometrium is called the *basal plate* (Fig. 29-23 E, *decidua basalis*), and it is on this side of the blastocyst that the

placenta will develop from the chorion. This is accomplished by the villi (with their cores of mesoderm) continuing in this site to grow and branch. In so doing, they of course continue to destroy and erode more and more endometrium. As they do this, the raw surface of the endometrium, as it becomes exposed, becomes lined with cytotrophoblastic cells from the tips of the villi. Since the lacunae between villi are filled with maternal blood and the capillaries of the villi with fetal blood, diffusion of dissolved substances can occur between the maternal blood in the lacunar spaces and the fetal blood in the capillaries of the villi.

The continuation of the processes described above in the region of the basal plate result in a structural formation of increasing size which in due course is known as the placenta; this will be described in more detail presently.

**The Deciduae.** All but the deepest layer of the endometrium of the uterus is shed when a baby is born. Since this portion of the endometrium of the pregnant uterus is destined to be shed, much like the leaves of deciduous trees in the Fall, all but the deepest layer of the endometrium in a pregnant uterus is referred to as the *decidua* (Fig. 29-23 E). Various areas of the decidua are called by different names which designate their positions relative to the site of the implanted ovum.

The *decidua parietalis* (*parietal* means forming, or situated on, a wall) lines the entire pregnant uterus except that in the area where the placenta is forming (Fig. 29-23 F).

The *decidua capsularis* is the portion of endometrium that overlies the developing embryo; it forms a *capsule* over it (Fig. 29-23 E and F). As the embryo becomes larger the decidua capsularis has to cover a larger and larger area, and it becomes very thin and atrophic. After 3 months, the size of the chorionic sac that contains the embryo has become so large that the decidua capsularis comes into contact with the decidua parietalis at the opposite surface of the uterus; hence, the uterine cavity is obliterated. Thereupon, the decidua capsularis blends with the decidua parietalis and as it does so it disappears as a separate layer.

The *decidua basalis* consists of the compact zone of the endometrium that lies between the chorionic sac and its contained embryo and

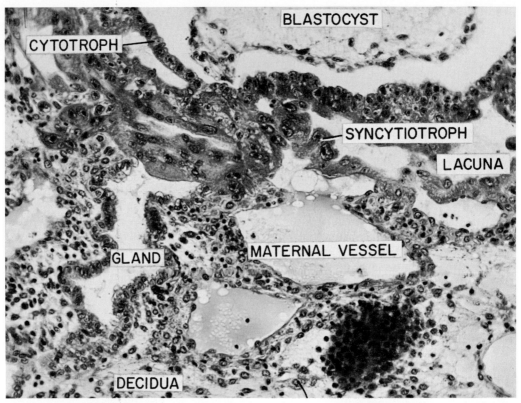

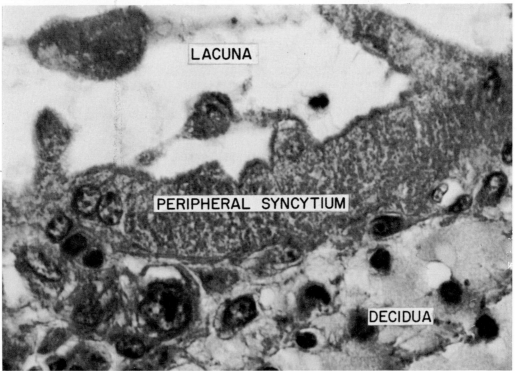

Fig. 29-25. (*Top*) Part of a 12-day implantation site. Lacunae are lined by syncytium; the latter has eroded a maternal artery and a uterine gland. The space near the top between embryonic membrane and trophoblast is an artefact. (*Bottom*) Site of contact between syncytium and maternal decidua. Note absence of cell boundaries in syncytium. (Both photomicrographs from Professors J. D. Boyd and W. J. Hamilton)

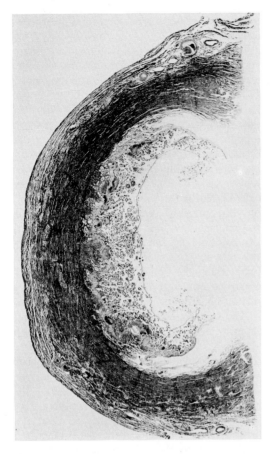

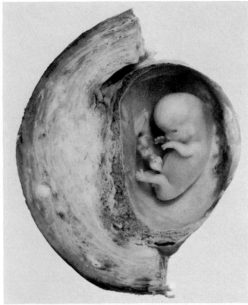

FIG. 29-26. (A, *Left*) This low-power photomicrograph is of part of the uterus with the placenta in situ, showing numerous villi cut in cross section lying in the intervillous space. The embryo, which was 15 mm. long, has been removed. (B, *Right*) This photograph is of part of the uterine wall with the placenta, fetus and fetal membranes. On the right, the wall of the chorionic sac (in which the fetus lies) is smooth. This is the chorion laeve. On the left, the fetal part of the placenta is formed by the chorion frondosum. This embryo was 36 mm. long. (From Professors J. D. Boyd and W. J. Hamilton)

the basal layer of the endometrium (Figs. 29-23 F, 29-26 A and B). The decidua basalis becomes the maternal part of the placenta. This is the only part of the placenta that is maternal in origin and after the placenta is delivered at term this layer is visible only as poorly defined bits of membrane.

Until about 12 to 16 weeks, the entire surface of the chorionic sac is covered with chorionic villi. As the sac enlarges those villi associated with the decidua capsularis degenerate and disappear, so that by 16 weeks the greater part of the surface of the sac is smooth. This large area is called the *chorion laeve* (*levis* = smooth) (Figs. 29-23 F and 29-26 B). The remainder of the surface of the sac, that is, the part adjacent to the decidua basalis, continues to be covered with villi which keep growing and branching. This part which constitutes the fetal part of the placenta is called the *chorion*

*frondosum* (Figs. 29-23 F, 29-26 A and B). By 16 weeks, the placenta is discoid in shape, consisting of the chorion frondosum and the associated decidua basalis. At the time of birth, the placenta occupies about 30 per cent of the internal surface of the expanded uterus. The progressive increase in its thickness from around the 3rd to the 7th month is due mainly to the villi becoming elongated. The relative weights of placenta and fetus at various stages of pregnancy are: 1 month, 6:1; 4 months, 1:1; birth, 1:7. At birth the placenta weighs about 450 Gm., is 15 to 20 cm. in diameter and about 3 cm. thick.

### HISTOLOGY OF THE PLACENTA

**The Villus.** The most important component of the placenta is the chorionic villus. The early villus is a compact, bushlike tuft with its base attached to, and arising from, the

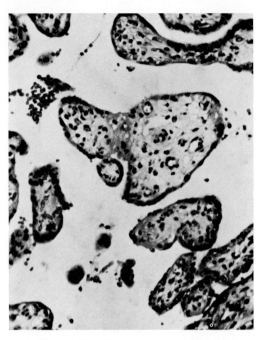

FIG. 29-27. This photomicrograph is of a section of a mature placenta showing villi lying in the intervillous space. Each villus is covered by a thin layer of syncytiotrophoblast and contains fetal capillaries and mesoderm.

chorion and its tip attached to the decidua (Fig. 29-24). By the 2nd month, side branches are formed with free tips, some of which later fuse with similar branches of adjacent villi to create a villous spongework. It is doubtful if such fusion permits anastomosis between fetal blood vessels contained in the respective cores of fusing villi. However, the cytotrophoblast at the tips of the main villi fuses to form a continuous placental covering for the eroded surface of the decidua basalis. In the fully formed human placenta, there are usually 8 to 15 large villi, each of which, together with its many branches, forms a *fetal cotyledon,* i.e., a fetal lobule.

Villi are alike histologically. A section of placenta cuts villi in all planes, and between them is maternal blood. From any one section is difficult for the student to visualize the of placenta viewed under the microscope, it morphology and the physiology of the respective fetal and maternal circulations, which will be described later, but the student can examine the tissue layers that comprise the *pla-*

*cental barrier* that separates fetal from maternal blood.

In each villus there is a fetal capillary blood vessel lined with typical endothelium, with the endothelial nuclei protruding into the lumen (Fig. 29-27). The capillary is contained in the loose connective tissue core of the villus. In the core there are some scattered smooth muscle fibers; recently these have been described by Arey as spindle-shaped or branching cells containing demonstrable myofibrils. Larger cells with large spherical nuclei (the cells of Hofbauer) also are seen in the cores of villi; possibly these are phagocytic. The trophoblast covering each villus consists of two well-defined layers until approximately the middle of the 3rd month of pregnancy, after which the cytotrophoblast progressively disappears until at term only isolated clumps of its cells are left.

The cytotrophoblast, also called Langhan's layer, consists of large, discrete, pale cells with relatively large nuclei; the cells rest on a well-defined basement membrane. Their cytoplasm contains vacuoles and some glycogen but no lipid. Wislocki and Bennett considered the vacuoles to be an expression of metabolic exchange instead of a sign of degeneration. Under the EM the cells of the cytotrophoblast, as described by Wislocki and Dempsey, reveal glycogen, mitochondria and ergastoplasm, the last being equivalent to the cytoplasmic basophilia seen with the light microscope. They found also some material of high electron density located interstitially between cells; this they consider to be iron, which is known to be abundant in the tissue.

The syncytiotrophoblast is a dark, variably thick layer in which numerous small nuclei are irregularly dispersed (Fig. 29-25 B). This layer becomes progressively thinner throughout pregnancy. Its outer surface has an irregular border, which often shows cytoplasmic streamers, an appearance which suggests a considerable plasticity of the cells during life. The EM shows the outer surface to have many microvilli. The cytoplasm ranges from being delicately vacuolated to foamy. It contains mitochondria, Golgi material and lipid droplets. The lipid droplets may be very large and abundant early in pregnancy, but later they become smaller and less numerous. Glycogen is usually absent, or present in very small amounts. After the cytotrophoblast has disappeared the syncytiotrophoblast rests on a condensed network of reticular fibers.

By the time of birth, the layers of tissue that constitute the placental barrier between maternal and fetal blood become very thin (Fig. 29-27). The outermost layer consists of only a thin layer of syncytium in which a few mitochondria and fat droplets are visible. The cytotrophoblast has mostly disappeared with only occasional cells persisting beneath the layer of syncytium. The middle layer is delicate connective tissue consisting chiefly of reticular fibers. The innermost layer is the endothelium of the fetal capillaries. Wislocki and Dempsey, with the EM, describe the placental barrier as consisting of a layer of syncytium bearing microvilli, a stout basement membrane, a connective-tissue space containing collagenic fibrils, a basement membrane around the capillary and finally the endothelium of the fetal capillary.

At intervals along a villus the syncytium is aggregated into protuberances of cytoplasm that contain many nuclei; these protuberances are called *syncytial knots* or *sprouts*. It is known that some of these syncytial sprouts break off to become free in the intervillous space; from here they can pass to the maternal circulation and on to the lungs of the mother.

Present in young placentae and becoming increasingly abundant in older placentae are irregular masses of an eosinophilic, homogeneous substance called *fibrinoid*. Its amount increases progressively during pregnancy; this gives an indication of the age of a placenta. At term aggregations of it may be visible to the naked eye. In sections, fibrinoid is eosinophilic.

As already noted, the maternal part of the placenta consists of the decidua basalis.

The zone where the trophoblastic shell is in contact with the endometrium is variously called the *junctional, composite,* or *penetration zone*. The last term relates to the fact that during the growth of the placenta the maternal tissue undergoes degeneration and necrosis in this zone as it is penetrated by trophoblastic villi. In this zone, it is possible to distinguish decidual cells (derived from endometrial stroma) from cytotrophoblastic cells because the former are surrounded with colla-

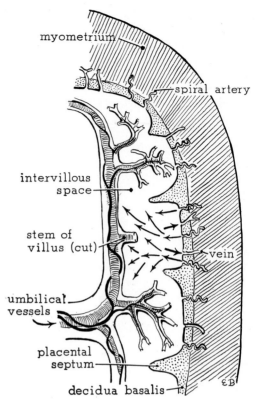

FIG. 29-28. This diagram illustrates the circulation of fetal and maternal blood in the placenta. Blood from the fetus reaches the placenta by the 2 umbilical arteries (*left, dark*), passes to the villi and is returned to the fetus by the single umbilical vein (*left, cross-hatched*). Maternal blood enters the intervillous space via numerous spiral arteries and returns to the maternal circulation through many veins. There is no mingling of the two bloods. Placental septae, which subdivide the placenta into cotyledons, are also shown.

genic and reticular fibers, but the latter have no fibrillar material between them. The endometrial stromal cells of the decidua basalis almost all take on the appearance of *decidual* cells; they become large, polygonal, and rich in glycogen and lipid droplets. The epithelial cells lining the endometrial glands during pregnancy are rich in mitochondria, glycogen and lipid droplets. By the 3rd month, these glands in the decidua basalis are stretched and appear as horizontal clefts. The decidua basalis as a whole (the basal plate) consists chiefly of a connective tissue stroma, the cells of which are of the decidual type; endometrial glands, fibrinoid, and small clumps of trophoblast cells are also present. As Boyd and Hamilton recently have described, the fetal syncytium may penetrate through all layers of the maternal endometrium and even into the myometrium. Giant cells may be present in the basal plate, and these are believed to be derived from the fetal syncytium. Passing through the basal plate are spiral arteries which open eventually into the intervillous spaces. They are lined with endothelium, but near their openings they are lined with cells of the syncytiotrophoblast type; these do not institute clotting. This growth of these cells into the maternal spiral arteries probably reduces the pressure at which maternal blood is delivered into the intervillous space.

The maternal decidua is eroded more deeply opposite the main villi than elsewhere, and this leaves projections of decidual tissue between the main villi, extending from the basal plate toward the chorion (Fig. 29-28). Such projections are called *placental septa*, and they divide the placenta into lobules or cotyledons, with each area of placenta between adjacent septa being a *maternal cotyledon* (Fig. 29-28). That the placental septa are mainly of decidual and not trophoblastic origin has been proved recently by Sohval, Gaines and Strauss, who showed that when the fetus was male the nuclei of the septa are of the female type. Maternal vessels, particularly veins, often make short excursions into the base of a septum; this also suggests that the septa are of decidual and not trophoblastic origin. However, some cells toward the apices of the septa are undoubtedly of fetal origin, being derived from trophoblast and deposited, as it were, on the summits of the septa. From the 4th month, the tissues of the decidua basalis become extraordinarily "loose," being composed chiefly of a very dense venous plexus with dilated and distorted uterine glands. The latter have very thin walls, and secretion persists in them until late in pregnancy. Toward the margins of the placenta, the decidua is more compact.

**The Intervillous Space.** *Blood Circulation.* The intervillous space develops very rapidly to become an enormous blood sinus bounded on one side by the chorion (chorionic plate) and on the other by the basal plate (Fig. 29-28).

The space is labyrinthine in development and in form because the villi in it are variously connected to each other. The space is incompletely divided into compartments by the placental septa. The intervillous space is much expanded toward the embryonic side; this expanded part is the *subchorial lake* or *space*. Here there are only the main stems of the villi, and, just as there is more air space in a dense forest between the trunks of the trees than there is further from the ground between the many branches, there is more space here for blood. The *marginal sinus* is the marginal prolongation of the subchorial lake at the periphery of the placenta, and thus is circular in form when viewed from the surface.

Maternal blood enters the intervillous space through several hundred arterioles that traverse the decidua basalis, there being many such arterioles in each cotyledon or lobule (Fig. 29-28). Blood drains into numerous veins which open over the entire surface of the basal plate. Maternal blood pressure drives the blood entering the intervillous space high up toward the subchorial lake. After bathing the villi, venous blood flows back toward the venous orifices in the basal plate. Contractions of the myometrium and the fetal pulse in the villi possibly assist the circulation.

**Attachment of Placenta.** One question, not yet definitely answered, is what mechanism holds the placenta in place. The association of degenerating maternal tissue and fetal trophoblast in the junctional zone, together with the presence of fibrinoid (Nitabuch's membrane), has been noted already, but this does not provide a firm attachment because it is here that separation occurs during labor. Probably the chief mechanism for holding the placenta in place is pressure. The chorionic sac is relatively tense throughout pregnancy, and early in development it fully occupies and obliterates the uterine cavity (Fig. 29-26 B). The growth of the chorionic sac and its contents requires that the uterus must grow to accommodate it; hence, the uterus hypertrophies, and hyperplasia occurs in the myometrium throughout pregnancy. With the pressure so engendered there would be little tendency for the placenta to move in relation to the uterine wall.

**Functions of the Placenta.** These may be summarized as: (1) Nutrition of the embryo, particularly with respect to carbohydrates, fats, proteins, water and salts which pass by diffusion from maternal to fetal blood. This has been discussed recently at some length by Dancis. (2) Respiration, oxygen passing from maternal to fetal blood and carbon dioxide passing in the reverse direction. (3) Excretion of metabolites and waste products. (4) As a barrier to particulate matter and bacteria, although some antibodies and viruses can pass the placental barrier. (5) Synthesis of estrogen, progesterone and chorionic or placental gonadotrophin. Enzymes with a local action, for example, those associated with digestion of maternal endometrium, also are formed in the placenta.

**Aging of the Placenta.** Some of the age changes seen in the placenta already have been described; for example, the thinning of the placental barrier and the virtual disappearance of the cytotrophoblast, and the formation of fibrinoid (Fig. 29-27). Paine has described the main features of aging in a *normal* placenta as a slow but progressive thinning of the syncytium, a gradual thickening of the walls of the fetal blood vessels in the villi, and a progressive conversion of the gelatinous fetal-type mesoderm of the stroma of the villi into an adult type of areolar fibrous tissue. These changes are accelerated in cases of hypertension and toxemia.

## THE CERVIX

The cervix is the lowest and relatively narrow segment of the uterus (Fig. 29-2). Both the substance of its wall and the mucous membrane that lines its canal are of a different character from those of the body of the uterus.

The recent study of Danforth indicates that the amount of smooth muscle and elastic tissue in the wall of the cervix is not as great as has been generally supposed. He finds that the wall of the cervix is composed chiefly of dense collagenic connective tissue and that smooth muscle fibers, on the average, comprise only about 15 per cent of its substance. Furthermore, he finds that elastic fibers, except in the walls of its blood vessels, are relatively scarce.

The cervix, it should be remembered, must become widely dilated at parturition in order to permit the passage of the fetus. It is important, for many reasons that will become obvious when clinical work is encountered, to know

whether the relaxation of the smooth muscle fibers in its wall is an important factor in permitting the cervix to dilate. Danforth's studies do not suggest that the cervix ordinarily contains enough smooth muscle to exert a very strong sphincter effect. Hence, it would seem that the main factor that permits the cervix to dilate at parturition, in response to the mechanical force exerted upon it, is the softening that occurs in its intercellular substance. This is associated with an increased blood supply and an increased tissue fluid content, which are probably due to the hormones of pregnancy.

Danforth has shown that so little elastic tissue is present in the cervix, except in its blood vessels, that it could scarcely be expected that stretched elastic fibers are a very important factor in bringing about the slow contraction of the cervix that occurs after parturition. What then makes the cervix become constricted again? It seems not unlikely that although the cervix does not contain enough smooth muscle to enable it to act as a true sphincter, it does contain enough smooth muscle to help it contract to some extent after birth, particularly since after birth the smooth muscle fibers would be in a stretched state and would have become sensitized to such oxytocin as is secreted by the posterior lobe of the pituitary gland at this time. But its further return probably involves a new organization of its fibrous tissue.

The cervical canal is flattened from before backward. A longitudinal ridge or raphe is present both on the anterior and the posterior surface of the canal, and from these ridges mucosal folds extend at angles toward each side. The ridges do not directly face one another, so that when the lumen is collapsed they fit alongside one another.

The mucous membrane of the cervical canal consists of epithelium and a connective tissue lamina propria. It contains numerous large, branched, tubular glands that, in the vaginal end of the canal, tend to slant from the lumen toward the body of the uterus (Fig. 29-29, *left*).

The epithelium of the mucous membrane consists of tall mucus-secreting columnar cells. In H and E sections their cytoplasm is pale, and their deeply stained nuclei are seen to be close to their bases (Fig. 29-29, *right*). Cili-

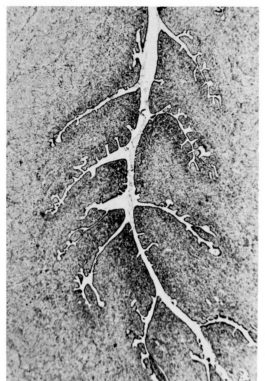
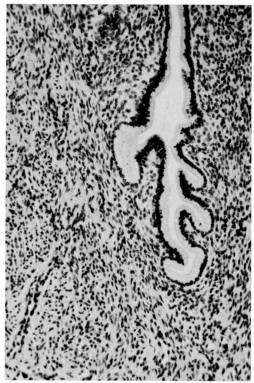

Fig. 29-29. (*Left*) Very low-power photomicrograph of a longitudinal section of the cervix, showing the cervical canal and the glands which extend out from it. The upper end of the photograph represents the end of the section nearest the vagina. (*Right*) Medium-power photomicrograph of the same section, showing the terminal part of one of the glands. The character of the stroma which immediately surrounds the glands and that of the general stroma of the cervix are also shown.

ated cells are sometimes seen. The same type of epithelium is found in the large, wide, branched tubular glands that extend deeply into the lamina propria and even somewhat beyond (Fig. 29-29, *right*). The lamina propria is a cellular type of fibrous connective tissue. The nuclei are of the fibroblast type and are relatively close together. The cytoplasm of the cells cannot be seen clearly in an H and E section, nor can the character of the not overly abundant intercellular substance between the cells be seen to advantage (Fig. 29-29, *right*).

On the whole, the mucous membrane of the cervical canal is of a dense structure and is firmly attached to the fibrous connective tissue wall that lies outside it. The lamina propria contains no coiled arteries and does not change much during the menstrual cycle. However, the secretion of mucus by the cer-

vical glands becomes increased at the time of ovulation; the secretion of the cervical glands is evidently stimulated by estrogen. The glands sometimes become closed off, whereupon they may become converted into cysts. These are called *nabothian follicles*. These may cause elevations on the surface of that part of the cervix that projects into the vagina and so be seen or felt on a vaginal examination.

The portion of the cervix that projects into the vagina is covered by stratified squamous nonkeratinizing epithelium similar to that which lines the vagina (which will be described presently) and with which it becomes continuous. This type of epithelium extends usually for a very short distance into the cervical canal, where it undergoes a transition into the columnar type that lines most of the canal (Fig. 29-30). In some instances the zone of transition between the two types of epithelium

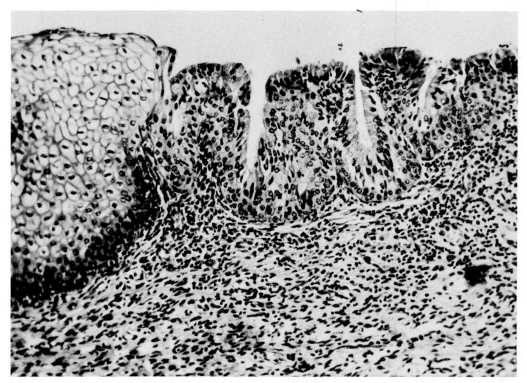

Fig. 29-30. High-power photomicrograph of a longitudinal section of the cervix near the site where the cervical canal opens into the vagina. The stratified squamous nonkeratinizing epithelium that covers the vaginal portion of the cervix and extends for a very short distance into the canal may be seen at the left, and the columnar epithelium that lines the remainder of the canal, at the right. The zone of transition between the 2 types of epithelium is immediately left of center.

is farther in; however, in others the columnar epithelium of the canal may continue out from the canal to cover little areas of the vaginal surface of the cervix close to the beginning of the canal; if so, these areas are termed physiologic erosions. (The stratified squamous nonkeratinizing epithelium which normally covers the cervix is pink-gray in color: columnar epithelium appears red. Hence the term "erosion.") A factor in producing these is that the lips of the canal may become somewhat everted as a result of childbearing; this tends to expose the columnar epithelium.

The portion of the uterus with which the cervix connects is sometimes termed the isthmus of the uterus. The isthmus is supposed to be the narrowed segment of the organ that begins, at its cervical end, where the typical mucous membrane of the cervix begins to change into the endometrial variety. The upper end of the isthmus is supposed to be the site where the lumen becomes constricted (the internal os) before opening out into the wide cavity of the body. However, the landmarks for both the beginning and the end of the isthmus are neither very obvious nor constant in position. The line of transition between the cervical type of mucous membrane and the endometrial type may be gradual and the so-called internal sphincter not at all obvious. Danforth has shown that the wall of the so-called isthmus is composed chiefly of smooth muscle, and so he regards the isthmus as part of the body. It does not become dilated in pregnancy as soon as does the body, but when there is a need for more room to accommodate the fetus and the membranes than can be conveniently provided by the body, the isthmus becomes expanded and elongated to provide extra accommodation. Eventually, the

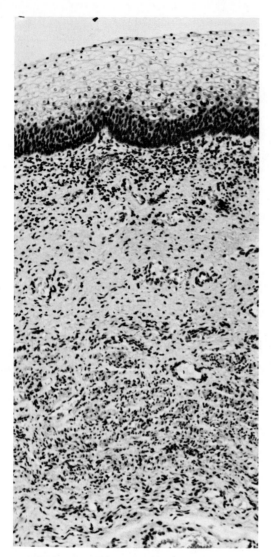

Fig. 29-31. Very low-power photomicrograph of a section of the wall of the vagina. Note that the more superficial epithelial cells are large and pale because of their glycogen content. The smooth muscle coats of the wall may be seen below the middle of the photograph.

more fibrous cervix itself becomes the only segment of the organ that is not expanded during pregnancy. The isthmus, then, is best considered, not as a separate part of the organ, but as the lower end of the body.

## THE VAGINA

The vagina is a musculofibrous tube lined with a mucous membrane (Fig. 29-31). Under ordinary conditions it is collapsed and the mucous membranes of its anterior and posterior walls are in contact. Except in the upper part of the tube, a longitudinal ridge is present on the mucosal surface of both the anterior and the posterior walls. From these two primary ridges numerous secondary ridges or *rugae* extend toward the sides of the tube (Fig. 29-2). No glands are present in the mucous membrane. The epithelium is of the stratified squamous type, and the way in which its character alters in relation to the level of sex hormones in the bloodstream will be discussed presently. The lamina propria on which the epithelium rests is of a dense connective-tissue type. It may exhibit lymph nodules. Farther out toward the muscle coat, the lamina propria—which in this site is sometimes regarded as a submucosa—becomes loose in texture and contains numerous blood vessels, particularly veins. Elastic fibers are numerous in the lamina propria directly under the epithelial lining, and they extend out through the mucous membrane to the muscular layer. The latter contains both longitudinally and circularly disposed smooth muscle fibers, but these are not gathered into discernible layers (Fig. 29-31). Longitudinally disposed fibers predominate. A fibrous adventitia lies outside the muscular coat and this connects the vagina with adjacent structures. The upper part of the posterior wall of the vagina is covered with peritoneum (Fig. 29-2).

**Vaginal Smears.** In recent years it has become common to study, particularly by means of films or smears, the cells that are found in the vagina. Such cells as are present in vaginal washings may be derived from: (1) the endometrium of the body of the uterus, (2) the cervical canal, and (3) the vaginal surface of the cervix or the lining of the vagina. Their study may be informative for two reasons. (1) Since the character of cells in these various sites is affected by the particular hormone concentrations that exist in the bloodstream, the cells found in vaginal washings may give some indication about the state of the hormone balance of the individual at the time they are obtained; and (2) cells indicative of having desquamated from an early cancer, growing in the cervix or the body of the uterus, may sometimes be found on an otherwise routine check of a patient and so indicate the need for more detailed examination for cancer. For

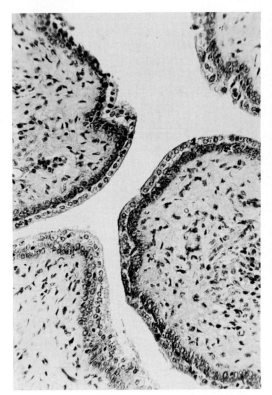 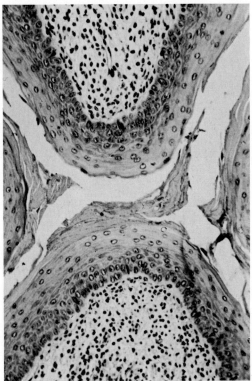

FIG. 29-32. (*Left*) Low-power photomicrograph of a portion of a cross section of the vagina of a rat from which the ovaries were removed. This shows that, under conditions of estrogen deficiency, the vaginal epithelium becomes thin, and the superficial cells nucleated. (*Right*) A similar preparation from a rat treated identically, except that it was given a large injection of estrogen 2 days before the section was obtained. Observe that the epithelium has become greatly thickened, and that the surface layers are heavily keratinized. This picture is similar to that seen in a normally occurring estrus.

both these reasons it has become common practice to study by the film method, cells obtained by gently wiping the lining of the vagina or the covering of the cervix and the cells aspirated or otherwise obtained from the entrance of the cervical canal.

**Cyclic Changes in the Vaginal Epithelium.** It is to be kept in mind that the earlier investigators who attempted to prepare ovarian extracts that contained sex hormones had no ready way to find out if their extracts contained the active hormones they sought. In other words, there were no biologic tests by which the hormone content of any given extract could be assayed conveniently and accurately. Therefore, it was of the greatest importance when Stockard and Papanicolaou discovered, in 1917, that the vaginal epithelium of the guinea pig becomes keratinized at the time of estrus. Hence, whether or not any

given guinea pig was in estrus could be ascertained by noting the presence or the absence of keratinized cells in a vaginal smear. A little later, Allen worked out the estrous cycle of the mouse and found that its vagina also became keratinized at the time of estrus. Therefore, it became obvious that the keratinization of the vaginal epithelium was one of the effects of the estrus-producing hormone. However, mature mice and rats come into estrus spontaneously every 4 days, so that they are not suitable animals to use to test for the estrus-producing hormone in any given extract. However, the vaginal epithelium of immature animals or of mature animals from which the ovaries have been removed remains nonkeratinized, so these serve as excellent test animals. Actually, mature female rats or mice whose ovaries have been removed are better test animals for several reasons. Using the keratiniza-

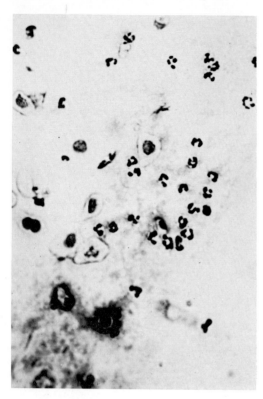 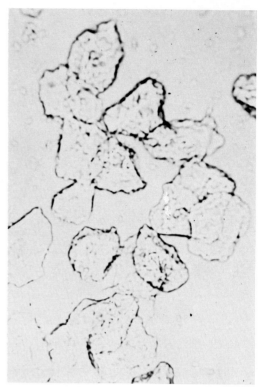

FIG. 29-33. (*Left*) High-power photomicrograph of a stained vaginal smear obtained from a rat in the later stages of metaestrus. Note the nucleated epithelial cells and the characteristic polymorphic nuclei of many granular leukocytes. (*Right*) High-power photomicrograph of a stained vaginal smear obtained from a rat in estrus. Observe that the smear contains nothing but large, very pale-staining, non-nucleated squames of keratin.

tion of the vaginal epithelium as a criterion of the presence of an estrus-producing hormone in the blood, Allen and Doisy, in 1923, were able to show that an extract made from follicular fluid aspirated from large follicles in hogs' ovaries contained the estrus-producing hormone. From this point on, progress was rapid, and soon estrus-producing hormones were obtained in pure form and their chemical structure elucidated.

The changes that occur in the vaginal epithelium throughout the 28-day cycle of the mature human female are not nearly so pronounced as those that occur in many lower animals. However, such changes as do occur are more easily interpreted in the light of a knowledge of the pronounced ones that occur in the estrous cycle of the rat or the mouse. Therefore, this will be described briefly.

As noted before, the rat and the mouse have

a 4-day estrous cycle. This is divided into 4 periods: *proestrus, estrus, metaestrus* and *diestrus*. In proestrus, follicles approach the surface of the ovary, the uterus becomes swollen with secretion, and its blood vessels become engorged. The epithelium of the vagina becomes thick as a result of proliferation in its deeper layers, but its most superficial cells are still nucleated. However, cells with keratohyalin granules appear beneath the superficial nucleated cells. The epithelial membrane thus comes to have a 2-layered appearance. In estrus or thereabouts, ovulation occurs, and throughout this stage the uterus remains swollen and red. The vaginal epithelium has now become thick and heavily keratinized (Fig. 29-32, *right*), and the mating impulse is aroused. The keratinized epithelium probably plays a protective function in the mating procedure. If mating does not occur, the animal passes into the metaestrus stage. As this progresses the uterus becomes smaller and the vaginal epithelium much thinner (similar to Fig. 29-32, *left*). The basement membrane disappears, and polymorphonuclear leukocytes invade the epithelium and pass through it to appear in great numbers among the epithelial cells that are seen in vaginal smears (Fig. 29-33, *left*). In diestrus, the uterus is small and pale, and the vaginal epithelium is still thin. However, polymorphonuclear leukocytes are confined mostly to the superficial layers of the epithelium. As proestrus develops, great mitotic activity occurs in the deeper layers of the epithelium, and it becomes thick again.

Since only the superficial cells desquamate, they are the only type seen in vaginal smears. Hence, in estrus, the vaginal smears contain only keratinized cells (Fig. 29-33, *right*). As metaestrus proceeds, vaginal smears contain, first, keratinized cells and then later nucleated cells and large numbers of the polymorphonuclear leukocytes that are making their way through the epithelium at this stage (Fig. 29-33, *left*). The diestrus stage is characterized by nucleated epithelial cells and leukocytes. In proestrus, the leukocytes have disappeared, so only nucleated epithelial cells are present.

**The Epithelium of the Human Vagina.** The epithelial lining of the human vagina is stratified and substantial (Fig. 29-31). Its deepest stratum consists of a single layer of cylindrical cells with oval nuclei. The next stratum is several cell layers in thickness. The cells in this stratum are polyhedral in shape, and it is said that they are joined together with intercellular bridges something like those in the stratum spinosum of the epidermis of thick skin; however, the cells in this stratum of the vaginal epithelium do not have a prickly appearance. The next stratum consists of a few layers of more flattened cells; these contain glycogen. Since this dissolves away in the ordinary preparation of sections, the cells of this and the more superficial strata appear swollen and empty. The most superficial stratum consists of several layers of more flattened but somewhat swollen cells, all of which possess nuclei.

The epithelium lining the vagina of the human female differs in two important respects from that lining the vagina of the mouse or the rat. First, since there is no true period of estrus in the human female, there is no time in the menstrual cycle when the epithelium becomes frankly keratinized. At the time of ovulation, which is the counterpart of estrus, the epithelium may show certain tendencies toward keratinization but, unless the epithelium is unduly exposed to air or some other unusual environmental factor, it does not develop true keratin; hence, the surface cells always contain nuclei. Secondly, the epithelial cells of the more superficial layers of the vaginal epithelium tend to accumulate considerable quantities of glycogen in their cytoplasm, particularly at the time of ovulation. This has two possible functions: (1) it may serve as nutriment for male germ cells during their passage through this organ, and (2) it is fermented by bacteria in the vagina which convert it to lactic acid, and this may be an important factor in maintaining a suitable type of bacterial flora in the vagina.

The appearance of the cells that desquamate from the lining of the vagina and from the covering of the vaginal surface of the cervix has been studied at great length by Papanicolaou by the smear method; his publications should be consulted for full information on this matter. Essentially, such progesterone as is secreted during the menstrual cycle appears to have no effect on the vaginal epithelium. The amount of estrogen secreted at the time of ovulation, while not enough to cause keratinization, does, however, have some effect. Papanicolaou considers that there is a relative increase in acidophilic cells with small dark nuclei in the vaginal smear at this time. The development of acidophilic properties by the surface epithelial cells is evidently preliminary to cells becoming keratinized, but this is as far as the process usually goes. There are also other criteria that may be employed. Evidently, in the hands of an experienced individual, the study of desquamated vaginal cells in smears may be helpful in determining the time of ovulation and the effectiveness of estrogen therapy and in diagnosing atrophic conditions of the vaginal epithelium that are due to estrogen deficiency.

The ability of estrogen to thicken and even keratinize the vaginal epithelium is taken advantage of in the treatment of certain vaginal infections, particularly those that occur in children, for in them the epithelium is thin and vulnerable.

## THE MAMMARY GLANDS
## (BREASTS OR MAMMAE)

**Development.** The first step in the development of mammary glands in man occurs near the end of the 6th week of embryonic life. At this time, in embryos of either sex, the ectoderm becomes thickened along two lines, each of which runs from the axilla to the groin of the same side. These are called the "milk lines," and their epithelial cells have the potentiality to grow down into the underlying mesenchyme at any point along either line to form mammary glands. Usually, in man, invasion of the underlying mesenchyme by epithelial cells destined to form mammary glands occurs at only one site along each line. However, in many animals mammary glands develop at many sites along each line so that in later life such animals have two rows of mammary glands with which to feed their large families. Occasionally, extra mammary glands develop along the milk line in man (and sometimes elsewhere); if so, they are called *supernumerary nipples* or *breasts*. Among civilized peoples supernumerary breasts are usually removed surgically for cosmetic and other reasons. Aberrant mammary gland tissue in the axilla may not become obvious until pregnancy or lactation causes it to swell.

As the embryo develops, the epithelial cells at the point along the milk line where a breast is to develop form a little cluster from which up to 20 or more separate cords of epithelial cells push into the underlying mesenchyme in various directions. Each one of these original cords of cells develops into a separate compound exocrine gland; hence, each breast is actually composed of many separate compound glands, each of which empties by a separate duct through the nipple. During fetal life the cords of cells that invade the mesenchyme branch to some extent and tend to become canalized so that at birth a rudimentary duct system has formed. At birth there is no obvious difference between the degree to which the glands of the female and the male infant are developed. During the first few days of life the glands of a baby may become distended for reasons to be described later. The condition soon subsides.

**Changes at Puberty.** As puberty approaches, the breasts of the female, which up to this time have been flat, become enlarged and more or less hemispheric in shape. The nipple becomes more prominent. The changes in the breasts constitute one of the secondary sex characteristics of the female that appear at this time. Most of the increase in their size is due to fat accumulating in the connective tissue between their lobes and lobules. At puberty the epithelial duct system develops beyond a rudimentary stage, but this change is not so striking as the increased amount of fat in the connective tissue. It is not believed that true secretory units develop at this time; the formation of these awaits pregnancy.

In the male, the mammary glands usually experience no or little change at puberty, remaining flat. Uncommonly some considerable enlargement closely resembling that which occurs in the female may occur: this condition is called *gynecomastia*.

Estrogen, probably in conjunction with some lactogenic hormone (the secretion of which would be dependent on estrogen appearing in the circulation), brings about the changes in the female breast described above. The progesterone that is periodically secreted from the time of puberty onward may play a contributing role. Estrogen given to males tends to make their rudimentary mammary glands develop into the feminine type.

**Histologic Structure of a Resting Breast.** The breast of a sexually mature nonpregnant female is termed a *resting breast* to distinguish it from one that is in the process of active growth in pregnancy or one that is functioning in lactation.

The *nipple* is a cylindrico-conical structure of a pink or brownish-pink color. It is covered with stratified squamous keratinized epithelium. Numerous papillae of an irregular shape extend into the epidermis from the dermis to approach the surface closely; hence, over papillae the epidermis may be very thin (Fig. 29-34). The main ducts from each of the many separate glands that make up the breast are called the *lactiferous ducts*, and they ascend through the nipple (Fig. 29-34) to open by separate orifices on its summit; the orifices are so minute that they cannot be seen with the naked eye. The epithelium of the lactiferous ducts, close to their orifices, is similar to that which covers the nipple. Deeper in the nipple the lactiferous ducts are lined with 2 layers of columnar epithelial cells that rest on a basement membrane.

The substance of the nipple consists of dense connective tissue and smooth muscle (Fig. 29-34). The fibers of the latter are arranged both circularly around the lactiferous ducts and parallel with, and close beside, them as they ascend through the nipple. Many blood vessels and encapsulated nerve endings are also present.

The epidermis of the nipple, like that of the vagina, is sensitive to estrogen. In relation to the problem of "sore nipples"—a condition which develops when some women attempt to nurse their babies—it is perhaps of interest to note that estrogen may be lacking in a woman shortly after she has given birth to a baby. The reason for this is that the function of estrogen production is largely taken over by the placenta during pregnancy; hence, when the placenta is delivered after birth, a woman is deprived of what has been her chief source of this hormone. Eventually, of course, her ovaries will produce a sufficiency, but it is possible that there may be a period of time when the epidermis of the nipple suffers from a lack of stimulation by estrogen. Indeed, Gunther ascribes one type of sore nipple to estrogen deficiency, and, in some experiments in collaboration with Gunther, the author found that feeding human placenta tissue to rats greatly thickened the epidermis of their nipples. However, there are certain complications, too involved to discuss here, in connection with attempting to use estrogen to thicken the epidermis of the nipples of women who have just begun to nurse their babies.

The skin surrounding the nipple, the areola, is of a rosy hue. It becomes pigmented in pregnancy, and after pregnancy never returns to its original shade; it always retains some pigment. Large modified sweat glands, but not so large or so modified as the mammary glands themselves, lie beneath the areola and open onto its surface; these are called the areolar glands (of Montgomery). Sebaceous glands and large sweat glands are present around the periphery of the areola. Smooth muscle fibers are disposed, both circularly and at right angles to the skin surface, beneath the areola.

The lactiferous ducts from the different lobes of the breast converge under the areola to enter the base of the nipple. As they near

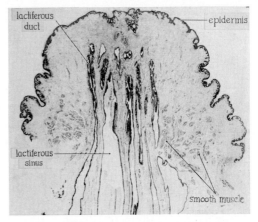

FIG. 29-34. Very low-power photomicrograph, lightly retouched, of a section of a nipple cut perpendicular to the skin surface.

the point at which they converge, the ducts are believed to become somewhat expanded. These widened segments of the ducts are termed the *lactiferous sinuses* (Fig. 29-34) and in the lactating breast, they are believed to act as little reservoirs for milk. Whether these expanded portions of the ducts may be seen in the gross when a resting breast is dissected is questionable.

The many separate glands that are drained by individual ducts through the nipple constitute the lobes of the breast. Each lobe consists of many lobules; hence, each main lactiferous duct gives rise to many branches that, since they run within lobules, are called *intralobular ducts*. The parenchyma of the lobes and the lobules is generally considered to be disposed in the subcutaneous tissue (the superficial fascia). Nevertheless, the parenchyma of the mammary glands which, it must be remembered, develops from the epidermis of the skin, does not, in a sense, entirely escape the confines of the dermis. It will be recalled that the dermis consists of 2 layers, and that of these the papillary layer that abuts directly on the epidermis is more cellular and of a finer texture than the coarser and noncellular reticular layer that lies deep to it (Fig. 29-35). When cords of epidermis grow down into the mesenchyme to form the duct system of the breast, it would seem that they carry, as it were, the developing papillary layer of the dermis along with them to form a soft cellular connective tissue wrapping for each duct. (Fig.

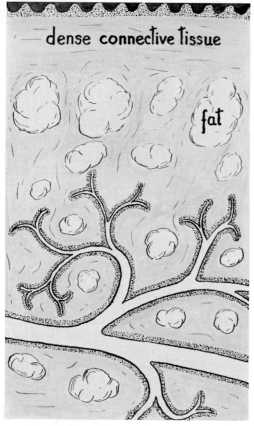

FIG. 29-35. Diagram to show the relation of the layers of the dermis to the connective tissue of the breast. The papillary layer of the dermis and the intralobular connective tissue of the breast are comparable and are both stippled in the illustration. The dense connective tissue dermis of the skin is seen to be prolonged deeply, in the form of septa or ligaments, which pass between lobules of fat, to become continuous with the interlobular connective tissue of the breast.

29-35) or a common wrapping for small adjacent groups of ducts. Then, between these single, or groups of, epithelial ducts so wrapped, substantial bundles and partitions of coarse noncellular connective tissue extend down from the reticular layer of the dermis that overlies the breast to separate the lobes and the lobules from one another and to hold the whole breast parenchyma tightly to the skin (Fig. 29-35). The larger of these bundles and partitions are termed the *suspensory liga-*

*ments of Cooper.* Fat accumulates in them (Fig. 29-35), so that they hold the fat of the breast in place as well as the epithelial parenchyma. Fat also accumulates in the connective tissue between the breast parenchyma and the skin that overlies it and the fascia that lies beneath it.

From the foregoing, the appearance of a section cut from almost any site in a resting breast, and in any plane, may be anticipated. In such a section; epithelial parenchyma will be scanty indeed, such as is present consists only of single ducts or little clusters of ducts widely separated from one another by connective tissue (Fig. 29-36). Most of the ducts seen in a section are cut obliquely or in cross section; occasionally, a portion of one may be cut in longitudinal section. Occasionally, a large lactiferous duct may be observed in a section that has been cut more or less haphazardly from the breast, but almost all the ducts that are commonly seen are of the different orders of branches that arise from the lactiferous ducts. Since the branches of the main ducts run out into the lobules that dangle, as it were, from the main ducts, most of the ducts seen in a section are inside lobules and hence are termed intralobular ducts. Their walls are generally composed of 2 layers of epithelial cells that have pale cytoplasm and pale oval nuclei. The long diameters of the nuclei in the inner layer of cells are commonly at right angles to the direction of the duct, and those of the outer layer are parallel with the duct. But the arrangement of epithelial cells in these ducts is variable. The epithelial cells of the ducts rest on a basement membrane.

Each duct is surrounded by a tunic of relatively cellular connective tissue that is about as thick as the duct is wide (Fig. 29-36). This cellular connective tissue that abuts on the epithelium of the ducts is the counterpart of the papillary layer of the dermis that abuts on the epidermis (Fig. 29-35). The cellular connective tissue that surrounds the individual ducts in a group of ducts may be confluent. Since this *cellular* connective tissue that invests the ducts is inside lobules, it is termed *intralobular* connective tissue. Fibroblasts are numerous in it and may be easily identified by their large, oval, pale and apparently naked nuclei (Fig. 29-36). Macro-

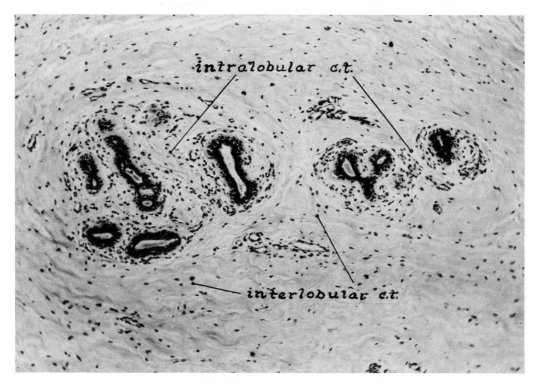

FIG. 29-36. Low-power photomicrograph of a section of a resting breast. Observe that the ducts are each surrounded by cellular intralobular connective tissue and that the 2 lobules shown are separated and otherwise surrounded by relatively noncellular interlobular connective tissue.

phages, lymphocytes and plasma cells are also normal cellular constituents of the intralobular connective tissue.

Single ducts or groups of ducts, invested with intralobular connective tissue, are separated from one another by thick partitions of coarse and *relatively noncellular* dense *interlobular* connective tissue. The connective tissue of these may be regarded, as is indicated in Figure 29-35, as a deep extension of the reticular layer of the dermis (the larger partitions seen are the suspensory ligaments of Cooper). The interlobular connective tissue often contains lobules of fat within its substance; the fat of the breast, then, is tied to the skin by the interlobular connective tissue.

**Changes That Occur in the Breast at Pregnancy.** The resting breast probably contains no secretory alveoli but consists only of a duct system. As pregnancy proceeds, a great development of the duct system occurs, and, finally, secretory alveoli develop at the ends of the smaller branches of the duct system. By the end of the 5th month of pregnancy the lobules are packed (and greatly expanded) with alveoli (Fig. 29-37). The intralobular connective tissue becomes broken up as alveoli bud from the ducts within lobules, so that the intralobular connective tissue eventually becomes reduced to a series of filmlike partitions between adjacent alveoli; however, these contain extensive capillary networks. The alveoli themselves are composed of a single layer of columnar cells. Curved myoepithelial cells are sometimes seen to be fitted around their periphery. Because of the great expansion of epithelial elements within the lobules, the partitions of interlobular connective tissue become greatly stretched and thinned (Figs. 29-37 and 29-38).

Most of the epithelial growth that occurs in the breast in pregnancy occurs before the end of the 6th month. In the later stages of pregnancy further growth occurs, but very slowly. However, the breasts continue to enlarge; this is due chiefly to the cells of the

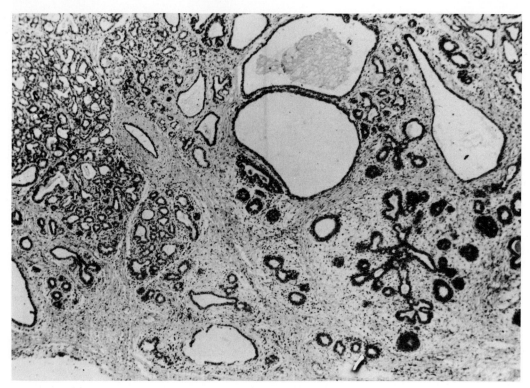

Fig. 29-37. Low-power photomicrograph of a section of a breast from a woman in the 5th month of pregnancy. The ducts have proliferated and, at the left side, they have given rise to alveoli.

alveoli beginning to secrete a fluid that expands them (and the breast) from within. This secretion is not milk; milk appears only after parturition, as will be explained presently.

CAUSE OF GROWTH OF BREASTS IN PREGNANCY. Any explanation for human breasts enlarging in pregnancy is based to a great extent on what has been learned from animal experiments. These experiments have yielded many contradictory results. One reason for this is that different workers have worked with different animals, and it seems that the hormone mechanisms that operate in pregnancy vary considerably throughout the animal kingdom. This makes it difficult to interpret such experimental results as have been obtained and to apply them to man with any precision. Nevertheless, certain facts have been established.

1. It has been clearly established that estrogens, suitably administered to intact animals, bring about a great development of their mammary glands. In some animals estrogen alone will prepare the breasts for function. However, in others progesterone also is needed to bring about a proper development of secretory aveoli at the ends of the duct system. Since large amounts of estrogen are made by the placenta during pregnancy, and since large amounts of progesterone are also produced, first by the corpus luteum and later by the placenta, it might seem that the explanation for the growth of the breasts in pregnancy is very simple: that their growth is stimulated directly by these two hormones. But the explanation is not quite so simple, as we shall see.

2. It has been established that a growth of the breasts comparable with that of pregnancy can be brought about by injecting animals with certain types of anterior pituitary extracts. In some instances this might be explained by supposing that the extracts, by containing gonadotrophic hormones, would stimulate the ovaries of the injected animals

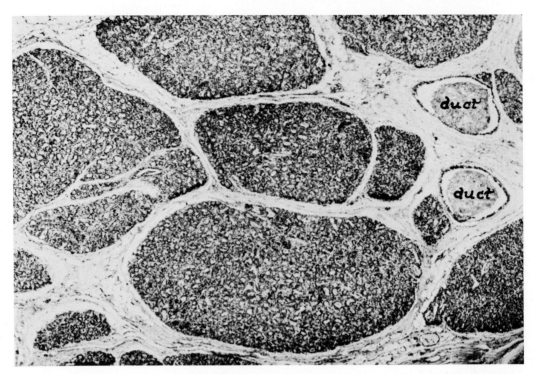

Fig. 29-38. Low-power photomicrograph of a section of a lactating breast. The lobules illustrated, although greatly expanded by a great content of alveoli, are not, in this section, cut through their widest parts. The interlobular septa are thicker in this photomicrograph than they are in most sites in the section.

to make estrogen and progesterone, which hormones, in turn, would cause the breasts to develop. But certain anterior pituitary extracts have been shown to cause the breasts to develop in female animals from which the ovaries have been removed. It is obvious, then, that anterior pituitary gland can itself make a hormone or hormones which can bring about the development of the breasts.

3. It has been shown that, although estrogen and progesterone induce a full growth of the breasts in intact animals, they cannot do so if the pituitary glands of the animals concerned are first removed.

4. It has been shown that in many different animals, including man, estrogen can be applied locally to a mammary gland so as to cause the growth of that particular mammary gland without having any effect on the other mammary gland or glands of the same individual.

5. It has been shown that the pituitary glands of animals can be removed when pregnancy is well advanced and that the mammary glands, under these conditions, continue their development provided that the placenta remains functional.

How are these facts to be reconciled in a working hypothesis? At least 2 theories should be considered in this connection. These differ primarily with regard to the question of whether or not the anterior pituitary makes a special hormone that causes breast growth. For convenience we shall term these theories 1 and 2.

*Theory 1.* According to this theory, the anterior pituitary gland makes a special hormone called the mammogenic hormone (mammotrophin), and this is the factor that directly stimulates breast growth. It is believed that this hormone is made by the anterior pituitary when this gland is stimulated sufficiently by estrogen. Indeed, it has been suggested that there are 2 mammogenic hormones, one made when the pituitary is stimulated by estrogen—and this brings about duct growth in the breast—and a second one —made when the pituitary is stimulated by progesterone—which brings about alveolar development. This theory has received support from experiments that show that the anterior pituitary glands of animals that have been injected with estrogen, or those of pregnant animals, contain more of the factor that stimulates breast growth than ordinary anterior pituitary glands. However, this theory does not explain why estrogen should have a local effect in causing breast growth.

*Theory 2.* This theory is opposed to the idea of there being a special anterior pituitary mammogenic hormone. In general, this theory attributes breast growth to the collaborative efforts of known anterior pituitary hormones and estrogen and progesterone. It depicts estrogen as having a local effect on the breast, not so much of a growth-stimulating one as an effect in making the vascular bed of the breast permeable to other hormones in the bloodstream which could cause breast growth if they were permitted to seep into breast tissue in sufficient amounts. The growth hormone, the adrenocorticotrophic hormone, the lactogenic hormone, the luteinizing hormone, chorionic gonadotrophin, adrenal cortical hormones and progesterone have all been suspected in this connection. It seems most probable that the lactogenic hormone is the most important, although the others are also necessary. This theory would explain why estrogen, though not capable of stimulating breast growth by itself, would, if it were applied locally, affect the capillary permeability of the part and so permit anterior pituitary and other hormones in the bloodstream to enter breast tissues and exert a growth effect. On the other hand, if the concentration of these hormones in the blood were great enough they would enter breast tissue in sufficient quantities without the help of estrogen; this could explain why anterior pituitary extracts, if given in large enough amounts, can bring about breast development in animals with no ovaries.

From all the foregoing it is obvious that the growth of the breasts in pregnancy involves very complex hormone interactions. The idea that estrogen acts to permit other hormones to enter breast tissue directly is attractive.

**The Lactating Breast.** As noted before, most of the increase in the size of the breasts from the 6th month on is due to secretion accumulating in the alveoli and the ducts. However, as this secretion is made, some appears at, and escapes from, the nipple (in women who have previously borne children, this may occur relatively early in pregnancy). This secretion is not milk but a somewhat different fluid termed *colostrum*. After parturition, colostrum is secreted more abundantly but only for 2 or 3 days, after which the breasts (in human females) begin to secrete milk.

Colostrum contains a higher concentration of protein than does milk but very little fat. It also contains fragments of cells and even whole cells of a large size. These frequently contain phagocytosed fat and are called *colostrum bodies*. It is probable that these cells are phagocytes that have made their way through the epithelium of the alveoli and so gained entrance to their lumens.

It was once commonly believed that a large proportion of the milk obtained by a baby at a single nursing was secreted during the nursing period. It is now generally accepted that almost no milk is secreted during this time and that milk is secreted and accumulates during the intervals between nursings.

MICROSCOPIC STRUCTURE. In the lactating breast the lobules are packed with secretory alveoli among which some intralobular ducts may be seen (Fig. 29-38). In general, the interlobular septa are greatly thinned; those illustrated in Figure 29-38 are wider than most. The appearance of alveoli in different parts of a lactating breast varies in that the alveoli in some parts of the breast have high columnar cells and others low columnar cells. Some are distended with secretion, and some contain only a little. It is probable that the alveoli of different parts of the same breast may, at the same time, be in different stages of a secretory cycle.

Milk contains proteins, lactose, fat and mineral salts. Of these constituents, fat is most easily demonstrated by histologic methods in the alveolar cells. In ordinary paraffin sections the fat droplets in the cytoplasm are dissolved, and the spaces they formerly occupied appear as cytoplasmic vacuoles. These are numerous between the free borders of the alveolar cells and their nuclei (Fig. 29-39).

The free borders of the alveolar cells that are in active secretion appear frayed. It is probable that part of the cytoplasm at the free borders of the cells is lost in the process of secretion; hence, the mammary glands are of the apocrine type.

CAUSE OF LACTATION. Hormones are necessary, not only to make the breast develop during pregnancy, but also to make it function after parturition. Furthermore, the hormones that induce lactation are at least somewhat different from those that induce breast growth.

It is generally conceded that a special anterior pituitary hormone, the lactogenic hormone, plays an important part in causing and maintaining lactation. Other hormones are also essential. Moreover, it seems probable that a pure hormone that has been recovered from the anterior pituitary gland (*prolactin*) does not account for all the effects that are exerted by the lactogenic hormone. There is evidence to show that lactogenic hormone may be present in the anterior pituitary glands at times other than during lactation. However, it is probable that the anterior pituitary gland makes more lactogenic hormone immediately following parturition and during lactation than at other times.

There is a very curious relationship between estrogen and the lactogenic hormone. There is much evidence to indicate that enough estrogen in the blood is a requisite for putting the anterior pituitary gland "into a mood," as it were, to make lactogenic hormone in large amounts. For example, if female animals of certain kinds are injected day by day with estrogen and then the estrogen injections are discontinued, the animals will begin to lactate. Yet, while estrogen seems to arouse the desires of the anterior pituitary with regard to producing lactogenic hormone, and causes it to secrete enough to cause breast development, it also tends to prevent the anterior pituitary from realizing its full secretory capacity in connection with lactogenic hormone, for enough estrogen in the blood seems to suppress lactation. Lactation, it must be remembered, does not begin during pregnancy but only after the placenta has been delivered and the body has been released from the effects of the estrogen and other hormones made by this structure. That estrogen can

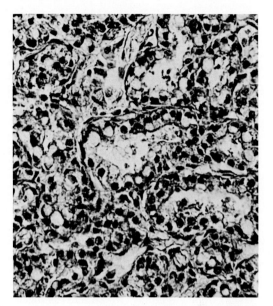

FIG. 29-39. High-power photomicrograph of a small area of a section of a lactating breast. Notice the vacuoles that represent fat droplets in the secretory cells of the alveoli, particularly at their free borders.

suppress lactation is further indicated by the fact that if sufficient estrogen is given a woman in the days following parturition, lactation is suppressed.

The foregoing could explain why the breasts of a newborn baby, whether male or female, tend to become distended with secretion shortly after birth, as if they, in their very undeveloped state, were attempting to function. This could be due to the estrogen produced by the placenta during pregnancy having stimulated the anterior pituitary gland of the fetus, as well as that of the mother, to try to make lactogenic hormone. Consequently, when the fetus is born and loses its connection with the placenta, its anterior pituitary gland, being now removed from the inhibitory effects of placental estrogen, could secrete enough lactogenic hormone to make the ducts of the mammary glands of the baby secrete a little fluid. This is called *witches' milk*. Since much of this is retained in the ducts, the ducts become temporarily distended.

The maintenance of breast function depends upon the anterior pituitary gland's continuing to secrete lactogenic hormone. This, in turn, depends upon the breasts being emptied regularly. The nervous stimulation from nursing and the psychological factors involved both contribute toward making the anterior pituitary continue the production of this hormone. While the anterior pituitary gland continues to make lactogenic hormone, it seems hesitant to make FSH, probably because the lactogenic hormone continues to exert a luteotrophic effect which results in a continued secretion of progesterone, which, in turn, suppresses FSH secretion. Hence, ovulation and menstruation may not occur during the time a mother is nursing her baby. However, this is by no means a universal phenomenon, and women can become pregnant again during the nursing period. It is of interest that while enough estrogen is made during pregnancy to inhibit the anterior pituitary gland from beginning to secrete lactogenic hormone, enough is not made to inhibit an anterior pituitary gland whose lactogenic function is well established from continuing to make the hormone. Consequently, pregnancy does not interfere with a well-established lactation, and a woman may continue nursing one baby after another has been conceived.

A thorough emptying of the breasts at nursing helps maintain and even increases their functional capacities, not only because the nervous stimuli involved somehow stimulate the anterior pituitary to continue to make lactogenic hormone, but also because increased demands for function tend to stimulate the growth of enough further structure to permit the increased functional demands to be met.

Lactation cannot proceed in the absence of the adrenal cortex. The cortical hormone that affects carbohydrate metabolism appears to be the essential factor from this gland. The thyroid hormone also facilitates lactation.

REGRESSION AFTER LACTATION. Since the breasts must be emptied regularly if their structure is to be maintained and if the secretion of lactogenic hormone is to be continued, the discontinuance of breast feeding, provided that the breasts are not regularly emptied by other means, leads to their gradually regaining almost the same type of microscopic structure as they exhibit before pregnancy begins. They do not return to precisely the same state as before because a few alveoli

persist in them. But most of the alveoli are resorbed, and the lobules shrink in size. The partitions of interlobular connective tissue again become thick and strong. It is very important that the breasts be properly supported during the time these partitions are thin, but it is particularly important during the period while the alveoli are being absorbed, the lobules are shrinking in size and the interlobular partitions are becoming thick again (the 2 to 3 months following the cessation of lactation). If the interlobular septa become "set" in a stretched state, the breasts will subsequently sag unduly.

The Mammary Glands After the Menopause. The changes that occur in the breast after the menopause are various. The general trend that the breast exhibits is toward atrophy, both of its epithelial and connective tissue components. The intercellular substance of the latter may undergo a hyalin change, but irregular growth and secretory changes may be superimposed upon the general atrophic changes. The epithelium of some ducts may proliferate and that of others secrete and convert the ducts concerned into cysts. Doubtless, estrogen and progesterone deficiency are chiefly responsible for the progressive atrophy that occurs after the menopause. The irregular growth and the secretory changes that are sometimes superimposed on the atrophic changes have been attributed to estrogen, but surely it seems more probable that those that occur around the time of the menopause are caused by anterior pituitary hormones that are secreted more abundantly when the anterior pituitary gland is being released from the restraining influences of estrogen. Certainly much more FSH is secreted by the anterior pituitary after the estrogen level of the blood falls at the time of the menopause, and quite possibly other anterior pituitary hormones, that might act to make the breasts grow and secrete a little, are secreted at the same time. Indeed, it is our opinion that there is some parallelism between the breasts of the newborn and those of a woman who has just experienced the menopause. In both individuals the anterior pituitary has been released from a prolonged period of stimulation by estrogen and, in both, the breasts tend to become cystic. So, whereas the effect of estrogen and progesterone deficiency might, in the end, lead indirectly to breast atrophy, it might be suspected that for a time after the menopause the secretion of some anterior pituitary hormones would complicate the histologic picture seen in the glands.

## REFERENCES

### SOME GENERAL REFERENCES

Bertalanffy, F. D., and Lau, Chosen: Mitotic rates, renewal times, and cytodynamics of the female genital tract epithelia in the rat, Acta anat. *54*:39, 1963.

Burrows, H.: Biological Actions of Sex Hormones, ed. 2, London, Cambridge, 1949.

Corner, G. W.: The Hormones in Human Reproduction, Princeton, Princeton Univ. Press, 1942.

Hartman, C. G.: The Time of Ovulation in Women, Baltimore, Williams & Wilkins, 1936.

Lillie, F. R.: The free-martin; a study of the action of sex hormones in the foetal life of cattle, J. Exp. Zool. *23*:371, 1917.

Papanicolaou, G. N., Traut, H. F., and Marchetti, A. A.: The Epithelia of Woman's Reproductive Tract, London, Oxford, 1948.

Parkes, A. S.: The Internal Secretion of the Ovary, London, Longmans, 1929.

Pincus, G., Thimann, K. V., and Astwood, E. B.: The Hormones, vols. 1-5, New York, Acad. Press, 1948-1964.

Young, W. C. (ed.): Sex and Internal Secretion, 2 vols., Baltimore, Williams & Wilkins, 1961.

### GENERAL REFERENCE ON FINE STRUCTURE OF PARTS OF THE FEMALE GENITAL SYSTEM

Rhodin, J. A. G.: An Atlas of Ultrastructure, pp. 114-130, Philadelphia, Saunders, 1963.

### GENERAL REFERENCE ON THE OVARY

Zuckerman, S. (ed.): The Ovary, 2 vols., New York, Acad. Press, 1962.

### SPECIAL REFERENCES ON THE OVARY

Allen, E.: The menstrual cycle of the monkey, *Macacus rhesus*, Contrib. Embryol. *19*:1, 1927.
——: The oestrus cycle in the mouse, Am. J. Anat. *30*:297, 1922.

Allen, E., Pratt, J. P., Newell, Q. U., and Bland, L. J.: Hormone content of human ovarian tissues, Am. J. Physiol. *92*:127, 1930.
——: Human ova from large follicles; including a search for maturation divisions and observations on atresia, Am. J. Anat. *46*:1, 1930.

Anderson, E., and Beams, H. W.: Observations on the ultramicroscopic anatomy of a mammalian ovum, Anat. Rec. *134*:525, 1959.

——: Cytological observations on the fine structure of the guinea pig ovary with special reference to the oogonium, primary oocyte and associated follicle cells, J. Ultrastr. Res. *3*: 432, 1960.

Aschheim, S.: Pregnancy tests, J.A.M.A. *104*: 1324, 1935.

Corner, G. W.: Cytology of the ovum, ovary, and fallopian tube *in* Cowdry's Special Cytology, ed. 2, p. 1565, New York, Hoeber, 1932.
——: Development, organization, and breakdown of the corpus luteum in the rhesus monkey, Contrib. Embryol. *31*:117, 1945.
——: Ovulation and menstruation in *Macacus rhesus*, Contrib. Embryol. *15*:75, 1923.
——: Relation between menstruation and ovulation in monkeys; its possible significance for man, J.A.M.A. *89*:1838, 1927.

Crocker, K. M., and Stitt, W. D.: Ovulation inhibitors, Canad. M. A. J. *90*:713, 1964.

Gatz, A. J.: A critique on the discussion of oogenesis in the textbooks of histology, Turtox News *33*:106, 1955.

Hartman, C. G.: Physiology of reproduction in the monkey and their bearing on gynecology and anthropology, Endocrinology *25*:670, 1939.

Lever, J. D.: Remarks on the electron microscopy of the rat luteum and comparison with earlier observations on the adrenal cortex, Anat. Rec. *124*:111, 1956.

Matthews, L. H.: Visual stimulation and ovulation in pigeons, Proc. Roy. Soc. London, s.B. *126*:557, 1939.

Ohno, S., Klinger, H. P., and Atkin, N. B.: Human oogenesis, Cytogenetics *1*:42, 1962.

Pederson, E. S.: Histogenesis of lutein tissue of the albino rat, Am. J. Anat. *88*:397, 1951.

Slater, D. W., and Dornfeld, E. J.: Quantitative aspects of growth and oocyte production in the early prepubertal rat ovary, Am. J. Anat. *76*: 253, 1945.

Sotello, J. R., and Porter, K. R.: An electron microscope study of the rat ovum, J. Biophys. Biochem. Cytol. *5*:327, 1959.

Yamada, E., Muta, T., Motomura, A., and Koga, H.: The fine structure of the oocyte in the mouse ovary studied with electron microscope, Kurume Med. J. *4*:148, 1957.

### SPECIAL REFERENCES ON THE OVIDUCTS

Novak, E., and Everett, H. S.: Cyclical and other variations in the tubal epithelium, Am. J. Obst. Gynec. *16*:449, 1928.

Snyder, F. F.: Changes in the human oviduct during the menstrual cycle in pregnancy, Bull. Johns Hopkins Hosp. *35*:141, 1924.

Stockard, C. R., and Papanicolaou, G. N.: The existence of a typical oestrus cycle in the guinea pig—with a study of its histological and physiological changes, Am. J. Anat. *22*:225, 1917.

### SPECIAL REFERENCES ON THE UTERUS

Bartelmez, G. W.: Histological studies of the menstruating mucous membranes of the human uterus, Contrib. Embryol. *24*:141, 1933.

————: Menstruation, Physiol. Rev. *17*:28, 1937.

Bartelmez, G. W., and Bensley, C. M.: Human uterine gland cells *in* Cowdry's Special Cytology, ed. 2, p. 1523, New York, Hoeber, 1932.

Bo, W. J., and Atkinson, W. B.: Histochemical studies on glycogen deposition in the uterus of the rat, Anat. Rec. *113*:91, 1952.

Corner, G. W.: Influence of the ovarian hormones oestrin and progestin upon the menstrual cycle of the monkey, Am. J. Physiol. *113*:238, 1935.

Daron, G. H.: The arterial pattern of the tunica mucosa of the uterus in *Macacus rhesus*, Am. J. Anat. *58*:349, 1936.

Markee, J. E.: Menstruation in intraocular endometrial transplants in the rhesus monkey, Contrib. Embryol. *28*:219, 1940.

Nicol, T., and Snell, R. S.: The appearances of lipoid in the genital tract of the mature virgin guinea pig during the oestrous cycle, J. Obst. Gynaec. Brit. Emp. *61*:216, 1954.

Nilsson, O.: Ultrastructure of mouse uterine surface epithelium under different estrogenic influences, pp. 1-387, Uppsala, Almqvist & Wiksells, 1959.

O'Leary, J. L.: Form changes in the human uterine gland during the menstrual cycle and in early pregnancy, Am. J. Anat. *42*:289, 1929.

Sharman, A.: An experimental study of postpartum endometrial repair in the guinea pig and rat, J. Endocrinol. *8*:162, 1951.

————: Post-partum regeneration of the human endometrium, J. Anat. *87*:1, 1953.

Smith, P. E., and Engle, E. T.: Differences in the time of onset of uterine bleeding after cessation of estrin and progestin treatments, Anat. Rec. *71*:73, 1938.

Sylvén, B.: The occurrence of ester sulphuric acids of high molecular weight and of mast cells in the stroma of the normal uterine corpus mucosa, Acta obst. gynec. scand. *25*:189, 1945.

Wislocki, G. B., and Dempsey, E. W.: Histochemical reactions of the endometrium in pregnancy, Am. J. Anat. *77*:365, 1945.

Young, A.: Vascular architecture of the rat uterus, Proc. Roy. Soc. Edinburgh *64*:292, 1952.

### SPECIAL REFERENCES ON THE PLACENTA

Arey, L. B.: The presence and arrangement of smooth muscle in the human placenta, Anat. Rec. *100*:636, 1948.

Barcroft, J., and Barron, D.: Observations upon form and relations of the maternal and fetal vessels in the placenta of the sheep, Anat. Rec. *94*:569, 1946.

Boving, B. G.: Implantation, Ann. N. Y. Acad. Sci. *75*:700, 1959.

Boyd, J. D.: Some aspects of the relationship between mother and child, Ulster M. J. *28*:35, 1959.

Boyd, J. D., and Hamilton, W. J.: The giant cells ·of the pregnant human uterus, J. Obst. Gynaec. Brit. Emp. *67*:208, 1960.

————: Development of the human placenta in the first three months of gestation, J. Anat. *94*:297, 1960.

Boyd, J. D., and Hughes, A. F. W.: Observations on human chorionic villi using the E/M, J. Anat. *88*:356, 1954.

Dempsey, E. W., and Wislocki, G. B.: E/M of human placental villi, Anat. Rec. *117*:609, 1953.

Hamilton, W. J., and Boyd, J. D.: Observations on the human placenta, Proc. Roy. Soc. Med. *44*:489, 1951.

————: Development of the human placenta in the first three months of gestation, J. Anat. *94*:297, 1960.

Mossman, H. W.: Comparative morphogenesis of the fetal membranes and accessory uterine structures, Contrib. Embryol. *26* (158):129-246, 1937.

Paine, C. G.: Observations on placental histology in normal and abnormal pregnancy, J. Obst. Gynaec. Brit. Emp. *64*:(5), 668, 1957.

Pierce, G. B., Jr., and Midgley, A. R., Jr.: The origin and function of human syncytiotrophoblastic giant cells, Am. J. Path. *43*:153, 1963.

Ramsey, E. M.: The vascular pattern of the endometrium of the pregnant Rhesus monkey (Macaca mulatta), Contrib. Embryol. *33*:113, 1949.

————: Vascular adaptations of the uterus to pregnancy, Ann. N. Y. Acad. Sci. *75*:726, 1959.

Sohval, A. R., Gaines, J. A., and Strauss, L.: Chromosomal sex detection in the human newborn and fetus from examination of the umbilical cord, placental tissue and fetal membranes, Ann. N. Y. Acad. Sci. *75*:905, 1959.

Terzakis, J. A.: The ultrastructure of normal human first trimester placenta, J. Ultrastr. Res. *9*:268, 1963.

Villee, C. A.: The Placenta and Fetal Membranes, Baltimore, Williams & Wilkins, 1960.

Wislocki, G. B., and Bennett, H. S.: Cytology of placental trophoblast, Anat. Rec. *100*:414, 1948.

### SPECIAL REFERENCES ON THE CERVIX AND THE VAGINA

Danforth, D. N.: The fibrous nature of the human cervix and its relations to the isthmic segment in gravid and non-gravid uteri, Am. J. Obst. Gynec. 53:541, 1947.

de Allende, I. L. C., Shorr, E., and Hartman, C. G.: A comparative study of the vaginal smear cycle of the rhesus monkey and the human, Contrib. Embryol. 31:1, 1945.

Gillman, J.: Cyclical changes in vaginal smear in the baboon and its relationship to perineal swelling, S. Afr. J. M. Sc. 2:44, 1937.

Nicol, T., and Snell, R. S.: The appearances of lipoid in the cells of the vaginal smear of the guinea pig, J. Obst. Gynaec. Brit. Emp. 61:85, 1954.

Papanicolaou, G. N.: The sexual cycle in the human female as revealed by vaginal smears, Am. J. Anat. 52:519, 1933.

Smith, B. G., and Brunner, E. K.: The structure of the human vaginal mucosa in relation to the menstrual cycle and to pregnancy, Am. J. Anat. 54:27, 1934.

## SPECIAL REFERENCES ON THE MAMMARY GLANDS

Bunting, H.: Cytochemical properties of apocrine sweat gland normally present in the human sweat gland, Anat. Rec. 101:5, 1948.

Corner, G. W.: The hormonal control of lactation: I. Non-effect of the corpus luteum; II. Positive action of extracts of the hypophysis, Am. J. Physiol. 95:43, 1930.

Cowie, A. T., and Folley, S. J.: Physiology of the gonadotropins and the lactogenic hormone *in* Pincus, G., and Thimann, K. V. (eds.): The Hormones, ed. 3, p. 309, New York, Acad. Press, 1955.

Dempsey, E. W., Bunting, H., and Wislocki, G. B.: Observations on the chemical cytology of the mammary gland, Am. J. Anat. 81:309, 1947.

Gardner, W. U.: The effect of ovarian hormones and ovarian grafts upon the mammary glands of male mice, Endocrinology 19:656, 1935.

————: Growth of the mammary glands in hypophysectomized mice, Proc. Soc. Exp. Biol. Med. 45:835, 1940.

————: Inhibition of mammary growth by large amounts of estrogen, Endocrinology 28:53, 1941.

Gardner, W. U., and Chamberlin, T. L.: Local action of estrone on mammary glands of mice, Yale J. Biol. Med. 13:461, 1941.

Gardner, W. U., and White, A.: Mammary growth in hypophysectomized male mice receiving estrogen and prolactin, Proc. Soc. Exp. Biol. Med. 48:590, 1941.

Gomez, E. T., Mammary gland growth in hypophysectomized castrated guinea pigs, Endocrinology 31:613, 1942.

Gomez, E. T., and Turner, C. W.: Initiation and maintenance of lactation in hypophysectomized guinea pigs, Proc. Soc. Exp. Biol. Med. 35:365, 1936.

Gunther, M.: Sore nipples; causes and prevention, Lancet 249:590, 1945.

Jeffers, K. R.: Cytology of the mammary gland of albino rat, Am. J. Anat. 56:257, 279, 1935.

Linzell, J. L.: The silver staining of myoepithelial cells, particularly in the mammary gland, and their relation to the ejection of milk, J. Anat. 86:49, 1952.

Nelson, W. O.: Endocrine control of the mammary gland, Physiol. Rev. 16:488, 1936.

Petersen, W. E.: Lactation, Physiol. Rev. 24:340, 1944.

Rawlinson, H. E., and Pierce, G. B.: Visible intraepithelial iron in the mammary glands of various species, Science 117:33, 1953.

Riddle, O.: Lactogenic and mammogenic hormones, J.A.M.A. 115:2276, 1940.

Selye, H.: Effect of chronic progesterone overdosage on the female accessory sex organs of normal, ovariectomized and hypophysectomized rats, Anat. Rec. 78:253, 1940.

Selye, H., Collip, J. B., and Thomson, D. L.: Nervous and hormonal factors in lactation, Endocrinology 18:237, 1934.

Trentin, J. J., DeVita, J., and Gardner, W. U.: Effect of moderate doses of estrogen and progesterone on mammary growth and hair growth in dogs, Anat. Rec. 113:163, 1952.

# 30  The Male Reproductive System

## THE PARTS OF THE SYSTEM AND THEIR FUNCTIONS

The male reproductive system (Fig. 30-1) consists of: (1) two gonads, the *testes*, which produce male germ cells and male sex hormone; (2) a copulatory organ, the *penis*, by which male germ cells may be delivered into the vagina of the female; (3) a long, complicated set of tubes and tubules which lead from the testes to the penis and so permit male germ cells made in the testes both to be stored and to be conducted to the male copulatory organ; and (4) certain glands called the male accessory glands, which have much smooth muscle in their walls. These glands not only provide a fluid vehicle for carrying male germ cells through the copulatory organ in the sexual act, but also, by the reflex contraction of the smooth muscle of their walls during the sexual act (certain voluntary muscles also participate), cause a mixture of their secretions and male germ cells (the mixture is called *semen*) to be expressed vigorously from the penis; this phenomenon, of brief duration, is termed *ejaculation*.

From the foregoing it may be realized that the male reproductive system consists of 4 structures or groups of structures that have somewhat different functions. Before considering the details of the microscopic structure of these and the relation of their microscopic structure to their function, it may be helpful to discuss, in a general way, some further features that they possess and their relation to one another.

**Some General Features of the Testes.** Although the testes develop in the abdomen from the indifferent gonads of the embryo, they migrate, in a way to be described in detail later, so that in postnatal life they are contained in the scrotum. This is a pendulous bag that hangs between the curved anteromedial borders of the proximal parts of the thighs (shown, but not labeled, in Fig. 30-1). Its wall is thin, being composed of skin, an incomplete layer of smooth muscle (the dartos) and some subcutaneous tissue. The wall of the scrotum has a considerable surface area, and it is believed that this permits its contents to be maintained at a temperature slightly below that of the body as a whole. This is probably an important requisite in man for the production of male germ cells by the testes. The dartos muscle in the wall of the scrotum contracts in response to cold and certain other types of stimuli; its contraction makes the scrotum smaller and its wall corrugated.

Like the ovaries, the testes perform the two functions of producing germ cells and sex hormone. Male germ cells are called *spermatozoa* (*spermà* = seed; *zōon* = animal). The generic term for substances having male sex hormone activity is *androgen* (*anēr* = man; *gennaō* = I produce).

The structure and the functions of the testes are governed by the gonadotrophic hormone of the anterior pituitary gland. As a boy approaches puberty, the anterior pituitary gland begins to secrete substantial amounts of gonadotrophic hormone. This, in turn, stimulates the testes to begin producing both spermatozoa and androgen. The androgen secreted as a result of the gonadotrophic stimulus brings about the development of the secondary sex characteristics of the male that appear at this time.

The testes have two important functional components. First, tubules, having walls of many cells in thickness and a total length of almost half a mile, are packed into the two testes (Fig. 30-2). These are the *seminiferous* (*semen* = seed; *ferre* = to carry) tubules. Their walls consist of many layers of cells; those cells of the innermost layers are more or less continuously turning into spermatozoa. These become free in the lumens of the tubules. The second important functional component of the testes consist of clumps of endocrine cells, the *interstitial cells*. These are disposed in the connective tissue stroma between the tubules. It is probable that these produce the androgen that is made by the testes.

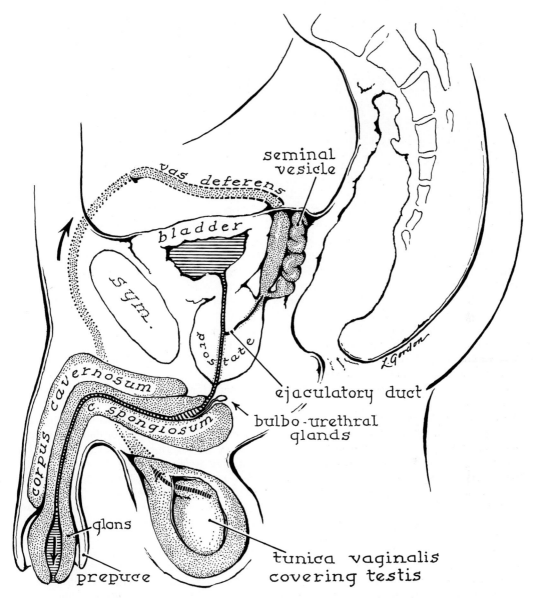

FIG. 30-1. Diagram of the parts of the male reproductive system, showing their connections with one another.

Each testis is an ovoid body, 4 to 5 cm. long. It is covered with a thick capsule called the *tunica albuginea* because it contains so much white fibrous tissue (Fig. 30-2). Along the posterior border of each testis, the capsule becomes greatly thickened and extends into the substance of the gland for a short distance to form an incomplete partition. Since it tends to be in the middle of the gland, this abortive partition and the thickened part of the capsule from which it arises are said to consti-

tute the *mediastinum* (*mediastinum* = being in the middle) of the testis (Fig. 30-2).

The mediastinum of each testis is riddled with a network of passageways that are lined with epithelium. These constitute the *rete* (*rete* = a net) testis (Fig. 30-2). The seminiferous tubules of the testis all empty into the spaces of the rete.

**General Features of the Set of Conducting Tubes and Tubules.** The spermatozoa present in the testis or seen in the rete testis are not

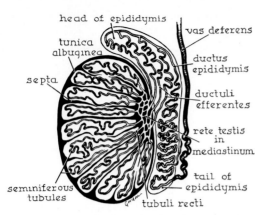

FIG. 30-2. Diagram showing the parts of the testis and the epididymis.

capable of fertilizing ova. It appears that spermatozoa complete their maturation outside the testis in tubules which are enormously long and convoluted. Some morphologic evidence of this maturation has been observed in the guinea pig in which the spermatozoa were seen to take their definitive shape in the distal part of the tubule only. The names and the general distribution of the tubules through which the spermatozoa must pass to reach the male copulatory organ will now be given.

The spaces of the rete testis, at the upper part of the mediastinum, drain into 15 to 20 tubules called the *ductuli efferentes* (*effere* = to bring out) that arise in this region (Fig. 30-2). These penetrate the tunica albuginea of the testis and emerge from its upper part. They thereupon pursue an extraordinarily convoluted course as they pass upward. Each tubule is so wound on itself that each forms a little cone-shaped structure. The cones are bound together by loose connective tissue and together they constitute most of the head of a narrow crescentic structure that caps the upper pole of the testis and extends down along one of its sides. Since the testes are alike (twins), this narrow structure that caps each of them is termed an *epididymis* (*epi* = upon; *didymos* = twin).

Each epididymis has a head, a body and a tail. The head fits over part of the upper pole of the testis and consists essentially of the cones of convoluted ductuli efferentes (Fig. 30-2). The body extends down along the posterolateral border of the testis and consists chiefly of the ductus epididymis. This duct

begins in the head where all the ductuli efferentes empty into it. In the body of the epididymis it pursues an extremely convoluted course (Fig. 30-2). This part of it, if unraveled, would be seen to be several yards long. In the tail of the epididymis, which reaches nearly to the lower pole of the testis, the ductus epididymis gradually assumes a less convoluted course and finally emerges from the tail to become the *ductus,* or *vas, deferens* (*deferre* = to carry away) (Fig. 30-2).

The ductus deferens ascends from the tail of the epididymis along the posterior border of the testis, medial to the epididymis. It becomes associated with blood vessels and nerves and becomes possessed of coverings derived from the anterior abdominal wall, whose lowest medial part it traverses in a region known as the *inguinal canal.* The ductus deferens, together with the blood vessels and the nerves associated with it and the wrappings it obtains from the tissues of the anterior abdominal wall, constitutes a structure known as the *spermatic cord.* The ductus deferens, in the spermatic cord, traverses the inguinal canal, which leads through the muscles and the fascia of the abdominal wall, to enter the abdominal cavity (however, the ductus remains outside the peritoneum). Here the ductus deferens becomes free of its coverings and, after entering and pursuing a course in the pelvis—a course that need not be described here—reaches the back of the urinary bladder (Fig. 30-1). An elongated epithelial-lined sac, the *seminal vesicle* (a blind outpouching of the ductus deferens), lies lateral to it on the back of the bladder (Fig. 30-1). Immediately beyond the point at which the seminal vesicle empties into the ductus deferens, the ductus—which is now the common duct of the testis and the seminal vesicle—is known as the *ejaculatory duct* (Fig. 30-2). This duct pierces the upper surface of the prostate gland, traverses the substance of this gland and empties into the urethra, which structure, in turn, courses through the prostate gland on its way from the bladder to the penis.

**General Features of the Glands That Supply the Fluid Vehicle for Spermatozoa.** As noted before, the fluid that is delivered through the penis in ejaculation is called semen, and it is a composite of spermatozoa and a fluid vehicle, most of which is supplied by the seminal vesicles and the prostate gland.

Moreover, these two structures, as well as containing epithelial secretory cells which provide the fluid vehicle described above, have a considerable amount of smooth muscle in their walls, and the sudden reflex contraction of these muscles at the time of ejaculation provides part of the force required to eject the semen.

The seminal vesicle has already been described as an outpouching from the ductus deferens near its termination. It does not contain glandular secretory units as such, but instead its lining is composed of secretory cells and is thrown into an enormous number of folds (Fig. 30-14). The secretion produced by its lining cells accumulates in the cavity of the vesicle, and the engorgement of the vesicle that results from this process, together with the filling of the glands of the prostate gland (to be described later), by stimulating the endings of afferent nerves, is probably a very important factor in arousing sex urge in the male. Moreover, it is probable that a very important reason for the sex urge of males decreasing with age is the fact that the secretory activity of the epithelial cells of these structures is controlled by the amount of male sex hormone in the circulation, and this decreases with age.

The prostate gland—about the size and the shape of a horse chestnut—is essentially a rounded mass of smooth muscle and connective tissue, the substance of which is thoroughly riddled by a great many separate compound tubulo-alveolar glands. The prostate gland surrounds the first part of the urethra as the latter emerges from the neck of the bladder (Fig. 30-1). The tubulo-alveolar compound glands that extend throughout its substance all drain, by means of about 2 dozen excretory ducts, into the prostatic portion of the urethra.

**The Copulatory Organ.** The urethra, which courses through the penis to open through its end, serves, in the act of copulation, as a means whereby semen can be delivered from the body. However, the penis, under ordinary conditions, is a flaccid structure and in this state it could not function as a copulatory organ. However, in a male subjected to sufficient erotic influence, the penis becomes greatly increased in size and assumes a more or less erect position. This phenomenon is known as *erection*, and it enables the organ to perform the sexual act. Erection is an involuntary act controlled by the autonomic nervous system. The increased size and the altered position of the organ that occur under these conditions are to be explained by the fact that most of its substance consists of erectile tissue, soon to be described. This is disposed in three long cylindrical bodies arranged, two side by side and known as the *corpora cavernosa*, and one placed medially below the paired ones and known as the *corpus cavernosum urethrae* because it, in its substance, conducts the urethra from one of its ends to the other (Figs. 30-1 and 30-18). The corpora cavernosa contain a vast number of little cavities, all connected with the vascular system. When the penis is flaccid the cavities are collapsed and contain only a little blood because the vascular arrangement is such that blood can drain from the cavities more easily than it can enter them. But, under conditions of erotic stimulation, nervous impulses flow to the organ and relax the smooth muscle of the arteries that supply the cavities. This causes greatly increased amounts of blood to enter them, more than can be drained away conveniently. As the cavities of the corpora cavernosa become distended with blood, some of the veins which ordinarily drain blood away from the cavities become compressed. The net result of the great increase of the arterial supply and the impeded venous drainage is that the cavernous bodies become longer, thicker, wider and straighter and, as a consequence, the whole organ becomes enlarged and erect. Subsequently, when the smooth muscle of the arteries that supply the cavities contracts, the rate of drainage of blood from the spaces in the erectile tissue comes to exceed the rate at which it is delivered into the spaces, and, as a result, the organ returns to its flaccid state.

## THE TESTES

**Development and Descent.** As was noted in describing the development of the ovary, different theories have been held regarding the source of primordial germ cells. It was formerly believed that in the male these developed from the sex cords of the testis, soon to be described. It has now been established, however, that as is true of the female also, the primordial germ cells are not formed in the gonad; those of males migrate to and enter the developing testis during the 5th week and become incorporated into cords of epithelial-like cells that are commonly believed to represent downgowths of the surface epithelium and are called sex cords. The primordial germ cells become the gonocytes of the child testis and eventually they become the spermatogonia of the seminiferous tubules that after puberty produce male germ cells, spermatozoa. The other cells in the sex cords give rise to what are termed the Sertoli cells of the seminiferous tubules.

Until the end of the 6th week there is little indication as to whether a developing gonad will become a testis or an ovary. However, in the 7th week the sex cords become much more clear-cut in the male gonad than in the ovary. Furthermore, the mesenchyme immediately beneath the germinal epithelium becomes thickened, indicating that the thick tunica albuginea of the male gonad will form later. As development proceeds, the sex cords become continuous with another group of epithelial cords that become organized somewhat more deeply in the testis and that are the forerunners of the rete. The development of the other ducts of the male genital system, and the manner in which they become connected with each other, involves embryologic considerations too detailed to be dealt with here.

By the 4th month, the elongated mass of tissue comprising the embryonic testis has become sufficiently condensed and rounded to have assumed a form suggestive of its adult shape. The cords of epithelium within it, destined to become the seminiferous tubules, have become more sharply defined from the mesenchyme that occupies the spaces between them which is differentiating into the connective tissue stroma of the gland. Some of the cells of the stroma enlarge and become grouped together to constitute clusters of *interstitial cells*. It appears established that these produce androgen during fetal life and that the testis is a much more active endocrine gland in the fetus than it is after birth until the time of puberty. It seems possible that the development of the interstitial cells of the testis in fetal life may be due to the gonadotrophin made by the placenta.

By the 6th month of fetal life, the cords of epithelial cells develop into seminiferous tubules. These, although called tubules, do not immediately develop lumens. Each seminiferous tubule becomes surrounded by a connective tissue layer which is continuous with the connective tissue of the mediastinum testis. In the testes of many animals the septa that radiate from the mediastinum out through the testis to the tunica albuginea divide the organ into lobules. However, in the testes of man the septa are incomplete.

Within the imperfectly separated lobules of the testes the seminiferous tubules become arranged in the form of long, convoluted, flattened loops (Fig. 30-2). At the point where each loop closely approaches the mediastinum, the tubule becomes continuous, by means of relatively straight canals (or caniliculi), the *tubuli recti* (*rectus* = straight) (Fig. 30-2), with the rete testis.

The testis originates in the body cavity behind the peritoneum at the medial side of the developing kidney. As development proceeds and the testis migrates downward, the peritoneum bulges out through the anterior abdominal wall, just above the medial end of the inguinal ligament, into the inguinal canal. The elongated tubular pouch of peritoneum so formed is called the *processus vaginalis* (sheathlike extension). The testis, which by this time lies immediately behind the peritoneum, is pulled down into the inguinal canal behind the processus vaginalis. The processus vaginalis traverses the inguinal canal and descends into the scrotum, arriving there at about the 7th month or somewhat later. The testis, pulling the ductus deferens behind it, follows along behind the posterior wall of the processus vaginalis to reach the scrotum shortly before the time of birth. The posterior wall of the processus vaginalis is invaginated by the testis and so covers its lateral and anterior wall as well as its two poles. In this way the testis comes to be provided with visceral peritoneum (the visceral layer of the tunica vaginalis). The remainder of the processus vaginalis lies in its own half of the inner wall of the scrotum and so constitutes the parietal layer of the tunica vaginalis. The canal by which the processus vaginalis communicates with the peritoneal cavity then be-

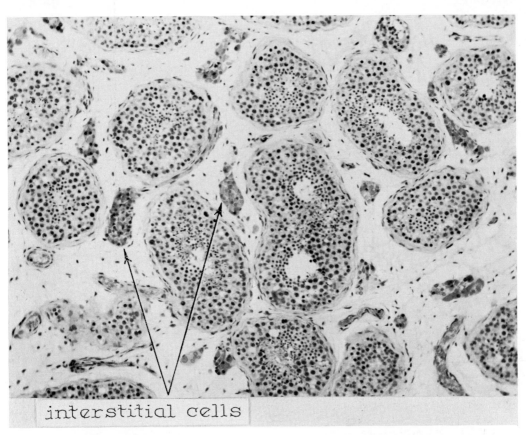

interstitial cells

Fig. 30-3. Low-power photomicrograph of a portion of a section of a testis of man. Seminiferous tubules, cut in cross and oblique section and separated from one another by a slight amount of interstitial connective tissue, may be seen, as well as some groups of interstitial cells.

comes obliterated (this may occur before birth but usually occurs after).

**Hormonal Control of Descent of the Testes and Maldescent.** Occasionally, one or both testes fail to descend into the scrotum during fetal life or immediately after birth. Testes that fail to descend may be held up at almost any point along the course that they normally follow. An individual with undescended testes is termed a *cryptorchid* (*kryptos* = concealed; *orchis* = testis). In some instances, undescended testes descend spontaneously during infancy, but in the majority of instances they do not, and measures must be taken to assist them to gain the scrotum. Unless the testes gain the favorable environment of the scrotum they do not produce spermatozoa; however, the interstitial cells may still produce androgens. As knowledge about sex hormones has increased, it has be-

come apparent that hormones to a considerable degree direct the normal descent of the testes.

As noted before, interstitial cells develop in the testis in significant numbers in the 4th month. This development and the general growth of the organ at this time suggest that it is being stimulated by some trophic hormone. It seems more likely that the trophic hormone concerned would be of placental than of pituitary origin. It is probable that this placental gonadotrophin stimulates the growth of the testis of the male early in fetal life and makes it a functioning endocrine gland.

The androgens thus secreted would bring about the changes in the inguinal canal that permit the testis to descend through it more readily. It would also facilitate the growth of the scrotum and the ductus deferens. So, it seems very probable that the androgen made

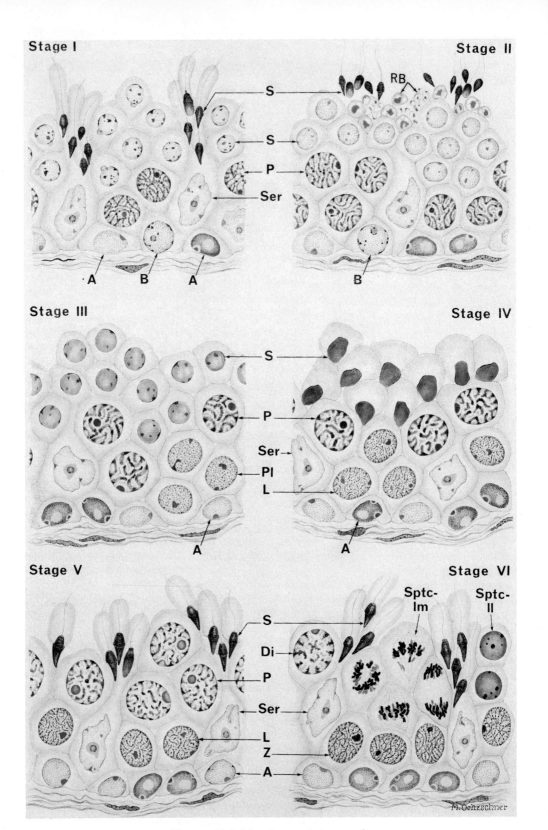

Figure 30-4 (*Caption on facing page*)

by the fetal testis is responsible for bringing about these important changes that permit its descent.

**Microscopic Appearance from Birth to Puberty.** The interstitial cells of the testes are not at all prominent during childhood (from birth to 10 years of age). The seminiferous tubules are small and are composed of two types of cells: the precursors of the definitive germ cells (gonocytes) and the supporting cells. The latter type of cells are numerous and show a small irregular nucleus and a poorly delimited cytoplasm. The gonocytes, fewer in number, have a spherical nucleus and a clearly visible cytoplasmic membrane. During adolescence (10 to 14 years of age), probably under the stimulation of the pituitary gonadotrophic hormone, the gonocytes start to proliferate and eventually produce, in large quantity, the spermatozoa. Simultaneously, the supporting cells increase in volume and each comes to have a large, pale-stained polymorphous nucleus and much cytoplasm which extends inwardly from the periphery of the tubule, through the many layers of cells that are concerned with forming spermatozoa, to the lumen of the tubule. These cells are called Sertoli cells (Fig. 30-4) and are believed to nourish the germ cells. During this period of active growth, the seminiferous tubules develop a lumen while the interstitial cells become distinguishable again in the stroma of the testes. A section of an adult testis showing seminiferous tubules in which spermatogenesis is occurring, and groups of interstitial cells, is illustrated in Figure 30-3.

**Spermatogenesis.** All the cells of the seminiferous epithelium, except the Sertoli cells, are involved in the production of spermatozoa. The process by which the initial germ cells proliferate and transform into free motile cells, the spermatozoa, is known as spermatogenesis. The initial germ cells, called *spermatogonia*

(*gone* = generation), which are generally seen close to the basement membrane of the tubule, are the direct descendants of the gonocytes that are observed in the sex cords of the fetal testis.

There are two main classes of spermatogonia, termed type A and type B, respectively. The type A spermatogonia have a spherical or ovoid nucleus containing fine chromatin granules and a nucleolus attached to the nuclear membrane (Fig. 30-4, A). The type B spermatogonia have a spherical nucleus containing, in addition to fine chromatin granules, several heavily stained chromatin masses attached to the nuclear membrane and to the centrally located nucleolus (Fig. 30-4, B). The type A spermatogonia multiply by mitoses. Half of the daughter cells remain as type A spermatogonia, and half differentiate slightly to become type B spermatogonia. The latter divide and differentiate to produce a new generation of germ cells, the primary spermatocytes. Therefore the spermatogonia as they proliferate both renew themselves and lead to the formation of generations of spermatocytes.

When they first appear, the primary spermatocytes (Fig. 30-4, PL) are difficult to distinguish from the spermatogonia (Fig. 30-4, B). Soon their nuclei stain to better advantage because of a reorganization of their chromatin into thin filamentous chromosomes (Fig. 30-4, L). The next step is indicated by the homologous chromosomes fusing to give coarser and hence more deeply stained threads (Fig. 30-4, Z), (see below for the significance of this phenomenon). These threads eventually contract into thick prophase chromosomes (Fig. 30-4, P). After this peculiar and long prophase the primary spermatocytes divide and, as a result of their division, two smaller cells, the secondary spermatocytes are formed (Fig. 30-4, Sptc II). These secondary spermatocytes have a

FIG. 30-4. Drawings illustrating the various steps of differentiation seen in seminiferous tubules. The illustrations are arranged to demonstrate the 6 typical cellular associations that are found repeatedly in the seminiferous tubules of man. The 6 associations (stages) are labeled I to VI, respectively. Ser = nucleus of Sertoli cell, A = type A spermatogonia, B = type B spermatogonia, PL = preleptotene primary spermatocytes, L = leptotene primary spermatocytes, Z = zygotene primary spermatocytes, P = pachytene primary spermatocytes, Di = diplotene primary spermatocytes, Sptc-Im = primary spermatocytes in division, Sptc-II = secondary spermatocytes in interphase, S = spermatids at various steps of spermiogenesis, and RB = residual bodies. (Clermont, Yves: Am. J. Anat. *112*:35)

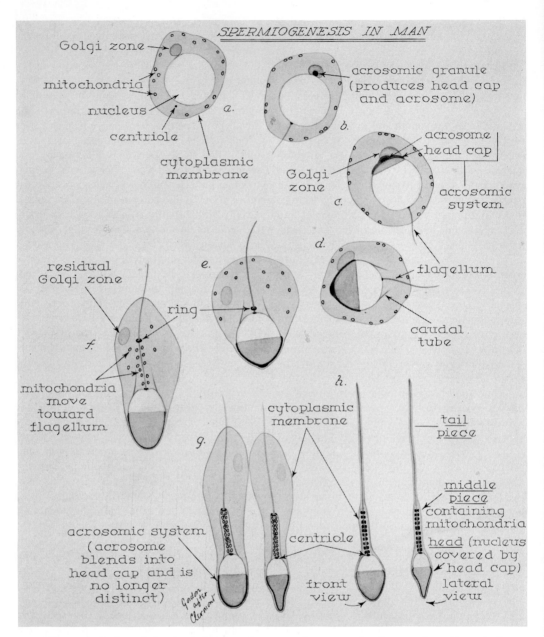

Fig. 30-5. Series of drawings showing the successive stages in the transformation of the spermatid into the spermatozoon. (Modified from Clermont and Leblond: Am. J. Anat. *96*:229)

very short life, and for that reason they are rarely seen in the seminiferous epithelium; they divide, each one giving rise to two smaller cells called *spermatids* (Fig. 30-4, S). Spermatids do not divide but instead each undergoes a metamorphosis into a spermatozoon (Fig. 30-5).

The cell divisions whereby each primary spermatocyte forms two secondary spermatocytes and the divisions whereby each secondary spermatocyte forms two spermatids are of a special character and are called *maturation divisions.* The first of these two divisions (whereby a primary spermatocyte becomes two secondary spermatocytes) is termed a *reduction* or *meiotic* (*meiosis* = a lessening) division, because in this division the number of chromosomes given each secondary spermatocyte is only half that of the number contained by the primary spermatocyte. Primary spermatocytes have the same number of chromosomes as the somatic cells of the body; in man, this is 46. Since these consist of 23 pairs, somatic cells are said to have a *diploid* (*diplous* = double) number of chromosomes. In the prophase stage of a reduction (meiotic) division of a primary spermatocyte, the two members of each pair of chromosomes approach each other so closely that it appears as if each pair were only a single chromosome. The phenomenon of the two members of each pair approaching each other closely is called *synapsis*. In the metaphase of a meiotic division the two members of each pair separate from one another, and in the subsequent phases of meiosis one member of each pair goes to one daughter cell and one member to the other. As a result, each of the two secondary spermatocytes that form as the result of the meiotic division of a primary spermatocyte has only 23 chromosomes—the *haploid* (*haplous* = single) number, instead of the diploid number. In the next division of maturation, by which each secondary spermatocyte gives rise to two spermatids, the number of chromosomes is not further reduced; thus each spermatid, and hence each spermatozoon, has 23 chromosomes, each of which is a single representative of a former pair.

In the female, the oocyte also undergoes two maturation divisions to form a mature female germ cell or ovum. The first of these occurs immediately before or at ovulation and the other after ovulation (Fig. 29-11). However, these divisions do not result in four equally mature germ cells, each with a haploid number of chromosomes, as it does in the male, but only in one mature ovum. Each time the ovum divides its cytoplasm is distributed to the two daughter cells so very unequally that only one of the two cells remains normal and survives; the other, called a *polar body*, eventually degenerates and disappears.

When a mature ovum, with its haploid number of chromosomes, is successfully fertilized by a spermatozoon, with its haploid number of chromosomes, the diploid number of chromosomes is restored in the nucleus of the ovum, with one member of each pair being obtained from the germ plasm of the mother and one from the germ plasm of the father. This provides the basis of inheritance from the two parents.

The two members of one pair of chromosomes—the sex chromosomes—in the primary spermatocyte are not identical, one being an X chromosome and one a Y chromosome. So, when the two chromosomes in a pair separate from one another in meiotic division, the X chromosome goes to one secondary spermatocyte and the Y chromosome to the other. As a consequence, half of the spermatozoa that develop in the testes have the X type of sex chromosome and half have the Y type. This is a different arrangement from that which exists in the female, for the sex chromosomes of ova are both of the X type. If a spermatozoon with an X chromosome fertilizes an ovum, the XX combination so formed determines that the embryo that results will be a female. If the spermatozoon concerned has a Y chromosome, the resulting XY combination determines that a male embryo will result.

**Transformation of Spermatids into Spermatozoa.** The spermatids that result from the division of secondary spermatocytes become enveloped by the cytoplasm of Sertoli cells near the lumen of the tubule, and in this environment they undergo a metamorphosis into spermatozoa. This entails a great change in their form. The formation of spermatozoa from spermatids is termed *spermiogenesis*.

The newly formed spermatid (Figs. 30-4 and 30-5) shows a centrally located spherical nucleus, a well-delimited Golgi zone close to the nucleus, numerous granular mitochondria lying to the inside of the cytoplasmic membrane and a small centriole (Fig. 30-5, a). The formation of a spermatozoon involves elaborate changes in all these cellular structures. The first sign of metamorphosis is seen within the Golgi zone; this is indicated by the formation of a dense granule at the surface of the nuclear membranes (Fig. 30-5, b). This granule, called the *acrosomic granule*, and its derivatives are PAS positive; this indicates the presence of carbohydrates within these structures. The growing acrosomic granule differentiates into two parts: (1) the *acrosome*, which is a small hemisphere on top of the

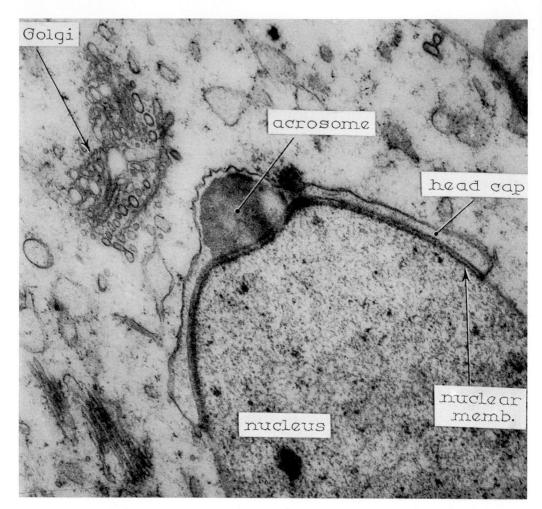

FIG. 30-6. Electron micrograph ($\times$ 39,000) of a section of a human spermatid (corresponding to Fig. 30-5 c), showing, in addition to the nucleus and the Golgi zone, the acrosomic system. The acrosome, a hemispherical dense granule, is inside a vesicular structure, the head cap, which also expands on the nuclear membrane. (Fawcett, D. W., and Burgos, M. H.: Ciba Foundation Colloquia on Ageing, vol. 2, p. 86, London, Churchill)

nucleus, and (2) the *head cap,* which is a membranelike structure growing around the acrosome on the surface of the nuclear membrane (Fig. 30-5, c and d, and Fig. 30-6). The head cap eventually covers approximately half of the nuclear surface. Once the acrosome and the head cap (the acrosomic system) are well developed, the Golgi zone becomes detached from the head cap and turns into a "residual Golgi zone" (Fig. 30-5, d and e). As the acrosomic system develops, the centriole becomes attached to the nuclear membrane in an area opposite to the acrosome and gives rise to the

vibratile organ of the future spermatozoon, the flagellum. An additional structure appears and surrounds this flagellum; this is the so-called caudal tube, which is made of submicroscopic filaments attached to the nuclear membrane.

At one stage of spermiogenesis, the acrosome and the head cap orient themselves toward the basement membrane of the seminiferous tubule. This is accompanied by a displacement of the nucleus within the cytoplasm toward the cell membrane (Fig. 30-5, e). The nucleus then becomes progressively condensed

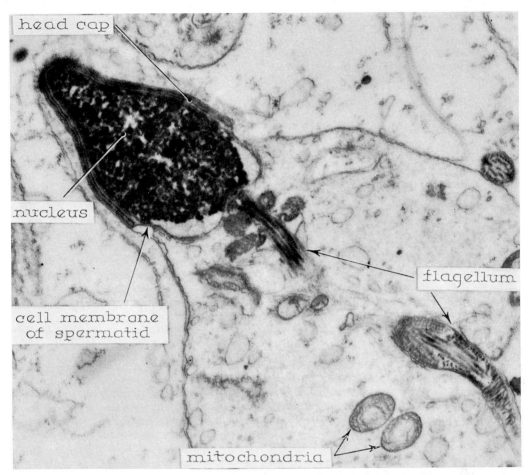

FIG. 30-7. Electron micrograph (× 25,000) of a section of a human spermatid at a more advanced stage of development (corresponding to Fig. 30-5 g). The nucleus shows a denser osmiophilic material. The head cap is still visible, but the acrosome can no longer be identified. A well-developed flagellum made of numerous filaments is seen extending from the lower end of the nucleus. Mitochondria can also be identified. (Fawcett, D. W., and Burgos, M. H.: Ciba Foundation Colloquia on Ageing, vol. 2, p. 86, London, Churchill)

and assumes a slightly flattened and elongated shape. Its anterior end is relatively sharp when it is seen in profile but rounded when it is seen in full face (Fig. 30-5, g and h). At the surface of the nucleus, the acrosome blends into the head cap from which it becomes indistinguishable (Fig. 30-7). Meanwhile, a small ring appears around the flagellum close to the centriole. This ring, once formed, slides along the flagellum for some distance (Fig. 30-5, e and f). The mitochondria which, up to this stage, have been disposed along the cytoplasmic membrane start to move in the cytoplasm toward the flagellum, more pre-

cisely toward the portion of the flagellum between the centriole and the ring (Fig. 30-5, f, g and h). The mitochondria line up along the flagellum, close to one another, and condense to form a striated collarlike sheath which delimits the middle piece of the future spermatozoon. The fate of the caudal tube is still not well understood. As the spermatid completes its development, the cytoplasmic surplus, which is not utilized in the formation of the spermatozoon, is cast off and forms a disintegrating *residual body*. However, a thin layer of cytoplasm, delimited by a cytoplasmic membrane, covers the nucleus, the

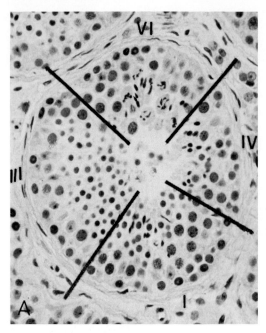

FIG. 30-8. Low-power photographs of human seminiferous tubules cut transversely (A) and longitudinally (B) to show examples of the distribution of the various cell associations or stages of the cycle in the seminiferous epithelium. In these two photographs the 6 stages of the cycle illustrated in Figure 30-4 can be identified.

Stage I (A) is characterized by spermatogonia (at this magnification the types cannot be identified), pachytene spermatocytes and 2 generations of spermatids (a young generation with spherical nuclei, an older generation with elongated condensed nuclei).

Stage II (B) shows, in addition to spermatogonia and pachytene spermatocytes, generations of young spermatids with spherical nuclei and maturing spermatids lining the lumen and discarding their residual cytoplasm.

Stage III (A and B) is characterized by spermatogonia and preleptotene spermatocytes (not distinguished at this magnification), pachytene spermatocytes and only 1 generation of spermatids with spherical nuclei.

Stage IV (A and B) is characterized by spermatogonia, generations of leptotene and pachytene spermatocytes and 1 generation of spermatids with slightly elongated nuclei.

Stage V (B) is composed of spermatogonia, leptotene orzygotene spermatocytes (not present in this field), pachytene spermatocytes and 1 generation of spermatids with elongated nuclei.

Stage VI (A) shows spermatogonia, 1 generation of early pachytene spermatocytes, maturation divisions of primary spermatocytes and 1 generation of spermatids with elongated nuclei. Note that the order in which the stages of the cycle are seen around the tubular lumen is not consecutive but on the contrary is variable. (Clermont, Yves: Am. J. Anat. *112*:35)

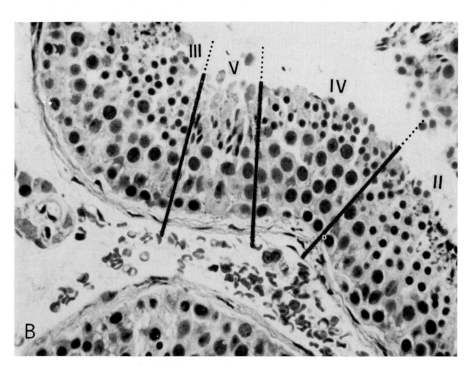

middle piece and the tail piece (except the extremity) of the spermatozoon.

The structure of the tail piece is basically similar to that of cilia (Fig. 30-7), the number and the arrangement of the longitudinal tubules being the same (see Chap. 8). However, along the tubules there are some additional coarse fibers, the nature of which is still a mystery and which make the flagellum of a spermatozoon different from an ordinary cilium. The net result is that the spermatozoon, though much smaller than the spermatid, retains nuclear elements of the spermatid in its head, some part of its Golgi apparatus in the acrosomic system, most of its mitochondria in the middle piece and its centriole. It is thus able to contribute cytoplasmic as well as nuclear components to the ovum.

When fully formed, spermatozoa leave the Sertoli cells and enter the lumens of the seminiferous tubules. Although their flagella beat, these spermatozoa are probably not very motile and are moved along the system of tubules until they reach the tail end of the epididymis. Then they become fully mature and actively motile and by lashing their tails can move 2 or 3 mm. a minute. This enables them to swim up the female reproductive tract when they are introduced into the vagina.

**The Cycle of the Seminiferous Epithelium.** A cross section of any given seminiferous tubule does not contain cells at all the various stages of development. Commonly in a cross section a given area of the seminiferous epithelium reveals 4 or 5 distinct generations of germ cells (the term generation is applied here to a group of germ cells at the same stage of development). The younger generations are seen close to the basement membrane; the older generations are close to the lumen of the tubule (Figs. 30-7 and 30-8). Furthermore, generations of germ cells have a clear-cut tendency to be present in association with other generations; these associations are of a constant composition. Thus, one or two generations of spermatids at given steps of spermiogenesis have a clear-cut tendency to be associated with one or two generations of spermatocytes and spermatogonia at given steps of their respective development. Six such well-defined cellular groupings were described by Clermont and were classified as 6 stages of a cycle of the seminiferous epithelium

since, in a given area of seminiferous epithelium, they follow each other in a cyclic manner (Fig. 30-4).

In man, the various cell associations occupy numerous and relatively small areas of the tubular epithelium; as a consequence, several distinct cell associations can be seen side by side in a single tubular cross section (Fig. 30-8, A). Furthermore, at the borderline of such typical cellular associations, cells can intermingle, giving irregular "heterogeneous associations which often disrupt the characteristic pattern of the stages of the cycle".

**Duration of Spermatogenesis.** It is of practical interest to know the duration of spermatogenesis in man (for example to forecast the time of a response to hormonal therapy). This information was provided by Heller and Clermont by injecting intratesticularly the radioactive DNA precursor, thymidine-$H^3$. This label was incorporated into the nuclei of some of the germ cells (spermatogonia and preleptotene spermatocytes). By analyzing the fate of these labeled cells, in radioautographed sections of biopsies collected at various intervals after injection, they evaluated first the duration of one cycle of the seminiferous epithelium. The cycle lasts close to 16 days. Then considering that spermatogenesis extends over the duration of several cycles, 4.6 according to these authors, the whole series of changes from the type A spermatogonia to the spermatozoa was said to consume approximately 74 days.

**Factors Affecting Spermatogenesis.** It has already been noted that spermatogenesis does not occur properly unless the testes are maintained at a temperature somewhat lower than that of the body as a whole and unless the cells of the seminiferous tubules are under stimulation by gonadotrophic hormones. A sufficiency of vitamin E in the diet is also essential. It will be recalled that the capacity of the ovary to produce mature germ cells, under the influence of FSH stimulation, ends more or less suddenly, usually when a woman is between the ages of 45 and 50. An event comparable with the menopause of women, a well-defined climacteric, does not occur in the average male. In the male, with increasing age, there is usually no more than a slow decline in the ability of the seminiferous tubules to produce mature germ cells, and there are many authentic cases of men having become fathers at a very advanced age.

**Abnormal Spermatozoa.** Abnormal spermatozoa are by no means uncommon products of the testes. There are a great variety of these (see Hotchkiss). There is much difference of opinion as to what percentage of spermatozoa may be abnormal without any loss of fertility. The evidence suggests that 10 per cent may be abnormal without any loss, and some investigators have found considerably higher percentages without any loss of fertility. But, although there seems to be a great amount of variation, there seems to be reason to believe that when a quarter, or somewhat fewer, of the spermatozoa are abnormal, fertility is impaired. For example, it has been shown that the semen of bulls with good breeding records average only about 16 per cent of abnormal cells, while those with poor breeding records average about 50 per cent of abnormal spermatozoa.

**Concentration in Semen.** There are usually more than 100,000,000 spermatozoa in each cubic centimeter of semen in fertile men, and 2 or more cubic centimeters of semen are usually delivered in each ejaculation. So, even if there are a considerable number of abnormal spermatozoa in any given ejaculation, there are a vast number of healthy spermatozoa present in it also. Although there is much variation in individual cases, men whose semen contains only around 50,000,000 spermatozoa per cubic centimeter are not usually so fertile as those whose semen contains considerably more, and those with 20,000,000 or less per cubic centimeter are generally sterile. Although such an enormous number of spermatozoa is produced by the testis, only one spermatozoon actually fertilizes the ovum.

**Metabolism of Spermatozoa.** In discussing cell respiration fermentative and oxidative types of metabolism were mentioned. It is of interest to note that spermatozoa obtain their energy requirements chiefly from fermentation; hence, they can live anaerobically. It is probably desirable that they should be able to do so, for in their long journey in the lumens of the various tubes of the male genital system, and in addition, if they are to fertilize an ovum, through the vagina, the cervix, the uterus and the oviduct of the female, they would be most unlikely to receive sufficient oxygen for their maintenance. Carbohydrate, on which they can survive anaerobically by fermentative mechanisms, is present in the secretions of at least several of the tubes through which they pass.

**Function of Interstitial Cells.** In discussing this matter it is necessary to understand at once that there is a profound difference between fertility and potency in the male. A fertile male may be defined as one who can produce at ejaculation, at least on some occasions, enough semen containing a sufficient number of healthy spermatozoa suspended in a sufficiently normal fluid vehicle to bring about the fertilization of an ovum in a fertile female. A sterile male cannot accomplish this function. Potency refers to another matter—the ability of the male to engage in intercourse. This depends fundamentally on the erection of the penis. A potent but sterile male may be able to ejaculate during intercourse, but the semen expressed will not contain a sufficient number of healthy spermatozoa to cause fertilization of an ovum.

The basis for fertility is spermatogenesis in the seminiferous tubules. The basis for potency is androgen production by the interstitial cells. Therefore, sterility need not cause impotence. Indeed, even eunuchs, though necessarily sterile, are not necessarily impotent unless their testes have been removed before puberty. The reason for this is that if there has been enough time for the androgen produced by the testes after puberty to have thoroughly masculinized the individual, to have established a heterosexual drive and to have permitted reflexes dependent on this drive to be formed, then the individual concerned may have remained potent because of the persistence of the reflexes even though his testes have been removed. Androgen, nevertheless, is concerned with the maintenance of the sex drive in the normal male, but it should be realized that psychological factors are also very important in the maintenance of the drive, once the basis for it has been established by androgen.

A male may be sterilized at operation either by removing the testes or by tying off and cutting the ducti deferentes (vasectomy). The latter operation prevents the egress of spermatozoa from the testes, but the interstitial cells continue to produce androgen, which leaves the testes by way of the bloodstream. The testes of the cryptorchid produce androgen but, usually, not spermatozoa. As it is possible for a male to be potent but sterile, it is also possible for an otherwise fertile male to be impotent. In such males, impotency is usually due to emotional factors which interfere with the functioning of the autonomic nervous system in such a way that the blood flow into the cavernous tissue of the penis is not sufficient to cause erection.

It is probable that the secretion of androgen by the interstitial cells is regulated by the anterior pituitary through a push-pull mechanism. When the amount of androgen in the bloodstream decreases, the anterior pituitary probably secretes additional gonadotrophic hormone. Then, when this stimulates androgen production and causes increased amounts to be delivered into the bloodstream, the secretion of gonadotrophin by the anterior pituitary is temporarily suppressed. It should be anticipated, then, that the administration of androgen to a male will tend to suppress the secretion of gonadotrophic hormone by his anterior pituitary gland and that this in turn will lead to diminished testicular function.

**Microscopic Appearance of Interstitial Cells.** It has been pointed out that in fetal life interstitial cells develop from the mesenchymal cells of the stroma between the developing seminiferous tubules and that they are much more prominent in the fetal testis from the 4th month on than they are in the postnatal testis between birth and puberty. In the sexually mature male these interstitial cells are distributed either singly or in clumps in the stroma between the tubules, usually in the angular crevices that are created by the round tubules being packed together (Fig. 30-3). They are large cells, measuring up to 20 or more microns in diameter (Fig. 30-9). Their spherical to oval nuclei are pale and contain one or more nucleoli. Some interstitial cells are binucleated. In H and E sections the peripheral cystoplasm may be vacuolated because lipoid droplets have been dissolved from it in the preparation of the section. The cytoplasm immediately surrounding the nucleus may appear to be granular; some investigators have described secretion granules in this site. Some interstitial cells contain a brown pigment; this is not melanin, and its precise nature and significance are not known.

The interstitial cells constitute an unusual type of endocrine gland. They do not develop

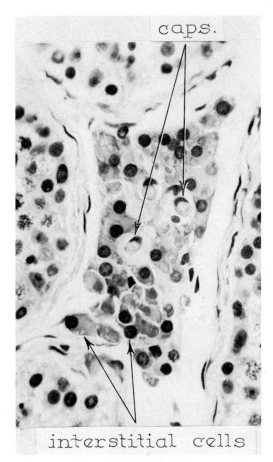

FIG. 30-9. High-power photomcirograph of a portion of a section of a human testis. Several blood capillaries (*caps.*) cut in cross section may be seen in an island of interstitial cells. This group of cells lies in the connective tissue between the seminiferous tubules. (Section provided by Y. Clermont)

from an epithelial surface, as do most glands, but from a mesenchymal stroma. Since they are scattered about in the stroma, which is abundantly provided with capillaries, they have access to the vascular system (Fig. 30-9). All in all, they constitute a very diffuse type of endocrine gland.

The cytoplasm of interstitial cells commonly contains lipid droplets and aggregates of a fatty osmiophilic granular material, as well as crystalloids (Fig. 30-10). Fawcett and Burgos have shown with the EM that the crystalloids have a complex but orderly internal structure; when they are sectioned they

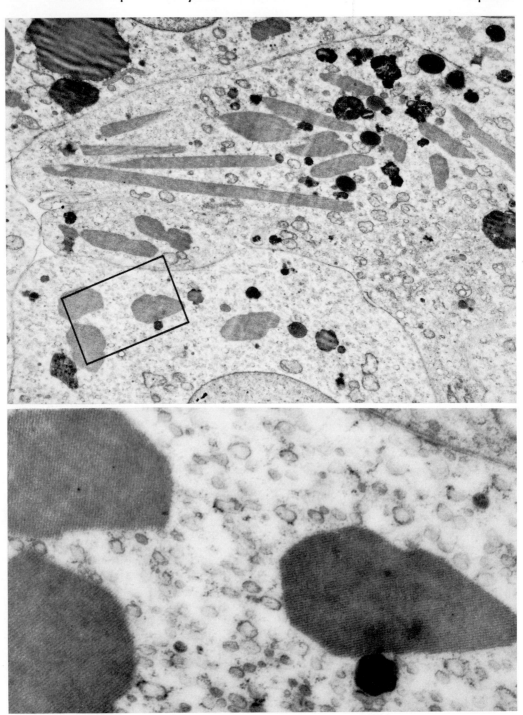

Fig. 30-10. (*Top*) Electron micrograph (× 8,550) of a section of parts of several interstitial cells. In the cytoplasm, in addition to dark osmiophilic bodies (lipid droplets and pigment granules of a lipoid nature), crystalline structures are visible (the crystalloids of Reinke). (*Bottom*) Electron micrograph (× 51,750) showing a higher magnification of a section of a crystalloid in which a highly ordered internal structure is apparent. (Fawcett, D. W., and Burgos, M. H.: Ciba Foundation Colloquia on Ageing, vol. 2, p. 86, London, Churchill)

present an appearance not unlike that of a woven fabric (Fig. 30-10, *bottom*). Christensen and Fawcett have further investigated the interstitial cells and find that the cytoplasm of these cells contains a meshwork of fine, interconnecting tubules (Fig. 30-11). There are no ribosomes associated with this reticulum. There is some evidence to suggest that this agranular reticulum is the site where male steroid hormones are produced.

**Tubuli Recti and Rete Testis.** The seminiferous tubules, as they approach the region of the mediastinum testis, become straight and are known as the *tubuli recti*; they empty into the rete testis of the mediastinum (Fig. 30-2). Spermatogenesis does not occur in the tubuli recti, which are lined by tall Sertolilike cells. The spaces of the rete are lined by cuboidal epithelium, the cells of which are each provided with a single cilium.

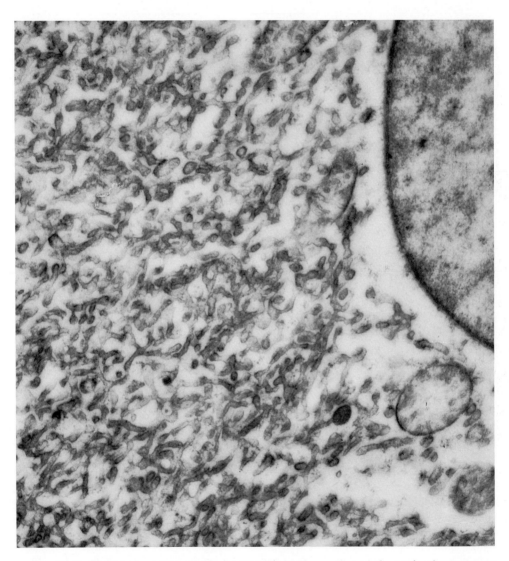

FIG. 30-11. This electron micrograph ($\times$ 33,000) is of a section of the testis of an opossum and shows part of an interstitial cell. Part of a nucleus is seen at top left, with 4 mitochondria adjacent to it. The remainder of the field is filled with a network of interconnected tubules of agranular endoplasmic reticulum. (From Drs. A. K. Christensen and D. W. Fawcett)

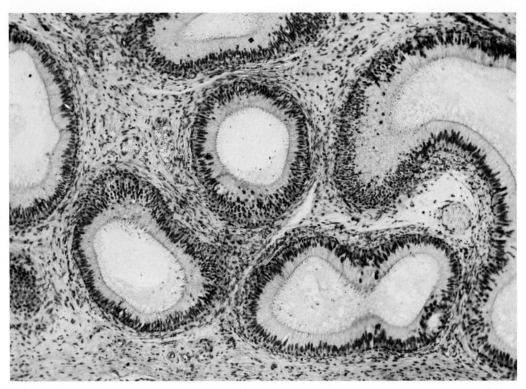

FIG. 30-12. Medium-power photomicrograph of a section of epididymis, showing the ductus epididymis cut in cross and oblique section. Observe the stereocilia of the tall epithelial lining cells.

## THE EPIDIDYMIS

The general structure of the epididymis is described in the first part of this chapter. The further details of its microscopic structure follow.

It is invested in a fibrous covering similar to, but somewhat thinner than, the tunica albuginea of the testis. The ductuli efferentes, in the cone-shaped bodies in which they are arranged, are held together by a delicate vascular connective tissue. The ductules themselves consist of an epithelial lining, a basement membrane and a thin layer of smooth muscle associated with some elastic fibers. The epithelium exhibits alternating groups of high columnar cells which have cilia and low columnar cells which usually do not. The latter cells are probably secretory. From a study of the epididymis of the guinea pig, Mason and Shaver suggested that the combined action of the rete testis, the ductuli efferentes and the proximal portion of the ductus epididymis is

to remove, from the excretory product of the testes, not only excess fluid but also extraneous materials carried with this mass. This reabsorption of fluid at the level of the epididymis would also create a negative pressure which would facilitate the transportation of the spermatozoa from the seminiferous tubule to the epididymis.

The convoluted ductus epididymis, which together with the connective tissue that holds its coils together (Fig. 30-12) comprises the body and the tail of the epididymis, consists of an epithelial lining, a basement membrane and a thin coat of circularly disposed smooth muscle fibers. The epithelium is tall and regular, and tufts of large nonmotile *stereocilia* (*stereōs* = solid) project toward the lumen from the free margins of the cells (Fig. 30-12). Cytoplasm extends between the stereocilia, and secretion occurs at this site. Secretion granules and vacuoles may be seen in the cytoplasm between the free margins of the cells and their nuclei.

## THE DUCTUS DEFERENS

The ductus or vas deferens is a sufficiently substantial structure to be palpated easily through the skin and the subcutaneous tissue. Its firm consistency is due to its very thick muscular wall and relatively narrow lumen (Fig. 30-13).

The mucous membrane consists of an epithelial lining and a lamina propria of connective tissue that contains a high content of elastic fibers. It is thrown into longitudinal folds of only moderate height. The epithelium is different in various parts of the ducts. Near the beginning of the duct it resembles that seen in the ductus epididymis. Farther along, the epithelium becomes nonciliated and tends to be pseudostratified.

The muscular coat consists of 3 layers (Fig. 30-13, *lower*). The inner and the outer layers are each thinner than the middle layer and are composed of longitudinally disposed fibers. The thick middle layer is composed of circularly disposed fibers. The adventitia consists of a loose elastic type of connective tissue and blends with the tissues comprising the spermatic cord which contains arteries, numerous veins, nerves and some longitudinally disposed striated muscle fibers (cremaster muscle). The veins are particularly prominent and form the *pampiniform* (*pampinus* = tendril) plexus; the plexus is so named because the veins wind around the duct similar to the way that tendrils of plants wind around other bodies for support. This is a common site for veins to become varicosed.

A short distance before the ductus deferens is joined by the seminal vesicle, it becomes dilated to form an ampulla. Here the muscular coat, though still thick, is thinner than in the other parts of the duct, and the lumen is considerably larger. The mucous membrane is thrown into very complicated folds similar to those of the seminal vesicle (Fig. 30-14).

## THE SEMINAL VESICLES

The size and the function of the seminal vesicles are controlled to a great degree by hormones; hence, the size and the shape of these structures vary considerably in relation to age. In the sexually mature male they are elongated bodies, 5 to 7 cm. or more long and somewhat less than half as wide at their

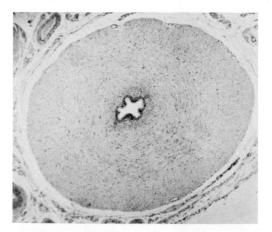

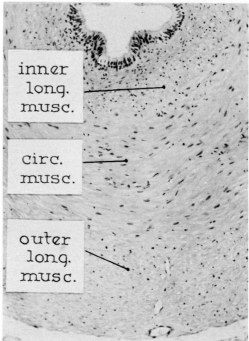

inner long. musc.

circ. musc.

outer long. musc.

Fig. 30-13. Low-power and high-power photomicrographs of an H and E section of the ductus deferens.

widest point. Their form tapers toward the end at which they join the ductus deferens.

To prevent confusion, it should be explained that the structure seen on gross dissection and called the *seminal vesicle* is essentially a tube that is much longer and much narrower than it appears at first sight. The vesicle is coiled and convoluted. The various coils and convolutions, where they touch one another, are adherent through the medium of

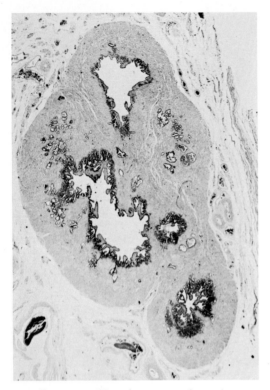

FIG. 30-14. Very low-power photomicrograph of a cross section of a seminal vesicle.

connective tissue (Fig. 30-14); this is the cause of the form and the organization of the body seen on gross inspection. This connective tissue must be dissected if the seminal vesicle is to be unraveled and seen in its true form; if this is done it will be found to consist of a tube about 15 cm. long. The coils and the convolutions are such that if a cross section is cut through the undissected body the seminal vesicle will be cut simultaneously at several points along its length (Fig. 30-14).

The wall of the tube exhibits 3 coats: an outermost one of fibrous connective tissue which contains a substantial content of elastic fibers, a middle muscular coat and a lining mucous membrane.

The muscular coat is substantial but not so thick as that of the ductus deferens. It consists of 2 layers: an inner one of circular fibers and an outer one of longitudinal fibers.

The mucous membrane of the seminal vesicle is thrown into an extraordinary series of folds (Fig. 30-14). These permit the vesicle to have an enormous area of secretory epithe-

lium; they also permit the tube to become distended with secretion without the undue stretching of the membrane of secretory cells that line the vesicle. The epithelial lining consists essentially of a layer of tall columnar cells but, between these and the lamina propria, small cells may be irregularly distributed. The small cells in some instances may form a continuous membrane, deep to the tall cells.

Since the folds of mucous membrane are so very numerous and may branch, the lamina propria of the seminal vesicle, as seen in a section, seems to contain glands. However, the glandular appearance, like that presented by the mucous membrane of the gallbladder, is due only to the extensive folding of the mucous membrane.

It was once believed that the seminal vesicle served as a storehouse for spermatozoa. The finding of spermatozoa in the seminal vesicle after death does not necessarily provide support for this theory because spermatozoa may migrate into the vesicles after death. The epithelial cells of the vesicles provide an elaborate, thick, yellow, sticky secretion. This is delivered into the ejaculatory duct during ejaculation and it serves as one of the fluids that constitute a vehicle and also provide nutritive materials for the spermatozoa.

The relation of the structure and the function of the seminal vesicles and the prostate gland to hormones is similar and will be discussed when the microscopic anatomy of the prostate gland has been considered.

## THE PROSTATE GLAND

The prostate gland is commonly described as being about the size and the shape of a horse chestnut but it is narrower below than above (Fig. 30-1). It surrounds the urethra as the latter emerges from the bladder. It is obvious that in this site enlargements of its substance might obstruct the outlet from the bladder. Unfortunately, enlargements of its substance that exert this effect are relatively common in men who have passed middle life. Their cause is obviously hormonal, for the reverse of enlargement—atrophy—occurs if the testes are removed. The removal of the prostate gland, or some part of it, to free the urethra from obstruction is a relatively common operation in older men.

The prostate gland is of a firm consistency. It is surrounded by a thin capsule that contains both connective tissue and smooth muscle fibers and is to be differentiated from the fascia that lies outside it.

As has already been noted, the substance of the prostate gland is made up of a large number of individual glands; these open by separate ducts into the prostatic urethra and are embedded in a stroma that is a mixture of smooth muscle and fibrous connective tissue.

A cross section of the prostate gland shows that the lumen of the prostatic urethra is V-shaped, with the apex of the V pointing forward (Fig. 30-15). The part of the posterior wall in the urethra that bulges forward to make the cross-section appearance of its lumen V-shaped is termed the *urethral crest* (Fig. 30-15). The two arms of the V that pass laterally and backward constitute the *urethral sinuses* (Fig. 30-15).

The glands that are embedded in the substance of the prostate are of three different orders of size and are distributed in three different areas that are arranged more or less concentrically around the urethra. The mucosal glands are the smallest and are disposed in the periurethral tissue (Fig. 30-15). They are of the greatest importance in connection with the enlargements of prostatic substance that occur in older men, for it is these glands that commonly overgrow to form *adenomatous* (*aden* = gland; *oma* = tumor) *nodules*. The submucous glands are disposed in the ring of tissue that surrounds the periurethral tissue (Fig. 30-15). The main, external or proper prostatic glands—and these provide the bulk of the secretion of the gland—are disposed in the outer and largest portion of the gland (Fig. 30-15). The mucosal glands open at various points around the lumen of the urethra, but the ducts of the submucous and main prostatic glands open into the posterior margins of the urethral sinuses (Fig. 30-15).

The prostate gland is imperfectly divided into 3 lobes by the passage through it of the ejaculatory ducts. Each lobe is imperfectly subdivided into lobules. The ducts that drain the lobules of the bulk of the organ sweep backward to empty into the urethral sinuses (Fig. 30-15). In the lobules, the ducts branch

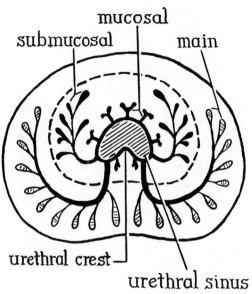

Fig. 30-15. Diagram of a cross section of the prostate gland, showing the distribution of the mucous, the submucous and the main glands and where their ducts open. (Redrawn and slightly modified from Grant, J. C. B.: A Method of Anatomy, ed. 4, Baltimore, Williams & Wilkins)

into tubulo-alveolar secretory units. These not only produce secretion but also are adapted to storing secretion. As a consequence they may be greatly dilated. To accommodate large amounts of stored secretion, the epithelial lining of the gland is greatly folded, and papillary projections of mucous membrane extend into their lumens at many sites (Fig. 30-16). This arrangement, together with the fibromuscular stroma that is disposed both between and within the lobules (Fig. 30-16), gives the gland a distinctive microscopic appearance.

In the healthy, sexually mature male the epithelium of the secretory units and ducts (except immediately before they enter the urethra) is of a tall columnar type. Smaller flattened or rounded cells may be distributed irregularly beneath the tall columnar cells. The tall cells have well-developed Golgi nets between their nuclei and their free borders. Blebs of secretion may sometimes be seen, apparently leaving the free surfaces of the cells. Concretions of secretion, which may be calcified to some extent, are not uncommon in the

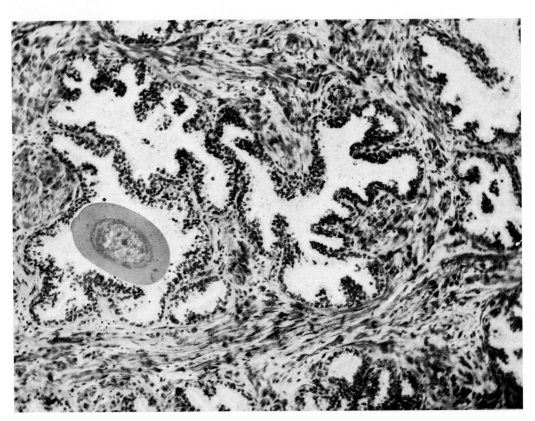

FIG. 30-16. Medium-power photomicrograph of a small area of a section of the prostate gland. Notice the smooth muscle fibers in the stroma of the gland and the concretion in the lumen of a secretory unit on the left.

secretory units of the prostate glands of older men (Fig. 30-16, *left*). The epithelium rests on a fibrous connective tissue lamina propria that contains an abundant supply of capillaries.

The secretion of the prostate gland is a thin, somewhat milky fluid. It contains, among other ingredients, quantities of an enzyme known as acid phosphatase; the function of this is not known, but its detection in the bloodstream is of use in the diagnosis of malignant tumors that arise from the secretory cells of the prostate gland.

**Effects of Hormones on the Seminal Vesicles and the Prostate Gland.** Androgen production by the testes is required to bring about the full development of the seminal vesicles and the prostate gland. Castration, after these structures have fully developed, causes them to atrophy. The most striking microscopic change brought about by castration occurs in the epithelium.

In a sexually mature male the epithelial cells of the seminal vesicles are of the tall columnar type. Their cytoplasm, between their nuclei and free borders, contains abundant secretory granules, each of which tends to be surrounded by a halo (Fig. 30-17, *left*). If the testes are removed, the epithelial cells shrink, becoming more or less cuboidal (Fig. 30-17, *middle*). Secretory granules disappear from their cytoplasm. Moore, Hughes and Gallagher have shown that both the height of the epithelial cells of the seminal vesicles and their normal content of secretory granules can be restored by injections of androgen (Fig. 30-17, *right*).

Moore, Price and Gallagher have shown also that the secretory cells of the prostate shrink in height if the testes are removed and that the prominent Golgi networks of the cells become greatly reduced in size. Both their height and their well-developed Golgi networks can be restored by injections of androgen.

Estrogen injected into male animals causes the epithelium of the seminal vesicles and the prostate gland to change from a tall secretory type into a low nonsecretory type. Moreover, estrogen induces a hypertrophy of the fibromuscular stroma of the prostate and the walls of the seminal vesicles.

The fact that the vigor of the secretory cells of the prostate gland is dependent on androgen is taken advantage of in the treatment of some malignant tumors that arise from these cells. A certain proportion of cancers of the prostate gland are benefited by castration. Being denied androgen, even malignant epithelial cells of the prostate gland may experience diminished function and growth activity. Likewise, in some instances prostatic cancers respond in a similar fashion to treatment with estrogens.

The hormonal basis for the nonmalignant overgrowths of prostatic tissue that so commonly obstruct the urethrae of older men is not thoroughly understood. Both the glandular tissue and the stroma of the prostate gland participate in these overgrowths. An interesting though unproved theory would relate the overgrowth of the stroma to an increased pro-

duction of estrogen in the older male. Such a condition could be visualized as arising as a result of the testes' making less androgen as a male ages, and, as a result, the anterior pituitary's making more gonadotrophic hormone which, in turn, might stimulate the latent capacities of the testes for making estrogen.

## THE PENIS

**Microscopic Structure.** The substance of the penis consists essentially of 3 cylindrical bodies of erectile (cavernous) tissue (Fig. 30-18). Two of these, the corpora cavernosa, are arranged side by side in the dorsal half of the organ (Fig. 30-18); this arrangement makes the dorsal surface of the otherwise more or less cylindrical penis somewhat flattened. The third long body of erectile tissue is called the corpus cavernosum urethrae because it conducts the urethra in its substance (Fig. 30-18) from one of its ends to the other (Fig. 30-1). It is also termed the corpus spongiosum. This cavernous body lies ventral to the paired corpora cavernosa. Moreover, it extends somewhat beyond the corpora cavernosa and becomes expanded into a more or less blunt cone-shaped body, the *glans*; this con-

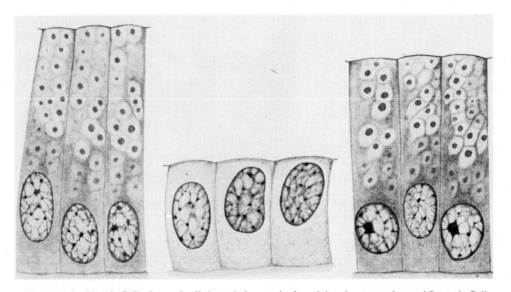

FIG. 30-17. (*Left*) Cells from the lining of the seminal vesicle of a normal rat. (*Center*) Cells from the same site 20 days after castration. (*Right*) Cells from the same site 20 days after castration; this rat received 29 injections of testis extract, beginning immediately after castration. (Moore, C. R., Hughes, W., and Gallagher, T. F.: Am. J. Anat. *45*:133)

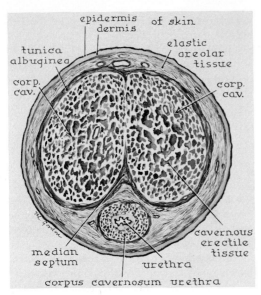

FIG. 30-18. Diagram of a cross section of the mid-section of the penis.

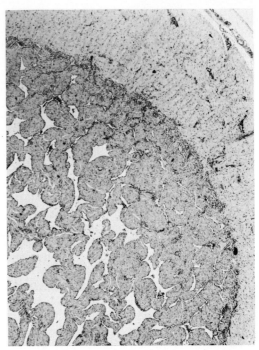

FIG. 30-19. Low-power photomicrograph of a portion of a cross section of a penis, showing the curved tunica albuginea at the upper right, with erectile tissue at the lower left.

stitutes the free end of the penis (Fig. 30-1).

Each cavernous body is surrounded by a stout sheath of connective tissue called a *tunica albuginea* (Figs. 30-18 and 30-19). In the corpora cavernosa, this sheath consists chiefly of collagenic fibers arranged in an inner circular and an outer longitudinal layer, but it also contains elastic fibers. The tunics covering the paired corpora cavernosa come into contact with one another along the midline of the penis and fuse to form a median septum (Fig. 30-18); this is thickest and most complete near the root of the penis. The sheath surrounding the corpus cavernosum urethrae is more elastic than that covering the other 2 bodies. In the glans, a true tunica albuginea is deficient; here the dermis of the skin that covers the glans serves as a tunica albuginea and is continuous with the cavernous tissue that is deep to it.

The 3 cavernous bodies (except where the paired corpora cavernosa are fused) are bound together by elastic areolar tissue called the *fascia penis* (Fig. 30-18). This also provides a flexible attachment for the skin that covers the penis. The epidermis of the skin of the penis is thin. No coarse hairs are present except near the root of the organ. A circular fold of skin extends forward to cover the glans; this is called the *prepuce* (Fig. 30-1).

It is usually sufficiently elastic to permit its being retracted. However, in some instances it is not, and it may fit too tightly over the glans; this condition is called *phimosis*. Modified sebaceous glands are present on the inner surface of the fold; the secretion from these, in a prepuce that cannot be retracted, may accumulate and serve as an irritant. The common operation by which the prepuce is removed is called *circumcision*.

The substance of the cavernous bodies consists of a 3-dimensional network of trabeculae. These are composed of connective tissue and smooth muscle and are covered with endothelium (Fig. 30-19). Between the trabeculae are spaces; since the trabeculae are covered with endothelium, the spaces are lined with endothelium. These spaces tend to be larger in the more central parts of the cavernous bodies and smaller near their periphery (Fig. 30-18). The substance of the glans is made up of convolutes of large veins rather than of spaces separated by trabeculae.

## Blood Supply and the Mechanism of Erection.

The arterial supply is of two sorts. Branches from the arteria dorsalis end in capillary beds which supply nutriment to the tissues of the organ, including those of the cavernous bodies. From the capillaries of the trabeculae, blood drains into the spaces. The spaces communicate in such a fashion that blood emptied into them can make its way to the more peripheral parts of the bodies, where the spaces communicate with plexuses of veins that are disposed close to the periphery of each cylindrical body. The blood that is instrumental in causing erection is derived chiefly from another and larger set of arteries that enters the substance of the bodies and there gives off branches that are conducted to the spaces by way of the trabeculae. These arteries have thick muscular walls and, in addition, many possess inner thickenings of longitudinal muscle fibers that bulge into their lumens. Many of these arteries that are disposed along the trabeculae are coiled and twisted when the penis is flaccid; this accounts for their being called *helicine* arteries. Many of the terminal branches of these arteries open directly into the spaces of the cavernous tissue.

The smooth muscle of the arteries and the smooth muscle in the trabeculae are supplied both by sympathetic and parasympathetic fibers. Under conditions of erotic stimulation, the smooth muscle of the trabeculae and the helicine arteries relaxes. The arteries tend to straighten, and as a result blood flows freely from them into the spaces. As blood collects in the spaces and dilates them, the venous plexuses in the peripheral parts of the bodies become compressed. With more blood being delivered into the spaces of the cavernous bodies, and with venous drainage from the bodies being impeded, the bodies become enlarged and turgid. The corpus cavernosum urethrae does not become so turgid as its two companions because its sheath is more elastic.

The phenomenon of the penis' returning to its flaccid state after erection is termed *detumescence*. This is brought about by the helicine arteries becoming constricted and by the smooth muscle in the trabeculae contracting; this slowly forces blood from the organ.

The penis is richly provided with a great variety of sensory nerve endings.

## THE MALE URETHRA

The male urethra is a tube of mucous membrane. In some sites its lamina propria, which is primarily fibro-elastic tissue, contains smooth muscle fibers and, in many sites, glands. Three facts about the urethra that the student will soon be able to verify when he learns, in his clinical years, to pass a catheter, are that it is about 8 inches long, its course is not straight but instead exhibits a reverse curve (Fig. 30-1) and (if the catheter employed is of too fine a caliber) that its lining is the seat of many small diverticulae.

The male urethra is commonly described as consisting of 3 parts. On leaving the urinary bladder the urethra enters the base of the prostate gland and courses through it to leave its apex. This portion of the urethra is described as its *prostatic part*. It then pierces the fasciae of the urogenital diaphragm. Accordingly, this portion of it is termed its *membranous part*. It then enters the expanded root (the bulb) of the corpus cavernosum urethrae (Fig. 30-1) and then extends through the entire length of this cavernous body to the apex of the glans (Fig. 30-1), where its *external orifice* is situated. The part of the urethra contained in the corpus cavernosum urethrae is called its *cavernous* or *spongy part*.

The prostatic portion of the urethra is more or less V-shaped in cross section. The apex of the V-shaped posterior wall points forward and is called the urethral crest (Fig. 30-1). A conical elevation on the crest is termed the *colliculus*, and a small diverticulum, the remains of the fetal müllerian ducts, opens through it. The slitlike openings of the ejaculatory ducts may be seen, one on each side of the colliculus, on the urethral crest. The sites of the openings of the prostatic ducts have already been described.

As was noted in Chapter 27, the epithelium of the urinary bladder is of the transitional type (Fig. 30-20 A). The epithelium that lines the first part of the prostatic urethra is of the same type (Fig. 30-20 B). However, in the part of the prostatic urethra nearest the membranous urethra the epithelium changes to the pseudostratified or stratified columnar variety (Fig. 30-20 C).

The lamina propria of the prostatic urethra is composed essentially of fibro-elastic connec-

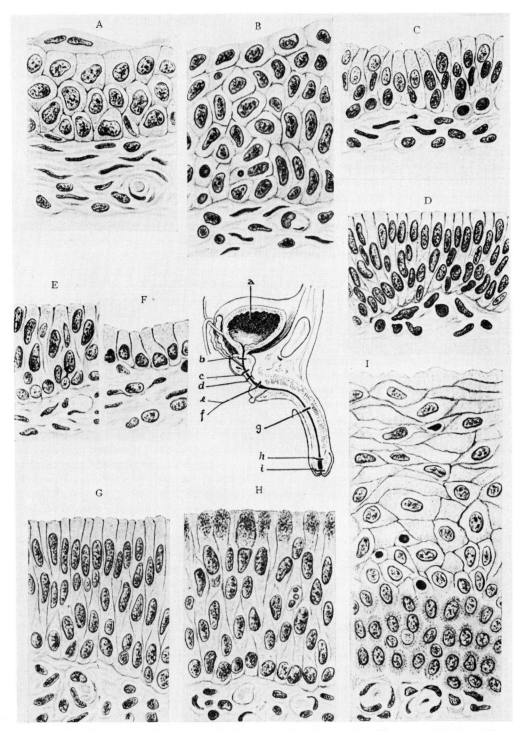

FIG. 30-20. The epithelial lining of the human male urethra at the different regions shown in the central diagram (× 600). (A) Wall of bladder. (B) Inner portion of prostatic urethra. (C) Outer portion of prostatic urethra. (D) Membranous portion of urethra. (E) Ampulla of urethra on sides and bases of folds. (F) Ampulla of urethra on crest of folds. (G) Middle of cavernous urethra. (H) Inner portion of fossa navicularis. (I) Outer portion of fossa navicularis. (Addison: Piersol's Normal Histology, ed. 15, Philadelphia, Lippincott)

tive tissue. It is very vascular, chiefly because of its great content of venules. Indeed, over the urethral crest the lamina propria contains so many venules and veins that it is sometimes described as erectile tissue. Smooth muscle fibers are also present in the mucous membrane of the prostatic urethra. These are disposed in 2 layers; the innermost one consists of longitudinal, and the outer layer, of circular, fibers. The latter are highly developed at the internal urethral orifice, where they, reinforced by certain smooth muscle fibers from another source, comprise the *sphincter of the bladder*.

The membranous part of the urethra is the shortest part, being about 1 cm. long. The lining cells here are tall columnar in type and are stratified (Fig. 30-20 D). Some smooth muscle is present in the lamina propria, but the circular fibers in particular are less numerous than they are in the prostatic portion of the urethra. However, in the membranous urethra, striated muscle fibers of the urogenital diaphragm surround the tube; these comprise the *sphincter muscle of the urethra*. This muscle is sometimes called the *external sphincter of the bladder*. Two small bodies, each about as large as a pea, the *bulbo-urethral* or *Cowper's glands*, are disposed on the undersurface of the membranous urethra, close to its midline (Fig. 30-1). Their ducts run forward and medially to open, sometimes by a common opening, on the lower surface of the first part of the cavernous portion of the urethra (Fig. 30-1), next to be described. The glands themselves are of the tubulo-alveolar type, and their secretory cells are mostly of the mucous type. These glands either secrete more copiously, or their secretion is expressed from them because of the contraction of the smooth muscle fibers in their stroma and the voluntary muscle outside them, under conditions of erotic stimulation. At any rate, their secretion, under these conditions, flows along the urethra to appear at the external orifice of the penis. The function of the secretion of these glands may be that of coating the lining of the urethra with a fluid that will provide a suitable environment for spermatozoa.

The cavernous or spongy part of the urethra is its longest part. As noted before, the urethra becomes expanded in the bulb of the corpus cavernosum urethrae to form the *bulb* of the urethra (Fig. 30-1). The urethra becomes ex-

panded again in the glans; this expansion of it is termed the *terminal* or *navicular fossa* (Fig. 30-1).

The epithelium in the cavernous part of the urethra is of the stratified columnar type, although simple columnar epithelium may be present on the crests of folds (Fig. 30-20 E, F and G). In the inner part of the terminal fossa some goblet cells may be present (Fig. 30-20 H). In the outer part of the terminal fossa the epithelium becomes stratified squamous in type (Fig. 30-20 I). This in turn becomes continuous with the stratified squamous keratinizing epithelium that covers the glans.

In the cavernous portion of the urethra the smooth muscle of the urethra proper fades out to be replaced, as it were, by the smooth muscle of the septa of the erectile tissue through which the urethra passes.

Two groups of glands are associated with the urethra. These are often termed the *glands of Littré*. One group, the *intramucosal* glands, consists of small, simple glands disposed in its lamina propria. Although these are present in all parts of the urethra, they are most numerous in its cavernous part. The second group constitutes the *extramucosal* glands. They are somewhat larger than the intramucosal type. Their ducts commonly pass to the urethra at acute angles. The extramucosal glands are not so widely distributed as the intramucosal glands. Both types secrete mucus. In addition to possessing glands, the lining of the urethra is beset by numerous small outpouchings of its mucous membrane; these are called *lacunae*. The glands described above may open into these.

## REFERENCES

### Male Reproductive System

Allen, E., Danforth, C. H., and Doisy, E. A. (eds.): Sex and Internal Secretions, ed. 2, Baltimore, Williams & Wilkins, 1939.

Burrows, H.: Biological Actions of Sex Hormones, ed. 2, London, Cambridge Univ. Press, 1949.

Clermont, Y.: The cycle of the seminiferous epithelium in man, Am. J. Anat. *112*:35, 1963.

Clermont, Y., and Leblond, C. P.: Renewal of spermatogonia in the rat, Am. J. Anat. *93*:475, 1953.

————: Spermiogenesis of man, monkey, ram and other mammals as shown by the "periodic acid-Schiff" technique, Am. J. Anat. *96*:229, 1955.

Fawcett, D. W., and Burgos, M. H.: Observations

on the cytomorphosis of the germinal and interstitial cells of the human testis *in* Ciba Foundation Colloquia on Ageing, vol. 2, p. 86, London, Churchill, 1956.

Ford, C. E., and Hamerton, J. L.: The chromosomes of man, Nature *178*:1020, 1956.

Grigg, G. W., and Hodge, A. J.: Electron microscopic studies of spermatozoa, Australian J. Sc. Res. *2*:271, 1949.

Hamilton, J. B.: The role of testicular secretions as indicated by the effects of castration in man and by studies of pathological conditions and the short lifespan associated with maleness, Rec. Prog. Hormone Res. *3*:257, 1948.

Heller, C. G., and Clermont, Y.: Kinetics of the germinal epithelium in man, Rec. Prog. Hormone Res. *20*:545, 1964.

Hodge, A. J.: Electron microscopic studies of spermatozoa, Australian J. Sc. Res. *2*:368, 1949.

Hotchkiss, R. S.: Fertility in Men, Philadelphia, Lippincott, 1944.

Huggins, C.: The physiology of the prostate gland, Physiol. Rev. *25*:281, 1945.

Koch, F. C.: The male sex hormones, Physiol. Rev. *17*:153, 1937.

Leblond, C. P., and Clermont, Y.: Spermiogenesis of rat, mouse, hamster and guinea pig as revealed by the "periodic acid-fuchsin sulfurous acid" technique, Am. J. Anat. *90*:167, 1952.

Macklin, C. C., and Macklin, M. T.: The seminal vesicles, prostate and bulbo-urethral glands *in* Cowdry's Special Cytology, ed. 2, p. 1771, New York, Hoeber, 1932.

MacLeod, J., and Hotchkiss, R. S.: Effects of hyperpyrexia upon spermatozoa counts in men, Endocrinology *28*:780, 1941.

Mason, K. E.: The specificity of vitamin E. for the testes, J. Exper. Zool. *55*:101, 1930.

Mason, K. E., and Shaver, S. L.: Some functions of the caput epididymis, Ann. N. Y. Acad. Sci. *55*:585, 1952.

Metz, C. W.: The male germ cells *in* Cowdry's Special Cytology, ed. 2, p. 1727, New York, Hoeber, 1932.

Meyer, R. K.: Hormones in reproduction, Ann. Rev. Physiol. *7*:567, 1945.

Moore, C. R., Hughes, W., and Gallagher, T. F.: Rat seminal-vesicle cytology as a testis-hormone indicator and the prevention of castration changes by testis-extract injection, Am. J. Anat. *45*:109, 1930.

Moore, C. R., Price, D., and Gallagher, T. F.: Rat-prostate cytology as a testis-hormone indicator and the prevention of castration changes by testis-extract injections. Am. J. Anat. *45*: 17, 1930.

Rasmussen, A. T.: Interstitial cells of the testis *in* Cowdry's Special Cytology, ed. 2, p. 1673, New York, Hoeber, 1932.

Roosen-Runge, E. C., and Giesel, L. O., Jr.: Quantitative studies on spermatogenesis in the albino rat, Am. J. Anat. *87*:1, 1950.

Stieve, H.: Entwicklung, Bau and Bedeutung der Keimdrüsenzwischenzellen, Ergebn. Anat. u. Entwicklungsgesch. *23*:1, 1921.

Swyer, G. I. M.: Post-natal growth changes in the human prostate, J. Anat. *78*:130, 1944.

Tjio, J. H., and Levan, A.: The chromosome number of man, Hereditas *42*:1, 1956.

# 31  The System of Sensory Receptors

## INTRODUCTION

In Figure 21-7 a variety of instruments are illustrated, each of which, when wired to a battery, could function to close an electrical circuit. Moreover, each of the instruments is specially designed to close a circuit if it is "stimulated" by a certain kind of stimulus. For example, the telegraph key would complete a circuit if it were touched lightly, another of the instruments would complete a circuit if it were heated, another if it were cooled, another if exposed to light, another if struck by sound waves, and another if its chemical environment were altered.

The same general principles are utilized in the human body. Special instruments, represented by different kinds of nerve endings, respond to different stimuli and convert the energy of the stimulus into the electrical energy of a nerve impulse which is conducted along a nerve fiber to the brain. Moreover, the nerve fibers that lead from these receptors travel to different parts of the brain; this is the anatomic basis for the recognition of different kinds of sensation.

The different sensations which may be perceived by the human body—man's different senses—are: touch, pressure, heat, cold, pain, smell, sight, hearing, taste, position and movement. It is to be realized, moreover, that the appreciation of a sensation is not necessary for reflex actions to occur in the body; for example, most of the afferent impulses that affect the operation of the autonomic nervous system do not appear in consciousness.

The receptors concerned with smell, sight, hearing, taste and perception of movement and position in relation to gravity, are aggregated into what are called *organs of special sense*. These will be described after considering the receptors that give rise to the sensations of touch, pressure, cold, warmth, pain and what may be termed *proprioceptive muscle sense* (a perception of the degree to which different muscles are contracted, and hence of the position of, for example, a leg or an arm in relation to the rest of the body). All the receptors of this latter group are commonly grouped together as those responsible for what is described as *cutaneous* and *deep sensibility*.

The terminations of the afferent nerve fibers concerned in cutaneous and deep sensibility are of 2 general types: *free* and *encapsulated*. The various members of these 2 main types of nerve endings will now be described.

## RECEPTORS CONCERNED IN CUTANEOUS AND DEEP SENSIBILITY

**Touch.** The sensation aroused by light (e.g., "cotton wool") touch is subserved by 3 types of receptors: *Meissner's corpuscles, Merkel's disks* and a basketlike arrangement of *naked nerve endings* disposed around the bases of *hair follicles*.

*Meissner's corpuscles* are distributed in the connective tissue papillae of the skin just below, and perpendicular to, the epidermis. These corpuscles are not distributed evenly, being most numerous on the palmar surface of the fingers, the lips, the margins of the eyelids, the nipples and the external genital organs. They are somewhat ovoid structures made up of a central mass of irregular cells penetrated by irregularly curved nerve endings (Fig. 31-1 B), and they possess a many-layered capsule of connective tissue that is continuous with the endoneurium associated with the afferent nerve fiber.

In the borders of the tongue, and probably in certain other sensitive epithelium, some rudimentary corpuscles of Meissner, called *Merkel's disks,* are found. These consist of expanded disks on the terminal twigs of the branches of nerve fibers that penetrate the stratified squamous epithelium. Each terminal disk is attached to a modified epithelial cell.

Many of the hair follicles are surrounded by

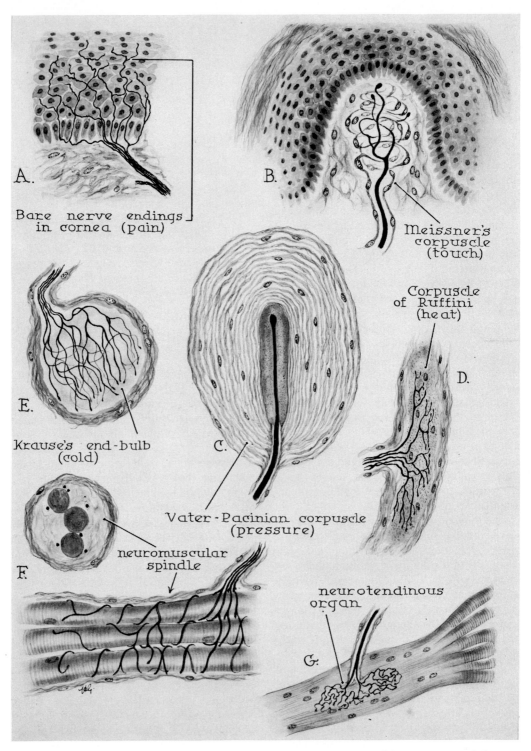

FIG. 31-1. Diagrams of the various types of nerve endings concerned in cutaneous and deep sensibility.

a basketlike arrangement of nerve fibers with several types of expanded endings. These are stimulated by the movement of the hairs. Around the hair follicles of rodents this arrangement is still more complicated, and special tactile hairs are present around the nose and the mouth.

**Pressure Receptors.** Pressure upon the skin of a greater degree than that which elicits the sensation of touch stimulates the more deeply lying receptors known as *Vater-Pacini corpuscles*. These are regarded as the organs of deep pressure, and possibly of vibration sense. They are distributed in the deep regions of the subcutaneous tissue, in the connective tissues near tendons and joints, in the interosseous membranes of the leg and the forearm, in the perimysium of muscles, in the pancreas and its mesentery, in serous membranes, under mucous membranes, in the mammary glands and in the external genitalia of both sexes.

The *pacinian corpuscle*, as it is often called, is made up of a central elongated granular mass covered with many concentric, thin layers of connective tissue (Fig. 31-1 C). This arrangement of cells results in a structure with an appearance not unlike that of an onion. The connective tissue laminae are separated by lymphatic spaces lined on their inner sides with a layer of endothelial cells whose nuclei bulge into the spaces. The peripheral laminae are thicker than those more centrally located. At one pole the nerve fiber, after losing its myelin, enters and terminates in a small swelling in the region of the central granular material. The neurolemma and the endoneurium of the nerve fiber become continuous with the capsule of the corpuscle.

**Heat Receptors.** The receptor of warmth is the *corpuscle of Ruffini*, lying deep in the skin or even in the subcutaneous tissue. These are present generally but are particularly numerous in the subcutaneous connective tissue deep to the plantar surface of the foot. This receptor is composed of a loose arborization of nerve fibers ending in flattened expansions and interspersed with a peculiar granular material dotted with nuclei. Elongated connective tissue bundles and fibroblasts give support to the structure (Fig. 31-1 D). Ruffini-type endings are probably concerned also with proprioceptive sense, as will be described under the latter heading.

**Cold Receptors.** The *Krause end-bulb* is believed to be the receptor for cold. These end-bulbs are most prevalent in the dermis of the conjunctiva, the mucosa of the tongue and the external genitalia. Two structurally different types have been described. The simpler is composed of a granular mass enclosed in a connective tissue capsule continuous with the endoneurium of the afferent nerve fiber; the nerve itself penetrates the end-bulb and terminates near the superior pole of the granular mass in a light thickening. The more complex variety is found in the conjunctiva. The afferent nerve, instead of ending bluntly, branches repeatedly in the bulb and ends in several free, enlarged terminations (Fig. 31-1 E).

**Pain Receptors.** The element or unit of the receptive mechanism for pain is not a small encapsulated structure innervated by a single nerve fiber but rather an appreciable area over which the naked terminal branches of one neuron are distributed. In the cornea, the naked branches of one neuron extend between epithelial cells (Fig. 31-1 A) over as much as one quarter to one half its surface area. In any area of normally innervated skin the terminals of many such units overlap intricately.

Pain fibers in the skin arise from a nerve plexus deep in the corium by way of a superficial plexus of unmyelinated and thin, myelinated fibers. The fibers leaving this superficial plexus are all unmyelinated, though they may have their origin in myelinated fibers. These naked fibers branch freely and end in fine, beaded terminals beneath and between the cells of the deep layers of the epidermis. Naked endings are also present in many of the connective tissues of the body, but not in all.

The pain endings do not respond selectively to one variety of stimulus but to any type, whether it be mechanical, chemical or thermal, provided that it is sufficiently intense. Therefore, the sensation of pain serves a protective purpose, giving warning of the injurious nature of a stimulus, rather than information as to its specific quality.

**Receptors for Proprioceptive Muscle Sense.** Certain encapsulated receptors in muscles and tendons are sensitive to the degree to which muscles are contracted and tendons are tensed; the nervous impulses they set up permit an individual to realize, for example, the position of a limb when the eyes are closed, and to adjust automatically a muscular effort to a particular load. There are 3 important types of these receptors.

*Neuromuscular spindles* are disposed in striated muscles. They consist of small groups of attenuated muscle fibers around which the endings of the sensory nerve fibers are coiled in corkscrew fashion (Fig. 31-1 F); they are so arranged that changes in the length of the muscle or in the tension exerted by it stretch the terminal parts of the nerve fiber. The muscle spindles are surrounded by a capsule of several layers of connective tissue (Fig. 31-1 F). After entering the spindle, the muscle fiber may branch and anastomose like a cardiac muscle fiber. Two or more large myelinated nerve fibers enter the spindle along with several unmyelinated fibers.

*Neurotendinous organs* are found at the junctions of muscles and tendons and in the aponeuroses of muscles. These consist of small bundles of collagenic fibers with numerous nuclei, enclosed within a capsule of connective tissue (Fig. 31-1 G). A large myelinated nerve fiber enters the spindle, usually at its middle, and there subdivides into smaller unmyelinated branches, terminating in leaflike plates.

*Ruffini Endings in Joint Structures.* As was noted under Nerve Supply in Chapter 19, which deals with joints, Gardner has pointed out the presence of numerous Ruffini-type endings in the capsules of synovial joints. These endings are in sites where they would be compressed by certain types of joint movement, so it seems probable that they also are important in connection with proprioceptive sense.

## THE OLFACTORY ORGAN

In the introduction to the chapter on nervous tissue it was explained that, as multicellular organisms were evolved, the first neurons that developed represented specializations of surface ectodermal cells (Fig. 21-2). Moreover, it was observed that as evolution proceeded, the nerve cell bodies of most afferent neurons came to migrate, as it were, along their axons (Fig. 21-6), eventually to take up a more central and better-protected position in cerebrospinal ganglia (Fig. 21-4). In addition, it was noted that there was one exception to this general rule; hence, that there is one site in the body where the cell bodies of afferent neurons remain, as it were, at the surface. This site is the *olfactory area*. Actually, the olfactory area consists of 2 areas, for there is one in each of the 2 nasal cavities. The mucous membrane lining the nasal cavities in the 2 olfactory areas constitutes the *olfactory organ*. The nerve cell bodies present in the epithelium of the mucous membrane at this site are highly sensitive with regard to being selectively stimulated by odors of different kinds. It should be kept in mind that having nerve cell bodies at the surface is a more hazardous arrangement than having them deeply disposed with their fibers running to a surface, for if a mucous membrane containing nerve cell bodies is injured by a disease process or by trauma, the nerve cell bodies that are destroyed cannot be regenerated, whereas a surface innervated by fibers alone can be reinnervated after an injury by the regeneration of fibers from the cell bodies of deeply situated nerve cells. So, as might be expected, the sense of smell is often impaired; indeed, Smith, from his investigations, has estimated that, on the average, about 1 per cent of the fibers of the olfactory nerve (which leads from the receptors to the brain) are lost each year of life. In some individuals, all olfactory fibers are lost at a comparatively early age, usually as a result of the destruction of the olfactory cells in the membrane by the infections to which the nasal mucous membrane is so commonly susceptible.

**Gross Characteristics.** The mucous membrane of the olfactory areas is of a yellow hue, in contrast with the pink hue of the mucous membrane lining the respiratory portion of the nose. It is disposed so as to line most of the uppermost part of the roof of each nasal cavity, beginning in front of the anterior termination of the superior concha and extending backward for about 1 cm. From the roof it extends down both sides of each nasal cavity; on the lateral side it extends so as to cover most of the superior concha, and on the medial side, for about 1 cm. down the nasal septum.

**Microscopic Structure.** The mucous membrane of the olfactory organ consists of a thick pseudostratified epithelium (Fig. 31-2) and a thick lamina propria.

The *epithelium* consists of 3 kinds of cells; (1) sustentacular, (2) olfactory or sensory and (3) basal.

The *sustentacular (sustentaculum = a*

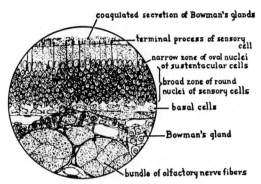

FIG. 31-2. Drawing of a portion of a section (low-power) of the olfactory area of a rat. (Smith, C. G.: Arch. Otolaryng. *25*:136)

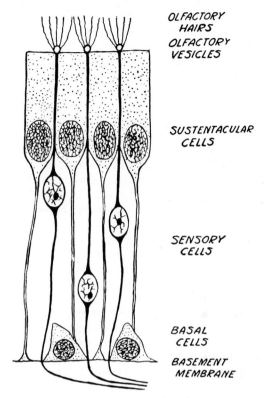

FIG. 31-3. Diagram showing the arrangement of the different types of cells in the olfactory area. (Smith, C. G.: Canad. M. A. J. *39*:139)

prop) cells are tall cylindrical cells disposed perpendicular to the surface (Figs. 31-2 and 31-3). In their deeper parts they are much narrower than in their superficial parts. Although, in the more superficial part of the membrane, they are packed closely together, their more or less cylindrical shape precludes their constituting an imperforate layer. The delicate processes (dendrites) of the sensory or olfactory cells, the cell bodies of which lie more deeply, are thus able to reach the surface by way of the crevices left between them (Fig. 31-3).

The cytoplasm of the sustentacular cells contains a yellow-to-brown pigment; this accounts for the yellow color of the olfactory area in the gross.

The nuclei of the sustentacular cells are disposed just above the middle of the epithelial membrane. They are oval, and since they lie in approximately the same plane, they appear in a section that is cut at right angles to the surface as a row or two of oval nuclei that runs parallel with the surface (Fig. 31-2). This row or two of oval nuclei is commonly referred to as the *narrow zone of oval nuclei* to contrast it with the more deeply disposed *wide zone of round nuclei* (of the sensory cells) that lies below it (Fig. 31-2).

Deep to their nuclei the sustentacular cells become much thinner, and in this region their cytoplasm becomes reduced to little more than strands (Fig. 31-3); these extend to the thin basement membrane. The basal cells, which are more or less triangular, are disposed ir-

regularly along the deepest layer of the epithelium (Figs. 31-2 and 31-3).

The *sensory or olfactory* cells are of the nature of bipolar nerve cells; hence, each has a cell body and a nerve fiber extending from each of its ends (Fig. 31-3): one, a dendrite; and the other, an axon. The sensory cells, like the sustentacular cells, are arranged perpendicular to the surface. Their cell bodies are fitted between the sustentacular cells in the region where these become greatly narrowed (immediately below the narrow zone of oval nuclei). The nuclei of the sensory cells in this region constitute the broad zone of round nuclei (Fig. 31-2). The dendrites of the bipolar cells ascend toward the surface in the crevices between the sustentacular cells. At the surface, each dendrite becomes expanded to form an *olfactory vesicle* and from this, delicate processes called *olfactory hairs* extend from the surface (Fig. 31-3). The axon of each sensory cell passes from the epithelial membrane into the lamina propria. The axons are unmyelinated, and in the lamina propria they become aggregated to form bundles of *olfactory nerve fibers* (Fig. 31-2).

The function of the *basal* cells is unknown; they may be of the nature of reserve cells for forming new sustentacular cells when the need arises.

The *lamina propria* is fibro-elastic connective tissue. In its deeper part it contains many veins, and in some of its deeper areas it is almost of the character of erectile tissue. The secretory portions of tubuloalveolar glands (the glands of Bowman) are disposed in the lamina propria of the olfactory mucous membrane (Fig. 31-2). Indeed, the glands of Bowman, according to Smith, are *confined* to the olfactory area; hence, if they are seen in what appears to be adjacent respiratory mucous membrane, it may be inferred that the latter was once olfactory mucous membrane but has suffered so much from injury that it has lost its olfactory character. The ducts of the glands lead through the epithelium to the surface. These glands make a thin secretion which presumably constantly freshens the thin layer of fluid which continuously bathes the olfactory hairs on the surface of the organ. The gases responsible for odors are thought to dissolve in this fluid and so affect the olfactory hairs.

Bundles of olfactory nerve fibers are encountered in the lamina propria. As noted before, these are composed of the unmyelinated axons of the sensory cells. Collectively, these constitute the *olfactory nerve*, which pierces the skull by way of the cribriform plate of the ethmoid bone to reach the brain.

**Relation of Structure to Function.** How an individual is able to distinguish different kinds of odors and their relative weakness or strength is a matter that is not well understood. Moreover, the problem does not lend itself to animal experimentation. Much of the factual basis for speculation on this matter has been obtained from studies made on individuals whose sense of smell has returned, at least in part, after the olfactory organ has been injured by a disease process which was not severe enough to destroy all the sensory cells but only of sufficient severity to render them functionless temporarily, after which

most of them recovered. Space does not permit a recital of the important studies made in this connection or an adequate discussion of their interpretation. Therefore, we shall only suggest some possible implications that could be derived from them.

First, as man is provided with certain receptors specialized to be stimulated easily by different kinds of stimuli (touch, pressure, etc.), it might be assumed that the sensory cells of the olfactory area itself are specialized so that different ones are sensitive to different odors. However, there are so many different kinds of odors that it is inconceivable that there could be special receptors for each and every kind; this leads, then, to the concept of the existence of olfactory cells specialized for only certain basic odors. The reason for man's being able to discern such a great variety of odors could be due to various combinations of the receptors for the basic odors being stimulated by these different and complex odors. Support for this idea has been derived from finding that when the sense of smell is being recovered after having been lost, a few odors may smell as before, others are different than they were before, and still others cannot be smelled at all.

Moreover, there is evidence to suggest that the different receptors for the different kinds of basic odors are not spread evenly throughout the olfactory area; hence, damage to one part of the organ may result in certain substances smelling differently from before or not at all, whereas, other substances, under these conditions, smell both quantitatively and qualitatively as before.

It would seem, then, that a reasonable working hypothesis in the light of present knowledge would be: (1) that olfactory cells are of different types, specialized to be easily stimulated by certain basic odors: (2) that the receptors for the basic types of odors are not distributed evenly throughout the whole olfactory area but are segregated to some extent; (3) that man's ability to recognize such a great variety of different odors is due to these different odors stimulating different combinations of the receptors for the basic odors and (4) that the strength of an odor bears some relation to the number of receptors stimulated by it.

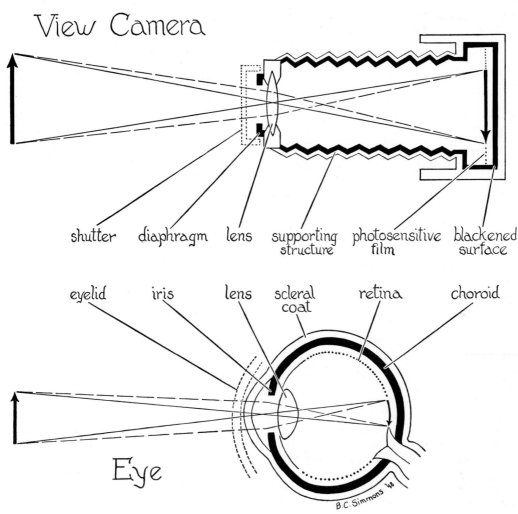

View Camera

shutter   diaphragm   lens   supporting   photosensitive   blackened
                                structure        film          surface

eyelid        iris        lens    scleral      retina        choroid
                                    coat

Eye

B.C. Simmons '48

FIG. 31-4. Diagram illustrating the similarities between the eye and a camera.

## THE EYE

### INTRODUCTION

The eye, except for being rounded, has most of the structural features of the common and familiar camera. The eyelids comprise its shutter (Fig. 31-4). The eye has an iris diaphragm (Figs. 31-4 and 31-10). This has an advantage over the kind found in cameras, for it contracts and dilates automatically in relation to the amount of light available. The eye has a lens (Fig. 31-4); this, being composed of altered transparent epithelial cells, is more elastic than the glass lens of a camera. Advantage is taken of its elasticity, for the lens of the eye is suspended in such a way that muscle action can alter its shape and so change its focal length. As a consequence, the eye need not be shortened or elongated when objects at different distances are successively brought into focus as is necessary in a camera with a rigid lens. The plastic or metal sides and back of a camera have their counterpart in the eye in a strong connective tissue membrane, the *sclera* (Fig. 31-4). The counterpart in the eye of the light-sensitive film used in a camera is a membrane of living cells of nervous origin, the *retina*, which lines, not only the back, but the sides of the eye as well (Fig. 31-4). Then, finally, just as black paint is used to blacken all the interior surfaces of a camera that might leak or reflect light, black pigment is distrib-

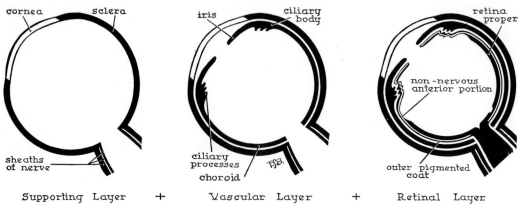

Supporting  Layer        +        Vascular  Layer        +        Retinal  Layer

FIG. 31-5. (*Left*) Diagram of the supporting coat of the eye. (*Center*) Diagram showing the vascular coat of the eye inserted on the inside of the supporting coat. (*Right*) Diagram showing the retinal coat of the eye on the inside of the outer 2 coats.

uted generously between the retina and the sclera and in other sites where it would be useful.

However, unlike many modern cameras, the lens of the eye is not placed at its very front; in this respect the eye is like an old-fashioned camera which has its external aperture covered with a glass window to keep out the dust, and its lens inside, a short distance behind the glass window. The transparent window in the central part of the front of the eye is of a curved form and is called the *cornea* (Fig. 31-6). This is composed chiefly of a tough but transparent type of dense connective tissue that is continuous with the opaque connective tissue of the sclera that surrounds and supports the remainder of the eye.

Windows not only permit householders to see out; they also permit the curious to see in. The cornea is like a window in this respect as well, for, with an instrument called an ophthalmoscope, the physician can direct a beam of light into the eye and at the same time look through the instrument and study the appearance of the various structures within the eye as they are successively illuminated. By this means much useful information, not only about the eye, but about the health of the body as a whole, may be obtained.

## GENERAL MICROSCOPIC STRUCTURE

The microscopic structure of many parts of the eye is complex, and an exhaustive treatment of the histology of this organ is not justi-

fiable in a general textbook. Reference books are listed at the end of this chapter for those who require specialized knowledge. Furthermore, even such details of structure as should be given in a textbook of histology are best postponed until the student has read a very general account of the structure of the eye and has learned the names of its various parts and how they cooperate in the functioning of the organ. For this reason, we shall first give a very general account of the structure of the organ and then, later, give some details about the structure of some of its more important parts.

The eye is a nearly spherical structure about an inch in diameter. It is contained in the anterior part of a bony socket, the *orbit*. Between the eye and the bony wall of the orbit in which it lies are fat, connective tissue, muscles and the glandular tissue that provides the tears. The eye is suspended by ligaments in such a fashion that voluntary muscles in the orbit (but outside the eye) can move the eye so that one can look up and down and from side to side.

In describing the microscopic structure of the eye it is convenient to describe first the structure of its *wall*, then its contents (these constitute the *refractive media* of the eye) and finally the *accessory structures* of the eye such as eyelids, tear glands and ducts and so on.

**The Wall of the Eye.** The wall of the eyeball consists of 3 layers which, from without in, are designated by the general terms of (1) supporting layer, (2) middle layer and (3) retinal layer (Fig. 31-5). All 3 layers are not present in all parts of the wall of the eye.

The *supporting layer* consists essentially of a dense connective tissue membrane. Around most of the eye this is called the *sclera* (*scleros* = hard) (Fig. 31-5). The sclera is white in color; the part of the sclera that shows is the "white" of the eye (Fig. 31-10). The part of the supporting layer covering the central part of the anterior portion of the eye bulges forward slightly and is transparent; this is called the *cornea* (Fig. 31-5). The supporting layer completely encloses the other layers of the eye except at one site posteriorly where there is an opening to permit the optic nerve to enter the eyeball.

The *middle layer* of the wall of the eye is often called the *uveal* (*uva* = grape) *layer* or *tract* because when the sclera is dissected away the middle layer is exposed and is seen to resemble the skin of a blue grape in that it is pigmented and surrounds the jellylike contents of the eye. The middle layer of the eye is very vascular; hence, it is sometimes called the *vascular layer* of the eye.

The middle illustration in Figure 31-5 shows the middle layer inserted on the inner surface of the supporting layer. In the posterior two thirds of the eye the middle layer consists of only a thin membrane; this thin posterior segment of the middle layer is called the *choroid*. Moreover, in this illustration it will be seen that toward the anterior part of the eye the middle layer becomes thickened to form what is called the *ciliary body*. This, as a thickened rim of tissue, encircles the anterior part of the eye. From it, what are termed the *ciliary processes* extend inwardly (Fig. 31-5, *center*). The middle layer of the eye continues anteriorly to constitute the *iris* (diaphragm) of the eye (Fig. 31-5, *center*). The iris is the pigmented part of the eye that may be seen through the cornea (Fig. 31-10); depending on the pigment content of the iris, eyes are said to be blue, brown or some other color. Indeed, pigment is abundant in all parts of the middle coat; this helps to lightproof the wall of the eye and to cut down reflection. The middle coat of the eye conducts blood vessels and, in addition, in its anterior part, it contains smooth muscle. The smooth muscle in the iris causes its aperture, the *pupil* of the eye (Fig.

31-10), to contract or dilate. The smooth muscle of the ciliary body affects the tension of the ligament that suspends the lens, not in the way that might at first be expected, i.e., by its contraction tensing the ligament that suspends the lens, but instead, by its contraction easing the tension on the ligament. This is how it permits the eye to accommodate its focus for near objects. The muscle of the ciliary body is, then, an important factor in the mechanism of accommodation.

The position of the *retinal layer* is illustrated on the right side of Figure 31-5. It consists of 2 layers; the outermost one is pigmented and lines the entire inner surface of the middle layer of the eye. The inner layer of the retina is composed of nervous tissue. The nervous part of the retina, as such, does not extend into the anterior part of the eye (Fig. 31-5, *right*), for there, light could not be focused on it. The nervous part of the retina contains special nerve cells called *rods* and *cones*; these are the *photoreceptors*. In addition, the retina contains the cell bodies of many conductor neurons and many nerve fibers. Most of the latter stream toward the site at which the optic nerve leaves the eye through the scleral layer.

**Refractive Media of the Eye.** A beam of light, on striking the surface of the cornea, passes through the following media before it reaches the retina:

1. The substance of the cornea (Fig. 31-6).
2. A space between the iris and the lens called the *anterior chamber* of the eye (Fig. 31-6); this is filled with a fluid called *aqueous humor*.
3. The lens (Fig. 31-6).
4. The transparent jellylike material of the vitreous body which fills the interior of the eye behind the lens (Fig. 31-6).

A beam of light is bent when it passes obliquely from a substance of one refractive index into that of another. The cornea is curved, and the difference between the refractive index of cornea and air is greater than the difference between the refractive indices of any of the media through which light subsequently passes to reach the retina. Hence, with regard to refracting light, the curved anterior surface of the cornea is of the greatest importance. The true lens of the eye has a refractive index which is only slightly greater

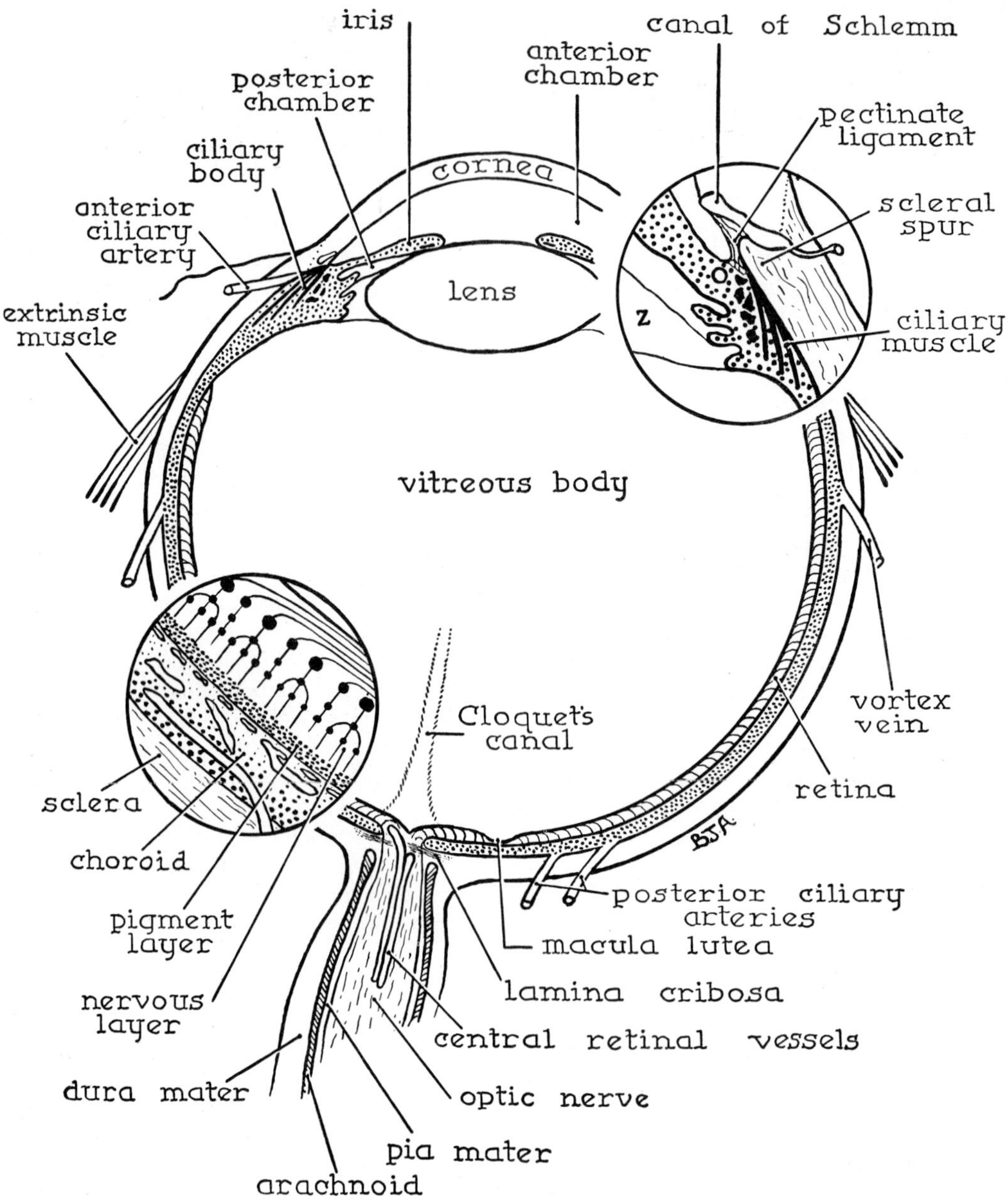

Fig. 31-6. Diagram of a longitudinal section cut through the middle of the eye.

than that of the aqueous humor in front of it and that of the vitreous body behind it; its function, then, of bringing light to a focus on the retina, is not of as great a magnitude as that of the cornea. Its unique importance lies in the fact that, being elastic, its focal length can be changed by the pull of muscles on the ligaments which suspend it; hence, it permits light from objects at different distances to be focused sharply.

On passing through the vitreous body and on reaching the retina, light does not immediately strike the photoreceptors, for these, as will be described in detail later, are in the outermost part of the nervous layer of the retina (Fig. 31-12). To reach the photoreceptors, light first must pass through the nerve fibers and the nerve cells present in the inner layers of the nervous coat of the retina (the layers adjacent to the vitreous body). Then,

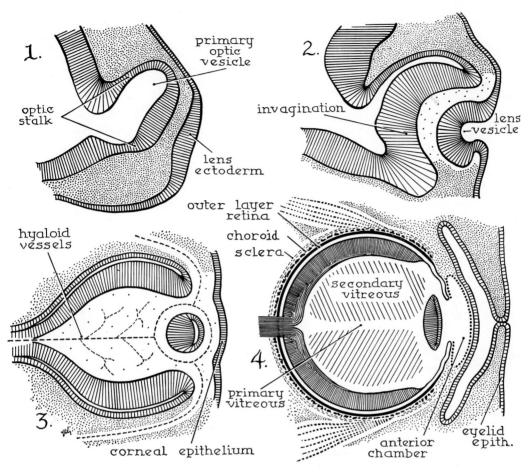

FIG. 31-7. Diagrams of 4 stages in the development of the eye.

when the light reaches and affects the photo-receptors in the outer layers of the nervous coat of the retina, the nervous impulses, set up by the stimulus of light, must pass in the reverse direction through nerve fibers and nerve cell bodies toward the vitreous body. Here, in the innermost layers of the retina (next to the vitreous), the nervous impulses are conducted by nerve fibers that run to the site of exit of the optic nerve, into which nerve they pass to reach the brain (Fig. 31-12).

## DEVELOPMENT

The retina of the eye develops as an outgrowth from the forebrain. This, early in development, is hollow and its anterior wall bulges forward to form the primary optic vesicle (Fig. 31-7, 1). The bulge then becomes constricted at its point of origin from the forebrain; the constricted portion of the bulge is

termed the *optic stalk* (Fig. 31-7, 1). While the forebrain is bulging forward to form the optic vesicle, the ectoderm immediately in front of it thickens (Fig. 31-7, 1) to form the lens plate. The anterior wall of the optic vesicle then becomes invaginated so that the optic vesicle becomes cup-shaped, with the wall of the cup having 2 layers (Fig. 31-7, 2 and 3). At the same time the thickened ectoderm in front of the optic vesicle bulges inwardly to form the lens vesicle (Fig. 31-7, 2). The lens vesicle then becomes pinched off from the ectoderm from which it arose (Fig. 37-1, 3). It is at first hollow, but the cells of its posterior wall elongate to make the posterior wall thicker than the anterior wall (Fig. 31-7, 3). Subsequently, its cavity disappears, and its posterior and anterior walls come together (Fig. 31-7, 4). In the meantime, the optic vesicle has become a deep cup, and since its origi-

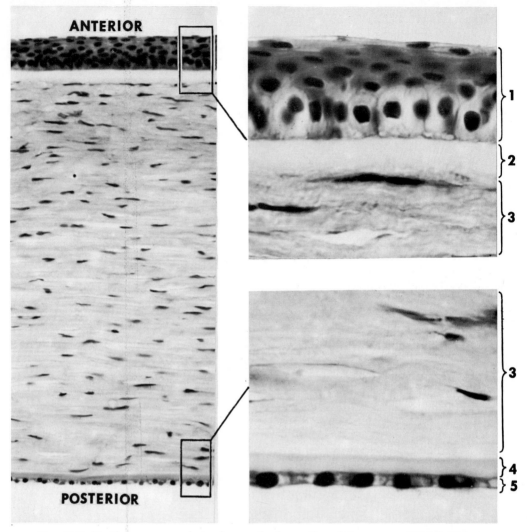

FIG. 31-8. (*Left*) Low-power photomicrograph of a section of the cornea. (*Right*) High-power photomicrographs of parts of the cornea: (1) stratified squamous epithelium, (2) Bowman's membrane, (3) substantia propria, (4) Descemet's membrane, (5) Descemet's endothelium.

nal anterior wall is pressed backward, its original anterior wall constitutes the inner layer of the cup (Fig. 31-7, 3), and this develops into the nervous layer of the retina. The outer wall of the vesicle becomes the outer pigmented layer of the retina which is black in Figure 31-7, 4.

The actively growing cells in the epithelial elements of the developing eye require a special blood supply, and this is provided, as the eye forms, by an artery that enters by way of the optic stalk. This is called the *hyaloid artery* (Fig. 31-7, 3). This subsequently atro-

phies as other sources of blood supply are evolved. The origin of the vitreous body is not thoroughly understood; probably both the cells of the optic and lens vesicles, together with the mesoderm into which both these vesicles grow, contribute to its formation.

The mesoderm surrounding the developing eye gives rise to both the middle and the supporting layers of the eye (Fig. 31-7, 4). Two folds of ectoderm with platelike cores of mesoderm extend over the developing cornea to form the eyelids (Fig. 31-7, 4). The substance of the cornea forms from mesoderm, but ectoderm persists over its anterior surface to form its epithelial covering (Fig. 31-7, 4). The anterior chamber develops as a result of the formation of a space in the mesoderm in this area (Fig. 31-7, 4). The epithelium of the 2 layers of the optic vesicle continues forward to form a lining for the back of the ciliary body and the iris, both of which form from mesoderm (Fig. 31-7, 4).

## DETAILS OF MICROSCOPIC STRUCTURE AND ITS RELATION TO FUNCTION

**Cornea.** The cornea is the anterior part of the supporting layer of the eye (Fig. 31-5, *left*). It is a transparent, nonvascular membrane. It has a shorter radius of curvature than the remainder of the wall of the eye; hence, it bulges forward from the remainder of the globe. Since it is exposed, it is subject to cuts, abrasions and other kinds of trauma. It is important in treating injuries of the cornea to know its thickness. Estimates based on measurements made on cadavers are not valid, since the cornea swells after death. In the living it is about 0.5 mm. thick at its central part and somewhat thicker at its periphery.

The cornea (Fig. 31-8) consists chiefly of a special kind of dense connective tissue, containing both cells and intercellular substance, called the *substantia propria* (Fig. 31-8, 3). This is bordered anteriorly and posteriorly by a homogeneous membrane of intercellular substance (Fig. 31-8, 2 and 4). Anteriorly, the cornea is covered with stratified squamous nonkeratinizing epithelium (Fig. 31-8, 1), and posteriorly it is lined by a single layer of endothelial cells (Fig. 31-8, 5).

The epithelium covering the cornea is several layers in thickness and is replete with nerve endings that are chiefly of the pain type (Fig. 31-1 A). Their stimulation results reflexly in the blinking of the eyelids and in the flow of tears. The surface of the cornea must be kept wet by tears (mucus from the conjunctival glands also helps keep the corneal surface wet); if the nerve pathways concerned in the reflexes described above are destroyed, the corneal surface, on not being frequently wiped by the wet lids, becomes dry and then ulcerated. There are no papillae projecting into the epithelium of the cornea. Furthermore, since the connective tissue beneath it has no capillaries, the epithelium of the cornea

is a comparatively long way from a source of nutrition. The diffusion phenomenon on which its cells depend must be very efficient, for corneal epithelium, on being injured, regenerates rapidly. Carbon dioxide is eliminated through the corneal epithelium.

The membrane of intercellular substance on which the basal cells of the corneal epithelium rest is called *Bowman's membrane* (Fig. 31-8, 2). This consists of a transparent homogeneous material. It is often spoken of as a condensation of the connective tissue of the substantia propria. It is regarded as an important protective layer, being resistant to trauma and bacterial invasion. Once destroyed, it does not regenerate. Bowman's membrane does not extend from the cornea into the sclera. The site at which cornea undergoes a transition into sclera (and consequently, where Bowman's membrane ends) is called the *limbus* (*limbus* = a border).

The substantia propria comprises about 90 per cent of the thickness of the cornea. It contains flattened connective tissue cells that are disposed between parallel bundles of collagenic fibers called *lamellae* (Fig. 31-8, *left*). While most of the fibers in a lamella are disposed parallel with the surface, those of one lamella run at an angle to those of the next. The fibers of some lamellae join with those of adjacent lamellae to bind the substantia propria together.

As was pointed out in Chapter 8, collagenic fibers, and perhaps fibrils, are bound together by an amorphous cementing substance. In the substantia propria this material is true hyaluronic acid sulfate. True hyaluronic acid sulfate has not been recovered from connective tissue elsewhere in the body. It is assumed that the binding together of collagenic fibrils and fibers in the substantial propria by this substance (as well as their regular arrangement) is responsible for the unique transparency of this membrane.

Deep to the substantia propria is Descemet's membrane (Fig. 31-8, 4). This is composed of a special kind of elastic material. In this respect it is different from Bowman's membrane, which does not stain with elastic tissue stains. Applied to the inner side of Descemet's membrane is a single layer of endothelial cells; this layer is called *Descemet's endothelium* (Fig. 31-8, 5).

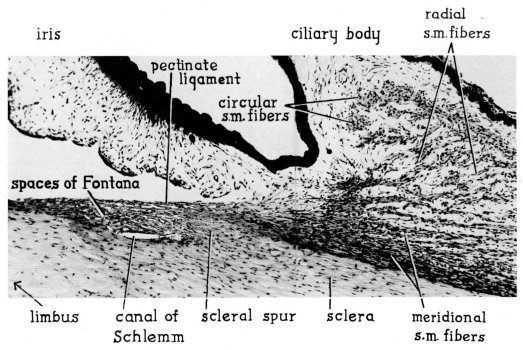

FIG. 31-9. Two low-power photomicrographs (mounted in continuity) of a portion of a longitudinal section of an eye, showing the region of the angle of the iris. The tissue labeled "spaces of Fontana" is now commonly referred to as the trabecular meshwork.

FINE STRUCTURE. The fine structure of the cornea has been investigated with the EM by Sheldon, and that of Descemet's membrane by Jakus. References to their studies are given at the end of this chapter.

TRANSPLANTATION. Homologous transplants of cornea are made with a considerable amount of success. In the past it was believed that cornea was an exception to the general rule about homologous transplants and that the cells of the transplants survived in their new hosts. There were reasons for thinking that cornea might be different from other tissues because the cornea is normally nonvascular, and it does not contain any lymphatics. Furthermore, it has a high proportion of intercellular substance to cells. Maumenee says that it has been shown experimentally that the epithelium and the endothelium of a homologous transplant of cornea are lost in a few days. The only cells of the transplant that survive for any length of time are some of the connective tissue cells within the substance of the cornea. Recently, it has been shown by Basu and Ormsby, by making corneal grafts from

female cats to males, and vice versa, and then determining the chromosomal sex of the cells by the sex chromatin technic, that the connective tissue cells of the graft do live for at least long periods of time. By the same technic it has been shown that the stromal cells of grafts in man live for at least a year, which is as long as they have been followed. The surface epithelium is regenerated from the host, so that it covers the transplant in a few days. The regeneration of the endothelium takes longer. The connective tissue cells within the substance of the cornea are replaced only very slowly from the host.

Sclera. The sclera is a tough, white, connective tissue membrane that consists of bundles of collagenic fibers with flattened fibroblasts between the bundles (Fig. 31-9). Some elastic fibers are mixed with the collagenic ones. The fibers are not arranged as regularly as those of the substantia propria of the cornea, and the cementing substance with which they are associated is probably of a somewhat different composition, since the sclera is opaque. The sclera is thick enough to permit its being sutured from the outside without the needle penetrating into the middle layer of the wall of the eye. It is not as thick as the cornea, except at its posterior pole; at the midportion of the globe (the *equator*) it is slightly less than 0.5 mm. thick. However, it is strong enough in adults to withstand very high intra-ocular pressures, should this condition occur, without stretching.

The relative opacity of the sclera, as compared with the cornea, is due to a very important degree to its greater water content. This can be shown very dramatically by blowing a jet of air on an exposed portion of sclera, for this makes it completely transparent. The reason the cornea remains transparent is that water is lost from its surfaces, so if either of its surfaces becomes damaged it may become opaque in that area. For example, if some of the vitreous comes and stays in contact with its posterior surface at any point, the cornea becomes opaque at that point.

It is important in connection with testing the intra-ocular pressure of the eye by means of a tonometer, which is placed on the cornea, to know that the scleras of different eyes are rigid to different degrees; hence, if the rigidity of the sclera is extreme, it may give an erroneous pressure reading.

At the posterior part of the eye the outermost part of the sclera is continuous with the dural sheath and usually with the arachnoid sheath also of the optic nerve (Fig. 31-6). Its innermost layers are continuous with the pia mater. Moreover, the innermost layer of the sclera, in the form of a perforated disk, bridges what would otherwise be a gap in the sclera, and through this the optic nerve leaves the eye (Fig. 31-17). The fibers of the optic nerve pass through the perforations of the disk. This part of the sclera is called the *lamina cribrosa* (*cribrum* = a sieve).

The sclera as a whole, being composed of dense connective tissue, is poorly supplied with capillaries. However, many larger vessels pierce it obliquely to gain entrance to the middle layer of the eye. The direction of these vessels, in passing through the sclera, is such that on reaching the inner aspect of the sclera they attain a point on the circumference of the eye closer to the anterior pole than the point at which they approached the exterior of the sclera (Fig. 31-6). The anterior ciliary arteries enter beside (or slightly in front of) the ciliary body (Fig. 31-6), and both short and long posterior ciliary arteries pass through the sclera behind the equator (Fig. 31-6). The long posterior ciliary arteries, on entering the middle coat of the eye, take a direct course to the ciliary body; the short ones branch. Four large vortex veins which drain most of the blood from the middle coat pass obliquely backward through the sclera near the equator of the eye (Fig. 31-6). The ciliary arteries have companion veins.

**Choroid.** The choroid is that part of the middle layer of the eye behind the ciliary body. It is only 0.1 to 0.2 mm. thick. It nourishes the outer layers of the retina. It consists of 3 layers.

1. THE EPICHOROID. This, its outer layer, consists chiefly of elastic fibers that are attached to the sclera. Many nerve fibers that terminate in *chromatophores* are present in it. The chromatophores are large pigmented cells that may be seen, although they are not labeled, in Figure 31-13. Some have branched irregular cytoplasm like that of an amoeba. Whether this pigment is actually produced by these cells or taken up from pigment produced in the retina has been a point of much controversy. During a short phase of early fetal life, before pigment is present, the future pigment cells of the choroid have been found to be dopa-positive. Moreover, the choroid has been shown at the same time to contain melanogen, the mother substance of melanin. This evidence, along with the fact that fuscin, the pigment of the retina, is slightly different from melanin, suggests that melanin is produced by the pigment cells of the choroid and thereafter stored *in situ*. It is interesting that melanin pigment, recovered from the uveal tract, has different immunologic properties from that of other parts of the body. Through the epichoroid run the two unbranching posterior long ciliary arteries. A few smooth muscle fibers are present in this layer in its anterior part; these represent the beginning of the ciliary muscle.

2. VESSEL LAYER. The choroidal vessels that are supplied by the short posterior ciliary arteries and drained by the 4 vortex veins lie in this, the middle layer of the choroid (Fig. 31-13). The stroma is similar to that of the epichoroid.

3. CHORIOCAPILLARIS. This, the inner layer of the choroid network (Fig. 31-13), consists of a single layer of capillaries which, however, are among the largest seen in the body. Some of them, especially those outside the macula (to be described presently), are as wide as sinusoids; these permit a rapid transfer of blood from the arterial to the venous side.

BRUCH'S MEMBRANE. Separating the choriocapillaris from the outer coat of the retina lies a glassy membrane (*Bruch's membrane*). This has both elastic and cuticular components, formed by the choroid and the retina, respectively. Bruch's membrane is semipermeable, and through it pass the essential metabolites for the photoreceptors.

**Ciliary Body.** The 3 strata of the choroid are continuous anteriorly with the ciliary body. This extends forward to a site where a narrow, short flange of sclera, called the *scleral spur,* projects inwardly (Figs. 31-6 and 31-9). The ciliary body, as a thickening of the middle coat of the eye, forms a ring on the inner side of the sclera, behind the scleral spur (Figs. 31-6 and 31-9). When an eye is cut in longitudinal section the ciliary body is cut in cross section. In cross section it appears as a triangle, with its base facing the anterior chamber and its apex passing into the choroid posteriorly (Fig. 31-6). The elastic epichoroid, in the ciliary body, is replaced by fibers of ciliary muscle. These are of the smooth variety and they comprise the bulk of the ciliary body (Fig. 31-9).

**Structures Involved in the Mechanism of Accommodation.** The smooth muscle fibers of the ciliary body are disposed so as to pull in 3 different directions. Accordingly, 3 groups of fibers are distinguished: (1) the *meridional* (a meridian runs from pole to pole, crossing the equator of a globe at right angles) fibers, which arise in the epichoroid near the ciliary body and pass forward to end in the scleral spur (Fig. 31-9); (2) the *radial* fibers, which are to the inside of the meridional fibers and fan out posteriorly to make a wide attachment to the connective tissue of the choroid (Fig. 31-9); and (3) the *circular* fibers, which lie near the inner edge of the ciliary body near its base and are arranged so as to encircle the eye at this site (Fig. 31-9).

To understand how the contraction of smooth muscle fibers in the ciliary body af-

fects the shape of the lens, certain features of the lens and the mechanism by which it is suspended must be described.

The lens (Fig. 31-6) is of the biconvex type, with its posterior surface exhibiting a greater convexity than its anterior. It is composed essentially of long prisms, called *lens fibers*, that are cemented together to constitute a transparent medium. The lens fibers evolve from epithelial cells. Most of the first fibers that form in the lens develop from the epithelial cells of the posterior layer of the embryonic lens (Fig. 31-7) and hence run in an anteroposterior direction. When epithelial cells become lens fibers they lose their nuclei; hence, lens fibers cannot reproduce themselves. But living epithelial cells persist at the equator of the lens and these proliferate and differentiate throughout life to give rise to new lens fibers which are added to the existing ones much as new layers are added to the sides of a tree. This results in the slow growth of the lens throughout life.

The lens is surrounded with a thick, homogeneous, elastic capsule of intercellular substance. The lens capsule is constantly under tension and hence constantly "seeks" to make the elastic lens assume a more globular form.

As the lens ages it loses water and becomes denser and less elastic. Consequently, its range of focus becomes diminished, often sufficiently for individuals to require supplementary lenses (in the form of glasses) for focusing near objectives sharply.

The lens is attached to the ciliary body by means of the *zonule* (Fig. 31-6, *upper right,* Z). In sections this exhibits a fibrillar form, and for this reason the zonule is sometimes called the *suspensory ligament of the lens.* But it is probable that much of its fibrillar appearance is due to fixation artefact and that in reality the zonule is composed of a gel and represents a specialized portion of the vitreous body, the mass of gel that lies behind it, which will be described presently.

The zonule has a broad zone of attachment both to the capsule of the lens around its equator and to the ciliary body (Fig. 31-6). Now, it might be thought, as was noted before, that matters would be arranged so that the contraction of the smooth muscle fibers of the ciliary body would pull on the zonule, which would in turn pull on the equator of the lens so that the lens would become flatter and hence accommodated for distant objects. Actually, the contraction of the smooth muscle of the ciliary body produces the opposite effect. Instead of tensing the zonule, the contraction of the smooth muscle of the ciliary body, the fibers of which are firmly attached to the sclera in the region of the scleral spur, pulls the part of the ciliary body to which the zonule is attached, *forward* and *inward*. This effect, since the attachment of the zonule to the ciliary body is posterior to its site of attachment to the lens, relaxes the tension of the zonule and hence permits the lens, which itself is under tension from its capsule, to assume a more globular shape, and hence become accommodated for close objects. It is to be noted, then, that muscular contraction is required for viewing close objects; this is one reason why reading "tires" the eyes more than viewing distant objects does.

**Iris.** The iris is a colored disk with a central, variable aperture, the pupil (Fig. 31-10). It is not a flat disk, for the lens pushes against its central part (the *pupillary margin*) from behind so that its more central part is more anterior than its periphery (Fig. 31-6).

The space behind the iris, and elsewhere limited by the lens, the viterous body and the ciliary body, is called the *posterior chamber* of the eye (Fig. 31-6); the space in front of the iris (and at the pupil, in front of the lens), and otherwise limited by the cornea and the most anterior part of the sclera, is called the *anterior chamber* of the eye (Fig. 31-6). Both the anterior and the posterior chambers are filled with a fluid called *aqueous humor*. A certain amount of circulation takes place in this fluid. In all probability the fluid is formed in the posterior chamber and then passes into the anterior chamber, from which it is resorbed by mechanisms to be described presently. Since the posterior border of the pupillary margin of the iris and the anterior surface of the lens press against each other, the iris acts like a valve in that fluid from the posterior chamber can force the pupillary margin of the iris away from the anterior surface of the lens to enter the anterior chamber, but fluid tending to move in the reverse direction presses the pupillary margin of the iris against the lens and so closes the opening between the 2 chambers. Posteriorly, the iris is lined by 2

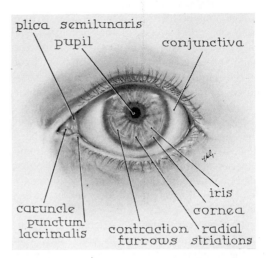

FIG. 31-10. The eye, as seen from in front.

layers of pigmented epithelial cells continuous with the 2 layers of retinal epithelium that line the ciliary body (Fig. 31-9). Anteriorly, the iris is covered imperfectly with squamous endothelial cells comparable and continuous with those of Descemet's endothelium.

The iris (Fig. 31-9) is well supplied with vessels and networks of nerve fibers. The arteries, branches of the major arterial circle, course spirally through its stroma like a corkscrew, so that their lumens will not be much affected by changes in the radius of the iris. They have a thick collagenous adventitia which prevents kinking when the spirals are compressed and makes the vessels appear as radiating gray lines in pale or blue irises. Throughout the stroma are scattered *chromatophores* which are concentrated mostly at the anterior border (Fig. 31-9). The vessels do not extend to this border.

Encircling the pupil, about 1.5 mm. from its margin, is a scalloped line formed, in a manner which need not be described here, by the regression of the membrane that extended across the pupil in embryonic life (Fig. 31-10). This line divides the iris into a pupillary and a ciliary portion (Fig. 31-10). Crypts opening anteriorly are found in the pupillary portion; they form as a result of the incomplete atrophy of the pupillary membrane. Shorter crypts are also found in the anterior surface of the ciliary portion. The contraction furrows (Fig. 31-10) appear as deeper folds encircling the anterior surface of the iris.

The muscle fibers of the iris are derived from the anterior cells of the pigmented epithelial layer; this is a continuation of the outer retinal layer of the eye. The constrictor of the pupil is the sphincterlike muscle composed of circularly arranged smooth muscle fibers near the pupillary margin. How firmly the iris is held against the anterior surface of the lens depends on the tone of these fibers. The dilator of the pupil is less distinct and consists of a thin sheet of radially disposed fibers near the back of the iris. The fibers are not typical smooth muscle fibers and are called *myo-epithelial* cells.

The pupillary size is automatically controlled by a nervous reflex in which the *retina* is the *receptor* organ, and the muscles of the iris the *effectors*. When the eye looks at a bright object the pupil is reflexly constricted, thereby decreasing the amount of light that can enter the eye, and vice versa. To anyone who has studied photography the pupillary size has a still further significance. A dilated pupil, like a dilated aperture in a camera, results in a diminished "depth" of focus. For this reason, glasses prescribed when the pupil is dilated are likely to be more accurate than those perscribed when the pupil is not.

The color of the iris is due to melanin pigment. As was noted in discussing the color of skin, melanin pigment, seen through a substantial thickness of tissue, appears blue. Hence, if the melanin pigment in the iris is limited to the epithelial cells that line its posterior surface, the iris (provided that the stroma ahead of the pigment is of a usual density) appears blue. If the stroma is somewhat denser than usual, the pigment at the back of the iris gives a gray color to the eye. If sufficient pigment is present in chromatophores in the substance of the stroma as well as in the epithelium at the back of the iris, the iris appears brown. In the white race the final color of the iris is not necessarily developed at the time of birth.

**Region of the Angle of the Iris.** It has already been observed that the site at which the sclera becomes continuous with the cornea is called the *limbus* (Fig. 31-9) and that immediately behind it the internal surface of the sclera is thrown into a ridge, the *scleral spur*, that extends inward and forward (Fig. 31-9). The scleral spur, of course, encircles the eye.

Immediately in front of the scleral spur a furrow dips into the inner layer of the sclera; this is called the *scleral furrow* (in Fig. 31-9 this is not labeled as such but as spaces of Fontana), and it too encircles the eye. At the bottom of the furrow a canal (or a group of anastomosing canals) lined by endothelium is situated. This is called the *canal of Schlemm* (Fig. 31-9), and it too encircles the eye. In a meridional section, the scleral spur, the scleral furrow and the canal of Schlemm are, of course, all cut in cross section (Fig. 31-9).

The scleral furrow is filled in (over the canal which lies at its bottom) with a loose meshwork of connective tissue; this extends from the cornea, at the anterior side of the furrow, backward to the anterior border of the scleral spur. The spaces in the meshwork were in the past called the *spaces of Fontana* (Fig. 31-9) and they communicate with the anterior chamber. The spaces which are now commonly referred to as the trabecular spaces are lined by endothelium; this is continuous with that which lines the cornea and covers the anterior surface of the iris. Hence, aqueous humor is present in the trabecular spaces. The middle (uveal) coat of the eye extends forward to provide a lining for the wall of the eye between the iris and the scleral spur. In the horse this lining is so strong and well developed that it is called the *pecinate ligament*. Sometimes this name is used for its relatively undeveloped counterpart in man (Fig. 31-9).

**Ciliary Processes.** About 75 little ridges, each about 2.0 mm. long, 0.5 mm. wide and about 1 mm. high, project inwardly from the ciliary body, immediately behind its point of junction with the iris, into the posterior chamber of the eye. These are termed the *ciliary processes*, and a few are usually to be seen in a single longitudinal section of an eye (Fig. 31-11, *left*).

As is indicated in Figure 31-5 (*center*), the cores of the ciliary processes are the counterparts in this particular region of the choriocapillaris since they consist chiefly of capillaries that are supported by a delicate connective tissue (Fig. 31-11, *right*). The processes are covered with two layers of epithelium; these represent the continuation of the 2 layers of the retina forward (compare the middle and the right drawings in Fig. 31-5). The cells of the deeper of the 2 layers

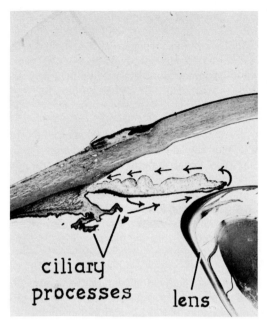
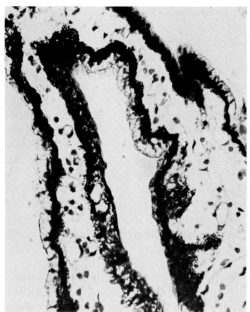

Fig. 31-11. (*Left*) Very low-power photomicrograph of part of a longitudinal section of the eye, showing the ciliary processes. The arrows indicate the course of the circulation of the aqueous humor. (*Right*) High-power photomicrograph of a section of the ciliary processes of a rabbit. Notice the large capillaries in the loose, delicate connective tissue that makes up the stroma of the processes.

are pigmented (Fig. 31-11, *right*). The superficial layer is called the ciliary epithelium. The epithelial layer, as a whole, rests on a membrane that is continuous with Bruch's membrane and separates the epithelium from the vascular stroma of the processes.

With the EM, Pease has shown that the ciliary epithelium (the layer that abuts on the aqueous humor) contains many deep folds of the cell membrane. These begin from the free surface and extend almost through to the deeper sides of the cells. Moreover, Pease has shown that the free surfaces of the cells are covered with a basement membrane. The folds and the basement membrane are both concerned, in all probability, with the transport of fluid required in connection with the secretion of aqueous humor.

**Aqueous Humor: Formation, Circulation and Absorption.** Aqueous humor is a thin watery fluid containing most of the diffusable substance of blood plasma and is very similar to blood serum in composition. For example, the albumin-globulin ratio is the same in both aqueous humor and serum. However, whereas

serum has a protein content of 7 per cent, aqueous humor contains only 0.02 per cent. Like serum, the aqueous humor contains no fibrinogen and therefore cannot clot. It has been a matter of some controversy as to whether it should be regarded primarily as a dialysate of blood plasma, comparable with tissue fluid, or as a secretion. For one thing it is hypertonic in relation to blood and in all probability not only the factors concerned in tissue fluid formation and absorption (hydrostatic and osmotic pressure), but specific cellular activities as well, participate in controlling its quality and its rate of formation and absorption. Friedenwald describes some of the complex cellular activities concerned in the matter, and his paper should be read for further information about this subject.

Although aqueous humor is thin and watery, it has been shown to contain considerable quantities of hyaluronic acid. However, this material, as was explained in Chapter 8, commonly appears in connective tissue as a soft, jellylike, amorphous type of intercellular substance. Its jellylike form in most connective tissues is due to its being present in a highly polymerized state, for its molecular aggregates are of a very large size. It was also observed in Chapter 10 that the enzyme hyaluronidase has the ability to depolymerize hyaluronic acid. It is of interest that it has been determined from studies made on the eyes of cattle that the hyaluronic acid in the aqueous humor is normally about 95 per cent depolymerized; this, then, is the reason for the aqueous having such a low viscosity. This suggests that hyaluronidase has a normal function in the eye in keeping the molecular aggregates of hyaluronic acid from becoming of a large size. If they did become of a large size, they probably could not drain away from the eye by the escape mechanism to be described presently; hence, hyaluronic acid would accumulate in the eye and so change both the physical state and the osmotic pressure of the aqueous humor to the detriment of the eye. It would appear, then, that the action of hyaluronidase in keeping the hyaluronic acid of the eye depolymerized represents a normal physiologic function of the enzyme.

Although the general principles with regard to the formation and the absorption of tissue fluid that have been explained in Chapter 10 are fundamental to the understanding of the formation and the absorption of aqueous humor, there are certain differences in the mechanism that operates in the eye from that which operates in most tissues. These differences are due to the fact that tissue fluid in the eye is under considerably greater pressure than it is in most sites in the body. In most sites the tissues surrounding capillaries are not under very great tension; hence, a relatively low hydrostatic pressure in the capillaries is sufficient to drive tissue fluid out through their walls at their arterial ends. Correspondingly, the tissue substance in which blood vessels are embedded is under so little tension that venules are not compressed, even though the hydrostatic pressure within them is extremely low. However, surrounded by a tough, inelastic, fibrous tunic, the contents of the eye are under constant tension; the usual intra-ocular pressure ranges from about 20 to 25 mm. of mercury. This requires, then, that the blood within the capillaries of the eye be under a considerably greater hydrostatic pressure than the general intra-ocular pressure if the osmotic pressure of the colloids of the plasma is to be overcome and tissue fluid (aqueous humor) elaborated. Furthermore, it requires that the blood in intra-ocular veins also be under considerable hydrostatic pressure; otherwise, the veins within the eye would be collapsed by the intra-ocular pressure.

Although it is possible that any capillaries close to the anterior or the posterior chambers could contribute to the formation and the absorption of aqueous humor, it is highly probable that the capillaries of the ciliary processes, and to a much lesser extent those at the back of the iris, elaborate most of it. It is not unlikely that the hyaluronic acid of the aqueous is also formed in the delicate connective tissue that forms the cores of the ciliary processes. The most important mechanism for the absorption of aqueous humor is situated in the angle of the iris and will be described presently.

It is to be noted that, since the fibrous tunic of the eye cannot stretch and since structures within the eye are normally of a constant size and incompressible, a normal intra-ocular pressure depends on a proper balance between the formation and the absorption of aqueous humor. If conditions should develop in the anterior part of the eye which in another part of the body would cause edema, for example, interference with the absorption of tissue fluid, the eye cannot swell; instead, the intra-ocular pressure becomes increased. An increase in intra-ocular pressure, sufficient to be incompatible with the continued health of the eye, constitutes the condition termed *glaucoma*, and it is obvious that the treatment of the condition would be directed toward increasing the absorption of aqueous humor and/or decreasing its production.

Although under certain conditions aqueous humor can be produced very rapidly and removed very rapidly, it appears that under normal conditions it is formed and absorbed very slowly, probably at about the rate of 2 cu. mm. a minute. After aqueous humor is formed it passes from the posterior chamber between the lens and the iris to enter the anterior chamber (Fig. 31-11). There it moves toward the angle of the iris, where most of it enters the trabecular spaces (Fontana), from which it is absorbed into the canal of Schlemm.

The canal of Schlemm (Fig. 31-9) probably has no direct communication with the trabecular spaces except perhaps very fine pores that can be seen only with the EM (see Holmberg, Garron, Speakman); hence, aqueous humor, to enter the canal, probably must pass through a delicate membrane, including the endothelium lining the canal. The canal contains aqueous humor during life; this drains outwardly through *collector trunks* in the sclera. These pass out under the bulbar conjunctiva where they are known as *aqueous veins* because they contain aqueous humor; in this position they may be seen with a slit lamp during life. The aqueous veins connect with blood-containing veins so that eventually aqueous humor is emptied into the venous system. Interference with the flow of aqueous humor in the collector trunks and the aqueous veins may be a factor in glaucoma. After death, blood may back up into the aqueous and the collecting veins and into the canal of Schlemm so that it may be seen in these sites in sections.

**The Vitreous Body.** The vitreous body is a mass of transparent gelled amorphous intercellular substance; the cells responsible for its formation are not known with certainty. It is bounded by the internal limiting membrane of the retina, the lens and the posterior zonular membrane (Fig. 31-6). In addition to transmitting rays of light, its bulk helps, anteriorly, to hold the lens in place, and posteriorly, to keep the inner coat of the retina in apposition with the outer pigmented coat. If vitreous is lost, as occurs unavoidably in some surgical procedures, the 2 latter coats of the retina may become separated.

The vitreous, as has been shown by Adler, also plays a part in the metabolism of the retina, allowing the transfer of metabolites through it.

Through the vitreous body runs Cloquet's canal, the remnant of the primitive hyaloid system or primary vitreous (Fig. 31-7, 4). Cloquet's canal runs from the papilla toward the posterior surface of the lens and is usually inconspicuous in life. In some instances the primitive hyaloid structures persist and may interfere with vision.

The vitreous is denser at its periphery. The dense peripheral vitreous, while it is adherent to the internal limiting membrane of the retina

over all its area, is particularly adherent at the papilla. It is also adherent to the posterior surface of the lens near its edge.

COMPOSITION OF THE VITREOUS BODY. The vitreous body is of the nature of a hydrophilic colloidal system. The dispersed phase of the system probably consists both of a complex protein (vitrein) which has pronounced hygroscopic qualities and *hyaluronic acid*. The dispersion medium of the system in a sense may be thought of as aqueous humor; in any event, it contains the crystalloids normally dissolved in aqueous humor. Under normal conditions the vitreous humor is gelled. It is very easily denatured by drying or fixation, and it then exhibits a fibrillar structure that may be seen with the light microscope. However, such fibrillar structure as it possesses during life and imparted to it by its molecular constitution cannot be seen with the ordinary light microscope. It was believed that lost vitreous was not replaced, but Pirie has shown that it re-forms in rabbits.

**The Retina.** In learning the layers of the retina the student should understand clearly that the terms "inner" and "outer" are used (as they are with regard to the layers of the wall of the eye) not with reference to the body as a whole but with regard to the *center* and the *exterior* of the eye. Hence, the inner of any 2 layers of the wall of the eye or of any 2 layers of the retina itself is the layer closer to the center of the eye. Moreover, the student should realize that from the study of skin and mucous membranes a habit of thinking of the layer next to the free surface of a membrane as its outer layer may have become established. Such a habit leads to difficulty in the study of the eye, for the free surface of the retina (the layer next to the vitreous body) is the *inner* layer of the retina and *not* its outer layer.

It will be recalled that the retina develops from the optic vesicle (an outgrowth from the brain) and that it is at first constituted of 2 main layers because the anterior wall of the optic vesicle (Fig. 31-7, 1) becomes invaginated backward into its posterior half to make a 2-layered optic cup (Fig. 31-7, 2, 3 and 4). It is the inner layer of the optic cup that develops into the nervous portion of the retina. The outer wall of the cup does not develop into nervous tissue but instead into a layer of

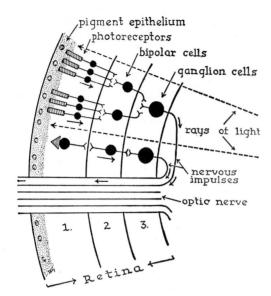

FIG. 31-12. Diagram showing the arrangement of the 3 layers of neurons in the retina. Observe that the light and the nervous impulses travel in opposite directions.

pigmented epithelium. The cells of this layer are of a somewhat flattened cuboidal shape (Fig. 31-14) when seen in profile and hexagonal when seen in full face. They contain a pigment which is probably an unusual type of melanin called *fuscin* (L., dusky) (Figs. 31-13 and 31-14). It has been reported that these cells, in embryonic life before they come to contain pigment, are dopa-positive; hence, there is reason for assuming that they make the pigment they contain.

The retina is commonly described as consisting of 10 layers. These are labeled from the outside in (Figs. 31-13 and 31-14). Therefore, the first layer of the retina is the layer of pigmented epithelium, the layer that develops from the original outer layer of the optic cup. This layer, it should be noted, becomes more firmly attached to the choroid than to the inner and nervous part of the retina from which, it must be remembered, it was originally separated by a cleft. Consequently, when eyes are removed for histologic study, the nervous portion of the retina commonly becomes detached from the layer of pigment epithelium, which remains adherent to the choroid (Fig. 31-17). The nervous part of the retina is 0.4 mm. thick posteriorly but thins out anteriorly to half this thickness.

Before considering the microscopic structure of the other 9 layers of the retina, it is helpful to recall that the cell bodies of most afferent neurons in the body are confined to cerebrospinal ganglia which, though close to the C.N.S., are not actually in the C.N.S. However, axons from these ganglion cells enter the C.N.S. to synapse there with connector neurons which in turn synapse with still others and so on. The neurons in the afferent chains sooner or later make connections with those of efferent chains, and so reflex phenomena are possible.

The arrangements with regard to the photoreceptor cells are quite different from the usual arrangement described above. The cell bodies of the photoreceptors are not disposed in ganglia but in the substance of the retina. Furthermore, the cell bodies of the first 2 neurons of the afferent chains that lead from the photoreceptors are also disposed in the retina (Fig. 31-12). If it is remembered that the retina is an outgrowth from the brain this does not seem so remarkable, for since connector neurons are confined to the tissue of the C.N.S. and since tissue of the C.N.S. migrates, as it were, into the retina, during embryonic development, the presence of connector neurons in the retina might be expected.

However, it might be expected that the photoreceptor cells would be present in the innermost layer of the retina because this is the first layer of the membrane that is struck by light after it passes through the vitreous body. Indeed, in some invertebrates this arrangement is to be found. But in vertebrates the photoreceptors are placed in the *outer part* of the retina, at right angles to its surface, so that their free ends abut on the first layer of the retina, the layer of pigmented epithelium.

With these few points in mind, Figure 31-12 should be consulted. In this diagram the layer of photoreceptors may be seen, apposed to the layer of pigment epithelium. Each cell in the photoreceptor layer has a dendritic process that extends from the region of the nucleus of the cell outwardly to the layer of pigmented epithelium. The dendritic processes of the photoreceptors are of 2 general shapes, resembling either *rods* or *cones*, and accordingly, the photoreceptors are classified as rod or cone

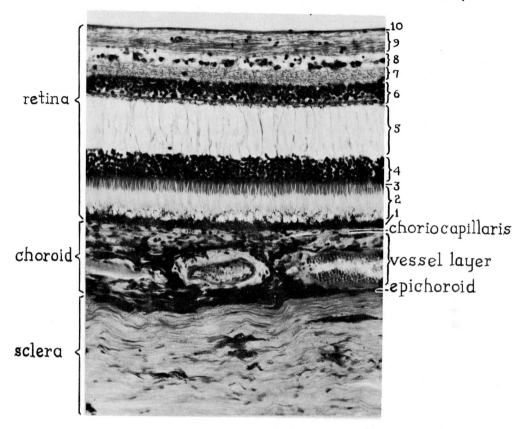

retina

choroid

sclera

10
9
8
7
6
5
4
3
2
1

choriocapillaris

vessel layer

epichoroid

FIG. 31-13. Low-power photomicrograph of a portion of a section cut through the wall of the eye, showing the retina, the choroid and some of the sclera. The numbers refer to the layers of the retina, which are described in the text and shown in diagrammatic form in Figure 31-34.

cells. The axons of the rod and cone cells pass inwardly and synapse with the dendrites of the nerve cells in the middle part of the retina. These, of course, are to the inside of the rod and cone cells and are called *bipolar cells* because they have only 2 processes: a dendrite and an axon (Fig. 31-12). The axons of the bipolar cells pass inwardly and synapse with the dendrites of the third and innermost layer of nerve cells, the *ganglion cells*. (It should be understood that these cells do not constitute a ganglion; they are called ganglion cells because they are large and otherwise resemble the nerve cells of ganglia.) The axons of the ganglion cells pass inwardly to the inner border of the retina, where they turn at right angles toward the site of exit of the optic nerve, running in the innermost part of the retina, parallel with the surface of the eye (Fig. 31-12).

To affect the rod- and cone-shaped processes of the photoreceptors, light from the vitreous must pass through the inner 2 layers of nerve cells of the retina and through the cell bodies of the photoreceptors themselves. Then, when the light reaches the rod- and cone-shaped dendritic processes of the photoreceptors and nervous impulses are set up, the nervous impulses must pass in the reverse direction, *inwardly*, through the bipolar and ganglion cells to the innermost part of the retina and from here, along the axons of the ganglion cells, to the site of exit of the optic nerve. Obviously, for this arrangement to be functional, the nerve cells and their processes that are situated to the inner side of the rod- and cone-shaped dendritic processes of the photoreceptors must be readily permeable to light.

Having gained some knowledge of the ar-

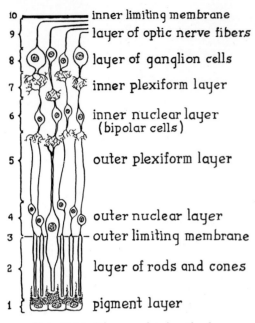

10 ─── inner limiting membrane
9 { ─── layer of optic nerve fibers
8 { ─── layer of ganglion cells
7 { ─── inner plexiform layer
6 { ─── inner nuclear layer
        (bipolar cells)
5 { ─── outer plexiform layer
4 { ─── outer nuclear layer
3 { ─── outer limiting membrane
2 { ─── layer of rods and cones
1 { ─── pigment layer

FIG. 31-14. Diagram showing the layers of the retina.

rangement of the nerve cells in the retina, it is easy to learn the 10 classic layers of this structure. These will now be described, and in the following description, the photomicrograph of the retina (Fig. 31-13) and the diagram of it, in both of which the layers are numbered (Fig. 31-14), should be consulted with reference to each layer described.

Layer 1, the *layer of pigment epithelium*, consists of the layer of pigmented epithelial cells (already described) that develops from the outer layer of the optic cup (see also Fig. 31-7).

Layer 2, the *layer of rods and cones*, consists of the dendritic cytoplasmic processes of the photoreceptors. These are packed closely together, side by side, in this layer, looking like bacilli; hence, this layer is sometimes known as the bacillary layer.

Layer 3, the *external limiting membrane*, is a sievelike membrane composed of the inward extensions of what are termed Müller's fibers. These are neurologic elements in the retina; the cells that are responsible for these fibers are in the same layer as the bipolar cells, as will be described presently. The dendritic processes of the photoreceptors extend through the holes in the sievelike external limiting membrane and are thereby supported.

Layer 4, the *outer nuclear layer*, is the layer formed by the closely packed nuclei of the photoreceptors.

Layer 5, the *outer plexiform layer*, is the layer in which the axons of the rods and the cones synapse with the dendrites of the bipolar cells. Since several rods may synapse with a single bipolar cell and, except at the fovea (to be described later), more than one cone, the dendrites of bipolar cells must branch into terminal networks; these, suitably stained, give this layer a plexiform appearance.

Layer 6, the *inner nuclear layer*, consists of the nuclei of the bipolar cells and the nuclei of the cells that account for Müller's supporting fibers. The nuclei of the latter have more cytoplasm surrounding them than have the nuclei of the bipolar cells; furthermore, they tend to lie in the outer part of the layer. To the inside of the layer of nuclei of the bipolar cells, the nuclei of some nerve cells of the association type, called *amacrine cells*, are present. Blood vessels, from the inner part of the retina, extend outwardly as far as this layer.

Layer 7, the *inner plexiform layer*, is the layer in which the axons of the bipolar cells synapse with the dendrites of the ganglion cells. The latter have fine networks at their terminations; these give the layer a plexiform appearance when sections are suitably stained.

Layer 8, the *ganglion cell layer*, is the layer in which the large ganglion cells are disposed, together with some neuroglial cells. Retinal blood vessels are also present in this layer.

Layer 9, the *layer of nerve fibers*, consists of the axons of the ganglion cells; these, after having reached the innermost part of the retina, have turned at right angles to pass thereafter parallel with the inner surface of the retina toward the site of exit of the optic nerve. To aid transparency they possess neither myelin sheaths nor sheaths of Schwann. Spiderlike neuroglial cells, the inner branches of Müller's fibers and blood vessels are also present in this layer.

Layer 10, the *inner limiting membrane*, is a delicate homogeneous structure composed of the fused, inwardly directed, terminations of Müller's fibers.

**The Fine Structure of Rods and Cones.** As has already been explained, the light that reaches the light-sensitive cone- or rod-

FIG. 31-15. Schematic drawing of rods in the guinea pig retina. Labeling has been added. For description see text. (Sjöstrand, F. S.: The electron microscopy of the retina *in* Smelser, G. K. (ed.): The Structure of the Eye, New York, Acad. Press)

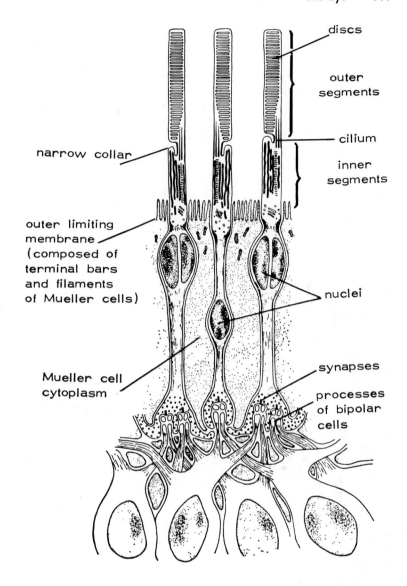

shaped processes of the photoreceptors (which are in layer 2 of Figs. 31-13 and 31-14) must pass from the vitreous through the 2 inner layers of nerve cells of the retina and then also through the cell bodies of the photoreceptors themselves. We shall now describe the structure of the photoreceptors in more detail and mention something of what is known of their function.

In reading the following it will be helpful to refer to Figure 31-15. This figure differs from preceding ones, not only in showing more detail but also by the fact that whereas in Figures 31-13 and 31-14 the outer layer of

the retina has been at the bottom, the light-sensitive portions of rods in this diagram are at the top.

Only the part of a photoreceptor which is farthest from the center of the eye is involved in the actual reception of light; this part of a photoreceptor is known as the "outer segment" and its fine structure will be described presently. Next is the inner segment, which is rich in mitochondria and rough-surfaced endoplasmic reticulum. The extremity of a photoreceptor that is nearest to the center of the eye carries the nucleus as well as a small swelling connected by synapses with processes of the bipolar cells to be mentioned below. Droz has shown that after injection of a radioactive amino acid, it is possible to see, by radioautography, that the inner segment synthesizes protein actively.

The junction between the inner and the outer segments is indicated by a narrow collarlike portion. On the inner segment side of this bottleneck there is a centriole from which a ciliumlike structure (labeled in Fig. 31-15) extends part way into the outer segment, presumably to provide it with rigidity. This structure contains the 9 peripheral and 2 axial filaments characteristic of the cilia in general and described in Chapter 8.

Most of the space in the outer segments of rods or cones is occupied by flat membranous disks that traverse the outer segments of rods or cones at right angles to their long axes. The flat membranous disks are stacked one upon the other but with spaces between them. Moreover, each disk has a space between its two membranous flat walls. According to Dowling, who has studied the disks in both the rods and the cones in the retina of the monkey, the disk membranes of the cones are about 50 Å in thickness whereas the membranes of the disks of rods are around 35 Å in thickness, except at their edges where they thicken into little buttonlike structures (left side of Fig. 31-16, *right*). The space between the two membranes of a disk is greater in cones than in rods, being 110 Å as compared with 40 Å in the cones, and the space between disks in cones is 180 Å as compared with 110 Å in rods. It is believed that the surfaces of the disks contains the substances which are the actual chemoreceptors of light.

In rods, the disks are associated with a substance known as rhodopsin. The absorption of light of various wavelengths by this substance follows a pattern identical with that of the sensitivity of the eye to low illumination. For this and other reasons, it is now accepted that rods are mainly active to collect light under conditions of twilight or low illumination. In fact, there are many rods, more than a hundred on the average, connected with each ganglion cell, so that small amounts of light received by each rod may add up and effectively pass on the small action potentials initiated by each rod, to the ganglionic cells. The manner in which the rod initiates an action potential is believed to be through a breakdown of rhodopsin to a retinene (an aldehyde form of vitamin A) and to the protein opsin. Whether this retinene can be transformed so as to reconstruct more rhodopsin is not clear. The evidence presented by Droz of a continuous synthesis of protein in the inner segment was completed by further radioautographic evidence that the new protein migrates to the outer segment. It was then suggested that the protein continuously supplied to the outer segment consists of new opsin to be built into rhodopsin by combination with the proper retinene.

As for the cones, there are 3 types, one mainly sensitive to blue light, one to green light, and the third to yellow light with some sensitivity to red light. It is believed that each one of the three types of cones has a special form of the visual pigment iodopsin, which would absorb the corresponding color and, in so doing, initiate an action potential, leading to color vision.

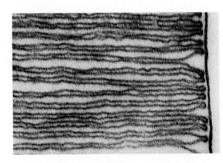 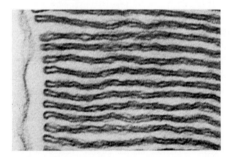

Fig. 31-16. Electron micrographs (× 100,000). (*Left*) Portion of foveal cone of monkey retina. (*Right*) Portion of outer rod segment of monkey retina. Description given in text. (Dowling, J. E.: Science *147*:57)

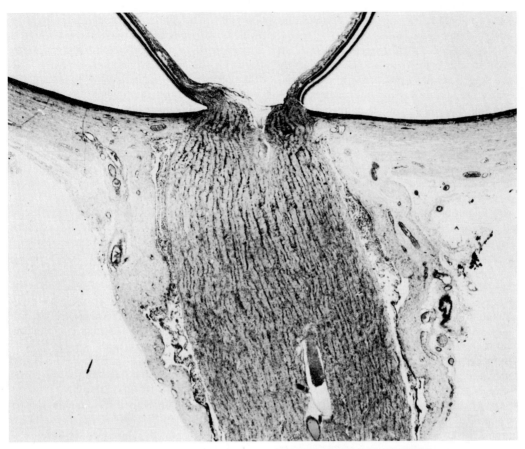

Fig. 31-17. Low-power photomicrograph of a section through the wall of the eye at the site of exit of the optic nerve. Observe that the inner layer of the retina is detached from the outermost layer of pigmented epithelium. Separation commonly occurs along this line when eyes are fixed and sectioned.

Since the layer of rods and cones contains no blood vessels whatsoever, all nourishment comes to this layer from diffusion and largely from the choriocapillares.

MACULA LUTEA AND FOVEA CENTRALIS. Very close to the posterior pole of the eye there is a little depression of the retina; here the retina is more yellow than elsewhere (after death); hence, it is called the macula lutea (yellow spot). The cells and the fibers of the inner layers of the retina diverge from the center of this area so that the photoreceptors in the central and most depressed part of this area, which is called the *fovea centralis*, are not covered to the same extent as the photoreceptors in other parts of the eye. No blood vessels are present in the retina over this area. The receptors here are all cones; moreover,

these, though longer than usual, are not so thick as usual; hence, more are packed into this small area than elsewhere. Therefore, this area is specialized in several ways for the greatest degree of visual acuity. Only the image formed in this area is interpreted clearly and sharply by the brain. For example, as one reads this page, although he is aware of words arranged in lines from top to bottom, he can see accurately only a very little at a time. In other words, in order that the brain may receive a detailed interpretation of this page, the fovea centralis, like the electron beam originating in the television picture tube, must scan the image of the page, letter by letter, word by word and line by line, from top to bottom. Fortunately, however, most words or groups of words can be recognized from experience merely by their general configuration, thereby saving much time.

Nerve fibers from this specialized area are provided with more room at the papilla (the site of exit of the optic nerve) and consequently are less heaped up and more securely arranged than are the other more converging retinal fibers. Hence, if edema should develop at the papilla, the fibers coming from the macular area are the last to be involved.

SENSITIVITY TO LIGHT. The sensitivity of the retina to stimulation by light is incredibly great. Hecht *et al.* have estimated that only a single quantum is sufficient to stimulate one rod and that 6 rods discharging into a common pathway may result in a nervous impulse along the path. There are practically 7 million cones in the human retina and 10 to 20 times that number of rods. Since the number of nerve fibers in the optic nerve has been estimated at from $\frac{1}{2}$ to 1 million, there is, of course, much overlapping of neurons.

**Optic Nerve.** Like the nerve fiber layer of the retina, the optic nerve at the papilla is composed of unmedullated nerve fibers, containing glial supporting tissue and some capillaries. At the lamina cribrosa, the nerve fibers, arranged in bundles, are interspersed by a fibrous meshwork extending from the sclera (Fig. 31-17). After piercing the lamina cribrosa, the nerve fibers become myelinated, thus swelling the size of the optic nerve (Fig. 31-17). They do not acquire a sheath of Schwann, and, consequently, they resemble the nerve fibers of the white matter of the cord or brain. The sheaths covering the nerve have already been described and are illustrated in Figure 31-6.

### INTERNAL APPEARANCE

It has been mentioned above that the eye is the window of the body, and that structures within the eye may be seen from the outside. Indeed, the eye is the only site where structures lying deep to the ectoderm of the body can be seen without artificial exposure or interruption of the integrity of the body surface. Since many of the functional and disease changes which occur in the body are reflected in changes in the structure of the eye, this fact is of great importance.

To look within the eye an instrument called the *ophthalmoscope* is ordinarily used. This provides a bright source of light, the rays of which are projected through the cornea into the patient's eye, thereby providing sufficient light for the operator of the instrument to see the fine structures in the back or fundus of the eye. With another instrument, the slit lamp microscope, the microscopic details of the conjunctiva, the cornea, the iris, the lens, the ciliary body and even the anterior portion of the vitreous can be studied in the living eye.

Figure 31-18 is a black-and-white representation of the fundus of a living right eye as viewed with the ophthalmoscope. The cup-shaped surface of the retina, gray in Figure 31-18, is red (the red reflex) in life because light is reflected back from the red blood cells in the vary large capillaries of the choriocapillaris. The whole background has a granular appearance, due in part to the irregular distribution of pigment in the retinal epithelium and in part to the coarse aggregation of pigment cells in the vascular layer of the choroid.

The unmedullated fibers of the retina (layer 9) converge at the site of exit of the optic nerve. Here, there is much heaping up of the retinal fibers. This constitutes what is known as the *papilla*. In this region the nerve fibers are loosely arranged; consequently, accumulation of tissue fluid in the nervous tissue of the retina results in an obvious swelling of the papilla; this is a valuable early clinical sign of certain pathologic conditions. Since the papilla is of a disklike shape about 1.5 mm. in diameter, it is often called the *optic disk*. It appears much larger when seen through the refracting media of the eye than it does if it is exposed. Because the white lamina cribrosa (white fibrous tissue) is pierced by gray nerve fibers and is supplied by a capillary network, the papilla has a pale pink color in contrast with the redness of the retina elsewhere. Should the capillaries become atrophied, the papilla appears gray, and the little perforations of the lamina cribrosa, now not so obscured, appear more prominent. Should the nerve fibers atrophy, the papilla becomes chalky white; this appearance may be exaggerated later by the proliferation of glial and fibrous tissue.

The central portion of the papilla, called the *physiologic cup*, is a funnel-like space created by the diverging nerve fibers. An in-

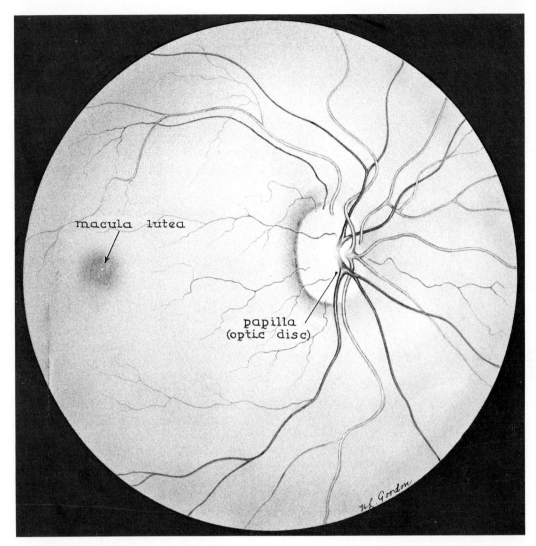

macula lutea

papilla
(optic disc)

H.E. Gordon

FIG. 31-18. Drawing, in black and white, of the appearance of the fundus of the right eye as seen through the ophthalmoscope.

crease in intra-ocular pressure (and other conditions) may displace the lamina cribrosa and its nerve fibers posteriorly. This results in the whole papilla becoming depressed and cup-shaped, a condition referred to as *cupping of the disk*.

The central retinal artery and vein make their appearance at the center of the physiologic cup, and, hugging its medial side (Fig. 31-18), they radiate over the inner surface of the retina, branching as they go (Fig. 31-18).

In placing the papilla inframedially, Nature reserved an area at the posterior pole of the eye, the *macula lutea* (Fig. 31-18), to sub-

serve the highest efficiency for visual acuity. The depressed central part of this area, the *fovea centralis* (L., central pit), lies about 2.5 papillary diameters laterally from the margin of the papilla and a little below its center. The size of the macula is variable but is usually only slightly larger or smaller than the papilla.

Naturally, large retinal vessels, which would otherwise interfere with vision, do not traverse the macula (Fig. 31-18). Instead, they pass well above and below it in wide curves; this aids the student in locating the macula with the ophthalmoscope. Smaller vessels extend from the curving blood vessels and also from

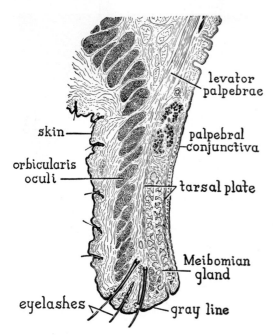

FIG. 31-19. Drawing of a section (low-power) cut perpendicularly through the upper eyelid. (After Duane, A.: Fuch's Textbook of Ophthalmology, ed. 8 revised, Philadelphia, Lippincott)

the medial side of the papilla itself into the macular area, but they never quite reach its center, which is left completely nonvascular. Because of yellow pigment in its superficial layers, the macular area appears yellow in the living (in red-free light) or on exposure after death. In ordinary white light it appears darker and redder than the remainder of the retina (Fig. 31-18). Its darker color is due to an increased amount of pigmentation in the outer pigmented retinal coat, and the increased redness is due to blood contained in the especially large choroidal capillaries disposed behind this area. The fovea centralis, viewed through the pupil, appears to be a minute bright point because light is reflected, as by a mirror, from its concave walls.

### ACCESSORY STRUCTURES (ADNEXA)

**Conjunctiva.** The conjunctiva is a thin transparent mucous membrane that covers the "white" of the eye as the bulbar conjunctiva (Fig. 31-10) and that lines the eyelid (which is not seen unless the lid is everted) as the palpebral conjunctiva (Fig. 31-19). The space

in the angle formed by the reflection of the palpebral conjunctiva from (and against) the bulbar is called the *fornix*.

The epithelium is characteristically stratified columnar in type with 3 layers of cells: a deep layer of columnar cells, a middle layer of polygonal cells and a superficial layer of flat or low cuboidal cells. The middle layer is absent in most of the palpebral conjunctiva. As the epithelium approaches the lid margin it changes to stratified squamous in type; this merges with the epidermis of the skin. Scattered through the conjunctival epithelium are mucus-secreting goblet cells. Near the limbus the epithelium of the bulbar conjunctiva becomes stratified squamous in type and is provided with deep papilla. It is continuous with the epithelium of the cornea.

The substantia (lamina) propria of the conjunctiva consists of delicate fibrous connective tissue; this is particularly loose over the sclera. In it are scattered accumulations of lymphocytes; these form nodules near the fornices. The substantia propria, except in the lid, merges into a more deeply situated and thicker meshwork of collagenous and elastic connective tissue.

The palpebral fissure is the space between the free margins of the 2 lids (Fig. 31-10). At the medial end of the palpebral fissure is a little lake of tears, the lacus lacrimalis. A free fold of conjunctiva, the concave border of which faces the pupil, is present at the medial end of the palpebral fissure; this is called the *plica semilunaris* (Fig. 31-10), and it is probably homologous to the nictitating membrane of birds. In the very angle of the palpebral fissure at its medial end, a little fleshy mass, the *caruncle* (Fig. 31-10), protrudes; developmentally, this is a detached portion of the marginal part of the lower lid; hence, it contains a few striated muscle fibers as well as a few hair follicles and sebaceous glands.

**Eyelids.** Each eyelid is covered on its anterior surface with delicate skin; this contains the follicles of some very fine hairs and some sebaceous and sweat glands (Fig. 31-19). The dermis is of an unusually loose texture, and the subcutaneous tissue, deep to it, in members of the white races, contains almost no fat. The keratin of the epidermis gradually thins out as the skin approaches the free margin of the eyelid, and here the epidermis becomes continuous with the epithelium of the palpebral conjunctiva, which has already been described as lining the inner (posterior) side of the lid (Fig. 31-19).

Each lid is reinforced with a plate of dense connective tissue, the *tarsal plate*. This is placed in the posterior part of the lid so that the palpebral conjunctiva is apposed to its posterior surface (Fig. 31-19). The secretory portions of long, vertically disposed, complex sebaceous glands, called *meibomian glands*, are embedded in the tarsal plate; these open onto the posterior part of the free margin of the lid (Fig. 31-19). Should one of these glands become infected, a painful pealike swelling develops in the lid.

Deep to the skin covering the anterior surface of the lid are bundles of striated muscle fibers of the orbicularis oculi muscle (Fig. 31-19). Some of the collagenic fibers from the aponeurosis of the levator palpebrae muscle pass between these bundles to be inserted into the skin that covers the eyelid. Others connect with the tarsal plate, and still others continue toward the margin of the lid in front of the plate. This latter sheet of connective tissue becomes more areolar as it approaches the margin of the lid, which it reaches to form the gray line, a surgical landmark of some importance. Along this gray line the lid may be split surgically, opening up the submuscular space known to the ophthalmologist as the *intermarginal space*.

The hair follicles of the eyelashes slant anteriorly as they pass to the surface. They are arranged in 3 or 4 rows, just ahead of the gray line. They are provided with sebaceous glands; these are termed the glands of Zeis. Between the follicles, the sweat glands of Moll are disposed. A sty is the result of the infection of either type of gland.

**Tear Glands.** Tears are produced by the lacrimal gland and several accessory tear glands. The lacrimal gland lies in the superolateral corner of the bony orbit. It is divided by the lateral edge of the levator palpebrae muscle into 2 lobes: a deep orbital lobe and a superficial palpebral lobe. Something less than a dozen ducts run from the gland to empty along the superior fornix. Most of the ducts from the orbital lobe, to reach their termination, pass through the palpebral lobe. Small accessory tear glands, the glands of

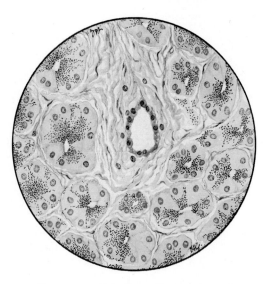

FIG. 31-20. Drawing of a portion of a section (high-power) of the lacrimal gland, showing secretory units and a duct.

Krause, are scattered along both fornices, but they are more numerous in the upper one. Still smaller glands are present in the caruncle. It is of interest that the eye may remain healthy in the absence of the lacrimal gland; this suggests that the function of the gland is to some extent that of providing floods of tears on special occasions.

The tear glands develop from the conjunctiva and are of the serous compound tubulo-alveolar type. The secretory cells are of a pyramidal columnar form and contain both fat droplets and secretion granules (Fig. 31-20). The secretory units are surrounded by myoepithelial cells which lie to the inside of the basement membrane.

The secretion of the tear glands is slightly alkaline. In addition to various salts, it contains an enzyme, lyzozyme, which is bactericidal. Tears, spread evenly over the cornea and the conjunctiva by the blinking of the lids, keep the surface of the cornea and the conjunctiva moist; this, as noted before, is an essential function. Floods of tears assist in washing foreign particles from the conjunctival sacs and the cornea.

DRAINAGE OF TEARS. On the free margin of each lid, near its medial end, is a little papilla called the *lacrimal papilla*. A small opening, which, however, can be seen with the naked

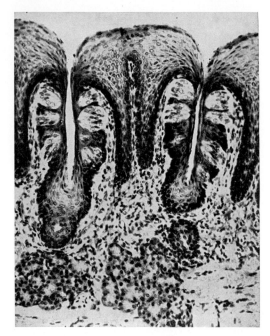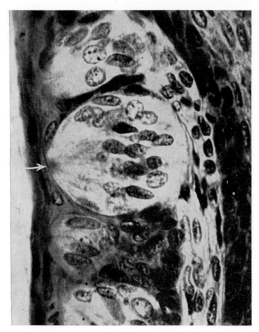

FIG. 31-21. (*Left*) Low-power photomicrograph of a portion of a section cut at right angles to the upper surface of the tongue of a rabbit in the region of the foliate papillae. These papillae, which are well developed only in certain animals, provide an especially good opportunity for seeing taste buds, which are numerous in this illustration. (*Right*) High-power photomicrograph of a taste bud in the epithelium of the side of a foliate papilla of a rabbit. The arrow occupies the approximate site where a pore (not shown) might be expected and it points to the pit (dark) into which the hairs of the neuro-epithelial cells project.

eye, exists near the summit of the papilla; this opening is termed the *punctum* and it leads into the *lacrimal canaliculus*. This is a small tube that runs first in the lid and then medially so as to meet its fellow from the adjacent lid in a little ampulla that extends outwardly from the lateral side of a tubular structure called the *lacrimal sac*. The latter descends as the *nasolacrimal duct*, to open through the lateral surface of the inferior meatus of the nose; by means of this mechanism, tears more or less continually drain into the nose. Should any part of this duct system become blocked, tears, produced at only an ordinary rate, run over onto the side of the face.

The puncta and the canaliculi are lined with stratified squamous nonkeratinized epithelium, and the lacrimal sac and nasolacrimal duct with 2 layers of columnar epithelium which contains goblet cells. The lacrimal papilla is rich in elastic fibers.

## TASTE BUDS

The nervous impulses responsible for the sense of taste are set up in little pale-staining bodies which resemble buds or little barrels and are arranged perpendicular to the surface in the epithelium of the mucous membrane of the mouth and the throat (Fig. 31-21). They are most numerous on the upper surface of the tongue, particularly along the sides of the grooves that surround vallate papillae. However, they are found on fungiform papillae and even in the epithelium between papillae. A few may be present in other parts of the mouth and in the lining of the throat. It is not unusual to see a taste bud in the epithelium on the laryngeal side of the epiglottis. They have been reported in other parts of the larynx.

A taste bud, like an onion, is constricted at both its ends. Moreover, taste buds, when seen in sections, appear to have a layered structure somewhat similar to that of an onion. This is due to the arrangement of their cells, of which there are 2 kinds: *sustentacular* cells and *neuro-epithelial* taste cells. The sustentacular cells are shaped like slices of cantaloupe; they are narrower at each of their ends than in their midsection, and they pursue a curved course from one end of the bud to the other. At the end of the barrel-shaped structure which reaches almost to the surface, they are arranged so as to surround a little central depression or *pit* which communicates with the surface by means of a fine passageway called the *inner taste pore* which extends through such epithelium as covers the end of the taste bud. The site of this is indicated on Figure 31-21 by an arrow, but the pore itself does not appear in the photomicrograph. (Pores are of such a small caliber that they show only occasionally in sections.) Neuro-epithelial taste cells are intermingled with sustentacular cells in the more central part of the bud. They are long narrow cells. The free end of each extends to the pit at the end of the taste bud, where it gives rise to a short hair that extends into the pit.

The sense of taste from the anterior two thirds of the tongue is mediated by way of the chorda tympani division of the facial nerve and from the posterior third by way of the glossopharyngeal nerve. Terminal fibers enter the deep ends of taste buds and end in intimate contact with the neuro-epithelial taste cells.

Any substance to be tasted must become dissolved in saliva and pass by means of a pore into the pit at the superficial end of a taste bud; here it affects the hairs of the neuro-epithelial cells in some fashion so as to cause a nervous impulse to be set up in the fibers associated with the neuro-epithelial cells. As is true of smell, there are only certain basic tastes: sweet, sour, salty and bitter, and perhaps alkaline and metallic. Doubtless, there are specialized receptors for each. These are not distributed evenly, so that some tastes are detected more easily in some parts of the tongue than in others. It seems incredible that the great variety of flavors of which we are aware are due to various combinations of these few basic tastes. Actually, it is easy to con-

fuse taste and smell to some degree, and many of the more exotic flavors are probably smelled rather than tasted.

## THE EAR

### INTRODUCTION

In beginning the study of this organ it should be explained that there is a certain amount of ambiguity about the meaning of the term ear. For example, the 2 delicately sculptured flaplike appendages that are attached, one to each side of the head, and termed ears in everyday speech, are, of course, only parts (the auricles) of the 2 organs known as ears by the anatomist. But even the anatomist is not precise about the meaning of the term ear because each ear, as we shall see, consists of 3 main parts (an external, a middle and an inner part), and each of these 3 parts is in itself termed an ear; hence, each (complete) ear is said to consist of an *external ear*, a *middle ear*, and an *inner ear*.

Before attempting to learn the structure of the various parts of the ear the student should understand that the ear is the organ where nervous impulses are set up that are responsible, not only for hearing, but for other senses as well. These include an appreciation of (1) how the head is orientated in space in relation to gravitational forces and (2) whether movement of the head takes place (the overcoming of inertia), or, if steady movement of the head is taking place, whether the rate or the direction of the movement is altered. It may seem curious that end-organs concerned in the maintenance of equilibrium are so closely associated with the end-organ for hearing in the body. Actually, however, in the evolutionary scale, the ear was an organ for permitting animals to maintain equilibrium before it was an organ for hearing; the latter function grew, as it were, in some fashion from the former.

It has already been emphasized that a set of mechanical contrivances could be built so that each would respond to a different type of "stimulus" by closing an electrical circuit. A variety of such contrivances is illustrated in Figure 21-7. Any good student, given the facilities of a physics laboratory, could easily build more. For example, it would be a simple matter to build one that would close a circuit

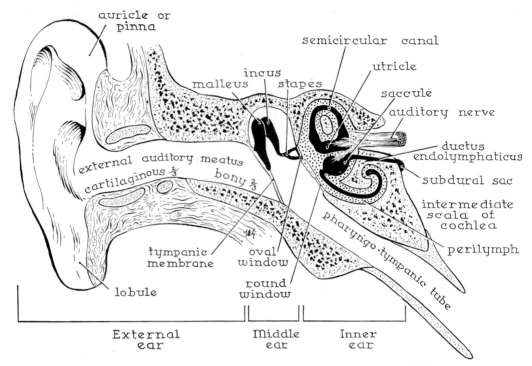

FIG. 31-22. Diagram of an ear, showing the relations of the external, the middle and the inner ear. (Redrawn and modified from Addison: Piersol's Normal Histology, ed. 15, Philadelphia, Lippincott)

if it were suddenly moved in a certain direction or, if it were in steady movement, if the rate of its movement were suddenly increased or decreased. All that would be needed would be a trough of water with a float at one end, which, on rising or falling, would close an electrical circuit. A sudden movement of the trough, in the direction of its long axis, would swish the water toward its back end, raise the float (if it were at that end) and so complete a circuit. Or, if the trough were in steady motion, with the water in it quite still, a sudden acceleration would produce the same effect, as everyone knows who has tried to hurry, while carrying a pail, full to the brim with water.

The student, then, may expect to find that a good amount of the structure of the ear is concerned with the "mechanical contrivances" that are present in it to permit sound waves, different positions in space and movement, to affect specific nerve endings (and these alone) in such a way as to set up nervous impulses which are then transmitted to the parts of the brain concerned in the interpretation of these sensations. However, before discussing the structure of these various arrangements in any detail, we shall first give a rough outline of the general structure of the ear and, as best we can, correlate the function of its chief parts with their structure.

### GENERAL STRUCTURE

The *external ear* consists of an appendage, the *auricle,* and a tube, the *external auditory meatus* (*meatus* = a passage or canal), which extends from the auricle into the substance of the skull (Fig. 31-22) to a tiny cavity in the petrous portion of the temporal bone, known as the tympanic cavity or middle ear (Fig. 31-22). The external auditory meatus, although it extends to the middle ear, does not open into it, because a membrane, called the *tympanic membrane* or *eardrum,* extends across the deep end of the external auditory meatus to form a partition between it and the middle ear (Fig. 31-22). This membrane, which thus forms a considerable part of the lateral wall of the middle ear, is of a suitable size and thickness and is maintained under a suitable tension to vibrate in accordance with sound waves that reach it by way of the auricle and the external auditory meatus.

Before discussing the general structure of the middle ear further, and explaining how the vibrations set up in the eardrum by sound waves are transmitted across the middle ear to the inner ear which lies still deeper in the petrous portion of the temporal bone, we shall comment briefly on the inner ear, for it is here that the special groups of nerve endings which are selectively stimulated by sound, changes in relation to gravity, and movement are located.

The inner ear consists of a series of membranous tubes that are disposed in various arrangements and planes, together with 2 membranous sacs with which the membranous tubes communicate (Fig. 31-22). This closed system of membranous tubes and sacs is filled with a fluid termed *endolymph*, and at appropriate sites, to be described later, neuro-epithelial structures, with special types of nerve endings, are arranged in the lining of the system. The whole system of membranous tubes and sacs is so like a maze that it is said to constitute the *membranous labyrinth* (*labyrinthos* = a maze). The membranous labyrinth is loosely fitted into a series of spaces and cavities in the bone; these are of a similar pattern to, though somewhat larger than, the membranous labyrinth. These tubular spaces and cavities, together with the thin layer of compact bone that forms their immediate walls, and in which the membranous labyrinth is loosely fitted, are said to constitute the *bony labyrinth*. Although in some sites the membranous labyrinth is attached to the periosteum that lines the wall of the bony labyrinth, the bulk of the membranous labyrinth is suspended in a fluid termed *perilymph* which fills all the space in the bony labyrinth that is not occupied by the membranous labyrinth.

The most expanded portion of the bony labyrinth lies deep to the bony medial wall of the middle ear; this part of the bony labyrinth is termed its *vestibule* because it is the hallway that would be entered by any microscopic visitor who entered the inner ear from the middle ear. There are no doors opening from the middle ear into the vestibule of the bony labyrinth, so any visitor from the middle ear would have to enter by way of a window.

There are two of these in the bony wall that separates the air-filled middle ear from the fluid-filled vestibule of the bony labyrinth; the upper is termed the *oval window*, and the lower one the *round window*. Both windows normally are closed, but in order to describe how they are closed we must digress for a moment.

It has already been explained how sound waves set the eardrum into vibration and that the eardrum constitutes a considerable portion of the lateral wall of the middle ear. A chain of 3 tiny bones, with joints between them, extends across the middle ear from its lateral to its medial wall (Fig. 31-22). The free end of the first bone of the chain is attached to the eardrum, and the free end of the last bone in the chain fits into, so as to close effectively, the oval window in the medial wall of the middle ear (Figs. 31-22 and 31-26). Hence, when sound waves set the eardrum in vibration, the chain of bones transmits these vibrations across the middle ear, and since the free end of the last bone of the chain does not fit rigidly into the window (beyond which is the perilymph of the bony labyrinth) but instead, a little like a piston in a cylinder, the vibrations are transmitted to the perilymph in the vestibule. However, fluid is incompressible; hence, every time fluid is pushed in at the oval window it must push out somewhere else. This occurs at the round window, for this is closed only by a membrane, and this has sufficient elasticity for this purpose. Having described the mechanical arrangements that exist in the ear to permit sound waves eventually to set up vibrations in the perilymph, we shall leave the matter of how these in turn affect nerve endings until certain other details of the bony and membranous labyrinth are considered.

Although the bony labyrinth (Fig. 31-23) has a complex form, it may be helpful to think of it as having 3 main parts. The first of these is the vestibule; this has already been described as its most expanded part which is disposed immediately medial to the middle ear. The other 2 main parts of the bony labyrinth may be regarded as 2 extensions of the labyrinth from the vestibule, and in these the bony labyrinth is tubular in form. The more anterior of the 2 tubular extensions of the bony labyrinth becomes wound into a spiral, the successive turns of which are of a decreasing radius

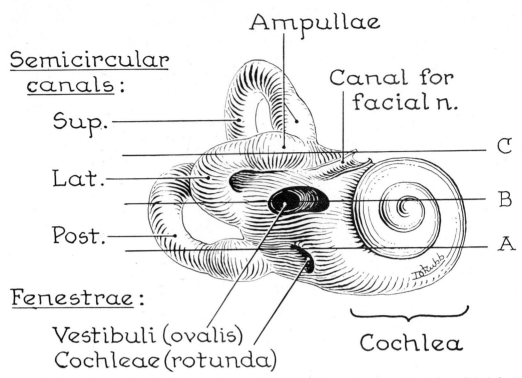

Ampullae

Semicircular
canals :

Sup.

Canal for
facial n.

C

Lat.

B

Post.

A

Fenestrae :

Vestibuli (ovalis)
Cochleae (rotunda)

Cochlea

FIG. 31-23. An anterolateral view of the bony labyrinth. The oval and round windows (labeled fenestrae) may be seen opening into the vestibule; the cochlea extends from the vestibule to the right, and the semicircular canals, to the left. (Grant, J. C. B.: Method of Anatomy, ed. 4, Baltimore, Williams & Wilkins; lines A, B and C have been added)

(Figs. 31-22 and 31-23). Since this coiled part of the bony labyrinth looks something like a snail's shell it is called the *cochlea* (L., snail shell). The more posterior of the 2 extensions of the bony labyrinth from the vestibule (actually this extension is regarded as a part of the vestibule) takes the form of 3 separate, round, bony tubes, each of which, on leaving the vestibule, follows a semicircular path so that each eventually returns to the vestibule (one may be seen in Fig. 31-22); hence, each tube communicates at both of its ends with the vestibule (Fig. 31-23). These bony tubes are referred to as *semicircular canals*, and it is of great significance that they be disposed in different planes, approximately so that the plane of each is at right angles to the planes of the other two (Fig. 31-23).

As noted before, the membranous labyrinth (Fig. 31-24) is comprised of a system of membranous tubes and sacs, and it is fitted loosely into the bony labyrinth. Actually, there are 2 sacs in the membranous labyrinth, and these are both present in the vestibule of the bony labyrinth. The more anterior and smaller of the two is called the *saccule* (*sacculus* = a small sac) and the larger and more posterior of the two, the *utricle* (*utriculus* = a little skin bag). The 2 sacs are in communication with one another by means of a fine membranous duct (Figs. 31-22 and 31-24).

As was explained before, the membranous labyrinth extends into all parts of the bony labyrinth. The membranous tube that extends into the cochlea is given off by the saccule. On entering the basal turn of the cochlea it becomes known as the *cochlear duct*. It is not, as might at first be imagined, a round tube, but instead it has more of the shape of a ribbon, particularly that of a thick wide ribbon that has been "ironed down" along one of its sides so that one side is much thinner than the other. Such a ribbon would be somewhat triangular in shape when seen in cross section.

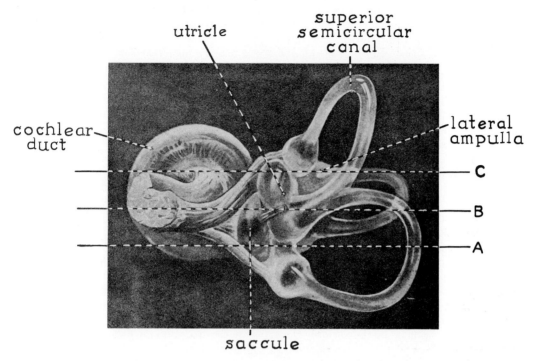

Fig. 31-24. Drawing of the right membranous labyrinth of a human adult (medial and posterior view). It shows the relation between the cochlear duct, the utricle, the saccule, the semicircular canals and the ampullae. (Spalteholtz, W.: Hand-Atlas of Human Anatomy, ed. 13, Philadelphia, Lippincott; lines A, B and C have been added)

The cochlear duct, of course, is not solid like a ribbon but is hollow and filled with endolymph (Fig. 31-28).

One side of the ribbonlike cochlear duct is attached to one side of the bony canal of the cochlea and the other side of the duct to the other side of the canal, so that the cochlear duct forms a rough shelf across the bony canal, splitting it into 2 parts along its whole length. In this fashion the cochlear duct ascends up the winding turns of the cochlea always keeping the part of the canal above it—and this is known as the *scala vestibuli* (*scala* = a stairway) (Fig. 31-28)—separated from the part of the canal that lies below it and which is known as the *scala tympani* (Fig. 31-28). Both the scala vestibuli and the scala tympani are filled with *perilymph*. (This is identical with cerebrospinal fluid and is in communication, in a way that need not be described here, with cerebrospinal fluid.) However, the cochlear duct keeps the perilymph in the scala vestibuli separated along the whole course of the

cochlea from the perilymph of the scala tympani. (Actually, there is a small opening between the scala vestibuli and the scala tympani at the tip of the cochlea, but this may be disregarded for the time being.)

It is obvious, then, that since the perilymph in the scala vestibuli and that in the scala tympani are not in free communication with each other, any vibrations in the perilymph in the scala vestibuli, to reach the scala tympani, would have to be transmitted through the thickness of the ribbonlike endolymph-containing cochlear duct. Now it so happens that the perilymph in the scala vestibuli connects with the perilymph that bathes the inner aspect of the oval window. This perilymph receives vibrations from the eardrum by way of the chain of bones, the last one of which fits into the oval window. Hence, the vibrations of the eardrum are transmitted up into the cochlea by means of the perilymph that extends from the oval window up into the scala vestibuli. However, as was noted before, fluid is incompressible; hence, the bone that fits into the oval window cannot push into the window unless the fluid in the bony labyrinth can push out somewhere else. It is of interest in this connection that the perilymph in the scala tympani is in free communication with that which bathes the inner aspect of the round window. Hence, vibrations transmitted into the oval window and through the perilymph of the scala vestibuli can be transmitted through the thickness of the cochlear duct into the perilymph of the scala tympani and from there to the round window, which "gives" sufficiently to permit the above-described mechanism to operate.

The above-described mechanism allows the vibrations set up by sound waves that strike the eardrum to be transmitted through the thickness of the ribbonlike but hollow cochlear duct along its full length. The end-organ for hearing consists of a narrow ribbon of special neuro-epithelial cells and nerve fibers that is disposed along the floor of the cochlear duct along its whole length. This long ribbonlike end-organ is called the *organ of Corti* (Fig. 31-28) and it is in it that the nervous impulses responsible for hearing originate when its special cells are stimulated by vibrations transmitted through the cochlear duct from the perilymph of the scala vestibuli into that of the scala tympani. In all probability, vibrations caused by high notes affect the receptors in the more basal part of the cochlea and those from low notes those in the terminal part of the cochlea.

From the foregoing, then, it should be clear that the more anterior tubular extension of the bony labyrinth (from the vestibule) houses the end-organ for hearing, and in a general way it may be understood that the special neuro-epithelial cells in the organ of Corti might be stimulated as a result of vibrations of the perilymph, set up by sound waves, being transmitted through the cochlear duct. We shall consider next the function of the more posterior extension of the bony labyrinth, the semicircular canals.

The semicircular canals (Fig. 31-23), like the cochlea, are filled with perilymph, but each contains, in addition, a membranous tube (part of the membranous labyrinth) which is filled with endolymph (Fig. 31-24). In a special expanded part of each membranous tube,

called its *ampulla* (Fig. 31-24), a little mound of neuro-epithelial cells called a *crista* (L., a crest) is present in its wall. The cristae react, in a manner somewhat similar to the float we described at the end of a trough of water, by setting up nervous impulses in response to a sudden movement, or if movement is in progress, to a change in the rate of movement. Since there are 3 of them, and since the membranous tubes that contain them are arranged in 3 different planes, they also react to a change in the direction of a movement. It is probable that, unlike the water in a trough, no current is set up in the membranous tubes in the semicircular canals or in the perilymph outside the membranous tubes when the head is moved, for the caliber of the tubes and of the canals is very small. Nevertheless, sufficient displacement of fluid does occur to affect the cristae when movement begins or ends, increases or decreases or when its direction is changed. The latter, of course, actually represents the beginning of a new movement in a different plane.

The end-organ that sets up the nervous impulses that are responsible for an appreciation of the position of the head in relation to gravitational forces is located in the *utricle*. It consists of a little mass of neuro-epithelial cells and nerve endings, together with some other features to be described presently, and is called a *macula* (L., a spot). A similar macula is also found in the saccule, but it is not thought that this one functions with regard to the sense of equilibrium; if anything, the sense organ in the saccule is probably related in some way to the sense of hearing.

## MICROSCOPIC STRUCTURE OF THE PARTS OF THE EAR

**Auricle.** In lower animals the auricle serves 3 purposes. Since it is movable and shaped like a funnel, it can be pointed at the source of a sound, acting as a natural ear trumpet to collect the sound waves and conduct them to the middle ear. With it the animal can determine the source of the sound by recognizing in what direction the auricle is pointed when the sound is loudest. Burrowing and aquatic animals can close the auricle over the meatus and in this way keep out dirt and water. In man, the auricle is a vestigial structure and can be moved but slightly; it is of little use

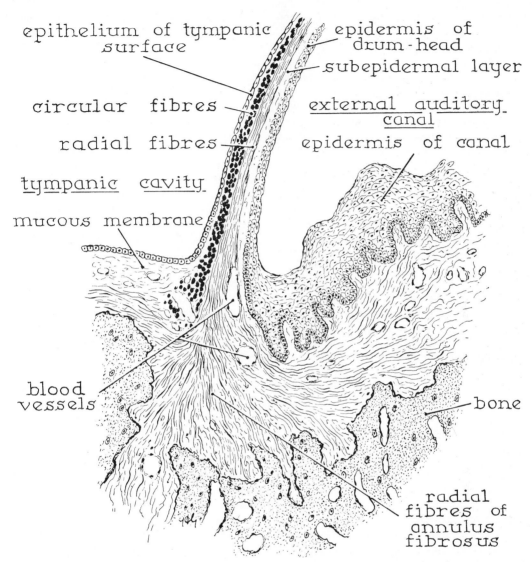

epithelium of tympanic surface

epidermis of drum-head

subepidermal layer

circular fibres

external auditory canal

radial fibres

epidermis of canal

tympanic cavity

mucous membrane

blood vessels

bone

radial fibres of annulus fibrosus

FIG. 31-25. Diagrammatic sketch of a part of the human tympanic membrane (low-power, cut in cross section). It shows the relation of the drum membrane to the external auditory canal and to the tympanic cavity and the attachment of the membrane.

as a sound-locating or protective structure, and its irregular and flattened shape (Fig. 31-22) would seem to detract from its function as a collector of sound waves.

The shape of the auricle is maintained by its content of yellow elastic fibrocartilage. It is easy to demonstrate the elastic quality of this cartilage by bending the auricle and then allowing it to snap back into position. The auricle is covered with skin on both sides. The subcutaneous tissue on the posteromedial surface is slightly thicker than that on the antero-lateral surface and contains some fat cells. Hair follicles with associated sebaceous glands can be found scattered through the dermis on both sides; these are most prominent near the entrance to the external auditory meatus. At the most dependent part of the auricle lies the *lobule*; this consists of a mass of fat, enclosed in connective tissue septa and covered externally with skin. The relative paucity of nerve endings and the rich capillary bed make the lobule a convenient site for obtaining blood for blood counts.

**External Auditory Meatus.** Since this canal leading to the drum is an invagination from the surface, it is lined with the stratified squamous epithelium of the skin. To prevent the canal from collapsing, its walls have rigid support. In the outer part this support consists of elastic cartilage continuous with the cartilage of the auricle; in the inner part of the meatus the support is provided by bone. In the outer one third of the canal there are many short hairs, and associated with their follicles are large sebaceous glands. In the submucosa deep to the sebaceous glands there are clusters of tubular *ceruminous* (*cera* = wax) glands; the ducts of these open either directly onto the surface of the canal or into the sebaceous ducts. The ceruminous glands are thought to be modified sweat glands, and their tubules are lined by tall cuboidal or columnar cells. The combined secretion of the sebaceous and the ceruminous glands, called *cerumen*, is supposed to lubricate the surface of the canal and the drum and to keep out insects. Often the cerumen is so efficient in this latter role that it also keeps out sound waves. Syringing the external auditory canal with water may be necessary to remove excesses of wax and to restore hearing. In the inner two thirds of the canal the ceruminous glands are confined to its roof.

**Tympanic Membrane.** The tympanic membrane is like a sandwich, the filling of which is collagenous connective tissue, and the bread, 2 epithelial coats (Fig. 31-25). The outer epithelial coat is continuous with the stratified squamous epithelium lining the external auditory meatus; it differs from it in having no papillae except short ones near the margin and also in that over the more central part of the drum it consists of only 2 layers of cells. The epithelium of the mucous membrane of the middle ear flattens out to exist as a single layer of low cuboidal cells; these form the inner covering of the drum. The middle fibrous filling of the drum consists of 2 layers of collagen fibers; the outer ones are dispersed radially and the inner ones circularly. The upper part of the drum is thin and flaccid because of a lack of collagen filling. Therefore, it is known as the *pars flaccida* or *Schrapnell's membrane*.

**Middle Ear.** The middle ear or tympanic cavity is a tiny epithelial-lined cavity in bone,

being roughly the shape of a red blood cell set on edge. The tympanic cavity is described as having 4 walls, a floor and a roof. It is about as high as it is long (about ½ inch), but is very thin; hence, its anterior and posterior walls are narrow. The lateral wall consists largely of the tympanic membrane, and the medial wall is the bone dividing the middle ear from the inner ear. There is a gap between the anterior and the medial walls for a canal, called the *eustachian tube*, which extends forward and communicates with the nasopharynx (Fig. 31-22).

The epithelium lining the cavity consists of simple nonciliated cuboidal cells with no basement membrane. The lamina propria is a thin connective tissue layer, closely adherent to bone. In some areas the cuboidal cells may become several layers thick. When infection occurs, the epithelium may become ciliated or may change to stratified squamous epithelium.

The middle ear houses 3 small bones or ossicles, 2 muscles and a nerve. When followed forward it leads to the pharynx through the *pharyngotympanic* or eustachian tube, and this communication makes it an air-containing cavity and offers a direct route for infection to reach it from the upper respiratory tract (Fig. 31-22). Indeed, middle ear infections are fairly common complications of head colds, particularly in children. Posteriorly, the tympanic cavity is continuous with a varying number of alveolar spaces in bone, the *mastoid air cells*. These too may become involved in retrograde infections from the nasopharynx.

OSSICLES. The 3 small bones of the middle ear cavity are the *malleus* or *hammer*, the *incus* or *anvil* and the *stapes* or *stirrup*. These bones were doubtless named in the days of the blacksmith shop and have little connotation for the modern student. The malleus is shaped like a crude hammer with a rounded head, a long handle and a spur in the region of the constricted neck which joins the head to the handle. The incus is shaped like a molar tooth with a body or "crown" and a vertical and a horizontal "root." The stapes, as its name suggests, is shaped like the stirrup of a riding saddle. It consists of a head, a neck, 2 limbs and an oval foot plate. The head of the malleus fits into the "crown" of the incus; the vertical "root" of the incus fits against the head of the stapes (Fig. 31-22).

The ossicles transmit the vibrations set up

in the tympanic membrane by sound waves to one of the two windows present in the medial wall of the middle ear. To do this, the handle of the malleus is firmly attached to the tympanic membrane and carries the vibrations to the incus; the incus transfers the vibrations to the stapes, causing the foot plate of the stapes, accurately fitted in the oval window, to rock to and fro. This carries the vibrations to the perilymph of the vestibule, as has already been explained. During this transfer, the amplitude of the vibration is decreased, but the force is increased because the ossicles are so arranged to exert leverage. The ossicles are atypical long bones, having no epiphyses and reaching approximately their full size during fetal life. The malleus and the incus have small central marrow cavities, while the stapes has none in the adult. The "ends" of these bones are covered with articular cartilage; they are held together by small ligaments, and the malleus and the incus are suspended by ligaments from the roof of the middle ear. The periosteal surfaces of these bones are covered by the mucous membrane of the middle ear cavity.

MUSCLES. The 2 muscles of the tympanic cavity are the *tensor tympani* and the *stapedius*. The tensor tympani muscle is housed in a bony groove (canal) above the cartilaginous roof of the eustachian tube; its tendon crosses the tympanic cavity mediolaterally to be inserted into the handle of the malleus. The stapedius muscle is housed in the posterior wall of the tympanic cavity (Fig. 31-26), and its tendon, issuing at the summit of a small projection of bone called the pyramid, is inserted into the neck of the stapes. The way in which these muscles affect the transmission of the sound waves by the ossicles is uncertain. The tensor muscle pulls the malleus inward, thus tensing the tympanic membrane and perhaps accentuating high-pitched sounds. The stapedius pulls the foot plate of the stapes outward, thus reducing the intralabyrinth pressure and perhaps making sounds of low frequency more audible. It has been found that reflex contractions of the stapedius occur during exposure to loud noise. Therefore, it seems that the stapedius plays a protective role, preventing too violent vibrations from injuring the special sense organs in the internal ear.

NERVES. The chorda tympani nerve traverses the middle ear in contact with the inner surface of the drum. It has no functional con-

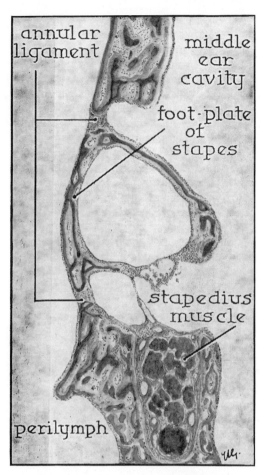

FIG. 31-26. Drawing of a horizontal section (low-power) of the foot of the stapes and the oval window of the right ear of a child taken approximately along the line B in Figure 31-23. It shows the relations of the stapedius muscle and the annular ligament to the stapes and the medial wall of the tympanic cavity.

cern with the ear. In addition, branches of many other nerves can be found in the mucous membrane and the bony walls of the middle ear. The facial nerve runs in a long canal in the medial wall of the middle ear. Its only concern with the ear lies in the fact that it supplies the stapedius muscle. The tympanic branch of the glossopharyngeal (Jacobson's nerve) is the great sensory nerve of the middle ear; the auricular branch of the vagus (Arnold's nerve) supplies the skin of the external auditory meatus. An attack of coughing or vomiting occasionally follows stimulation of the external auditory canal, for example, when a speculum is introduced into it. This is thought to be due to a reflex whose afferent arm is Arnold's nerve.

THE OVAL WINDOW. The foot plate of the stapes sits and is fitted accurately in the oval window. Its periphery is attached to the cartilaginous rim of the oval window by an annular ligament composed of strong collagenous and elastic fibers (Fig. 31-26). The mucous membrane lining the middle ear cavity is reflected from this onto the stapes. Through the oval window, vibrations are conducted to the perilymph of the vestibule.

THE ROUND WINDOW. Since fluid is incompressible, there must be some movable object which the perilymph can displace when it is thrust inward at the oval window. This movable object is a moderately elastic membrane which fills in the round window like a flexible windowpane. The membrane has a core of connective tissue and is lined on its middle ear surface by mucous membrane; on its inner side it is lined by the connective tissue of the perilymphatic space of the vestibule (Fig. 31-27).

**The Pharyngotympanic Tube.** The simple cuboidal epithelium of the middle ear cavity gives way to respiratory epithelium; i.e., pseudostratified ciliated columnar epithelium, in the pharyngotympanic or eustachian tube. There are rugae in the epithelial coat here, and goblet cells can be found in the lining of the cartilaginous part of the tube. Near the pharyngeal end, a mixed mucous and serous gland is present in the submucosa. Normally, the mucous surfaces of the tube are in contact, and the tube is open only during swallowing. The pressure in the middle ear can be adjusted

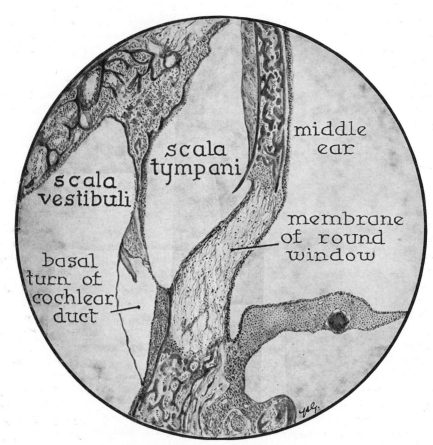

FIG. 31-27. Drawing of a section (low-power) through the round window of the right ear of a child. It shows the relation of the membrane of the round window to the tympanic cavity and the vestibule.

rapidly to that of the atmosphere only when this tube is open. Thus, when coming down in an airplane, one can prevent discomfort from too high pressure in the middle ear cavity by swallowing; this opens the tube and permits the pressure in the middle ear to become equalized with that of the atmosphere.

**The Mastoid Air Cells.** In early life the mastoid process and all the petrous bone surrounding the inner ear are normally filled with hemopoietic marrow. In the adult, small air pockets continuous with the middle ear cavity have replaced this marrow in the mastoid region. The process whereby the bone is invaded by these air sacs is known as *pneumatization*; it starts as early as the 3rd fetal month, with the greatest extension occurring between the 3rd year and puberty. However, the degree of pneumatization cannot be used to tell the age of the fetus or of a baby, since some 6-month fetuses show marked pneumatization. The degree of pneumatization of the mastoid area varies greatly from person to person, and some investigators believe that minor infections of the middle ear, common in childhood, favor obliteration of the air spaces. From a roentgenographic study on pneumatization in a large series of twins, it was concluded that heredity plays a much more important role than middle-ear infection in determining the extent to which the mastoid and the surrounding petrous temporal bone become pneumatized.

It is often of considerable importance to the surgeon to know the extent of pneumatization of the temporal bone in order that he may drain the pus from infected air cells. To do this he takes roentgenograms of the mastoid area. Unfortunately, however, the roentgenogram does not always distinguish between air pockets filled with pus and marrow spaces filled with fatty marrow, and the disease process can go undetected until the bony trabeculae are eroded.

The lining of the mastoid air cells is a thin mucoperiosteum; the cuboidal cells of the middle ear cavity here become flattened to a simple squamous type and lie adjacent to the periosteum of the mastoid air cells.

**The Cochlea.** The bony cochlea, as explained before, is part of the bony labyrinth and consists of a bony tube. In describing the cochlea further it is convenient to speak of it as if it were laid flat on its base; then it can be said that the bony tube of which it is composed winds spirally upward around a central pillar of bone called the *modiolus*. Actually, in position in the body, the apex of the cochlea is directed anterolaterally. However, in describing the microscopic anatomy of this structure, we shall assume that it has been laid flat on its base.

In the account of the general structure of the ear it was explained that the portion of the membranous labyrinth that extends into the bony cochlea was of the shape of a hollow ribbon flattened along one of its edges, and that its 2 edges were in apposition with the 2 sides of the bony canal in which it lies so that it separates the bony canal along its whole length into 2 long spiral chambers, the scala vestibuli and the scala tympani. Whereas it is true that the cochlear duct is more or less ribbonlike and that it extends from one side to the other of the bony canal in which it lies, it should be stated now that this explanation is somewhat simplified. The matter will now be elaborated further.

The relations of the cochlear duct, which is part of the membranous labyrinth, to the bony canal in which it lies, which is part of the bony labyrinth, and the position of the organ of Corti in relation to the floor of the cochlear duct, are best learned in a section cut through the center of the cochlea as a whole, but cut through a bony canal at some point along its spiral course at approximately right angles. A portion of such a section, showing a cross section of the *bony canal*, is illustrated in Figure 31-28, and this figure should be referred to frequently as the following description is read. The term inner, as used in the following description of the cochlea, refers to the central pillar of the cochlea, the modiolus, a portion of which may be seen housing the spiral ganglion (to be described later) at the bottom of the illustration.

The floor of the cochlear duct, in order to extend from the inner to the outer side of the bony canal of the cochlea, is not so wide as might be thought because both the outer and the inner walls of the bony canal of the cochlea bulge toward the center of the canal of the cochlea to support the floor of the cochlear duct and so make the distance it must bridge narrower. The bulge from the inner wall of the bony canal takes the form of a thin shelf of bone called the *osseous spiral lamina* (Fig. 31-28) because it winds up the modiolus like the thread on a screw. The bulge from the outer surface of the bony canal is not bone but is of the nature of a thickening of the periosteum that lines the canal; this line of thickened and primarily fibrous periosteum that

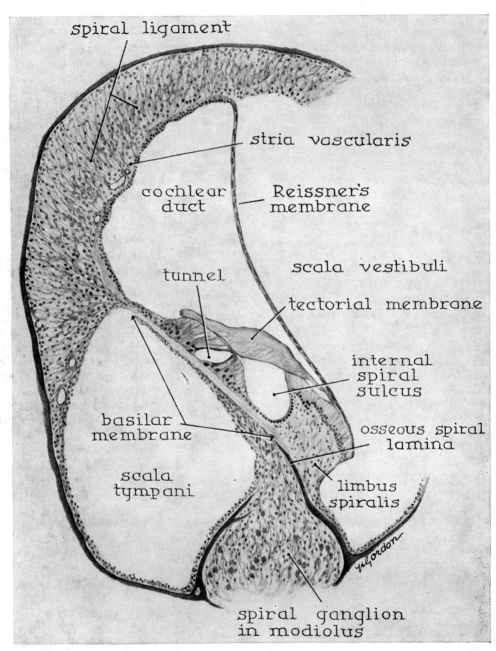

Fig. 31-28. Drawing of a portion of a section (low-power) of the bony cochlea cut parallel with the modiolus and through it along the line B in Figure 31-23. A section cut in this plane cuts the bony tube, as it pursues its spiral course, approximately at right angles at several different sites. Only one cross section of the bony tube is illustrated in this figure; it shows the cochlear duct extending across the bony canal, as well as the features described in the text.

winds up the turns of the cochlea is called the *spiral ligament* (Fig. 31-28). The floor of the cochlear duct, the *basilar membrane* (Fig. 31-28), bridges the gap between the osseous spiral lamina and the crest of the spiral ligament. The basilar membrane is made up of a dense mat of collagenic and some elastic fibers. The fibers of this membrane were once called *auditory strings*, and different ones were believed to vibrate selectively with different vibrations. The roof of the cochlear duct, in contrast with its floor, is thin, being composed of only 2 layers of squamous epithelial cells; this is called *Reissner's membrane* (Fig. 31-28). The outer wall of the cochlear duct is made up of the spiral ligament already described. The upper and larger part (the part nearer Reissner's membrane) is known as the *stria vascularis* (Fig. 31-30) and is rich in blood vessels which lie directly below a surface layer of deep-staining cuboidal cells. A small part of the outer wall of the cochlear duct, close to the attachment of the basilar membrane to the crest of the spiral ligament, is arranged to form what is known as the *sulcus spiralis externus*. Here, long protoplasmic processes from the surface epithelial cells extend down into the connective tissue of the spiral ligament. Moreover, Shambaugh has found secretory cells, which, though deeply buried in this area, have access to the surface; he suggests that they constitute a secretory mechanism for replenishing endolymph in the cochlear duct.

**The Spiral Organ of Corti.** Running along the whole length of the floor of the cochlear duct like a ribbon, and hence resting on the basilar membrane, is the highly specialized end-organ of the nerve of hearing. This is the spiral *organ of Corti* (Fig. 31-28). When the organ of Corti is sectioned at right angles to its long axis, a triangular central space can be seen. This is known as the *tunnel* (Fig. 31-28). Situated at the basal angles of this triangle, and forming part of its walls, are, in any given section, 2 darkly staining cells called the *internal* and the *external pillar cells*, respectively. On the outer side of the external pillar cell and on the inside of the inner pillar cells are *hair cells*, usually 3 on the outside and 1 on the inside. These cells are so named because hairs arise from their free surface and give them a ciliated appearance. Underlying and supporting the hair cells are columnar

cells, called *Deiter's cells*. Lateral to the outer hair cells is another collection of columnar cells; these are called *Hensen's cells*. Their function is unknown.

Except in the area of the organ of Corti the basilar membrane is lined by low cuboidal cells. To the inside of the organ of Corti the periosteum of the upper surface of the osseus spiral lamina forms a fleshy elevation, the *limbus spiralis* (Fig. 31-28), which bulges into the duct. The outer margin of this limbus presents a groove known as the *internal spiral sulcus* (Fig. 31-28); the edge of the limbus spiralis that overhangs this is called the *vestibular lip*. From this lip of the limbus a thin, homogeneous, jellylike membrane extends over, and is in contact with, the cilia of the hair cells of the organ of Corti. This is the *tectorium* or *tectorial membrane* (Fig. 31-28).

The lining of the scala tympani and of the scala vestibuli (apart from that provided by the basilar membrane, Reissner's membrane and the spiral ligament) is composed of the internal periosteum or endosteum of the bony cochlear canal.

The sound waves, conducted to the organ of Corti by the endolymph of the cochlear duct from the perilymph in the scala vestibuli, affect the hair cells in some way. The stimuli so produced are conducted by nerve fibers which begin as telodendria around the bases of the hair cells; these run in the basilar membrane, between the 2 thin plates of bone that constitute the osseous spiral lamina, to their nerve cells in the *spiral ganglion*, which is housed in the modiolus (Fig. 31-28). These peripheral fibers may be considered dendrites of the spiral ganglion cells. A single dendrite may have many peripheral branches and so receive stimuli from many hair cells. The bipolar cells of the ganglion send their central processes or axons (as the cochlear division of the acoustic nerve) to end synaptically in the cochlear nuclei of the brain stem.

**The Vestibule.** In the bony vestibule, filled with perilymph, are suspended the sacs of the membranous labyrinth—the utricle and the saccule. These 2 sacs, filled with endolymph, are joined by the short arms of a Y-shaped tube, the *ductus endolymphaticus*. The long arm of the Y extends through the petrous bone to the posterior cranial fossa, where it ends in a blind subdural swelling, the *subdural endo-*

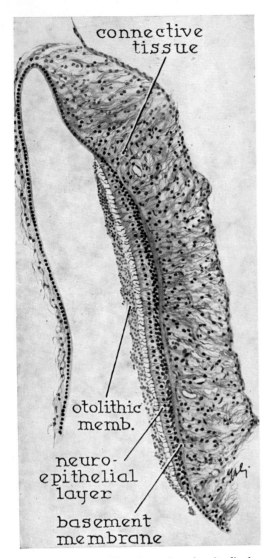

connective
tissue

otolithic
memb.

neuro-
epithelial
layer

basement
membrane

Fig. 31-29. Drawing of a longitudinal section (low-power) cut through the macula sacculi of a child along the line marked A in Figure 31-24. It shows the relationship of the macula to the lining of the saccule and the relationship of the otolithic membrane to the neuro-epithelial cells.

*lymphatic sac.* This is a safety valve for endolymph.

Into the utricle open the ends of the 3 membranous semicircular canals. Each has one expanded end or ampulla (Fig. 31-24). The nonexpanded ends of the superior and the posterior ducts have a common opening into the utricle, while the others open independently.

Hence, for the 3 canals there are 5 openings.

The utricle and the saccule are lined by flattened epithelial cells, usually called *mesothelium*, resting on a connective tissue membrane. The membranous sacs do not fill the bony vestibular space, nor do they lie free in this space, since fine strands of connective tissue connect them to the endosteum lining the bony vestibule. The saccule and the utricle each contains a flat, plaquelike sensory ending, called a *macula* (Fig. 31-29).

**Maculae.** A macula is somewhat similar cytologically to the organ of Corti. It consists of a thickened epithelium, containing 2 types of cells and separated from a connective tissue layer by a basement membrane. One type of cell, the neuro-epithelial cell, is plump, pale-staining and provided at its free end with a tuft of fine hairs. The other type is the supporting cell. These are packed around and between the hair cells. The hairs of the neuro-epithelial cells do not float freely in the endolymph but are embedded in a gelatinous membrane called the *otolithic membrane* (Fig. 31-29). This membrane contains many fine granules of minute crystalline particles composed of calcium carbonate and protein. Slight changes in pressure or tension on the otolithic membrane, produced by changes in the position of the head, affect the hair cells of the utricle. The stimuli so produced set up nervous impulses which pass into the peripheral terminal branches of the vestibular nerve.

If the otolithic membranes are removed from the maculae of the guinea pig by centrifuging, the animal loses its static sense of position. If both utricles are destroyed, the animal is unable to maintain its balance. It is possible to destroy the saccules in a dog without impairment of balance.

**The Semicircular Canals.** The membranous semicircular canals are lined with a squamous epithelium similar to that lining the saccule and the utricle. This also rests on a framework of connective tissue. The membranous tubes take up only a small part of the bony canal and are eccentrically placed, being in contact with the concave wall of the bony canal. Filaments of connective tissue join the tubes to the more distant parts of the canal, and perilymph fills the interstices.

The outer wall (most distant from the center of the rough circle made by each tube) of each ampulla presents a transverse ridge in its lining, the *crista*. This is composed of connective tissue, nerve fibers and capillaries. The surface epithelium of the crista is similar to that of the macula, possessing hair cells with large, oval, deep-staining nuclei and supporting cells packed closely, next to the basement membrane (Fig. 31-30). Resting on the surface of the crista is a membrane which closely resembles the tectorial membrane; this is called the *cupula* (L., a cup) (Fig. 31-30). It is a gelatinous noncellular membrane which covers the crista and projects up into the endolymph of the ampulla. The cupula differs from the otolithic membrane in that it contains no crystals. The function of the crista has already been explained.

Each crista is supplied by a branch of the vestibular division of the acoustic nerve. These branches of the vestibular nerve to the middle part of the membranous labyrinth are peripheral dendrites of nerve cells which lie in the vestibular (or Scarpa's) ganglion. Their central processes or axons constitute the vestibular division of the 8th nerve and end synaptically in the vestibular nuclei of the brain stem and in the cerebellum, where they initiate postural reflexes to maintain balance.

FINE STRUCTURE. The fine structure of the cristae ampulares of the guinea pig has been studied comprehensively with the EM by Wersall. His study embraces many matters, including the fine structure of the nerves and the nerve endings, and it represents a magnificent contribution.

### DEAFNESS

As can be seen from considering the anatomy and the physiology of the ear, anything which interferes with the transmission of the sound waves to the cochlear duct or damages the organ of Corti or the cochlear division of the 8th nerve will interfere with hearing. This may be a thing as easily removed as wax in the external auditory meatus or as permanent as nerve injury. A very serious cause of gradually increasing deafness in the adult is a disease which involves the bony case of the middle and the internal ear. This disease is known as *otosclerosis* and results in the formation of sharply circumscribed bony growths within the otic capsule. The site of predilection of this lesion is near the oval window. Whenever

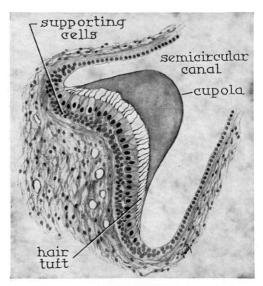

FIG. 31-30. Drawing of a cross section (low-power) cut through the ampulla (slightly collapsed) of the lateral semicircular canal of the right ear of a child along line C in Figure 31-24. It shows the crista ampullaris in cross section and the relation of the cupula to the hair cells of the sense organ.

the otosclerotic patches remain within the bony capsule, hearing is not impaired. When they spread beyond the periosteal or endosteal layer in the region of the oval window, they cause immobilization of the foot plate of the stapes. At operation, most of the clinically diagnosed cases show fixation of the stapes.

If this disease progresses to the point where it causes serious deafness, it may be relieved by operation. This operation, called *fenestration*, consists of drilling a hole in the bony medial wall of the middle ear over the lateral semicircular canal. The opening is covered by skin taken from the posterior wall of the external auditory meatus. It is probable that the direction of the sound waves in the inner ear is then reversed, that the waves are transmitted through the round window and that the displacement of fluid is permitted by the artificial window. Occasionally, however, in spite of the most careful operative technic the opening becomes closed by bone; we think that this is a result of regeneration from the osteogenic cells that line the bony canal through which the fenestrum is made.

## REFERENCES

### A GENERAL REFERENCE FOR FINE STRUCTURE OF VARIOUS PARTS OF THE SYSTEM OF SENSORY RECEPTORS

Rhodin, J. A. G.: An Atlas of Ultrastructure, pp. 144-166. W. B. Saunders Co., Philadelphia, 1963.

### DEEP AND CUTANEOUS SENSIBILITY

Adrian, E. D.: The Physiological Background of Perception, Oxford, Clarendon, 1946.

Duthie, H. L., and Gairns, F. W.: Sensory nerve-endings and sensation in the anal region of man, Brit. J. Surg. 47:585, 1960.

Lewis, T.: Pain, New York, Macmillan, 1942.

Loewenstein, W. R.: Biological transducers, Scient. Am. 203:98, 1960.

Merrillees, N. C. R., Sunderland, S., and Hayhow, W.: Neuromuscular spindles in the extraocular muscles in man, Anat. Rec. 108:23, 1950.

Nafe, J. P.: The pressure, pain and temperature senses in Murchison's Handbook of General Experimental Psychology, p. 1037, London, Oxford, 1934.

Olmsted, J. M. D.: The special senses, Ann. Rev. Physiol. 7:509, 1945.

Sanders, F. K.: Special senses, cutaneous sensation, Ann. Rev. Physiol. 9:553, 1947.

Takashi, M., Sakai, I., and Usizima, H.: On the terminal neural apparatus detectible in the retroperitoneum of man—a complex pattern of Pacinian corpuscles, Anat. Rec. 122:17, 1955.

### TASTE AND THE OLFACTORY ORGAN

Crozier, W. J.: Chemoreception in Murchison's Handbook of General Experimental Psychology, p. 987, London, Oxford, 1934.

Smith, C. G.: Changes in the olfactory mucosa and the olfactory nerves following intranasal treatment with 1 per cent zinc sulphate, Canad. M. A. J. 39:138, 1938.

———: Incidence of atrophy of the olfactory nerves in man, Arch. Otolaryng. 34:533, 1941.

———: Pathologic changes in olfactory mucosa of albino rats with "stunted" olfactory bulbs, Arch. Otolaryng 25:131, 1937.

———: Regeneration of sensory olfactory epithelium and nerves in adult frogs, Anat. Rec. 109:661, 1951.

### THE EYE

#### A General Reference on the Eye

Smelser, G. K. (ed.): The Structure of the Eye, New York, Acad. Press, 1961.

#### Special References on the Eye

Ascher, K. W.: Further observations on aqueous veins, Am. J. Ophth. 29:1373, 1946.

Ashton, N.: Anatomical study of Schlemm's canal and aqueous veins by means of neoprene casts; aqueous veins, Brit. J. Ophth. 35:291, 1951.

Aurell, G., and Holmgren, H.: Metachromatic substance in cornea with special reference to question of its transparency, Nord. med. 30:1277, 1946.

Basu, P. K., and Ormsby, H. L.: Identification of sex chromatin in corneal stroma cells for the determination of the fate of corneal transplants, Trans. Bull. 23:435, 1959.

Basu, P. K., Miller, I., and Ormsby, H. L.: Sex chromatin as a biologic cell marker in the study of the fate of corneal transplants, Am J. Ophth. 49:513, 1960.

Cook, C., and Macdonald, R. K.: Effect of cortisone on the permeability of the blood-aqueous barrier to fluorescein, Brit. J. Ophth. 35:730, 1951.

Davson, H.: The Physiology of the Eye, New York, Blakiston Division of McGraw-Hill, 1949.

DeRobertis, E.: Electron microscope observations on the submicroscopic organization of retinal rods, J. Biophys. Biochem. Cytol. 2:319, 1956.

———: Morphogenesis of the retinal rods; an electron microscope study, J. Biophys. Biochem. Cytol. (Supp.) 2:209, 1956.

DeRobertis, E., and Franchi, C. M.: Electron microscope observations on synaptic vesicles in synapses of the retinal rods and cones, J. Biophys. Biochem. Cytol. 2:307, 1956.

Dowling, J. E.: Foveal receptors of the monkey retina: Fine structure, Science 147:57, 1965.

Droz, B.: Dynamic condition of proteins in the visual cells of rats and mice as shown by radioautography with labeled amino acids, Anat. Rec. 145:157, 1963.

Duke-Elder, W. S.: Text-book of Ophthalmology, ed. 2, St. Louis, Mosby, 1938-1940.

Duke-Elder, W. S., and Davson, H.: The present position of the problem of the intra-ocular fluid and pressure, Brit. J. Ophth. 32:555, 1948.

Duke-Elder, W. S., Davson, H., and Maurice, D. M.: Studies on the intra-ocular fluids, Brit. J. Ophth. 33: part 1, Jan., 1949, p. 21; part 2, June, 1949, p. 329; part 3, July, 1949, p. 452; part 4, October, 1949, p. 593.

Friedenwald, J. S.: The formation of the intra-ocular fluid, Am. J. Ophth. 32:9, 1949.

———: Recent studies on corneal metabolism and growth, Cancer Res. 10:461, 1950.

Garrow, L. K., and Feeney, M. L.: Electron microscopic studies of the human eye, Part 2, Arch. Ophth. 62:966, 1959.

Greaves, D. P., and Perkins, E. S.: Influence of the sympathetic nervous system on the intraocular pressure and vascular circulation of the eye, Brit. J. Ophth. 36:258, 1952.

Holmberg, A.: The fine structure of the inner wall of Schlemm's canal, Arch. Ophth. 62:956, 1959.

Jakus, M. A.: Studies on the cornea: II. The fine structure of Descemet's membrane, J. Biophys. Biochem. Cytol. (Suppl.) 2:243, 1956.

Krause, A. C., and Sibley, J. A.: Metabolism of the retina, Arch. Ophth. (N.S.) 36:328, 1946.

Langley, D., and Macdonald, R. K.: Clinical method of observing changes in the rate of flow of aqueous humour in the human eye, Brit. J. Ophth. 36:432, 1952.

MacMillan, J. A.: Disease of the lacrimal gland and ocular complications, J.A.M.A. 138:801, 1948.

Mann, I. C.: The Development of the Human Eye, London, Cambridge Univ. Press, 1928.

Meyer, K.: The biological significance of hyaluronic acid and hyaluronidase, Physiol. Rev. 27:355, 1947.

Meyer, K., and Chaffee, E.: The mucopolysaccharide acid of the cornea and its enzymatic hydrolysis, Am. J. Ophth. 23:1320, 1940.

Oppenheimer, D. R., Palmer, E., and Weddell, G.: Nerve endings in the conjunctiva, J. Anat. 92:321, 1958.

Pease, D. C.: Infolded basal plasma membranes found in epithelia noted for their water transport, J. Biophys. Biochem. Cytol. (Supp.) 2:203, 1956.

Pirie, A.: The effect of hyaluronidase on the vitreous humour of the rabbit, Brit. J. Ophth. 33:678, 1949.

Polyak, S. L.: The Retina, Chicago, Univ. Chicago Press, 1941.

Reyer, R. W.: Further studies on lens development from the dorsal iris of Triturus viridescens in the absence of the embryonic lens, J. Exp. Zool. 125:1, 1954.

———: Regeneration of the lens in the amphibian eye, Quart. Rev. Biol. 29:1, 1954.

Sheldon, H.: An electron microscope study of the epithelium in the normal mature and immature mouse cornea, J. Biophys. Biochem. Cytol. 2:253, 1956.

Sheldon, H., and Zetterqvist, H.: An electron microscope study of the corneal epithelium in the vitamin A deficient mouse, Bull. Johns Hopkins Hosp. 98:372, 1956.

Speakman, J.: Aqueous outflow channels in the trabecular meshwork in man. Brit. J. Ophth. 43:129, 1959.

Tokuyasu, K., and Yamada, E.: The fine structure of the retina studied with the electron microscope, J. Biophys. Biochem. Cytol. 6:225, 1959.

Walsh, F. B.: Clinical Neuro-Ophthalmology, Baltimore, Williams & Wilkins, 1947.

Wanko, T., and Gavin, M. A.: Electron microscope study of lens fibers, J. Biophys. Biochem. Cytol. 6:97, 1959.

Wilmer, W. H.: Atlas Fundus Oculi, New York, Macmillan, 1934.

Wislocki, G. B.: The anterior segment of the rhesus monkey investigated by histochemical means, Am. J. Anat. 91:233, 1952.

Wolff, E.: The Anatomy of the Eye and Orbit, ed. 3, London, Lewis, 1948.

———: The origin of the malignant melanomata, Brit. J. Ophth. 32:72, 1948.

Woodin, A. M.: Hyaluronidase as a spreading factor in the cornea, Brit. J. Ophth. 34:375, 1950.

Wyburn, G. M., and Bacsich, P.: Survival of retinal elements in subcutaneous homografts, Brit. J. Ophth. 36:438, 1952.

Young, M. W.: Photoreception and phonoreception, Neurology 10:662, 1960.

## THE EAR

Anson, B. J., and Cauldwell, E. W.: The developmental anatomy of the human stapes. Ann. Otol. 51:891, 1942.

Bast, T. H.: A historical survey of the structure and function of the cochlea, Ann. Otol. 52:281, 1943.

Bast, T. H., West, R., Backus, O. L., Krasno, M., and Eyster, J. A. E.: Electrical currents associated with sound reception by the ear, Proc. Soc. Exp. Biol. Med. 30:638, 1933.

Davies, D. V.: A note on the articulation of the auditory ossicles and related structures, J. Laryng. Otol. 62:533, 1948.

Eggston, A. A., and Wolff, D.: Histopathology of the Ear, Nose and Throat, Baltimore, Williams & Wilkins, 1947.

Flock, Å.: The ultrastructure of the macula utriculi with special reference to directional interplay of sensory response as revealed by morphological polarization, J. Cell Biol. 22:413, 1964.

———: Electron microscopic and electrophysiological studies on the lateral line canal organ, Acta otolaryng. Supp. 199, 1965.

Flock, Å., and Wersäll, J.: A study of the orientation of the sensory hairs of the receptor cells in the lateral line organ of fish, with special reference to the function of the receptors, J. Cell Biol. 15:19, 1962.

Guild, S. R.: Comments on the physiology of

hearing and the anatomy of the inner ear, Laryngoscope *47*:365, 1937.
——: Hearing by bone conduction: the pathways of transmission of sound, Ann. Otol. *45*: 736, 1936.
Hagens, E. W.: Anatomy and pathology of the petrous bone, Arch. Otolaryng. *19*:556, 1934.
——: Pathology of otosclerosis, Arch. Otolaryng. *21*:297, 1935.
Jackson, C., and Jackson, C. L. (eds.): Diseases of the Nose, Throat and Ear, Philadelphia, Saunders, 1945.
Kimura, R., Lundquist, P. G., and Wersäll, J.: Secretory epithelial linings in the ampullae of the guinea pig labyrinth, Acta otolaryng. *57*: 517, 1963.
Kobrak, H. G.: Animal experiments on the mechanism of the acoustic irritation in the cochlea, Laryngoscope *47*:453, 1937.
Lempert, J.: Lempert fenestra nov-ovalis with mobile stopple, Arch. Otolaryng. *41*:1, 1945.
Lindsay, J. R.: Pneumatization of the petrous pyramid, Ann. Otol. *50*:1109, 1941.
Lundquist, P. G., Kimura, R., and Wersäll, J.: Ultrastructural organization of the epithelial lining in the endolymphatic duct and sac in the guinea pig, Acta otolaryng. *57*:65, 1963.
——: Experiments in endolymph circulation, Acta otolaryng., Supp. *188*:198-210, 1964.

Mackenzie, G. W.: The appearance and behavior of the normal tympanic membrane, Laryngoscope, *34*:497, 1924.
Montagna, W.: The pigment and fatty substances of the ceruminous glands of man, Anat. Rec. *100*:66, 1948.
Montagna, W., Noback, C. R., and Zak, F. G.: Pigment, lipids and other substances in the glands of the external auditory meatus of man, Am. J. Anat. *83*:409, 1948.
Polyak, S. L., McHugh, G., and Judd, D. K.: The Human Ear, Elmsford, N. Y., Sonotone Corp., 1946.
Potter, A. B.: Function of the stapedius muscle, Ann. Otol. *45*:638, 1936.
Shambaugh, G. E.: Cytology of the Internal Ear *in* Cowdry's Special Cytology, ed. 2, p. 1333, New York, Hoeber, 1932.
Wersäll, J.: Studies on the structure and innervation of the sensory epithelium of the cristae ampullares in the guinea pig; a light and electron microscopic investigation, Acta otolaryng., Supp. *126*:1-85, 1956.
Wersäll, J., and Flock, A.: Physiological aspects on the structure of vestibular end organs, Otolaryngologica, Supp. *192*:85-89, 1964.
Wiggers, H. C.: The functions of the intra-aural muscles, Am. J. Physiol. *120*:771, 1937.

# Index

Acetylcholine, 501, 573
Acid(s). *See under individual names*
Acidophilic substances, 814
Acinus, 124, 191
  liver, 721
Acromegaly, 821
Acrosome, 955
ACTH, control of secretion of, 863
  effects on adrenal cortex, 859
  secretion and stress, 863
Actin, 489
Addison's disease, 856
Adenohypophysis, 817
Adenoids, 749
Adenosine triphosphate, 140, 489
Adipose tissue, 248
Adrenal cortex, 855
  fetal, 853
Adrenal gland(s), 852
  cortex. *See* Adrenal cortex
  development of, 852
  medulla. *See* Adrenal medulla
Adrenal medulla, 860
Adrenergic nerve fibers, 573
Adrenocorticotropin. *See* ACTH
Agglutination of platelets, 299
Aging, changes in, 221
Albino, 633
Aldosterone, 856
Alimentary tract, 645
All or none law, 498
Allergy, 246
Alpha cells, 824, 872
Altitude, effect on erythrocyte count, 291
Alveolus(i), of gland, 199
  of jaw, 653
  of lung, 757
Amacrine cells, 998
Ameloblasts, 657
Amino acids, 11
Amphicytes, 555
Ampulla(ae), of ductus deferens, 965
  of oviduct, 909
  of semicircular canals, 1010
  of Vater, 657, 739

Anabolism, 58
Anaphase, 77
Anaphylaxis, 246
Anastomoses, arteriovenous, 600
Androgens, 946
Anemia, 292
  hyperchromic, 295
  hypochromic, 295
  iron deficiency, 295
  macrocytic, 294
  microcytic, 294
  normochromic, 294
  pernicious, 296
  sickle-cell, 288, 295
Aneuploidy, 85
Ångstrom unit, 24
Anomalies, 71, 83
Anterior horn cells, 540
Anterior lobe of pituitary, 815, 819
  cells of, 823
  development of, 816
  hormones of, 820
Anthracosis, 150
Antiagglutinants, 304
Antibodies, 37
  details of kinds of, 326
  fluorescent, 38
  seen in the EM, 46
Antibody formation, 234
Antidiuretic hormone, 793, 828
Antigens, 37, 236
  secluded, 844
Aorta, 585
Aortic valve, 603
Apocrine glands, 199
Apparatus, Golgi. *See* Golgi apparatus
  juxtaglomerular, 785
Appendices epiploicae, 700
Appendicitis, 701
Appendix, vermiform, 700
Appositional growth, of bone, 387
  of cartilage, 377
Aqueous humor, 991, 993
Arachnoid, 547
Arachnoid villi, 551
Areolar tissue, 204
Argentaffine cells, 694

Argyrophilic fibers. *See* Reticular fibers
Arrector pili muscle, 627
Artefacts, 25
Arteries, 582, 583
  coiled, of endometrium, 915, 917
  compared with veins, 598
  distributing, 586
  elastic, 585
  helicine, 971
  nervous control, 588
  nutrition of walls, 583
  vasa vasorum, 586
Arteriolae rectae spuriae, 804
Arteriolae rectae verae, 804
Arterioles, 587
Arteriosclerosis, 585
Arteriovenous anastomoses, 600
Articular cartilage, development, 414
  fine structure, 465
  growth, 467
  metabolism, 466
  microscopic structure, 463
  nourishment, 466
  repair, 467
Articulations, 458
Artifacts, 25
Aschheim-Zondek test, Friedman modification, 904
Asthma, 768
Astrocytes, 536
  fibrous, 536
  gliosomes of, 536
  protoplasmic, 536
ATP (Adenosine triphosphate), 489
Atrophy of disuse, 436
Auerbach's plexus, 676
Auto-antibodies, 844
Autographs, using radioactive isotopes, 31
Autonomic nervous system, 567
  craniosacral outflow, 572
  emotion and, 861
  ganglia. *See* Ganglia
  gray rami communicantes, 571
  nerve endings in, 572
  parasympathetic division, 572

Autonomic nervous system—
    (*Continued*)
  postganglionic fibers, 571
  preganglionic fibers, 571, 572
  sympathetic division, 570
  thoracico-lumbar outflow, 570
  white rami communicantes,
    570
Autosomes, 69
  anomalies, 83
Axons, 509, 530, 556
Azurophilic granules, 262, 270

Baldness, 629
Barr bodies, 69
Basement membranes, 169, 220
Baroceptor, 590
Basal metabolic rate, 831
Basket, myoepithelial cells, 197
Basophilia of cytoplasm, 117
Basophilic leukocytes, 269
Basophilic substances, 14
Basophils, of anterior pituitary,
    824
Beta cells, of islets of Langer-
    hans, 868
Betz cells, 543
Bile, 713
Bile canaliculi, 719, 727
  fine structure of, 727
Bile ducts, 733, 737
Bilirubin, 151, 713
Birth, effect on lymphatic tis-
    sue, 313
Bladder, urinary, 808. *See also*
    Urinary bladder
Blastocyst, 918
Blood, in anemia, 292
  cells, 257. *See also* Erythro-
    cytes *and* Leukocytes
  circulation, 581
  hemoglobin content, 291
  plasma, 257
  platelets, 298
  preparation of films, 257
  pressure, diastolic, 582
    factors in, 582
    systolic, 582
  sludging, 296
  stains for, 258
  sugar level, 871
    control, 871
Blushing, 591
Body (bodies), Barr, 69
  carotid, 590
  ciliary, 983, 990
  Herring, 830
  Nissl, 527

Body (bodies)—(*Continued*)
  pineal, 875
  polar, 896
  residual, 145
Bone(s), 384
  alveolar, 653
  appositional growth, 385
  atrophy of disuse, 436
  blood supply, 449
  calcification, mechanism, 390.
    *See also* 378
  canaliculi, 384
  cancellous, 396
    transplanted, 447
  cells of. *See under their names*
  cementing lines, 400
  compact, 396
    transplanted, 444
  decalcified, 387
  development, 388. *See also*
    Ossification
  differences from cartilage, 384
  effects, of estrogen on, 820
    of growth hormone on, 820
    of parathyroid hormone on,
    848
  endochondral ossification, 408
  endosteum, 436
  epiphyseal disks, 415
  fine structure, 389
  formation, 388. *See also*
    Ossification
    of compact, from cancel-
    lous, 396
    from marrow cells, 441
  grafting. *See* Transplantation
  ground sections, 388
  growth, in length, 416
    as a whole, 420
    in width, 424
  haversian systems, 423
  immature, 392
  intercellular substance, 390
  lamellae, 393
  maintenance growth in, 428
  marrow, 351. *See also* Mye-
    loid tissue
  mature, 393
  membrane, 394
  methods of study, 387
  mineral metabolism and, 428,
    434
  nutrient arteries, 450
  nutrition, 384
  opacity to x-rays, 431
  osteitis fibrosa, 848

Bone(s)—(*Continued*)
  osteoclasts. *See* Osteoclasts
  osteoporosis, 431
  periosteum, 436
  phosphatase in, 379, 419
  radioactive isotopes and, 388
  radioautographs, 420
  remodeling during growth,
    422, 428
  repair of fractures, 436
  resorption, 402
    in rickets, 434
    in scurvy, 432
  Sharpey's fibers, 468, 665
  spicules, 395
  stem cells, 386, 402
  trabeculae, 395
  transplantation, 444
  turbinate, 748
  uncalcified, 434
  undecalcified section, 388
  vascularity, 385, 451
  Volkmann's canals, 426
  watermarks in, 400
  Wolff's law, 436
  Wormian, 459
Border, brush, of cells. *See*
    Striated border of cells
  striated, of cells, 174
Bowman's capsule, 783
  glands, 980
  membrane, 987
Brain, capillaries, 547, 550
  cerebral cortex, 543, 544
  cerebral hemispheres, 520
  coverings, 546
  gray matter, 543, 544
  histogenesis, 525
  medulla oblongata of, 518
  morphogenesis, 518
  ventricles, 520
  white matter, 544
Breasts, 934. *See also* Mammary
    glands
Bronchi, 753
Bronchioles, 755, 756
  innervation, 768
Brown atrophy of heart, 504
Brown fat, 251
Bruch's membrane, 990
Bud, periosteal, 441
  taste, 1006
Bulbo-urethral glands, 973
Bundle, atrioventricular, of His,
    604
Burns, 638
  plasma loss in, 218

Calcification, in hypercalcemia, 848
  in hyperparathyroidism, 848
  mechanism in cartilage and bone, 379, 390
  zone of, in epiphyseal disk, 416
Calcitonin, 851
Calcium, role in clotting, 300, 306
Callus of fracture, 439
Calyces of kidney, 780
Canal(s), cloquet, 995
  haversian, 423
  hyaloid of vitreous, 995
  of Schlemm, 992
  semicircular, 1020
  Volkmann's, 426
Canaliculi, bile, 719-727
  of bone, 384
Cancellous bone, 396
  transplantation, 447
Cancer, 62
Capillaries, absorption of tissue fluids by, 214
  appearance in sections, 590
  control of circulation in, 591
  development, 226
  fenestrated endothelium, 594, 790
  fine structure, 594, 610
  formation of tissue fluid by, 213
  lymphatic, 610
  of skin, 635
Capsule cells of ganglia, 555
Carbohydrate, absorption, 696
  chemistry of, in tissue, 13
  role of Golgi apparatus in secretion of, 136
  storage in cells, 146, 732
Cardiac glands, 679
Cardiac muscle, 501
Cardiac sphincter, 679
Caries, dental, 668
Carotid body, 590
  sinus, 590
Carotinoid pigments, 150
Cartilage, 373
  appositional growth, 377
  articular. See Articular cartilage
  calcification, 378
  cells, 375
  classification, 374
  development, 377
  elastic, 380
  fibro, 381

Cartilage—(Continued)
  fine structure, 465
  in healing fractures, 441
  hyaline, 374
  intercellular substance, 375
  interstitial growth of, 377
  nutrition, 378
  perichondrium, 375
  transplantation, 381
Caruncle, 1004
Casts in kidney, 801
Catabolism, 58
Cavities, nasal, 746
  pericardial, 600
  pleural, 744
  pulp, of tooth, 652
  tympanic, 1014
Cell(s), 49. See under individual names. See also Nucleus and Cytoplasm
  binucleated, 85
  cancer, 62
  cultures, 61
  cycle, 95
  cytoplasm of. See Cytoplasm
  dead, 112
  definition, 57
  difference between male and female, 68
  differentiation, 59, 152
  division, 71
  families in the body, 59
  fixed and free, 352
  foreign body giant, 232
  general features, 57
  glycogen in, 146
  graft rejection, 235
  growth, 59
  history of term, 57
  inclusions, 115, 145
  membrane, 120
  metabolism in, 58
  nests, 375
  nucleus, 64. See also Nucleus
  organelles, 116. See also under individual organelles
  postmortem degeneration, 112
  potentiality, 60
  reproductive capacity, 60
  respiration in, 138
  size, 59
  specialization, 4, 59
  specificity, 60
  stem, 61
  totipotent, 60
  turnover, 61
  web, 174
Celloidin method, 16

Cementum, 652, 664
Central nervous system, 516. See also Brain, Spinal cord
Centrifugation, differential, 126
Centrioles, 75, 116
Centrosphere, 116
Centro-acinar cells of pancreas, 708-709
Centrosome(s), 75, 116
Cerebellum, 545
Cerebral cortex, 543
  histogenesis, 525
Cerebral hemispheres, development, 518
Cerebrospinal fluid, 549
Ceruminous glands, 1014
Cervix, 927
Chamber, transparent, 52
Cheeks, 648
Chief cells, of parathyroid, 846
  of stomach, 684
Chimera, 356
Cholecystokinin, 739
Cholinergic fibers, 573
Chondrocytes, 375
Chondroitin sulfuric acid, 210
Chordae tendineae, 602
Chorion, 921, 923
Choroid coat of eye, 983-989
  choriocapillaris, 990
  formation, 986
Choroid plexus, 549
  fine structure of, 550
Chromaffin reaction, 860
Chromatids, 74
Chromatin, 66
  fine structure, 109
  histochemistry of, 86
  sex, 68. See also Sex chromatin and Barr bodies
Chromatolysis, 527
Chromatomere of platelets, 302
Chromatophores, 634
Chromidial substance of cytoplasm, 117
Chromophils of pituitary, 824
Chromophobes of pituitary, 824
Chromosomes, 67-71
  acrocentric, 83
  aneuploidy, 85
  classification, 81
  diploid number, 85
  effect of radiation on, 98
  fate of DNA in, 93
  fine structure, 97
  functions, 73

Chromosomes—(*Continued*)
  haploid number, 85
  karyotyping, 83
  metacentric, 83
  morphology, 81
  number in cells of man, 69
  polyploidy, 85
  protein, 88
  sex, 69
    determination by, 68
Chyle, 610, 697
Chyme, 680
Cilia, 183
  fine structure of, 183
Ciliary body, 983, 990
Ciliary muscle, 990
Ciliary processes, 992
Circulatory system, 581. *See also* Arteries, Arterioles, Capillaries, Heart *and* Veins
Circumcision, 970
Cisterna chyli, 610
Cisternae, of cytoplasm, 116
Clasmatocytes. *See* Macrophages
Clearing, 8
  of tissues, 8
Climacteric, female, 906
Clitoris, 889
Clotting mechanism, 300
Cochlea, 1010, 1017
  basilar membrane of, 1019
  Deiter's cells of, 1019
  external pillar cells, 1019
  Hensen's cells, 1019
  internal pillar cells, 1019
  modiolus, 1017
  organ of Corti, 1019
Colchicine, effects on mitosis of, 80
Cold receptors, 977
Collagen, formation of, 227
  molecule, 11
  periodicity, 206
Collagenic fibers, 203
  formation, 227
Collagenic fibrils, 204
  electron microscopy, 207, 229
  formation, 227, 229
  microfibrils, 204
Colloid(s), of blood, 213
  of thyroid, 834
Color, of eyes, 992
  of hair, 630
  of skin, 632, 637
Colostrum, 940
Compact bone. *See* Bone

Complex, junctional, 117
Conception, control of by hormones, 907
Conchae of nose, 748
Conditioned reflexes, 515
Conductivity, definition, 58
Cones of eye, 998
Conjunctiva, 1004
Connective tissue, 200
  areolar, 204
  cells of, 225
  classification, 166
  collagen, 203
  dense fibrous, 251
  development, 224
  loose ordinary, 200, 226
  mesenchyme, 224
  metaplasia in, 224
Contractility, definition, 58
Contraction, mechanism, 489
Cord(s), spermatic, 948
  spinal. *See* Spinal cord
  umbilical, 918
  vocal, 751
Cornea, 983, 987
  transplantation, 988
Corona radiata, 896
Corpora cavernosa, 969
Corpus luteum, blood supply, 898
  corpus albicans, 903
  effects of luteinizing hormone on, 897
  follicular lutein cells, 898
  formation, 897
  function, 893, 898
  granulosa lutein cells, 898
  involution, 903
  length of life, 903
  and placental gonadotrophin, 904
  in pregnancy, 903
  theca lutein cells, 898
Cortisol, 856
Cortisone (Hydrocortisone), 856
Cowper's glands, 973
Crenation, 289
Cretinism, 832
Crypts, of Lieberkühn, 691
  of tonsil, 652, 673
Cumulus oophorus, 895
Cupula, 1021
Cyanosis, 291
Cycle, menstrual, 912. *See also* Menstrual cycle
Cysts, 188
  fatty, 147

Cytoplasm, 115
  basophilia, 117
  centrioles, 75
  centrosome, 75
  chromidial substance, 117
  cytomembranes, 120
  endoplasmic reticulum, 123. *See* Endoplasmic reticulum
  ergastoplasm, 117
  fat in, 146
  fibrils, 116
  filaments in, 116
  glycogen in, 146
  Golgi apparatus. *See* Golgi apparatus
  inclusions, 145
  lysosomes, 142
  membranous vesicles, 116
  microsomes, 126
  mitochondria, 137
  organelles, 115
  pigments, 149
  ribosomes, 119
  RNA of, 113
  secretion granules, 133
  stored foods in, 146
Cytotrophoblast, 918

Deafness, 1021
Decalcification, 13
Decidua, 921
Decidual reaction, 915
Deciduous teeth, 653
Degeneration, postmortem, 112
Dehydration of tissues, 8
Deiter's cells, 1019
Demilunes, serous, 197
Dendrites, 509
Dental caries, 668
Dental lamina, 654
Dental papilla, 655
Dental sac, 657
Dentin, calcification, 661
  fibers, 661
  formation, 660
Dentinal tubules, 661
Deoxyribonucleic acid. *See* DNA
Dermis, 614
Descemet's, endothelium, 987
  membrane, 987
Desmosome(s), 176, 617
Desoxyribonuclease, 87
Desoxyribose nucleic acid, 90. *See also* DNA
Diabetes, insipidus, 828
  mellitus, 867

Diabetogenic effects, of adrenal cortex, 856
of anterior pituitary, 870
Diastole, 582
Differential count of leukocytes, 259
Differentiation, 59, 152
consequences, 60
Diffusion, in intercellular substances, 202
Digestion, 645
Digestive system, parts, 645
Diploe, 408
Diploic veins, 408
Disks, A, I, J, Q and Z, 484
intercalated, 502
intervertebral, 462
of striated muscle, 484
DNA, amount in cells constant, 87
as chemical basis of genes, 88
form and duplication, 90
how it controls protein synthesis, 99
labeling with radioactive thymidine, 91
staining of, 86
storage of information in, 89
synthesis, 90
Dopa-oxidase, 633
Dopa reaction, 633
Duct(s), 188
alveolar, of lung, 757
of Bellini, 800
bile, 655, 739
cochlear, 1017
cystic, 737
development, 188
ejaculatory, 948
intercalated, 711
interlobular, 191
intralobular, 194
lactiferous, 934
nasolacrimal, 1006
pancreatic, 706
right lymphatic, 610
thoracic, 610
Ductuli efferents, 948
Ductus deferens, 948, 965
endolymphaticus, 1019
epididymis, 948
Duodenum. See Small intestine, 688
Dura mater, 547
sinuses, 549
Dust cells. See Phagocytes, alveolar
Dusts, 150

Dyes. See Stains
Dwarfism, 820, 832

Ear, 1007
auricle, 1012
ceruminous glands, 1014
cochlea, 1010, 1017
cristae of canals, 1021
cupula of cristae, 1021
deafness, 1021
ductus endolymphaticus, 1019
eustachian tube, 1014, 1016
external, 1008
general structure, 1008
maculae, 1021
mastoid air cells, 1014, 1017
middle, 1014
modiolus, 1017
muscles, 1015
nerves, 1015
organ of Corti, 1019
ossicles, 1014
otolithic membranes, 1020
otosclerosis, 1021
oval window, 1016
pharyngotympanic tube, 1014, 1016
round window, 1016
semicircular canals, 1020
transmission of sound waves in, 1019
tympanic membrane, 1014
vestibule of inner, 1019
Eardrum, 1008
Ectoderm, 167
Edema, 216
Ejaculation, 946
Ejaculatory duct, 948
Elastic cartilage, 380
Elastic fibers, 208
age changes in, 221
Electrocardiograms, 607
Electron microscope, 39
Embedding, 9
for electron microscopy, 43
Emotion, and autonomic nervous systems, 861
and epinephrine secretion, 861
Enamel, calcification, 663
formation, 662
lines of Retzius, 663
maturation, 663
Enamel organ, development, 655
differentiation in, 657
Endocardium, 601
Endocrine glands, 814
development, 188
general structure, 197

Endocrine glands—(Continued)
how knowledge developed, 815
storage of secretion in, 814
Endocytosis, 145
Endoderm, 167
Endometrium, 911
blood supply, 915
decidual reaction in, 915
in menstrual cycle, 914
Endomysium, 496
Endoneurium, 560
Endoplasmic reticulum, 123
rough-surfaced (granular), 123, 135
smooth-surfaced (agranular), 127
Endosteum, 436
Endothelium, 167
fenestrated, 594
Enterochromaffine cells, 694
Enzyme(s), definition, 58
histochemical tests for, 29
induction, 154
Eosinophils, 268
formation of, 366
Ependyma, 520
Epicardium, 600
Epichoroid, 989
Epidermis, 614
Epididymis, 948, 964
Epidural space, 548
Epiglottis, 749
Epimysium, 496
Epinephrine, 861
Epineurium, 560
Epithelial tissue, 165. See also Epithelium and Glands
Epithelium, basement membranes, 169
classification, 166
defined, 165
junctional complexes, 177
nutrition, 169
pseudostratified, 183
simple, 169, 170
ciliated, 183
columnar, 171
cuboidal, 171
squamous, 170
stratified, 184
columnar, 185
squamous keratinizing, 186
squamous nonkeratinizing, 184
terminal bars, 181
terminal webs, 175
transitional, 185
Eponychium, 641

Equatorial plate, 76
Erectile tissue, 949
Erection, mechanism, 949, 971
Ergastoplasm, 117
Erythroblasts, 360
Erythrocytes, 287
  counting of, 291
  fragility, 289
  liberation into circulation, 363
  polychromatophilic, 293
  reticulocytes, 293
  ronleaux formation, 296
Erythropoiesis, control, 363
Erythropoietin, 363
Esophagus, 678
Estrogen, 892
  assay, 931
  effects, on anterior pituitary, 898
    on breasts, 938
    on nipples, 935
    on sex organs, 892
    on vagina, 931
  in estrous cycles, 931
  withdrawal, effects on endometrium, 903
Estrous cycle, 899, 931
Eustachian tube, 1014, 1016
Excretion, definition, 59
Exocrine glands, 188-197
Eye(s), 981
  accessory structures, 1004
  adnexa, 1004
  anterior chamber, 991
  aqueous humor, 991, 993
  aqueous veins, 995
  blood supply, 989
  canal of Schlemm, 992
  caruncle, 1004
  choroid. See Choroid coat of eye
  ciliary body, 983, 990
  ciliary processes, 992
  color, 992
  conjunctiva, 1004
  cornea, 983, 987
  cupping of disk, 1003
  development, 985
  drainage of tears, 1005
  equator, 989
  eyelid. See Eyelid
  fornix, 1004
  fundus, 1002
  general structure, 981
    microscopic, 982
  glassy membrane of choroid of, 990
  glaucoma, 994

Eye(s)—(Continued)
  internal appearance, 1002
  intra-ocular pressure, 994
  iris. See Iris
  lacrimal canaliculus, 1006
  lacrimal glands, 1005
  lacrimal sac, 1006
  lamina cribrosa, 1002
  layers of wall, 982
  lens, 990
  limbus, 987, 992
  mechanism of accommodation, 990
  optic disk, 1002
  optic nerve, 1002
  optic stalk, 985
  optic vesicle, 985
  papilla, 1002
  physiologic cup, 1002
  plica semilunaris, 1004
  pupil, 983
  refractive media, 983
  retina. See Retina
  sclera, 982, 988
  spaces of Fontana, 992
  tear glands, 1005
  use of ophthalmoscope, 1002
  uveal layer of. See Choroid coat of eye
  vitreous body, 995
Eyelid(s), formation, 986
  glands, of Moll, 1005
    of Zeis, 1005
  intermarginal space in, 1005
  lacrimal papilla, 1005
  meibomian glands, 1005
  punctum, 1006
  tarsal plate, 1005

Fallopian tube. See Oviduct
Fat, absorption, 696
  brown, 251
  staining by Sudan III, 30
  storage in cells, 146, 248
Fat cells, 248
Fat depots, 248
Feed-back theory, of hormones, 822
Female reproductive system, 884
  cervix. See Cervix
  clitoris, 889
  external genitalia, 889
  fallopian tubes. See Oviduct
  glands of Bartholin, 890
  hymen, 890
  labia, majora, 889
    minora, 889

Female reproductive system—(Continued)
  mons pubis, 889
  mons veneris, 889
  ovaries. See Ovary
  oviducts. See Oviduct
  parts, 885
  vagina. See Vagina
Feulgen reaction, 86
Fibers, adrenergic, 573
  cholinergic, 573
  collagenic, 203
  defined, 203
  elastic, 208
  formation, 227
  muscle, 476
  nerve, 555
  postganglionic, 571
  preganglionic, 571
  purkinje, 607
  reticular, 208, 220
  Sharpey's, 468, 665
  spindle, 76
  unmyelinated, 555
  vasoconstrictor, 588
  vasodilator, 589
Fibrils, cytoplasmic, 116
  fine structure, 204
  myofibrils, 484, 486
Fibrin, 298, 300
Fibrinogen, 300
Fibroblasts, 226
  local and hematogenous source, 230
Fibrocartilage, 381
Fibrocytes, 226
Filaments, 486
Filiform papillae, 650
Fine structure, 40
Fingerprints, 615
  biologic significance, 615
Fixation, 7
  for electron microscopy, 43
Fixatives, action on proteins, 11
Fluid, cerebrospinal. See Cerebrospinal fluid
  follicular, 894
  pericardial, 600
  pleural, 744
  tissue, 211
Fluorescence microscopy, 36
Follicle(s), of endocrine glands, 198
  hair, 623
  lymphatic, 311, 317
  nabothian, 928
  of ovary. See Ovary
  of thyroid, 833

Follicle-stimulating hormone, effects on ovary, 892
in menstrual cycle, 898
relation to puberty, 892
secretion after menopause, 906
Fontanelles, 398
Foreign body giant cells, 232
Fracture(s), of head of femur, 442
repair, 437
Freckles, 633
Free cells, 352
Freemartin, 885
Freeze-dry method, 15
Freezing, method of sectioning, 15
Fungiform papillae, 650

Gallbladder, 737
Ganglia, 513
autonomic, 569
celiac, 571
cerebrospinal, 554
mesenteric, 571
microscopic features of, 554, 569
paravertebral, 570
posterior root, 554
prevertebral, 570
spinal, 554
stellate, 570
sympathetic, 570
terminal, 572
Gastric glands, 682
Gastrointestinal tract, general plan, 674
Gels, definition, 10
Germ layers, 167
Germinal centers, 317
Gigantism, 821
Glands, acinous, 190
adrenal, 852. See also Adrenal glands
alveolar, 190
anterior pituitary, 815. See also Anterior lobe of pituitary
apocrine, 191
areolar, of Montgomery, 935
of Bartholin, 890
Bowman's, 980
of Brunner, 690
bulbo-urethral, 973
ceruminous, 1014
classification, 188-190
compound, 191
Cowper's, 973

Glands—(Continued)
development, 188
ductless. See Endocrine glands
endocrine. See Endocrine glands
exocrine, 188
gastric, 682
hibernating, 251
holocrine, 191
lacrimal, 1005
of Littré, 973
lobules, 715
lymph. See Lymph nodes
mammary, 924. See also Mammary glands
meibomian, of eyelids, 1005
merocrine, 191
mixed, 193
of Montgomery, 935
mucous, 193
nerve endings, 572
parathyroid, 845
parotid, 669
pineal, 875
pituitary, 815
prostate, 949, 966
salivary, 669
sebaceous, 630
serous, 193
simple, 191
sublingual, 670
submandibular, 669
submaxillary, 669
suprarenal, 852. See also Adrenal glands
sweat, 620
tear, 1005
thymus, 338. See also Thymus gland
thyroid, 831. See also Thyroid gland
tubular, 191
tubulo-alveolar, 191
urethral, 973
of Zeis, 1005
Glans of penis, 970
Glaucoma, 994
Glomerular arterioles, 783
capillaries, 786
filtrate, 773
Glomerulus(i), 782
afferent arteriole, 783
basement membrane, 788
capillaries, 786
efferent arteriole, 783
epithelium, 782, 792
fine structure, 790
function, 774

Glomerulus(i)—(Continued)
juxtamedullary, 805
lobules, 787
mesangium, question, 787
physiologic atrophy, 804
podocytes, 792
root, 785
surface area of capillaries, 788
vascular pole, 785
Glomus, 635
Glucagon, 874
Glycogen, 13
in cells, 146, 732
in muscle fibers, 494
Glycogen formation, effect of insulin on, 871
staining by P A S technic, 30
Glycolysis, 138
Glycoproteins, 14
Glycosuria, 867
Goblet cell, 136, 175
Goiter, 832
exophthalmic, 833
Golgi, apparatus, 127
fine structure, 130
negative image, 129
role, in secretion, 133-136
study, by radioautography, 135
method, 534
Gonadotrophic hormone, 822. See also Follicle-stimulating hormone and Luteinizing hormone
Gonadotrophs, 826
Gonads, indifferent, 884
Gonocyte, 950
Grafts. See Transplantation
Graft rejection cells, 235
Granules, azurophilic, 262-270
interchromatinic, 111
keratohyaline, 619, 624
Palade. See Ribosomes
perichromatinic, 111
RNA. See Ribosomes
zymogen, 133, 708
Gray matter, 522, 540, 543
Ground substance, 202-209. See also Hyaluronic acid
Growth, appositional, 373, 385
definition, 59
interstitial, 377
Growth hormone, 820
Gynecomastia, 934

H and E section, 14
Hair, 623
cyclic growth of, 628

Hair—(*Continued*)
   follicles, 623. *See also* Hair
      follicles
Hair cells of organ of Corti, 1019
Hair follicle(s), 623
   arrector pili of, 627
   connective tissue sheath, 627
   cyclic growth, 628
   development, 623
   external root sheath, 624
   germinal matrix, 624
   internal root sheath, 627
   nerve endings, 975
   sebaceous glands, 630
Hashimoto's disease, 844
Hassal's corpuscles, 341
Haversian systems. *See* Bone
Hay fever, 246
Heart, 600
   atrioventricular bundle (His)
      of, 604, 606
   atrioventricular node, 606
   electrocardiograms, 607
   endocardium, 601
   epicardium, 601
   impulse-conducting system,
      604
   innervation, 589, 605
   muscle, 501
   pacemaker, 605
   pericardium, 600
   sinu-atrial node, 605
   skeleton, 601
   valves, 601
Heat receptors, 977
Hemal lymph nodes, 327
Hemal nodes, 327
Hematoidin, 151
Hematoxylin, 14
Hemoconcentration, 219
Hemoglobin, 289
   amount in blood, 291
   carbon monoxide, 291
   methemoglobin, 291
Hemolysis, 289
Hemophilia, 305
Hemopoietic tissue, 308. *See*
      Lymphatic tissue *and*
      Myeloid tissue
Hemorrhagic disease of new-
      born, 306
Hemorrhoids, 699
Hemosiderin, 151
Hemostasis, 298
Henle's loop, 777, 794, 799
Henson's cells, 1019
Heparin, 243
   relation to mast cells, 243

Heredity, chemistry of, 88
Hermaphrodites, 885
   sex chromatin, 885
Hertwig's epithelial sheath, 660
Heterochromatin, 68
Heteropyknosis, 68
Histamine, 246
Histiocytes, 231
Histochemistry, 29
   methods for,
      carbohydrates, 30
      enzymes, 29
      inorganic salts, 31
      lipids, 30
Histologic technics, ordinary, 7
   special, 28
Histology, definition, 3
Histones, 153
Holocrine glands, 191
Homogenous transplants, 279
Homograft reaction, 277
Homologous transplants, 279
Hormones. *See also under indi-*
      *vidual names*
   definition, 814
   development of knowledge
      about, 815
   enterohepatic circulation of,
      714
   functions, 815
   push-pull theory, 822
Humor, aqueous, 991, 993
Hyalomere of platelets, 302
Hyaluronic acid, in aqueous
      humor, 993
   general, 209
   in synovial fluid, 472
Hyaluronidase, in aqueous
      humor, 993
   general, 209
Hydrocephalus, 550
Hydrochloric acid, formation in
      stomach, 684
Hydrocortisone, 856
Hydrothorax, 746
Hymen, 890
Hyperglycemia, 871
Hyperparathyroidism, 832
Hypersensitivity. *See* Allergy
Hypertension, 786
   arterioles in, 587
Hyperthyroidism, 832
Hypoparathyroidism, 847
Hypophysioportal circulation,
      818
Hypophysis cerebri, 815. *See*
      *also* Pituitary gland

Hypothalamus, development of,
      520
   hypothalamo-hypophyseal
      tract, 829
   neurosecretion in, 829
Hypothyroidism, 832

Idiocy, mongolian, 84, 615
Ileum, 688
Immunity, 37, 234, 275, 320, 345
   effects of radiation on, 356
Immuno-electrophoresis, 326
Immunofluorescence technics, 37
Immunologic tolerance, 237
Impulse-conducting system of
      heart, 604
Inclusions, 8
   cytoplasmic, 145
Incus, 1014
Induction, of enzyme, 154
Infection of tissue, 265
Inflammation, 265
Ingrown toenail, 642
Insulin, action, 871
   control of secretion, 872
   discovery, 869
   shock, 872
   storage in cells, 872
Interalveolar partitions, 758
Intercalated disks, 502
Intercalated ducts, 711
Intercellular substance(s), 200
   aging in, 221
   diffusion in, 202
Interference, microscope, 48
Intermedin, 822
Interphase, 65, 95
   duration of stages in, 95
Interstitial cells of testis, 951,
      960
   in fetus, 950
Interstitial growth, 377
Interstitial lamellae, 423, 425
Intestine, large. *See* Large in-
      testine
   small. *See* Small intestine
Intramembranous ossification,
      393, 394
Involution of thymus, 340
Iodine, 838
Iris, angle of, 992
   color, 992
   general features, 991
   myo-epithelial cells, 992
Iron, test for, 31
Irritability, definition, 58
Islets of Langerhans, 866

Islets of Langerhans—
  (*Continued*)
  alpha cells and their functions,
    872
  cells, 872, 874, 875
  in diabetes, 869
  neuro-insular complexes of,
    875
  relation to anterior pituitary,
    870
Isologous animals, *275*

Jaundice, 739
Jejunum, 688
Joint(s), age changes in, 473
  capsules, 468
  classification, 458
  definition, 458
  effects of compression on, 473
  function, 458
  intervertebral, 462
  sutures, 459
  symphyses, 461
  synchondroses, 460
  syndesmoses, 459
  synostoses, 460
  synovial, 462. *See also* Syn-
    ovial joints
Junctional complex, 117
Juxtaglomerular complex, 785

Karyolysis, 112
Karyorrhexis, 112
Karyotype, 81
Keratin, 617, 624
  hard and soft types, 624
Keratohyalin granules, 619, 624
Kidney, 772
  arcuate arteries, 802
  basement membranes in, 788,
    792
  blood vessels, 802
  calyces, 780
  casts in, 801
  circulation through, 802
  collecting tubules, 800
  columns of Bertin, 779
  connective tissue, 801
  cortex, 777
  cortical labyrinth, 780
  counter current osmotic mul-
    tiplier in, 792
  crush syndrome, 804
  distal convoluted tubules, 800
  ducts of Bellini, 800
  fetal lobulation, 779
  glomeruli, *782. See also*
    Glomerulus(i)

Kidney—(*Continued*)
  hypertonic urine explained,
    792
  interlobar arteries, 802
  interlobular arteries, 803
  intralobular arteries, 803
  juxtaglomerular complex, 785
  juxtamedullary glomeruli, 805
  labyrinth of cortex, 780
  lobes defined, 779
  lobules defined, 779
  loop of Henle, 777, 794, 799
  lymphatics, 805
  macula densa, 785
  malpighian corpuscles, 782
  medulla of, 777, 779
  medullary rays, 778
  nephron of human, 781
  concentration of urine in, 792
  nerve supply, 809
  papilla, 777-780
  P A S staining, 788
  pelvis, 777, 778, 781
  physiologic hypertrophy, 806
  postnatal growth, 806
  proximal convoluted tubules
    795
  relation to high blood pres-
    sure, 786
  renal corpuscles, 782
  stellate veins, 804
Knife, diamond, 43
  glass, 43
  microtome, 9
Korff's fibers, 661
Krause's end-bulbs, 977
Kupffer cells, 724

Labia, majora, 889
  minora, 889
Labels, used in radioautography,
    33
Lacrimal sac, 1006
Lactation, 940
Lacteals of villi, 695
Lactiferous ducts, 935
Lactogenic hormone, 821, 941
Lacunae, Howship's, 401
Lamella(e) of bone, circumfer-
    ential, 424
  haversian, 423
  interstitial, 425
Lamina, dental, 654
  propria, 674
Lanugo, 623
Large intestine, 697
  rectal columns of, 699
  teniae coli, 700

Large intestine—(*Continued*)
  vermiform appendix, 700
Larynx, 749
Law, all or none, 498
Lens, 990
Leukocytes, 257. *See also under*
    *individual names*
  how counted, 259
Ligament, suspensory, of lens,
    990
Line(s), milk, 934
Lingual tonsil, 652
Lipids, 12
Lipochrome(s), 150, 733
Lips, 647
Liver, 711
  acini, 721
  bile canaliculi, 719, 727, 733
  bile ducts, 735
  canals of Hering, 735
  capsule of Glisson, 711
  classic lobule, 715
  development, 712
  ductules, 735
  endocrine function, 715
  exocrine function, 713
  fine structure, 726
  hemopoiesis in, 724
  von Kupffer cells, 724
  lobules, 715
  lymphatics, 726
  of pigs, 716
  portal areas, 717, 720
  preductules, 736
  regeneration, 740
  reticuloendothelium of, 724
  sinusoids, 717, 723
Lobule(s) of glands, 715
Lung(s), 744
  acinus, 757
  alveolar ducts, 756
  alveolar pores, 759
  alveoli, 757
  blood supply, 766
  changes at birth, 765, 766
  development, 763
  fine structure, 761
  growth, 766
  innervation, 768
  Lambert's sinuses, 759
  lobules, 755
  lymphatics, 767
Lunule of nail, 640
Lutein cells, 898
Luteinizing hormone, 822, 896
Lymph, filtration, 317
  formation, 214

Lymph—(*Continued*)
 return to venous system, 273, 610
Lymph glands, 313. *See also* Lymph nodes
Lymph nodes, 313
Lymph nodules, 311
Lymphatic(s), 609
 capillaries, 609, 610
Lymphatic follicles, 311-317
Lymphatic tissue, 309
 response to antigen, 308
Lymphatic vessels. *See* Lymphatics
Lymphoblasts, 319
Lymphocytes, 270
 as immunologically competent cells, 276
 fine structure, 272
 formation, 317
 function, 273, 275
 life span, 273
 recirculation, 275
 runt disease and, 276
 sensitivity to radiation, 281
Lymphoid tissue, 309
Lysosomes, 142, 730

Macrocytes, 287
Macrocytic anemia, 294
Macrophages, 231
 relation to reticuloendothelial cells, 231
 system, 352
Macromolecules, 10
Macula densa of kidney, 785
Male reproductive system, 946
Male urethra, 971
Malleus, 1014
Mammary glands, 934
 at birth, 941
 cause of growth in pregnancy, 937
 cause of lactation, 941
 development, 934
 effect, of hormones on, 938
 histologic structure, 934
 in lactation, 940
 after the menopause, 942
 nipples, 934
 supernumerary nipples, 934
 suspensory ligaments of Cooper of, 936
 witch's milk, 941
Mammogenic hormones, 939
Marble bone disease, 399

Marrow, bone, 351. *See also* Myeloid tissue
Mast cells, 242
 fine structure, 244
 histamine and, 246
 relation of heparin, 243
Matrix, of bone. *See* Bone, intercellular substance of, 390
 of hair follicles, 624
 of nails, 640
Mechanism, hemostatic, 296
Mediastinum, definition of, 947
Medulla oblongata, 518
Medullary cords, 315
Medullary rays, 778
Megakaryocytes, 304, 368
 fine structure, 304
 formation of platelets by, 304, 368
Megaloblasts, 364
Meiosis, 892, 896, 954
Meissner's corpuscles, 975
Meissner's plexus, 676
Melanin, 151, 632
Melanoblasts, 633
Melanocytes, 633
Melanocyte-Stimulating hormone, 822
Membrane(s), arachnoid, 547
 basement, 169, 220
 Bowman's, 987
 Bruch's 990
 cell, 120
 Descemet's, 987
 intracytoplasmic, 116
 mucous, 647, 674
 nuclear, 107
 otolithic, 1020
 periodontal, 665
 plasma, 120
 Reissner's, 1019
 Schneiderian, 747
 Schrapnell's, 1014
 synovial, 470
 tectorial, 1019
 tympanic, 1014
Membranous labyrinth, 1009, 1017
Meninges, 546
Menopause, 906
 mammary glands after, 942
Menstrual cycle, 912
 endometrium during, 912
 summary of hormone control of, 898
 vaginal changes in, 931
Menstruation, anovulatory, 903

Menstruation—(*Continued*)
 endometrium during, 912
 relation to ovulation, 898
Merkel's disks, 975
Merocrine glands, 191
Mesangium, discussed, 787
Mesenchymal cells, 225
Mesenchyme, 224
Mesoderm, 167
Mesoglia. *See* Microglia
Mesothelium, 167
Messenger RNA, 100
Metabolic rate, 831
Metabolism, definition, 58
Metachromasia, 211
Metamyelocytes, 365
Metaphase, 75
Metaplasia, 224
Methemoglobin, 291
Mice, inbred strains, 275
Microbodies, 729
Microcytes, 287
Microdissection, 52
Microfibril(s), 204
Microglia, 534, 536
Micro-incineration, 35
Micromanipulation, 52
Micron, 24
Microscope, electron. *See* Electron microscope
 fluorescence, 36
 interference, 48
 light, 21
 phase, 48
 ulraviolet, 40. *See also* Fluorescence microscopy
 use, 21
Microsomes, 126
Microspectrophotometry, 87
Microtome, 9
Microvilli, 174
Micrurgy, 52
Middle ear, 1008, 1014
Milk, composition, 940
 line, 934
Millimicron, 24
Mitochondria, 137
 enzymes, 140
 fine structure, 139
 nucleic acids in, 141
Mitosis, 74
 effects of colchicine on, 80
 interphase, 95
 times taken for different stages of, 95, Fig. 6-27
Mitotic figure, 71
Modiolus, 1017

Mongol spot, 634
Mongolism, 84
Monoblasts, 283
Monocytes, 281
  fine structure of, 282
Morula, 918
Motor end-plates, 498
Mucin. *See* Mucus
Mucoperichondrium, 747
Mucoperiosteum, 747
Mucopolysaccharides, 13
Mucous membrane, 647, 674
Mucus, 136, 172
Muscle, 476
  cardiac, 501
  how to distinguish 3 kinds, 504
  involuntary, 477. *See also*
    Smooth muscle
  mechanism of contraction in,
    489
  skeletal, 482. *See also* Striated
    muscle
  smooth. *See* Smooth muscle
  striated. *See* Striated muscle
  voluntary, 482. *See also* Stri-
    ated muscle
Muscular tissue. *See* Muscle
Muscularis externa of intestine,
  676
Muscularis mucosae of intestine,
  674
Myelin, 522, 558
  composition, 522
  fine structure, 558
  formation, 558
  staining, 525
Myelinated fibers, 558
Myelinization, 522, 558
Myeloblasts, 359
Myelocytes, 364
Myeloid leukemia, 370
Myeloid tissue, 351
  cells, 352
  colony formers of, 356-359
  development, 351
  effects of radiation on, 353,
    356
  formation, of erythrocytes in,
    359
    of granular leukocytes in,
    364
  lymphocytes, 369
  megakaryocytes, 368
  monocytes, 370
  myeloblasts, 359
  plasma cells, 370
  platelet formation in, 368
  red and yellow, 351

Myeloid tissue—(*Continued*)
  reticuloendothelium, 352
  sinusoids, 353
  stem cells, 355
  study of, in clinical medicine,
    370
    by spleen colony technic, 356
  transplantation, 356
Myenteric plexus of Auerbach,
  676
Myocardium, 501, 601
Myo-epithelial cells, 197, 477,
  620
Myofibrils, 484, 486
Myofilaments, 486
Myometrium, 911
Myosin, 489
Myxedema, 832

Nabothian follicles, 928
Nails, 640
Nasolacrimal duct, 1006
Negative staining, 46
Nephron, 773, 781
Nerve(s), blood supply of, 561
  cells. *See* Neurons
  cleft of Schmidt-Lantermann,
    555
  after crushing, 564
  degeneration, 564
  endings, afferent, 975
    in autonomic nervous sys-
      tem, 572
    chemical effects produced by
      efferent, 572
    for cold, 977
    corpuscles of Ruffini, 978
    for cutaneous and deep sen-
      sibility, 975
    efferent, in glands, 572
      in smooth muscle, 572
      in striated muscle, 498
    encapsulated, 975
    for heat, 977
    Krause's end-bulbs, 977
    Meissner's corpuscles, 975
    Merkel's disks, 975
    motor end-plates, 498
    naked, 975
    neuromuscular spindles, 978
    neurotendinous organs of
      Golgi, 978
    pacinian corpuscles, 977
    for pain, 977
    for pressure, 977
    for proprioceptive muscle
      sense, 977

Nerve(s), endings—(*Continued*)
  for touch, 975
  endoneurium, 560
  epineurium, 560
  fibers, 555
    fine structure, 556
    injuries, types, 564
    myelinated fibers, 552, 558
    nodes of Ranvier, 555
    perineurium, 560
    regeneration, 564
    structure, 560
    transplantation, 567
    unmyelinated fibers, 555
Nervous system, 507
  autonomic, 567. *See also* Auto-
    nomic nervous system
  central, 516
  peripheral, 552. *See also* Pe-
    ripheral nervous system
Nervous tissue, 507
  neurons. *See* Neurons
Neural crests, 517
  folds, 517
  groove, 517
Neurilemma, 555
Neuroblasts, 522
Neuro-ectoderm, 517
Neurofibrils, 526
Neuroglia, 532
  staining, 534
  turnover of cells, 532
Neurohypophysis, 828
Neuro-insular complexes, 875
Neurolemma, 555
  development, 555
Neuromuscular junctions, 498
  spindles, 978
Neurons, 509
  afferent, 511
  association, 516
  axon hillock, 530
  axons, 530
  cell bodies, 526
  chromatolysis in, 527
  chromidial substance, 527
  continuous renewal of cyto-
    plasm, 528
  dendrites, 528
  efferent, 511
  fine structure, 527
  Golgi apparatus, 527
  neurofibrils 526
  Nissl bodies, 527
  nuclei, 526
  perikaryon, 526
  pigment in, 528
  sex chromatin, 526

Neuropil, 545
Neurosecretion, 829
Neurotendinous organs of Golgi, 978
Neutrophilic myelocytes, 364
Neutrophils, 262
  band forms, 263
  fine structure, 263
  formation, 364
  juvenile forms, 263
  sex chromatin, 262
Nipple, 934
Nissl bodies 527
Node(s), atrioventricular, 606
  hemal, 327
  lymph, 313
  of Ranvier, 555
  sinu-atrial, 605
Nodules, lymphatic, 311
Norepinephrine, 861
Normoblasts, 361
Nose, 746
  olfactory organ of, 978
Nucleic acids, 12, 86
  in mitochondria, 141
Nucleolonema, 103
Nucleolus(i) chemistry of, 103
  fine structure, 103
  formation, 103
  hypertrophy, 107
  nucleolonema, 103
  numbers, 103
  pars amorpha, 106
  staining, 103
Nucleoproteins, 12
  DNA. See DNA
  Feulgen reaction and, 72
  RNA. See RNA
Nucleus(i), 64
  changes after death, 112
  chromatids, 73
  chromatin, 66
    granules, 66
  chromosomes, 71, 81, 86
  condensed chromatin type, 66
  constancy of DNA content, 87
  fine structure, 107, 109, 111
  interphase, 65
  karyolysis, 112
  karyorrhexis, 112
  membrane, 107
  in mitosis, 74
  nucleolus. See Nucleolus
  open-faced type, 65
  polyploidy, 85
  pores, 109
  pulposus, 462

Nucleus(i)—(Continued)
  pyknosis, 112
  sap 109

Oddi, sphincter of, 739
Odontoblasts, 660
Olfactory organ, 978
  Bowman's glands, 980
Oligodendroglia, 534, 536
Oocyte, 896
Oogonium, 891
Ophthalmoscope, 1002
Oral cavity, 647
Organ(s), of Corti, 1019
  enamel, 655
  of special sense. See Olfactory organ, Eye, Taste buds and Ear
Organelles 115
Ossicles of ear, 1014
Ossification, 388, 393
  center, 395, 411-414
  endochondral, 393, 408
  heteroplastic, 393
  intramembranous, 393, 394
Osteitis fibrosa, 399
Osteoblasts, 388
Osteoclasts, 402
  fine structure, 405
  and foreign body giant cells, 407
  functions, 406
  and megakaryocytes, 403
  origin 406
  striated borders, 403
Osteocytes, 388
Osteogenesis. See Ossification
Osteogenic cells, 386, 402
Osteoid tissue, 434
  in rickets, 402
Osteopetrosis, 399
Osteophytes, 473
Osteoporosis, 431, 851
Otolithic membrane, 1020
Otosclerosis, 1021
Ovary, 890
  anovulatory cycles, 903
  atretic follicles, 894, 905
  changes at puberty in, 892
  corpus albicans, 903
  corpus luteum. See Corpus luteum
  cumulus oophorus, 895
  developing follicles, 894
  development, 891
  after menopause, 906
  hormonal factors in 28-day cycle, 898

Ovary—(Continued)
  ovulation in, 896
  primordial follicles, 891
  theca externa, 895
  theca interna, 895
Oviducts, 909
  cyclical changes in, 910
Ovulation, 896
  time of, 913
Oxidation, 139
Oxyhemoglobin, 289
Oxyphil cells of parathyroid 847
Oxytocin, 828

Pacinian corpuscles, 977
Pain appreciation, 977
Palade granules. See Ribosomes
Palate, hard, 671
  soft, 671
Palatine tonsils, 673
Pancreas, 706
  control of exocrine secretion of, 711
  development, 706
  exocrine secretion, 689
  islets of Langerhans, 866. See also Islets of Langerhans
Pancreozymin, 711
Paneth cells, 691
Papilla(e), of hair follicles, 624
  of kidney, 777, 780
  of tongue, 650
Paraffin method, 7
Paraganglia, 866
Parasympathetic division of autonomic nervous system, 572
Parathyroid glands, 845
Parathyroid hormone, theories of action of, 847, 851
Parenchyma, definition of, 581
Parietal cells, 683
Parotid gland, 669
Pars nervosa of pituitary gland, 828
P.A.S. technic, 30
Patches, Peyer's, 696
Pelvis of ureter, 777, 778, 781
Penicilli, penicillar arteries, 331
Penis, 946, 949, 969
Pericardial cavity, 600
Pericardium, 600
Perichondrium, 375
Pericytes, 592
Perilymph, 1011
Perimysium, 496
Perineurium, 560
Periodontal disease, 667

Periodontal membrane, 665
Periosteal bud, 411
Periosteum, 436
Peripheral nervous system, classification of, 552
  ganglia, 552. *See also* Ganglia
  nerve endings of. *See* Nerve endings
  nerves of. *See* Nerves
Peristalsis, 676
Peritoneum (serosa), 677
Pernicious anemia, 296
Peyer's patches, 696
Phagocyte(s), alveolar, 760
Phagocytosis, 59
Pharyngeal hypophysis, 817
Pharyngeal tonsil, 749
Pharynx, 672
Phase microscope, 48
Phimosis, 872, 970
Phosphatase, 29, 379, 417
Phosphoric esters, 379
Phosphorus of blood, effect on calcification of, 322, 434
Photomicrography, 24
Phytohemagglutinin, 82
Pia-arachnoid, 547
Pia mater, 546
Pigments, 149
Pillar cells, 1019
Pineal body (gland), 875
Pinocytosis, 122
Pitocin, 829
Pitressin, 829
Pituitary gland, 815
  blood supply, 818
  as a link between nervous and endocrine systems, 817
  pars anterior. *See* Anterior lobe of pituitary
  pars intermedia, 828
  pars nervosa, 828
  pars tuberalis, 828
  portal circulation, 818
Placenta, 917
  age changes, 927
  attachments of, 926
  decidua, 921
  development, 918
  functions, 926
  histology, 923
  intervillous space, 926
  villus, 923
Placental barrier, 924
Placental gonadotrophin, 904, 927
  effect on testis, 951
Plasma, loss of, 219

Plasma—(*Continued*)
  membrane, 120
  thromboplastin, 300
Plasma cells, 234
  fine structure of, 239
Platelets, 298
  chromatomere, 302
  counting methods for, 304
  fine structure, 303
  formation, 304, 368
  function, 298, 302
  hyalomere, 302
  life cycle, 304
Pleura, 744, 767
Plexus, Auerbach's, 676
  Meissner's, 676
  myenteric, 676
  submucous, 676
  subpapillary, 635
Plica(e), circulares, 689
Pneumothorax, 746
Podocytes, 792
Poikilocyte, 295
Polar body, 896
Polarized light, 484
Polymorphonuclear leukocytes, *See* Neutrophils
Polyploidy, 85
  polyribosomes, 120
  polysomes, 120
Pons of brain, 518
Pores, alveolar, 759
  nuclear, 109
  of taste buds, 1006
Postmortem degeneration, 112
Potency in male, 960
Potentiality of cells, 60
Precursor, in radioautography, 33
Predentin, 661
Pregnancy, 917
  tests, 904
Prepuce, 970
Pressure receptors, 977
Prickle cells, 617
Primitive reticular cells, 312, 352
Process(es), ciliary, 992
Processus vaginalis, 950
Product, in radioautography, 33
Proerythroblasts, 360
Progesterone, effects on anterior pituitary, 899
  effects on endometrium, 915
  and pseudopregnancy, 901
Prolactin, 941
Promyelocytes, 364
Prophase, 74

Proprioceptive muscle sense, 977
Prostate gland, 949, 966
Protein, chemistry of, 10
Prothrombin, 300
Protoplasm, 57
  properties of, 58
Pseudohermaphroditism, 857
Pseudopregnancy, 900
Pseudostratified epithelium, 183
Puberty, cause of, 892
Pulp of tooth, 668
Purkinje cells, of cerebellum, 545
  of impulse-conducting system, 607
Purpura, essential thrombocytopenic, 306
Push-pull theory of hormone secretion, 822
Pyknosis, 112
Pyloric glands, 687
Pyloric sphincter, 687
Pyramidal cells, 543

Quartz-rod illuminator, 52
Quick-section diagnosis, 16

Rachitic rosary, 434
Radiation, 98
  effects of, on chromosomes, 98
  on immunity, 356
  myeloid tissue of, 356
Radioactive isotopes, 31
Radioautography, 31
  with the EM, 47
Radioiodine, 838
Rami communicantes, 570, 571
Rathke's pouch, 816
Rays, astral, 75
  medullary, 778
Reaction, Feulgen, 86
  Schiff, 30
Reconstructions, 17
Rectum, 699
Red blood cells. *See* Erythrocytes, 287
Red pulp of spleen, 331
Reflex arc(s), 511
Refractive media of eye, 983
Regeneration, of adrenal cortex, 858
  of articular cartilage, 467
  of beta cells of pancreas, 875
  of bone, 436
  of epidermis, 638
  of liver, 740
  of nerves, 564
  of smooth muscle, 477

Regeneration—(*Continued*)
　of striated muscle, 495
　of tendons, 253
Renin, 786
Reninactivator, 786
Repair. *See* Regeneration
Reproductive system. *See* Fe-
　male reproductive system
　*and* Male reproductive
　system
Respiration, definition of, 6
Respiratory bronchioles, 756
Respiratory movements, 744
Respiratory system, 744
Reticular cells, 312, 342, 352
Reticular fibers, 208, 220
Reticulocytes, 293
Reticuloendothelial cells, 231,
　352
Reticuloendothelial system, 352
Reticulum, endoplasmic, 123
　sarcoplasmic, 485, 494
Retina, 983, 995
　development, 985
　fovea centralis, 1001
　layers, 998
　light reception by, 1000
　macula lutea, 1003
　nutrition, 1001
　photoreceptors of, 999
Ribonuclease, 87
Ribonucleic acid. *See* RNA
Ribosomes, 117
Rickets, 434
Rima glottidis, 751
RNA, cytoplasmic, 117
　demonstration, by radioautog-
　　raphy, 34
　distinguished, from DNA, 86,
　　100
　messenger, 100
　in nucleolus, 103
　polysomes, 120
　site of synthesis, 106
　transfer, 102
Rods of eye, 998
Ruffini corpuscle, 978
Runt disease, 275

Saccule, of cytoplasm, 116
　of ear, 1010, 1019
　of larynx, 751
Saliva, 669
　control of secretion, 670
Salivary glands, 669
Sandwich technic, 38
Sap, nuclear, 109

Saphenous vein, 596
Sarcolemma, 483, 485
Sarcomere, 484
Sarcoplasm, 478, 484
Sarcoplasmic reticulum, 493
Satellites, of nerve cells, 536
　perineural, 536
　perivascular, 536
Scala, media. *See* Duct, cochlear
　tympani, 1001, 1019
　vestibuli, 1001, 1019
Sclera, formation, 986
　general features, 988
　lamina cribrosa, 989
　spur, 992
　structure, 988
Scurvy, 432
Sebaceous glands, 630
Sebum, 630
Secretion, definition, 59
　granules, 135-137
　mechanism, 133-137
Section, mounting, 9
　study of, 19
　ultra thin, 45
Sectioning, of tissues, 9
Sella turcica, 815
Semen, 946, 960
Semicircular canals, 1010, 1012
Seminal vesicles, 948, 965
Seminiferous tubules, 953
Sensation, basis for, 514
Senses of man, 975
Sensibility, cutaneous and deep,
　975
Septa, interlobular, 191
Septal cells, 760
Serosa, of intestine, 677
Serotonin, 248, 304, 695
Serous demilunes, 197
Serous secretory units, 193
Sertoli cells, 953
Sex, chromatin of interphase
　nuclei, 69
　chromatin of neurophils, 262
　determination, 885
　hormones and, 885
　reversal, 885
Sex cycles, in lower animals,
　899
Sharpey's fibers, 468, 665
Sheaths, of hair follicles, 624,
　627
　of Schwann, 555
　tendon, 253
Shock, and kidney circulation,
　804
　surgical, 218, 220

Silicosis, 150
Silver impregnation methods,
　534
Sinu-atrial node, 605
Sinus(s), carotid, 590
　of dura mater, 549
　lactiferous, 935
　of larynx, 751
　of nose, 748
　subcapsular, of lymph nodes,
　　315
Sinusoids, of myeloid tissue, 353
　of spleen, 331
Size, estimating with microscope,
　24
Skeletal muscle, 482. *See also*
　Striated muscle
Skeleton of heart, 601
Skin, 613
　blisters, 637
　blood supply, 635
　burns, 638
　grafting, 638
　hair follicles. *See* Hair fol-
　　licles
　interpapillary pegs, 616
　layers of epidermis, 617
　nails, 640
　papillae, 616
　pigmentation, 632
　repair after burns, 637
　ridges, 615
　sebaceous glands, 630
　sweat glands, 620
　thick, 615
　thick and thin compared, 615
　thin, 621
Skull, growth of, 407
Sludging of blood, 296
Small intestine, 688
　absorption from, 696
　argentaffine cells, 694
　Brunner's glands, 690
　crypts of Lieberkühn, 691
　lymphatic tissue, 695
　mucous membrane, 692
　Paneth cells, 692
　Peyer's patches, 696
　plicae circulares, 689
　villi of, 689
Smooth muscle, 477
　distribution, 481
　fine structure, 479
　function, 481
　growth and regeneration, 477
　identification, in sections, 482
　microscopic structure, 478
　nerve endings, 480

Smooth muscle—(*Continued*)
  origin, 477
  shape of nuclei on contraction, 479
Soft palate, 671
Sol, definition of, 10
Sole plasm, 498
Somatotrophin, 819
Space(s), epidural, 548
  of Fontana, 992
  perivascular, 342, 346
  subarachnoid, 547
  subdural, 548
Spermatic cord, 948
Spermatids, 954
Spermatocytes, 953
Spermatogenesis, 953
Spermatogonia, 953
Spermatozoa, 955
  abnormal, 960
  concentration in semen of, 960
Sphincter, of bladder, 868, 973
  of Boyden, 739
  of Oddi, 739
  pyloric, 687
Spinal cord, appearance at different levels, 539
  cells of anterior horn, 540
  central canal, 522
  coverings, 546
  histogenesis, 520
  horns, 522
  microscopic structure, 538
  morphogenesis, 517
  neurons. *See* Neurons
  segmentation, 539
Spinal ganglia, 554
Spindle, 75
Spleen, 327
  arteries, 330
  capsule, 329
  circulation according to Knisely, 337
  colony technic, 356
  ellipsoids, 336
  functions, 327
  gross characteristics, 328
  lymphatic nodules, 329
  microscopic structure, 329
  penicilli, 331
  plasma cells in, 334
  pulp of, 329
  pulp cords, 332
  red pulp, 331
  sinusoids, 331
  trabeculae, 330
  white pulp, 330

Spongioblasts, ependymal, 520
  free, 534
Spreading effect, 209
Stains and staining. *See also*
    Histochemistry, 29
  acid and basic, defined, 14
  blood stains, 258
  Bowie's, 785, 872
  brilliant cresyl blue, 293
  electron, 44
  fluorescent, 36, 37
  hematoxylin, and eosin, 14
  metachromatic, 211
  mordants, 14
  negative, 46
  Periodic-acid Schiff (PAS) technic, 30
  Romanovsky, 258
  silver, 534
  supravital, 51
  vital, 232
Stapes, 1014
Stellate reticulum, 657
Steriocilia, 964
Sternal puncture, 370
Steroid hormones, 856
Stomach, 680
  chief cells, 684
  control of secretion, 687
  fine structure, 684
  gastric pits, 615, 682
  mucous neck cells, 684
  parietal cells, 684
  pyloric glands, 687
  renewal of cells in, 686
  secretion of hydrochloric acid in, 684
Stress, effects of, 862
    on secretion of ACTH, 863
Striated border, 174
  of epithelial cells, 174
  of osteoclasts, 403
Striated muscle, 482
  A bands of, 484, 487
  ATP in, 489
  attachments to tendons of, 496
  blood supply, 497
  centrotubules, 493
  changes on contraction in, 489
  Cohnheim's fields of, 494
  connective tissue components, 496
  contraction, 489
  cross-striations, 484, 487
  efferent innervation, 498
  endomysium of, 496
  epimysium, 496
  fine structure, 486

Striated muscle—(*Continued*)
  glycogen in, 494
  growth, 494
  H disk, 486
  I band, 486
  innervation, 498
  J band, 484
  lymphatics, 497
  mechanism of contraction, 489
  motor end-plates, 498
  motor unit, 498
  myofibrils, 484, 486
  myofilaments, 486
  myosin, 489
  nerve endings, 498, 977
  organelles, 486
  perimysium, 496
  proprioceptive sense from, 977
  Q band, 484
  regeneration, 495
  sarcolemma of fibers, 483, 485
  sarcomere, 484
  sarcoplasmic reticulum, 493
  study of, with polarized light, 484
  Z lines of, 484
Striped muscle, 482. *See also*
    Striated muscle
Stroma, definition, 581
Sty, 1005
Subcapsular sinus, 315
Subcutaneous tissue, 614
Subdural space, 548
Submucosa of intestine, 675
Substance, central gelatinous, of spinal cord, 538
  chromidial, 117
  intercellular. *See* Intercellular substance(s)
  interchromatinic, 111
Substantia propria, 987
Sugar, in blood, 871
  storage in liver, 715
  in urine, 871
Sulfated mucopolysaccharides, 243, 375
Sustentacular cells, 978, 1007
Sutures, 398
Sweat glands, 620
Sympathetic division of autonomic nervous system, 570
Sympathetic ganglia, 569
Sympathetic trunks, 570
Symphyses, 346

Synapse, 510, 532
  fine structure of, 532
Synchondroses, 460
Syncytiotrophoblast, 924
Syndesmoses, 459
Synostoses, 460
Synovial fluid, 466, 472
Synovial joints, 462
  absorption from, 472
  age changes, 473
  blood supply, 471
  capsules, 468
  development, 462
  lymphatics, 471
  menisci in, 471
  nerve supply, 471
  nourishment of cartilages, 466
  osteoarthritis, 473
  osteophytes, 473
  synovial membranes, 470
  transition zone, 470
System, of articulations, 458. See
    also Joints
  blood-vascular, 581. See also
    Circulatory system
  circulatory. See Circulatory
    system
  definition, 581
  digestive, 645
  endocrine, 814
  female reproductive. See Fe-
    male reproductive system
  integumentary, 613. See also
    Skin
  male reproductive. See Male
    reproductive system
  nervous, 507. See also Central
    nervous system and Pe-
    ripheral nervous system
  respiratory. See Respiratory
    system
  of sensory receptors, 975
  urinary, 772
Systole, 582

Taste buds, 1006
Tastes, different, 1007
Technics. See under individual
    names
Teeth. See Tooth
Telophase, 78
Tendon, 253
  transplantation of, 253
Teniae coli, 700
Terminal bar, 181
  web, 175
Testis(es), changes at puberty
    in, 953

Testis(es)—(Continued)
  coverings, 950
  cryptorchid, 951
  crystalloids in interstitial cells,
    961
  descent, 949
  development, 949
  ductuli efferentes, 948, 964
  effects of gonadotrophin on,
    946, 953
  formation of spermatozoa in,
    953
  hormones and descent, 951
  interstitial cells, 951, 960
  maldescent, 951
  mediastinum, 947
  primary spermatocytes, 953
  rete of, 947, 963
  secondary spermatocytes, 953
  seminiferous tubules, 946, 953
  Sertoli cells, 953
  spermatogonia, 953
  spermatozoa, 955
  tubuli recti, 963
  tunica albuginea, 947
  undescended, 951
Tests for pregnancy, 904
Tetany, 847
Theca interna and externa, 895
Thiouracil, 843
Thoracic duct, 610
Three-dimensional visualization,
    17
Thrombin, 300
Thrombocytes, 298
Thromboplastin, 300
Thrombosis, 298
Thrombus, 299
Thymidine, tritium-labeled, 91
  study of DNA synthesis, 91
Thymus gland, 338
  barrier in, 339
  blood vessels of, 342
  development, 340
  effects of removal at birth,
    345
  fine structure, 342
  involution, 340
  lymphocytes, 341, 343
  migration of lymphocytes in,
    344
  microscopic structure, 342
  possible functions, 345
  relation to endocrine glands
    of, 345
  size at different ages of, 340
  steroid hormones and, 345

Thyroglobulin, 834
  breakdown, 839
  synthesis, 837
Thyroid gland, 831
  colloid goiter, 842
  effect of thiouracil on, 843
  effect of thyrotrophic hor-
    mone on, 840
  exophthalmic goiter, 833
  factors affecting histology of,
    839
  fine structure, 837
  gross structure, 831
  hypofunction and hyperfunc-
    tion, 832
  hormones, 831
  microscopic structure, 833
  parenchymatous goiter, 841
  possibility of a secluded anti-
    gen in, 844
  relation of iodine to structure
    of, 842
  testing function, 844
  thyroglobulin, synthesis in,
    838
  uptake of iodine, 838
  use of radioiodine, 844
Thyrotrophic hormone, effect on
    thyroid, 840
Thyrotrophs, 826
Tissue(s), adipose, 248
  areolar, 204
  bone, 384
  cartilage, 373
  chemical components, 10
  classification, 166
  connective, 200
  culture, 61
  definition, 3
  dense fibrous, 251
  embryologic origin, 167
  epithelial, 165
  erectile, 949, 971
  four primary, 166
  glandular, 188
  granulation, 231
  hemopoietic, 309
  lymphatic, 309
  muscular, 476
  myeloid, 351
  nervous, 507
  transplantation of, 277
Tissue fluid, composition of, 211
  and edema, 216
Tolerance, immunological, 237
Tomes' fibers, 661
Tone of muscle, 481
Tongue, 648

Tonofibrils, 617
Tonsil, lingual, 652
  palatine, 673
  pharyngeal, 749
Tooth (teeth), 652
  alveolar process, 653
  ameloblasts of, 657
  anatomic crown of, 652
  clinical crown of, 653
  deciduous, 653
  dentin of, 660. *See also* Dentin
  development, 654
  enamel, 662
  enamel organ, 655
  eruption, 660
  Hertwig's sheath of, 660
  Korff's fibers of, 661
  periodontal membrane of, 665
  pulp chamber of, 668
  wisdom, 654
Touch appreciation, 975
Tracers, radioactive, 33
Trachea, 751
Tract, hypothalamo-hypophyseal, 829
Transformation, 88
Transitional epithelium, 185
Transparent chambers, 52
Transplantation, of tissues, general, 277. *See also under different tissues*
Trigonum fibrosum, 601
Triiodothyronine, 831, 839
Tritium, as label, 33
Trophic hormones, 822
Trophoblast, 918
Tropocollagen, 207
Tropomyosin, 489
Tubule(s), collecting, of kidney, 800
  distal convoluted, of kidney, 800
  proximal, convoluted, of kidney, 795
  spindle, 76
Tunica propria, 674

Tunics of blood vessels, 585
Turbinate bones, 748
Tympanic cavity, 1014
Tympanic membrane, 1014


Ultrastructure, 40
Ultraviolet microscope, 40
Undifferentiated mesenchymal cells, 225
Unit, Ångstrom, 24
Ureter, 807
Urethra, female, 808
  male, 971
Urinary bladder, 808
Urinary system, 772
Urine, 772
Uterus, 888
  cervix, 927
  endometrium, 911
    in menstrual cycle, 912
    histology, 911
    stratum vasculari, 911
Utricle, 1012, 1019
Uveal tract, 983


Vagina, 930
  cyclical changes in, 931
  smears, 930
Vallate papillae, 650
Valve(s), of heart, 601
  of Kerkring, 689
  in lymphatics, 609
  in veins, 598
Varicose veins, 599
Vas deferens, 948, 965
Vasoconstrictor nerves, 588
Vasodilation, mechanisms of, 589
Veins, 596
  aqueous, 995
  compared with arteries, 598
  large, 597
  lymphatics in walls, 598
  of medium size, 596
  pampiniform, 965

Veins—(*Continued*)
  stellate, of kidney, 804
  valves, 598
  varicose, 599
  vasa vasorum of, 597
Vellus, 623
Ventricles of brain, 520
Venules, 594
Vesicles, membranous of cytoplasm, 116
  pinocytotic, 122
Vestibule, of inner ear, 1009, 1019
Villi, arachnoid, 551
  of intestine, 689
  of synovial membranes, 470
Villus, placental, 923
Viruses, 37, 46
  appearance, in sections, 47
  negatively stained, 47
Vital staining, 232
Vitamin, A, and retina, 1000
  $B_{12}$, 296
  D, effect of deficiency on bone, 432, 434
  E, 959
  K, 306
Vitreous body, 983
Vocal cords, 751
Volkmann's canals, 426
Voluntary muscle, 482. *See also* Striated muscle


Wasting disease, 275
Web, cell, 174
  terminal, 175
White matter of central nervous system, 522
White pulp of spleen, 330
Witch's milk, 941
Wolff's law, 436


Z lines of muscle, 484
Zona pellucida, 894
Zymogen cells, of stomach, 684
Zymogen granules, 133, 708